Under the editorship of

LEONARD CARMICHAEL

SECRETARY, SMITHSONIAN INSTITUTION;
FORMERLY PRESIDENT, TUFTS COLLEGE, AND DIRECTOR,
TUFTS RESEARCH LABORATORY OF SENSORY PSYCHOLOGY
AND PHYSIOLOGY

Personality Development

✠ A DYNAMIC APPROACH

Houghton

and Psychopathology

Norman Cameron

YALE UNIVERSITY

Mifflin Company · Boston

For Jean

Editor's Introduction

Personality Development and Psychopathology: A Dynamic Approach, is written by a professor at Yale University. Many readers of the present volume will remember his two previous distinguished books, *The Psychology of Behavior Disorders,* and, with Ann Magaret, *Behavior Pathology,* both published by Houghton Mifflin Company.

This book is similar to the two previous ones in that it is a broad and comprehensive consideration of human mental life, both in its normal and abnormal aspects. The earlier books were written from what may be called a general biosocial point of view. In both of these volumes the author emphasized the importance of inborn biological make-up as it is molded by individual social experience in the development of the specific patterns of mental life in each individual.

In this new volume the comprehensive and broad point of view of the two earlier books is maintained but the presentation is much more profoundly influenced by a psychodynamic approach to psychology. It should be emphasized, however, that Dr. Cameron has given here no mere historical interpretation of classical Freudian concepts. Rather, he has worked out a modern and refreshingly novel synthesis of psychoanalytic teachings in the terms of the current discoveries of general psychology and especially of dynamic psychopathology. In reading the present book it is not hard to remember that the author not only holds the degree of Doctor of Philosophy in psychology from the University of Michigan but also holds the degree of Doctor of Medicine from the Johns Hopkins University. A special feature of the book is its enrichment by many case studies drawn from the author's own long and varied experience as a physician who has specialized in the treatment of mental illness.

While at Johns Hopkins Dr. Cameron was closely associated with the late Dr. Adolf Meyer. It is true that the present volume is less directly a development of the point of view of Dr. Meyer than were its two predecessors but it still retains much of the biological orientation of that distinguished American psychiatrist.

This book very explicitly deals with what the author characterizes as the *inner life of man.* As every student of the history of psychology knows, this subject is a difficult one for productive research, but it is most important. Each person reacts in his own way to the stimuli presented by the social world in which he lives. Somehow these differences in response to identical external energies must be due to special characteristics of the inner life of the behaving individual. Some psychologists attempt to explain these individual characteristics of behavior in terms of known facts about the anatomy and physiology of the nervous system and of the chemistry of the body fluids. Some students further postulate still undiscovered anatomical and physiological processes and supplement known biological facts with such constructs. Older psychologists for similar reasons formulated constructs such as volition and many other conscious mechanisms as a means of accounting for the special reactions that they observe in their own mental life and in that of others.

Many psychologists and psychiatrists are not content with either of these sets of so-called "explanations" of the individual character of behavioral reactions. The author of the present book is a distinguished member of the group that recognizes not only the importance of neurological processes and of conscious events but also wishes to emphasize the significance of unconscious mechanisms, many of them of a most irrational sort, as basic to an understanding of abnormal and even of normal behavior.

It must be recognized that many modern students of scientific psychology do not wish to postulate conscious or unconscious mechanisms in their effort to understand mental life. Such puristic objective students try to be satisfied with a systematization that deals with the quantification of the energies of the environment acting upon the organism and with the measurement of the responses that the organism makes to the environment in which it exists. Such students consider the full history of the reactions of the organism and especially what it has learned during the full course of its life from prenatal days to death. More than forty years ago John B. Watson formulated this point of view concerning the aim of a strictly behavioristic psychology in the following famous words: ". . . the goal of psychological study is the ascertaining of such data and laws that, given the stimulus, psychology can predict what the response will be; or, on the other hand, given the response, it can specify the nature of the effective stimulus." More recently a similar point of view has been clearly presented by B. F. Skinner: "The practice of looking inside the organism for an explanation of behavior has tended to obscure the variables which are immediately available for a scientific analysis. These variables lie outside the organism, in its immediate environment and in its environmental history."

The present volume is a distinguished contribution to the study of mental life by one who is not at all content with such a purely external or behavioristic view of the organism-environment relationship. The chapters of the present book, without underestimating the importance of the make-up of the nervous system, deal most effectively with the conscious and especially the preconscious and unconscious mechanisms which are postulated as basic to "normal" and "abnormal" human behavior.

In considering the various approaches to an understanding of mental life mentioned above, the editor cannot help thinking of the physicist's "black box." In recent years nonelectronically-trained individuals have purchased what they like to call "black boxes" which contain in working order elaborate complexes of circuits and tubes that have been assembled by electronic engineers to perform very specific functions. Later, when such a "black box" no longer operates correctly it is discarded and a new complete and unopened box is put in its place. The purchaser does not try to know and may not even wish to ask what the box contains; he really buys what the box can do.

Some very good modern psychologists are content to think of the human living organism as such a "black box." Many orthodox behaviorists indeed are almost violently determined to keep the box closed. Others who may call themselves physiological psychologists are interested in attempting to understand to the greatest degree possible how the known facts of the physiology and anatomy of the nervous system and of the composition of the body fluids help them understand human reactions. Other psychologists and psychiatrists, as this present book most ably testifies, are more venturesome. These students wish to view normal and abnormal behavior as explained by constructs involving not only neurological and conscious events but also in terms of elaborate unconscious mechanisms which at times are held to comprise almost a separate and "deep" systematic existence in the mental life of the individual.

The present volume is indeed an advanced and coherent presentation of this latter important modern way of considering psychology. According to this approach, an understanding of the very specific and divergent patterns of behavior shown in normal as well as in neurotic and psychotic behavior can only be fully understood in terms of such unconscious processes. Observed behavior is thus considered to have its true genesis in many cases in the irrational dreamlike world of the unconscious.

An interest in what is spoken of as the depths of the human personality is not new. But the present book has developed in a novel and effective way the description of the constructs that have been formulated to give coherence to the treatment of these deep phases of the personality. A stanza of an English poem of about 1615 dealing with *Tom o'Bedlam* illustrates the fact that perceptive observers have long recognized the great and deep role of such processes:

> "With an host of furious fancies
> Whereof I am commander
> With a burning spear, and a horse of air,
> To the wilderness I wander.
> By a knight of ghosts and shadows
> I summoned am to tourney
> Ten leagues beyond the wide world's end.
> Methinks it is no journey."

One who neglects these furious fancies and mental ghosts and shadows, in the opinion of the author of this book, will never gain a deep and therapeutically helpful understanding of the true mechanisms that underlie mental life. From the psychodynamic point of view of this book the behavioristic approach to psychopathology mentioned above is not a study of the real mind of man but it is rather a point of view that assumes that man is in fact not a living human being but an inanimate computer.

In every section of the present volume the author presents a persuasive and clearly formulated exposition of the way in which he himself as an experienced clinician with a full understanding of all the divergent trends of modern psychology and psychiatry can view what is for him the all important dynamics of the inner life of man, both in its surface and in its deep manifestations.

The book thus becomes much more than a treatise written in terms of one school of psychology or psychoanalysis. This is not to say, however, that the author ever fails to admit his deep debt to Freud. In this connection it may not be inappropriate to remember words of the last paragraph of Freud's own autobiography written in 1925:

> Looking back, then, over the patchwork of my life's labours, I can say that I have made many beginnings and thrown out many suggestions. Something will come of them in the future, though I cannot myself tell whether it will be much or little. I can, however, express a hope that I have opened up a pathway for an important advance in our knowledge.

Such a pathway was indeed opened by Freud. No one who surveys the intellectual climate of our day can doubt that psychoanalysis has had a deep effect on the religion, the philosophy, the social sciences and even the art and literature of our age. Even those who reject the teachings of psychoanalysis cannot afford to be ignorant of its postulates if they are to be in touch with the well springs of much modern thought.

Dr. Cameron, in the opinion of the editor, in this current volume has made a new and important advance along the pathways indicated by Freud. Thus, it can be said with assurance that every serious student of psychology, psychiatry, education or any of the social or behavioral sciences will profit by a detailed study of its pages. Some people will not agree with every statement in the book, but no one who studies it with care can fail to recognize that it is an important addition to the professional literature of its field. This volume is thus one of those rare contributions to knowledge that no one who claim competence in psychology or in fields related to psychology can afford not to have studied in detail.

LEONARD CARMICHAEL

The Smithsonian Institution

Preface

The purpose of this book is to present a picture of the inner life of man, as it interacts with the surroundings, as it is experienced, and as it is expressed in normal behavior and psychopathology. Man's inner life is always a significant source of action; and it arouses in other persons, through its behavioral expression, some of their most important experiences. The dynamic interplay of each person's inner life, his behavioral expressions, and the experiences he arouses in others, are the major forces that constitute society and go to form the culture in which human beings live. Comparisons with the circumstances of animal life, where the environment is much simpler and the reactions to it far less flexible, bring out sharp contrasts as well as some similarities.

The human being is equipped with a few fixed patterns of response, which are necessary for survival and for the development of a human kind of society, but his greatness lies in his incomparable plasticity. We can predict with some accuracy how an infant will behave during the first few months; but even then we have to take into consideration the life patterns of the family into which he is born. Soon prediction, excepting for a limited number of relatively simple variables, becomes inaccurate. The child is father to the man; but he lives out his infancy and childhood among persons who determine the nature of this fatherhood, who provide the influences that stress certain factors and minimize certain others. By the time a child reaches adolescence, his original patterns have been enormously affected by his human environment. Many of them are eliminated entirely. Some of them may even be reversed.

Throughout this book the importance of infancy and early childhood is strongly emphasized. This is in accordance not only with a dynamic approach, but also with the findings of all modern students of psychopathology, to say nothing of those who work with infants and children themselves. Two of the early chapters are devoted to an account of personality development in which the emphasis upon the early years is obvious. Decades of direct clinical experience have influenced this presentation — the experience of the author over a period of thirty years, and the experience of a great community of clinical and experimental workers. The product of this experience is not mere theory, any more than the product of professional experience in other behavioral sciences is.

Of particular importance is the current nationwide study of the nature

ix

of fixation and regression in patients with psychopathology as this is related to the observation and testing of normal infants and preschool children. Each of these two fields illuminates the other. The Gesell and the Piaget studies, for example, have had a constructive impact upon our understanding of abnormal behavior or experience in childhood and adolescence, in adulthood and the senium. Often it is the contrast that counts; often it is some remarkable similarity; sometimes it is practically an identity.

Any science that goes beyond a description of what can be directly seen, tasted, heard, smelled or felt, must make use of *constructs* or *intervening variables*. It must make certain assumptions about what goes on when direct observation does not account for what can be observed. Otherwise the descriptive scientist must stop with his description and go no farther. The history of advance in the so-called exact sciences has been a history of such assumptions and their ultimate verification, modification or elimination. The modern physical scientist, for example, often speaks of atoms, electrons, protons and neutrons, as though anyone could buy them in a hardware store. In psychopathology, a similar use is made of such constructs as motive, emotion and memory, of ego-systems, the id, the superego and the ego-ideal, of the unconscious, the preconscious and the conscious. In this book we shall make use of these *constructs* or *intervening variables* in much the same way that physical scientists make use of theirs. It is understood from the start that all such conceptions are provisional, that they may have to be modified or even abandoned as the objective evidence materializes.

There is no advantage in being timid about constructs and intervening variables. They are the tools of scientific logic. Without them we would be lost. It is even widely accepted nowadays in our field that what we call *external reality* is a construct rather than a "given." It is something which each person must evolve for himself, as he grows from infancy through childhood to adulthood, something which he must continually validate through his interactions with other human beings in the same culture.[1] In this book, I have repeatedly emphasized the primitive nonverbal and often illogical undercurrent of everyone's behavior and experience. I have over and over again called attention to the many similarities between neuroses and psychoses, on the one hand, and the universally familiar experiences of dreams and intoxications.

I have also called attention, over and over, to the remarkable effects of *sensory deprivation* or *perceptual isolation* in normal adults, because in many ways they duplicate psychotic experiences. This seems to me one of the major breakthroughs of contemporary psychopathology. It is especially significant because no chemical substances are introduced into the subject, as they are in producing the so-called "model psychoses." The only factors seem to be the isolation of the subject from normal perceptual stimulation and his immobilization. The inferences which one can draw from sensory deprivation experiments are that primitive processes are normally going on all the

[1] Nash, H., "The behavioral world," *J. Psychol.*, 1959, 47, 277–288.

time, during the day as well as at night, and that they can produce psychotic experiences if a person is prevented from a normal interchange with his surroundings for a prolonged period. It seems to me that it is worth pointing out this comparison between psychopathology and the experimental products of sensory deprivation in normal persons whenever the strangeness of pathological experience or behavior becomes prominent.

This book has a history of its own as well as a purpose. In 1952, John C. Whitehorn appointed a *Special Commission on Psychodynamics* whose purpose it was to prepare and publish a concise account of the psychodynamic principles which were generally accepted at that time. Dr. Whitehorn became chairman of the *Commission* and I became its reporter. The other members were Daniel Blain, Thomas French, Frieda Fromm-Reichmann, Maxwell Gitelson, Theodore Lidz, Sandor Rado and John Romano. There were others appointed to the *Commission;* but they rarely appeared and contributed little or nothing. We met several times during the ensuing year; and I worked on the material between meetings. Everything that was said during the conferences was recorded, typed up, and turned over to me for the final report.

As time went on, it became more and more obvious that we were not likely to achieve our goal. There were many dissident opinions about basic concepts among the members of the *Commission.* Our conferences seemed to result only in repetitions of the disagreements, and in an enormous amount of typed copy which I found impossible to assimilate. Eventually, when our time was nearly up, we managed to work out a report together, going over every item in the tiresome way that is characteristic of most committee meetings. In the end, no one was satisfied with the report. Dr. Fromm-Reichmann said that it had no life in it. Dr. Whitehorn called it unnecessarily wooden, and took it away to revise it. Eventually, however, the report was published essentially unchanged, excepting for a footnote by Dr. Whitehorn in which he expressed his own dissatisfaction. It was only after its publication that we all recognized how inadequate it was. We had forgotten, for example, to include a substantial account of anxiety, even though every one of us knew that anxiety is central to psychodynamics.

Soon after the report had been completed, Frederick C. Redlich invited me to come to Yale to write a fuller account of psychodynamics myself. I accepted the invitation. Unfortunately, my work has been delayed by a series of unavoidable interruptions, each involving long periods away from my manuscript, so that the final account has taken twice as long as I had anticipated. The writing has benefitted, however, by the need I experienced to think things over afresh each time I returned to my work.

At this point, a distinction must be made between a *psychodynamic approach* and *psychoanalysis.* They are not the same. Psychodynamic approaches owe their origin to psychoanalysis, but they have greater latitude. They go beyond the necessarily rigorous practice of psychoanalysis. A psychodynamic approach forms a bridge between psychology and psychoanalysis, as the growing number of dynamically oriented experimental psychologists indicates. Hilgard has recently pointed out, for example, that although Freud's theories have been largely characterized as *affective* or *conative*, they are also *cognitive*.[2] This ties them up with the contemporary trend toward cognitive as well as ontogenetic emphases.

The greatest change in my own outlook has come from a training analysis, from the extended experience of participating in clinical conferences in a dynamic setting, and from listening to my own patients with this background. Much of what my patients say, when they free associate, carries me back to the years at Johns Hopkins where therapists were given freedom to interact with their patients, and the in-patient load was limited to about eight patients for each therapist. The senior staff at Hopkins, including Adolf Meyer, showed little interest in unconscious determinants and no interest whatever in dreams. This is all the more remarkable because our psychotic and borderline-psychotic patients often expressed primitive material quite clearly, and almost all our patients mentioned their dreams. The primary interest of the staff lay in observing and reporting whatever the patients actually said and did.

The advantages of such attitudes are obvious. They fostered accurate observations and reporting. Their disadvantages are also obvious. What patients said or did was treated as though it had no deeper significance. The major emphasis was upon getting the patient symptomatically well as quickly as possible. A patient who was ready to be discharged was considered a well person. This was almost a behavioristic climate.

The trouble with a behavioristic approach in psychopathology is that it leads a person to study human beings almost as though they were computers. It emphasizes information input, it makes mechanistic assumptions about how intervening variables may achieve their immensely complex computing, and it examines the output almost as though it were the output of a machine. Such an approach ignores the inner life of man.

Everyone knows that there are all kinds of private experience going on within him, whether he includes them in what he reveals to others or not. Almost everyone realizes that private experience, often rich and complex, gives character to what a person does, to what he says and what he thinks. Private experience is now generally acknowledged as determining a person's style of life. Whether or not this can all be objectified, quantified, and expressed in measurable units constitutes a completely separate problem.[3] The experience is there all the time. At some level it is always effectual.

This book deals with normal as well as pathological behavior and experience. It focusses upon the inner life of man, with its logical and its magical processes, because that is where things go on which are mainly responsible

---

[2] Hilgard, E. R., "Impulsive versus realistic thinking," *Psychol. Bull.*, 1962, *59*, 477–488.

[3] *Cf.* Fowler, W., "Cognitive learning in infancy and early childhood," *Psychol. Bull.*, 1962, *59*, 116–152.

for what a person says and does. It also recognizes that, just as no one has a perfect body with perfect physiology, so no one has a perfect inner life. We are all so organized that we have active infantile and magical processes going on within us, at the same time that we are behaving adequately as mature adults. There is not the slightest possibility of eliminating all these irrational unconscious components; and if there were, we should lose all of our warmth, most of our ideals, and the greater part of our feeling and emotion. We would then be nothing but automatons, with receptors, internal hook-ups, and a fully predictable, measurable output. But we would not be human beings.

The theme is central to this book that we all operate simultaneously at different levels of maturity and rationality. Our learned, adaptive ways of life, and our defensive organization, keep us unaware of these immature and irrational components during most of the daytime. Recent experiments have shown that we all have periods of dreaming every night. Irrational thinking — the so-called *primary process* — appears to reign in dreams. Since everyone indulges in such lapses from realistic logical thinking, we may conclude that some irrationality is essential to mental health. There is, for example, every evidence that what appears in dreams at night has already been at least partially worked out during the day. In short, irrational and often infantile unconscious processes are normal components of everyday behavior and experience.

It is impossible to understand this peculiar split-level thinking without some knowledge of how human personality develops. If we are to ready ourselves for the strange experiences and behavior of persons who suffer from neuroses, psychoses or personality disorders, we must begin with some understanding of the way in which infants appear to develop, as they evolve from biological neonates to biosocial children, adolescents and adults. Fortunately, the past few decades have witnessed many contributions to such an understanding, coming from many different disciplines.

From the work of psychologists, sociologists and psychiatrists, it is clear today that personality development always includes processes of internalization. Infants do not behave like reflex machines. They take into themselves *en masse* the characteristics of their surroundings, and especially the characteristics of the people who care for them. They develop an inner life which at first seems to be indistinguishable from the realities of their bodies and the external world. Eventually, this inner life becomes a separate existence, or at least an existence which most people can separate from their experiences with their bodies and their surroundings. The inner life of man poses many contradictions for his social behavior. It is basic to the complexity of man's psychopathology, as well as to the richness of his personal experience.

This book could not have been written without long periods of freedom from other tasks, and without the opportunities to learn from living patients, in therapeutic interaction, what they were experiencing and what they had experienced earlier in their lives. I owe my freedom first of all to Frederick C. Redlich, who has made good the promises originally made to me. Within the past three years, I have owed a large measure of freedom also to Thomas Detre, a talented teacher and clinician, who has carried a great deal of the clinical teaching load which I had earlier accepted as part of my work at Yale. The conception and execution of the manuscript, however, have been mine alone; and I take complete responsibility for the product.

For a critical reading of the manuscript, I wish to express my gratitude to Ingeborg Gross, Ellen Mead and Inez Montgomery, who have been unsparing in their criticism and approval. Most of all I am indebted to my wife and colleague, Eugenia S. Cameron, to whom this book is dedicated. She has followed the growth of the manuscript during the past three years with deep interest and understanding. She has made many suggestions and constructive criticisms, some of which I have incorporated in the finished product. I am also grateful for the suggestions and criticisms of Dr. Leonard Carmichael, who has carefully gone over the manuscript, and to Mr. Richard N. Clark of the Houghton Mifflin Company, who has provided me with advice and encouragement. Finally, I wish to acknowledge the consistent protection from unnecessary interruptions which Mrs. Arthur Gagné has provided while I worked.

NORMAN CAMERON

Institute of Human Relations
Yale University

Contents

1

Introduction

✣

Neuroses and psychoses, personality disorders and psychosomatic disorders have now been established as the most common sources of illness, of personal unhappiness, and of socially unacceptable behavior. Our contemporary novels, our short stories, biographies and mystery stories make free use of this common knowledge. Some of the greatest dramatists of our day have devoted themselves to the tragedies and the comedies of psychopathology.[1] Anyone who is old enough to read adult literature, to watch television or go to the movies — and this includes preadolescent children — cannot help learning something about pathological experience and behavior, even though he has no special interest in them.

Books and popular articles abound that interpret juvenile delinquency and some adult crimes as the outcome of abnormal social situations, or of childhood deprivation and childhood seduction.[2] Many of these interpretations are basically sound, even though they sometimes lead to unsound conclusions, such as the idea that to be socially irresponsible is to be natural. This is untrue. In our society, to be socially irresponsible is to be undependable, maladapted and immature. Some writers have gone so far as to say that everyone is neurotic and should be thankful for it. This also is untrue. To

---

[1] Cf. Sievers, W. D., *Freud on Broadway: A History of Psychoanalysis and the American Drama.* New York: Hermitage House, 1955.

[2] Earle, A. M., and Earle, B. V., "Early maternal deprivation and later psychiatric illness," *Amer. J. Orthopsychiat.,* 1961, *31,* 181–186; Sanua, V. D., "Sociocultural factors in families of schizophrenics," *Psychiatry,* 1961, *24,* 246–265.

1

be neurotic is to be in conflict, to be more vulnerable to anxiety than the average person, and to settle for a compromise which includes pathological symptoms. This is not a disgrace, but neither is it an advantage.

Everyone has potentialities for developing psychopathology — personality disorder, psychosomatic disorder or psychosis, as well as neurosis — just as we all have potentialities for other kinds of illness. The vast majority of people do not develop significant psychopathology unless they are subjected to intolerable stress; and a great many people manage to maintain their psychological equilibrium even under extreme duress. No one, however, can avoid relationships with persons who have been unfortunate in their experiences during childhood and adulthood.

Psychopathology in everyday life

Children and adults with a significant degree of psychopathology make up a natural part of our everyday environment. There may be someone at the supermarket or the department store who is always irritable and brusque. The driver of the school bus may be unreasonably permissive with the children in his charge and incredibly angry with any adult who crosses his path. Perhaps the child next door is being unintentionally trained by his overanxious mother to worry as much over his health as she does. An otherwise effective teacher at school may be unable to tolerate the least disorder or disarrangement in the classroom, or the slightest change in the curriculum. She must have everything around her under control if she is to be able to control herself.

There are adults who develop anxiety attacks whenever they hear footsteps behind them on a lonely street, even in the daytime. There are others who have no trouble during the day, but are as frightened by the dark as any anxious small child. Men moved from a day shift to a night shift sometimes have to give up their jobs because of such a fear. Children whose mothers are terrified by lightning and thunder are likely to become themselves terrified, and to join their parents in a dark closet until the storm has passed. In this way specific fears and nonspecific anxieties can be culturally transmitted through several generations. They may have originated in an ancestor who, as a small child, received from his parents too little protection and relief from his inevitable infantile anxieties.

A child's own father may be a man who sleeps poorly, has temper tantrums and shouts when he is displeased. He may, instead, be passive and ineffectual in the home; or — and this amounts to the same thing as far as the child is concerned — he may be absent from the home most of the time. A child's mother may be domineering and overprotective for her own neurotic reasons. She may be a rigid, ritualistic woman who cannot resist two or three nightly patrols of the home, to make sure that the doors are really locked securely, that all the lights and the television are turned off, and that the deep freeze and the refrigerator are tightly closed. Such rituals, no matter how they may be rationalized, come from neurotic attempts to keep one's inner anxieties under control.

A child may have a brother who dares not go to sleep for a long time each night because he is afraid that he might stop breathing in his sleep and never wake up again. A sister, otherwise healthy, may lose her voice and go limp whenever she is emotionally upset. In the background there may be an aunt with perpetually frayed nerves, or an uncle who is always worried, complains of ulcer pains, and cannot seem to get relief anywhere. Sometimes we find whole families in which every member shows some form of psychopathology, yet none of them is incapacitated.

Frank psychotic illnesses are much less common than the relatively minor disorders that we have been describing: and they usually lead to hospitalization. On the other hand, it is impossible to estimate the incidence of mild, boderline or "ambulatory" psychotic states, in which people often get along as well as most neurotics do. The number is probably much higher than any of the statistics indicate.

Every child at some time runs across frankly psychotic people, or at least hears others talking about them. He reads about them in story books, and sees them represented in comic strips and television shows. He will occasionally notice someone in the street who seems confused, glances about furtively and talks to himself. In many neighborhoods there is some adult who threatens child trespassers, or who responds suspiciously and antagonistically to the doorbell. Children hear their elders discuss this person's maniacal outburst or that one's suicide in a depression. Not a few children are reared with a mixed-up, forgetful grandmother right in the home who, because of a failing brain, calls a child by the name of some relative long dead, wanders about at night, and sometimes tries to prepare breakfast for the family at two in the morning. The average child can have only the haziest idea about the meaning of such disturbances, since his elders are usually not too clear about them; but he cannot escape some contact with them, directly or through vivid hearsay.

We adults also come into frequent close contact with psychopathology, in the home or out of it, at business, in shops or in the street. Who does not know at least one person who seems always on edge, no matter what the situation? Most of us know some businessman, neighbor or professional person who flies into a rage whenever his judgment is called into question or whenever someone else makes a mistake. Many of us have among our friends a compulsive housewife, whose home must be always spotless, uncomfortably clean and neat, not because she takes a womanly pride in her home, but because dirt and disorder make her intolerably anxious. We all know of some man or woman who complains of perpetual fatigue and discomfort, in spite of constant resting, but who paradoxically seems to have no systemic disease, and lives to a ripe old age without ever developing anything related to his lifelong complaints.

Among our business and social acquaintances, or within our circle of relatives and intimate friends, we can usually find someone who seems chronically uneasy about the intentions, attitudes and inferences of other people. One of these may feel himself the target of unjust criticism, for reasons that are unclear to him, and may never be understood by others. He is likely to expend fruitless effort in attempting to justify himself and what he does. Another shows continual preoccupation with the impression he makes upon other people. When he feels misunderstood, he tries to explain, even though nobody wants an explanation. He may plant protective hedges of qualifying phrase and clause to guard whatever he says against a possible misinterpretation, so that it is hard to understand him.

Most of us know a vague, perplexed man or woman who seems not to be quite living the lives of others, who is still preoccupied with unanswerable questions about the meaning of life, and speaks of semimystical experiences which no one else can share. All of us know the inadequate person who lives only for approval and praise, but can never get enough of them. He may be one who says that he feels inferior to others; or he may feel unfairly treated because other people get more than they should. We all hear about persons with tremendous wealth or power who seem driven on to gain more and more wealth, to bring more and more under their domination. To make ten million seems only a challenge to make ten million more, no matter what the personal cost. To hold sway over a million people sparks the ambition to hold sway over another million. There is something within the power-driven person that forces him on. It is only when he tumbles from the height to which his impulses have driven him that we begin to see how childlike and basically insecure he must have been from the beginning.

Many of these persons we shall meet in the clinical chapters. We shall go on meeting them, or hearing about them, in our daily lives; and as time goes on we shall come to understand them better and better.

Psychopathology as a national problem

Never before in their history have the people of the United States shown as great a desire to understand psychopathology as they have shown in recent years. There are good reasons for this awakening. Since the beginning of World War II our people and our government have come face to face with the fact that psychopathology is common all over the world and in all classes of people. They have found that it accounts for more illnesses in our own country than all other sources of illness combined; and they have come to realize that psychopathology is as treatable as other illnesses are.[3] We have been fortunate in having large numbers of competent men in the armed services, psychiatrists and psychologists, who were trained to recognize and deal intelligently with the psychopathology they encountered. It

---

[3] We are not including the mentally subnormal as a special class, although they have special problems, as all handicapped persons do. Persons of less than average intelligence can be found among any of the syndromes of psychopathology.

was a United States Army bulletin, produced by the combined efforts of regular army and reserve personnel, that laid the foundation for our present official classification. A great many able men, who might never have become interested in this area, have been trained in it as a direct result of their military experience, or because of training grants, research grants and other opportunities supplied by private foundations and the government.

Today there are more than 12,000 members of the American Psychiatric Association, 1000 members of the American Psychoanalytic Association, and 3000 members of the Clinical Division of the American Psychological Association. Most psychoanalysts are also members of the American Psychiatric Association, and some are members of the American Psychological Association. But even allowing for overlap, the number of trained personnel in these three groups alone comes close to the 15,000 mark. To this figure must be added some 3000 psychiatric social workers and the 15,000 professional nurses employed in mental hospitals. There are also a great many psychotherapists who do not belong to any of these groups. The demand for trained personnel in this area far exceeds the supply; and the demand is rising steadily everywhere in the country, but especially where existing facilities are of high calibre.[4]

It is as difficult as ever to estimate the full magnitude of our national problem in mental health.[5] We know that in the United States today there are about half a million patients in psychiatric hospitals, nearly all of whom are psychotic, and over one-half schizophrenic. This number is greater than the total patients hospitalized for all other illnesses put together. The annual public expenditure for psychiatric care and treatment in the United States amounts to well over $800,000,000. If we add to this figure the estimated loss of income suffered by persons hospitalized because of psychoses, the total annual loss to the nation rises to over two billion dollars. This total does not tell the whole story, even for hospitalized patients, and it tells nothing of the patients who are ill but not hospitalized.[6]

Those who have studied the national situation estimate that, if reasonably good facilities were available in all our states, instead of in only some of them, more than a million and a half psychotic men and women would now

---

[4] For a description of national, state and private facilities, training programs and mental hygiene activities, see Arieti, S. (Ed.), *American Handbook of Psychiatry.* New York: 1959, Part 14, "Management and care of the patient" (various authors), pp. 1827–1982. Also see Albee, G. W., *Mental Health Manpower Trends.* New York: Basic Books, 1959.

[5] Fein, R., *Economics of Mental Illness.* New York: Basic Books, 1958; Hollingshead, A. B., and Redlich, F. C., *Social Class and Mental Illness: A Community Study.* New York: Wiley, 1958; Leighton, A. H., *My Name is Legion.* New York: Basic Books, 1958; Myers, J. K., and Roberts, B. H., *Family and Class Dynamics in Mental Illness.* New York: Wiley, 1959; Jaco, E. G., *Social Epidemiology of Mental Disorders.* New York: Russell Sage Foundation, 1960.

[6] There are workable alternatives to hospitalization which have been demonstrated in other countries, but have not as yet been widely practiced in the United States. See Linn, L., "Hospital Psychiatry," in Arieti, S., (Ed.), *American Handbook of Psychiatry.* New York: Basic Books, 1959, pp. 1829–1839.

be in hospitals. In a great many communities, even in some of the wealthiest, the facilities provided by their citizens for early psychiatric diagnosis and treatment are well below the minimum standards observed for other medical and surgical specialties. This situation alone discourages potential patients and their families from seeking in-patient and out-patient help when they need it. It also creates a misleading picture of community need, since the proportion of the population getting help for psychopathological problems is highest where the facilities are best.[7]

Another influence that holds down the national admission rate for psychoses is our ancient cultural tradition of guilt, shame and superstition when it comes to what the public calls *insanity*. To a great many people, a psychosis still seems to be a kind of visitation, something which must be concealed. There still are families which, because of such attitudes, refuse to consider psychiatric treatment. Although a more informed and intelligent understanding of psychoses has developed within the last two decades, stories are still coming out in print, and shows are still appearing, that misrepresent psychotic illness as something inevitable and dangerous, in ways that other illnesses are not.

A vast amount of evidence has accumulated within the past half century to substantiate the natural and avoidable etiology of most psychoses. The rate of accumulation of evidence has accelerated tremendously within the past fifteen years, both from the direct study of normal and pathological early development, and from the clinical studies of psychotic patients by therapists who have learned to master their own anxieties. Any experienced clinician knows that psychotic patients get well and stay well for decades, and even for a lifetime. He knows that normal people experience in dreams the same kind of things that a psychotic patient may experience when he is awake. We are clearly not dealing with two different worlds — a normal world and a psychotic world — but with a difference in the adequacy of a person's defenses. The normal man experiences things only in his dreams; during the daytime he remains unaware of them. The psychotic man experiences them when he is wide awake.

The public still does not fully realize that clinicians today are able to treat enormous numbers of mildly and moderately psychotic patients — depressed, hypomanic, paranoid and schizophrenic — without resorting to hospitalization.[8] A great many such patients are able to go about their work, with psychotherapeutic help, and eventually to recover. These never get into the national statistics. Many of them do not know that a few decades ago they would have been quickly hospitalized because of the anxieties they aroused in others. If one patient, out of the thousands being treated today in out-patient clinics and office practice, has an acute episode or makes a

[7] Gurin, G., Veroff, J., and Feld, S., *Americans View Their Mental Health.* New York: Basic Books, 1960.

[8] Scher, S. C., and Davis, H. R. (Eds.), *The Out-Patient Treatment of Schizophrenia.* New York: Grune & Stratton, 1960.

suicidal attempt, the cry is still raised at once, "Why wasn't he in a hospital?" It is as though the proper place for a psychotic person is always in a hospital.

Persons with a psychotic illness who cannot control their own actions have to be hospitalized for their own protection and for the welfare of others. But there are dangers even in hospitalization, such as the danger of giving up the struggle and settling down to a dependent routine in an artificial setting. In the United States, and in other countries, there is evidence that the outlook for many patients is poorer in a hospital than outside it. This is more especially the case when the hospital is drab and understaffed, as most public mental hospitals are, and if the patient seldom sees relatives or friends, and feels abandoned by them.

In psychopathology there are always risks, whether the patient is in a hospital or not. The patient, the family and the clinician must be prepared to undertake the inherent risks, and not make maximum security the only goal. Most important of all, the general public needs to learn to accept the inevitability of risks in the treatment of psychopathology, just as it accepts the risks involved in surgery.

A word should be said here about the growing army of persons who are suffering from brain disorders, most of whom are in the upper age brackets. As every one knows, there is a rapidly increasing number of aged men and women in our population. In 1960 more than 17 million persons had passed the age of sixty-five years in the United States. Among these we must expect to find thousands of persons, being cared for at home, who nevertheless are suffering from serious memory defects, personality decline and episodes of confusion. The aged are more likely to survive and to preserve more of their mentality in their familiar home environment than if they are removed to a strange place, no matter how sanitary and comfortable the strange place may seem.

There is still another army of patients which does not usually get into the statistics of mental disorders. This is made up of persons who develop a transient brain disorder — usually some kind of a delirium — because of an infection, high fever or intoxication, or as a by-product of some systemic disease or a surgical procedure. Such patients, as a rule, are best cared for where they are, in a general hospital or at home, provided that they are continuously protected against the dangers of their own disoriented behavior.

When it comes to the incidence of neuroses, personality disorders and psychosomatic disorders, it is next to impossible to make an estimate of the number of persons who need or get therapy. Few of them ever need to be hospitalized. Judging from the large numbers we chance upon through casual contact or routine consultation, or in the course of some unrelated investigation, it seems clear that the great majority in these categories do not understand the nature of their difficulty and never ask treatment for it.

It has been loosely calculated that perhaps one child in every five now of grade-school age will at some time during his life need expert help because of neurosis, personality disorder, or psychosomatic disorder. It has also been estimated, admittedly from incomplete data, that approximately one person in twenty will at some time during his life be hospitalized for a psychosis, while another one in twenty will be incapacitated by a psychosis, but will not be hospitalized. It has been estimated that about 40 per cent of those who come to out-patient clinics in general hospitals, regardless of their initial complaint, are suffering mainly or solely from neurotic, psychotic, personality or psychosomatic disorders. Even before World War II, when hospital personnel were not as alert to these disturbances as they have become since, a study of the clientele of one metropolitan general hospital placed this figure at 30 per cent.

Is psychopathology on the increase? This is an important question: but it cannot be answered. There are too many sources of unreliability.[9] The past, with which our uncertain figures would have to be matched, also had its own special uncertainties. The clinical and social records of today are incomparably superior to those earlier in the century, especially when it comes to anxieties, fears and conflicts, the problems of infancy and childhood, of sexual gratification, of marital and social relationships, and of the management of aggression. Many complaints are now recognized as signs of psychopathology which earlier in the century would have been dismissed as trivial or distasteful, or simply as signs that the patient needed a vacation. The power of imagination has also become widely recognized. Competent persons in this area no longer expect a patient to be helped by being told that he is just imagining things. To imagine something can be more stressful than to experience it in reality.

The plain truth is that professional attitudes and methods have changed so much within the past few decades that we shall never know how prevalent what we now call psychopathology was in times past. In its mild and moderate forms it seems to have gone largely unrecognized; in its severe forms it was often concealed or provided with a euphemistic nonpsychiatric label. The character distortions, immaturities and deviations which are now grouped as personality disorders used to be looked upon with ridicule, or regarded simply as obstinacy, showing off, snobbishness, vanity, degeneracy, or inherent wickedness. Psychosomatic medicine has only come into its own within recent years. In short, we have to accept the fact that comparisons between the incidence of psychopathology in the past and present are little more than guesses.

Normal and abnormal personality

The task of differentiating between what is normal and what is abnormal has always been a vexatious one. Different people define normality and abnormality in different ways, from different points of view, and for different purposes. There are so many shadings, in so many dimensions, that most

---

[9] Cf. Caplan, G. (chairman), *Problems of Estimating Changes in Frequency of Mental Disorders.* New York: Group for the Advancement of Psychiatry (in press).

writers avoid the subject altogether. But even though we still cannot settle the problem, it deserves at least to be discussed.

Normal, perfect and ideal personality. One source of common confusion can be cleared up quickly. This is the tendency to equate normal personality with perfect or ideal personality. There is the same difficulty here as in defining physical health, and we have to take as realistic an attitude in one as in the other. The "normal human body" is really an abstraction; to describe it is to describe no one. The range of normal variation, for both sexes within a given age, is enormous and multidimensional. The anatomist or physiologist who attempted to cover all the possible variations of normality in his specialty would never finish his subject, and he would lose his audience. The same is true of the behavioral, psychological and psychic life — that is, the experience and behavior of the normal social person, internal and external, independent and interdependent.[10]

Normality and conformity. It is often said that normality means the ability to conform to the cultural expectations of one's society. To be unable to conform is then considered abnormal. For some purposes this is a useful criterion. It makes allowances for the striking differences that students of different societies find in cultural expectations; and it stresses the *ability* to conform rather than conformity itself. Conformity, however, is not necessarily a sign of normality; and an inability to conform is not always pathological.

A great many persons conform out of anxiety. We have their own word for it, or their rationalizations make it clear. Many conformists have an excessive need for social approval; they are too afraid of risking censure to do or think differently from the average person. Some of the most meticulous conformists are compulsive persons who accept all social customs as ritualistic means for controlling their own internally generated anxiety. Some conformists suffer from excessive guilt, conscious or unconscious, which makes them afraid that at any moment they will do wrong. Conformity such as this can hardly be called normal.

Complete conformity is possible only in a static culture. We know that in our culture the standards of conformity are continually shifting, so that there is always considerable conflict between succeeding generations. Nonconformity with cultural expectations often leads to the discovery of valuable new customs in a society, and to the shedding of other customs which have lost their social value. It may thus be a basis for social progress. Within recent decades this has been especially obvious in the arts and sciences. Innovations of all kinds have not led to disintegration in the arts, but on the contrary have opened up brand new avenues of expression.

[10] A proposal for the inclusion of the behavioral sciences in medical undergraduate curricula has been outlined by Cameron, N., "Human ecology and personality in the training of physicians," in Whitehorn, J., Jacobsen, C., Levine, M., and Lippard, V. (Eds.), *Psychiatry and Medical Education.* Washington, D.C.: Amer. Psychiatric Ass. 1952, pp. 63–96.

Personal nonconformity in a society such as ours cannot be assessed without taking into consideration what is permissible for each sex at different ages and in relation to status and personal background. We expect adolescents to conform less to adult customs than either latency children or adults themselves; but we also expect adolescents to show rigid conformity in relation to the current standards of their own adolescent peers. They insist upon doing what other adolescents are doing, and consider their parents' ways absurd. We expect girls and women, in most respects, to be more conformist than boys and men. An inability to conform, provided it does not isolate a person from human contact or lead to antisocial conduct, may be an expression of unusual talent. It may even be the beginning of a revolt against something pathological in the customs of the culture itself. There are many persons who are *able* to conform, but *choose* not to do so. Their non-conformity may also lead to beneficial results for their society as a whole.[11]

Normality and adequacy of performance. Another useful criterion of normality is that of the relative adequacy of performance, in comparison with an individual's previous levels, and with the cultural norms in his society for persons of his sex, age and status. This adds the dimension of previous performance, and it emphasizes competence in an objective way. It has, however, its own weaknesses as a criterion.

It does not allow for the wide fluctuation which a great many persons show in their general or their occupational adequacy, without being in any sense disturbed or ill. Most people have their good days and their bad days without being able to say exactly why. This criterion also pays only lip service to the normal decline in adequacy that comes with ageing. Above all, it does not take into account the personal cost of adequate performance. For one person a position of leadership or of subordination may come easily, for another person it may be ruinous, even though both look alike on the surface.

Normality and the inner life. Neither cultural expectancy nor adequacy of performance pays enough attention to the inner life of human beings. It is possible to meet the cultural expectations of a society, to perform adequately within its specifications, even to excel beyond precedent, and still to have an impoverished inner life, or to live always with serious conflicts and frustration, or to feel always unloved and alone. In discussing normality from the standpoint of the inner life of human beings, we shall be discarding neither of the two preceding criteria, but only adding something significant to them.

We shall not attempt a definition of normality at this point, or make a clear distinction between normality and psychopathology. This distinction will grow out of the rest of the book; and it will always remain a difficult one to make, excepting in the extremes of clinical syndromes. Here we shall limit discussion to some of the relationships between — or rather within —

[11] Milgram, S., "Nationality and conformity," *Scientific Amer.*, 1961, *205*, 45–52; Berg, I. A., and Bass, B. M. (Eds.), *Conformity and Deviation*. New York: Harper, 1961.

cultural expectations, personal adequacy and the inner life of perception, feeling, emotion, thought and action.

Human personality, as we shall see, grows out of early introjections and identifications, by means of which every infant internalizes what he experiences. It is nothing new or strange to say that we take into ourselves what we see and handle, what we hear and mouth and feel. By such processes we set up inside us the culture that surrounds us, giving it something of our own individualistic stamp, but leaving it much like the internalized culture of the other persons among whom we live.

Unless the cultural expectations of a society are based upon early childhood identifications that enrich a person's inner life, and are readily available while he is growing up, the price of seeming to meet them may be that of accepting an inner impoverishment. We see tragic examples of this among institutionalized infants who, although they may receive routine care and nourishment that are fully adequate, do not have readily available the products of constant maternal devotion which they need to build an inner life. We see it to a much lesser degree during childhood and early adolescence, in those who are compelled or encouraged to take on major adult responsibilities before they have had the chance to experience the flowering of their childhood and adolescence within them. Such precocious assumption of adulthood is likely to result in a responsible man or woman who is relatively empty, who performs well and meets expectations, but who can operate only within a narrow range like an automaton.

Unless a society provides reasonable opportunities for children and adolescents to work out solutions for their major conflicts, and unless the frustrations to which they are exposed fall within moderate limits, they will grow into adults who cannot tolerate conflict and frustration, adults who act impulsively, resort easily to violence, or escape from life by falling into comparative apathy. Such a society will produce few adults who know the art of being maturely interdependent, few who can take pleasure in giving and receiving love, few who are not afraid to take the initiative, to be enterprising, to cooperate and compete, to be aggressive without being hostile, and to tolerate aggression in others. It will produce few adults who find genuine pleasure in fulfilling their social roles, and who at the same time give pleasure to those who fulfill reciprocal roles with them.

These are not easy goals to achieve. We all have many different needs, some of them mutually exclusive; and the needs of others frequently clash with ours or fail to provide a satisfying reciprocal relationship. It is impossible to resolve all of these incompatibilities; and the art of compromise is a difficult and delicate one, demanding patience, understanding and tolerance.[12]

Our own society is far from having reached optimal levels in these dimensions, as the multiple evidence of cultural conflict and personal unhappiness

[12] Cohen, M. B. (Ed.), Advances in Psychiatry: *Recent Developments in Interpersonal Relations.* New York: Norton, 1959.

testifies. At the same time, let it be said that there is no other society, as diverse in opportunities and expectations as ours, that is devoting as much serious concentrated effort in seeking solutions for its infinitely complex human problems. We shall see examples of failure to reach optimal levels in the disruptive emotional ambivalence in some of our patients. We shall see that other patients have too great a need to be dependent, and that still others cannot tolerate a healthy dependence because they lack a *basic trust,* which they should have developed as infants. We shall see persons suffering from too much or too little guilt, of which they are not always aware. We shall see the familiar overprotective and overindulgent mothers, the unresponsive and the hypersensitive children. We shall see some wide deviations from cultural expectations in maturity and in a capacity for reciprocal interdependence. Finally, we shall see examples of what we all know, that a person can be physically healthy, able to meet the cultural expectations of his society and fulfill adequately his social roles, without being at peace within.

Some criteria of normality. In the chapters that follow, we shall use a set of rough criteria in distinguishing normal from pathological personality functioning. These will include *cultural expectations.* Everyone lives in the presence of cultural expectations. They are internalized from infancy on, to help construct the ego and superego, and to prepare a person for his social interactions as a child, as an adolescent and as an adult.

Our criteria will also include *adequacy of performance,* in comparison with each individual's previous level of adequacy, and with the cultural norms current in his society for persons of his sex, age, background and present status. This criterion will allow for wide fluctuations, such as those between being awake and being asleep, being sick and being well, feeling optimistic and feeling discouraged, being able to rejoice and being able to grieve.

Our criteria will include not only a person's overt behavior and his physiological levels of function, but also his *internal integrative functions* at psychological levels — conscious, preconscious and unconscious. They will include the ways in which a person's internal psychological functions influence his conception of his body, his conception of himself and of the world around him. They will include the ways in which a person's psychological functions determine how he shall interact with his human environment.

A certain degree of internal stress and strain is normal and inevitable for everyone. Part of this is a result of the difference between the *internal organization of a human being* and the *organization of the environment* in which he lives. We master as much of the human environment as we can, and we come to some kind of a working compromise with what we cannot master. It is the human being and not, of course, the inanimate environment that has to work out compromises and maintain them. Part of the internal stress and strain comes from the *conditions of group living,* in which attempts are made to strike a balance between group need and personal need, group harmony and personal gratification, between the integrity of the individual, and of the family, of the community, the state and even the world. Part of the internal stress and strain arises because of the complexity of the internal personality system itself, or as we prefer to call it, *the psychodynamic system.*

All experience and behavior at conscious and preconscious levels appear to have unconscious components and to stimulate unconscious activities. These unconscious components and activities *remain* unconscious; but they are still active and effective. They are living operations within the psychodynamic system itself. They have to be dealt with somehow — expressed in action, fantasy or dream; incorporated into preconscious activity but not directly expressed; sublimated, defended against or neutralized.

The human being also cannot escape conflicts between needs which must remain unsatisfied in order that other needs may find expression. There are automatic scanning, selecting and defending systems within the psychodynamic system. These make it possible for a person to engage in socially organized ("secondary process") perception, emotion, thought and action, without the disruption that unconscious processes might bring if they were allowed to intrude on a massive scale. But although their general effect is to stabilize the psychodynamic system, they also create sources of conflict within it.

The degree of stress and strain to which the psychodynamic system is normally subjected can be appreciated by the urgency of the normal demand for sleep every night. The kinds of intrusions that are kept out during the day can be judged by what happens when we fall asleep and dream. To fall asleep is to regress, to relax our daytime vigil, to give up some of the differentiation into unconscious and preconscious, to loosen our ties with external reality and to revel in fantasy.

To be normal, the psychodynamic system must include effective ego boundaries which protect the preconscious and conscious life during the daytime against threats of disruptive intrusion — whether the threat comes from external reality, from the superego, from the unconscious ego or from derivatives of the id. This separation, however, is not normally a complete one. There is a certain amount of intercommunication between what is preconscious and what remains unconscious. When the separation is too rigid, as it sometimes is, we find a general all-around inhibition, which makes a person emotionally restrained, cold, formal and lacking in spontaneity. Neither may the situation go to the opposite extreme, and make a person completely uninhibited, impulsive and unpredictable. Between these extremes there are many varieties of normality and abnormality. It is not even normal to be good if the goodness is sustained by a pervasive sense of worthlessness or guilt. Most psychopathology includes major defects in the organization of ego boundaries, such as too rigid a separation between preconscious and unconscious, too permeable a separation, and the inclusion of a distorted defense system. Any of these may prevent a person from making full use of his potentialities.

The normal person in our society is one who first of all gains a basic confidence or trust through his interactions with a mother figure early in life. This leaves him free to take a great deal for granted in his relationship to the world around him, to feel reasonably secure about himself and others. He is one who, in growing from infancy to adulthood, has managed to weather the succession of weanings and emotional crises which all maturing normally entails. He has been able to resolve his major conflicts without the serious personality distortions which leave a person vulnerable to adult psychopathology. He has learned to give and to get love and loyalty, at each phase of his development, in ways that are appropriate for each level. He has learned to control his aggressions without becoming passive, without losing enterprise and initiative, and without missing the enjoyment of competition and cooperation. He takes pleasure in mutual interdependence, in needing others and in being needed by them. He is a person who experiences a reasonable degree of self-fulfillment in his major social roles, feels warmth toward other human beings, and is able to communicate his feelings acceptably in such a way that they are reciprocated by other persons in his daily life.

Dreams and the psychopathology of everyday life

All this is not to say that the normal person achieves perfect equilibrium, or that he never shows the slightest sign of psychopathology. What is true of the anatomical and physiological systems is true also of psychodynamic systems. They are never ideal or perfect. There are always minor defects which might conceivably lead to major difficulties under conditions of stress, deprivation or illness. Under ordinary conditions people manage to compensate for their defects, one way or another, and to keep their psychological equilibrium oscillating within normal bounds.

What this equilibrium includes at unconscious levels, in every human being, was first set forth systematically by Freud in two of his major works, published within a year of one another. The first is *The Interpretation of Dreams,* which came out in 1900, and the second is *The Psychopathology of Everyday Life,* which appeared in 1901. In their recent translations they are without peers in their respective fields.[13] They are not only classics which everyone interested in psychopathology should read; they are also fascinatingly written and replete with illustrations taken from everyday experience. Our modern conceptions of psychopathology are still based upon these original presentations of the unconscious meanings of nighttime dreams and daytime slips.

Every one of us, no matter how good or bad his psychological equilibrium, loses his reality-testing functions and has psychotic experiences when he falls asleep and dreams. Everyone agrees that sleep is essential. Not everyone realizes that dreaming seems also to be essential. It does not matter if we forget our dreams, which we almost always do. They have done

[13] Freud, S., *The Interpretation of Dreams.* (1900), Standard Edition (trans. J. Strachey), vols. 4–5; Freud, S., *The Psychopathology of Everyday Life.* (1901), Standard Edition, 1960, vol. 6.

their work and we awake refreshed, ready for another day of realistic experience.[14]

We all know how unrealistic dreams usually are and how extravagant they may be. They are strange forms of personal artistic creation, plays which provide their own stage and their own scenery. The dreamer, who at times is a watcher and at times an active participant, accepts his dreaming fantasy while he is asleep as though it were objective fact. He sees or takes part in strange performances which undergo unexpected shifts and kaleidoscopic changes. Magic is in the air, miracles occur, the dead come to life, the past and present are indiscriminately mingled. There may be all kinds of contradictions, impossible substitutions and absurd distortions which follow one another without apparent reason.

In dreaming we experience many desires and fears, many anxieties and conflicts, fantasies of hatred and destruction, of love and possession, that are unacceptable to us when we are awake. For such reasons, and because dreams seem so fantastic when we are awake, we laugh about them or dismiss them as so much nonsense. The fact remains, however, that they are our own individualistic creations. We sometimes suspect that there may be some hidden truth in them and wonder what they might mean.[15]

This is an ancient story. More than two thousand years ago it was written that the good man dreamed what the bad man did. It was even believed then that incestuous dreams were normal. In Sophocles' play, *Oedipus Rex*, which was played in the fifth century B.C. and is still staged today, we hear Jocasta reassuring her husband, who unknown to either of them is also her son. She says, "Many a man ere now in dreams hath lain with her who bare him. He hath least annoy who with such omens troubleth not his mind."[16] We shall remember these lines when we discuss early childhood development.

Recent research indicates that everybody dreams every night.[17] Some dreams, perhaps all dreams, are in part prepared during the daytime, by primitive processes operating at unconscious levels. They only come to full expression after we have gone to sleep. It is then that we exclude all that we can of our realistic surroundings and give up our realistic thinking. The ego boundaries that protect our daytime thinking from unconscious intrusion partially dissolve. The defensive organization grows lax, superego control goes primitive or disappears, and the lid of repression opens. Abstract and metaphorical thinking is replaced by processions of concrete imagery. It is often said that we can afford to let our dream fantasies emerge because we are immobilized and cannot act out what we fantasy. There is some truth in

---

[14] Cf. De Martino, M. F. (Ed.), *Dreams and Personality Dynamics.* Springfield, Ill.: Thomas, 1959.

[15] Lewis, H. B., "Organization of the self as reflected in manifest dreams," *Psychoanalysis & Psychoanal. Rev.*, 1959, *46*, 21–35.

[16] Cited from Freud, S., *The Interpretation of Dreams.* (1900), Standard Edition, 1953, vol. 4, p. 264.

[17] Goodenough, D. R., Shapiro, A., Holden, M., and Steinschriber, L., "A comparison of 'dreamers' and 'nondreamers': eye movements, electroencephalograms, and the recall of dreams," *J. abnorm. soc. Psychol.*, 1959, *59*, 295–302.

this; but we shall see that sleepwalkers go on dreaming while they dress, go down the stairs, open the door and walk along the street.

What about the daytime? This is where the psychopathology of everyday life comes in. When we are awake we all occasionally give little signs that more is going on beneath the surface than we fully realize. A slip of the tongue reveals a sentiment quite different from the one we consciously intended to express, sometimes different from what we were actually feeling at the time. An intended positive comes out unexpectedly as a negative; an intended denial comes through as an affirmation. This kind of thing has also been recognized from ancient times and expressed in literature through the ages. In *The Merchant of Venice*, Shakespeare has Portia say to the suitor whom she favors, "One half of me is yours, the other half yours — mine, I would say." She had already given her word that she would leave the selection to chance; but her feeling gets through in spite of her conscious intent.

Slips of the tongue need not be as transparent as Portia's misspeaking; and what slips through the defenses may not have ever been fully conscious. There is often a strange condensation of meanings in what one says. The meaning we had intended comes out with something else which is embarrassing, something that makes others wonder privately or laugh outright. Slips of the pen and typewriter, misreadings, bungled actions, and the many varieties of selective remembering and forgetting, hearing and not hearing, seeing and overlooking, losing and finding — all point in the same general direction. There is much more going on within us than we reveal to others or to ourselves, and a great deal of it is beyond our own control.

The selective exclusion of unpleasant, unacceptable and contradictory trends is something more than a desire to present ourselves in a favorable light, more even than a desire to think well of our own intentions. It is a matter of preserving our integrity as human beings, of maintaining an ability to experience the realistic world in realistic ways, an ability to adapt to these realities and master some of them. It is a matter of maintaining a necessary self-respect and keeping the respect of others. We can do this without ourselves becoming automatons because, through our semipermeable ego boundaries, we still remain in touch with a vast magical world that operates beneath the surface. In this world of magic there are infinite interactions among impulses, fantasies, intuitive evaluations, symbols and feelings, all of them beyond the reach of reality-testing and logic.

The great human achievement in growing up is to set boundaries which will contain this magical world and allow its forces to be energized into realistic experience and behavior. The boundary-setting is structured and maintained by a complex organization which includes the defense mechanisms. We shall often speak as though the defenses functioned like a protecting wall, but in reality they are alive and they are selectively permeable in both directions. It is true that we need the stimulation of external reality in the daytime to keep us realistically oriented; but it is equally true that we need the warmth, vitality, inspiration and playfulness which our unconscious world of magic contributes. There are difficulties in constructing boundaries and in maintaining them so that both demands are met. If the boundaries are too rigid, we have said, a person may be without adequate spontaneity. He gives up his freedom in exchange for rituals that protect him from the threat of anxiety. If the boundaries are too permeable, a person may be plagued by continual anxiety, which means a constant threat of ego disintegration. He may even suffer a partial disintegration and be unable to distinguish between normal metaphorical thinking and the concrete meanings it always contains. Some of these defects in functional boundaries, in the organization and use of defense mechanisms, and in ego-superego relations, will become clear when we examine the clinical syndromes of psychopathology.

Syndromes of psychopathology

Psychopathology is a multidimensional continuum. We have to break it up into groups of related phenomena in order to be able to handle it and particularly to discuss it. In working with a patient on his problems it is often necessary to make a diagnosis and attach a label to what he presents. Often it is impossible to do either. When it comes to communicating with someone else, however, the formulation may be so vague and inclusive that it only communicates confusion. This, too, is an old tale. About a century ago, experts working in this general area decided that classification was worse than useless. They lumped all psychopathology together and called it all by one name. It was not long before this solution proved vain. The groupings began again; and they have continued to evolve up to the present day.

In presenting clinical material to illustrate psychopathology, we shall in general follow the official classification of the American Psychiatric Association.[18] Wherever we deviate from it, we shall note the deviation and explain it. Classifications of illness, in other fields as well as in psychopathology, are always somewhat arbitrary and in some respects unsatisfactory. This is inevitable. They are the products of committees appointed for the task, and made up of representatives of more than one school of thought and more than one generation. What comes out of such a committee is always a compromise between opposing points of view, the best compromise that could be worked out.

In our clinical chapters we shall recognize fourteen major syndromes, or groupings, in each of which the psychopathology has certain basic characteristics in common. Although the case illustrations have been selected for their clarity, it goes without saying that in each syndrome there will appear also some characteristics belonging to another syndrome. Each is a "typical case," which is not to say that it is an average case, but rather that it is unusually free of admixtures. The first six are officially grouped together as *neuroses*

---

[18] *Mental Disorders.* Diagnostic and Statistical Manual, Washington, D.C.: Amer. Psychiatric Ass., 1952.

or *psychoneuroses* — the terms have now become synonymous. The next five are officially grouped as *psychoses*. When psychoses are severe they usually distort reality sufficiently to disable the patient temporarily; when they are mild they may interfere little with normal life. In addition to these eleven, we shall describe what are now called *personality disorders*, a rather heterogeneous group, as we shall see in the next pages, *psychosomatic disorders*, in which the prime disturbance is expressed directly in some form of physical illness, and those *brain disorders* which include significant psychopathology. At this point we shall characterize each syndrome briefly, and leave a more extended discussion for later chapters.

The Neuroses

1. Anxiety reactions

These are states of diffuse nameless apprehension, in which attempts are made to discharge internally generated tension and reduce anxiety by increasing bodily activity. The increased activity may be simply a sustained tenseness; it may also include restlessness and vigorous action. Sleep is usually light, fitful, and often disturbed by night terrors. Appetite is sometimes diminished; but sometimes it is increased. Various visceral disturbances occur as part of the discharge of tension. Some patients have acute anxiety attacks which frighten them. In rare instances a full-fledged panic develops, involving a generalized regression, which may lead to an acute psychotic episode.

2. Phobic reactions

Phobias are like anxiety reactions; but the anxiety is focused upon some definite object or situation. The internally generated tension and the anxiety are displaced from within and projected on to something which can usually be avoided. The fear is therefore an irrational one; but the phobic reaction is somewhat more adaptive than is generalized anxiety, because the apparent source of fear can be controlled through a specific avoidance. When phobias spread to include many kinds of external excitant, they lose this advantage. Children commonly develop transient phobias early in life when they have not yet organized adequate means of handling their tension and anxiety. The adult phobia is a revival of the childhood device, although the object or situation feared need not be the same as the childhood ones. An irrational fear of height, of closed in places or of wide open spaces, are common examples of adult phobia.

3. Conversion reactions

By a conversion reaction we mean a process that transforms (converts) an unconscious conflict into a body symptom. This reduces tension and anxiety by expressing the conflict symbolically. The disturbed function may express forbidden impulses, the defenses against them, and self-punishment for having such impulses. A single symptom often has many unconscious meanings, some of them infantile or childish, some of them adult. Blindness, deafness and paralysis in otherwise healthy persons are dramatic examples. The dramatic, classical conversion symptoms used to be more common than they are today, at least in urban communities. They are still to be found in remote, underdeveloped communities, where knowledge of psychodynamics has not become general. Minor conversion symptoms are still common everywhere. They often occur as exaggerations of organically produced symptoms and may be difficult to distinguish from psychosomatic disorders.

4. Dissociative reactions

The dissociative reaction is an attempt to escape from excessive tension and anxiety by isolating or separating some parts of ego function from the rest. It appears in a variety of forms and intensities, including sleepwalking, trances, estrangement and depersonalization, massive amnesia, fugues or flights, and multiple personalities. Some of these are close to normal functioning, such as sleepwalking, and others are close to psychosis. Multiple personality has always been rare; but it apparently still occurs. A recent case is the one written up and dramatized as *The Three Faces of Eve*.[19] The classic in this field is Morton Prince's *Dissociation of a Personality*, which has recently been reprinted as a paperback.

5. Obsessive compulsive reactions

Obsessive compulsive reactions consist of repetitious actions, words or thoughts, which seem absurd and useless, but actually enable a person to reduce intolerable tension and anxiety by magical means. In the symptoms of this group, also, one can often find expressions of forbidden impulses or fantasies, of defenses against these expressions, and of self-punishment for having the impulses or fantasies. Guilt plays a prominent part in the syndrome, although it is usually unconscious. The symptoms range in complexity from trivialities, such as tapping, counting or snapping the fingers, all the way to complex rituals which are time-consuming, fatiguing, and must always be repeated in exactly the same manner. Abstract speculation, rumination and doubting are sometimes the only symptoms present. Obsessive compulsive reactions are related to normal ceremony, magic and the sciences.

6. Neurotic depressive reactions

The neurotically depressed person is typically dejected and self-depreciatory; often he is also restless and anxious. Guilt plays a leading role in producing the symptoms, as it also does in obsessive compulsive reactions; but the symptoms are not magical or ritualistic, and they control tension and

19 Thigpen, C. H., and Cleckley, H. M., *The Three Faces of Eve.* New York: McGraw-Hill, 1957.

anxiety less effectively. The symptoms consist of repeated complaints of feeling inferior, worthless and hopeless. These complaints stimulate others to protest and to reassure the patient; but his unconscious sense of guilt makes him reject all protestations and reassurances, and to insist upon his inferiority, worthlessness and hopelessness. He thus arouses further protest and further reassurance, which he again treats as he did the earlier attempts, and the cycle begins again. The neurotic depression may be distinguished from the psychotic depression by the severity of general personality disturbance and the depth of the regression. A neurotically depressed person can nearly always keep at his work; the psychotically depressed person usually cannot.

The Psychoses

A clear-cut distinction between neuroses and psychoses is not universally accepted. One of the most influential books in the field of psychopathology discusses both as neuroses.[20] Nevertheless, the official classification does make the distinction and we shall do the same. As we have already indicated, when psychoses are severe, reality is usually much distorted. Delusions and hallucinations represent attempts to deal with previously unconscious material, which invades preconscious and conscious organizations, as regression becomes widespread and ego boundaries begin to dissolve. It should be repeated that mild or "borderline" psychotic states may interfere little with normal life, and are not inconsistent with great talent at times. They are sometimes chronic and are not recognized under ordinary conditions. We shall begin with paranoid reactions because they seem often to be a combination of neurotic and psychotic mechanisms, and because the denial and projection used are similar to normal denial and projection, as, for example, in the universal practice of scapegoating.

1. Paranoid reactions

Paranoid reactions are attempts to escape the effects of previously unconscious impulses and fantasies, which have erupted into preconscious and conscious organizations, by processes of denial and projection. The patient tries to remain in contact with external reality by reconstructing it in accordance with the impulses and fantasies which he can no longer keep unconscious. The delusional reconstructions are in this sense spontaneous attempts at self-cure. Sometimes the product is a *delusional pseudocommunity* of persecutors, which includes real and fictitious persons with real and fictitious roles. Delusions in any of the psychoses may be creative in the same sense that dreams are. The projective mechanisms used relate paranoid reactions to the phobias; but whereas the phobic patient agrees that his fears sound absurd, the paranoid patient believes in his delusions. Paranoid elements enter into all of the other psychoses to some extent.

[20] Fenichel, O., *The Psychoanalytic Theory of Neuroses.* New York: Norton, 1945.

2. Psychotic depressive reactions

Psychotic depressions are mood disorders in which dejection, self-depreciation and self-condemnation reach delusional proportions. An acutely conscious sense of worthlessness and guilt develops and persists. There is a sweeping regression which revives conflicts between an *infantile ego*, which speaks with an adult voice, and a *primitive superego*, which persecutes the patient. The patient identifies now with the regressive, helpless, remorseful ego, now with the harsh, punitive superego. Often he tries to project his self-hatred as the attitudes of others toward him; but usually he is less successful in this maneuver than paranoid or paranoid schizophrenic persons are. The danger of suicide is a grave one. Prospects for recovery, regardless of the form of therapy, are excellent.

3. Manic reactions and manic-depressive cycles

Manic reactions are psychotic excitements which are characterized by overactivity and delusional elation or self-assertion, but show relatively little disorganization. The behavior of manic patients is a caricature of joy and optimism, of self-assurance and self-assertion. Often the caricature is childish. In a small minority of patients manic attacks alternate with psychotic depressions. This relationship, which was recognized even in ancient Greece, is the origin of the term *manic-depressive psychosis*. Many look upon the manic reaction as primarily a defense against an imminent threat of a psychotic depression, that is, a denial of depressive trends and a reaction-formation against them, in fantasy and action. It is not unusual for a manic patient to burst into tears, make depressive statements about himself, and then to become manic again.

4. Schizophrenic reactions

These are the most interesting of all the psychoses. More than 15,000 articles and books have been written about them. They are attempts to escape tension and anxiety by abandoning interpersonal relations and replacing them with delusions and hallucinations, which reconstruct external reality for the patient, in accordance with the previously unconscious fantasies which have invaded preconscious and conscious organizations on a large scale. They are baffling to the normal observer because the patient who has not given up completely continues to operate at several different levels of regression. These represent his multiple points of immature fixation. He may shift from concrete, infantile thinking to adult metaphorical thinking and back again to concrete thinking, several times within the same hour, or even mix the two in the same statement.[21]

21 The writer is indebted to Dr. William L. Pious for first calling his attention to this conception. For a recent discussion, see Searles, H. F., "The differentiation between concrete and metaphorical thinking in the recovering schizophrenic patient," *J. Amer. Psychoanal. Ass.*, 1962, *10*, 22–49.

To understand an active schizophrenic patient, the participant observer must be flexible enough, intuitive enough, and sufficiently free from anxiety himself, to be able to shift his own levels of interaction so as to coincide with the patient's shifts. Such flexiblility, intuition and freedom from anxiety, in the face of strange, primitive thinking, are uncommon. If, however, a therapist is able to exercise them, he not only brings help to the isolated patient, but he also gains insights into human thinking which no other experiences provide.

It has been recognized for at least half a century that the group of schizophrenias includes a rich variety of unrealistic experience and behavior. Attempts to organize the variety into subtypes have so far failed. Patients themselves shift in their predominant experience and behavior from one subtype to another. A person may enter a hospital, for example, in a rigid stupor, and within a few days become excited and overactive; or he may come out of the stupor, express frank delusions and hallucinations, and give every evidence that during the stuporous phase he was still acutely observant. Sudden unexpected recoveries are not unknown, without the intervention of special therapy. They are most likely to occur when interaction with therapists is available at whatever level of thought is possible for the patient at the time. The outlook for recovery is not good; but in a suitable environment about 50 per cent get well; and these may stay well for a lifetime if not subjected to unusual stress.

5. Involutional psychotic reactions

This designation has only historical precedent to justify it. In the official classification it is an obvious compromise between those who would like to preserve the old concept of *involutional melancholia*, which it includes, and those who would like to drop it altogether. The commonest syndromes now included in this grouping are psychotic depressions and paranoid reactions appearing for the first time in middle or late life. There is no doubt that depressive and paranoid reactions to signs of senescence are common; but they are no different from depressive and paranoid reactions to other crises. Even the tendency of the psychotic state to persist is hardly surprising, since senescence and senility persist. It is unlikely that this group will survive another revision of our classification.

Other Major Disorders

1. Personality disorders

Under this designation, the official classification includes many diverse syndromes for which it has not been able to find a place elsewhere. We shall describe the following five groups in the chapter on personality disorders:

(*i*) *Character disorders.* These include all of the "personality trait and pattern disturbances" of the official classification that correspond to neurotic and prepsychotic character structures. In these, some personality distortion develops early in life, and persists as the individual's "style," that is, as the characteristic way in which he copes with his environment and fends off anxiety, without developing outspoken neurotic or psychotic symptoms. We shall follow the official classification in distinguishing compulsive, paranoid, cyclothymic (i.e., manic-depressive) and schizoid personalities; but we shall add the hysterical personality, a histrionic temperamental character disorder commonly encountered in clinical work, which seems to have been overlooked.

(*ii*) *Inadequate and unstable personalities.* This group includes chronically inadequate persons, emotionally unstable persons, and chronically passive-aggressive persons.

(*iii*) *Sociopathic personality disturbances.* We include here three groups: (a) irresponsible and emotionally shallow persons, who repeatedly commit offenses without much anxiety and with little material gain; (b) antisocial persons, who are constantly in open rebellion against society for unconscious reasons; and (c) dissocial persons, who are easily corrupted, but seem to be neither antisocial nor emotionally shallow.

(*iv*) *Sexual deviation.* The official classification names a few examples without discussing them. We shall discuss six of the commonest forms: (a) *overt homosexuality;* (b) *exhibitionism;* (c) *voyeurism;* (d) *fetishism;* (e) *transvestism;* and (f) *sadomasochism.*

(*v*) *Addiction.* As in the official classification, we include here separately addiction to *alcohol* and addictions to *drugs,* since both clinicians and research workers find basic differences in the character of alcohol addicts and drug addicts.

2. Psychosomatic disorders

In these disorders, a person reacts to stress, tension and anxiety with some direct physiological malfunction, which may eventually lead to irreversible organ or tissue damage. There seems to be no symbolism involved such as there is in conversion symptoms. Among the commonest examples of psychosomatic disorders are the development of stomach ulcers in persons who are in perpetual conflict over their needs to be dependent upon someone, and the development of ulcerative colitis in persons who continually repress hostility because they also have a great need to please. If we realize that the internal organs are always responsive in emotional situations — for example, almost everyone suffers digestive disturbances when he is angry or depressed — the psychosomatic disorders are not difficult to understand.

3. Acute and chronic brain disorders

Many brain disorders involve significant psychopathology; many do not. We shall discuss the following syndromes which do: (a) *delirium,* including acute intoxication; (*b*) *head injury;* (*c*) *general paresis;* and (*d*) *senile* and *arteriosclerotic brain disorders.* The severity of brain damage is not always proportional to the severity of the psychopathology, nor is the latter specific for the character of the brain injury. It will be seen, for example, that ageing persons differ markedly in their reaction to a decline, and that the differences are related both to current circumstances and to a person's life history.

Nowadays it is taken for granted that most psychopathology has its roots in infantile, childhood and adolescent experiences. There are flaws in the personality structure of vulnerable persons, and these seem to be the result of early misfortunes. Accordingly, we shall begin our account with a discussion of what is known about personality development that may have a direct bearing upon adult psychopathology. In personality development, as in embryological development, there are successive phases which must be lived through, each with its special problems. If the problems of one phase are left unsolved, the following phases may be burdened with the consequences, and may be seriously distorted. It is true in personality development, as also in embryological development, that failures in *early phases* are likely to leave more serious defects than failures in later phases. For this reason we shall begin with a chapter devoted to infancy and early childhood, and follow it with a chapter on latency and adolescence where some of the earlier difficulties may leave a mark.

After we have finished discussing the making of a person, we shall turn to the special problems of need, drive and motivation, as these appear in the psychodynamic system, and then go on to a description of the psychodynamic system as we currently conceive of it. Finally, we shall take up the special topics of conflict, regression, anxiety and the defense mechanisms, as an introduction to the clinical chapters which then follow. First of all let us see how human personality develops, and what the major difficulties are in achieving ultimate maturity.

2

Personality Development:
Infancy and Early Childhood

⊕

EACH OF US IS BORN INTO THIS COMPLEX WORLD IN SUCH A HELPLESS STATE that if some adult did not immediately take charge of us, meet our daily needs and protect us, we could not even survive. A newborn infant can do next to nothing for himself. He cannot speak or understand a word he hears. The facial expressions of others around him mean nothing to him; neither do their gestures nor their tones of voices. He cannot grasp the most obvious intentions of the people about him. He does not even see people or things as separate objects. He cannot distinguish between himself and the person who holds him, between his own body and his surroundings. In the beginning he is human in form, beautifully made, but animal in conduct.

Over the long years of infancy, childhood and adolescence, the human being is transformed from a *biological baby*, immersed in an almost structureless universe, into a *biosocial adult*, who becomes an integral part of a world that he understands. Each infant, through his own activity and effort, learns to single out things and persons from the kaleidoscopic shifts of patterns in his environment. He learns to recognize movements and time sequences, to distinguish his body from what surrounds it, to distinguish what is near from what is far away. He evolves complex techniques of adaptation, defense and mastery. He establishes personal interactions that help determine his own personality structure. He learns to differentiate eventually between private fantasy and social fact, between things actually happening and things

25

that he is merely remembering or imagining. Much of this hard-won organization of internal and external reality, as we shall see in later chapters, can be lost under a variety of conditions.

Personality development is the name given to the gradual transformation from biological organism to biosocial person. Each child, through continual interaction with other human beings in a human environment, comes in time to feel, to think and to act fundamentally as others feel and think and act. He builds for himself a stable external world of space and time, containing persons, things and causal relations, a world that eventually corresponds to the one that the adults in his culture experience. In short, the sweeping changes in outward appearance and behavior, which continue throughout a child's growth and maturing, are paralleled by sweeping perceptual and cognitive changes within him. Every human being builds within him a stable mental organization, one that continually adapts to the external world and absorbs it, while at the same time it keeps shifting the balance of its internal forces to cope with the internal shifting needs which continually arise, and to find means of satisfying them.[1]

The earliest development of personality is in direct relation to needs and satisfactions that are direct, simple and concrete. The moment we are born we experience new biological needs for such things as food, air, warmth and contact. The main task is to get these needs satisfied, in infancy and childhood with a great deal of help, and later on with little help. The human society that receives the infant at birth understands his needs and is prepared to help him to meet them.

The social organization of human beings is built around animal want — hunger and thirst, the need for warmth, love, shelter and protection, sex desire and its many consequences, the human urge to express love and aggression, self-assertion, initiative, pleasure and anger. Even our most treasured customs, our values and our highest ideals, emerge out of needs which at some time were concrete, biological and basic to human existence. Many of these still bear the marks of their origins, in eating and drinking, in loving, mating and parenthood, in striving and competition, and in the covering, guarding and housing of our biological bodies. Eating and drinking show many such origins and functions. We eat and drink, not just to satisfy hunger and quench thirst, but also to celebrate feasts together, to honor one another, to express mutual acceptance. We eat and drink together to experience spiritual closeness, to increase mutual understanding, to heal personal wounds, to signify the sharing of sorrow as well as joy, and even in token form to symbolize deep religious beliefs.

During earliest infancy we begin, through the satisfaction of concrete physiological needs, to bind ourselves closely to a mother figure, who is the immediate source of nearly all our early satisfactions. Through this early bond, which is literally vital, the mother first helps her infant develop a

[1] Ritholz, S., *Children's Behavior.* New York: Bookman Associates, 1959.

basic trust in her, and then gradually prepares him to enter into family activities and human society. The mother herself, long before she has a child, has already internalized the social organization within which she has been living. Her ways are the ways of her society; her values reflect its values. These ways and values she transmits to her child, in her own personal idiom, through her maternal behavior during a relationship of many years. This relationship, after the infant has matured enough perceptually, develops such intimacy that mother and child seem for a time to be almost one. It continues through successive phases of weaning or emancipation until the child, now grown to adolescence or adulthood, leaves his home. In what follows, we shall escort our human being swiftly through his first two decades to see what influences he comes under, how he experiences them and what he does, what seems to favor personality growth, and what contributes to its arrest or its distortion.

Life in the uterus

A human being is created when an errant sperm penetrates a receptive ovum within the mother's oviduct. Sperm and ovum immediately reorganize and fuse to form a single unitary cell, the fertilized ovum. With this fusion the sex of the child-to-be is determined, and so also is his entire biological inheritance. The newly created organism is now launched upon a career of growth and development. It moves down the oviduct and becomes implanted in the uterine wall. Cell divisions begin and multiply with almost explosive rapidity. An organized mass forms, then the ground plan of the embryo appears, and the embryo develops and grows into a "fetus," or unborn child. Membranes meanwhile develop to form a sac and secrete a fluid in which the fetus floats. A *placenta* organizes and connects the growing fetus with its mother. This placenta acts as a complex digestive and respiratory organ, bringing fetal blood into functional relationship with the mother's blood, but not mixing them together. Eventually this new creation emerges as a new-born baby.

From the moment of conception to the moment of birth the new organism's progress is governed by physiological factors. Its intrauterine development depends in the first place upon the goodness of physiological interaction between mother and unborn child. There is, of course, no direct nervous system connection between them; and the fetal blood does not mingle directly with the maternal blood. The relationship between mother and unborn child is mediated through the semi-permeable membranes of the placenta, where there is a continuous interchange of chemical substances and gases, day and night.[2]

Intrauterine development also depends upon countless biological interac-

---

[2] For a review of the literature on the biological aspects of prenatal life, see Carmichael, L., "The onset and development of behavior," in Carmichael, L. (Ed.), *Manual of Child Psychology*. (2nd ed.) New York: Wiley, 1954, pp. 60–185.

tions within the embryo and fetus itself. At first there are no recognizable organs. Then, what appear to begin merely as energy concentrations and energy relations lead to the formation of enduring structures. Tissues and organs evolve, systems and subsystems emerge and become interrelated. Given a normal internal milieu and a normal immediate environment, the growing organism seems to work out biologically its own self-governing plan and its own timetable of maturational sequences.

An especially interesting feature of growth and maturation is that embryonic and fetal structures form and begin to function before they are actually needed, and before what they do is useful to the organism as a whole. There is, for example, a well-developed gastrointestinal system, engaged in peristaltic movement and in secreting digestive juices and enzymes, long before any food is in prospect. The heart appears and begins to beat before there are blood vessels and blood to pump. Even breathing movements occur several weeks before birth, while the fetus is immersed in amniotic fluid and cannot benefit from breathing.

What is true of internal organ functioning is also true of external behavior. There are all kinds of movements during prenatal life. Before the sixth month the fetus is already making complex chewing movements and swallowing. His arms and legs move about, his hands can grasp, and his eyelids open and close, even though there is nothing much to see and no light to see it in. Later on, the head begins making turning movements of a kind that will be useful after birth in seeking food, but are useless while the child is still in the uterus. In short, when organs and systems and body parts are physiologically ready to function, they begin to function, whether or not what they do serves any immediate purpose.

The environment in which the fetus carries on its vast developmental changes is itself a tranquil one. The unborn child is protected from cold and heat, from bright lights and loud sounds, from blows and sudden stresses. He dwells in a warm, dark chamber, immersed almost weightlessly in a fluid, cushioned by it, and provided through the placenta with continuous room service. The pregnant uterus is, in fact, a miracle of automation. As long as the unborn child gets from his mother's blood what he requires for growth, maintenance, and a little moving about, and as long as his waste products are removed fast enough, by the same route, he can have little experience with the tensions of physiological want that flood him after he is born.

Birth and the newborn

Birth expels the child from the warm, dark monotony of the uterine waters, into a world of everlasting change and infinite space. Here he is exposed to noise and light, to tastes and smells, to warmth and cold. He breathes in air, lies heavily on solid surfaces, is picked up bodily and put down, carried around, and handled and moved about in wholly unfamiliar ways. He experiences the pangs of hunger, learns to ease them through his own action, and gains a new enjoyment as his stomach fills. But from now on, in order to get food he must grasp a nipple with his lips; he must learn the art of sucking and swallowing while he breathes. He must digest and assimilate the food he takes in, and eliminate waste products by his own muscular efforts. All this means work, and often it means discomfort, emptiness and pain.

During his first two or three weeks the newborn performs few organized actions in relation to objects excepting when he nurses.[3] Most of the time he seems to be asleep or dozing. When apparently awake and not hungry, he may lie more or less inertly with his head turned to one side, and perhaps with one arm thrust out, his legs flexed and eyes staring. He gives no specific response to faces or voices and he never smiles. What activity he does engage in, except for the symmetry of arm and leg movements, is rather poorly integrated. He gives occasional starts and shudders which at times are almost convulsive in pattern. His response systems are obviously immature.[4] Even his sleeping and waking are not clear-cut; they lack the definiteness and the rhythm of older children.[5] His first few weeks are little more than a continuation of the life he lived in the uterus.[6]

There is one notable exception to all this. When the very young infant is hungry, and awakens, he shows a dramatic change. He may cry violently, turn bright red, flail his limbs, and twist and squirm all over. If he is put in position for feeding, he pushes forward eagerly, clutches ineffectively with his hands, roots and searches with his mouth and, as soon as he contacts the nipple, seizes it with his lips and begins to suckle. When his hunger has been appeased, the suckling dies down and stops, the nipple slips away, and the sated infant falls into what looks like the oblivion of sleep. He behaves once more as though he were back in the uterus.

Newborn infants are helpless but they are not defenseless. Freud long ago postulated a *protective barrier* of some kind that seems to keep stimulation from becoming effective. Even though very young infants do not yet have a well differentiated sleep-awake cycle, and appear most of the time to

3 Kessen, W., Williams, E. J., and Williams, J. P., "Selection and test of response measures in the study of the human newborn," *Child Develpm.*, 1961, *32*, 7–24; Ross, S., Fisher, A. E., and King, D., "Sucking behavior: a review of the literature," *J. genet. Psychol.*, 1957, *91*, 63–81.

4 For a summary of the information concerning the instability of functioning in the newborn and the sensitivity to stimulation, see Michaels, J. J., "A psychiatric adventure in comparative pathophysiology of the infant and adult," *J. nerv. ment. Dis.*, 1944, *100*, 49–63; Richmond, J. B., and Lipton, E. L., "Some aspects of the neurophysiology of the newborn and their implications for child development," in Jessner, L., and Pavenstedt, E. (Eds.), *Dynamic Psychopathology in Childhood*. New York: Grune & Stratton, 1959, pp. 78–105.

5 Gifford, S., "Sleep, time and the early ego," *J. Amer. Psychoanal. Ass.*, 1960, *8*, 5–42.

6 For a review of the literature on the neonate, see Pratt, K. C., "The neonate," in Carmichael, L. (Ed.), *Manual of Child Psychology*, pp. 215–291. (2nd ed.) New York: Wiley, 1954. See also the references given in Stone, L. J., and Church, J., *Childhood and Adolescence: A Psychology of the Growing Person*. New York: Random House, 1957; and in Landreth, C., *The Psychology of Early Childhood*. New York: Knopf, 1958.

be in a sort of dozing state, they do appear to withdraw behind some kind of a protective barrier.

This behavioral withdrawal is really not hard to understand. We adults also know how to erect a protective barrier against incoming stimulation. When we want to, we can retire into daydreams and inaction. We can shut out the busy world around us. More than this, even when we are engaged in organized activity, we have to exclude whatever does not belong to the activity if we are to maintain the integration we need to carry it through. The most drastic exclusion that we adults practice is the one we call going to sleep. We may be sitting in a crowded plane, in a business meeting or in a classroom; but if we let go and relax, everything around us fades into apparent silence. Previously adequate stimulation becomes ineffectual, the external world vanishes and, except for periods of dreaming, both the internal and the somatic worlds seem also to vanish as if by magic. Even though neonates and very young infants lack a clear differentiation between being asleep and being awake, they seem to have much the same ability to block stimulation that we adults have in going to sleep and, for that matter, in daydreaming also. We shall meet this kind of blocking of stimulation again when we come to such defenses as repression, denial and isolation.

The neonate has another source of protection against stimulation that we adults lack. This comes from the rudimentary state of his perception, the physiological immaturity of his brain, and the poverty of his integrated movements. The complex, meaningful perceptual patterns, which we adults experience in the newborn's environment, make no demand upon him at all. They simply do not exist for him. He is incapable of taking them in; he cannot react to them specifically; and this very incapacity shields him from the barrage of external stimulation which assails his sense organs. He is thus enclosed in a shell of perceptual inadequacy and protected by it.

Individual differences: the child

Everyone who deals with newborn infants is impressed with the individual differences which they show in their various sensitivities and behaviors. At one end of the scale are the extremely sensitive neonates; at the other end are those who require strong stimulation before they react. Likewise, the tempo of some neonates is consistently fast in everything, while the tempo of others is consistently slow. In the feeding situation, for example, there are neonates who quickly develop rooting and searching for the nipple. At the other extreme, there are neonates who are more or less indifferent, those who need to have the nipple placed in their mouths, and even then require coaxing to make them suckle and keep on suckling.[7]

[7] Bergman, P., and Escalona, S. K., "Unusual sensitivities in very young children," *Psychoanal. Study Child*, 1949, *3/4*, 333–353; Greenacre, P., "Toward an understanding of the physical nucleus of some defence reactions," *Internat. J. Psychoanal.*, 1958, *39*, 69–76; Spitz, R., "Some early prototypes of ego defenses," *J. Amer. Psychoanal. Ass.*, 1961, *9*, 626–651; Escalona, S. K., and Heider, G. M., *Prediction and Outcome*. New York: Basic Books, 1959.

For nearly thirty years, Fries and her co-workers have been engaged in a systematic study of the activity levels of newborns.[8] They have found that newborns range from extremely active to extremely quiet. Each newborn has his own activity level, and he persists in it. Their studies imply that there are consistent, characteristic differences in tension level and tension discharge among newborns, apart from experience and learning, and that these innate differences may determine individual differences in the infant's toleration of delay, frustration and discomfort. Their findings agree with the observation of other workers that infants show striking differences in the degree to which common stress situations disturb their equilibrium.

Other individual differences at birth have been reported by skilled observers on every hand.[9] We know, for example, that newborns show marked differences in their characteristic modes of internal organ functioning. This is especially clear in the whole feeding cycle — in nursing, in retaining or regurgitating food, in digesting and assimilating it, and in elimination. The feeding cycle, of course, is one of the focal points of maternal care and one of the earliest significant mother-child relationships.

Swallowing and retaining food also form biological patterns for such symbolic ego maneuvers as *incorporation, introjection* and *identification,* whether these are used defensively or adaptively. Regurgitation and vomiting form the earliest biological patterns for such symbolic ego maneuvers as *projection.* This, as we shall see, has also its symbolically adaptive and its symbolically defensive functions. We shall have a great deal to say about these processes when we come to our various discussions of ego adaptations, of superego formation and of the defense mechanisms.

There are obvious and important individual differences at birth in general autonomic stability. Because autonomic functioning is basic to emotional experience and emotional expression, innate differences in this sphere of physiological activity may have crucial effects upon the character of mother-child interaction from the start. An expressive baby will have a definite effect upon his mother, and upon her interaction with him, which may be lacking in a phlegmatic child. Here, once again, we are dealing with physiological characteristics which may determine the nature of early mother-child relationships.

It is clear that each newborn enters into the formation of the early mother-child relationship with unique, persistent qualities. He has his own individual patterns of sensory equipment and neural organization. He quickly develops his own distinct set of rhythms, tempo and coordinations — internal as well as external, perceptual as well as motor. He has his own peculiar combination of sensitivities, his own levels of readiness to discharge tensions

[8] Cf. Fries, M. E., "Some factors in the development and significance of early object relationships," *J. Amer. Psychoanal. Ass.,* 1961, *9,* 669–683.

[9] Sears, R. R., Maccoby, E. E., and Levin, H., *Patterns of Child Rearing.* Evanston, Ill.: Row, Peterson, 1957; Brody, S., *Patterns of Mothering.* New York: Internat. Univ. Press, 1956; Carmichael, L., (Ed.), *Manual of Child Psychology.* (2nd ed.) New York: Wiley, 1954.

and to achieve satisfaction, in relation to oral experiences, body contact, warmth, sound, light, smell, taste and movement. To top it all, each infant has his own rate of maturing; and this rate may be different for his different functions. Every newborn is congenitally different from every other newborn.

Individual differences such as these can be of considerable importance in the earliest mother-child relationships. It is well known, for example, that mothers react quite differently to the varying characteristics of their different children.[10] Most babies seem soft and easy to cuddle, but some seem stiff when they are held, from the very beginning. Others feel like a bag of bones. These congenital differences are by no means trivial. Mothers themselves comment spontaneously on the pleasure they get from holding a "cuddly baby," and their disappointment that a stiff baby gives them. Perhaps we need to add to the old concepts of accepting and rejecting mothers the newer ones of accepting and rejecting babies.

While an active and sensitive mother may be continually disappointed by a slow-moving, unreactive baby, a phlegmatic mother may find an active, energetic baby disturbing to her, and a sensitive baby quite unintelligible. Greedy energetic rooters and feeders actually frighten some mothers; they seem to be attacking, devouring little monsters. To other mothers a greedy, rooting infant seems only an amusing, eager little trencherman. Indifferent, apathetic little feeders seem to frustrate and annoy some mothers, while in other mothers they arouse tender concern.[11]

Individual differences: the mother

The newborn's mother is also a unique individual. Unlike her baby, she enters the relationship already equipped with a highly complex personality, the product of many years of social living and of private thinking and feeling. This personality she has built upon the biological foundations with which she herself was born; and her biological foundations may have been different in more than one respect from those of her newborn child. Besides this, she has been reared in a particular kind of family, with its own special values, ideals, prejudices and expectations, its own emotional qualities and its own variety of sub-culture. The mother was once herself a baby who entered into a mother-child symbiotic unit with her mother.

To the mothering situation, the mother brings the background of her own childhood experiences of having been mothered. She brings also the background of her lifelong fantasies, her daydreams and games of being a

[10] Sears, R. R., Maccoby, E. E., and Levin, H., *Patterns of Child Rearing*. Evanston, Ill.: Row, Peterson, 1957; Wenar, C., "The reliability of mothers' histories," *Child Develpm.*, 1961, *32*, 491-500; Tuddenham, R. D., "The constancy of personality ratings over two decades," *Genet. Psychol. Monogr.*, 1959, *60*, 3-29; Thomas, A., Chess, S., Birch, L., and Hertzig, C. E., "A longitudinal study of primary reaction patterns in children," *Comprehensive Psychiat.*, 1960, *1*, 103-112.

[11] See Levy, D., *Behavioral Analysis: An Analysis of Clinical Observations of Behavior as Applied to Mother-Newborn Relationships.* Springfield, Ill.: Thomas, 1958.

mother. She brings whatever realistic experience she may have had with younger babies in her own family, her experiences in baby-sitting, or in playing the role of substitute mother for someone else's baby. If she has already been a mother she will have certain expectations and advantages or disadvantages because of this.

Marriage and pregnancy give a woman opportunities for crystallizing her attitudes toward becoming a mother for the first time and toward caring for her child.[12] If she has already found consistent pleasure in giving and receiving love, and if she has a healthy degree of self-esteem as a woman and a wife, the chances are high that she will greet her new baby with a generous measure of maternal love. If, on the other hand, her love experiences have been disappointing and her self-esteem is low, it is probable that her gift of maternal love will be something less than adequate.[13]

But whether or not she is the best of mothers, a woman's personality patterns are of prime importance for her child's personality growth.[14] It is she who will help the child structure and enter into a close symbiotic relationship with her. In her person she embodies the society and culture to which she and the baby belong, and in which he will be reared and live out his life. It is this embodiment of society and culture, bearing the mother's own individual stamp, that she brings her child to be his constant companion.

It is mainly through his mother, as we shall see, that a child prepares to become a part of human society. She it is who helps him to form an intimate attachment to her, and she it is who guides him more and more toward the goal of becoming an autonomous member of his family. Her ways of loving will give rise to his ways; and the kind of welcome that she then gives to his ways of loving will help determine their future development. It is also his mother who, by denying or frustrating him — since a small child's demands cannot all be met — must inevitably arouse his rage at times or drive him into apathy. Finally, it is the mother who must cope with his rage or his apathy. She may do this by soothing, comforting and diverting him, remaining openly and steadfastly loving toward him; or she may attempt it by ignoring or punishing him, or by emotionally deserting him. Whatever her chief ways are of meeting her child's love, his anger and his indifference, these ways will play a major role in molding his personality.

Unlike her baby, we have said, the mother enters the new relationship with a complex matrix of expectations, fears and faiths, much of which she may

---

[12] Bibring, G. L., Dwyer, T. F., Huntington, D. S., and Valenstein, A. F., "A study of the psychological processes in pregnancy and of the earliest mother-child relationship," *Psychoanal. Study Child*, 1961, *16*, 9–72; Newton, N., *Maternal Emotions; A Study of Women's Feelings toward Menstruation, Pregnancy, Childbirth, Breast Feeding, Infant Care and Other Aspects of Their Femininity*. New York: Hoeber, 1955.

[13] Ourth, L., and Brown, K. B., "Inadequate mothering and disturbance in the neonatal period," *Child Develpm.*, 1961, *32*, 287–295.

[14] See Bowlby, J., *Maternal Care and Mental Health*. Geneva: World Health Organization, 1952. For a popular account, see Winnicott, D. W., *Mother and Child*. New York: Basic Books, 1957; and for a more technical account, see Winnicott, D. W., *Collected Papers*. New York: Basic Books, 1958.

never have clearly formulated to herself. Out of this matrix will come her maternal behavior, her contribution to the symbiotic mother-child unit. Some mothers are eager to have the child, feel comfortable with him from the start, and find motherhood in every way rewarding. They welcome the baby as a form of self-fulfillment, as a new object of affection and a living symbol of loving and being loved. Many mothers who are not eager to have the child find its appeal irresistible when it comes, and quickly lose the feeling of unwillingness.

Even among accepting mothers many problems arise. There are women who want the baby all through their pregnancy, welcome it when it arrives, and then discover that for them the tasks and restrictions of motherhood outweigh the satisfactions. A new baby is usually the center of attention; and some new mothers feel pushed to the sidelines and valued only as caretakers of the child. Others are overwhelmed by the responsibility of caring for an infant. They find themselves anxious all the time; and they do not succeed in taming their anxiety. Some mothers feel uncomfortable with a particular baby, or even frightened by it, whereas their previous experiences with babies have been pleasant. Considering the wide range of individual differences among newborns and among mothers, it is hardly surprising that sometimes the match is not a good one, especially as there is no free choice on either side.

A new baby may pose a special problem if it comes too soon after its nearest sibling. The symbiotic mother-child unit, once it has been formed, takes time to dissolve again; and both mothers and children vary in the amount of time they require to work through their close relationship. If another child arrives before this dissolution is well under way, the mother may be thrown into serious conflict by the demands on her affection made by her second baby, at a time when she is still deeply involved with the first. Other more obvious problems are posed by prolonged ill health in mother or child, which may retard or disturb the development of the mother-child unit — as may also, of course, the demands made by the ill health, physical or emotional, in older children or the husband. The tensions of marital discord, and the interferences from the parents' relatives, can seriously disturb early mother-child relationships.

For a variety of reasons, motherhood or the addition of a new child to the family can be unwelcome to a woman from the start; and it may continue to be unwelcome. We have already mentioned illness, anxiety, the burdens of responsibility and the restrictions of freedom. In marital discord a new baby may be disliked and resented as a symbol of the unhappy marriage and of the unloved husband, and as something that makes separation more difficult or impossible. Even where there is no marital discord, women who are unusually narcissistic sometimes look upon the baby as a rival for their husband's love and attention.

Maternal rejection is seldom expressed openly. Society's attitudes toward motherhood make maternal rejection or neglect an unforgivable offense.

Therefore, it is rarely that a hostile or indifferent mother puts into plain words any socially condemned attitudes which she may have toward her baby.[15] Furthermore, because of her own moral code, derived during her childhood from her own society, it is unusual for a mother to admit even to herself that she has such attitudes, unless they are merely transient and superficial. As a rule, hostile and indifferent maternal attitudes find subtle, devious, disguised, defensive and often unconscious expression, in what the mother does or fails to do. It has long been known, for example, that over-protective mothers are commonly hostile mothers who restrict their child's freedom, and that overprotection by indifferent or rejecting mothers is an exaggerated denial of their indifference and rejection. We call such defensive denial which takes the form of an exaggerated opposite attitude, *reaction formation*.[16] Other people are more likely to be aware of what a hostile, indifferent or rejecting mother is expressing than she herself is.

But whether anyone else recognizes a mother's negative attitudes or not, they are communicated to the infant at nonverbal levels. Since infants can neither speak nor understand speech, they experience maternal behavior as simply the kind of mothering they receive, as the kind of world they are living in, the only one they know.[17] A mother's accepting, indifferent or rejecting attitudes, which an infant experiences for years at nonverbal or practically nonverbal levels, significantly influence his initial dependency relationships and the later evolution of his independence.

A world without objects

We have implied that the infant seems at first to live in a world without objects, a world devoid of persons and things, of space, time and causality. In the nursing situation, for example, what we adults recognize as a nipple yielding milk, as the mother's supporting hand, arm and body, as her prattle and her loving face — all these exist for the very young baby as only comfort and pleasure, as a pervasive satisfaction that has no structure. What we recognize as the baby's hunger, his discomfort, his emptiness or loneliness, exist for the baby only as boundless misery and want. He can have no understanding of how or why he is miserable, or what it is he wants. And when, through his mother's intervention, his misery and want give way again to comfort and pleasure, he cannot in the least realize what is being done for him, what he himself does, or even that there are people around him and that he himself has a separate existence.

This concept of a world without stable objects, and without organization

---

[15] Crandall, V. J., and Preston, A., "Verbally expressed needs and overt maternal behaviors," *Child Develpm.*, 1961, *32*, 261–270.

[16] *Reaction formation* will be discussed further in Chapter 6, under the defenses, and in Chapter 11 on compulsions.

[17] For examples of personality distortions in early childhood, resulting from the presence of ambivalent, hostile or seductive parents, see Chapter 19, "Personality disorders," which includes references to the recent literature.

in time, space and causality, is difficult for an adult to picture. Our familiar world of external reality seems to us solid, permanent and self-evident. But careful studies of infants over several decades have made it unmistakably clear that this apparently self-evident world of ours is actually a personal construction, the product of long and costly individual effort. Each of us has had to build up his own world of reality, and at the same time tie it in functionally with the realities that other persons experience. The apparent firmness and permanence of the external world are in part the projections of our own firm, enduring personality organization.[18] If our personality organization disintegrates — and this happens in mental health as well as in mental illness — our adult world of external reality begins to lose its organization at the same time. It grows unstable and confused; and it may even disappear.

Adult experiences with an objectless world. We have today a wide variety of evidence that goes to show the dependence of organized external reality upon mental and physiological integrity. The sense of reality can easily be lost. For centuries it has been known that intoxication, whether with alcohol or with some other drug, makes the world grow confused for the intoxicated person. He may seem to be adrift in a strange universe of unpredictable, shifting forms and events. Even his own body undergoes weird transformations. If the intoxication goes far enough — and some drugs produce extraordinary effects — the distortions and the dissolution of organization approach the experience of an objectless world. This kind of thing is under vigorous investigation today.[19]

Adults who are otherwise normal report similar experiences as they go under a general anesthetic, or as they come out of it. Some have weird experiences even under the heavy sedation which nowadays precedes surgery. They feel, for example, that everything is somehow changing, that the world is dissolving or that some body part has become detached. A patient on the way to surgery, under sedation, tells the attendant quite seriously that his arm has come off, that it is lying on the floor and had better be picked up before they go on.

Similar phenomena have long been observed in persons under hypnosis;[20] and they have been reported from more than one source by adults who observe their own experiences as they fall asleep.[21]

Within recent years many investigations have cropped up which report the loss of external reality, and distortions in the perception of the subject's

[18] Kaplan, B., "An approach to the problems of symbolic representation: nonverbal and verbal," *J. Commun.*, 1961, *11*, 52–62.

[19] See, for example, Uhr, L., and Miller, J. G. (Eds.), *Drugs and Behavior*. New York: Wiley, 1960.

[20] Gill, M. M., and Brenman, M., *Hypnosis and Related States*. New York: Internat. Univ. Press, 1959.

[21] Isakower, O., "A contribution to the pathopsychology of phenomena associated with falling asleep," *Internat. J. Psychoanal.*, 1938, *19*, 331–345.

own body, when a normal adult is simply deprived of nearly all external stimulation and self-stimulation, under strict laboratory conditions. It has become evident from these investigations that a certain amount of external stimulation is essential to preserve realistic perception in normal adults, and that, without this, one begins to experience strange dreamlike or hallucinatory activities. This method of isolation is called *sensory deprivation*. It indicates that unrealistic processes may be going on all the time, of which we are ordinarily unaware, processes which are masked by everyday conscious and preconscious experience or integrated with it. The method of sensory deprivation has great advantages over the use of drugs and of hypnosis. It does not introduce something foreign to the subject, it merely subtracts as much as possible from his normal external stimulation.[22]

We are also getting abundant evidence that external reality can change, and even partially dissolve, from another direction, from the experiences of deep regression in mental illnesses. Some adult patients speak of being alone in an empty universe, of being lost in a world without time or space. Others say that the world and they themselves have somehow become one. There seem to be no boundaries, nothing appears to be real, things and experiences flow in and out of them, or seem to fuse with them. For some, everything that actually happens around them appears to be happening inside them; they seem to encompass everything. Here are a few examples, each from a different patient.

(1) "Everything is thrown into space. No one will know my name because they are all dying. Even my body will go. My soul is in space which is limitless and boundless. It is floating and I cannot get it back. I will go on forever. I must be a million years old. I will just live in space."

(2) "I'm bordering on another world. I feel I've been pulled over the brink. There's such a clamoring there. This is the end of the world. Death and dark angel picked those to go over."

(3) "There is no feeling and no time. It could be 1958 and it could be 1000 B.C. Every minute is like forever. There's no place, nothing but space, and I go into it and come out of it, and nothing makes any difference or any sense. I have no brains, only a skull with pictures that go up into the sky, a panorama of life that is floating. If I were only hallucinating there wouldn't be this torture."

(4) "I was conscious of my own actions at first. Now mine and others are mixed up. If somebody touches me it's part of me touching me. If there's a noise it's in me like my heart beating. A furnace noise brings different thoughts and it's all inside me. If something moves it moves inside me. Everything is in me and I am nothing, or I don't know where I begin."

Such descriptions of a world or a self that is not like the world or the self of normal adult reality, although given often with considerable anxiety,

[22] Solomon, P., *et al., Sensory Deprivation.* Cambridge, Mass.: Harvard Univ. Press, 1961.

are often given clearly and consistently. They have the same general characteristics from patient to patient, those of a universe lacking in stable objects and definite boundaries. All of the patients from whom these complaints
were taken were able to do the ordinary basic things of everyday life, such
as eating and drinking, dressing and bathing, even conversing with other
patients who did not know of the bewilderment they were experiencing in
their dissolving worlds.

Infantile experience of an objectless world. The objectless world of early
infancy is not the same thing, of course, as the adult experience of lost
reality and ego disintegration. The examples we have given above retain
obvious language organization. But even in patients whose language also
disintegrates — something that happens often — there are basic differences.

When an adult regresses he loses something which he has built up over a
period of many years. The infant at first has no world to lose. His world is
undoubtedly far simpler, more homogeneous and more formless. It is not
the product of regression and disintegration, but of total inexperience and
of an ego organization which is extremely rudimentary.

The newborn is an organism without a perceptual focus, living in a
universe that for him has no boundaries and no structure. Out of his nebulous
and fleeting experiences he must gradually construct external reality and at
the same time build within himself an effective ego organization. He has
nothing to begin with but the biological organization of his own body, and
a world around him which will take him decades to understand.

As soon as he recovers from the shock of being born, the sucking movements of his hungry mouth provide him with his first perceptual focus. The
hungry sucking mouth requires something outside his body to complete it,
something with a yield that will fill his empty stomach. It is this incompleteness, this organismic demand, that first orients an infant toward what will
ultimately become for him his external reality. His first active nursing begins
the slow work of constructing a reality in terms of his infant need.

We shall see in this and in succeeding chapters that, as he matures and
learns, the child's reality grows more and more differentiated. He will ultimately distinguish clearly between what he thinks or imagines (*internal
reality*), what his body is like (*somatic reality*) and what the world around
him is like (*external reality*). In the beginning, however, it is certain that
he can make no such distinctions.

The concept of erogenous zones in child development

Freud and his earliest associates were first interested in the neglected field
of sexuality. They divided up childhood development into maturational
sequences which emphasized the pleasure-giving or erogenous zones, that
seemed to predominate at a given age. Thus, the earliest phase of infancy

they called the *oral phase,* since mouth pleasures obviously dominate at first. During the second year of postnatal life, the child begins to assert himself and to gain control over his bowel function. This has been named the *anal phase.* After a time, when bowel control has become established, interest in it diminishes and interest in genital functions and genital differences holds the center of the stage. This period was at first called the *genital phase;*[23] but later it was more accurately named the *phallic phase.* (Both uses still appear, however, in the contemporary literature.) The final phase of sexual development, the *genital phase,* begins with the onset of puberty and adolescence, when interest in genital function has reached sufficient maturity to make the adolescent aware of his approaching adult sex role and of a realistic preoccupation with persons of the opposite sex.

This general scheme has the advantage of being simple and straightforward. It calls attention to normal maturational sequences in the focus of erogeneity which may, through fixation, through distortion or regression, lead to various forms of psychopathology. There is a disadvantage in the fact that it was conceived before aggression was given a coordinate position with sexuality. Attempts have been made, particularly by Abraham,[24] to subdivide the sexual phases into retention and destruction periods; but such subdivision is often called into question. It seems probable that the *oral, anal, phallic* and *genital phases* will remain the fundamental maturational sequences.

In what follows, we shall in general continue in this now traditional sequence. For the sake of greater latitude in dealing with the interactions that take place between a developing person and others around him, we shall include these phases in six personality stages. Through these every human being must pass in moving from birth to adulthood. As might be expected in dealing with anything as complex as human development, these stages overlap. They are not always clearcut and mutually exclusive; but they are always useful and interesting. We shall take them up in the following order:

1. The oral dependent phase (the first year).
   a) Early perceptual development (the first two or three months).
   b) The symbiotic mother-child unit (the next six months or more).
2. The phase of self-assertion and sphincter control (the second year or so).
3. The edipal phase (somewhere between the third and fifth years).
4. The phase of latency (from the close of the edipal phase to about the eleventh or twelfth year).
5. Adolescence.
6. Adulthood.

[23] References made in the literature to phases of development preceding the *phallic phase* are still as a rule called *pregenital phases.*

[24] Abraham, K., *Selected Papers.* London: Hogarth Press, 1927.

The oral dependent phase of the first year

We call the first year of postnatal life *oral* because during this period the mouth plays a leading role in experience, and oral experiences lay the first foundation for an infant's construction of reality. They give to his reality and to his early ego organization an oral stamp which he will never lose. Even as mature adults we still utilize unconsciously a great deal of oral imagery. It appears constantly in everyday speech without our paying it any attention or even realizing it.

We say, for example, that memories are sweet or bitter, and we say the same about revenge. We speak of having taste in clothes, in housing, furniture, automobiles, literature and art, even though we have no intention of eating any of these. We also speak of tasting victory and defeat. In the business world, there are suckers whose funds are swallowed up because they are too greedy — all feeding terms. We say a man uses biting sarcasm, that he spits out his anger, that he is thirsty for adventure, and that he eats up flattery and the news. There are thousands of such examples of habitual oral imagery in normal adult life. When we come to psychopathology, we shall meet examples of oral imagery which often illuminate otherwise obscure, meaningless symptoms.

The first year is dependent. We call the first year *dependent* because infants are helpless. They can do next to nothing for themselves. They cannot even defend themselves in matters of life and death. They can suckle, they can move about and eliminate waste; but even in feeding and eliminating they need adult help, to bring food almost to their lips, and to keep them clean and healthy. This is the negative side of dependence.

Dependence and the symbiotic relationship. Dependence also has a positive side, one that expresses what a dependent baby can do. After a few weeks of perceptual maturing and learning, every infant can and must form an intimate attachment to a mother figure, who will act as his temporary ego substitute. Infants are not born with such an attachment. They have to develop it, with their mothers' help, as they organize their earliest experiences into a primitive perceptual world. It is only after this primitive perceptual world begins to crystallize that an infant can enter into a symbiotic relationship with his mother, in which mother and child become practically one.

In what follows we shall first discuss oral experience and imagery, as we conceive them in young infants. their role in early ego development, and their coordination with other early perceptual experience and imagery. This experience and imagery, along with the well-known motor development of the first two or three months, make the subsequent symbiotic phase possible. We shall then go on to describe the symbiotic relationship, which unites mother and infant, and lays the behavioral and experiential basis for all later personality development, as well as for some of the most interesting neurotic and psychotic symptoms.

Early perceptual developments that lead to symbiosis. During the first year of postnatal life, human perception develops rapidly, far in advance of motor strength and motor coordination. It is customary, in theoretical discussions, to speak about the opposition between "fight and flight" in early mental life, but this talk has little to do with the facts. For a long time the human infant can neither fight nor flee. There are very few things he can do in the way of defending himself; and as for flight, the very idea is absurd, because the human infant is virtually rooted to the spot. There is little that he can do in the way of coping with what he perceives. On the other hand, there is every evidence that during their first year, even during their first six months, infants are capable of enormously complex perception in several different fields. The world as first perceived must include several perceptual components, among which the oral seems to predominate, for reasons which will soon become apparent.[25]

1. *Oral experience in the earliest ego developments.* Oral experience dominates early ego development because the mouth is at first the most efficient center of adaptation and mastery. It is not only a mature adaptive organ at birth. It is also the only feeding organ, and therefore a major source of pleasure, of comfort, and of meaningful contact with what will in time become external reality. The mouth combines a richly endowed receptor system with an agile motor system, both housed in the same unit. The unit is already integrated at birth with inborn patterns for suckling, engulfing, mouthing, tasting and rejecting.

The mouth also has the anatomical advantage of having definite boundaries, the lips, which can be opened like garage doors to admit things, or closed to deny them admission. These opposed functions, of admitting and excluding, form the basis for an early discrimination between *external reality*, that which can be taken in or denied admission, and *internal reality*, that which is always present, in this case the organs that make up the mouth. In short, the mouth is a self-contained sensorimotor system, ready almost from the moment of birth to engage in activities that relate to the world around it, and thus ready to act as a center for early ego differentiation. These congenital characteristics make oral experience the basis for the earliest ego organization, which has been called *the mouth ego*.[26]

2. *The mouth as a sensorimotor unit.* We have called the mouth a richly endowed receptor system, one whose activities contribute much to early ego

[25] For a general discussion of perception, see Allport, F., *Theories of Perception and the Concept of Structure.* New York: Wiley, 1955; Murphy, G., and Solley, C. M., *Development of the Perceptual World.* New York: Basic Books, 1960; Wohlwill, J. F., "Developmental studies of perception," *Psychol. Bull.* 1960, 57, 249–289.

[26] Cf. Hoffer, W., "Development of the body ego," *The Psychoanalytic Study of the Child.* New York: Internat. Univ. Press, 1950, vol. 5, pp. 18–23.

development. On the lips and scattered all over the inside of the mouth are sense organs of touch and pressure, of temperature and pain. It is a physiological fact that the tip of the tongue yields the finest touch discrimination of the whole body. Muscles of the lips, the tongue and the cheeks contain kinesthetic sense organs which are stimulated by every muscle movement, providing a constant source of feedback. The tongue itself has, in addition to all the sense organs already mentioned, large numbers of specialized taste buds, which yield countless combinations of flavors.[27]

Because this great variety of sense organs is mounted on a supple, acrobatic muscular organ, the tongue, an infinity of perceptual variations becomes possible. The tongue can explore the mouth cavity in which it is rooted, carrying along its multiplicity of receptors. It can manipulate whatever enters the mouth, push fluids and solids about, run over and around and under them, tasting in this way their texture and form as well as their flavor. Manipulations of the tongue and lips give the infant organism its first taste of three-dimensional experience. The first *reality-testing* is thus actually a *reality-tasting*, something which we acknowledge obliquely when we speak of tasting experience and tasting life. The first highly organized activities which satisfy an irresistible, primitive id need are thus the first to form a differentiated ego structure.

3. *Oral discrimination.* The earliest discriminations are made by the mouth. The hungry mouth turns toward anything that stimulates the face, grasps it with the lips and, if the lips can hold it, the infant begins to suckle. If what is grasped yields milk, the process of suckling, at first imperfectly coordinated with breathing, will go on until the infant is satisfied. If there is no such yield, the suckling stops, and crying or rooting and searching may appear. This difference is obviously a primitive form of discrimination, between what does and what does not yield milk. It is the precursor of ego choice and ego discrimination.

4. *Pleasure sucking.* It should be mentioned at this point that infants also enjoy sucking when they are not hungry. Sometimes a hungry infant even prefers sucking his thumb or finger to nursing, and has to be coaxed or gently coerced to nurse. Sometimes an infant introduces his finger along with the nipple, apparently for double pleasure.[28] It is this pleasure sucking (sometimes called "empty sucking") that Freud regarded as erotic. It is interesting that, when engaged in alone, pleasure sucking is backed up by postural patterns of head and neck muscle action which are different from

[27] The sense of smell should be included as an oral function. The smell of food, both before and after it enters the mouth, is a normal component of "tasting," and sometimes its most important component.

[28] This corresponds with Freud's speculation about an infant's imaginary gratification, and with the view that man is a symbol-making organism from the time of birth, put forward by Langer, S., *Philosophy in a New Key.* Cambridge, Mass.: Harvard Univ. Press, 1942.

those of the postures assumed during ordinary feeding.[29] This non-nutritive use of sucking is the earliest example of the active self-satisfaction of a need, without the help of someone else, the first example of what one day will become self-sufficiency.

5. *Oral anticipation.* The appearance of oral anticipation is another landmark in the development of the ego. After a little experience, the hungry nursling begins to quiet down as he nears the nipple, or when he is merely placed in the nursing position — in either case well before any food enters his mouth. Active rooting and searching with the mouth, both of which are forms of oral anticipation, appear as early as the first postnatal week. Anticipation introduces delay and often some frustration into the nursing act, a delay between an active approach to the nipple and the moment of orally seizing it with the lips and beginning to suckle.

Delay and moderate frustration are essential to the development of ego organization. They interpolate a period of anticipation between the urge to suckle and the actual beginning of suckling. This period of delay, however brief, can be considered a *phase of desire*, while the moment of grasping the nipple with the lips can be considered the beginning of the *phase of satisfaction*. Such a split in the act of nursing, into desire first and satisfaction later, marks the beginning of mental structure. It is an example of an early internal rearrangement, or reorganization, in which the unitary need-satisfaction sequence is replaced by a more flexible need-delay-satisfaction sequence. During the period of delay a great many things can happen, and mental organization can become highly elaborate.

6. *Oral perception, oral imagery and the central nervous system.* As an integrated process, perception always means a corresponding patterned activity of the central nervous system, which in some way represents the perceptual experience, including its emotional as well as its sensorimotor components. The central nervous system is also peculiarly fitted to retain the effects of its own patterned activity. Its own functional organization grows as its patterns multiply. In this way, the organism's experiences with external and somatic reality find their stable representation, or imagery, in organizational changes in the brain.

The delays and moderate frustrations, which we have been discussing, give the organism time for the appearance of mental imagery. The food source — the nipple and its yield — can be imagined during the delay. This imagery, based upon previous experiences keeps the infant "on course" and eager. It introduces purpose into his act; and, as we have seen in his anticipatory behavior, it helps him to endure the delay for a little while quietly.

[29] Brody, S., *Patterns of Mothering: Maternal Influence During Infancy.* New York: Internat. Univ. Press, 1956; Sears, R. R., Maccoby, E. E., and Levin, H., *Patterns of Child Rearing.* Evanston, Ill.: Row, Peterson, 1957; Ross, S., Fisher, A. E., and King, D., "Sucking behavior: a review of the literature," *J. Genet. Psychol.*, 1957, *91*, 63–81.

This appearance of *imagery*, or *central representation*, marks the beginning of an internal functioning which is now generally called *mental* or *psychic functioning*.

As used throughout this book, the term *imagery* means an active central representation, originally based upon perceptual experience. The term *representation* is too clumsy for common use. It must be borne in mind, however, that *imagery* means more than just a picture. It includes emotional or feeling components; and it need not have the same *form* as the thing perceived, recalled or imagined. Much the same applies to *thinking* and *cognition* (*knowing*). Neither occurs ordinarily without some contribution from feeling and emotion. It is possible, of course, to perform logical and mathematical feats with little preconscious or conscious emotion; and when we discuss impersonal matters, we try to exclude all personal considerations of an emotional character. Nevertheless, as we shall point out further in Chapter 5, there are still emotional components operating at unconscious levels; and these have an effect upon the way discussion goes. We all know that even scientists and logicians, if they are devoted to their intellectual work, are apt to show a good deal of personal emotion when their results or conclusions are challenged.

7. *The internalization of experience.* The importance of imagery is that, once organized, it can be aroused by the need alone, i.e., without the presence of the nipple or the milk. Provided that the delay is not too long between hunger need and its realistic satisfaction, such imagery can provide temporary gratification. It can fill in the period of delay with an imagined satisfaction, much as we adults can help ourselves through a day of routine work by imagining the pleasure of the coming evening. With such a beginning, the infant has already begun the process of ego organization, which now includes delays and imagery, as well as the realistic integrations that lead from desire immediately to active satisfaction.

Subsequent experiences consolidate and elaborate the perceptual organizations and their imagery, which now have stable representation in the new functional patterns of the central nervous system. In this way, experiences that originate merely as temporary adaptations to somatic and external need, can bring about enduring changes in actual brain organization. It is in some such sense that we speak of the *internalization of experience*. Experiences produce lasting changes in the brain-as-an-organ, in the same sense that exercise produces lasting changes in the muscles, and in the same sense that skilled coordinations — such as one develops in tennis or baseball — produces lasting changes in both brain organization and muscular development.

We speak of the internalization of experience as *incorporation* if it seems to be actually taken into the body. We call it *introjection* if the taking in is only a *symbolic* taking in. We speak of *identification* if the internalization makes a person feel like that which he has internalized. Under certain circumstances, which we shall specify when they arise, the three terms may be used interchangeably. For example, an *introjection* may be a *symbolic incorporation* which is partly experienced as a physical taking in (*actual incorporation*) and makes one feel *like* the person or thing introjected (*identification*). As we shall soon see, internalization of experience occurs in visual, auditory and manual forms, as well as in oral.

8. *Primacy of oral experiences and oral imagery.* During the first weeks of postnatal life, the mouth is the only organ capable of purposive holding and engulfing. For a long time it maintains superiority in these functions over such modes as manual holding and engulfing. We have seen that, when the mouth seizes hold of the nipple and begins to milk it, this is literally an act of incorporation. The nipple is actually taken into the body or incorporated temporarily, while the milk is incorporated permanently. The anticipation of such action represents the earliest specific attitudes taken toward external reality, or what will become external reality.

The mouth is thus the first organ to take up specific attitudes toward external reality. It is also the first to experience regularly the possession of something vital and its subsequent loss. The mouth loses by swallowing; it loses by spitting out or vomiting; it loses through the slipping away of the nipple, especially at the end of feeding. These experiences are believed to play significant roles in oral imagery, in oral transactions within the symbiotic mother-child unit, and later on, in unconscious fantasies and symptom formation.

There is no way of finding out when oral symbolization begins in infancy. Symbolization has sometimes been said to begin with the beginning of verbalization; but this is certainly not true. Preverbal imagery and symbolization play an important part in primitive, infantile fantasy, such as we see revived in adult dreams, in psychoses, and in the deep therapy of neuroses. It must be remembered that infants and small children learn to interact in very complex ways with their surroundings long before words have an important place in their thinking. Preverbal interaction at human levels would be impossible without symbolic representation in oral and other forms. It is more in keeping with the facts to assume that symbolization begins around the same time that perceptual organization begins, in other words, soon after birth.

9. *Oral imagery, oral incorporation and introjection.* As we suggested earlier, oral incorporation provides experiences and imagery which are the first models for the act of symbolic incorporation which we call *introjection*. Infant and child are able to imagine (represent to themselves) swallowing or otherwise taking things in which cannot actually be swallowed or otherwise taken in. When children become able to communicate their experiences to some extent, they often express oral incorporation, in their playful or fearful fantasies, which is primitive and unrealistic. Symbolic incorporation (*introjection*) is still more often expressed. We assume that these experiences

do not spring suddenly to life with the advent of speech, but go back a long way toward the beginning of postnatal life. In the psychotic regressions of adults we sometimes hear introjective wishes or fears expressed primitively in terms of actual incorporation.

A schizophrenic violinist, in her middle twenties, brought her violin in its case to the in-patient service with her. She had an unusually possessive attitude toward it, trying to carry it everywhere she went. Twice, when she mislaid it, she became agitated because she felt sure that she had swallowed it. She gave as her only reason the fact that it belonged to her. She seemed to be fusing the notions of possessing, belonging to and being within her. She was making concrete the feeling she had that it was an inner part of her being, as symbolically it was.

We shall see something comparable when we come soon to discuss the mother-child symbiotic unit. In later chapters, we shall meet with introjection in relation to psychotic depression, mourning and schizophrenia.

10. *Oral refusal as a model for denial.* It was pointed out earlier that the mouth has definite anatomical boundaries, the lips, which separate its interior from what will later become external reality. Just as opening the mouth is the earliest form of acceptance, so closing the lips is the earliest form of denying admission of something.[30] This act of closing the mouth, with its attendant imagery, contributes to forms of denial other than the purely oral, as, for example, the symbolic denial of something which threatens to be painful or dangerous. We shall see later that denial is used as a common defense, by normal as well as by neurotic and psychotic persons.[31]

11. *Oral ejection as a model for projection.* The mouth is also instrumental early in life in active ejections and rejections. The infant can spit out and vomit, sometimes reflexly, sometimes with apparent intent. These acts, with their imagery, become the models for *projection,* which is a symbolic ejection or rejection. Just as an infant, by spitting out or vomiting, can make something within him become something which is outside him, so the older child and the adult can symbolically project something, and in so doing make it appear to himself as something outside him, as something which is not a part of him.[32]

The objectionable qualities and intentions which even normal persons ascribe unjustifiably to others, or to "the facts of life," are often projections

---

[30] Spitz, R., *No and Yes.* New York: Internat. Univ. Press, 1957.

[31] Closing the eyelids is another physiological origin of the mechanism of denial. One can refuse to accept something by refusing to see it. "There are none so blind as those who *will* not see."

[32] Anal expulsion probably does not act as an early model for projection. During the first three or four months, infants seem to be unaware of anal function. Cf. Spitz, R., "Some early prototypes of ego defenses," *J. Amer. Psychoanal. Ass.,* 1961, 9, 626–651.

of their own unacceptable qualities and intentions. The universal use of scapegoats is an example both of denial and projection. There is the *denial* that one has certain impulses or desires; and there is the *projection* of them on to persons considered to be licentious or inferior.

12. *Orality persists throughout life.* Before going on to discuss nonoral infantile experience, it should be made clear that man never ceases to function as an oral being. Tasting, eating and drinking remain vitally important throughout life, not only on physiological grounds, but also as symbolic expression. Mouthing, chewing, sucking and smoking remain sources of pleasure for vast members of adults. Kissing is a major expression of affection and acceptance in most contemporary cultures. As speech develops, the mouth finds still other ways of expressing affirmation and denial, of expressing taste and discrimination, of symbolically incorporating and symbolically rejecting. Through talking and singing, man expresses vast ranges of feeling, maintains and enriches his social intercourse, and masters an infinity of complex situations.

Eyes, ears and hands in early ego development. If the mouth is the infant's first active perceptual focus, the eyes, the ears and the hands are his second groups of perceptual foci. Each of these seems to develop and function at first independently of the others, and independent also of oral activity.[33] The organization of the visual system gets a somewhat later start than the oral; and the visual system matures relatively slowly, over a considerable period. In the beginning it seems to provide a more or less independent perceptual world.

For a long time, what the infant sees he does not bring to his mouth or manipulate. If his own hand appears in his visual field, he merely stares at it, sometimes with apparent surprise, as if it were something emerging out of the void. When it disappears again, the infant promptly loses interest in it, just as he does with regard to other disappearing objects.

If visual pursuit and visual searching go on, they do so without reference to oral or manual action. What the hands feel and grasp is not subjected to oral or manual examination. Only the ears seem to be tied up, almost from the start, with optical movements.[34] This tie-up is a primitive forerunner of an orientation in space.

It is not until the second month that pursuit movements of the eyes develop which permit them to fixate and hold a moving object by moving with it.

[33] For numerous protocols and discussions of this and succeeding materials, see Piaget, J., *Origins of Intelligence.* New York: Internat. Univ. Press, 1952; Piaget, J., *Construction of Reality in the Child.* New York: Basic Books, 1954; Murphy, L., *Personality in Young Children.* New York: Basic Books, 1956. A series of replications of Piaget's studies is being conducted by Elkind. See, for example, Elkind, D., "Children's conceptions of right and left: Piaget replication study IV," *J. genet. Psychol.,* 1961, *99,* 269–276.

[34] Wertheimer, M., "Psychomotor coordination of auditory and visual space at birth," *Science,* 1961, *134,* 1692.

A little later, the eyes develop an increased ability to converge upon a visual stimulus and to make spontaneous conjugate movements of both eyes. Such fixating and following movements enable the child to maintain visual contact with things he sees. They are visual forms of grasping and holding. By the third month, the infant has perfected his coordinated head movements, and these head movements help the eyes to prevent moving things from escaping. The infant has now extended his reality in space and time. He has begun to gain control over his world.

From the second month on, the infant's hand becomes more and more systematically adaptive. Movements of fingering, touching, scratching, grasping, pulling and letting go, are repeated over and over, for long periods. The hands explore each other, the face, the body, and the surroundings. In time, the hand begins searching for things that have escaped it; but for a long time, searching with the hand seems to be guided solely through manual perception, and without any visual aid whatever. Even when an infant looks directly at his hand while the hand is grasping something, his visual perception seems not to influence what his hand does. Sometimes when the hand loses something, both hand and eyes search for it, but each system searches in accordance with its own formula. The hand moves around in the general area where it last made contact; but the eyes search inappropriately by turning from side to side, and not by turning toward the hands.

1. *Visual and auditory incorporation.* We have said that the eyes and ears "incorporate" experience. This is not a mere metaphor. Whatever the eyes and the ears can take in, and whatever of this the central nervous system is able to assimilate, become true "nutriment" for the visual and auditory organizations of mental life. More than this, the eyes, the ears and their nervous system representation must have appropriate stimulation if they are even to develop physiologically along normal lines. Visual and auditory incorporation is thus a biological necessity for normal receptor maturation and for the normal development of the brain as an organ.

The internalization of visual and auditory experience proceeds as it does in oral experience. That which originates outside the body brings about changes in body structure, that is, changes in brain organization. These changes, of course, need not mirror the experiences which they represent. Incorporation always involves some alteration of what is incorporated. The organism selects and eliminates. It digests and assimilates whatever it takes in, so that what becomes finally incorporated bears some relation to the perceptual organizations which are already present.

In short, anything that is incorporated is always somewhat altered by being included in the body's organization — here chiefly the organization of the brain. On the other hand, the inclusion of new perceptions always brings about alterations in the organization of the brain also. Mental organization, which is based physiologically upon the organization of the brain, is particularly adaptable in this respect. It tends to preserve the effects of whatever it incorporates.

2. *Visual and auditory incorporation in relation to oral incorporation.*
During the first few weeks, we have said, oral experience is superior to all
other kinds of experience, because of the more mature organization of the
infant's mouth and of its activities soon after birth. As time passes, however, the superiority of oral functions, including oral incorporation, is lost
as visual and auditory experience grows in importance.

The eyes and ears can "take in" distant things, whereas the mouth is limited
to direct contact. Gradually the eyes and ears assume leadership in perceptually organizing a space-time world. They are destined to become the
major sources of information-input for child and adult, both directly and
through the medium of language. They are among the chief agencies through
which the child organizes an objective world in which he lives.

The eyes and ears also have special significance for unconscious and preconscious processes. Visual imagery, for example, makes up most of our
manifest dreaming. Auditory imagery, although less important in this respect than visual, still contributes more to manifest dreams than any of the
remaining senses. Both auditory and visual imagery play a prominent role
in most hallucinations.

Oral incorporation undergoes no comparable elaboration. There is, of
course, the shift from suckling to eating; and there is the shift from playful
babbling to speech. Nevertheless, oral incorporation remains a primary
source of imagery in dreams, and presumably in the unconscious, even
though its *manifestation* in dreams is nearly always visual. Oral incorporation is also a source of symptom formation in neuroses and psychoses.

We have already mentioned that the mouth and its accessories, together
with hearing, develop an extraordinary elaboration of *output* in the form of
language. This becomes the supreme achievement in the fields of human expression and communication. Even here, however, hearing is an essential
component of speech, and vision plays a highly important role the moment
a person is able to read.

3. *Manual incorporation.* The fact that the hands also incorporate is still
less obvious than visual and auditory incorporation; but it is of great significance in perceptual development and in the construction of reality. At
birth the hands are of little use; but with the passage of time they become
more and more adept in exploring whatever comes in contact with them.
They touch, feel, pass over and scratch things very early in life, long before
they are integrated with oral, visual or auditory perception.

The peculiarly flexible form of the human hand makes it possible for it
eventually to enclose things, to adapt it own form to the forms it encounters
in external reality, including the manipulable realities of its own body. This
enclosing, even though it is only temporary, is still a kind of *engulfment*
which is comparable to the temporary incorporations executed by the mouth
— in suckling, for example. The hands are also able to mold things into
new forms, and then to incorporate perceptually the new forms they have
created.

Manipulation by the hands — including finger exploration and general manual exploration — contributes constantly to an infant's construction of reality. One has only to think of the supreme importance of manual exploration and incorporation for the congenitally blind to realize the potentialities of the hands and of the imagery they produce. Ordinary children and adults never give up reality-testing through actual handling. In the end, manual manipulation supersedes oral manipulation as the principle means of directly exploring external and somatic reality.

The use of manual imagery, in sharpening one's perception of something seen or recalled, can be observed directly in the way a person shapes his hands as he tries to grasp, to comprehend, the form which he sees or remembers visually. We are all familiar with the now standardized manual symbolization of flying in airplanes and astronaut capsules. These manual manuevers are effective and illuminating as well as amusing.

Final intercoordination of the perceptual systems. Between the fourth and the sixth postnatal months, true eye-hand coordination is established. Both the eyes and the hands can now initiate activity and carry it out cooperatively. The eyes, from their watchtower in the head, gradually gain control over the guidance of visible hand movements. They guide the hands toward things which the eyes can see but cannot reach, toward things which the hands can reach but cannot see. The eyes come to act as scanning and tracking instruments. They keep the hand "on course" toward what is essentially a visualized goal.

It may help us to understand this early experience by comparing it to what an adult amputee experiences as he watches his artificial hand move awkwardly, and often unpredictably, across his visual field. The amputee is learning to guide an unfamiliar hand visually, and through his own internal effort, just as every infant has to do. Both adult amputee and infant have to utilize an unfamiliar feedback from new muscular patterns. The amputee, of course, has many advantages over the infant, not the least of which is his ability to verbalize and to communicate his new experiences. This ability may well give us a greater insight into the struggle through which every infant must go in acquiring his intercoordinations between visual and manual fields.

With the passage of time, the planes of oral, visual and manual perception intersect. The hand that is seen goes with uncertain movements toward the mouth; while the hand that has just been mouthed can be held within the visual field and gravely inspected, sometimes with an assist from the other hand. Here, again, we are dealing with suspended action, with delay, which is generally considered to be essential for the development of an *ego*.

As the functions of mouth, eyes, ears and hands become integrated with one another, the evidence multiplies of more and different kinds of *anticipation*. Thus, for example, the eyes and the ears as distance receptors can initiate sucking movements, drooling and hypersecretion, while an adult is making preparations for the feeding situation, and long before food comes near the mouth itself. It is clear that the eyes and ears can "take in" the feeding situation before the mouth takes in the food. This "taking in" of a situation is what is meant by *incorporation,* whether it is the eyes, the ears or the mouth that does the "taking in."

Oral, visual, auditory and manual incorporation — with the central nervous system changes they induce in perceptual organization, imagery and cognition — are all prime sources of ego structure. They constitute the models for *symbolic incorporation* or *introjection,* which the human organism uses to build up ego and superego structures, as well as for defensive purposes. Symbolic incorporations or introjections enter into the most highly integrated secondary-process thinking, as well as into more primitive, unrealistic thinking, such as we see in the formation of unconscious fantasies, manifest dreams and symptoms. The lack of clear differentiation, and particularly the lack of ego boundaries, make introjection much simpler to carry through in infancy than in later childhood and in adulthood. In psychotic regression, as we shall see, introjection may again become a prominent maneuver, with confusing and sometimes disintegrating results.

Lack of functional boundaries in early mental functioning. When we turn next to a discussion of the symbiotic mother-child unit, we shall find that infants seem at first to lack the functional boundaries which we adults take for granted. Among these are the boundaries between external and internal, between fantasy and socially shared reality, between the self and others. It is difficult to imagine what existence must be like without such differentiations.

The lack of functional boundaries seems more mysterious and unimaginable than it actually is. We all experience it repeatedly in our dreams. One moment a dreamer seems to be watching something that is being done, and the next moment he is the one who is doing it, or it remains unclear whether it is he or someone else who is doing it. The boundaries between *me* and *thee* often fluctuate unstably in a dream, in a way that would be extremely disturbing if one were awake.

In other dreams, activity and passivity seem to be interchangeable. A person dreams of doing something to somebody else; and then, without a break in the continuity, he seems to be the one to whom it is being done. Once again, if such fluctuating identity were present in an adult who was awake, the effect would be confusing and anxiety-provoking. The actual inactivity in sleep protects us.

Functional boundaries are sometimes inadequate or even lacking when a person, an adult, is awake. The simplest demonstration of this can be made in *intoxications.* A wide range of intoxicating agents, from ordinary alcohol to mescalin and lysergic acid, can dissolve the functional boundaries of most adults. When the intoxication clears up, the boundaries reestablish themselves. The ego organization which depends upon the integrity of such boundaries soon reappears.

A demonstration that is more difficult to arrange is that of *sensory deprivation*. Here, without the intervention of an intoxicating agent, an otherwise normal adult may lose his functional boundaries and hallucinate, just because the sensory input is lacking upon which his ego integrity depends.

Functional boundaries also dissolve in the psychoses, and most strikingly in the schizophrenias. Many schizophrenics, without having ingested a drug or having been denied sensory stimulation, nevertheless re-experience the inability to distinguish between themselves and someone else, or between themselves and other things, which they experienced as infants. A schizophrenic patient may complain that he does not know whether it is he or someone else who is doing something — much as dreamers seem to feel. He is often unable to distinguish clearly between his own imaginings and the events that are occurring in the world of external reality or in the reality of his own body.[35]

Such patients often complain openly that they seem to be "falling apart" or "disappearing," that the world seems to be changing unaccountably, or that something terrible is happening which they cannot put into words. These all seem to be attempts to describe the experience of ego disintegration which occurs in deep regression. Since in schizophrenic disorders the patient is neither intoxicated nor alseep, nobody can put a halt to his disintegration, or to the regression of his ego functions, by detoxifying him or by waking him up. The path back to normality is a difficult one. There are some who never succeed in finding it.

Sometimes a regressing schizophrenic patient suffers intense anxiety over the feeling that he is losing his identity, that he is falling apart, disappearing or dissolving. In addition to the weird dreamlike experiences that go with deep regression, there is often also a fear of sinking back into something like the mother-child symbiotic state, or into something that preceded it. In either case, the fear is a fear of losing one's individuality, of losing one's existence as an individual person.

If we remember that external reality and ego organization are interdependent, that "the world" and "the self" are two aspects of the same unity, it is easy to understand why ego disintegration appears to the regressing person as the disappearance of the world, as well as the disappearance of the self. We have only to remind ourselves that every night both the world of external reality and the self disappear (when we fall asleep) to be able to understand how such a thing is possible. The difference is that, when we fall asleep every night, there is no other world present to confuse and be-

[35] This we call *overinclusion*. See the discussion in the chapter on schizophrenia. Also Cameron, N., "Experimental investigation of schizophrenic thinking," in Kasanin, J. (Ed.), *Language and Thought in Schizophrenia*. Berkeley, Calif: Univ. of Calif. Press, 1944, pp. 50–64. The literature on overinclusion has been reviewed by Payne, R. W., "Cognitive abnormalities," in Eysenck, H. J. (Ed.), *Handbook of Abnormal Psychology*. New York: Basic Books, 1961, pp. 245–250; Goldman, A. E., "A comparative-developmental approach to schizophrenia," *Psychol. Bull.*, 1962, *59*, 57–69; Payne, R. W., Mattusek, P., and George, E. I., "An experimental study of schizophrenic thought disorder," *J. ment. Sci.*, 1959, *105*, 627–652.

wilder us, whereas in schizophrenia the world of reality presents itself to the patient as something that does not fit into his imaginings.

We have now given the background of early perceptual development, and of early perceptual coordination in infancy.[36] We have emphasized appropriately the outstanding significance of oral functions and of oral imagery for early life, and for a good deal of regressive psychopathology, such as we shall see especially in the psychoses. We are now ready to discuss the characteristics of the symbiotic mother-child unit, the first important love relationship of an infant's life.

The symbiotic mother-child unit

We have been discussing the early maturation and development of the infant almost as though he were an isolated organism, capable only of perceiving, behaving and coordinating his perceptual fields and motor activities through his own solitary effort. This initial approach is justified by the complexity of human beginnings, by the need to simplify them so that they can be described, by the initial loneliness of the infant and by the early superiority of perceptual growth over motor coordination. The picture, however, is at best only half true. It virtually ignores the vital role of mothering and being mothered. It leaves out the affective aspects of the first year and the internal organization of a rudimentary ego system. In this section we shall take for granted the perceptual and cognitive developments already discussed, and focus upon the mother-child interaction, without which no infant can grow into a normal human being.[37]

Early in this century a pediatrician published some startling statistics on the high incidence of deaths among institutionalized infants, and the relatively low incidence among those adopted early and brought up by a foster mother.[38] In spite of the vigor and insistence of his articles they seem to have been largely ignored. Institutionalized infants went on dying in spite of adequate nourishment and clean surroundings. Perhaps the hardy spirit of the times fated the reports to be disregarded as mere sentiment; perhaps a lack of understanding of the power of behavioral interaction was responsible.

The crusade for adequate mothering was revived three decades later by workers with a psychodynamic orientation, but once again disbelief and ridicule met the reports.[39] This was in part due to the lack of specific published data and the emotionality of the appeal for adequate infant care. Soon, however, careful objective clinical research began to appear, and the data aroused

[36] Solley, C. M., and Murphy, G., *Development of the Perceptual World.* New York: Basic Books, 1960.

[37] Harris, I. D., *Normal Children and Mothers: Their Emotional Opportunities and Obstacles.* Glencoe, Ill.: Free Press, 1959.

[38] Chapin, H. D., cited in Rollman-Branch, H. S., "On the question of primary object need," *J. Amer. Psychoanal. Ass.*, 1960, *8*, 686–702.

[39] There are still residuals of this attitude among research workers and theoreticians who reject the possibility of psychogenesis in their professional work, even though they may accept it in the practical interaction of everyday life.

interest and alarm among those working in the field. The problem of mothering became a major issue.[40]

There are still orphanages today where infants may receive meticulous physical care and perfect feeding formulas, but get little or no real mothering. Death rates are much lower than they were earlier in the century; but the incidence of severe infant and child personality disturbance is high. Perhaps the government will include this factor in its new plans for the study of feeblemindedness. Severe emotional deprivation is known to be a contributing factor in many cases of irreversible developmental defect.[41]

Today it is widely recognized that the ministrations of a devoted mother or mother substitute are essential to an infant's physical welfare as well as to his emotional development and personality organization. It is essential that such a mother figure enter into an intimate symbiotic relationship with the infant, and that she maintain it without serious ambivalence during much of the first postnatal year. Fortunately, the maternal needs of normal mothers take care of this situation. As the term symbiosis implies, both mother and infant gain by their mutual experiences in such a relationship.[42]

The concept of symbiosis in psychopathology. The term *symbiosis* is borrowed from biology. There it refers to mutual and sometimes vital benefits derived by both host and parasite in a biologically parasitic relationship.[43] The host and the parasite belong to different species.

The *mother-child symbiosis* in psychopathology has the same connotations. For even though mother and child belong to the same species, they are entirely different in their biosocial levels of organization. The infant, because of his unparalleled slow maturation, is at first *functionally parasitic*. He cannot interact with his mother. The mother, with her highly developed personality organization and her role membership in an enormously complex society, is the *functional equivalent* of her infant's *host*. We have described the vast differences between newborns earlier in the chapter. They can be summarized in a few words here.

The mother in the symbiotic relationship. A willing mother receives each newborn as a new love object. Even though she may be clumsy and awkward

[40] For a review of this work, see Brody, S., *Patterns of Mothering.* New York: Internat. Univ. Press, 1956.

[41] Provence, S., and Lipton, R., *Infants in Institutions: A Comparison of Their Development with Family Infants: Report of a Five-Year Research Study.* New York: Internat. Univ. Press, 1962; Yarrow, L. J., "Maternal deprivation: Toward an empirical and conceptual re-evaluation," *Psychol. Bull.*, 1961, *58*, 459–490; Provence, S., and Ritvo, S., "Effects of deprivation on institutionalized infants," *Psychoanal. Study Child*, 1961, *16*, 189–205; Earle, A. M., and Earle, B. V., "Early maternal deprivation and later psychiatric illness," *Amer. J. Orthopsychiat.*, 1961, *31*, 181–186.

[42] Cf. Benedek, T., "Parenthood as a developmental phase," *J. Amer. Psychoanal. Ass.*, 1959, 7, 389–417.

[43] For an account of the development of this concept in psychodynamics, see Chapter 16 in Bellak, L. (Ed.), *Schizophrenia: a Review of the Literature.* New York: Logos Press, 1958, pp. 555–693.

with her firstborn, and even though each new addition to the family may make her anxious in advance, it is usual for a mother to find the helplessness and need of her baby irresistibly appealing.[44] The newborn calls out infinite maternal tenderness and the desire to care for and to give. He has a double appeal. The mother has borne him; he has been at one time a part of her own body, and he comes from it. She also possesses him and realizes that she can care for him in ways that no one else can. She becomes sensitive to his every want and to every change in his appearance and behavior.

The infant is an object to the mother from the start, a little person, something tiny, but complete in itself. It is something that grows more and more a part of her again, but in a new sense, outside the mother's body, and by means of the whole process of mothering. For the mother the baby represents self-fulfillment, completeness and creation. To her relationship with the newborn, she brings a world of maternal understanding, of willingness to comfort, to protect and to nourish.

The newborn in the symbiotic relationship. For the newborn the situation is entirely different. He does not perceive his mother as an object at all. He does not have the means necessary for recognizing her as a separate being who watches over him, feeds and cares for him, makes him comfortable and safe. *Before* birth he floated aimlessly in the amniotic fluid; *after* birth he is adrift in a shoreless world without objects of any kind. He can in no way reciprocate the love he gets; he is unable to return love or even to long for it. All that he can contribute is his own body; and he is not even aware that he has one. His mother is vividly aware of motherhood; whereas the child at first has no self to be aware of, and he cannot know that he is "a child."[45]

During the first few weeks the infant is incapable of entering into a genuine interpersonal relationship. With the exception of his feeding periods, he remains for the most part a passive and an isolated object of maternal care and affection. He has to acquire a capacity for mutual interaction. As he develops perceptual, emotional, cognitive and motor abilities, he grows more and more capable of participating actively in the relationship which his mother offers him. His initial loneliness — lost in a shoreless ocean of diffuse experience — gives way gradually to a growing closeness in the symbiotic relationship which reaches its peak around the sixth month.

Growth of the symbiotic relationship. The symbiotic relationship begins, then, with a *mother* acutely aware of motherhood, and ready for what her role demands, and an *infant* who can only accept love, care and protection passively, without understanding anything. The great achievement of the infant's first few weeks is that of developing enough perceptual maturity, acquiring

44 Sears, R. R., Maccoby, E. E., and Levin, H., *Patterns of Child Rearing.* Evanston, Ill.: Row, Peterson, 1957.

45 Cf. Levy, D., *Behavioral Analysis: An Analysis of Clinical Observations of Behavior as Applied to Mother-Newborn Relationships.* Springfield, Ill.: Thomas, 1958.

enough adaptive behavior, and incorporating enough of his surroundings, to enable him to become an active, participating partner in the symbiosis. Ultimately he becomes even more involved in the partnership than his mother. He has almost no role other than that of a symbiotic infant, whereas his mother occupies several important roles. She is wife, homemaker, perhaps the mother of other children, and an active participant in activities outside the family.

Since an infant can understand nothing said to him, and cannot himself speak, his media of communication with his mother must lie at nonverbal levels. Communication must come at first from what his mother does, the way she picks him up and puts him down, how she carries him, feeds and diapers him, bathes him and covers him up, takes him out and brings him in. Contact with her body, with her warmth and softness, her nearness, the smell of her and the music she makes with her voice — all these mean everything to him, while words mean nothing.[46]

The mother as temporary ego. A mother does things for her child which he will later be able to do for himself. By carrying him around, handling him, bringing things to him, and giving him changes of scene, she nourishes him with a vast variety of perceptual and motor experiences which he could otherwise never have. In doing these things she is performing the work that his adaptive ego, with its autonomous functions, will eventually perform. This service is all the more essential because a young infant's perceptual development far outpaces his motor development. He can perceive things for a long time before he is able to reach them. Without the variations which his mother's action provides him the infant would sink into apathy for want of adequately varied stimulation.[47]

It is under these conditions, with infinitely repeated and varied experiences which he and his mother share, that the infant develops a confident expectation that his needs will be met as they arise, including the need for multiple stimulation. This helps him form the *basic trust* which, as we said earlier, may determine his emotional future, particularly the emotional health and richness of his interpersonal relations. Through her own dependability, a mother structures the shared situation in such a way that both she and her child are confident.

Because at the beginning the infant does not have specific ego defenses, his mother must also provide substitutes for these if she is to protect him.[48] At birth he seems unreactive, excepting to massive stimulation which for the moment overwhelms him. In part this is accounted for by assuming the existence of an inborn *protective barrier* against stimulation, out of which

---

[46] Compare the importance of contact, etc., in Rollman-Branch, H. S., "On the question of primary object need," *J. Amer. Psychoanal. Ass.*, 1960, *8*, 686–702.

[47] Certain American Indian mothers perform the same kind of service by strapping an infant to their backs while they work, providing for him a richly varied field of moving perceptual stimulation.

[48] Spitz, R., "Some early prototypes of ego defenses," *J. Amer. Psychoanal. Ass.*, 1961, *9*, 626–652.

specific ego defenses may later evolve. In part it is also the result of a lack of organized specific perceptual response patterns.

As an infant develops more and more capacity for specific and differential response his need to be shielded grows proportionally. Protection from excessive external stimulation means that the mother must arrange her child's environment so that it will not impinge upon him with too great intensity, for too long a period, or with too much emotional excitement. Protection from internal stress means relieving pain and discomfort by removing their cause, and when that is not possible by such countermeasures as holding, carrying, rocking, soothing and bubbling. All such protection represents maternal substitutes for the child's own defenses, which have not yet matured.

Maternal protection also includes help in taming and channeling early emotional drives. At first the most a mother can do is to avert emotional build-up so as to minimize the necessity for massive discharge, and to intervene when cycles of frustration and rage become self-sustaining. She must also act as temporary ego in protecting the child from the consequences of his own activities when — because of inexperience, inability to differentiate objects and himself as entities, and inadequate motor coordination — he puts himself in danger of injury or of intolerable anxiety. As drive differentiation grows, and as the infant begins to gain control over action, he can be helped to channel drive discharge along socially acceptable lines, in ways that are least disruptive and most satisfying in the end.[49]

The failure of a mother to provide an early protective substitute ego for an infant may drive him into self-protective apathy such as one sees in institutionalized infants who get no mothering. Excessive stimulation may also force an infant to develop defenses before he is physiologically prepared to develop them. In the latter case he may develop a premature distorted defensive organization and, in consequence, a precocious pathological ego structure. When this happens, all the later sequences of defensive and adaptive ego maturation may show distortions.[50]

Primary identification with the mother. We have good reason to assume that, during the first few weeks of postnatal life, no human infant is capable of distinguishing between himself and his mother. This state of affairs is known as *primary identification*. It is not an abnormality; it is not an act of perception or cognition; it is not a defense. It is simply an incapacity to distinguish objects, a lack of ego organization and an absence of self-feelings. It is an expression of the lack of functional boundaries which characterizes early infancy, and which we have compared to the kaleidoscopic shifting of imagery commonly experienced in adult dreaming.

Primary identification early in life is the result of perceptual and cognitive

---

[49] Finney, J. C., "Some maternal influences on children's personality and character," *Genet. Psychol. Monogr.,* 1961, *63,* 199–278.

[50] The importance of early maternal protection for the normal development of young infants will be further discussed in the chapters on the neuroses, psychoses and personality disorders; Bishop, B. M., "Mother-child interaction and the social behavior of children," *Psychol. Monogr.,* 1951, Whole No. 328.

immaturity, and in this sense the expression of a defect. Nevertheless this situation carries with it certain advantages for the young infant. Among these advantages is an inability to differentiate between what happens because of maternal action and what happens because of infant action and perception. Since the infant has not yet developed functional boundaries, and cannot recognize such differences, he experiences the results of maternal action, of his own action and his perception, as the equivalent of what he will later identify as his own. He lives in a magical world where, for example, he seems at times to move swiftly, while his perceptual world undergoes tremendous change with little or no experience of effort. Many normal regressive experiences, such as dreams of flying and floating effortlessly through the air, probably come from the imagery belonging to this phase of primary identification. So also do many hallucinatory experiences in schizophrenia, and some of the equilibratory disturbances seen in intoxications and sensory deprivation.

For the infant, these and many other experiences, in which he participates in what his mother does without knowing it, provide him with apparent magical activity and protect him from having to recognize his actual helplessness and passivity, and the poverty of his resources. Whenever he is moved about, turned over, bathed, diapered, carried around or taken out of doors, he perceives the endless variety of experiences as things that happen and, as he matures a little more, as things that he himself is doing.[51]

Another consequence of the symbiotic fusion is that the infant presumably also experiences his joy and his mother's reciprocal joy as a unitary undifferentiated global joy. Or if he experiences a diffuse angry tension, and his mother responds with her anger, he experiences the whole as his universe of fury. From the studies of emotionally deprived infants we conclude that a very young infant cannot experience full joy and pleasure without the simultaneous joy and pleasure expressed overtly by a symbiotic mother figure. In adult terms, her emotional expressions are his, and his experiences are his also. The two supplement each other to form an undifferentiated whole.

The importance of such fusion can be imagined in situations where the child is flooded by feelings of angry frustration, but the mother, conscious of the child's helplessness, and of her own role as rescuer and comforter, responds consistently with soothing, loving intervention. The infant's total emotional experience will then include his mother's behavior, still undifferentiated from his own. He will learn to expect to experience relief confidently whenever he grows intolerably tense or becomes enraged. The dependence which is characteristic of this period includes such a looking-to-the-mother (even before she has become a separate object) for the satisfactions of his desires and the taming of his rage. It is easy to understand how such maternal participation can become the most significant factor in determining a child's emotional development.

[51] Solomon, J. C., "Brief communication: passive motion and infancy," *Amer. J. Orthopsychiat.*, 1959, 29, 650–651.

Ego development and dissolution of the symbiotic unit

We shall defer further discussion of ego development until we come to Chapter 5 on the psychodynamic system. Here it will be enough if we give a bare outline to supplement what has already been said.

1. *Autonomous ego functions and the conflict-free sphere.* The infant's maturation and development of perceptual, cognitive and motor functions make it possible for him to organize external reality, as we have seen. These functions form the basis of what have been called *autonomous ego functions.* They are primarily adaptive in character, rather than defensive, and they give rise to a *conflict-free sphere* in ego organization.[52]

2. *Id and ego, primary and secondary processes.* We assume that at birth there is an *id-ego* nucleus from which an *id drive system* and a *reality-oriented ego system* will be elaborated. The *id system* (Freud's *system unconscious*) will continue to operate in terms of the *primary process,* that is, in terms of mobile cathexes or energies, of displacement, condensation, and an archaic form of symbolization. The *ego system* grows more and more differentiated from the earlier id-ego nucleus, as *delay, frustration* and *conflict* enter more and more into the infant's experience. The ego system develops a complex series of defensive organizations, most of them unconscious, and it develops more and more elaborate systems of adaptation and mastery. It operates more and more in terms of the *secondary process,* that is, in terms of realistic perception and cognition. The extreme example of secondary process thinking is logical reflection, which begins around the fifth or sixth year, that is, after the edipal phase has been worked through and repression established, but does not reach full maturity until just before puberty.

3. *The defenses and boundary setting.* Early in life the defenses play a leading role in establishing and maintaining functional boundaries between the id system, with its primary process, and the ego system, with its secondary process. The defenses also help set functional boundaries between ego and external reality, and between both these and somatic reality. We shall have opportunities to see what happens if these boundaries begin to dissolve when we come to the clinical chapters on neuroses and psychoses.

4. *Ego introjects.* While perceptual, cognitive and motor functions are maturing and developing through use, and while the ego is differentiating from the id, from external and somatic realities, there are also incorporations of certain aspects of maternal behavior taking place. We call the results of such incorporation *ego introjects.* They are actually derived in part from the

[52] Cf. Hartmann, H., *Ego Psychology and the Problem of Adaptation.* New York: Internat. Univ. Press, 1958.

mother's behavior and in part from the simultaneous experiences of the infant. As we have seen, the infant cannot at the time distinguish between the two sources of his experience, that which comes from his mother, and that which comes from himself.

To a lesser degree, but still to a significant extent, the ego introjects also include aspects of the father's and the siblings' behavior, and of that of any other significant person in the household. It must be remembered that father, siblings and other significant figures enter somewhat into the *mother-child symbiosis,* even though to a much lesser degree than the mother.

5. *Internal objects.* As ego boundaries crystallize, these early ego introjects organize into what we call *internal objects.* The internal objects represent external objects, especially parental objects. They organize the early fundamentals of personality. They also help the infant to control his behavior along the general lines of parental approval and disapproval. In other words, the infant becomes more and more like his parents by introjecting their aspects; and these introjections help determine what he does. They are therefore precursors of what will later become suprego control. Early in life he tries to please the internalized parents as well as the parents in external reality.

6. *The infant as an autonomous individual.* By the time an infant can sit up alone and stand, his active relations with what is becoming external reality, and his parallel organization of an ego system within, have progressed to a point where he can begin to operate as an *autonomous individual.* From the second or third month these abilities, and the corresponding ego elaborations, begin to evolve and their rate of evolution rapidly accelerates. By the end of the first year the infant has already become a separate person.

Failures to resolve the symbiotic relationship. In exceptional instances, an infant fails to dissolve his symbiotic relationship and to gain full membership in the family unit.

(a) *Autistic children.* Some of these failures appear to be the result of an inability on the part of the infant to enter into a full symbiotic relationship before the time comes to dissolve it. Such are the *autistic children,* first identified and described by Kanner,[53] and subsequently studied by him and others. Autistic children remain permanently incapable of forming effective object relationships and of constructing external reality or an effective ego organization.

(b) *Symbiotic children.* Other failures appear in children who seem to have entered into a full symbiotic relationship with a mother figure, but who cannot successfully resolve it. They go on to develop an extremely distorted,

[53] Kanner, L., "Early infantile autism," *J. Pediatrics,* 1944, 25, 211–217.

dependent relationship with the mother figure. The syndrome is called a *symbiotic childhood psychosis*.[54] The outlook for the symbiotic child is also bleak, even though his level of fixation is less primitive than that of the autistic child.

Both autistic children and symbiotic children are often said to be suffering from *childhood schizophrenia*. There are, however, such wide differences between these childhood syndromes and those of adolescent and adult schizophrenia that many objections have been raised to the use of this term.[55]

As we shall see later on, in the clinical chapters, there are many partial failures to resolve the problems raised by the symbiotic mother-child relationship that result neither in austistic nor in symbiotic childhood disorders. They do give rise to personality structures which are vulnerable to neurotic or psychotic breakdowns, later on in childhood, in adolescence, or in adulthood. More often than not, partial failures in dissolving the symbiotic relationship with the mother leave a child poorly equipped to develop into an autonomous individual. This, as we shall also see, leaves him unready to enter into and resolve the later edipal phase of personality development. Let us turn next to the phase of self-assertion and sphincter control.

The phase of self-assertion and sphincter control

This phase of personality development occupies the second year of postnatal life. It begins with the beginning dissolution of the symbiotic mother-child unit, and ends with the child becoming entangled in edipal strivings and edipal conflicts. In this phase the child strives for independence as a separate individual with his own identity, but within the family group. Normally he succeeds. His principal means consist of vigorous self-assertion — at times appearing as pure negativism — a growing ability to stand, walk and run alone, and the mastery of sphincter control.

The chief pitfalls in this phase are the overdoing of self-assertion, the abuse of freedom in walking, climbing and running about, and the use of sphincter control to frustrate his parents — either by withholding bowel movements when they are asked for, or by making them at times or in places which are inappropriate. The self-assertion in most directions can be easily controlled by parents. The danger to the child is that if he is frustrated too much he will become either a chronically angry child or a submissive one who lacks normal initiative. The same is true of his freedom of movement. He needs to have this as much as possible; but because of his lack of skill and lack of experience he can easily put himself in danger. In the matter of sphincter

[54] Mahler, M. S., "On childhood psychosis and schizophrenia. Autistic and symbiotic infantile psychosis," *The Psychoanalytic Study of the Child.* New York: Internat. Univ. Press, 1952, vol. 7, pp. 286–305.

[55] For an excellent review of the problem, see Ekstein, R., Bryant, K., and Friedman, S. W., "Childhood schizophrenia and allied conditions," in Bellak, L. (Ed.), *Schizophrenia: A Review of the Syndrome.* New York: Logos Press, 1958, pp. 555–693.

control, it is more difficult for parents to have their way, because the child really does have the chance to please them or foil them by what he does. We shall return to this topic after a few paragraphs because it has a special place in normal and psychopathological development.

A growing ability to understand speech and to use it are also characteristic of this phase of development. Talking and understanding speech hasten the child's integration into the family unit, and lead to an almost unlimited elaboration of secondary process ego organization.[56] Language also has its pitfalls. They are too well known and too numerous to merit a description here. We may mention, as an example, the confusion of things with the words that symbolize them, the misunderstanding of what is said because of inexperience and a peculiarly concrete manner of thinking,[57] and the use of speech to tantalize adults, as in the perpetual "why's." Even as adults, we are still many times confused and trapped by the apparent dichotomy between what we experience in nonverbal ways and what we try to say about such experience — or what others say about similar experiences. Language has its own structure and its own rules, which are not always the same as the structure and the rules of nonverbal experience.

Any division of childhood development into separate phases is bound to be somewhat arbitrary, and to lead to misunderstanding itself. For example, we see attempts at self-assertion, and even negativism, during the symbiotic phase; and neither self-assertion nor negativism disappear completely when the child enters his edipal phase. Locomotion and general coordination go on increasing in efficiency well into adulthood. The mastery of language and the acquisition of knowledge may not be complete until late maturity. Even sphincter control is not achieved all at once. There may be frequent lapses, especially if a sibling is born soon after sphincter control has been achieved. Obstinacy finds many other channels of expression. The *reaction formations* against soiling, characteristic of this early period, become important mechanisms of self-control which precede formation of the superego by several years.

Transitions from symbiosis to self-assertion and sphincter control. Before dissolution of the symbiotic mother-child unit, and leading up to it, the child reacts to "outsiders" — including father and siblings — in certain specific ways which represent the mother's attitudes rather than the child's own. The child is carried along with the mother in these ways because he is a part of her in the symbiosis. She is able to have these attitudes, and to react in their terms, because she is already a full-fledged member of the larger family unit, which the child still is not. In such ways, the mother carries her infant into

---

[56] For a review of recent work on cognitive learning in infants and young children, see Fowler, W., "Cognitive learning in infancy and early childhood," *Psychol. Bull.*, 1962, *59*, 116–152.

[57] Although we emphasize the mother in the early years, the father nowadays plays a much more important and intimate role than in the past. This is an example of social role change which may significantly change the infant's basic psychological structure.

all kinds of relations with other members of the family while he is still part of the symbiotic mother-child unit. For her infant, the mother has one foot in each world, the world of the symbiotic unit and the world of the family unit.

As the infant begins differentiating *the I* or *the me* from *the mother*, both externally and in his internal imagery, he can go right on having the attitudes which he originally shared with his mother before the differentiation; and he can go right on responding to the other members of the family as he had been doing before. This kind of behavior is a direct outgrowth of the original confusion which we have described earlier as *primary identification*. Moreover, the child can also apply these attitudes and responses to his mother, as she in turn becomes a differentiated, external object for him.

As he differentiates himself further and further from the original mother-child unit, he assumes these attitudes and takes these reactions more and more as his own. This process, of course, is also a form of incorporation or introjection. The child modifies and elaborates what he introjects (his *ego introjects*) in accordance with his own developing childhood personality. He begins to function more and more as an individual person in his own right. Every now and then, when the stress of life becomes too much for him, he may run back into his mother's arms, thus momentarily re-establishing the old mother-child unit.

Normal parents and siblings encourage and support a child's efforts to differentiate himself as a separate little person. For the mother this is a matter of relief as well as of pride. She looks forward to greater liberty for herself, even though it may mean entering into another symbiotic relationship with a new baby. The child, for his part, has to achieve certain advances before he is fully acceptable as an independent family member — in eating habits, in channeling his love and his rage, in becoming predictable, in gaining self-control, and in achieving sphincter control.

The special place of sphincter control. During this phase of development it is normal for a child to show special interest in bowel control and in bowel products. Bowel control can be a new and pleasurable accomplishment, a further step toward mastery and maturity, which parents and siblings can appreciate and encourage. Interest in bowel products is also understandable. The child creates them by a voluntary act; they obviously come from his own body; they have a recognizable form; and in a sense they are infantile sculptures. Moreover, the child's mother openly values them and expresses her satisfaction to her child. She sees them as evidence of good health and of increasing maturity. The great majority of young children lose most of their pride and interest in bowel functions as they mature further, and as they find other forms of mastery to awaken their pride and hold their interest.

It is of importance to psychopathology that the childhood problem of bowel control can easily become a call to battle within the family. A child quickly learns that his parents want him to produce movements on schedule and in the right place. He also learns that he can easily frustrate them by not complying. If a child's noncompliance arouses anger or anxious insistence in the parent, it can become the focus of serious warfare.[58]

Some mothers react with marked tension, and even with rage, when their child becomes constipated, especially if it seems to them to be the result of willful negativism. The trouble with such reactions is that they also make the child tense and angry. He is then actually incapable of having a move-ment. Occasionally we find mothers who, when their child makes them anxious and angry, threatens to give an enema as retaliation whenever the child refuses to conform. Combats over bowel function may result in a patho-logical fixation at this general level. We shall mention four kinds of outcome here.

1. *The compulsive character.* A person grows to adulthood with a well-recognized cluster of characteristics. He is unreasonably obstinate, parsi-monious and constricted. He often frustrates and controls others through invoking arbitrary rules and laws, just as his parents once frustrated him and arbitrarily controlled him. The compulsive person usually does not recognize what he is doing or why he has to do it. Either the memory of his childhood battles over sphincter control has vanished, or, if the memory remains, the adult can see no relationship between these childhood battles and his current insistence upon routine, ritual, order and excessive cleanliness.

2. *The personality vulnerable to obsessive compulsive regression.* Another result of fixation at the level of sphincter control is to make a person always vulnerable to regression, under stress, to frank obsessive compulsive neuroses, even though when things go well there may be no compulsive character. Some obsessive compulsive patients, who have regressed under stress, can recall battles over bowel function that extended right through the edipal phase and into the latency period. We shall give one such example in the chapter on obsessive compulsive reactions. It is impossible to disregard the patho-logical nature of the mother's behavior that allows the contest of wills to go to such extremes.

3. *The overcompliant person.* If a child, embroiled in some such contest of wills at this level of development, finally accepts defeat and becomes over-compliant, he may go into adolescence and adulthood as an intimidated, compulsively "good" person. In this situation, the person is not "good" because of any inherently constructive values, but only because he has become reconciled to the conformity enforced upon him. He has been so intimidated that he is incapable of rebelling, incapable of showing aggression even when

[58] Maccoby, E. E., Maccoby, N., Romney, A. K., and Adams, J. S., "Social reinforce-ment in attitude change," *J. abnorm. soc. Psychol.,* 1961, *63,* 109–115; Sears, R. R., Maccoby, E. E., and Levin, H., *Patterns of Child Rearing.* Evanston, Ill.: Row, Peterson, 1957; Brody, S., *Patterns of Mothering: Maternal Influence During Infancy.* New York: Internat. Univ. Press, 1956.

he should. It is easy to overlook the pathology of such behavior, and to see only its virtue.

4. *Anal fixation and sadomasochistic pleasure.* This clinical relationship appears concretely in obsessive compulsive neuroses. It is apparently, however, more general than this. Studies of children, normal as well as neurotic, suggest that emotional ambivalence is experienced by every child during the phase of self-assertion and sphincter control. Love and hate for the same person are still intermingled and still unresolved. Pleasurable erotic experience during this phase seems to include bowel function and anal stimulation. Sadomasochistic pleasure and anger appear to be related both to infantile self-assertion, and to the rage which fills a frustrated child who is able to do so much, and yet is subjected to so much control by others. The sadistic pleasure is usually regarded as a fusion of erotic and aggressive drives; more recently it has been formulated as being wholly erotic.[59]

In the past educated people have been reluctant to accept the role of bowel function and bowel products in ordinary human motivation and in psychopathology. This may be in part a natural disgust with anal functions, a disgust which those animals who bury their excrement seem to share.[60] In part, however, it stems from a reluctance to relate them to sex and anger. Nevertheless, there is much evidence that such relations are almost universally recognized, in our own culture as well as in the more primitive ones. Slang and obscenity, all over the world today, and in centuries past, relate bowel functions and their products with anger, hatred, contempt and erotic pleasure. The connection between sadomasochism and sexuality has long been recognized openly. Adults who have been thrown with earthy human beings of their own culture in the recent past are aware of these relationships; so also are nursery school teachers and child psychiatrists.

This brief excursion into resistance and cultural prejudice, which often makes an adult deny what he actually knows, will prepare us to discuss sex identification and object love. This we shall do in relation to the pre-edipal period, which is our next topic, and in the edipal period to which we shall soon turn.

Pre-edipal sex identification and object love. An infant's first love object is always his or her mother. The love object, even though fragmentary and incompletely perceived at first, is recognized early by the child as the major source of repeated gratification — of hunger, of love, of action-pleasure and so on. The mother also provides the earliest conditions for infant identification, even though, as we have seen, this is at first an undifferentiated primary identification. We assume that these simultaneous experiences of object love

---

[59] Gero, G., "Sadism, masochism and aggression: their role in symptom formation," *Psychoanal. Quart.*, 1962, *31*, 31–42.

[60] We call it *natural* because many animals without special training express distaste for their excretions as they grow up and, like good campers, bury them.

and identification bring about alterations in personality structure even before the phase of primary identification has passed, and before the mother has been given up as sole love object.[61]

As an infant's ego organization matures and begins to set boundaries, he internalizes aspects of both parents in relation to his own immediate needs and satisfactions. These introjects, composed of part parent and part infant experience, retain the emotional qualities of drive experience until the child masters his edipal phase.[62]

Before a growing child is able to develop secondary identification (*true identification*), the kind that older children and adults use, he identifies through imitating parental action.[63] Thus, a little girl of our acquaintance always runs her toy carpet sweeper vigorously over the rugs while her mother is doing the same with a full-sized one. Imitation among both boys and girls in the pre-edipal period is at first imitation of the mother. Soon, however, the boy turns toward a male identification figure, his father, an older brother or some other adult male. If his own father is an adequate affectionate male, he presents the boy with a needed model, while he himself can enjoy and profit from his son's admiration. The little girl continues to identify with her mother, but more fully and more realistically than before, playing house and caring for dolls. Her mother can enjoy the daughter's wish to be like her and she gains in self-esteem. In such ways the child internalizes both parents in different ways, while he or she is in part losing them through the dissolution of the symbiotic relationship.[64]

Innate sex drive patterns appear spontaneously under favorable conditions during the pre-edipal phase of both boys and girls. The small boy often declares openly his intention of marrying his mother; he may show a protective attitude toward mothers, sisters and other females, if he is allowed to do so. The small girl is normally flirtatious with her father and other males, and she focuses interest upon her graceful body and its adornment. Parents normally reciprocate with appropriate behavior which distinguishes between the masculine behavior and aspirations of the pre-edipal boy, and the feminine behavior and aspirations of the pre-edipal girl.

Normal parents are able to do this with increasingly mature expressions of object love for their child, that is, love in the form of sublimated, openly expressed affection. They thus help the boy to establish his masculine identity, and the girl to establish her feminine identity, before the edipal phase opens. By contrast, emotionally immature or pathological parents may behave se-

[61] Freud, S., *The Ego and the Id.* (1923), Standard Edition, 1961, vol. 19, pp. 13–66.
[62] Benedek, T., "Parenthood as a developmental phase," *J. Amer. Psychoanal. Ass.,* 1959, 7, 389–417.
[63] McDavid, J. W., "Imitative behavior in preschool children," *Psychol. Monogr.,* 1959, 73, Whole No. 486; Rosenblith, J. F., "Learning by imitation in kindergarten children," *Child Develpm.,* 1959, 30, 69–80.
[64] Emmerich, W., "Parental identification in young children," *Genet. Psychol. Monogr.,* 1959, 60, 257–308; Mussen, P., and Distler, L., "Masculinity, identification, and father-son relationships," *J. abnorm. soc. Psychol.,* 1959, 59, 350–356.

ductively toward their pre-edipal child, exhibit jealousy of him or her, or experience such strict, rigid superego attitudes that they become incapable of showing normal, sublimated parental affection.[65]

Meanwhile, the pre-edipal child has already internalized parental value systems through progressive identification. He has acquired numerous hierarchies of most preferred and less preferred values, whose rank orders correspond more or less to those of one or both parents. At the same time, however, the child gives these his own individual stamp, as he integrates them into his pre-edipal ego organization. To the extent that such value systems and hierarchies deal with what seems *good* or *bad, right* or *wrong, moral* or *immoral,* they become the precursors of the superego which develops toward the close of the edipal phase. Such pre-edipal moral distinctions need not correspond to the more realistic postedipal ones. They are usually even more strict and rigid, often showing the meticulousness and the sadism of reaction formation against soiling and losing control. They usually also include much concern about relatively trivial matters, some of these are the infantile equivalents of adult snobbery as to "what is done" and "what is not done."

From all that has been said above it is evident that the edipal phase, when it finally comes, has a long history of dynamic interaction between child and parents, reaching back to early pre-edipal situations. These interactions, together with the child's infantile sexual maturing, make the edipal phase inevitable. If the transactions between child and parents, during the pre-edipal phase, have been good ones, they will not only help structure the edipal situation but help resolve it also, with benefit to all concerned.

In turning now to a consideration of the edipal phase, we must bear in mind one great difference between child and parent, aside from matters of skill and knowledge. This fundamental difference is that, whereas an emotionally mature parent already has a mature superego to maintain an integrated balance within his psychodynamic system, the pre-edipal child enters his edipal phase with only infantile precursors of a superego, with his largely untamed drives, and with his fears of parental disapproval, rejection, punishment and retaliation. These fears, as we shall soon see, reflect the child's sadomasochistic immediate past, and expose him to unrealistic anxieties with regard to his survival and the integrity of his body.[66]

The edipal phase

Until the time of Freud it was customary to speak of the small child as asexual, in spite of everyday experience to the contrary, and to hail puberty as the first flowering of human sexuality, instead of its second. Not one of the many nineteenth-century books on childhood that Freud examined had

[65] See the discussion of parental seduction and sex deviation in Chapter 19, "Personality disorders."

[66] Rangell, L., "The role of the parent in the Oedipus complex," *Bull. Menn. Clinic,* 1955, *19,* 9–15.

a chapter in it on the sexual interests of little children. When he was forty-five, Freud made a clear reference to infantile sexuality in his *Interpretation of Dreams*, and he followed the reference with a lively discussion of the Oedipus legend and of Shakespeare's *Hamlet*.[67] When he was almost fifty he gave the *coup de grâce* to the myth of the asexual little child in his book, *Three Essays on the Theory of Sexuality*.[68] In subsequent publications, Freud and others established the edipal complex as the infantile nucleus of adult neuroses. Thus, while disposing of the legend of asexual childhood, Freud and his associates transformed the ancient legend of unconscious incest, which is the theme of Sophocles' Greek tragedy *Oedipus Rex*, into the contemporary real drama which every little child must himself enact.

The legend. According to an ancient legend, which Sophocles has one of his characters compare to normal incestuous dreams, an infant prince was exposed to die because of a prophecy that he was destined to murder his father. He was rescued by strangers and brought up as a prince in an alien court. When he sought to learn his true origin from an oracle, he was given the kind of confusing information in which oracles seem to specialize. He was simply told to avoid his home because he was destined to kill his father and marry his mother. The prince, whose name was Oepidus, then took to the road as a warrior, thinking that he was indeed leaving his home. In a quarrel on the way, he killed the King of Thebes, who actually was his father although he did not know it. He then went on to solve the riddle of the Sphinx which saved the Thebans from her murderous attacks. The grateful Thebans put Oedipus on the now empty throne and, as was the ancient custom, gave him the slain king's widow as his wife.

The new king, Oedipus Rex, had a long and peaceful reign, during which the queen bore him two sons and two daughters. Then a plague broke out in Thebes. The oracle declared that the murderer of his father must be driven from the land if the land was to be saved. After an objective but tragically personal searching, which Freud compares to psychoanalysis, Oedipus discovered that the slain king was his father, and that he had married his own mother. Before either he or his mother realized the truth, and while Oedipus was beginning to suspect it, we find his wife and mother trying to reassure and comfort the distraught Oedipus by saying, "Many a man ere now in dreams hath lain with her who bare him."[69] When the truth is finally revealed the queen commits suicide. Oedipus blinds himself and leaves his home forever.

The edipal tragedy in normal childhood. Some time during the third or fourth year of postnatal life the child loses what autonomy he has gained and

---

[67] Freud, S., *The Interpretation of Dreams.* (1900), Standard Edition, 1953, vol. 4, pp. 257–266.

[68] Freud, S., *Three Essays on the Theory of Sexuality.* (1905), Standard Edition, 1953, vol. 7, pp. 135–243.

[69] Lewis Campbell's translation as given in the Standard Edition of the *Complete Psychological Works of Sigmund Freud.* London: Hogarth Press, 1953, vol. 4, p. 264.

falls deeply in love with his parent of the opposite sex, at the same time developing intense jealousy toward his other parent, as toward a competitor. If they are not too inhibited or frightened, children express openly and spontaneously their intention of marrying the parent of the opposite sex when they grow up. This avowal is based upon a firm conviction and a passionate emotional need. Around it develops the most complex and significant struggle of a child's emotional life.[70] This development, the edipal complex, is made inevitable by the pre-edipal identifications and object love preceding it, which we have already discussed.[71] It is not only inevitable. It is also essential that a child develop the *grand illusion* of one day marrying a parent and, after a painful struggle, experience the tragedy of having to give it up. This is the natural human way for little boys to prepare to grow into men who can love women, and for little girls to prepare to grow into women who can love men.

Animals do not go through an edipal phase. The human being is unique in this respect. There are at least two reasons for his uniqueness. One is the close-knit character of human family formation and the utter helplessness of children during their first few years. The other is the ability of helpless little boys and girls to construct fantasies and daydreams about sexuality, including ideas about parental intercourse, to entertain fantastic hopes of possessing a loved parent, and in most cases to recognize the anatomical root of sex differences, even though they may misinterpret its source.

It seems useless to seek parallels for the edipal complex among animals, since they are incapable of such high-level fantasy and daydream. Moreover, most animals mate readily with parents and, in the case of domestic animals and herds, they do so with the blessing of their human owners. These animals bear or beget offspring through intercourse with their parents without trace of reluctance, repugnance or guilt. The situation among human beings who honor the incest taboo is incomparably different.[72]

Edipal sex identification and object love. We have already said that the edipal phase has a long history in the interactions between parents and child, stretching back to early pre-edipal situations, and that this history makes the development of an edipal phase inevitable. Normal parental behavior toward children undoubtedly contributes to the structuring of the edipal situation, since they do differentiate their own love for a boy from their own love for a girl. The major difference between the differentiated love of edipal children and that of emotionally mature parents, we have said, is that, whereas the normal child's edipal love is frankly sexual in intent and aim, the love of parents at this time is sublimated, warm, tolerant affection. It becomes

---

70 See the well-balanced discussion by Rangell, L., "The role of early psychic functioning in psychoanalysis," *J. Amer. Psychoanal. Ass.*, 1961, *9*, 595–609.

71 The edipal complex "has apical importance . . . as the nucleus of normal character formation," according to Gitelson, M., "Re-evaluation of the role of the edipus complex," *Internat. J. Psychoanal.*, 1952, *33*, 351–354.

72 Hersko, M., Halleck, S., Rosenberg, M., and Pacht, A. R., "Incest: a three-way process," *J. soc. Ther.*, 1961, *7*, 22–31; Stephens, W. N., *The Oedipus Complex: Cross-Cultural Evidence.* New York: Macmillan, 1962.

obvious that the mature superego of parents helps them to keep their parental love sublimated as soon as one studies the effects of seductive parents, whose superego is defective, in promoting sex deviation in their children. In short, what we have been saying is that the edipal child normally experiences sexual feelings and jealousy toward his or her parents, even though full sex maturity is about a decade away, while normally mature parents reciprocate with an increase of sublimated love, treating their child always as a child, and not as a lover.

(a) *The edipal boy.* The edipal boy develops intense pride in his clearly visible genital, and an intermittent urge to use it aggressively and to exhibit it. This intense pride, the sexual feelings that a boy experiences toward his mother, and the jealousy that he feels toward his father, are generally believed to be major sources of an intense spontaneous anxiety. The anxiety appears in relation to a fear that he may suffer bodily injury, that he may lose what he so highly values (*castration anxiety*). The boy's genital pride, and his sexual and aggressive fantasies — of possessing his mother and eliminating his father — appear in some way to precipitate the edipal climax.

Why should a small boy have sexually possessive attitudes toward his mother at an age when he is incapable of carrying out the sex act? The answer to this question, as also to the question about the small boy's castration fear, can hardly be expected to follow the lines of adult logic, since the small child does not reason logically about matters as strongly emotional and personal as this. It seems probable that the edipal phase is biologically predetermined, or at least that, given such a close-knit unit as the human family in Western culture, it is biologically inevitable.[73]

Both the boy's masculine pride and his sexually possessive attitude are part of his normal identification with the dominant male figure in the home, his father. The boy wants to be as much like his father as possible, and to do the things his father does. It is too much to expect of a three-year-old child that he should be capable of realistically sorting out what society considers proper and feasible for him, from among all the masculine things he wants to be and do. Even matter-of-fact adolescents and adults, in spite of their incomparably greater experience and knowledge, at times grossly overestimate their abilities and powers.

The edipal boy's identification with his father also introduces further complications into the edipal situation. He admires the man with whom he identifies, his father, and at one level or another he also loves him. This affection, this identificatory pride in a loved fellow male, increases the guilt he feels over also having vengeful and destructive fantasies about his father, and over his competitive wish to displace him and possess his mother. We

[73] It has also been suggested that unconscious sexual attitudes of the parents, which the small child responds to as though they were conscious, are in part responsible for the edipal phase. Cf. Benedek, T., "Parenthood as a developmental phase," *J. Amer. Psychoanal. Ass.*, 1959, 7, 389–417.

shall consider some of these complexities further in relation to the edipal boy's somewhat incomprehensible castration anxiety.

(*b*) *Castration anxiety*. We have just said that castration anxiety, the fear of losing the genital or of having it damaged, seems to arise spontaneously among small boys in the edipal phase of personality development. We shall discuss this a little more at the end of this section, especially in connection with the talion principle of primitive law, and the use of castration as punishment within recent centuries, and even in some parts of western civilization today. Before doing this, we shall point to a few sources of reinforcement which castration anxiety receives in our society generally.[74]

One source of reinforcement is the small child's discovery that not everyone has a visible genital. Studies of small children indicate that they do not make the kind of differentiation between male and female that adults do. They seem to group human beings into those who have and those who lack a visible genital. Two conclusions, which both boys and girls appear to draw, are that persons lacking a visible genital have no genital whatever, and that they have probably lost one. This seemingly bizarre conclusion appears to arise in boys from the natural assumption that everyone is constructed as they themselves are. In girls, the discovery, that others have a visible genital while they do not, leads them to conclude that they have lost one, or have not yet grown one. Castration anxiety arises in the boy if he makes this discovery when he is acutely anxious because of his fantasies, or if he *recalls* this lack in girls and women when he is acutely anxious. If they have lost their genital, then he might lose his also, particularly when it is the center of his sexual feelings, his aggressive urges and his hostile fantasies.

Another common source of anxiety reinforcement comes from the angry jealousy and resentment that a boy feels toward his father. The father, after all, really is a powerful person. He really does love the boy's mother. He possesses her and has sex relations with her. Under these circumstances, it seems almost inevitable that the boy should take refuge in sadomasochistic fantasies. His active sadistic fantasies may picture the father as destroyed, emasculated, dead — or merely away. It is not unusual for boys to express such fantasies openly during their edipal phase. The passive masochistic fantasies picture the boy himself rendered harmless through being maimed or even killed by a supposedly jealous father. Shifts from the active sadistic to the passive masochistic are familiar in all primitive imagining, including the fantasies expressed in manifest dreams.

A third source of reinforcement, which we tend to forget, is that some adults still threaten little boys with castration as punishment for genital play. Mothers as well as fathers say that the genital will be cut off, or that the child will permanently damage himself. When this is expressed, a small boy's anxieties are greatly intensified.

In spite of all this, castration anxiety still remains something of a mystery.

[74] Sarnoff, I., and Corwin, S. M., "Castration anxiety and the fear of death," *J. Pers.*, 1959, 27, 374-385.

Children develop it who seem never to have been threatened. Now that many hundreds of non-neurotic adults have been psychoanalyzed, as part of their training in becoming psychoanalysts, and in view of the careful screening to which such candidates have been subjected, there is no longer any justification for restricting castration anxiety to neurotic persons. It seems to be practically universal, at least in western culture.

Freud invoked the *talion principle* to account for castration anxiety in small boys. This principle was at one time legally accepted in our culture. It appears in the biblical pronouncement, "An eye for an eye; a tooth for a tooth." In the old days, if anyone knocked out a tooth of his adversary, he was condemned to have a tooth of his own knocked out. If he gouged out his adversary's eye, he was condemned to have an eye gouged out, sometimes by his adversary, sometimes by a relative of his adversary. Injury to another's genitals involved the same punishment.

It is easier to understand the talion principle if we consider the current use of capital punishment in most of our states. Most people accept it as right and natural that a killer be himself killed, even though capital punishment is not considered effective, by experts, as a deterrent against murder. The state has taken over this talion principle task presumably to avoid the feuds which used to be common when the relatives of a murdered man themselves executed the killer.

Castration as a preventive against sexual assault has been practiced for ages. Millions of eunuchs have been created in times past for this reason. Castration was used as punishment for treason in Europe as late as the sixteenth century. In Scandinavia it is still legal today, both as a preventive and as a punishment in cases of sex deviation. None of this explains the small boy's irrational castration anxiety, since he knows nothing of this history or, in the United States at least, of the legal status of castration in other countries. It does, however, give some historical perspective for the notion of expecting like punishment for like crime; and it indicates that the notion of castration, however repulsive it may seem, is not entirely alien even to contemporary Western civilization.

(c) *The edipal girl.* The edipal girl has a more complex and more difficult situation to cope with than has the edipal boy. For one thing, she has no visible genital upon which to focus her pride, even though her sex feelings are centered in her genitals. Like the small boy, she begins by believing that others are constructed as she is. When she finds out her mistake, she is likely to feel cheated. She is likely to make the same misinterpretation that boys make, to think that she has been deprived of a visible genital. It is this realization that she has apparently been short-changed which precipitates the girl's edipal phase. Her occasional pre-edipal flirtations now give way to sexual feelings centered in her genitals. Her increased sexuality calls for more expression, and it is this that emphasizes to the girl her apparent lack of means.

According to some who work with small children, all girls blame their mother for having denied them a penis; according to others, most little girls do.[75] In any case, one result seems to be that of turning away from the mother and toward the father. Such a move means a radical change in the object of the girl's love. As a baby, she takes her mother as her first love object, just as the boy does. She, too, at one time formed a symbiotic union with her mother; and she was also initiated by her mother's care into membership within the family group. Now she turns away from her mother in disappointment and toward the father who seems able to give her what she wants. In this way she develops a love-hate conflict that is the counterpart of the boy's. She falls in love with her father and feels contempt and hatred toward her mother, whom she would like to eliminate.

The edipal girl, in spite of feeling that she has been denied a penis, or has lost one, manages to develop her own anxieties in relation to this privation. These are collectively known as the *female castration anxiety*. The most obvious anxiety in small girls arises in the form of feeling incomplete or inferior, or envying what small boys have, and even as the fantasy that the girl will one day grow a visible genital, or that she will rob a baby brother of his. She likewise develops intense fear of retaliation, but from her mother rather than from her father. This fear arises out of the girl's vengeful fantasies of getting rid of her mother, of having her go away or die.[76] She is certain that she could look after her father better than her mother does. At the same time she fears what she finds out about a woman's sex role. Her fears are necessarily vague, because of her imperfect knowledge, but vague fears need not be any less frightening than specific ones. Since she has no clear ideas about her own internal structure, she may be frightened by the notion that her body may be penetrated and injured because of her feminine sex desires.[77]

In identifying with her mother, the edipal girl has the same kind of problems that the edipal boy has. Unless she rejects the feminine role completely, which is most unusual, she will want to be like her mother and do the things she does. Like the boy, she has her troubles in deciding in what ways she can carry out her identification. If she must give up the sex role what shall she keep? In many ways she admires her mother's femininity which, after all, has been successful in winning and keeping her father. In spite of all the contempt and hatred she feels toward her mother for barring the way to her edipal goals, she also has some of the old object love which she enjoyed so long as her mother's child. She still needs her mother in her everyday life, even more than she needs her father, who is away most of the time. It is said that the girl never gives up her love of her mother as an object, but remains to a greater degree ambivalent toward her mother than

[75] Cf. Praeger, D., "An unusual fantasy of the manner in which babies become boys or girls," *Psychoanal. Quart.*, 1960, 29, 44–55.

[76] Derivatives of all these childhood illusions are often found in neurotic and psychotic women during therapy. Nursery school children also express them freely.

[77] Cf. Deutsch, H., *The Psychology of Women.* New York: Grune & Stratton, 1944.

the boy does toward his father. Her affection for her mother likewise increases her guilt over the hatred and contempt she feels.

Disappointment and humiliation of the edipal child. As it has been pointed out ever since Freud's day, the intense edipal love of small children is doomed to disappointment. Not only are small children incapable of carrying out their edipal wishes, of begetting or bearing babies, and of being the consort of the opposite-sexed parent. They are also exposed to the humiliation of being treated only as children. No matter what they have thought, and no matter what people tell them, they discover that they are not little men or little women but little children.

Normal parents, we have said, love their children as children, and not as suitors or competitors for adult sexual love. It is nonetheless a bitter experience for the small boy, who has already made public his intention of growing up and marrying his mother, to realize finally that no one takes his declarations at face value. He at last recognizes what everyone else seems to have known right along — that his love and his intentions have all been based upon a grand illusion. Not only is he physically incapable of being his mother's husband at the time; he also finds out that his mother does not in the least share his desire for their marriage when he grows up. The same fate awaits the edipal girl. She has lovingly asked to be her father's wife. She must come at last to realize that she is incapable of having babies, that her father does not want her as his wife, and that he will not wait for her to grow up.

These realizations do not come to edipal children all in one day, any more than the edipal phase itself arrives all in one day. But as they come, one after another, and long before the child acknowledges his defeat to himself, he experiences the anger and hate that his repeated frustrations arouse. Anger and hate are aroused now, not only by the like-sexed parent who has always seemed a competitor, but also by the opposite-sexed parent who rejects the proffered love, and seems to the child to be rejecting him or her altogether. The child in this phase, as much as at any other period of life, needs the patient, kindly, understanding help that an emotionally mature, loving parent can give. If he gets this from both his parents, and his pre-edipal conflicts have been reasonably well worked through, there is no reason why he should not resolve his edipal problems successfully and emerge as a healthy child free from emotional entanglements in the home and ready for the latency period.

Mastering edipal conflicts in childhood. From what we have been saying, it is clear that a child is destined to develop a grand illusion, the illusion of becoming a spouse and parent while still a child. It is clear also that he must somehow then give up the illusion. In other words, he must accept a *grand disillusionment.* These are the conditions which every child must fulfill in our culture today if he is to work through his infantile attachments and to use his edipal experiences constructively in his later love life.

The grand illusion, we have said, is the normal climax of a small child's developing identification with a like-sexed parent and his object love for the other parent. Even if a child is not allowed to express his edipal wishes and intentions openly, he will still experience the same powerful emotional needs. Children who actually lack one or both parents during this phase, or even earlier, normally create fantasied parents to repair the lack. There are, after all, many models for such creations around the child.

If the grand illusion never appears early in childhood, even unexpressed, this can only mean that the child has been unable to evolve an effective model on which to build his later adolescent and adult sex role as husband or wife and parent. Fear of one parent or of both parents is the usual source of such a failure. It means that the child will probably never experience a full capacity for mature heterosexual love.

Even though a child does not understand the full implications of adult love, he experiences the rejection and disillusionment as keenly as a loving suitor does. He must learn the hard lesson of modifying both his identification with the one parent and his object love for the other, so as to bring both into line with what is possible. The boy must give up his childish hope of ever having his mother to himself, the girl of ever becoming her father's wife. Identification with the like-sexed parent must now exclude whatever sexual rights that parent has. Object love for the other parent must now exclude its sexual aspects. Such identification and such object love are the kind that emotionally mature parents offer their children, the kind that we have called *sublimated*. In resolving his edipal conflicts, the child of such parents has before him the living and loving models that he needs for his own emotional growth.

The edipal child must also master his anger and his fears in relation to each parent. Anger is the natural response to frustration. The like-sexed parent arouses it by barring the child's way to his or her love object. The opposite-sexed parent arouses it by ignoring, rebuffing or belittling the child's advances. Even though a small child's desire may seem wicked to an adult and his advances absurd, they are both rooted in passionate needs which seem to the child neither wicked nor absurd. We have already discussed the edipal child's fears in relation to the characteristic castration anxiety, which appears in both boys and girls during this phase, in somewhat different forms and for somewhat different reasons. Castration anxiety, if it is too severe and unrelieved at the time, or if it is not overcome in resolving the edipal complex, may play a pervasive and decisive part in later neurotic development and character structure.[78]

To be successful in the edipal struggle a child must realign his sexual and aggressive drives, fuse them to form more realistic fantasies, and develop a defensive organization which utilizes enough but not too much repression. He must internalize the aspects of his parents that he needs, the biosocial roles and the reciprocal roles necessary for new ego and superego identi-

[78] Gitelson, M., "Re-evaluation of the role of the edipus complex," *Internat. J. Psychoanal.*, 1952, *33*, 351–354.

fications. These will come particularly from the parent who is experienced as most frustrating, since introjection and identification are most commonly the product of a loss which the introjecting person overcomes by taking in symbolically what he has lost in reality.

The best adult illustration of this can be found in the process of normal mourning for a lost one. The mourner takes in the image[79] of the lost one and makes it a part of himself. Sometimes he adopts some of the leading personality characteristics of the person he mourns, and occasionally he even seems to look like the mourned one. In doing this, the mourner repeats the process by which he resolved his edipal tragedy in childhood. When the mourning process has been completed, the mourner is usually a more sober and sometimes a sadder person than before; but he is ready and able to resume normal interpersonal relationships with other people.

The child who is successful in resolving his edipal conflicts will emerge with a greatly strengthened *ego organization,* richly endowed and ready for rapid, realistic growth, a well-organized *defensive structure,* which maintains functional boundaries between primary processes and secondary processes without deadening either, and between internal and external reality without distorting either, and an integrated *maturing superego,* which provides an internal source of self-control, self-esteem and ideals. Such a child will enter the long period of latency free from the old entangling alliances normal to dependent infancy, and free from the frightening fantasies of parental retaliation for his forbidden loves and hates. Later in life, when he reaches puberty and enters adolescence, he will be far better able to cope with the resurgence of his edipal conflicts which normally appear, than if he had never met them before and resolved them. Barring serious later difficulties, he should not suffer undue turbulence as an adolescent, and he should be successful in finding his way to normal adult aggression and normal adult love.

[79] Superego development, the primary process and the defenses will be discussed in Chapter 5, "The psychodynamic system."

3

Personality Development: Latency, Adolescence and Adulthood

AFTER THE EDIPAL STORM PASSES, THE RELATIVE PEACE OF LATENCY COMES. This gives the child a chance to explore and master his human environment, to become a member of the wider community where a cooler emotional atmosphere prevails, before he must face the second storm of puberty and adolescence. Latency does not mean quiescence. The latency phase is by no means free from serious problems. It does not even free the child from family domination. He is still dependent upon his family and the home for his support, emotional as well as physical, and for his security and guidance, while he learns to set limits and goes on constructing his realities. He must still adapt to home schedules, to parental restrictions and parental demands. At the same time he is able to continue to participate in the strength and wisdom of his parents which, however little they may seem to them, seem enormous to him.

During the early years in his home the average child receives protection, privileges and intimate emotional acceptance. Through such parental treatment he satisfies his early needs, builds his *basic trust* and *general security*, and evolves a complex *ego organization*. He acquires a multitude of manual skills and freedom in handling objects and materials, both of which are necessary if he is to play on equal terms with the neighborhood children. He gains mastery over the use of his own body and over its functions. He learns at home some of the essential social techniques in associating with other persons in group situations, and in behaving as one member of a family group.[1] The frequent presence in the home of family friends, relatives and usually siblings gives the child much experience, while he is still under protection of home and parents, that he will need later when he is outside the home. He will enter the wider community, not as a solitary waif, but as the member of a family unit with which other children identify him.

There is another momentous change which needs mention here, and which we shall take up in a later chapter in more detail. This is the evolution of a *superego,* differentiating within the ego organization. Resolution of the edipal complex, while it brings early grief and a massive repression of infantile experience, brings also the adaptive internalization of parental standards, parental love and parental controls, in the form of a highly integrated super-ego organization. This postedipal superego system, whose conscious part we call *conscience,* always functions in relation to the ego from which it has differentiated, and always in relation to reality and to the now wholly un-conscious *id,* which is also intimately tied up with the ego. The postedipal superego — which is what is usually meant when the term *superego* is used — supersedes the archaic control by internalized objects which is believed to prevail early in infancy; and it supersedes the pre-edipal superego fore-runners, largely sadomasochistic, which help control behavior just before the edipal phase starts, and which we shall meet again in obsessive com-pulsives, in depressives and in schizophrenics. The postedipal superego matures along with ego maturing, often throughout life. But its presence as a differentiating grade within the ego contributes enormously to the child's maturation.[2]

Paralleling the evolution of the postedipal superego is the equally impor-tant *separation between ego and id.* This separation is achieved through a massive repression of infantile experiences, somewhere around the age of four or five years. The repression is instrumental in establishing firm boundaries between ego organizations and the now wholly unconscious id, which operates according to the primary process. Without the presence of such boundaries there can be no satisfactory development of secondary process thinking and realistic perceiving.

The perception and cognition of the *pre-edipal child* are continually con-taminated by *primary process intrusions,* that is, by products of id func-tioning. We see this in the child's frequent inability to distinguish clearly what he recalls from what he imagines, in his frequent confusion of fantasy and fact. He maintains magical, inconsistent and even obviously contradic-tory beliefs and interpretations, without being disturbed when his incon-sistencies and contradictions are pointed out, and without being able to overcome them. The edipal child continues in the same general tradition, although his greater mastery of the external environment, his maturing ego organization, and the logical structure of speech may conceal it.

[1] Bell, N. W., and Vogel, E. B. (Eds.), *A Modern Introduction to the Family.* Glencoe, Ill.: Free Press, 1960.
[2] Ego, id and superego will be discussed as an interlocking system in Chapter 5.

It is not until firm ego boundaries have been set, mainly through the development of effective repression, that realistic secondary process thinking can be established and progress can be made toward a mature logic. It is interesting that Piaget, from the standpoint of a philosopher and logician turned child psychologist, independently confirmed Freud's distinction between *prelogical* and *logical*, forty years ago. The child of five or six is still more or less comfortable with glaring inconsistencies and contradictions which, by the time the period of latency is over, have disappeared from his thinking. Thus the evolution of logical reflection roughly parallels the period of latency, beginning near its beginning and ending near its end.[3]

The Phase of Latency

The small child emerges from his home into the wider community, equipped with basic confidence and basic motor, perceptual and social skills. He has already gained considerable mastery over his body and he has learned to channel his emotional drives. He has evolved a superego organization which enables him to supply himself with guidance, control and self-esteem, derived from his parents' guidance, control and esteem. The superego contributes greatly to the internal stability of the psychodynamic system. Now mere shifts in internal cathexis (energy) provide much that previously the child had had to get from his parents, and about which he often remained in suspense. The child no longer depends upon policing for self-control. The latency child has established ego boundaries which decrease primary process intrusion from id functioning, and thus create the conditions necessary for secondary process developments (e.g., for realistic perception and cognition, and for the evolution of logical reflection).

The latency child still remains a member of his own family. From it he gets emotional and physical support. It provides a safe harbor to which he can return whenever frustrations outside are more than he can bear, when others fight him or reject him. The major social change in latency is that, while he is still a member of his family group, the child goes forth alone into the world outside his family, expands his physical and social horizons, and supplements membership in his own family with membership in groups outside it.

The early neighborhood group

The moment that a child steps out of his own home unaccompanied, he loses the status of a protected and privileged son or daughter, and becomes merely another child in the neighborhood. The patterns of friendliness, aggression and defense which he now encounters are different and less predictable for him than are those to which he is accustomed at home. It is

[3] Piaget, J., *Language and Thought in the Child* (1923), (trans. M. Gabain). London: Kegan Paul, Trench, Trubner, 1932.

quite normal for a child to be a bit timid and tentative until he gets his new bearings by testing his new reality. The emerging child finds that other children are apt to be casual and unconcerned about him, once the novelty of his appearing among them has worn off. Some of them seem surprisingly critical and even hostile.

Friendly adults treat a neighborhood child more objectively than his own parents do, more as a person, perhaps less approvingly but also less critically, and with different emphases. Differences arising between children are usually settled directly by the contestants and their respective supporters, without adult intervention. When adults do intervene in a children's squabble it is often to aid their own child against the others.

The standards prevailing in the neighborhood are those of the children composing it, each child differing in some respect from each other, because he comes from a different family background. Sex differences are at first less decisive than age differences. The solitary and parallel play of infancy gives way to associative and cooperative play, in which children learn to share objects and activities with other children, and prepare to take part in group competitive play. Eventually they learn to participate in joint projects; this leads over into a readiness to subordinate individual needs and aims to the needs and aims of the group as a whole.[4]

Some of the earliest participative games involve simple forms of social role-taking. The small child must play the baby or the pupil, as directed, so that an older child may play being mother or teacher or leader. There are also marching games, dancing and running games, and weavings about with other children in structured patterns. In all of this the small child plays a variety of simple roles and learns the elements of social cooperation and competition without adult supervision. He learns the penalties for non-cooperation; and he learns how to avoid physical and emotional upset from the impact of larger and quicker children, intent upon their own games. Talking plays a significant role in neighborhood groups, especially during the earliest phase of neighborhood socialization, when boys and girls are still playing together.

The peer culture

Children soon separate spontaneously into groups of their own sex and age, with whom they have much more in common than with members of the opposite sex or with older children. This pattern persists as the preferred one until puberty. Boys play with boys as soon as they are big enough and skilled enough to enter into the rough and tumble competition of boys' games. Their first attempts to join a group of boys may be rudely rebuffed, but eventually they make the grade. Girls play with girls in physically milder games, some of which are highly competitive, and some more on the ex-

[4] Sutton-Smith, B., and Rosenberg, B. G., "Peer perceptions of impulsive behavior," *Merrill-Palmer Quart.*, 1961, 7, 233–238.

pressive side. Girls include very small boys in their play if it suits them. With few exceptions, children regard a child who tries to play with an opposite-sexed group as odd and unwelcome.[5]

Sex differences in play are obvious long before the latency phase; and they continue into it. Little boys are, in general, more aggressive, self-assertive and independent than little girls.[6] They identify with achievers, initiators and leaders. They show a greater interest in power symbols as toys — in trucks, trains, rockets, planes, machines and soldiers. They emphasize strength, dexterity, courage and adventure. The group games of boys are predominantly aggressive, vigorous, highly competitive and boisterous. Fighting is normal and common. Boys are typically too much concerned with things and with action to care about appearance and cleanliness when they are playing.

There is less variety, less violence and less boisterousness in girls' play than in boys'. Girls continue to identify with their mothers in elaborate doll play, keeping house and cooking, although they seldom include adult male figures among their dolls.[7] This doll play is more directly related to the girl's expected sex role as an adult than the play of boys is to theirs. Girls enjoy caring for and protecting little children of either sex, like little mothers, although because they are still children they cannot be completely depended upon to carry this role without sometimes forgetting it or thoughtlessly abandoning it. Girls' group games may also be highly competitive, involve quarreling and invective, but seldom physical violence. Girls are much more concerned with physical appearance, grooming and cleanliness than are boys, even though these considerations limit their play. They are more interdependent, more mature socially, less individualistic and more conformist than boys of the same age.[8]

In all of this differentiation, extending from pre-edipal years through the edipal phase and into latency, we see progressive role-differentiation which expresses a child's growing sex identity and prepares him in many ways to assume it in adolescence and adulthood. It must grow out of biological sex typing as well as out of social pressures.

The school

Early in latency the child begins going to school. Here he enters into new, highly formalized relationships with other children and adults, in which

[5] Sutton-Smith, B., and Rosenberg, B. G., "Manifest anxiety and game preferences in children," *J. genet. Psychol.*, 1960, *31*, 307–311.

[6] Rosenberg, B. G., and Sutton-Smith, B., "A revised conception of masculine-feminine differences in play activities," *J. genet. Psychol.*, 1960, *96*, 165–170; Moore, T., and Ucko, L. E., "Four to six: constructiveness and conflict in meeting doll play problems," *J. Child Psychol. Psychiat.*, 1961, *2*, 21–47.

[7] Josselyn, I., *The Happy Child.* New York: Random House, 1955.

[8] Weinstein, E. A., and Geisel, P. N., "An analysis of sex differences in adjustment," *Child Develpm.*, 1960, *31*, 721–728.

kinship plays no part and there is little regard for previous friendships. He is expected to be on time each day and to control his own behavior for about six hours — to be quiet and orderly, to suppress many of his individual impulses and to engage in supervised work. What with mealtimes, home chores and school homework, formal schooling leaves the child with little free time. If he is fortunate, his school will give him new companions and new identification figures, as well as formal training and knowledge which are essential to his future as an adolescent and an adult.[9]

It has been recognized for centuries that unsublimated sexual preoccupation and unchanneled aggression interfere with learning. The normal child replaces most of his edipal curiosity with a general curiosity, an eagerness to learn, which he retains for most of his lifetime. His aggression is tamed and channeled along lines of mastering more and more knowledge, of elaborating external reality, and of enriching a corresponding development of ego and superego organization.

We have said that latency does not mean quiescence. The emotional drives from id functioning are still present and active. They always will be present and active as long as life lasts. The latency child is a highly competitive person. Even his learning, for all the channeling and repression of naked id drive, remains normally an aggressive process. Sexuality no longer dominates the latency child; but he is still sexually curious and interested. Curiosity and interest have generalized without leaving the child asexual. In spite of sublimation and superego control, there is normally a certain amount of sex curiosity and sexual experimentation during the phase of latency.[10]

The church and other formal groups

The church and most other formal groups are dominated one way or another by adults; and, unlike the school, they have a high proportion of adults in them. Children tend to look upon such organizations as belonging to the adults, and see their membership in them as extensions of their membership in the family. Churches are organized along lines different from the neighborhood and the peer culture, and different from nonsectarian schools. They may increase family and in-group solidarity by representing an extrafamilial source of identification in which the whole family joins.

The church and other similar organizations may represent to the child systems of special belief which demand of him a high degree of conformity. They may also provide institutionalized systems of personal guilt, of penitence, and of complex ritual, early in the child's life. They often provide

---

[9] For a general discussion of this phase, with bibliography, see Jersild, A. T., *Child Psychology*. (5th ed.) Englewood Cliffs, N.J.: Prentice-Hall, 1960.

[10] It is assumed nowadays that a certain amount of limited early sexual gratification promotes a child's general development. Cf. Mohr, G., and Despres, M., *The Stormy Decade: Adolescence*. New York: Random House, 1958, Chapter 3; Bornstein, B., "On latency," *The Psychoanalytic Study of the Child*. New York: Internat. Univ. Press, 1951, vol. 6, pp. 279–285.

also systematic group recreational facilities, including in-group social gatherings. When their ideals and demands clash with individual or with family
ideals and demands, they may raise conflicts of considerable importance.
Political and other social creeds, if they call for unquestioning belief and submission to appointed authority, may operate psychologically in much the
same way that strict, authoritarian religions do.

Stresses inherent in the phase of latency

Contrary to some popular beliefs, the phase of latency has within it inevitable sources of stress. To enumerate and discuss them all would require
a volume in itself.[11] Here we shall limit ourselves to a brief account of some
of the stresses and what they may mean to the child. The major stresses arise
from the daily separation from the family, from the necessity for adapting
to the peer culture and the school system, and from the increasing demands
made upon the child, coming from every direction, that he master new skills,
exert more and more emotional control, acquire more and more knowledge,
and enter into a number of new and often conflicting social roles.

Even the most capable, intelligent adult knows how difficult it is to learn
entirely new things, to acquire new skills and new forms of control, to move
into a new neighborhood or job and to establish himself with strangers.
Most adults avoid this kind of experience with every resource they have, because they know from their own past experience the rigors of such demands.

The latency child must first of all move out among comparative strangers
and learn to survive and enjoy himself without the protection and guidance
to which he is accustomed. Within a year or two he must enter an entirely
new kind of culture, *the school,* and diligently apply himself to concentrated
learning during a six-hour day, which is almost as long as the average
workingman's day. He must also continue adapting himself to the neighborhood group and his peer culture, mastering new skills, even at play, and entering into group participation with play groups whose pattern continually
changes.

The stresses of this phase are often overlooked by adults, who tend to
idealize latency as a period of no responsibility. It is not unusual for an
adult, who is himself lounging in a chair taking his ease after seven or eight
hours at work, to rebuke a child for not working harder, when the child has
spent six hard hours at school and perhaps three more hard hours competing
with children his own age.

The acquisition of new knowledge and new skills, at school, at play and in
the home, the gaining of more and more emotional control, and the entering
into new role relationships, together comprise a common source of problems

---

[11] American Psychiatric Association, Committee on Academic Education, *Sources of
Information on Behavioral Problems of Adolescence.* Washington, D.C.: Amer. Psychiat.
Ass., 1960; Mussen, P. H. (Ed.), *Handbook of Research Methods in Child Development.*
New York: Wiley, 1960.

during the latency phase. Life between the ages of five or six and twelve or thirteen demands a great deal. In the home a child is expected to be obedient, loyal, orderly and self-controlled, even when he is tired out and irritable. At school he is expected to be obedient, orderly and self-controlled, to work diligently, and to cooperate with other children or compete with them in accordance with pre-established rules. He is expected to conform to standards which he does not set, and which keep going higher and higher the older he gets.

Everyone knows that children usually greet their release from school with joy. The play in which they then become engaged, however, is rarely relaxed and easygoing. It is not like the play of an adult who goes for a drive, tinkers in his shop, sails a boat or works in the garden. The child plays as a member of a peer group with rigid standards of its own, which may be quite different from the standards at home and in school.[12] The peer group always has its pecking order — based upon age, strength, size, skill and special know-how — to which adults have given the grand name of *hierarchy*. The same child is likely to rank differently in the hierarchies of his three societies — the home, the school, and the peer group. This variation in itself demands flexible adaptations of the child as he moves from one society to the next in the same day. In each situation, at home, in school and in the peer group, he is expected to behave appropriately; and because his status in each shifts as he grows older, he must also make basic shifts in his standards of behavior at different ages.[13]

Need for emotional support and guidance from adults

We have said that a child remains a member of his family throughout latency, and that the family continues to give him support and to provide a refuge for him when frustrations outside the home become unbearable. Children need help throughout latency in setting limits, in solving personal problems and conflicts, and in making choices and decisions. Their horizons expand more rapidly than their ego-superego organizations grow. The wider community presents them with more opportunities for action and for gratification than they get at home, as well as with more sources of frustration. This means that the latency child must structure further his world of reality, and that he must strike new balances between new freedoms and new needs for self-control.[14] Identification with the parents is in itself not enough for a child. He obviously cannot do everything that adults do. He cannot even foresee and plan as adults can. He lacks the necessary experience and wisdom

[12] Strauss, A., "The development of conceptions of rules in children," *Child Develpm.*, 1952, *25*, 193–208.

[13] Clark, A. W., and van Sommers, P., "Contradictory demands in family relations and adjustment to school and home," *Hum. Relations*, 1961, *14*, 97–111.

[14] Josselyn, I., *The Psychosocial Development of Children*. New York: Family Service Ass., 1948; Josselyn, I., *The Happy Child*. New York: Random House, 1955.

to be able to sort out what is appropriate at his age, and in his circumstances, from what is not.

Some of the most serious childhood anxieties come from the failure of parents to set limits to a child's impulsive behavior, and to provide him with wise guidance and wise discipline when these are indicated. A child is not born with self-control; he has to acquire it. He needs kindly help in structuring his behavior in accordance with conditions, situations and regulations which are all new to him. Some of this he learns through direct interaction with other children and adults; but a great deal of it he learns best through the experienced, sympathetic help of his parents.

Certain essential distinctions must be made here between *demands for blind compliance*, which tend rather to infantilize a child than to lead him toward maturity and responsibility, and *reasonable demands for conformity*, where conformity is absolutely essential. A generation or so ago, it was common among intellectuals to give their children almost complete freedom, and to expect them to make choices and decisions for which they were not psychologically ready. The result was often to leave the child impulsive, anxious, and unpredictable, even to himself. The ability to choose and to make decisions varies with age, experience and intelligence. Freedom to do so must be tailored to meet these variations.

Two or three generations ago, much greater unquestioning compliance was demanded of children than today. The trouble with unquestioning compliance, which still prevails in some families, is that it promotes the passive acceptance and control by other people, or else it leads to an almost indiscriminate rebellion against all guidance and control. Neither passive compliance nor blind rebellion favors a mature ego-superego development; and without such development a child cannot grow up to be a self-reliant, dependable adult.

To achieve self-confidence, a child needs freedom and encouragement to make his own choices and decisions, at least in minor matters, within the limits of his age, experience and intelligence. If he is called upon to make important decisions for which he is not prepared, or simply left to make them without judicious adult help, he is likely to become unnecessarily anxious. Such decisions often themselves call for adult intervention to protect the child from their consequences; and this only breeds further insecurity and lack of self-esteem.

The situation in the child world is not qualitatively very different from that in the adult world. We adults often find ourselves beyond our depths in unfamiliar seas. We feel justified, not humiliated, when we turn for help to relatives, friends, associates, lawyers or priests, if our own experience seems insufficient to us, or our personal resources seem inadequate to meet new or more complex situations.

This is essentially the child's position when he faces complexities that exceed his capacities. The major difference is that, whereas mature adults rarely need special support and guidance, and then only in complex situations, children during the latency period need them frequently, and in relatively simple situations. It is self-evident that a child who has been unsuccessful in mastering edipal and pre-edipal problems will encounter much greater difficulty in mastering the problems of competition, cooperation and group interaction which characterize the phase of latency. Let us see what some of the commonest sources of such failures are.

Stresses resulting from failures to resolve edipal problems

The child who enters latency without having resolved his edipal problems reasonably well, enters it poorly equipped to handle the stresses inherent in this phase. He is not ready to practice its freedoms or to exert optimal self-control. He will lack adequate practice in reality-testing and he will not have the ego-superego organization necessary for making full use of his new opportunities. He will continue using infantile forms of dependence; his ego boundaries will still be too permeable to primary process intrusions from the id; and he will still rely upon infantile, sadomasochistic forerunners of the mature superego for self-control. In a small but important number of children, self-control may even rest upon the use of archaic internal objects. The occasional boy may still be assailed by direct derivatives of edipal castration anxiety, and the girl by a sense of physical inferiority, of incompleteness or envy of the male.

1. *Need for self-reliance and security with parents.* It is obvious that a child must be reasonably secure in his relationships with his parents before he sallies forth into his new world outside the home. As we have said, he needs the home as a secure haven to which he can retire, at least during the first months of latency, whenever frustrations exceed his capacity to tolerate them. He also needs the self-assurance which grows out of self-reliance, out of the unspoken certainty that his parents have confidence in him, and that they will always be available and dependable when he needs them. In short, the child who has not achieved reasonable security with his parents in the home is ill-prepared to meet the new stresses of the peer group and the school.

Put in its simplest terms, the tasks which the edipal child must complete before he is ready for latency are as follows. He must have learned to love passionately and aggressively with irrational expectations. He must then succeed in weathering the frustration and humiliation of defeat. He must transform his passionate love into tender affection for his parents and a capacity for affection for his like-sexed peers. He must give up his irrational expectations without losing hope for the remote future when he will come of age. He must transform his naked aggression and his feeling of omnipotence into a channeled, socially acceptable struggle for mastery over the human environment, in both its physical and its social aspects.

A small proportion of children, grossly lacking in these transformations, remain little children emotionally, and sometimes behaviorally also.[15] They fail to master the human environment even to the extent of being able to learn, and of forming minimal social relationships. These are the autistic, symbiotic and chronically antisocial children. The vast majority, even of those who have been relatively unsuccessful in resolving edipal conflicts, develop compensatory mechanisms of adaptation and defense which may carry them through latency without evidence of overt psychopathology. They remain, however, especially vulnerable to adolescent and adult neuroses, psychoses or sociopathic disturbances.

2. *Maternal overprotection.* Overindulgent mothers, and domineering, possessive ones do not prepare their children for latency. The overindulged child is a relatively undisciplined child who has been allowed to continue utilizing infantile forms of demand and aggression long after they have ceased to be appropriate. When he enters the wider community, he expects to have his way in everything; and when he does not, he tries bullying, fighting, temper tantrums and obstructionist tactics. These tactics fail in the wider community. The overindulged child then may avoid his peers and play with younger children whom he can dominate.

The child of a domineering, possessive mother is, in contrast, a dependent, submissive child, who has been overtrained not to take initiative or to rebel. When he emerges from his home into the wider community, he is likely to remain timid, submissive or withdrawn. He is likely to avoid the company of his peers also, to play with children who treat him as a baby or, if he is a boy, to try to join a group of girls. The dependent, submissive, infantilized child of a dominating, possessive mother, like the overindulged child, also fails to be accepted into the normal play group of his childhood peers.[16]

The basic importance of experience in the home, for adaptation to the conditions of latency, is clear in both these products of maternal overprotection. Children carry over the kind of reciprocal role relationship, learned in the home, into their situations outside the home. The *overindulged child* tries to dominate others as he has dominated his mother; the *dominated child* offers dependence and submission to children who scorn such attitudes. Neither child can meet his peers on an equal footing, and neither is likely to be given equal status by his peers. Many such children, in spite of gross failures in social adaptation, are unable to change their ways sufficiently ever to gain acceptance by their peers. Consequently, they never become integrated fully with normal play groups, where children get the chance to practice endlessly the techniques of social give-and-take. The behavior of an overprotective mother, with her own unusually strong symbiotic needs, develops in her child reciprocal needs that are equally imperious, and can be satisfied

[15] Cf. the panel discussion in Kaplan, E. B., "Classical forms of neurosis in infancy and childhood," *J. Amer. Psychoanal. Ass.*, 1962, *10*, 571–578.

[16] Finney, J. C., "Some maternal influences on children's personality and character," *Genet. Psychol. Monogr.*, 1961, *63*, 199–278.

only by the mother or a replica of her. No like-aged average child can possibly take her place.[17]

3. *Sibling rivalry.* The birth of a sibling into the family constellation means a redistribution of attention and affection. This event is usually hardest on a previously only child. He has been receiving all the maternal love and care up to this time, but suddenly the focus of his mother's care shifts to the new interloper. It is impossible for a willing mother to conceal her new attachment from her firstborn, but it is not difficult for her to prepare him well in advance for the approaching change in status. Neither is it difficult for her to see to it that the change has rewarding aspects for him, and that he is genuinely included as an important member of the new family set-up. The mother who slights her first child for the pleasures of her second, or who rebuffs him for interfering in them, is emotionally rejecting him just as seriously as though she felt indifference or hostility toward him.

It is almost impossible for an adult to anticipate the intensity of feeling with which a first child greets his new sibling. The first child enjoys an intimate dependent relationship with his mother which he need not share with another for years. Even if his father has been his rival, the child has had the field to himself all during his father's working days; and their competition has been at different levels. The new baby is quite another kind of rival. He can be obtrusively present, day and night, and he competes at the small child's level. As an infant he can easily win any contest based upon helplessness, without even trying.

Under these circumstances, the older child is likely to resort to whatever aggressive tactics, or regressive tactics, that he can hit upon to regain his lost sense of significance and belonging, or, failing that, to avenge his displacement in his mother's affection. If these maneuvers do not succeed, or if the child is already cowed, he may drift to the fringe of life in the home, and take refuge in fantasy and solitary play.

It is hardly surprising that the larger and stronger child should resort to simple aggression in order to prevail over his infant competitor. Siblings from the very start are potential rivals for the same love and consideration, the same life-space and the same supplies. It is too much to expect of a small child that he clearly recognize the meanings of the new situation and the rights of infants, considering how unclearly he understands the complex world in which he lives. Sometimes the aggression takes the form of direct action. The new baby is covered up, restrained, poked, slapped, deprived of something it has, or even allowed to fall. There are many reports in the literature of assaults and attempted assaults on babies by the next older child. In Levy's classical study, a four-year-old girl tried twice to throw her baby sister out of the window.[18] Threats to strike the baby are made by siblings often; sometimes they are carried out.

[17] The classical study of such children is that of Levy, D., *Maternal Overprotection.* New York: Columbia Univ. Press, 1943.

[18] Levy, D., *Maternal Overprotection.* New York: Columbia Univ. Press, 1943, pp. 25–26.

As a rule, under the influence of social learning, redirection of aggression and rudimentary self-control, the original hostility becomes quickly indirect, subtle or covert.[19] Often it is limited entirely to belittling comments, which have their constructive aspect since they tend to emphasize the child's own greater maturity, or to amused unfavorable comparisons which are flavored with contempt. Sometimes the effort to keep aggression suppressed makes a child irritable or anxious; and his obvious irritability or anxiety may be misinterpreted by both the mother and the child himself.

Following the birth of a sibling, the older child may exhibit regressive behavior, either alone, or along with aggressive acts. He suddenly loses some of his gains in biosocial maturity and reverts to behavior that belongs to earlier infantile levels. New skills and newly acquired controls, which are not yet fully consolidated, are most likely to be involved. Such regressive behavior is usually incidental to the older child's general emotional disturbance over the new situation, and not unlike other regressive behavior which he has shown before, when lonely or in conflict.

Regression sometimes appears in the form of direct, open competition with the new baby for the kind of care he is getting. The older child begins to whine again, speaks babyishly, wets and soils, lies on the floor, crawls like an infant or wants to take to the bottle again. A certain amount of temporary indulgence in regressive behavior does no harm under these circumstances of stress, as long as the child understands that it is just for the moment, and that his mother understands and sympathizes with him.

Both aggressive and regressive tactics disappear as the child learns that he is still genuinely loved and wanted, that he is still significant and secure. As in so many other childhood crises, the problem of sibling rivalry is more easily resolved by children who are treated with consistent and intelligent affection, by parents whose difficulties do not interfere with their parental functions, than by children whose parents have psychopathology which distorts parental functions, or whose parents are inconsistent and who lack intelligent sympathy.

Sibling jealousy can distort edipal developments and interfere with successful resolution of edipal conflicts. The jealousy may generalize so that when the child emerges into the wider community he is abnormally quick to become jealous, angry and spiteful. Such behavior will interfere with his acceptance in play groups and may make him into a lone wolf early in his career. These are some of the hazards of unresolved sibling rivalry.

Sibling rivalry in childhood never disappears; it merely undergoes socialization along with the rest of behavior. Many of its fruits have a positive, constructive social value and a maturing effect upon the growing child. The distribution of parental affection in itself can be beneficial, provided each child feels that he is getting his share of the time. Siblings can be comrades as well as rivals. The presence of siblings in the home gives each child prac-

[19] Kagan, J., "Socialization of aggression and the perception of parents in fantasy," *Child Develpm.*, 1958, *29*, 311–320.

tice in multilateral interaction. This prepares him for the later direct impact of other children in the neighborhood, the gang and the school.[20]

If both sexes are represented among siblings, the highly important discovery of sex differences can be made in the home at childhood levels, instead of merely from parental differences which may be disturbing to a small child, or from neighborhood exploration which is likely to create crises between the children's families. It is generally considered important that children have opportunities early in life to discover that there are anatomical sex differences between children.

Brothers and sisters learn the techniques of sharing in one another's company, not only parental love and parental displeasure, but also objects, materials and activities. They learn at home how to cooperate, compete and compromise, how to defend, evade, attack and escape. Because they are like-aged and do the same kinds of things with the same general kind of motivation, siblings unwittingly train one another in skills and methods which parents alone cannot always manage with ease. An older sibling learns to enjoy the experience of having and protecting a younger one. This may increase his own self-reliance. Younger siblings benefit by the diversions and the extra stimulation which an older one provides at childhood levels. When one has brothers and sisters there is a greater tendency for *we-ness* to develop, the sense of belonging to a clan. All of this may give a small child a head start when the time arrives for him to cruise about the neighborhood. If, however, the presence of siblings has aroused more jealousy and hatred than pride and affection, a child is almost sure to act out his unresolved sibling rivlary in relation to other children, and thus to complicate his adaptations in the latency period and to multiply its stresses.

4. *Sex role differentiation and its failures.* Under ordinary circumstances, there is a continuing process of sex role differentiation throughout pre-edipal, edipal and latency phases of development. This process, with its biological basis and its social pressures, establishes each child as a boy among boys or a girl among girls. At puberty, the child stands on the threshold of becoming fully *a man among men*, interested in men's things and in girls as potential love objects, or of becoming fully *a woman among women*, interested in women's things and in boys as potential love objects. The process is in effect an elaborate and extensive apprenticeship in learning the cultural expressions, techniques, feelings and future of the sex role to which each child is assigned at birth. This process, abetted by the child's biological strivings and identifications, readies him for the inevitable upheavals and the strong social pressures of adolescence, so that when these come he can play his part. The cultural influences in childhood help determine not only the differences in sexual behavior expected of young men and young women, but

[20] Ferguson, E. D., "The effect of sibling competition and alliance on level of aspiration, expectation and performance," *J. abnorm. soc. Psychol.*, 1958, 56, 213–222.

also differentiated patterns of aggression, and of behavior and experience considerably removed from both sexuality and aggression.

Almost all children pass successfully through their pre-edipal and edipal sex role differentiation, and go on more or less uneventfully through latency until they come to adolescence. Some, however, because of their incomplete resolution of the edipal complex, have an exceedingly difficult time; and a small number fail to resolve it. These last have either *failed to experience* the grand illusion during their edipal phase, and have remained infantile or severely inhibited emotionally; or else they have *never overcome* the edipal grand illusion, and are therefore unable to embark wholeheartedly upon the *great adventure*, which is the phase of normal latency.

We have already discussed, in Chapter 2, the problems of sex identification and object love in the pre-edipal and edipal phases of personality development. Here it will be sufficient to point out what the child needs if he is to construct a normal edipal situation for himself — in which he should experience intense love and pride in being what he is — and what he needs in order to be able to resolve his edipal conflicts, as his disillusionment becomes final. That is, he needs to be able to fall in love hopelessly between his third and fifth years, and to emerge into a new equanimity after he gives it up.

In brief, what he needs is an ideal identification figure of his own sex, who is neither frightening nor ineffectual, and he needs an ideal love-object of the opposite sex, who is neither seductive nor too forbidding. The best possible identification and the best possible love-object should be the child's own parents, since they are or should be always with him, and since they love him as a child. If they accept their child's declaration of love without becoming anxious and without arousing their child's anxiety, and if they give the child overtly, not a reciprocal passionate love, but the warm, tender affection of an emotionally mature parent, they will provide everything that the child needs, both to experience his edipal situation and to resolve it.

If the parent of the same sex as the child is emotionally a reasonably mature adult, the child has a model whom he can admire and emulate, even though he also envies his admired parent,[21] and is at times unreasonably jealous of him. Such happy circumstances are usually approximated; but they are by no means universal. Let us look at some of the common defects which often underlie adult psychopathology.

5. *Faulty identification: the boy.* At one extreme is the parent who seems frightening to the child; at the other extreme is the parent who seems weak and ineffectual.[22] A too *formidable father,* or a father who seems violent, may frighten his son to such a degree that he cannot identify profitably with him. Either the son is afraid of some terrible punishment from his father

[21] Pishkin, V., "Psychosexual development in terms of object and role preferences." *J. clin. Psychol.*, 1960, *16*, 238–240.

[22] It must be borne in mind throughout this discussion that what counts is the way the parent *seems to the child* in the home. This may or may not correspond to the objective facts of the situation.

for wanting to usurp the paternal role — which is what normally uninhibited edipal boys openly express — or he is afraid that he will become as violent as his father appears to be. If it is his mother who seems to be the frightening parent, her son may feel identification with his father too dangerous because of what his mother might do to him in his relatively helpless state. It goes without saying that a child at this stage thinks vaguely, not specifically as an adult does, and that he experiences magical omnipotence and misunderstandings as great as those in his fairy tales.

A *father* who seems to his son *weak and ineffectual* in the home leaves him without a worthy model for identification and without protection. The need for an identification model to nourish a boy's masculinity is obvious.[23] A boy's need for paternal protection is twofold. He needs protection against his own sexual and aggressive impulses toward his mother, at a time when his ego organization is weak, but his id impulses are strong. He also needs protection against being engulfed by his mother's symbiotic love; that is, he needs masculine protection against the danger that he will regress to a symbiotic phase in which he will lose his identity again, and in this sense cease to exist. If a boy's father seems weak and ineffectual to him, while his mother seems powerful, the boy feels placed in double jeopardy.

Weak, ineffectual mothers, on the other hand, are resented and looked down upon by their small sons, who feel the need of a worthy love object during their edipal phase. Such mothers present their sons with a depreciated model for their later adolescent and adult love. Thus a low opinion of women may come not alone from observation of anatomical differences and the physiological subordination of the woman sexually, but also because a mother fails to earn her son's respect by being an adequate woman.

6. *Faulty identification: the girl.* A *frightening father* may also inhibit his daughter in her attempts to identify with her mother. She dares not put herself in a feminine, submissive position in relation to such a terrifying male as her father seems to be, even in her imagination. It goes without saying that the daughter of a *weak, ineffectual mother* lacks a worthy identification figure to help her evolve her own femininity; but in addition she lacks the protection of a wise, effectual woman to protect her against her own infantile wishes and her fears with respect to her father.

A *frightening mother* may have similar deleterious effects for different reasons. Her daughter may feel so helpless, as a small child, that she dares not identify with a woman who, instead of offering protection and comfort,

---

[23] When there is no father present in the home, similar problems may arise. Cf., Stephens, W. N., "Judgments by social workers in fatherless families," *J. genet. Psychol.*, 1961, *99*, 59–64; Leichty, M. M., "The effect of father-absence during early childhood upon the Oedipal situation as reflected in young adults," *Merrill-Palmer Quart.*, 1960, *6*, 212–217; Wylie, H. L., and Delgado, R. A., "A pattern of mother-son relationship involving the absence of the father," *Amer. J. Orthopsychiat.*, 1959, *29*, 644–649; Lynn, D., and Sawrey, W. L., "The effect of father-absence on Norwegian boys and girls," *J. abnorm. soc. Psychol.*, 1959, *59*, 258–262.

seems always on the verge of attacking her.[24] Girls carry the special burden of resentment against their mothers for having made them girls, along with guilt for harboring such resentment. The daughter of a frightening mother cannot express her feeling of having been short-changed, even indirectly. Some little girls, we know, play at having a penis; some pretend that they actually have one, or continue to believe that some day they will grow one; some maintain the pretense or the actual belief unconsciously right into adult life, as the analysis of women reveals.

The daughter of a seemingly *weak, ineffectual father* may despise him, when what she badly needs is a male figure whom she can look up to and admire. Little girls are sometimes outspoken about needing someone to keep mother under control. This comes in part from their fear of being engulfed by their symbiotically inclined mother which, to the little girl, means a loss of her individuality, and which she equates with oblivion, with ceasing to exist. The little girl is also expressing the need for a dominant, worthy love object to whom she can imagine herself surrendering. A weak, ineffectual father frightens the little girl because of her first need; and he frustrates her and offends her because of her second need.

7. *Some results of faulty identification.* Whether it is the father or the mother who seems frightening to the child, the outcome may be essentially the same. The child becomes intimidated. He gives up trying to identify as he should in the edipal phase or he gives up trying to find a suitable love object. This of course robs the child of his most important experiences in love and aggression, after he emerges from the symbiotic union with his mother. It also denies him normal experiences of frustration. The apparently paradoxical benefits from frustration, among which is ego growth through internalization of frustrating situations, are thus lost to such a child. Because he has not loved and lost when he was a small child, he remains unable to love freely as an adult and remains immature in his ego organization.

In extreme instances, which are not rare in psychopathology, we find emotionally immature adults who appear incapable of forming permanent and meaningful love relationships. Among these are the Don Juans and their feminine counterparts who, contrary to popular belief, are not sexually powerful but as a rule sexually immature. We find some adults also who seem to have identified with the parent of the opposite sex (*cross-identification*), or with an older sibling of the opposite sex, and choose as their love object a person of the same sex. These persons make up one group of overt homosexual adults. A third possibility is that the child retains an infantile attachment for one or the other parent, succeeds only in repressing its sexual aspect, and remains with the parents as a more or less asexual dependent. Such a person may, of course, be intellectually superior, even though emotionally immature; sometimes he may appear to be asexual.

[24] A clearcut example of such fears will be seen in the case of Sally J. See her name in the alphabetized list of cases in the index under *Cases*.

In actual life one sees a great many more cases of compromise, somewhere along the line of emotional development, than of these clear-cut extremes. In the first place, parents are rarely frightening or ineffectual in *every* respect. A child has many kinds of parental behavior with which he can identify, or which qualify the imperfect parent as a reasonably good love object. In the second place, small children have vivid imaginations. They can sometimes create effectual identification figures and love objects through the cooperation of their own strong desires with what they see going on around them. Children, in other words, can create imaginary parents just as they can create imaginary companions. They thus try to remedy what is denied them, what frustrates them, by setting up something satisfying within them. Finally, we repeat that many children who are unfortunate in having unsatisfying parents are fortunate in finding a worthy parent substitute among adult relatives or among the parents of their friends — provided that parental jealousy does not intervene.

One important reason for early adequate sex identification, prior to the onset of latency, is that during latency, at least in our culture, children seek out children of their own sex and for several years avoid close relationships with like-aged children of the opposite sex. It is common and normal for latency children to develop strong loyalties and affections for their like-sexed peers, usually on an idealistic basis, but with many of the characteristic possessiveness and jealousy which they will later show, in adolescence and adulthood, toward persons of the opposite sex. If latency begins before adequate identification with a like-sexed parent has developed, in relation to adequate love for an opposite-sexed parent, there is greater possibility of homosexual attachments than would otherwise be the case. There is also a greater likelihood that the latency child will feel a stronger need to depreciate the other sex than is necessary for affirming his own, and establishing his membership in it.

8. *Negative edipal complex* (*inverted edipal complex*). When we discussed the development of the edipal complex and its resolution, in Chapter 2, we omitted one normal complication in order to keep the discussion clear. This complication is the love that little boys have for their fathers and that little girls have for their mothers. With this normal love for the like-sexed parent goes also a certain amount of identification with the opposite-sexed parent. Thus, the edipal boy is able to picture himself in his mother's role as wife and mother — imperfectly, because he is only a small child as well as a boy. The edipal girl, similarly, can picture herself in her father's role as father and husband — imperfectly, because she is only a small child as well as a girl. This paradoxical emotional and imaginal relationship, which is probably confined to the human species because of the freedom that human things have to conceptualize something apart from action and contrary to fact, is known as the *negative edipal* or *inverted edipal complex*. It is basic to what Freud has called the bisexual nature of the human being.

The negative edipal complex remains a normal part of every child's personality development provided that it plays only a minor role in the child's imagining. It seems to be a necessary component of human personality development if the child is to grow to adulthood with a workable understanding of members of the opposite sex, as well as a desire for them. Members of the opposite sex always remain something of an enigma, in spite of this internal representation of their reciprocal role, because of their differents goals, ideas and experiences.

It is pathological for a man to be completely unable to understand women, wives and mothers, and for a woman to be completely unable to understand men, husbands and fathers. Such defects, which may be compared with an adult inability to conceive of a baby's orientation, are probably the result of failure to develop the negative edipal complex normally, or to resolve it.[25]

On the other hand, if the intensity of the negative edipal complex experienced in childhood is as great as the positive edipal experience, or even greater, the child will suffer some distortion in his personality development. As an adult, he will be vulnerable to difficulties that range from relative ineffectuality in his appropriate sex role all the way to a reversal of it. The ineffectuality may be no more than weakness or passivity in men, and aggression or domineering in women. We see common products of such an unpromising beginning in timid men who cannot occupy a strong masculine role and enjoy it, and in women who cannot take and enjoy a receptive feminine role. If the timid man or the strident woman still has a predominantly heterosexual orientation, and can find a marital partner with reciprocal needs, the general adaptation to life that results may fall within normal limits.

An overdeveloped negative edipal complex that remains essentially unresolved underlies some overt homosexuality, but by no means all. We have already mentioned the part played by early cross-identification in creating a homosexual orientation. In addition, there is the complication that many overt homosexual men play an essentially masculine role in relation to a man, and many overt homosexual women play a feminine role in relation to a woman. It is their choice of love object, rather than their choice of sex role, that shows the more basic pathology. Finally, we have the fact that many overtly homosexual men suffer from severe castration anxiety, which seems to be fundamental to their abnormality; while many overt homosexual women suffer from a sense of having been deprived of an adequate sex organ, and because of this they cannot accept their femininity or overcome a lasting resentment toward men. In short, overt homosexuality can arise from failure to resolve a *positive* edipal complex, as well as from failure to resolve a *negative* one.[26]

9. *Failure to overcome castration anxiety or penis envy.* We said in Chapter 2 that the end of the edipal phase comes when a child gives up his

---

[25] Stephens, W. N., *The Oedipus Complex: Cross-Cultural Evidence.* New York: Macmillan, 1962.

[26] Overt homosexuality will be discussed further in Chapter 19, "Personality disorders."

or her infantile sexual and aggressive aims, develops a mature superego that internalizes both the loving and the critical aspects of parental behavior, and is then able to enter latency. What happens to the castration anxiety in boys, and to the sense of loss or inadequacy in girls? As is the case with most early primitive organizations, neither is completely overcome; both remain latent at some level. If the edipal resolution is adequate, the castration anxiety or its feminine equivalent is successfully repressed. It is not reactivated unless a person is subjected to extreme stress, or seeks personality reorganization through psychotherapy or through psychoanalysis.

If the edipal resolution is defective, a child enters upon the phase of latency without the freedom that he or she might otherwise have enjoyed. A common pathological device is that of denying the fact that girls and women lack a penis. This denial may persist unconsciously into adult life in either sex. The lack of freedom in latency may appear more diffusely as a too great dependence upon one's parents, as an unwillingness to join the neighborhood or peer group, as a school phobia, or as a generalized fearfulness.

Such latency defects are treatable; and they may be overcome spontaneously through good experience in the home, the neighborhood, the peer culture or the school. The difficulty is that a chronically anxious child is usually an unhappy child. As far as socialization outside the home is concerned, he is usually an ineffectual child. Nevertheless, anxious children find ways of compensating for their anxiety, especially if they have some special ability which their peers admire, or which in some other way brings them self-esteem.[27]

There is a certain amount of de-emphasis of the edipal complex and of castration anxiety today among some psychoanalysts, in favor of a greater preoccupation with pre-edipal phases, including the mother-child symbiosis and the relatively autonomous phase of self-assertion and sphincter control. This newer emphasis does not, however, detract from the importance of either the edipal phase or the castration anxiety. It merely gives both a longer history.

It is widely held today that many or most of the difficulties experienced in the edipal phase, including difficulties in overcoming castration anxiety or penis envy, are themselves the consequences of unresolved problems belonging to pre-edipal phases.[28] In other words, satisfactory resolution of pre-edipal problems prepares a child for a normally intense edipal relationship, normally structured. It prepares him for the normal resolution of the edipal complex as he enters latency.

It has been noted that parents who experience little or no difficulty with their child's pre-edipal problems are sometimes disturbed by his edipal phase.

[27] Koppitz, E. M., "Relationships between some background factors and children's interpersonal attitude," *J. genet. Psychol.*, 1957, *91*, 119–129.

[28] See the discussion by Rangell, L., "The role of early psychic functioning in psychoanalysis," *J. Amer. Psychoanal. Ass.*, 1961, *9*, 595–609; Sarnoff, I., and Corwin, S. M., "Castration anxiety and the fear of death," *J. Pers.*, 1959, *27*, 374–385.

They then become less free to be helpful to the edipal child than they had been during symbiotic and autonomous pre-edipal phases.

10. *Superego defects.* The differentiation of a superego organization from the edipal ego is one of the most momentous events in a child's life. It occurs toward the end of the edipal phase and makes a latency phase possible. The superego organization "involves internalization by the child of parental approvals and disapprovals, of love and rebuke, of taboos, standards, ideals and tastes — each system with its hierarchy of less important and more important. Superego organization cannot reach the level of postedipal control unless there is clear separation of the self from others. The child's reality construction must include fairly clear object representation, as well as self-representation.[29]

It should be emphasized at this point that the superego organization goes on maturing throughout life, that it is being continually modified through maturation and experience. Latency is obviously not a phase of suspended animation for the superego, any more than it is for the ego, with which and with the id, the superego is in constant interaction.

This brings us to some of the defects in superego structure and functioning. Since the superego differentiates from ego organization, it is likely to carry over some of the ego defects which belong to moral and ethical control, standards, ideals and self-esteem. To the extent that a child's parents are defective in some of these areas, the child's superego may also be defective. There is thus a certain amount of cultural inheritance in superego organization. It must not be forgotten, however, that a child has two parents, either of which may be dominant in different areas, and that other significant figures influence superego identifications just as they do the ego identifications. It is not always easy either to predict what a child will internalize from his human environment, or to say what it is in the past that has had a determining influence upon superego development.

There has been a good deal of work within the recent past upon superego development and superego defect, which we shall take up in the chapter on the psychodynamic system (Chapter 5), and again in the chapter on personality disorders. Suffice it to say here that in clinical studies, in which a parent was in treatment at the same time as the child, and at times in the same room, observers were often able to detect obvious signs of encouragement on the part of a parent to commit misdeeds. The parent seemed not to be aware of his own attitude of connivance at the time; but it showed through clearly as eagerness while the child was describing antisocial or deviant behavior, and as unconscious but still obvious seduction outside the treatment situation. The child whose parent has clinically obvious superego defects, or whose

---

29 Cf. Jacobson, E., "The self and the object world," *The Psychoanalytic Study of the Child.* New York: Internat. Univ. Press, 1954, *9*, 75–127; Loewald, H. W., "Ego and reality," *Internat. J. Psychoanal.*, 1951, *32*, 10–18; Loewald, H. W., "The problem of defense and the neurotic interpretation of reality," *Internat. J. Psychoanal.*, 1952, *33*, 444–459.

parent for any reason has a need for the child to act out forbidden impulses, will not himself develop a normal superego organization at the close of his edipal phase, or afterwards during latency. Its defects may reflect similar defects in a parental superego, or it may represent the fulfillment of frustrated parental impulses. It may even include in its organization a parent's unconscious vengeful feelings toward the child, and toward what the child represents in the parent's own ego attitudes.

This last is seen in cases where parents unconsciously communicate to the child the misdeeds or the inappropriate behavior which they expect or even want. When the child complies by showing the expected behavior, the parent is likely to respond with ambivalent attitudes of condemnation and encouragement, simply because he consciously condemns the behavior but unconsciously wants it. Superego corruption is seen also in cases of inadequate sex identity and sexual cross-identification, where on the basis of parental psychopathology a parent fosters attitudes and interests characteristic of the opposite sex from that of the child. The parental encouragement may be subtle and unconscious; but in some of the cases reported it was done openly, and "justified" to the therapist on the grounds that the child "wanted" it.[30]

Preadolescence

Toward the end of latency there is a brief period during which marked emotional and social changes occur without much biological change.[31] The child is often touchy, defiant and resentful toward his parents. His behavior may seem disorganized, even to the point of vagueness and unintelligibility of speech.[32] Boys take pleasure once more in disorder and dirt; girls become uncertain, and some become tomboys again. In their fantasies and daydreams preadolescent children express edipal wishes openly with little distortion. At the same time they turn critical of their parents and of parental values. They seek the company of nonparental adults, and seek experiences which exclude their parents.

Preadolescent peer groups exclude members of the opposite sex toward whom the preadolescent expresses a contempt which contrasts sharply with the attitudes in mid-adolescence and in mature adulthood. If there is any association with members of the opposite sex, this is in accordance with the demands of like-sexed peers, and not because of genuine sex attraction. Need for peer group approval is more imperative than ever. Nevertheless, the peer groups themselves are often unstable in their make-up because their members are seeking new experiences.

[30] See, for example, Johnson, A. M., and Szurek, S., "The genesis of antisocial acting-out in children and adults," *Psychoanal. Quart.*, 1952, *21*, 323–343.

[31] See Blair, A. W., and Burton, W. H., *Growth and Development of the Preadolescent.* New York: Appleton-Century-Crofts, 1951.

[32] See the account of verbal disorganization in girls given by Kestenberg, J. S., "Menarche," in Lorand, S., and Schneer, H. J. (Eds.), *Adolescents.* New York: Hoeber, 1961, pp. 31–35.

The preadolescent child tends to be uncommunicative with his parents, both because he is beginning to feel the need for independence, and because sexual fantasies are growing prominent which he conceals. Preadolescence must be regarded as an ill-defined period during which a child passes from the relative calm of latency toward the turbulence of adolescence.

Latent into adolescent

Whether a child has resolved his epidal conflicts and developed a satisfactory superego or not, the major part of his latency will be absorbed by innumerable tasks and adventures through which he gains mastery over the human environment and himself, develops appropriate role behavior of his own, and develops reciprocal role behavior in relation to children and adults of both sexes. He acquires physical skills and social skills, stores up prodigious quantities of knowledge, and develops an ego-superego organization in accordance with his prevailing culture. In time he will become a separate person who knows how to behave interdependently with other persons, and has at his disposal representations of their attitudes to guide his behavior and experience, as well as his own established stable attitudes. He usually terminates latency with a brief transitional period of preadolescence, such as we have just described.

Adolescence, the next phase, is ushered in by rapid physiological growth and maturation, especially marked in genital and secondary sex characteristics, both visible and invisible. These are predetermined by the sex of the child at the time of conception. They provide us with some excellent examples of innate growth and behavioral patterns which do not come to full expression for more than a decade and a half of postnatal life.

If the child has been normally reared, and is himself normal, the experiences of his symbiotic, pre-edipal, edipal and latency phases will have prepared him for his further development into an adolescent, and eventually into an adult person. Nevertheless, in our culture, the phase of adolescence is normally one of behavioral instability and emotional turbulence. During it, as we shall soon see, both pre-edipal and edipal problems may be reactivated with all their original emotional intensity and ambivalence, but now under very different circumstances. Let us turn next to a consideration of adolescence and how it prepares a person for adulthood.

The Phase of Adolescence

Students of the adolescent phase are now of the opinion that it is not merely a transition from childhood to adulthood, but as distinct a phase of development as is childhood, and as deserving as childhood is to be considered in its own right.[33] Adolescence occupies most of a decade of life, during which

[33] For a fuller account of the psychodynamic development in adolescence, see Mohr, G., and Despres, M., *The Stormy Decade: Adolescence.* New York: Random House,

momentous changes take place before its culmination in full adulthood — changes in anatomical, physiological, emotional and intellectual functions, and changes in social relationships. In our account we shall pay scant attention to anatomical and physiological changes, important as these are, in order to focus more clearly upon the psychodynamic characteristics of adolescence.

Adolescence is turbulent and unstable. Unless a pathological arrest of development occurs as, for example, in the perpetually adolescent rebellious, dependent person, this phase is also transient. Nevertheless, to become a fully mature adult in our culture, it is essential to experience fully a phase of adolescence.[34] It is during this period that the rapidly growing person organizes his external, somatic and internal realities in accordance with the realities of an increasingly adult world. He greatly enriches his ego organization by means of a prodigious amount of new learning, by a series of rapidly shifting experiences and orientations, and by new identifications. He channels or sublimates his emotional drives without sacrificing their vigor, if he is successful, and he builds further his superego organization — also through learning, experiencing, orienting and identifying — which acts as a scanning and evaluating device, as a reassuring and critical companion, and as a semi-independent source of self-esteem and self-condemnation.[35]

If for any reason the phase of adolescence is cut short, as for example when adult responsibilities are assumed precociously, the resulting adult personality is characteristically impoverished, however efficient and mature it may appear. Adolescence offers a vast range of choices from which to select the materials for one's adult organization. It affords a range of experience before that organization has crystallized out. These advantages must be weighed against the apparent wastefulness and stress of adolescent experience.

Adolescent turbulence and instability

Anatomical, physiological, emotional, intellectual and social factors all enter into the adolescent picture to make it turbulent and unstable. Changes in these various realms do not necessarily coincide in time. Even the rate of change in any one of them is not wholly predictable. As everyone knows, two adolescents of the same chronological age and the same sex may show

1958; Peck, R. F., Havighurst, R. J., Cooper, R., Lilienthal, J., and More, D., *The Psychology of Character Development.* New York: Wiley, 1960; Blos, P., *On Adolescence: A Psychoanalytic Interpretation.* Glencoe, Ill.: Free Press, 1962; Benimoff, M., and Horrocks, J. E., "A developmental study of relative needs satisfactions of youth: equilibrium-disequilibration," *J. genet. Psychol.,* 1961, *99,* 185–207; and Pearson, G. H., *Adolescence and the Conflict of Generations.* New York: Norton, 1958.

[34] For accounts of growth and development in childhood and adolescence, see Carmichael, L. (Ed.), *Handbook of Child Development.* (2nd ed.) New York: Wiley, 1954; Gesell, A., *et al., The First Five Years of Life.* New York: Harper, 1940; Gesell, A., *et al., The Child from Five to Ten.* New York: Harper, 1946; Gesell, A., Ilg, F. L., and Ames, L. B., *Youth: The Years from Ten to Sixteen.* New York: Harper, 1956.

[35] Hawkes, G. R., and Pease, D., *Behavior and Development from Five to Twelve.* New York: Harper, 1962.

great differences in physical maturity. Girls in general reach puberty about two years earlier than the average boy.[36] It is obvious that the adolescent who matures early has greater demands placed upon him than the adolescent of the same sex who matures later. At the same time, the more mature adolescent is more likely to be chosen as a leader than the immature one.

Adolescence is precipitated by hormonal changes which define the onset of puberty. The relative calm of latency is replaced by the rising adolescent storm. New imperious drives toward sexual and aggressive activities are experienced by the young adolescent almost without warning. While he still acts as a child, he feels a demand to be treated as an adult; and while he demands adult treatment he is afraid of adulthood because of his inexperience. He may seem impulsive and unpredictable, even to himself. He experiences rapid mood changes which he usually cannot fathom, and which no one around him seems to understand. His body keeps growing, and changing its proportions, faster than he can adapt to them. At a time when he may be exquisitely sensitive to the opinions of others, his body makes him clumsy and ridiculous. New social demands are being continually made upon him, without his fully understanding what the demands are, why they are made, and how he ought to fulfill them or avoid them. Because the society in which he lives is itself undergoing rapid changes, he can expect little help even from those whom he trusts. Adolescent orientations, daydreams and fantasies change progressively as the young man or woman moves anatomically, physiologically, experientially and socially nearer and nearer to full sexual and social maturity.[37]

Some sex differences in adolescent experience

A boy's sexual feelings focus upon his prominent, visible external genitalia, and upon the obvious changes which they undergo. There is little of the diffuseness that characterizes a girl's sexual feelings. We have seen that, even early in childhood, the average boy shows more vigorous activity and initiative than the average girl. During adolescence his drive toward active mastery of the physical world becomes outstanding. He is vigorous and boisterous in his competitive play, varied and constructive in his solitary play. He is, in general, object-oriented and relatively little concerned with personal appearance. He has daydreams of glory and ambition, and a continued interest in power symbols and mechanical things.[38] Since he reaches puberty on the average two years later than the girl, he presumably has two

---

36 Kestenberg, J. S., "Menarche," in Lorand, S., and Scheer, H. I. (Eds.), *Adolescents.* New York: Hoeber, 1961, pp. 19–50.

37 Engel, M., "The stability of the self-concept in adolescence," *J. abnorm. soc. Psychol.*, 1959, *58*, 211–215.

38 Cf. Bandura, A., and Walters, R. H., *Adolescent Aggression: A Study of the Influence of Child-Training Practices and Family Interrelationships.* New York: Ronald, 1959; Lansky, L. M., Crandall, V. J., Kagan, J., and Baker, C. T., "Sex differences in aggression and its correlates in middle-class adolescents," *Child Develpm.*, 1961, *32*, 45–58.

valuable years more than she has to devote himself to mastering skills and his own body, without being disturbed by pubertal changes.

Once a boy enters puberty, however, his sexual maturation progresses more rapidly than does the girl's, unless he has been intimidated earlier in life. Among young adolescent boys, masturbation is almost universal, whereas in girls it is the exception. This difference is probably related both to the genital differences and to the greater conformist tendencies among girls. The aggressive, adventurous attitudes of boys lead them to show general initiative and to be vigorously competitive in behavior, plans and orientations.

In girls puberty appears, on the average, two years earlier than in boys.[39] The onset of menstrual function (*menarche*) appears to influence the interests of the pubertal girl at once. It sets the seal upon her femaleness. She can settle down to almost a lifetime of monthly cycles, which make her sex role and its implications now undeniable, and introduce a form of regularity and predictability into her life over which she has no control. Preceding and following the menarche, the girl's body undergoes extensive changes in form. This not only makes her more aware than ever of her body but also gives her direct experience in being an object of sex attraction.

In the United States today the menarche and the appearance of secondary sex characteristics seldom come with the sense of shock or shame that seems to have been common two generations ago. Girls are usually adequately informed and prepared, if not by their mother, then by their girl friends. Nevertheless, the single most important factor in a girl's acceptance of her femininity, and her pride in it, still comes from the prevailing attitudes of her mother. If a mother accepts her own femininity, and takes pride in it, her daughter is almost certain to feel the same way when her puberty arrives. If a mother resents being a woman, and envies men their lot and their masculine functions, her daughter is likely to have similar attitudes and to have a bad time at puberty. The maternal attitudes in either case need not have been communicated verbally. Daughters pick up their mother's attitudes toward the woman's lot even though they are never spoken.

Because her sex feelings are relatively diffuse, the girl has a predominantly inward orientation, no matter how practical and worldly she may be. Her external genitalia do not provide her with the kind of objective, thing-like experience that a boy's do. Sexuality concerns the interior of her body. She is much more concerned with secrets than the boy, and less concerned with vigorous activity. The girl tends to see life from a subjective point of view. She daydreams a great deal. She is much concerned about the appearance of her body and its adornment. It is highly important for her that she be considered attractive.

Sex differences in general and differences in sexual attitudes, such as we have been discussing, seem to be present in almost all forms of contemporary society, and seem to have prevailed in past ages wherever there was freedom

[39] Douvan, E., "Sex differences in adolescent character processes," *Merrill-Palmer Quart.*, 1960, *6*, 203–211; Howard, L. P., "Identity conflicts in adolescent girls," *Smith Coll. Studies Social Work*, 1960, *31*, 1–21.

to develop differences.[40] It is reasonable to conclude that they are not merely products of custom, excepting as regards particular forms, but also the results of innate biological sex differences.

Adolescent rebellion

Sooner or later, in both sexes pubertal changes precipitate adolescent rebellion. Although the young adolescent badly needs adult guidance and protection, he hates his dependent needs; he is afraid that they will defeat him in his drive toward emancipation. He cannot stand being treated as a child when he is vividly aware that he is growing up. One result of this fear is that he may alienate his parents, that he may isolate himself psychologically from them. At a time when he actually needs supervision, he may berate his parents for attempting to supervise him. To establish his independence the adolescent may even disappear for a day, an evening or a weekend, and when he comes back he is likely to refuse to say where he has been and what he has been doing.

As everyone knows, adolescence often places a heavy burden upon parents as well as upon the adolescent. It is usually a period of mutual misunderstanding and frustration. The parents find themselves sometimes treated with indifference, coldness, scorn or hostility by a child whom they may have always loved unselfishly, and still love. They hear themselves addressed condescendingly and their cherished values ridiculed or rudely challenged. A growing son or daughter may ignore parents, avoid them or look at them hatefully. If the parents feel sure that their attitudes toward their child and their treatment of him have not changed, they are bewildered by this new experience.

It is the adolescent who usually initiates the change in parent-child relationships, even though he may be as baffled by it as his parents are. The fact is that the child is no longer a child; and yet in some ways he is more childish than ever. In one way or another he demands privileges and protection, as a dependent member of the family, but he objects violently to the least curtailment of his activity. This contradictory situation seems to be peculiar to the human species, just as the phase of the flowering of infantile sexuality appears to be. It may even be peculiar to Western civilization and to the family structure in our society.

With the onset of puberty, at least in our society, there comes a reactivation of pre-edipal and edipal urges and conflicts in the young adolescent. At the same time there may also be revived experiences of separation anxiety or castration anxiety. The situation, however, is basically different from that of the edipal period or anything preceding that. During the *edipal phase*,

[40] Cross-cultural studies have been reported in this area. Cf., for example, Asayama, S., "Comparison of sexual development of American and Japanese adolescents," *Psychologia*, 1957, *1*, 129–131; Fleming, C. M., Digaria, D. F., and Newth, H. G. R., "Preferences and values among adolescent boys and girls," *Educ. Res.*, 1960, 2, 221–224; Hsu, F. L. K., Watrous, B. G., and Lord, E. M., "Culture pattern and adolescent behavior," *Internat. J. soc. Psychiat.*, 1961, 7, 33–53.

as we have seen, there was a profound identification with the like-sexed parent, often outspoken, and a drive toward taking the opposite-sexed parent as love object, also often openly declared. Now the young adolescent, whatever his unconscious motivations, is seeking consciously to escape from his parents, by whom he feels repelled even before he feels attracted to persons of the opposite sex outside his family. This can be understood only in terms of his unconscious impulses toward his parents, which rearouse the old edipal guilt with even greater force than it originally had.

The normal pride which parents experience in their growing child may well include unconscious edipal components of love, envy and guilt. The hypersensitive normal adolescent, like the paranoid sensitive adult, may be more aware of such temptations than his parents are. This may help to explain the exaggerated anger, derision and avoidance which many adolescents show their parents without apparent provocation. If edipal components are also exceptionally strong in parental responses to the maturation of an adolescent, the home atmosphere may become highly charged with incomprehensible emotional stresses that seem to affect everyone within reach.

Whether or not his parents react unconsciously with edipal love or edipal envy, the adolescent's own conflicts make it imperative that he turn away from his parents and toward comparative strangers. He still needs love, guidance and protection; but he can no longer accept them from his parents because of his reactivated unconscious attitudes. He needs intensely to separate himself from them, to rid himself of his childhood affectional ties, with their intolerable burden of guilt, and to avert the danger and temptation of remaining in subjection to them. This he must accomplish if he is ever to become a self-respecting, self-reliant adult.

Adolescent rebellion may appear ungrateful, callous and senseless to parents. To the adolescent, who does not understand his unconscious reasons for revolting any more than his parents do, his behavior appears somehow justified, even though he may at times regret it. He usually seeks to account for it on the grounds of external circumstances, the parallel behavior of other adolescents, and of his conscious need for greater freedom and maturity. The rebellion is certainly justified, but not on rational grounds, and not in terms of verbal logic. The rebellion is essential in our culture, but it is still irrational, for its sources lie among the now unconscious fantasies and conflicts which come from early childhood.[41]

Years later, after the separation has been made, and the adolescent has established new relationships outside the home, he may become fully reconciled to his parents, and even love them again, but now as an adult among adults. Nonetheless, at the time of emotional separation there is pain and sorrow on both sides. To parents, the adolescent rebellion seems a heartless desertion, a betrayal of confidence and love. To the adolescent, it seems to be a period of hopeless misunderstanding by the very persons whom he has

[41] Bandura, A., and Walters, R. H., *Adolescent Aggression: A Study of the Influence of Child-Training Practices and Family Interrelationships*. New York: Ronald, 1959.

trusted so unquestioningly in the past. An occasional adolescent seems to effect the separation serenely, without making his parents suffer.

At the other end of the distribution, there are adolescents who never suc-ceed in emancipating themselves. Some of them remain as grownup children in their parents' home forever; some transfer a childlike attachment to a marital partner who may be satisfied with it; some remain forever in chronic rebellion without clearly realizing what they are rebelling against. Failure to find satisfactory identifications and love objects outside the home may leave a person vulnerable later in life to one or another form of psycho-pathology. If such pathology appears when the vulnerable adult becomes himself a parent, he is likely to pass on to his child the same vulnerability to the development of psychopathology. Thus what looks like a clear case of biological heredity may actually be one of cultural inheritance.

New identification figures and new love objects

Meanwhile, the lonely adolescent must find new identification figures out-side the family, to take the place of his once idealized parents whom he now scorns. He must also find fresh sources of emotional support and guidance, since he has cut himself off from parental help. Eventually he will have to find new love objects to whom he can attach himself without fear of edipal guilt. These processes go on in somewhat random fashion and at variable rates. A new advance may be followed by a retreat to a more infantile or at least a less confident level. A retreat to an infantile, withdrawn or con-fused state may be followed by another advance. Retreats in one area of functioning are often accompanied by advances in another area. The total effect upon both the adolescent himself and upon those in daily contact with him is bewildering. Let us look at some of the reasons.

For one thing, puberty and early adolescence upset the equilibrium estab-lished during latency between ego, id and superego *within*, and between this *psychodynamic system* within and the *external reality* which surrounds it. This situation results from the simple fact that puberty means a tremendous increase in emotional drive energy. The young adolescent, like the edipal child, finds himself faced with powerful sexual and aggressive drives which his ego organization cannot handle. This time, however, he cannot escape his predicament by renunciation, unless he is willing to renounce the world. He must somehow come to terms with his imperious drives; he must use them to establish himself finally as an adult among adults. This is a mo-mentous task which will call for the employment of every means at his dis-posal.

The young adolescent has certain great advantages over the edipal child. One of these is that he has achieved greatly in *intellectual growth*. He has perceptual and cognitive organizations undreamed of by the edipal child. He has *motor skills*, *physical mastery*, the gift of *language* and *logic*, and tremendous experience in *social interrelationships*. We may lump these gains together as the gains in *ego strength* which come from the long period of learning, experience, identification and maturing which we call the *phase of latency*.

Another advantage stems from the growth, during the edipal phase and during latency, of *systems of ideals, standards* and *controls*. When the young adolescent abandons his parents, he does not abandon their values and ideals, though he may seem to do so, and even though he may intend to do so. Regardless of what he consciously thinks, and regardless of what his parents think, he retains his early superego identifications, with their hierarchies of values and ideals. The apparent escape of the nonconformist child of conservative parents into a radical reaction may be followed by a return to conservatism; and even when it is not, the standards now utilized in the service of a new ideology will usually turn out to be the parental standards, differently formulated and differently applied.

At first the young adolescent's intellectual powers will be used as a powerful defense; and his idealism will be similarly utilized to ward off a too threatening reality. But after a period of maturation, which goes on behind the façade of these defenses, the adolescent will utilize his intellectual powers to gain new knowledge and further mastery; and he will match his idealism against a realistic world. Both of these processes, with all their innumerable variations, call for a continual exercise of *reality-testing*. Through such reality-testing the adolescent slowly evolves his new worlds of socially shared *external reality* and of internally experienced, often incommunicable, *psychic reality*.[42] Through the fresh impetus of pubertal and early adolescent thrusts, personality development gains new dimensions in new relationships. In one direction, the young adolescent seeks *new identification figures* and *new object love* among the adults around him; in another direction he seeks them among his contemporaries. The first we shall consider here; the second we shall defer for separate consideration in the next section on the adolescent peer culture.

If the young adolescent is fortunate, he will find among the adults around him, who are not connected with his parents, persons whom he can idealize. These are sometimes teachers who seem to the adolescent to possess the uncontaminated qualities which his parents lack. They are usually adults of the same sex whom the young adolescent can idealistically admire and at the same time take as models of identification. Among adolescent boys, the admired model is likely to be an athletic coach who embodies the health, skill, vigor and eagerness which the boy's middle-aged father has long ago lost. Among girls the admired adult with whom one can also identify may be an attractive teacher of the same sex about whose personal life the girl knows little, and can therefore conjecture much. Both boys and girls supplement an available, admired identification figure with some inaccessible person

---

[42] We shall often use the term *psychic*, rather than *psychological*, because it is now widely used with these connotations, and because it is shorter and less contaminated with extraneous meanings.

in the public eye, who can supply an indefinable mystery and therefore serve as an identification figure and a love object to which almost any qualities may be ascribed.

The new identification figure or love object may not be an adult but an admired older sibling, or someone outside the family, who is two or three years older. Such apparently small differences in age may make a world of difference to the young adolescent. The essential thing is that the older contemporary have already the qualities which the young adolescent admires. It is easy to understand why a contemporary outside the family is preferable to an older sibling, since in the latter case the attachment is more likely to involve edipal complications than in the former. In some instances, the adolescent becomes attached to persons of the opposite sex who are at first much like their own parent; but in time his or her choice lights upon a younger person who need not resemble a parent at all.

These intermediate love objects and identification figures must be recognized as compromises. The adolescent has strong unconscious desires for his opposite-sexed parent who is a forever forbidden person. At first, he cannot possibly accept someone in the role of beloved or admired who is too different from the parent whom he consciously renounces and unconsciously loves and hates. Time allows the adolescent to experience emotional attachments and yearnings gradually, which would be frightening if they came all at once. Moreover, he can at first fuse both his need to identify with an idealized person and his equally pressing need to have a new love object. As he approaches closer and closer to full sexual and social maturity, he will have had these intermediate compromises as his sexual and social background. On such a foundation he will be prepared to build his heterosexual choices among the members of the adolescent peer culture.

The adolescent peer culture

However satisfying his identifications and object love may be in relation to idealized adults, the average adolescent finds his most helpful emotional support and understanding in the close companionship of his peers. Here he discovers that others of his own age have the same problems with their parents, the same resentment, loneliness, disdain, anxiety and guilt. They can understand one another even without understanding what their rebellion involves, excepting that they feel aloof from their elders and need independence and recognition as individuals. The result is a feeling of belonging instead of a feeling of being alone and misunderstood. Adolescents of the same sex who are at the same level of maturity can share their experiences, join in depreciating their parents, admiring certain adults and hating others.

Traditionally, the early adolescent phase, like the preadolescent phase, has been called a "homosexual phase," even though it involves little overt sexual activity. It does involve strong loyalties, strong though often shifting affection, and group identifications which are significant for later adult group interaction and adult love. In both the boy groups and the girl groups, young adolescents can discuss the opposite sex as well as their own feelings much more freely than with adults. They can share admirations, hostility toward parents — other parents are as bad as theirs are — and the various strategies which they may have developed individually for handling their mutual problems. These early like-sexed adolescent groups tend to be exclusive, and to be antagonistic toward other peer groups. Nevertheless, their composition changes; they are unstable organizations. Girls usually give up their contempt for boys when the menarche arrives; boys continue to depreciate girls until a later age, and some continue it throughout life.

It is common for boys to form gangs; girls almost never do. The boys' gangs are not by any means necessarily delinquent, although masculine aggression, competitiveness and initiative often lead to acts of antisocial violence which the individual boy might never contemplate alone. Middle-class boys are less likely to form delinquent gangs because their day-to-day experience is not as frustrating as that of lower-class boys. They have usually been better trained in self-control and provided with greater inner resources.

Delinquent gang hostility is directed both against adults, especially against adults in authority, and against other adolescents, against adolescents in more fortunate circumstances or against those belonging to another gang, to another race or to another country of origin. Gang loyalties are usually powerful forces. They may be accompanied by implacable hatred of out-groups and a willingness to follow a leader who in some cases is antisocial for entirely personal reasons. A good deal of what adults call crime arises among adolescents as competition in daring. Gangs tend to dissolve as their members begin to establish themselves as older adolescent and young adult members of their heterosexual society.

There is normally a progressive transition from the like-sexed peer groupings to heterosexual groups, which are also as a rule unstable in composition. Early dating is motivated not so much by sexual desire as by curiosity and the demands of the peer group. There is a curious transitional phase, common among girls but very uncommon among boys, in which two close friends of the same sex share an attachment for an adolescent of the opposite sex. Its commoner occurrence among girls may be on the basis of a not wholly unrealistic anxiety, since the boy to whom a girl feels attracted is usually older and always stronger than she is. The common "double date" has similar protective advantages over the single dating. This transitional phase gives the adolescent opportunities for trying out a variety of social roles, including interactions with members of the opposite sex, while he or she is still under the protection of the group. There is still a strong preoccupation with status and a tendency to form cliques in which the adolescent experiences, not only a sense of belonging, but also practices of censure and approval that may be far stricter than those of parents.

Older adolescents and young adults almost universally form heterosexual peer groups. The exceptions are the lonely ones, the isolates who have not learned to get along with their contemporaries, a few dependent persons who fail to emancipate themselves from their families or from the middle adolescent state, and a few who retain a homosexual orientation because of faulty identifications or edipal fears.

Members of the older adolescent peer group may continue their antagonism for parents and other adults in middle life. They can now share mutual interests much more realistically with one another than they could at an earlier age; and they have much more in common with one another than they have with their parents. They still have their anxieties and their soul searchings; but they feel themselves to be individuals. They can experience and learn to master their anxieties in close association with members of the opposite sex. This facilitates pairing off, reconsideration and reshuffling, before it becomes necessary to settle upon one's marital partner.

The search for individuality or identity

The upheaval at puberty awakens the preadolescent to a need to become an individual in his own right. He experiences the adolescent upheaval first, the biological and social disturbance of a previously established equilibrium; then he begins a series of advances and retreats, a succession of partial disintegrations and reintegrations, which eventually culminates in adulthood. It is possible that this whole process is peculiar to Western civilization, which emphasizes the more or less free-wheeling individual rather than group solidarity. The demands in early adolescence for conformity with adolescent peers, the demands that an adolescent be as much as possible the same as others, give way to a kind of typing, a search for what one wants to be like and what one can be. The powerful upthrusts of sexual and aggressive drives, the need for individual freedom, the close contact with peers, and the growth of ego-superego organizations, propel the adolescent toward a reorganization of his conceptions about himself. He ceases to be the complacent, protected member of his family. He moves toward becoming an independent member of his community.

The adolescent is quicker than his parents in recognizing that he is no longer a child, that he now needs the sympathetic companionship of others like himself. He enters upon a phase of experimenting with different social roles in different relationships. This is less a period of progress than one of trying out. Unquestionably the most beneficial product of a long period of adolescence is that it allows the individual to experience many changes before he must crystallize his personality into its adult form. Many different kinds of solution are worked out for the same and for different problems, as they come up in a realistic context. Some preadolescent and early adolescent defenses, such as intellectualization, idealization and reaction formation, become ego methods for coping with and mastering realistic situations. If the adolescent is to grow into a self-reliant, self-respecting adult, his self-esteem must keep pace with his growing self-identity.[43]

[43] Cf. Bronson, G. W., "Identity diffusion in late adolescents," *J. abnorm. soc. Psychol*, 1959, *59*, 414–417.

The adolescent search for identity has both aggressive and sexual aspects. The male, in particular, is required in our culture to take the initiative in choosing his life work, whether it be that of a farmer, an artisan, a business man or a professional man. The demand for such a choice is one of the major sources of anxiety among late adolescents and young adults. This is in part because there are actually many choices open to the adolescent or young adult, and the nature of his choice may determine his future way of life more than any other factor. Certain family attitudes tend to increase an adolescent's anxiety over his choice of work, such as parental expectations, family tradition, the demand that a son enter his father's business, or simply the parental hope for upward mobility of their children.

The male adolescent or young adult in our culture must also make his own choice of a marital partner. This will usually be the outcome of pre-edipal, edipal and latency identification and object love, as well as of experiences during latency and adolescence. Accidental factors, such as proximity and availability, also enter into the final choice. The success or failure of his choice will depend in part upon the extent to which the chosen woman fulfills the man's conception of the kind of wife a person of his identity should have.

A woman's choice of her marital partner in our culture is more important in determining her status and her identity than her choice of a vocation. This is because whatever vocation she chooses is likely to be set aside by her functions as wife and mother. Vocational choice, therefore, is usually a temporary expedient.

The woman in our culture seeks to establish her identity within the role of homemaker, wife and mother, and builds her adult self-esteem upon the quality of her performance in these roles. Like the male, she will make her choice of a marital partner on the basis of her pre-edipal, edipal and latency experiences, as well as in relation to the outcome of her latency period and her adolescence. The identifications and the object love of her early childhood form the groundwork of her adolescent and young adult sex choices. Like the male, she will also be influenced by such accidental factors as availability and proximity. Because of her much greater dependence upon her marital partner to provide her with her adult status, the woman in our culture must seek and find fulfillment of her identity needs in the nature and the outcome of her marriage. She is thus dependent upon her husband, not only for her sexual satisfaction, her children and her home, but also for the kind of life she will lead and, to that extent, for the structure of her adult identity.

Adolescent into adult

In the United States the end of adolescence is not necessarily heralded by socio-economic independence as it used to be. The growing young man, no matter how responsible and capable he may be, can no longer look forward confidently to gainful employment. When he is able to work he may have to be satisfied wtih odd jobs and intermittent idleness. Employment insurance, necessary as it is today, often blunts the edge of early adult determination. It makes steady work less a source of personal stability and self-esteem than it once was. In the more advanced technological and professional areas, the young man can usually find adequate financial support from governmental grants and from colleges, or from his own parental family. This he receives for several years beyond his coming of age. For the less fortunate, marriage must be postponed or, at best, undertaken under conditions which guarantee the support of the young people in their parents' home.

These socio-economic developments make it more and more difficult to pinpoint the transition from adolescence to adulthood on the old bases of an independent job and the capacity for marrying and forming a new family unit. The youthful unemployed now tend to remain in their parental family, in a dependent relationship which has some of the characteristics of adolescence and some of the strivings toward independent adulthood. The youthful technological or professional trainee has a greater opportunity to detach himself from dependence upon a parent; and he is usually compelled to move out of his parental home because his training takes place in an industrial or educational setting elsewhere. Because of the economic support he receives, and the promise of an independent future, he is likely to go ahead and marry, to begin procreative activities with his wife, and to assume the obligations and reap the rewards of parenthood while he is still financially dependent. To take such steps, which used to be accompanied by the socio-economic independence of adulthood, indicates a degree of enterprise, faith and courage, both in the husband and in the wife, that deserves to be called mature.

Adulthood

The changes and uncertainties in the modern socio-economic situation, and the prolongation of the period of tutelage and dependence into the middle or late twenties, throw us back upon psychological criteria in determining the change from adolescence to adulthood. No one who has worked with grownup persons preparing themselves for a career, while also raising a family, can doubt that they are for the most part responsible adults. In many ways they seem more mature personally than did their forebears, who postponed marriage and family formation until after they had completed their postgraduate or on-the-job training.

What are the psychological criteria of adulthood? They are the disappearance of the turmoil, uncertainty and conflict of adolescence, the appearance of emotional control and general predictability, the establishment of self-confidence and self-respect, a willingness to accept adult responsibilities even within the framework of economic dependence, and a self-assertive independence of thinking and judgment. These are the marks of emotional maturity, of the channelling of sexual and aggressive drives, of adult ego integration, of the stabilization of superego functioning — in providing both self-criticism and self-esteem — and of a realistic construction of a person's external and internal worlds. A brief discussion of maturity and the normal adult personality will prepare us to consider in more detail the organization of experience and behavior and its disturbances.

Maturity is always relative. It is justifiable to speak of an infant, a child or an adolescent as mature for his age. It is also justifiable to look upon maturity as something that comes only with middle age or old age, if indeed it comes at all. Many adults, as we shall see, marry and have children without ever becoming themselves psychologically mature. On the other hand, some who choose a life of celibacy, in the pursuit of some ideal, show a degree of mature responsibility and predictability greater than that of many of their married adult peers.[44] Many adults who seem wild and irresponsible in their twenties or thirties, and even in their forties, develop personal and social responsibility in middle or late life. Some of these become models of maturity, and a few become saints. Many of the criteria proposed by experts for *normal personality* are not to be found among the millions whose socio-economic status and family background do not provide them with realistic material security.

In what follows we shall use the term *maturity* to designate a post-adolescent equilibrium which allows a person to pursue the life he chooses or is given, without undue stress and strain, and which enables him to cope with his inevitable frustrations and conflicts with a minimum of infantile behavior and experience. The post-adolescent equilibrium of which we speak is mainly *internal*, as we shall see in the chapters following this one; but it demands a vast amount of *external experience* for its development and for its maintenance. The equilibrium changes in character as a person grows older, as his physiological and social equilibrium changes. It can be seriously impaired and even destroyed by adult catastrophe; and the less firm its infantile, childhood and adolescent foundations are, the more vulnerable it will be to adult impairment or destruction.

Adult normality, like maturity, is always relative. The normal adult of twenty-five would be abnormal at fifty if he remained the same. On the other hand, he would be abnormal at twenty-five if he thought and acted like a man of fifty. Normality follows a different pattern in the two sexes.[45] As we said earlier, men are expected to show initiative, enterprise and aggression, even to the point of belligerence if necessary, in the world of adult men outside the home. Women normally look to their husbands for such qualities. They themselves are expected to show a different kind of initiative and enterprise in domestic affairs, in the rearing of children, in managing their immediate neighborhood and in providing the family with comfort and entertainment. The passive dependence often incorrectly ascribed to women

44 Cf., for example, the thought-provoking account in the chapter on the *mature personality* in Allport, G., *Pattern and Growth in Personality*. New York: Holt, Rinehart & Winston, 1961, pp. 275–307.

45 Bennett, E. M., and Cohen, L. R., "Men and women: personality patterns and contrasts," *Genet. Psychol. Monogr.*, 1959, *59*, 101–155.

is actually the prerogative of their infants. Sexual competence, and a reasonable degree of control of aggression in the home, are expected of both adult men and adult women.

When it comes to the achievement of adult equilibrium, we are faced with innumerable normal patterns. Their components will be discussed in some detail as we pass on to the psychodynamics of human behavior and experience. Here it is enough to say that adult normality requires a person to achieve and to maintain a reasonably effective psychodynamic balance within, and reasonably effective interpersonal relationship without. For this, he must be able to control and channel his emotional drives, without losing his initiative and his zest, without having to employ excessive inhibitions, and without suffering character distortions. He must have an adequate defensive organization, which protects him from excess anxiety and does not expose him to the intrusion of infantile primary process material,[46] and from unnecessary superego interference. He must have developed adequate ego adaptations, so as to be able to cope successfully with the unavoidable external and somatic stresses of life, to be able to enter into normal social interactions, and to experience the enjoyment of life in its many aspects. He must have developed a superego organization capable of providing normal self-esteem, of supporting him in adversity, and of scanning what he does or wants to do. His superego should be able to represent ethical and moral standards in the absence of other persons, or even in opposition to their opinions, and provide a kind of balance wheel that is neither too permissive nor too punitive.

The interactions of the different components of personality should be smooth most of the time. They should be capable of shifting cathexes (*energy commitments*) when circumstances demand a redistribution of internal energies, rather than a change in external conditions.[47] The normal adult must be able to weather ordinary personal storms, and the inevitable frustrations and disappointments of human life, without more than temporary disequilibrium. He must be capable of throwing himself wholeheartedly into adult work and adult play with the cooperation and competition of his adult peers. He must be able to give and to experience adequate heterosexual gratifications in a stable relationship. He must be capable of expressing a reasonable degree of aggression, anger, joy and affection, under socially appropriate conditions, and with neither undue effort nor unnecessary guilt.

In actual life we do not meet paragons of perfection. There are always regrettable flaws and lapses. In fact, adult life cannot be considered normal unless it shows some defects, at some level, in some area. Those who treat the neurotically or psychotically sick, or deal with character distortions, know that even grave imperfections can be compensated for, or masked, by defensive and adaptive structures. We can go even further than this and say that, just as absolute perfection of physique and physiology are rare rather

[46] A distinction between primary process or prelogical thinking, and secondary process or logical thinking, will be made in Chapter 5, "The psychodynamic system."
[47] We shall discuss such shifts in Chapter 5, "The psychodynamic system."

than normal, so perfection of adult equilibrium in behavior and experience is rare rather than normal. We expect to find minor imperfections in normal body function and in normal mental function. We often find reasonably normal body or mental function in persons who suffer from a serious defect which they have learned to master; and we find poor body or mental function in persons with a mild defect who have not learned to master it.

Let us now turn to a systematic account of the roots of human experience and behavior, as seen from a number of different aspects. After we have finished that, we shall be prepared to understand the neuroses, the psychoses, and the other disturbances of psychological functioning, which taken together are the sources of by far the greatest amount of preventable human unhappiness and suffering.

4

Need, Drive and Motivation

NEED, DRIVE AND MOTIVATION ARE AT THE HEART OF CONTEMPORARY BE-
havior pathology. All the rest is built around them. To be born is to be
separated from the automatic biological machinery of need-satisfaction which
supports life within the uterus. The newborn is now dependent for the
satisfaction of his needs upon his own efforts, as in suckling and breathing,
and upon the love and good will of a separate person, who can fulfill or deny
his wants. In all phases of personality development this dual dependence
persists, upon one's own efforts and upon the love and good will of a separate
person. Each one of us must learn to cope effectively with our own growing
needs and with the delays, frustrations and denials we meet as we pass from
the asocial behavior of the biological baby, through the complexities of
domestic, neighborhood and school life, into adolescence and into adulthood.
In the two preceding chapters we have sketched some of the difficulties involved in growing up.[1]

---

[1] There is a vast literature on *need, drive* and *motivation*. The interested reader may
begin with some of the more recent reviews in Brown, J. S., *The Motivation of Behavior.*
New York: McGraw-Hill, 1961; Hall, J. F., *Psychology of Motivation.* Philadelphia:
Lippincott, 1961; Young, P. T., *Motivation and Emotion: A Survey of the Determinants
of Human and Animal Activity.* New York: Wiley, 1961; Olds, J., *The Growth and
Structure of Motives.* Glencoe, Ill.: Free Press, 1956. Also see the *Annual Review of
Psychology* which includes a review of current literature on motivation each year.
There is an ambitious attempt to bring together psychological, neurological and physiological factors, in relation to emotion and personality, which contains much on *motivation*, in Arnold, M. B., *Emotion and Personality.* New York: Columbia Univ. Press, 1960,
2 vols.

Difficulties in adapting to and mastering the conditions of human group living, and in tolerating delay, frustration and denial, do not disappear when a person reaches adulthood, no matter how mature he may become. In fact they never disappear. Throughout the successive phases of our life span new and different demands continually arise. These require us to develop new and different orientations, new and different techniques with which to meet them, defend against them or avoid them. Finally, after we pass life's zenith, there lies ahead of us the downward path, with its demands for further adaptation, with its special disappointments, denials and rewards.

We differ from one another in the patterns of adaptation, defense and mastery which we habitually employ in our daily life. We differ also in the intensity and the variety of our internally generated demands. We differ in the relative effectiveness with which we are able to handle our personal crises as these confront us. Each of us has his special areas of weakness and his special areas of strength; and each has limits to the frustration he can tolerate without experiencing excessive anxiety. All of us, however, have certain fundamental needs in common; and each common need demands its special kind of satisfaction.

Need and satisfaction

At birth our organization is such that we at once generate some needs which only the environment can satisfy. It is infant need that structures infantile dependence. The satisfaction of infant need requires the continual loving, dependable help of an older person, usually the child's mother. It is through this help, with its emotional components and its close physical contact, that the biological baby begins his development toward becoming an interactive human being. An infant's first requirements are those which enable him to maintain biological equilibrium (*homeostasis*) and to recover it whenever it is disturbed. If he does not establish and maintain homeostasis he cannot stay alive. In addition to this minimal requirement, the infant also needs the protection and the richly varied experiences of someone with a healthy devotion to his care and an ability to give for a long time without receiving affection in return.

Many of the needs of infants and children persist with little change throughout life. Many undergo fundamental changes, as complete dependence gives way to interdependence, and as the growing organism develops new capabilities, and experiences new modes of satisfaction. Further new needs and new satisfactions proliferate as life goes on.[2] Most of them are elaborated along conventional lines through social interaction, social sanction and personal interdependence. Many of them appear to lose their original connection with biological urges and to continue in their own right, as autonomous needs. In a crisis, however, links between apparently autonomous needs and primitive drives are often re-established in the process of what we call *regression*.

[2] Maslow, A. H., *Motivation and Personality*. New York: Harper, 1954.

Infantile and childhood needs which persist throughout life: Normal persistence. Among the early needs which persist more or less unchanged throughout life are such obvious ones as the need for food, fluid, warmth or coolness, and shelter. The need for protection against being overwhelmed by excitation also persists. It is in part satisfied by ego defenses and defensive armoring, by learning to shut out certain demands or to ignore them, by periodically isolating oneself and by retiring into sleep. There is a need for continual, varied stimulation of receptors and the nervous system, while one is awake, if the human organism is to develop normally and to maintain its normal reactivity and its relationship to external reality. This need has only recently been fully recognized by experiments using *sensory deprivation* or *perceptual isolation.*[3]

The need for repeated, intermittent relief of accumulated tensions has long been recognized. This is met in a vast array of different activities, ranging from organized work and play, through innumerable varieties of vicarious discharge in entertainment, hobbies, daydreaming, fantasying and dreaming. Creative activities and group interactions seem to furnish the most lasting vicarious satisfactions. Sex relations with a loved marital partner provide the most constructive avenue of direct sexual satisfaction as well as the basis for an enduring human tie.

Another group of needs includes some of those just mentioned, but they are important enough in human life to deserve separate consideration. One is the need for varied human companionship, varied enough to give a person opportunities for satisfactions and discharge of tensions which his immediate family does not fully provide. Another is the need to have persons around us whom we can confide in and completely trust. This need derives from the original *basic trust*[4] which arises out of the mother-child symbiosis. There is in most persons another derivative of the symbiotic relationship, but experienced on an adult heterosexual level, the need for a dependable, intimate contact with a loved and loving person, such as sleeping with a marital partner provides. Parenthood brings to most parents a different kind and level of intimacy. For most adults a frequent, more or less periodic need arises for temporary fusion with an adult sex partner, which is sometimes accompanied by a pleasant loss of identity. This, too, seems to represent a persistence of infantile symbiotic needs in healthy, mature adults. There are, of course, innumerable human needs which continue normally the needs of infancy and childhood. The ones given above are only samples.

Pathological persistence. A great deal of behavior pathology is concerned with the pathological persistence of infantile and childhood needs into adulthood. A few common examples will be mentioned here; others will come up as we discuss clinical material later on. There is, first of all, the indefinite continuation of an infantile kind of dependence upon others for food, warmth

[3] Solomon, P., *et al.*, *Sensory Deprivation*. Cambridge, Mass.: Harvard Univ. Press, 1961.

[4] Erikson, E. H., *Childhood and Society*. New York: Norton, 1950.

and shelter, which leads in adulthood to many types of dependent relation-ships, involving other adults, social groups and agencies, and in time even one's own children. Such persistent infantile needs, and most of the others we shall discuss below, can often be satisfied vicariously and indirectly, al-though this does not alter the fact that the persistence is abnormal. For example, an infantile degree and kind of dependence upon being fed may take the form of an addiction; and it may also appear as an insatiable hunger and thirst for knowledge which does not lead to a socially useful product.

The need that every infant and child normally has to be led, guided and controlled by a loving parent may persist in its original form, especially if one's parents are unusually possessive. Thus, we often see adults who remain in the parental home, usually unmarried, and sometimes quite contented with their dependence. A persistent need for parental love may be strong enough to cause failure if the dependent person does marry. It is sometimes a factor in creating the Don Juans and the seductive, dissatisfied women who never succeed in finding among their contemporaries the kind of love they want. It is likewise a factor in producing chronically infantile adults who seek, and occasionally find, a repetition in their marriage of the dependent relationship which they never resolved in childhood.

The pathological persistence of infantile and childhood need is also seen in sex deviations, many of which represent fixation in some early form of sexual satisfaction.[5] Of particular importance among these is the per-sistence of strong latent or overt homosexual trends. We have seen that there is a certain amount of normal homosexual love in the young child's affection for his like-sexed parent or sibling. This affection is usually tamed and sublimated at the same time that edipal love for the opposite-sexed parent or sibling is. It normally survives after that as continued, maturing affection for persons of one's own sex, and as reinforcement of normal self-love and self-esteem. In its tamed and sublimated form, under the control of the maturing superego, this affection plays a highly important role in the formation of close friendships during latency, preadolescence, and early adolescence, while the child has not yet reached the point where he is ready for heterosexual love, and while he is still engaged in developing his own sex identity through identification with his peers.

If the child or adolescent is fixated in a homosexual orientation, or is made intolerably anxious by conflicts over heterosexual drives, a full heterosexual orientation may not develop during adolescence and early adulthood. The commonest outcome is a latent homosexual orientation, of which an adult may not be aware. Sometimes it appears masked by exag-gerated virility in men and exaggerated femininity in women. Sometimes it is responsible for a succession of heterosexual affairs, in which there is an unconscious attraction toward a like-sexed lover or toward the like-sexed spouse of a supposed lover. This somewhat resembles the sharing of a boy

[5] Some of these will be discussed in the chapter on personality disorders.

friend which seems to occur normally among adolescent girl chums.[6] Sometimes a strong, latent, unconscious homosexual orientation leads a person to ally himself in a socially acceptable, sublimated devotion to groups or causes which involve association with like-sexed adults. This is closely related to normal sublimated affection and devotion.

Sometimes a latent homosexual orientation has less fortunate consequences. One of these is a confused identification, such as we see sometimes in schizophrenic or borderline patients. Another is cross-identification which, although it does not necessarily appear as overt homosexuality, does appear as an interference with the mature development of a person's sex role, and a tendency to identify with the interests and destinies of members of the opposite sex. The occasional pathological outcome in adulthood is overt homosexuality, which we shall discuss more fully in the chapter on personality disorders.

A widely distributed persistence of infantile need appears in the many forms of *impulsive aggressive discharge*. We call the need infantile because it is not successfully integrated into some pattern of socially acceptable aggression. It is found most commonly among individuals and groups who have not acquired competence in controlling their own hostility, or who are suffering from greater frustration of their needs than they can endure. Its simplest form is the individualistic temper tantrum in which the outburst of rage may take the form of shouting, stamping, threatening or minor assault on things and people. An extreme but helpful illustration appears in the following case.

A sixty-two-year old lawyer, unmarried, was hospitalized because he was depressed and malnourished. Whenever he could not have his own way on the psychiatric service he would throw himself to the floor with a yell, shout and curse, move around on all fours and bang his head against the wall. Relatives reported that he had controlled a numerous household of dependents — he was the only professionally trained person in the family — by having such temper tantrums whenever he was crossed by them. He had exhibited this behavior as far back as any of them could remember. He learned to control himself with surprising good nature in the hospital, as of course he had had to do in his professional work. It was doubtful that he would change permanently at home, where this technique worked well and where his dependents accepted it.

Less dramatic, and usually less infantile, examples of this kind of reaction to frustration, delay or denial, can be found in most ordinary families and many ordinary neighborhoods, in stores and in traffic competition and traffic mishaps. It is true that, in general, most adults have learned that a reasonable degree of control and socially acceptable channeling of their own ag-

[6] See the discussion in Mohr. G. J., and Despres, M. A., *The Stormy Decade: Adolescence.* New York: Random House, 1958.

gressions make them less costly, less disruptive, and more likely to succeed in gaining eventual satisfaction. Nevertheless, infantile discharge of aggression is by no means uncommon at all levels of society, even among adults in positions of responsibility and leadership. A great many impulsive assaults by adolescents and adults are infantile in character and origin, no matter how mature the person may otherwise be. There is a notable sex difference in the predominant antisocial acting-out of adolescents and adults. Male delinquents commit a very much higher proportion of hostile aggressive assaults; female delinquents are much more likely to "act out" in impulsive sexuality.

Passing mention should be made here of a more or less indirect, but common, mode of expressing infantile rage among inhibited adults. This takes the form of a sullen, aloof withdrawal, in response to the feeling of having been frustrated, rejected or not given the preference which the person thinks he should have. Whether or not the judgment of having been frustrated, rejected or slighted is justified, the technique used in handling the situation is definitely infantile.

Two opposed infantile needs that persist pathologically in adults deserve brief special consideration. The first is an inability to remain alone without developing anxiety. The other is an insistence upon solitude.

Anxiety developing when one is left alone has well-known infantile antecedents. Most infants pass through a phase during which they become anxious whenever they are left alone, especially when their mother is absent. Such *separation anxiety* may persist in adulthood as an intolerable anxiety or an intolerable boredom when alone. It may be expressed in restlessness which can only be appeased by seeking out the company of other persons, by having parties or going to the theater — not in search of pleasure, but in flight from anxiety.[7] It persists in adulthood also in the form of never being able to take the love and acceptance of others for granted, of not finding general affection and intermittent intimacy sufficiently reassuring. The basic defect may be a failure in resolving the symbiotic mother-child unity of early infancy, or the failure to master the loneliness that follows rejection in the edipal phase, and again in adolescence. The defect may also be a partial failure in superego development, which leaves one exposed to temptation in fantasy or in action, and requires the company of other adults as protection against carrying the forbidden impulses out.

An insistence upon solitude is sometimes only a persistence of the insistence upon being left alone, upon being independent, which the pre-edipal child expresses in the *self-assertion phase* of development. It may also be the persistence of a withdrawn phase which many preadolescents and young adolescents pass through, especially those who dread and resent their approaching adult role. It goes almost without saying that any of these per-

[7] Kessen, W., and Mandler, G., "Anxiety, pain and the inhibition of distress," *Psychol. Rev.*, 1961, 68, 396–404.

sistent infantile modes may be found complicating a neurotic or psychotic reaction, or entering into a more generalized personality disorder.[8]

Regression to infantile and childhood needs under stress. Infantile and childhood organizations of need and satisfaction, like the infantile reality constructions we discussed in Chapter 2, are not lost when they are given up. They may not even become permanently inactive or inert. We have evidence of this in adult manifest dreams, some of which require scarcely any interpretation to reveal their infantile nucleus. Further evidence of adult regression to infantile need comes from the behavior and experience of persons who become intoxicated, go under a general anesthetic, suffer from delirium, develop a "catastrophic reaction" because of brain damage, or become psychotic under a stress they cannot tolerate. Infantile needs also reappear in sensory deprivation and in therapeutic regression.[9]

It is generally believed that, if internal or external stress becomes sufficiently intense, almost *anyone* will regress and exhibit infantile needs. Adults who have been left especially vulnerable, because of innate hypersensitivities (such as we discussed in Chapter 2) or because of failure to resolve major infantile and childhood crises, are likely to regress under relatively minor stress. This is particularly the case when the minor stress is one to which they are selectively susceptible — for example, the temporary absence or the illness of a loved person, in adults with unresolved *separation anxiety*. We shall see abundant evidence of regression in the clinical chapters.

The concept of regression is often misunderstood. It does not mean a return to infancy or childhood, or even a general reversion to behavior that is normal for an infant or a child. Adults are organized in ways that infants and children are not. When they regress, they reactivate infantile conflicts, wishes and fears, but most of their adult defensive and coping organization remains. The regressed adult does not act, speak or look like a child. The most obvious example is the neurotic adult who, although partially regressed, carries on as usual in his daily life, in spite of his reactivated infantile needs.[10] He may not even realize that he has infantile needs. Psychotic persons suffer more sweeping and deeper regressions than do neurotic. Yet in psychoses there are countless residues of the thinking and behavior that belong to the now disintegrated adult organization. Indeed, much of the confusion in

[8] Sensory deprivation has also been cited as a motivational variable. See Jones, A., Wilkinson, H. J., and Braden, I., "Information deprivation as a motivational variable," *J. Exp. Psychol.*, 1961, *62*, 126–137; Jones, A., "Supplementary report: information deprivation and irrelevant drive as determiners of an instrumental response," *J. Exp. Psychol.*, 1961, *62*, 310–311.

[9] Azima, H., Vispo, P., and Azima, F. J., "Observations on anaclitic therapy during sensory deprivation," in Solomon, P. (Ed.), *Sensory Deprivation.* Cambridge, Mass.: Harvard Univ. Press, 1961, pp. 143–160.

[10] See, for example, the obsessive compulsive case of Sally J., listed in the subject index under *Cases*.

neurotic and psychotic experience results from the mingling of simultaneously present adult and infantile components in consciousness.

A good example of regressive need is seen in persons who become unreasonably anxious or depressed when they are *promoted*. The situation seems quite unintelligible until one discovers what is involved. A man wants a promotion, works hard for it, and celebrates his achievement when it comes. Before long, however, he finds himself under enormous strain which his new duties cannot explain. He is unable to relax, he is unhappy, lonely and frightened. He can no longer eat and sleep as he did before his promotion.

If such a person gets competent therapy he may find out for himself that he has unresolved infantile needs to be dependent, to do well for the sake of an immediate superior, to be accepted as one of the crowd by his equals. In his new post he misses all of these satisfactions; and the position of leadership makes him terribly anxious instead of confident and proud. What has happened is that a stress, to which he is especially vulnerable, has reactivated all these needs with all the strength and irrationality of early childhood. The potential seriousness of such regression appears when a vulnerable person develops a psychotic depression, and may even attempt suicide, following a much-desired promotion.

Language and thought in human need and satisfaction. Need and satisfaction are enormously enriched and complicated in human beings by the development of speaking and thinking. We have said earlier that there is no way of finding out when thinking begins in the young child or exactly what it is like. It is often assumed that the dawn of thinking is linked to the dawn of speech, that is, toward the end of the first year or the beginning of the second. There are many observations that contradict such an assumption, and none that support it.

Manifest dreams, which express infantile need so clearly, seldom make use of words; and when they do, this is usually evidence that the dreaming person is beginning to wake up. Dreaming nearly always takes the form of visual, plastic imagery. It has many archaic characteristics that are absent from spoken language. Manifest dreams, even the most expressive ones, are notoriously difficult to put into words; and when this is done, it always involves a secondary revision or distortion of the manifest dream.[11] The verbal description of a dream seems cold and impoverished, like the verbal description of a painting.

Like manifest dreams, daytime fantasies and daydreams, and the expressive productions of true artists in any field, can rarely be formulated adequately in words. Even in artistic prose, the effectiveness of what is said depends more upon the imagery evoked than upon what is actually verbalized. Genuine poetry often uses words in ways that make little sense as plain communica-

[11] Bartlett, F., *Thinking: An Experimental and Social Study.* New York: Basic Books, 1958.

tion; it also depends upon evoking imagery and feelings in the reader which cannot otherwise be expressed.

There is every indication, short of objective proof, that infants begin to think in some form before they begin to speak.[12] Their painstaking, sustained examination of objects — orally, visually and manually — during the first year strongly suggests some kind of inner representation in imagery and symbols.[13] Very early attempts to repeat interesting perceptions, through manipulating the environment and changing body position, have been well documented by Piaget.[14] Both of these performances described by Piaget suggest an inner structured need, formulated in terms of imagery and fantasy. Neither makes sense in terms of transient stimulus-response relations.

Definitions. Before going on with a discussion of need, drive and motivation, we shall give definitions of need, of frustration and of frustration tolerance.

(*a*) *Need.* By *need* we mean *a state of unstable or disturbed equilibrium, appearing typically in the organism as increased tension, in relation to some more or less specific source of potential satisfaction.* It is clear from this definition that, even though environmental conditions may contribute to the appearance of many needs, the need itself is an expression of a dynamic imbalance within the organism itself. It is, therefore, a function of the human being's internal organization.

(*b*) *Satisfaction.* By *satisfaction* we mean *the restoration of equilibrium in an organism which has lost it.* This does not necessarily mean a return to the same stable state that preceded appearance of the need. A different stable state may bring satisfaction to the organism. Satisfaction, like need, is determined by the structure of the human organism, including whatever modifications have developed as the result of experience. We speak of the linkage between a need and its satisfaction as a *need-satisfaction sequence.*[15] The variety of need-satisfaction sequences in human life is so great that, as we shall see in a moment, students of human behavior and experience have been driven to "reductionism," that is, to attempts to reduce them to a few basic ones, so that they may become manageable.

(*c*) *Frustration tolerance.* By *frustration tolerance* we mean *the degree of delay, thwarting or denial that a person can endure without personality disintegration and regression.* As might be expected, different persons show

[12] This is essentially the position implied in Freud's basic hypothesis of the hallucinated breast in early infancy, and of the logician, Susanne, K. Langer. Cf. *Philosophy in a New Key.* Cambridge, Mass.: Harvard Univ. Press, 1942.

[13] See Chapter 2 for a discussion of these exploratory activities which are carried on at first in each domain separately, and only later fuse. See also Gonzales, R., and Ross, S., "The basis of solution by preverbal children of the intermediate-size problem," *Amer. J. Psychol.,* 1958, 71, 742–746.

[14] Piaget, J., *Origins of Intelligence in Children.* New York: Internat. Univ. Press, 1952; Piaget, J., *Construction of Reality in Children.* New York: Basic Books, 1954.

[15] Cameron, N., and Magaret, A., *Behavior Pathology.* Boston: Houghton Mifflin, 1951, Chapter 2, "Need, stress and frustration," pp. 21–52.

differences in frustration toleration in different areas of experience. The same person shows variation in his frustration tolerance, not only in different kinds of experience, but also under different external conditions, including differences in social organization and different physiological conditions.[16] Such factors as fatigue, hunger, thirst, loneliness and hopelessness are likely to reduce frustration tolerance. Good health, high morale, good company and self-confidence increase one's tolerance for frustration.

Frustration is everyone's lot and it is an essential condition for normal development. It is fully as necessary for a child to learn to endure delay, thwarting, opposition and denial as it is for him to experience full and appropriate gratifications. There is no need to introduce a child prematurely to frustration, or to expose him to more than he can handle. One of the major functions of parenthood is that of protecting a child from exposure to more frustration than he can handle, and of introducing him to the experience of trying something new before he is quite capable of managing it alone, but ready to learn how to do it with adult help.[17]

The child who does not learn, with sympathetic help, to tolerate the inevitable frustrations that he will meet, cannot grow up to be a healthy member of adult society. This is only a restatement of the *reality principle*. A person must learn to organize his behavior, his experiences and his expectations more or less in accordance with the *realities of the physical and social world*, including the realities of his own body and its potentialities. Experiences of mastery, with sympathetic adult help, are among the best of early preparations for independent mastery.

Need, need-disposition and drive

For several decades, the concept of *drive* has rivaled those of *need* and *need-disposition* in the study of normal behavior and experience and in the study of psychopathology.[18] The concept of *drive* expresses primarily a *dynamic, organismic push from within*, a force generated in the organism. The concept of *need*, and particularly of *need-disposition*, expresses a *relationship* between organismic imbalance and some external source of satisfaction.

Need and need-disposition fit into a stimulus-response way of thinking, one in which the organism is conceived as always reacting to something outside it, which determines its need. This way of thinking is in line with a conception of the human organism as a complex system of more or less reflex reactions with its environment, a conception that has proved most fruitful in experimental psychology and in the laboratory study of learning. The

---

[16] Triandis, L. M., and Lambert, W. W., "Sources of frustration and targets of aggression: a cross-cultural study," *J. abnorm. soc. Psychol.*, 1961, *62*, 640–648.

[17] Lawson, R., and Marx, M. H., "Frustration: theory and experiment," *Genet. Psychol. Monogr.*, 1958, *57*, 393–464.

[18] Hinde, R. A., "Unitary drives," *Animal Behavior*, 1959, *7*, 130–141; Hinde, R. A., "Concepts of drive," in Brazier, M. (Ed.), *The Central Nervous System and Behavior*. New York: Josiah Macy, Jr., Foundation, 1960.

introduction of Gestalt psychology, in its many forms, all of which emphasize perception and cognition, has greatly modified the originally mechanical conceptions of conditioned and unconditioned responses. So also has the development of the concept of operant conditioning, with its "emission" of behavior.

Reductionism. One general movement, mentioned above, has been evident for decades among those dealing with normal behavior, including the study of animal behavior. This has been the attempt, one way or another, to reduce the number of basic needs or need-dispositions to a few, ranging usually from half-a-dozen to a score. Such attempts always raise the cry of *reductionism,* and the claim that any attempt to reduce human behavior and experience to a few root needs or need-dispositions gives an impoverished, distorted conception of human life.

There is some truth in this objection. Human behavior and experience are infinitely rich, while the needs and need-dispositions proposed to represent them are simple and bare. Nevertheless, some kind of reductionism is inescapable. Without it, one must be content with a conception of human life that leaves every moment incomparable with every other one.

Reductionism has been established practice in physics and chemistry for ages. No lay person can question the tremendous strides that these fields have made by reducing the immense complexities of their observations to a few abstract entities which can be easily manipulated according to a set of rules. No sophisticated scientist mistakes his abstract units for what they are meant to represent.[19] The manipulation of abstract formulations must be repeatedly compared with further observation of what they represent; and where the abstract entities prove to be inadequate, they have to be modified to correspond closer to external reality.

Reductionism in psychopathology. In the field of psychopathology, the reductionism practiced seems at first glance drastic. The concept of *drive,* often called *instinct,* is now firmly established and well-defined. The term *need* is employed only in its more or less popular sense, as a general want or lack. We speak, for example, of *dependency needs.* The concept of *need-disposition* has not been found useful. Only two basic drives seem to be recognized as underlying psychopathology, the *sexual* and the *aggressive drives.*

Closer examination, however, shows that the reductionism in psychopathology is much more apparent than real. The sexual and aggressive drives are not treated as single forces but as *groups* of emotional drives whose members are by no means all the same. In addition to this source of variation, there is also the concept of *the unconscious,* which has varied historically during the present century and varies in its levels and functions even today. The exploitation of the concept of the unconscious has been one of the most fruit-

19 Lowe, C. M., "The self-concept: fact or artifact?", *Psychol. Bull.,* 1961, *58,* 325–336.

ful, if not the single most fruitful, in contemporary psychopathology. If we add to this the concept of a *preconscious* (described in 1900 in *The Interpretation of Dreams* but relatively little used until recently)[20] the concept of *narcissism*, of *fixation* and *regression*, of *cathexis*, of *primary process* and *secondary process*, of *unconscious defenses*, and, since 1923, the reorganization of mental life in terms of the *id*, the *ego* and the *superego*, we have a complex, variegated system of theoretical constructs, without even including the many modifications after 1923, or such fundamental ideas as *anxiety, conflict, sublimation* and the like. In the rest of the present chapter we shall confine our discussion to the drives and to the general topic of motivation.

Sexual and aggressive drives

The concept of *emotional drive*, which most psychoanalysts prefer to call *instinct* or *instinctual drive*, clearly dominates contemporary psychopathology. Freud conceived of the drive, or instinct, as representing an endosomatic, continuously flowing force from within, which either appeared at the threshold between the physiological and the psychological, or sent its derivatives into unconscious, preconscious and conscious systems. Freud changed his formulation of the drive, or instinct, from time to time; and he frequently expressed his dissatisfaction with his formulations.[21] In spite of this dissatisfaction, however, the *Trieb* remained a fundamental concept throughout all of his writing. It remains today a fundamental concept both in the theory and the practice of psychoanalysis, and it is still central to most contemporary clinical and therapeutic formulations.[22]

Sex drives. In Freud's early formulations, and for several decades thereafter, sexuality with its many ramifications, its conflicts, anxieties, distortions and deprivations, reigned alone in psychodynamic theory and therapy.[23] This emphasis was in part a reaction against the hypocritical Victorian prudishness which prevailed at the turn of the century. At that time even the mention of sex was looked upon as indecent; while at the same time what was condemned was given romantic exaggeration and worshiped in literature, poetry and drama. Freud's emphasis upon sexuality was a courageous, straightforward expression of the important role that it plays in normal life, as well as in psychopathology — something which Freud heard furtively acknowledged by other physicians all around him, but never heard publicly admitted. Sex drives still reign in contemporary accounts of human experience and behavior, but they have been given a coordinate partner within recent years, as we shall see in the next section.

[20] Kris, E., "On preconscious mental processes," in *Psychoanalytic Explorations in Art.* New York: Internat. Univ. Press, 1952.

[21] There are many discussions of this in current psychoanalytic literature. A brief summary of Freud's changing concepts appears in the introduction to the new translation of *Instincts and Their Vicissitudes.* Standard Edition, 1957, vol. 14, pp. 111–116.

[22] Cf. Colby, K. M., *Energy and Structure in Psychoanalysis.* New York: Ronald, 1955.

[23] This omits consideration of the early "ego-instincts" which Freud later discarded.

We have already discussed most of the important sexual complications inherent in normal infancy, childhood and adolescence, when we described personality development. We have also mentioned their significance for behavior pathology, which we shall expand in the clinical chapters. It is obviously no easy task to control, channel and socialize infantile sexuality, without unduly inhibiting or distorting it. The same is true for later childhood, preadolescence and adolescence. Even among adults who have enjoyed a favorable personality development, sexuality still poses many problems. There are always conflicting demands within a person, a certain degree of ambivalence which may create conflict on occasion, and many ambiguities in relation to sexual expression in the structure of society.[24]

The general orientation toward sex has certainly undergone great changes since the Victorian era. Sexuality has become in most circles a decent and acceptable subject for discussion and for study. But the changed orientation has not made sexual problems vanish. All of its power and most of its inherent difficulties remain with us. It is still hard to integrate so powerful a group of drives for personal gratification and personal expression into a social organization which depends for its existence upon adequate sex control. It is as necessary as ever, in the interest of peaceful coexistence and social stability, to restrict direct sexual expression and satisfaction among adults to certain well-defined, institutionalized relationships. The alternative is to invite open conflict among adults with respect to the rights and limitations involved in sexual possession and parenthood.

Aggressive drives. Within recent decades, *aggression* has been added to sexuality as a coordinate basic drive, or "instinct," in psychopathology. Freud, in his later years, went further than this, admittedly on a speculative basis, to establish a *life instinct* and a *death instinct* as opposed groups of fundamental drives.[25] This late development has not received general acceptance, but the position of aggressive drives, on a par with sexuality, is now firmly established.

A certain amount of freely acting aggression is essential to normal life. It is, therefore, as vital to preserve its potentialities during infancy, childhood and adolescence as it is to preserve the potentialities for mature sexuality. The channeling, organizing and socialization of aggression pose some of the same problems that sexuality poses.[26] Let us take as one example, from among hundreds, the necessity for aggression in normal adult initiative, independence, and the mastery of one's environment and of oneself. Too

24 Colley, T., "The nature and origins of psychological sexual identity," *Psychol. Rev.*, 1959, *66*, 165–177.

25 Freud, S., "Beyond the Pleasure Principle," Standard Edition, 1955, vol. 18, pp. 1–64.

26 Kagan, J., "Socialization of aggression and the perception of parents in fantasy," *Child Develpm.*, 1958, *29*, 311–320; McCord, W., McCord, J., and Howard, A., "Familial correlates of aggression in nondelinquent male children," *J. abnorm. soc. Psychol.*, 1961, *62*, 79–93.

great an inhibition of aggressive action and expression during infancy and childhood may well produce an intimidated adult, one who is incapable of taking normal initiative, of being independent, of mastering his environment or of mastering himself.

Aggression is essential to many of the crises of development. When an infant begins to emerge from his symbiotic attachment to his mother he needs aggression, in the form of initiative and self-assertion, if he is to succeed in dissolving his now too close identification with her. This is one source of the temper tantrums and the irrational negativism which many small children develop while they are trying to establish their separateness and individuality. What looks like senseless, stubborn opposition or ill humor to an adult seems to the inexperienced small child a natural expression of his identity. A certain amount of aggression is necessary throughout childhood and adolescence, both to assert oneself and take initiative within the home, and to master the environment, establish and re-establish one's identity, and engage in cooperative and competitive activities with one's peers.

In a favorable environment the growing boy or girl learns the uses, the penalties and rewards of aggression, and the limits set by peers and older persons within which aggression may be exercised. Normal aggression is needed by anyone who expects to be self-supporting, and by anyone who expects to be respected. Ordinarily, a greater degree of aggression and self-assertion is required in the male than in the female role. Aggression and initiative are masculine prerogatives in sex relations; relative passivity and receptivity are feminine prerogatives. The man finds his major daily outlets for aggression in his work, the woman in running the home and presiding over her children's welfare and activity.[27]

Like sexuality, aggression poses many problems for the individual and for society. Learning its uses and control is one of the major tasks of childhood and adolescence. At the present time, while most of the world is preoccupied with war and the threat of war, and in a period which has witnessed some of the most barbaric, murderous aggression in history, the control and constructive use of aggressive drives have become more difficult than ever to achieve. All of us who live in the atomic age realize that hostile aggression and destruction are potentially unlimited in scope and completeness. It is necessary to train many millions of adults in the techniques of killing human beings, and to educate the rest to live in the presence of a real danger that any day they may die a violent death.

At the same time, and in the same lands, it is also necessary to rear children and adolescents so that as civilians they will control their aggressive drives, conform to social expectations, and live at peace with their kin and their neighbors. Even a peaceful life at home, at work, or in the neighbor-

---

[27] Buss, A. H., *The Psychology of Aggression.* New York: Wiley, 1961; McNeil, E. R., "Psychology and aggression," *J. Conflict Resolution,* 1959, *3,* 195–293; Moore, T., and Ucko, L. E., "Four to six: constructiveness and conflict in meeting doll play problems," *J. Child Psychol. Psychiat.,* 1961, *2,* 21–47.

hood, does not mean a life of absolute nonaggression. The problem of establishing and maintaining one's identity in several different roles — at work, at play and at rest; as a subordinate or coordinate member of this or that group, or as a leader; in cooperative and competitive relationships as well as in isolation — presents itself over and over, as a person moves through life. Over and over the necessity for self-assertion and enterprise, for protecting others, for guarding against the encroachment of others, for starting up new projects and bringing others to completion — all these call for aggressive action within the framework of what one's society encourages and permits.[28]

The normal fusion of sexual and aggressive drives. It is a truism that, in actual human experience, sexual and aggressive drives (or "instincts") rarely, if ever, occur separately. We have already mentioned the essentially aggressive character of the normal masculine role in courtship and in sexual relations, and the pleasurable expectation of aggression on the part of the female. As a matter of fact, aggression is best controlled and tamed by fusing it with love; and love itself is made manifest through acts of initiative and aggression, or through acceptance of such acts.

Early in life there are already present all kinds of aggressive impulses in combination with recognizable precursors of adult sexuality. Near the beginning of the century, Freud pointed out the coupling of hunger and sexuality in the infant.[29] He was apparently the first among moderns to have the courage to call general attention to this relationship, although not, as he himself says, the first to recognize it. Thirty years later, an experimental psychologist reported the occurrence of erections in male sucklings during nursing, thus giving objective support to Freud's contention.[30] (It is presumed that something homologous occurs in female infants.) The vigorous attack of nurslings in the feeding situation, the periodicity of the feeding act, and its termination in blissful satiety, have likewise been compared with sequences in normal adult sexuality.

Aggression is normal in the pre-edipal child who is engaged in the process of establishing his identity and independence, as we have already said. It is also normally present during the edipal phase, where it assumes more personal and more destructive forms. The edipal child is torn between the love and emotional support that he needs from his parents, and the demands he makes that he be treated as an independent person capable of sexual love. It is generally believed that edipal children harbor hateful, death-dealing wishes and fantasies in relation to their like-sexed parental rival, and that these wishes and fantasies generate equally exaggerated fears of being

[28] Lansky, L. M., Cranfall, V. J., Kagan, J., and Baker, C. T., "Sex differences in aggression and its correlates in middle-class adolescents," *Child Develpm.*, 1961, *32*, 45–58.

[29] Freud, S., "Three essays on the theory of sexuality," (1900), Standard Edition, 1953, vol. 4, pp. 257–266.

[30] Halverson, H., "Genital and sphincter behavior of the male infant," *J. genet. Psychol.*, 1940, *56*, 95–136.

harmed or destroyed by the like-sexed parent in retaliation. Here once again we meet sexual and aggressive drives fused in a single situation.

Some of these edipal longings and fears may reappear during adolescence, although not as a rule at fully conscious levels. To grow from adolescence into a fully mature adult is to have successfully resolved the conflicts involved in sexuality and aggression, so that one can enter into affectionate relationships, as well as into competitive ones, without endangering others or oneself. This means that the adult becomes fully socialized, or civilized, without losing the capacity for enjoying sexuality and aggression.

The emotionally mature man or woman will be able to enter into adult sexual relationships without feeling impulses to injure or be injured, and without impulses to devour and destroy or fears of being devoured, of being swallowed up and losing personal identity. He or she will be able to enjoy aggression, as well as sexuality, without having impulses to destroy or irrational fears of being damaged or killed. There will be no irrational guilt feelings growing out of irrational unconscious superego pressures.

Impulses and fears such as these, always irrational and usually infantile in origin, we shall find as components of many neurotic and psychotic symptoms. In these symptoms we shall find also evidence of defensive maneuvers, which guard against the emergence of archaic fears and impulses, and signs of intense anxiety when the emergence of archaic material seems imminent.

Normal parenthood brings to the adult the maturing experience of an intimate, emotional relationship with a helpless, dependent infant. In it, he or she will identify with infant and growing child, and in this way re-experience infancy and childhood all over again.[31] It is true that infantile impulses and conflicts may be reactivated in a parent by identification with an infant. If such impulses and conflicts can be worked through successfully once again, the identifying adult may achieve still greater stability. If, however, the adult is unsuccessful in working them through, his instability may be increased, and he will be likely to increase corresponding difficulties for the child.

The concepts of instinct and drive in contemporary psychodynamics

We have mentioned earlier that most psychoanalysts prefer to use the term *instinct* rather than *drive*. Freud himself seems to have preferred the term *Trieb*, even though the term *Instinkt* was available to him and he sometimes used it. The word *Trieb* may be translated either as *drive* or as *instinct*. The difference seems not to have been of any importance in German, whereas in English it is of great importance. *Drive* has a dynamic connotation, while *instinct* is static and inflexible.[32] The choice of *instinct* as a translation of

[31] Benedek, T., "Parenthood as a developmental phase," *J. Amer. Psychoanal. Ass.*, 1959, 7, 389–417.

[32] Cf. Josselyn, I., *Psychosocial Development of Children*. New York: Family Service Ass., 1948.

Trieb seems to have been more or less accidental. It has certainly been unfortunate for two reasons, one lying in the history of modern psychology and the other in the contemporary rise of ethology.

During the first quarter of the century, psychologists were brought face to face with the fact that *instinct*, which until then had been in wide use, was impeding progress in the behavioral sciences by supplying hundreds of "first causes," which were used to account for almost every form of human activity. This realization became suddenly widespread in the United States when a book on the subject was published listing the hundreds of instincts then in current use.[33]

Publication of this book led psychologists in the United States to abandon entirely the use of *instinct* as an explanation of human experience and behavior. The concept became the property of students of inherited behavior patterns in subhuman organisms, patterns which are little influenced by individual learning. Psychologists accepted this shift from their static concept of instinct because they were primarily interested in the learning and the flexible, varied, individualistic patterns which characterize the human being. So much for the demise of the concept of instinct as an explanation of human experience and behavior.

It is worth considering what the development of psychodynamic thinking might have been in the United States if the early translators had used the dynamic term *drive* instead of the term *instinct* for Freud's *Trieb*. What, for example, might have been the early reception given to one of Freud's most basic and brilliant contributions, *Triebe und Triebschicksale* if it had appeared on the American scene as *Drives and Their Vicissitudes*?[34] Sophisticated psychologists at that time might have found psychodynamic formulations more assimilable if they had not come face-to-face with the apparent primacy of *instinct* just when they were weeding it out of their own thinking. There were, of course, many innovations and great originality in the psychodynamic approach which would have aroused opposition anyway; but the pseudo problem of instinct need never have been posed in the United States had it not been for an accident of translation.

The contemporary rise of ethology, as exemplified in the work of Lorenz and Tinbergen,[35] has given new life and broader scope to the term *instinct*. Their discovery of *imprinting* in many lower forms of life has brought the study of innate patterns of complex behavior once more into the limelight. The claims of the ethologists have also touched off a lively controversy over the whole concept of instictive behavior.[36] Ethology and these controversies seem to have little if any significance for psychopathology; but already speculations about ethological problems in relation to psychopathlogy have begun

---

[33] Bernard, L. L., *Instinct.* New York: Holt, 1924.

[34] The English translation first appeared in 1925.

[35] Lorenz, K., *King Solomon's Ring.* London: Methuen, 1952; Tinbergen, N., *The Study of Instinct.* Oxford, England: Oxford Univ. Press, 1951.

[36] Loewald, H. W., "On the therapeutic action of psychoanalysis," *Internat. J. Psychoanal.*, 1960, *41*, 16–33.

to appear in the literature, apparently because of confusion over the use of *instinct* and *instinctual* in the two fields.

This digression is intended to alert the person interested in psychodynamics to the unnecessary and increasing hazard of continuing to use *instinct* instead of *drive*. In the rest of the book we shall speak of *drive* or *emotional drive*, in the sense of Freud's *Trieb*, and only occasionally couple this with *instinct* to remind the reader that the latter is still the usual rendition of *Trieb* in English-speaking countries.[37]

Why we confine ourselves to sexual and aggressive drives. Hunger and thirst are actually prepotent over sexual and aggressive drives. If hunger or thirst becomes sufficiently intense, it blots out sexual interest entirely. It can even blot out aggression, as when a person finds that he has to be submissive if he is to get food or drink. There are many other human needs that cannot be long denied. The need for sleep becomes irresistible in everyone sooner or later. Even the need to dream, according to recent research, seems to be irresistible. Needs for human companionship, for freedom of action,[38] for varied perceptual stimulation, for comfort and privacy, to name only a few, play significant roles in preserving personal integrity. We have learned how vital these are from the effects of their sadistic denial in "brainwashing," and from experiments on the effects of sensory deprivation.[39] Why do we leave these out?

We confine ourselves to sexual and aggressive drives because under ordinary conditions these are the drives, or "instincts," which create major problems in behavior pathology. The others raise major problems in Western civilization only when they are used in torture or in deliberate experiment. To include them in our account of everyday behavior pathology would be to indulge in pedantic excursions and to confuse and complicate matters unnecessarily. In our civilization they do not appear as common sources of neurotic, psychotic or character disorders. They belong to societies where people are severely deprived and to cultures which, from our point of view, are themselves sick and distorted.

We have already discussed the advantage, even the necessity, of reducing the infinite complexities of nature in scientific studies to a few manageable units or abstract principles. The layman usually looks upon the abstract units of any science as more real than the phenomena that he can himself observe.

---

[37] See the thoughtful discussion in the preface to Freud, S., *Instincts and Their Vicissitudes* in the Standard Edition, 1957, vol. 14, pp. 111–116. Also J. Strachey's comment that "the word 'instinct' is, with some misgivings, used to render the German *Trieb*." Freud, S., *An Outline of Psychoanalysis*. (1938) New York: Norton, 1949, p. 14.

[38] Mendelson, J. K. *et al.*, "Physiological and psychological aspects of sensory deprivation, a case analysis," in Solomon, P. (Ed.), *Sensory Deprivation*. Cambridge, Mass.: Harvard Univ. Press, 1961, pp. 91–113.

[39] Lifton, R. J., *Thought Reform and the Psychology of Totalism: A Study of "Brain Washing" in China.* New York: Norton, 1961; Sedman, G., "'Brain washing' and 'sensory deprivation' as factors in the production of psychiatric states: the relation between such states and schizophrenia," *Conf. Psychiat.*, 1961, *4*, 28–44.

Actually scientific abstractions are unreal. They are subject to change whenever they turn out to be inadequate, as witness the numerous changes in the concept of the atom since Niels Bohr formulated it and won the Nobel Prize. They are most useful when they are recognized and treated as abstractions which need continual reality testing and modification in relation to what they represent.

Such are the abstract concepts of sexual and aggressive drives or instincts. They are *constructs* which clarify and enrich the thinking of those who realize their abstract and tentative character, and who look always to the observed phenomena for justification of their use (*scientific reality-testing*). The numerous changes which Freud himself made in most of his fundamental concepts over the years provide an excellent example of scientific reality-testing which never loses sight of observation.

Some special characteristics of sexual and aggressive drives. Sexual and aggressive drives, with their derivatives, are fundamentally different from hunger and thirst and the periodic need for sleep. The major differences significant for psychopathology are as follows:

(1) *Unlike hunger, thirst or the need for sleep, sexual and aggressive drives can be indefinitely frustrated, delayed or even completely denied without killing the organism.* Some adults choose to give up direct sexual or aggressive expression for a lifetime without apparently suffering harm, other than an impoverishment of personality organization and some limitation of their interpersonal relationships. Many celibates and completely nonaggressive persons succeed in enriching themselves by their devotion to religious, altruistic, scientific or artistic occupations. Such devotion produces a different kind of person from the average, a person who may contribute much of value to his associates and to society at large. This is often done at the cost of great personal sacrifice in material comforts. Sometimes it sacrifices the devoted person's general happiness or that of his associates, especially that of his close relatives.

Some frustration, delay and denial are, of course, inevitable for all persons, even for those who are not especially devoted to anything. The demands and proscriptions involved in ordinary social living often run counter to individual wishes and needs.[40]

(2) *Sexual and aggressive drives seem to be constantly present in human beings.* Sometimes they are imperious and direct; sometimes they are neither imperious nor direct, but their derivatives are always active. Because these drives, or their derivatives, produce a disequilibrium in the organism, they always contribute a certain amount of stress or push toward satisfaction, however mild or indirect this may be.

If sexual and aggressive drives cannot be satisfied directly, they inevitably

[40] Lowe, C. M., "The self-concept: fact or artifact?" *Psychol. Bull.*, 1961, *58*, 325–336.

lead to sublimation in the form of nonsexual or nonaggressive ways, or to derivatives which may retain little recognizable sexual or aggressive flavor. Sublimations and derivatives of drives appear in the dreams, fantasies and daydreams of persons who have renounced them in overt action and conscious intent. This explains the disturbing imaginings which such people often experience, and which seem to them to be temptations of an evil spirit. Actually, they are temptations coming from an unregenerate id which, as we shall see in the next chapter, remains infantile and unsocialized in everyone throughout life.

(3) *Direct sexual and aggressive drive-satisfaction requires the reciprocal behavior of another person if it is to be complete.* This is not true of satisfying hunger or slaking thirst. No one can experience full adult sexuality or give vent to full adult aggression alone. Solitary masturbation and solitary temper tantrums provide at most a partial relief, not the kind of full realization that comes with close personal interaction. Sexuality offers the most intimate of all adult relationships. When it leads to the sex act, the consummation is typically carried out in strict privacy with a reciprocal sex partner, so that nothing extraneous interferes with the experience of blissful union.

If direct sex satisfaction is achieved alone, without the reciprocal sex activity of an adult partner, a person misses the deeply emotional experiences of heterosexual intercourse. He also misses the aggressive possession of a beloved or, for the female, the receptive possession of him. Pleasurable fantasies and pleasurable relief are the most that he can expect.

Perhaps because of social taboos, which people internalize early in life, solitary sex satisfaction usually stimulates conscious or unconscious superego condemnation. Latency children, adolescents and adults experience this consciously as guilt, or as revulsion after the satisfaction. Adults who have not resolved their edipal conflicts, or have not completely accepted the sex role which their anatomy and physiology assigns to them, may also experience guilt or revulsion after even socially sanctioned heterosexual relations. This is a source of much dissatisfaction with marriage and its consequences.

(4) *Sexuality and aggression are more subject to suppression, repression and distortion than are such equally fundamental needs as hunger, thirst and sleep.* In human beings, this seems to be related to the precocious appearance of sexuality and hostile aggression during infancy and early childhood, when they assume unrealistic and unacceptable direct forms. The precocious flowering of sexuality, a decade before sex relations are appropriate or even possible, exposes the small child to disturbing emotional storms, all of which may leave their residues in persistently infantile unconscious strivings, expectations and interpretations. The regressions that we see in neuroses and psychoses often bring these close to the surface again. In exceptional cases, a seductive or sadistic parent or older child takes advantage of a child's early

sexual excitement or hostile aggression to act out his or her own neurotic needs.[41] This is responsible for many sex deviations and antisocial acting out in the child when he grows to adulthood.

The suppression, repression and distortion of sexual and aggressive drives are also related to something which we have already mentioned. This is that (unlike hunger, thirst and the need for sleep) sexual and aggressive drives can easily be frustrated or denied expression in any recognizable form, without endangering a child's life. Such denial or frustration can be inflicted upon the growing person for most of two decades. It may be the result of accidental circumstances, in which there is neither conscious nor unconscious malice on the part of parents or other older persons. It may also be the outcome of abnormal domination by possessive or unconsciously sadistic persons, or the result of overindulgence which fails to provide a child with the limits he needs. In either case the developing person lacks sufficient experience in self-expression and self-control.

In the past, sexual distortions have received far more professional attention than have pathological aggressions. Today the problems of pathological aggression, which often go hand in hand with sexual pathology, are coming more and more into focus. The current interest in pathological aggression stems in part from the rise of violence and antisocial hostility in gangs and among nations today, in part from recognition that the aggressive drives are coordinate with the sexual drives.[42]

Ego and superego in the control of sexual and aggressive drives. It is one of the major functions of *ego organizations* to tame and channel sexual and aggressive drives, to integrate them and their derivatives into ongoing ego activity. Creative and constructive behavior, reciprocal cooperation and competition, social conformity and self-control, all involve ego integration of drive energy. The ego, which we shall discuss in the next chapter, includes such all-encompassing functions as perception, cognition and action. In many respects it is the most realistic and efficient system of organizations in the personality.

At the same time, as we shall see later on, ego organizations also include much that is childish and unrealistic, particularly at unconscious levels, much that belongs to early phases of development, and should not be directly relevant for adult experience. These primitive childhood residuals sometimes participate actively in the ego control of sexual and aggressive drives, thus complicating human experience and behavior in ways that are not intelligible at conscious adult levels.

The ego also has available a host of fantasies and daydreams, at preconscious and unconscious levels, into which derivatives of sexual and ag-

---

[41] Johnson, A. M., and Szurek, S., "The genesis of antisocial acting out in children and adults," *Psycholanal. Quart.*, 1952, *21*, 323–343.

[42] Cf. Redl, F., and Wineman, D., *The Aggressive Child*. Glencoe, Ill.: Free Press, 1957; Saul, L. J., *The Hostile Mind*. New York: Random House, 1956.

gressive drives can be incorporated. The product often yields personal satisfaction and, in exceptional instances, artistic creation.

Finally, ego organizations also control the drives and their derivatives in response to pressures from the superego, which is by no means always realistic. It is one major function of the superego, and of its infantile precursors, to react to the drives and to their derivatives whenever moral or ethical standards are threatened with violation. Another major function is that of supplying moral support, criticism or condemnation, whenever ego activity arouses it.

Superego pressures include the familiar conscious experiences which we call *conscience,* and which seem almost a separate person inside us. They may also include powerful, and often irrational, pressures that remain unconscious in adults and are responsible for much otherwise inexplicable guilt, and feelings of worthlessness or inferiority. In psychotic regression, some of these superego pressures lead to savage self-condemnation which may endanger the patient's life; others appear as projected external persecutors.[43] In both, we witness the operation of an internalized part of the personality system as though it were somehow another individual, an exaggeration of what we normally experience when we listen to the voice of our conscience, or feel a little guilty about something without really knowing why.

Summary. We can sum up and put together what we have just been saying as follows:

(*a*) *The drives* provide a continual, powerful and sometimes irresistible supply of sexual and aggressive impulses or urges. The broader sense in which Freud finally came to use his concept of sexual and aggressive drives — so that the one group was constructive and unifying, while the other group was destructive and fragmenting — will be discussed later on in this chapter.

(*b*) *The ego,* a system of integrative, defensive and adaptive functions (including perception, cognition and action), controls the drives and their derivatives by integrating as much as possible into its ongoing activity. Much of the remainder it absorbs in fantasies and daydreams, some of which may be conscious, but most of which are preconscious or unconscious. Much that the ego can neither integrate into its own activities nor absorb in fantasies and daydreams it represses or otherwise defends itself against.

(*c*) *The superego* functions in relation both to the drives and to the ego, but almost as a separate system. In part it is a kind of *Trojan horse* that was taken in during early infancy and early childhood. It is a representative of the parents and society; but, like the ego, it includes much that is childish along with much that is idealistic and realistic. It constitutes a stabilizing, regulatory system within the personality structure when it uses the ego-ideal as a multiple calibrating instrument for evaluating ego function and drive demand.

---

[43] See the cases of Constance Q. and of Charles G. listed in the index under *Cases.*

It is hardly necessary to re-emphasize the fact that *the id, the ego* and *the superego* are constructs, or intervening variables, and not things. They have been evolved for the purpose of making human experience and human behavior more intelligible than was the case when the equally conceptual intervening variables which we call reflexes were the mainstay of psychology. It has been pointed out that even our apparently self-evident *objective reality* is also a construct, and that its intent is one of making the behavior of other persons more intelligible.[44]

When we come to the clinical study of the neuroses, psychoses and personality disorders, we shall find many compromises, distortions and substitutions in the expression of drives and drive-derivatives. Most of these are the direct or indirect result of unfavorable conditions during personality development in infancy and childhood. Even in normal maturation and development, the functioning of ego and superego imposes many conditions upon the expression or satisfaction of the drives, and at the same time gives their derivatives almost limitless complexity.

In the mature adult, direct aggression, especially direct hostile aggression, and direct sexuality, are limited to a relatively few occasions, and to certain prescribed situations. Indirect expression and indirect satisfaction enjoy far greater liberty. Drives that are being indirectly expressed and satisfied may be obvious to everyone at the time, as in courting, flirting and kissing, in competitive games, and in the use of wit and sarcasm. On the other hand, they may be so disguised or transformed that no one, not even the behaving person himself, recognizes what is being expressed or satisfied.

Drives and their derivatives often get no satisfaction or expression at all. This is especially true when a person's dominant motivation is the defense against drives, which originates in ego function or in superego pressure. We are now ready for a discussion of the levels of motivation.

All significant human behavior is motivated from within. The motivation of most human behavior cannot be formulated simply in terms of sexual and aggressive drives, at least not in terms of the drives as we have been discussing them. With maturation and development, human beings elaborate an extraordinarily complex matrix of *internal stimulation* for external action. In this matrix the *drives and their derivatives* are imbedded; but so also are whole systems of *ego adaptation, defense* and *mastery*. At preconscious and unconscious levels there are *impulses, fantasies, daydreams* and *dreams*, all of which can be effective determinants, and all may lead to expressive satisfaction, without ever reaching full consciousness. The *superego* and even its infantile precursors add their contributions to motivation. Human beings also give specific responses to specific external and somatic stimulation (stimulus-response patterns), but always with a background of ongoing organismic activity. Drives and specific motives are thus seen to be *abstractions*. They are constructs, not things or separate forces, even though in the interest of making human behavior and experience more intelligible, we speak and think as though they were.[45]

Changing concepts in Freud's formulation of the drives

Before going on to discuss the different levels of motivation, a word or two about the historical development of drive or instinct concepts in Freud's thinking must be said. Freud began with sex drives as basic to human motivation in part because disturbed sexuality was recognized, even in the nineteenth century, by such eminent physicians as Charcot to be at the root of neurotic symptoms. Freud made *sexuality* the keystone of the psychoanalysis which he invented, and for a long time sex drives, in almost naked form, dominated his thinking about motivation and symptom formation. This, we have said, was also in part a reaction against Victorian hypocrisy, which made even professional men at the turn of the century avoid more than a passing mention of sex.

Rather late in his life, in his sixties, Freud gave to *aggression* a coordinate status with sex, as a group of basic drives or instincts in psychopathology. Today aggressive drives are being given special attention without, however, decreasing the emphasis upon sexuality. A more subtle change also took place gradually in Freud's thinking about the drives, as his clinical experience steadily increased and his preoccupation with theory continued. This change was in the general direction of enriching and expanding his conception of drive or instinct.

Originally he discussed sex drives as forces which appeared somewhere at the boundary between the physiological and the psychological. Even then, however, he insisted that sex drives were not single but multiple. They passed through oral, anal and phallic phases to arrive at the point, in adolescence, where mature genitality and concern for a peer of the opposite sex took the leading role. This expanded conception of sex drives and sexuality lost none of its force and none of its primacy. But it clearly included all kinds of love, at many levels, in all kinds of behavior and experience. It involved a rich variety of objects relations, identifications and interactions, many of which the man in the street would never think of as sexual. When Freud gave aggression a coordinate position with sex in human motivation, he likewise enriched and expanded its meaning to include such widely separated normal strivings, activities and attitudes as initiative, competition and hostility.

Eros and Thanatos. As Freud's theories grew, his formulations of the drives, or "instincts," became more and more complex. By the time he had published *Beyond the Pleasure Principle,* in 1920, the already multiple sex drives had been transformed into *Eros,* the life principle, and the aggressive drives had become *Thanatos,* the death principle. This was an important

---

[45] For a review of research in emotional development, see Jersild, A. T., "Emotional development," in Carmichael, L., *Manual of Child Psychology.* (2nd ed.) New York: Wiley, 1954, pp. 833–917.

change which introduced modifications in the conceptions of sadism and masochism, as well as an expansion of the concepts of the drives.[46]

(a) *Eros.* In Freud's hands, *Eros,* the life principle, now embraced not only the naked sex drives, at various levels, but also strivings toward union, creation, construction and integration, the striving of adults toward fusion in sex intercourse, the cohesion involved in family formation, and even the cohesion of particles to form organic units.[47] *Eros* could also be made to include friendliness and cooperative undertakings, the growth and maturing of organic systems and entities, and the reproduction of new units, including human offspring.

(b) *Thanatos.* The death principle or death instinct embraced all the opposites of *Eros* — naked aggression, hostility and attack, strivings toward destruction, disunion, fragmentation and disintegration, the decay and dissolution of organisms, as well as of interpersonal relationships, all urges to lose individuality and merge with nature. In the end, the destructive death instinct was conceived as permitting new units to form, through separation from the old. The cycle was thus completed, from life to death, and from disintegration to new life.

What this seems to represent is the philosophical development of Freud's thinking, from a mechanistic view of the organism which was at the same time personal and subjective, to a purposive, almost religious view. *Eros* and *Thanatos,* the sexual and aggressive drives, were formulated by Freud in such a way as to approach the age-old preoccupation with birth, death and resurrection, the ageless cycle of life in spring and summer, of decline and death in autumn and winter, and the miracle of rebirth with each return of spring.

The presence of such intensely opposed strivings in the human organism would lead to all kinds of conflicting trends, including mankind's pervasive ambivalences. It would include such complex combinations of sexual and aggressive drives as occur in ordinary cooperative and competitive work and play, in sex intercourse, in sleep (Shakespeare called sleep "the death of each day's life"), and in constructive, aggressive enterprise.

This whole development of the drive or instinct concept, whether we follow it to its metaphysical conclusions or stop at some point along the way, is an evolution from almost unstructured blind forces toward structured, purposive organizations. The "seething cauldron" and the "chaos," which Freud sometimes spoke of in relation to the unconscious, was given an organization dominated by the *pleasure principle* and the *primary process* at one level. At a more advanced level it acquired a different organization,

---

[46] The changes in Freud's conceptions of sadism and masochism are too complex to be discussed here.

[47] Cf. *Beyond the Pleasure Principle.* (1920), Standard Edition, 1955, vol. 18, pp. 7–64; *Group Psychology and the Analysis of the Ego.* (1921), Standard Edition, 1955, vol. 18, pp. 67–143; *The Ego and the Id.* (1923), Standard Edition, 1961, vol. 19, pp. 12–59.

which was at least partly dominated by *secondary processes* and the *reality principle*. The drives or instincts could now represent a conflict between creation and destruction, and by implication the conflict between good and evil. The originally simpler strivings of desire and destruction had now become opposing trends in a matrix of motivation.

The great majority of persons trained in classical psychoanalysis do not fully accept Freud's *Eros* and *Thanatos*.[48] Relatively few seriously believe in a death instinct. But most people find the expansion and enrichment of the sexual and aggressive drive concepts, to include the *integrative* and *creative* as opposed to the *disintegrative* and *destructive*, a valuable development in psychodynamic theory. It is in this last sense that we shall follow Freud in our interpretation and use of the general concept of human motivation.

Levels and complexities of human motivation

We have said that all significant human behavior is motivated, that it is directed towards expression or satisfaction. The motivation of every significant human act or thought has unconscious components as well as preconscious or conscious ones. This means that whatever we do, say or think expresses more strivings than we are aware of. Even a very simple, passing thought may be determined by complex, enduring drives, which usually include both sexual or integrative and aggressive or disintegrative components. Slips of the tongue, flashing impulses and manifest dreams often give clear evidence of unconscious, preconscious and conscious intent; but other experiences, less easy to analyze, reveal the same multiplicity of origin. Complex behavior and experience may represent complex motivation; often it stems from fairly simple strivings. But whether motivation is simple or complex, and whether its expression or its satisfaction is direct or indirect, we can take it for granted that human beings are always motivated in some direction, that as a rule many motivations are simultaneously present, and that expression or satisfaction of one need is soon followed by the appearance of another need.[49]

Experts in psychopathology concentrate upon hidden, unexpressed and unsatisfied motivation because this is the major source of neurotic, psychotic and personality disorders. The openly "acted out" antisocial sexual or aggressive impulse is the rare exception, even though it gets the headlines. Inhibited, concealed, disguised and subtly distorted experience and behavior are the rule. Behind any symptom may lie motivation at all levels, including unconscious drives and unconscious defenses against them, including futile

[48] Freud himself took notice of this resistance to his conception of the "basic forces or instincts." See Freud, S., *An Outline of Psychoanalysis.* New York: Norton, 1949, p. 21. See also the clear discussion in Hendrick, I., *Facts and Theories of Psychoanalysis.* (3rd ed.) New York: Knopf, 1958, pp. 124–139.

[49] Allport, G., *Personality and Social Encounter.* Boston: Beacon Press, 1960; Witkin, H. A., *et al., Psychological Differentiation.* New York: Wiley, 1962.

attempts at ego adaptation and mastery, and unconscious as well as conscious superego pressures.[50] We need to take account of all levels of human motivation before we are ready to understand psychopathology.

(a) *Conscious motivation.* The most familiar motivation is that of which we are conscious. At first glance, it seems also the most realistic and rational; and even after careful study, this first glance may turn out to have been the truth. It is sometimes nonsensical to dig for deeper motives when what is conscious is adequate and nonconflictual. A recognition of this fact is expressed in the concept of *conflict-free areas* of ego function, especially those ego functions which are the product of growth and maturation, rather than of conflict. The student of psychopathology must always consider the possibility that things are really what they seem.

It is true that unconscious, infantile strivings enter into the motivation of most thoughts and acts; but this does not mean that the unconscious, infantile contributions always reveal a person's dominant motives. The unconscious drive may be only a parisitic rider. It is well known that unconscious strivings are adept at utilizing conscious and preconscious expressions as avenues for discharge. If some repressed, infantile need can be relieved indirectly and incidentally, during a socially approved and socially motivated action, this is pure gain. It does not mean that therefore the socially acceptable and socially motivated conscious action was nothing but a disguise for the asocial or antisocial impulse. It usually means that the conscious or preconscious action served as a convenient vehicle for discharge, and often without in the least distorting the overt act.

People who are eternally searching for hidden meanings and hidden symbols in what their friends say or do, are apt to become public nuisances who have a distorted orientation toward social life. They are like the occasional medical student who makes uncalled for, off-the-cuff diagnoses at social gatherings. The mature psychotherapist and the mature psychoanalyst, like mature internists and surgeons, confine their professional activities to professional situations. If they observe something unusual in a social setting, they respect their companions' need for privacy, and therefore keep their observations to themselves. It is nonetheless true that by far the most widespread, varied and interesting motivations originate at preconscious and unconscious levels.

(b) *Preconscious motivation.* The scope of preconscious motivation is vast. We can be fully aware of only a little at a time. We are conscious only of this or that reason for what we do and think about, for what we remember from the past, and for what we anticipate in the future. But whenever we talk over a conscious motive with someone else, or even ruminate about it alone, we nearly always find that it has many ramifications.[51] These ramifica-

[50] Buskirk, C. V., "Performance on complex reasoning tasks as a function of anxiety," *J. abnorm. soc. Psychol.*, 1961, *62*, 201–209.
[51] Pine, F., "Incidental stimulation: a study of preconscious transformations," *J. abnorm. soc. Psychol.*, 1960, *60*, 68–75.

tions can, as a rule, easily be made conscious, and they can as easily disappear when they are no longer needed. This vast reservoir of easily available preconscious motivation provides us with our ordinary conscious explanations for what we do, say or think. It gives us a sense of continuity and integrity in our lives which the fleeting conscious experience cannot yield.

There are also vast areas of preconscious motivation that require special effort to make them conscious. To some extent this difficulty is a product of forgetting, since no one can possibly remember everything. To some extent it is a product of the modifications which the structure of our ego-superego organization imposes. We may, for example, progressively reshape the memory of our motivations in such a way as to fit them into the organization of our culture, and into the image that we already have of our individual selves.[52]

We usually forget or omit the motivations that we do not like; and sometimes we deny them even though we may have an uncomfortable feeling that we once had them. We see this kind of defensive forgetting most clearly in *denial* and *rationalization,* when a person knows that his real motives are unworthy or unacceptable, when he refuses to acknowledge them even to himself, when he disowns them and substitutes a socially approved, rationalized motive as whitewash. The work of undoing the denial of what is preconsciously present, and of recognizing a rationalization for what it is, may not be any easier than working through the defenses that conceal unconscious motivation. What is revealed as preconscious motivation, however, has the advantage of being usually organized more in accordance with external reality than is unconscious motivation.

Three levels of motivation so far discussed. We have now discussed three levels of motivation. They are as follows:

1. *Conscious motivation.* This is familiar to us all. It states our conscious purposes and the reasons we recognize for acting as we do, the reasons for what we experience and the way we experience it.

2. *Readily available preconscious motivation.* This is simply the vast reservoir of available motivation from which we draw whatever we need in order to account for our behavior and experience. It allows us a sense of continuity and integrity, as we move toward our goals. It may provide explanations for what we have done, or what we plan to do; and these, when we confront them, may deflect us from an undesirable course, as well as guide us toward a desired one.

3. *Preconscious motivation which is not readily available.* This includes a great deal of motivation, present in our preconscious life, but defended against by such mechanisms as *denial* and *rationalization.* It also includes

---

[52] Cf. Bartlett, F., *Remembering, a Study in Experimental and Social Psychology.* Cambridge, England: Cambridge Univ. Press, 1932; also, Bartlett, F., *Thinking: An Experimental and Social Study.* New York: Basic Books, 1958.

motivation that has been reshaped to conform with familiar cultural norms and with our own self-image. This summary brings us to the subject of unconscious motivation.

Unconscious motivation

Throughout the ages, human beings have realized that they often do, say or think things for inexplicable reasons. This goes beyond the limitations imposed by consciousness which, as we have said, can encompass little at any one time. It even goes beyond the difficulties inherent in preconscious motivation. Unconscious motivation is not only inaccessible by ordinary routes; it often contradicts everything we know about ourselves. It may be incredibly infantile. It may be unintelligible on any rational grounds.

The concept of unconscious motivation has not had the hard going, in gaining general acceptance, that the concept of unconscious thinking has had. It is true that when inacceptable, ego-alien motivation was clearly involved, the custom was usually to ascribe it to the intervention of invisible but external agents, and that when a person's motivation seemed superhuman it was usually ascribed to inspiration from the outside. But even so, motivation was recognized as sometimes lying outside the realm of conscious human reason, and even beyond the limits of human responsibility.

During the nineteenth century there were many demonstrations that in a hypnotic trance ordinary adults could be motivated to carry out some activity many hours after the trance had been terminated. Not only would the subject carry out the activity as instructed but, if he had been told during the trance that he would not remember having been so instructed, he would often rationalize his behavior when it appeared later, and seem to believe his own spurious explanations. Although this behavior is not the same as ordinary unconscious motivation, and although it involves hypnosis which is still little understood, it has served in the past to focus attention upon the fact that a person can do things without knowing why and without having any recollection about what induced him to need to do it in the first place. Such evidence of unconscious motivation is dramatic, and it can be repeated as a demonstration almost at will.

Less dramatic, but more impressive in the end, is the vast array of *parapraxes*, that is, the slips of the tongue and pen, the selective forgetting of unpleasant events and the name of an unpleasant person, the misreading something closer to the heart's desire, and a great many mistakes, bunglings, accidents and symptomatic acts. Freud made these the subject of one of his longest treatises, first published only a year after his *Interpretation of Dreams*. It is still the most complete and most interesting book on the subject.[53]

The most profound, most extensive, and most clearly illustrated account

[53] Freud, S., *The Psychopathology of Everyday Life.* (1901), Standard Edition, 1960, vol. 6, pp. 1–289. We shall discuss further the existence of two conceptual systems within classical psychoanalysis in the next chapter.

of unconscious motivation appears in Freud's *Interpretation of Dreams* which to the end of his life Freud considered as his greatest contribution. When he revolutionized psychodynamic theory in 1923 by introducing systematically the interrelated concepts of ego, id and superego, he made no important changes in the book on dreams. This has the disadvantage that it leaves us with two somewhat different theories, originated by the same person, to account for the same kind of phenomena. It has the advantage of leaving us an extensive account of Freud's early theories to compare with his later ones and with the theories of those who succeeded him.[54]

Unconscious motivation refers to the established fact that explanations of what we do, say or think, of what we avoid or fail to do, say or think, and even of some things that repeatedly happen to us in one form or another, seemingly without our connivance, are not exhausted by the fullest accounts of conscious and preconscious motivation. They appear to be motivated by something of which we are not aware, by motives that we might not recognize or believe even if they were pointed out to us. The contributions to motivation that come from unconscious levels include some of the most significant and most fundamental. To discover what they are usually requires prolonged and systematic work, and the cooperation of a specialist. More often than not the unconscious motivation has to be patiently and carefully reconstructed on the basis of whatever fragments a prolonged therapeutic investigation yields.

Freud has compared the task of reconstruction in psychoanalysis to that of an archaeologist who must reconstruct a vanished culture on the basis of the remnants of a ruin. He has also pointed out an important difference. Whereas the archaeologist's fragments are dead pieces of a dead civilization, the fragments of unconscious motivation are still alive, and the inaccessible unconscious systems to which they belong are also alive and active. This is a restatement of something to which we have already alluded, namely, that early primitive experiences and ways of handling crises and conflicts continue to exist in mental life, even though they may be deeply repressed, and they continue to influence experience and behavior in adulthood. We shall meet clear examples of this among the clinical syndromes in later chapters, where the patient's symptoms, his anxieties and conflicts, and his ways of trying to master them, all show evidence of infantile situations which current stresses have regressively revived.

Two levels of unconscious motivation

At this point it is necessary to distinguish two levels of unconscious motivation, just as we have distinguished two levels of preconscious motivation. The criteria, however, are here quite different.

[54] Freud, S., *The Interpretation of Dreams.* (1900) (trans. J. Strachey), Standard Edition, 1953, vol. 4–5.

At one level, the level closest to preconscious functioning, the unconscious motivation arises from repressed ego and superego functions, which persist typically in the form of unconscious fantasies and daydreams. These may be fairly well organized even though kept in repression. As a rule, however, unconscious fantasies and daydreams are subjected to some degree of primary process distortion, because of their proximity to the id. Their organization may be almost incredibly infantile, representing conflicts, needs, fears, wishes, love and anger, as they were experienced in early childhood.

At the deepest level lies the most primitive unconscious motivation. It operates strictly in accordance with the primary process which, as we shall see in the next chapter, is characteristic of the id. In what immediately follows, we shall limit discussion to a brief account of the less deep unconscious fantasies and daydreams, leaving the primary process for our description of the id.

The more superficial but still unconscious fantasies and daydreams, which represent the products of early repression, are often the fantasies and daydreams of a child who is unclear about the distinction between himself and others, between himself and inanimate objects, and between internal, external and somatic reality. They may show distortions and exaggerations of the conflicts, the needs and fears, the wishes, loves and hatreds of early childhood. Activity and passivity may also be confused, just as they often are in adult dreams. What was originally the child's primaeval rage appears in his primitive fantasies as an immense, pervasive fury, of which he seems somehow to be the victim. What was once a primitive desire to possess something by swallowing it, appears in fantasy as a monstrous threat of being swallowed or devoured.

A repressed, but still alive and active, infantile fantasy may have been so anxiety-ridden, when it was formed in childhood, that it still distorts beyond recognition what was actually experienced. Thus, for example, a justifiable rebuke in early childhood reappears in unconscious fantasy as a monstrous injustice or a terrible threat, because that is the way the small child originally experienced it.[55] What was in reality a reasonable denial, or the unavoidable absence of the mother, reappears in unconscious fantasy as a deliberate hideous desertion. Punishment or the mere threat of punishment may appear in unconscious fantasies as the frightening certainty of mutilation (castration anxiety in boys, the feeling of having been castrated in girls).

Motivational gradients or hierarchies

It can be demonstrated, even in animal experiment where both the organism and the situation are kept relatively simple, that every organism has gradients or hierarchies of motivation, some motives being prepotent over others in

[55] Johnson, A. M., and Szurek, S., "The genesis of antisocial acting out in children and adults," *Psychoanal. Quart.*, 1952, *21*, 323–343.

any given series or in a given area of function. The gradients vary in organization, as one prepotent need is satisfied and another takes its place. Moreover there may be interactions between motivation in one series, or in one area of function, and motivation in other series or areas.

Human motivation likewise has its gradients or hierarchies of relative strength and relative value. These change in prepotency with need-satisfaction; and members of one motivational series or area of functioning interact with members of others. Motivations in human beings cannot be as easily delineated and defined as they can in lower forms of life under controlled laboratory conditions, especially in lower forms without a complex societal structure. As one might expect, motivation in man, his motivational gradients or hierarchies, and the interactions among motivations are exceedingly complex.[56]

The complexity of motivation in human beings arises in part from the enormous complexity of the human organism but more especially because of human psychodynamic organization, which is unlike anything else in nature. The internal psychodynamic structure of every person is a reflection of the intricate complexity of human society, of its continually varying demands and opportunities for expression and adaptation. Human society, represented early in life by the structure of the family, demands of each person that he take over the prevailing standards around him, and that he make them an integral part of himself. It demands that he establish himself in a specific role, at first as a child among other children, subordinated to adults, and later as an adult himself with a certain degree of latitude as to the identity or style of life that he evolves. Even his sex role, which is predetermined by his biological beginning, can be expressed in more than one acceptable way.

On top of all this, or more accurately stated, within all of this, the human being has infinitely varied systems of expression, symbolization and communication. These further augment the prodigious complexities of human life, until it is unlike that of any other living thing. All through the ages earnest attempts have been made to categorize human motivation. None of them so far has proved to be satisfactory. Most of them deal only with conscious and preconscious motivation. A review of these attempts would go beyond the scope of this book.[57]

Motivation and psychodynamic structure: a résumé

As we turn now to a discussion of psychodynamic structure, we shall not be turning away from the concepts of conscious, preconscious and uncon-

[56] See, for example, Shibutani, T., *Society and Personality*. Englewood Cliffs, N.J.: Prentice-Hall, 1961.

[57] Cf., for example, Allport, G., *Pattern and Growth in Personality*. New York: Holt, Rinehart & Winston, 1961; Stagner, R., *Psychology of Personality*. (3rd ed.) New York: McGraw-Hill, 1961; Maslow, A., *Motivation and Personality*. New York: Harper, 1954; Shibutani, T., *Society and Personality*. New York: Prentice-Hall, 1961; Hall, C. S., and Lindzey, G., *Theories of Personality*. New York: Wiley, 1957.

scious levels of experience and behavior. On the contrary, we shall be extending them and defining them further.

Conscious. What we have been calling *conscious*, for example, belongs to both ego and superego organizations. We are consciously aware of an infinite number of things that we perceive, think and do, along with our emotional feelings and motivation. This awareness, an ego function, is restricted at any one time to a relatively few things; but the total even in a single day is astronomic. We also become aware of moral judgments and verdicts that we make about the worth, fitness or rightness of what we perceive, think or do, and about the acceptability and appropriateness of our motives and our emotions. This awareness is the surface part of superego functioning that has long been known as *conscience*.

Preconscious. (a) What we have been calling *preconscious* includes all that can *easily become conscious* as we shift our orientation, and change what we perceive, do or think, from one thing to another. It is the vast reservoir of readily accessible perceptions, thoughts, memories and actions, with their motivational components, which lie near the surface of conscious experience, and are barred from it only by the limited scope of conscious experience at any one time. All of this involves ego and superego activity. It includes a vast amount of adaptive, automatic behavior which makes up the ordinary coordinations of everyday life, of which we have become completely unaware, and the automatic scanning of the superego, which only becomes conscious when we face moral doubts and dilemmas.

(b) The *less readily accessible preconscious* is also a great reservoir of perception, thought, memory, action, judgment and motivation. To use the same metaphor as above, it lies further from the surface of consciousness than does the readily available preconscious. It includes much that is barred from consciousness by certain defenses, such as *denial, reaction formation* and *rationalization*. A person may be dimly and uncomfortably aware of what lies behind these defenses, even though he does not admit it.

Unconscious ego and superego. A large proportion of both ego and superego activity is unconscious, that is, it cannot be made conscious by ordinary rational methods. The general organization of much of this functioning is like that of the conscious ego and superego of small children;[58] but to a certain extent it has been modified in the direction of the primary process because of the proximity of the id with which there may have been some interaction. There are unconscious repressed fantasies, conflicts, urges and daydreams. These vary all the way from the fairly well organized daydreams of latency, through the less organized and less realistic daydreams of edipal

---

[58] In the case of edipal and pre-edipal organizations it is more exact to speak of *precursors* of the superego, since the mature superego results from resolution of edipal conflicts.

and pre-edipal phases, to mere fragments and distorted derivatives of early conflicts, hopes, wishes, fears, loves and hates, with all their childhood confusions, misinterpretations and exaggerations still intact. Some writers include this last group with the id; but, as we shall see, the id cannot become conscious, whereas many of these deeply unconscious ego and superego experiences under special circumstances can. We shall meet them in full daylight when we come to study the neuroses and psychoses.

The unconscious ego also includes most of the defenses. They help form functional boundaries between the ego and the id, and prevent id impulses and unconscious motivation from reaching consciousness or the preconscious in their pristine forms. The unconscious ego defenses also prevent unconscious fantasies and daydreams from breaking through into conscious and preconscious life, but allow many of them a certain degree of expression and discharge in derived, disguised, more or less acceptable forms. This separation between *unconscious fantasies*, which are for the most part unrealistic and infantile, and the *preconscious* and *conscious organizations*, is one condition for the development of secondary process thinking, and for maintaining it.

Under normal circumstances, while we are awake, the unconscious ego mechanisms of defense operate silently. We are not aware of them. During sleep, they enter into some of the organization and revision of manifest dreams. When ego defenses become inadequate while a person is awake, they take an active part in symptom formation, as we shall see in the chapters on the clinical syndromes. It is then, in particular, that the products of deeply repressed, unconscious fantasies and daydreams make their appearance in consciousness. Some of them can be frightening or grotesque. The unconscious ego defenses are normally responsive to superego pressures applied also at unconscious levels.

Unconscious id. The rest of the unconscious constitutes the id, with its naked drives, its primitive motivation, and its push toward immediate gratification. The id operates in accordance with the pleasure principle and the primary process. It produces derivative effects in experience and behavior that seem strange, illogical, contradictory and even weird to conscious thinking. Id activities themselves never become conscious or preconscious. We have to infer them from the otherwise unintelligible experiences to which they give rise, as we shall see in the next chapter.

5

The Psychodynamic System

⁂

THE *psychodynamic system* IS A CONCEPTUAL ORGANIZATION OF INTERLOCK-
ing mental functions. It has been developed during the past seventy years in
attempts to make human experience and behavior intelligible without leaving
out their irrational components. It is still in process of evolution, but its major
features are now firmly established. The rational and irrational components
of the psychodynamic system which we shall discuss in this chapter are the
id, the *ego*, the *superego*, and the mental representations of the *body*, the
self, biosocial roles, and *reality*.

The psychodynamic system and the central nervous system

Each of the components of the psychodynamic system depends upon the
integrative action of the central nervous system for the integrity of its function. When the physiological activities of the central nervous system disintegrate, the psychodynamic system also disintegrates. This we shall clearly
see when we come to the chapter on *brain disorders*.

There are, however, important differences between the two systems. For
one thing, the different components of the psychodynamic system, as we have
listed them above, cannot be assigned to the different individual components
of the central nervous system. The ego, for example, involves the physiological action of the whole brain. It is simply that the principles of organization in the one system do not correspond to the principles of organization
in the other. Moreover, the psychodynamic system can disintegrate while the

central nervous system continues to function normally at physiological levels. This is most obvious in panic states, in mania, in the depressions and in schizophrenia. There is also a limited amount of disintegration of the psychodynamic system even in the neuroses, where symptom formation shows signs of the influence of the primary process.

Freud never gave up the hope of his youth that some day the structure of psychopathology, of mental organization, and of social interaction, would all be reduced to problems of physiology and pharmacology. His hope was in the spirit of his times. By a strange irony of fate, it was he who was destined to become the greatest genius of our age in establishing the primacy of experiential and behavioral concepts in these fields over the necessarily more limited concepts of physiology and pharmacology.[1] He also endured the contempt and partial ostracism of his medical colleagues without swerving from his path or losing heart, without wasting time in polemics, and without ever taking refuge from the complexities of human experience and behavior by transmuting them into something simpler and easier to investigate.

The two conceptual developments of psychodynamics

With the passage of years, and the accumulation of clinical data, Freud sensed the growing need that his theories had for a more definitive structure than he had provided. It is true that in both *The Interpretation of Dreams* (1900), and in an earlier unpublished manuscript,[2] Freud has spelled out many detailed and original conceptualizations, all based upon years of clinical investigation. These are still worth reading for their freshness and the fruitfulness of their concepts. Many of these concepts, such as the differentiation between primary and secondary processes, are still basic to psychodynamic theory. They reveal a remarkable insight into mental functioning at a time when no one else seems to have had it. Nevertheless, the conceptual structure remained inadequate.

During more than thirty years, Freud was continually preoccupied with innovations, modifications and elaborations of his psychodynamic concepts, while he went on with his clinical work. Many of his contributions to theory appeared more or less incidentally in the articles which he kept publishing. They are perhaps most systematized in his article, "On narcissism" (1914), in the so-called *Papers on Metapsychology* (1915–1917),[3] and in his semi-

---

[1] Reference has already been made to the two-volume work by Arnold, M. B., *Emotion and Personality*. New York: Columbia Univ. Press, 1960; and to Uhr, L., and Miller, J. G., *Drugs and Behavior*. New York: Wiley, 1960. There is an earlier bibliography published by the Department of Health, Education and Welfare. See *Psychopharmaca: A Bibliography of Psychopharmacology*. Washington, D.C.: U.S. Govt. Printing Office, 1958 (approximately 2500 articles between 1952 and 1957).

[2] Freud, S., "Project for a scientific psychology," (1895), in Freud, S., *The Origins of Psychoanalysis* (ed. M. Bonaparte, A. Freud, and E. Kris). New York: Basic Books, 1954, pp. 347–445. (Freud actually left this paper untitled and unpublished.)

[3] Freud, S., "On narcissism," (1914), Standard Edition, 1957, vol. 14, pp. 73–102; Freud, S., "Papers on metapsychology," which include "Instincts and their viscissi-

popular *Introductory Lectures on Psycho-Analysis* (1920).[4] Freud was his own most candid and ruthless critic. He appears always to have been dissatisfied with these earlier conceptual structures and outspoken about their shortcomings.

In 1923 Freud suddenly crystallized a new conceptual organization of mental functions and published it in *The Ego and the Id*.[5] This title should have been expanded to include the superego, because here for the first time Freud presented his conception of the superego, with a section all to itself, and in the form which he was to utilize with little change from then on.[6] The concepts of id, ego and superego contained in this work have given direction to psychodynamic theory ever since. They have also influenced directly the practice of psychoanalysis, and more indirectly a large segment of psychology and psychiatry, in theory, in experiment, in psychotherapy, and in social studies. Today the division of mental organization into ego, id and superego seems so natural that it is almost self-evident.

For some reason, Freud made no systematic attempt to revise his earlier writings to bring them into line with *The Ego and the Id*. Even in his last revision of *The Interpretation of Dreams* (1932), he left the theoretical structure much as it had appeared in 1900. The result is that we have today two distinct accounts of the psychodynamic system which, although not mutually exclusive, approach it from somewhat different perspectives. The account which follows will draw upon both formulations and try to do violence to neither.

The Id and the Primary Process

As Freud himself liked to point out, the *id* is an abstraction, though a lively, energetic one. We cannot observe id functions directly. We cannot see them or demonstrate them. We can only infer their existence and characteristics from certain otherwise unintelligible experience and behavior, such as an absurd dream or a neurotic symptom. Nevertheless, as in the case of many other invisible scientific abstractions, the id has turned out to be so fruitful that we cannot get along without it.

We assume that the organization of the id of adults must be close to what the mental organization is like in early infancy. From the moment of birth, all infants are exposed to external reality; and every now and then they have

---

tudes," "The unconscious," "A metapsychological supplement to the theory of dreams," and "Mourning and melancholia," (1915–1917), Standard Edition, 1957, vol. 14, pp. 105–258.

    [4] Freud, S., *Introductory Lectures on Psychoanalysis*. (1920) To appear as Volumes 15 and 16 of the Standard Edition. At present this is available in a paperback, Freud, S., *A General Introduction to Psychoanalysis* (trans. J. Riviere). Garden City, N.Y.: Doubleday Permabooks, 1953.

    [5] Freud, S., "The ego and the id," (1923), Standard Edition, 1961, vol. 19, pp. 12–59.

    [6] See the preface to "The ego and the id," cited above, pp. 3–11, presumably written by J. Strachey.

to interact with it in order to feed and survive. External reality forces itself upon neonates in many other ways; but still the demands it makes are slight and intermittent. Only very gradually the reality-demands multiply and come to occupy more and more of the infant's time and to increase the precision of his interaction. It is this gradually increasing impact of the surrounding world that helps an ego organization grow and mature in such a way that it can cope directly with external reality. Nevertheless, there always remains an active core of mental organization that seems almost impervious to the influence of external reality and is never socialized. This core we call the *id*.

What are the characteristics of the id? And how do we get our information about it? The id, first of all, is governed by the *pleasure principle*. It is made up of *drives* or *"instincts"* which strive for immediate satisfaction or discharge. It operates by certain peculiar maneuvers which we call the *primary process*. We get our information about the id through studying the end-products of the primary process which appear under certain circumstances in preconscious or conscious life. Among these are the *manifest dreams* which anyone may experience during normal sleep, and the *symptoms* which we shall discuss in some detail when we come to the clinical chapters.

At this point we shall describe what the id seems to be like, its characteristics which have been inferred from more than half a century of study of its end-products.[7] After that, we shall go on to discuss the changes in mental function which the ego and the superego organizations introduce.

The id and the pleasure principle

The id operates strictly in accordance with the pleasure principle. Its drives always seek immediate gratification or immediate discharge, without regard to consequences other than the attainment of pleasure. In terms of *energy* or *cathexis,* this means immediate reduction of the drives to an optimal level where they are no longer disturbing. It does not mean reduction of energy to zero, any more than optimal temperature for the human being means a reduction to zero. In ego-superego terms, the goal of the *pleasure principle* is the attainment of a stable state in which a person feels comfortable and contented as he is, with no desire to change.

The goal of complete comfort and contentment is one that human beings seldom reach and cannot long maintain. Human beings have been noted throughout the ages for their difficulty in finding contentment, and for the brevity of any state of equilibrium that they manage to achieve. The *pleasure principle* really expresses a theoretical goal, one about which many people

---

[7] Primary process thinking can be found even among normal school children. Cf. Burstein, A. G., "Primary process in children as a function of age," *J. abnorm. soc. Psychol.,* 1959, *59,* 284–286. There are abundant protocols showing the same thing in many of Piaget's books. See, for example, Piaget, J., *Language and Thought in the Child* (1923) (trans. M. Gabain). London: Kegan Paul, Trench, Trubner, 1932. Replications of the Piaget studies generally confirm Piaget's findings.

daydream, and many hope to attain on earth or in an afterlife. In psychopathology, this hypothetical state of perfect equilibrium (toward which the id drives push) helps us to understand not only the partial satisfactions and contentments which human beings actually achieve, but also the compromises and distortions that appear in manifest dreams and in symptoms.

There are certain inevitable limitations to our achieving the goals of the pleasure principle, and of the asocial id drives, which may be mentioned here. One of them is that many different needs normally coexist at the same time in the same person, and some of them are in direct conflict with others. This makes no difference to the unrealistic id; but in reality there has to be some selection, depending upon the circumstances. A gradient or hierarchy has to be formed, with some needs prepotent over others; and since this is a *realistic compromise*, it is no longer an example of id function. Another limitation is the fundamental imbalance between the human organism and its environment. External reality is simply not organized in such a way as to satisfy all human needs and keep them satisfied. Human beings have to reorganize their environment and reorganize themselves, just to stay alive, and this demands realistic efforts which are also not part of id function. Finally, we have the structure of social living, a special limiting group of realistic conditions, which permits one satisfaction in an acceptable way under certain conditions, while it forbids other satisfactions and other ways or conditions. Again, we are up against considerations which go beyond id drives.

Id drives or instincts

The id is the source of the drives or instincts which we discussed in Chapter 4. It is the source of an unfailing upthrust of mental energy which the ego and superego must somehow tame and modify, so that it can achieve expression, discharge and pleasure, in accordance with external reality and internal standards. Otherwise the energy has to be fixed in some fantasy organization, repressed, denied, projected or otherwise kept from disturbing the ego functions.

We said in Chapter 4 that the drives most commonly involved in psychopathology are the *sexual* (or *constructive*) *drives* and the *aggressive* (or *destructive*) *drives*. These are the ones that can be greatly modified, and even suppressed completely, without apparently doing harm to the organism. Their complete repression or distortion may impoverish the personality structure or bring it into conflict with society; but the result is not comparable with that of the complete frustration of hunger, thirst or the need for sleep. Freud believed that all other human drives could be comprehended within these two groups.[8] We assume that in the id they appear as naked impulses toward immediate gratification or discharge.

[8] Freud, S., *An Outline of Psychoanalysis* (1938) (trans. J. Strachey). New York: Knopf, 1949.

Many writers insist that mental energy or cathexis is wholly unlike anything else in nature, and that it constitutes a closed system. They maintain that it is entirely different from the energy manifested in physiological function, that it cannot therefore come from physiological sources. Other writers feel free to compare mental energy to physiological energy, without having to specify the exact relationship between the two. Some go so far as to compare the concept of optimal level of drive cathexis with the physiological concept of *homeostasis*.[9] Neither position seems to do violence to the basic tenets of psychodynamics. The choice between them remains one of relative fruitfulness. We shall choose to regard mental energy as derived from physiological energy, but organized in psychological systems in accordance with mental functions. This choice is not only in harmony with observable clinical facts; it also leaves the door open for a closer relationship between physiological and psychological levels of explanation.

The concept of cathexis

The term *cathexis* means *the amount of mental energy involved*. It may be *bound energy*, such as we find in relation to organized fantasies, daydreams, conflicts, object relationships, the self and social roles. Or it may be *mobile energy*, ready to discharge immediately, by any means available, such as we assume for the id. The concept of cathexis is useful in describing id functions, in understanding ego adaptations and defenses, in formulating the superego and its precursors, in discussing object relationships and in many other psychodynamic interactions. These uses will become apparent as we move through this and the succeeding chapter, and on into the discussion of clinical material.

No method has yet been devised for measuring drive energies and their derivatives in human beings. Their quantification, therefore, is limited to estimates of relative strength, e.g., whether id drives seem strong or weak in relation to ego and superego forces, whether they seem irresistible or inhibited, whether they are controllable or overwhelming. Such crude quantification is far from satisfactory, but it has the virtue of being unpretentious. Here are a few examples of the use of the concept of cathexis.

We speak of a powerful drive cathexis in infancy, against which the relatively weak ego defenses and adaptive mechanisms cannot prevail. We can point to the violent but poorly organized, impulsive temper tantrum, a familiar form of general nonadaptive tension discharge during infancy and early childhood. We can point out, within the same frame of reference, that as soon as *ego organization* develops which can partially contain the rush of id forces and channel them, a powerful aggressive cathexis can be discharged in a more integrated and more realistic form. This may be a coordinated attack upon an obstacle blocking satisfaction, or upon another

[9] Hendrick, I., *Facts and Theories of Psychoanalysis*. (3rd ed.) New York: Knopf, 1958.

child who has been provocative or has aroused envy. Neither the attack upon an obstacle nor upon another child may be a welcome social event, but it does show a more realistic integration of drive discharge than that of merely flailing the arms, stamping and yelling. This "more realistic integration," however, has already carried us beyond id function, which cares nothing about consequences but only about immediate tension relief.

There is another upsurge of sexual and aggressive drive tension at puberty which, although it involves far more than id function, illustrates the use made of the concept of cathexis. Both physiological changes and social pressures give to id drives indirectly a sudden impetus which proves to be more than the adolescent ego organization can handle. There may be all kinds of infantile behavior, including pointless negativism, sexual "acting out," and even temper outbursts. The adolescent rarely reverts to the infantile pattern of flailing his limbs and yelling.

When he has matured a little further, and worked through his new and difficult situation as an adolescent in our culture, the young person will find the cathectic balance once more favoring ego and superego control, as it did during latency. He will be able once again to utilize, channel, tame and defend against the now more powerful than ever *drive cathexes* or *energies*. The turbulence will settle down and the adolescent will grow into an adult. As in the first example, that of the temper tantrum developing into coordinated attack, we have had to turn to ego function to illustrate id activity. This will be evident also, and much more interesting, when we come to the symptom formation of neuroses and psychoses.

The primary process of the id

The name *primary process* implies a mode of operation which precedes in time the development of all other forms of mental function in the individual. It includes throughout life the primitive rock-bottom activities, the raw strivings and strange unconscious maneuvers of the human being. It includes prelogical archaic symbolism, a peculiar interchange of expressive vehicles, a tendency to condense the cathexes of several drives into one, and an absence of such logical necessities as negation, resolution of contradiction, and the recognition of time and spatial relations. These characteristics, which are hardly surprising when we recall the perceptual and cognitive primitivity of young infants,[10] are responsible for much of the weird experiences that we have in dreaming, and that occur in delirium, intoxications, psychotic symptomatology and sensory deprivation.[11]

Freud originally developed his concept of the primary process in his clinical work with neurotic symptom formation, and he later applied it to

[10] Discussed in Chapter 2, in the section on the oral dependent phase.

[11] Cf. Jones, A., Wilkinson, H. J., and Braden, I., "Information deprivation as a motivational variable," *J. exp. Psychol.*, 1961, *62*, 126–137; Jones, A., "Supplementary report: information deprivation and irrelevant drive as determiners of an instrumental response," *J. exp. Psychol.*, 1961, *62*, 310–311.

work out the meanings of manifest dreams (*dream interpretation*). As a concept it proved so fruitful that for the first time in history neuroses and manifest dreams, which had always seemed nonsensical, became intelligible. Psychoses also reveal striking derivatives of the primary process; and so do slips of the tongue and other parapraxes, wit and humor, mythology and many artistic creations. As a matter of fact, primary process thinking and feeling are present to some degree in the unconscious activity of everyone and lead to a great deal of deeply satisfying experience. We shall confine our discussion here to the two original sources of information about the primary process, dreaming and symptom formation.

Mobile cathexes of the id. Freud conceived of the cathexes or energy charges of the id as being highly mobile, in contrast to the cathexes of ego and superego which are bound in stable organizations.[12] Theoretically, if it were not for the presence of an ego organization, the drive cathexes of the id would be continually discharging as they built up, regardless of the effects upon the environment or even upon the organism itself. The most that would be formed in the way of object relationships would be a transient, impersonal one with anything or anyone that can serve as a medium of discharge. (This is what one sometimes finds in autistic children, whose ego development is minimal.) Since immediate discharge or gratification is the only driving force in the id, it makes no difference how or where the cathectic discharge occurs, as long as tension is lowered to an optimal level, consonant with the pleasure principle. Two common results of this cathectic mobility are seen in *displacement* and *condensation*.

Displacement. In terms of id energy, this means the complete transfer of cathexis from one process, which may be unable to gain access to an available outlet, to another process which is free to discharge energy. The means or vehicle of discharge seems to be of as little importance as the choice of a taxicab to get to a theater. If one driver cannot get through, the cathexis is displaced on to one that can, and if the second one gets blocked, something quite different may be used for discharge.

We shall see obvious examples of this kind of almost mindless displacement when we come to study symptom formation in neurotic illness. In some of our obsessive compulsive patients, for example, the same conflict over hostile aggression and contamination may be expressed in a dozen different ways by the same patient, without his having any conscious awareness of what is happening or why. Forbidden impulses, which have no chance of direct expression, come through clearly in a phobia whose terrifying object seems far removed from the forbidden impulse. It goes without saying that symptoms are end-products, not only of primary process procedures, but also of defensive maneuvers. Nevertheless, as we shall show a

[12] See Holt, R. R., "A critical examination of Freud's concept of bound *vs.* free cathexis," *J. Amer. Psychoanal. Ass.*, 1962, *10*, 475–525.

little further on, they illustrate what happens to a preconscious organization when it is subjected to the primary process during a regression.

Condensation. Because id cathexes are mobile, several of them can be condensed in one drive or drive derivative; everything is then discharged at once. To use the analogy of the taxicab again, it is as though only one cab were able to get through, and everyone from the blocked cabs crowded into the one with free access. Condensation is really only a special form of displacement of cathexes.

Condensations are common among the neurotic symptoms. A single phobia may represent several different drive cathexes. The same conversion symptom may represent the energies of completely opposite drives, just as a caricature or a piece of sculpture may carry entirely different meanings at the same time. Obsessive compulsive patients commonly represent two opposed impulses, one of which may be used defensively to hold the other in check. Such defensive functions do not belong to the id, of course, any more than do caricatures and sculptures; but all represent the use of primary process maneuvers in gaining simultaneous discharge or expression for more than one impulse.

Lack of negation. Negation cannot be represented in a system of freely mobile cathexes which are all striving for discharge, and which will make use of any available avenue whatever. Negation is a direct ego function and an indirect superego function. It implies a recognition of reality and an ability to accept it, both of which are lacking in the id. When a patient makes a negation, particularly if it is uncalled for in the situation and is related to known conflictual material, it usually means an unconscious expression of what is being denied. When a patient recounts a manifest dream, and states that a woman in it was *not* his mother, the chances are good that his mother actually was represented in the dream, although one must find other evidence for it as confirmation.

Unresolved contradictions. In the primary process opposites exist side by side without entering into a compromise, even without mutual confrontation. One drive demand may immediately accompany another drive demand without producing any change in either of them. This is only another way of expressing the cathectic mobility of the drives, their push toward discharge or expression, without regard for consequences and without regard for integration.

Primitive symbols. This characteristic was originally ascribed to Freud's *System Unconscious*, before the division had been made into id, ego and superego. It was carried over into the concept of the primary process of the id. It has always been, and still is, the subject of controversy. In its original form, the concept of *primitive symbolization* pictured the symbols as probably universal, and presumably not capable of further analysis, a sort of innate "given." It has been suggested that man may have inherited them from prehistoric experience.

It seems more likely today that the primitive symbols arise *de novo* in each infant and small child. Their apparent universality, at least in societies with our type of family unit, is more likely the result of universally similar primitive experiences in each little child than the result of an inheritance of acquired experience. The paucity of associations, which is characteristic of primitive symbols, may be a function of the relatively simple, syncretic character of infantile thinking at the time when the symbols first appeared in the child's life.

The most extensive and easily accessible discussion of primitive symbols appears in the *Tenth Lecture,* "Symbolism in Dreams," in Freud's *A General Introduction to Psychoanalysis.*[13] Freud listed there, among others, symbols of the human body as a *house,* of parents as *royalty,* of children and siblings as *little animals* and *vermin,* of birth by some direct reference to *water,* of death as *journeying* or *traveling,* and of nakedness as *clothes* or *uniforms.* Freud gave a lengthy account of primitive sexual symbolism, the variety and prominence of which is easy to understand in terms of a small child's fascination and perplexity concerning sex relations and their consequences.

A nonsensical manifest dream and some of its unconscious roots

Freud demonstrated at the turn of the century that the manifest dream which we remember when we wake up is not the whole dream process but only an end-product of unconscious processes. The same is true of a neurotic symptom. A study of either will show that what is being expressed has been subjected to the primary process, as we have just described it, and in addition to ego defensive and adaptive mechanisms, and usually to superego influences as well.[14] In the clinical chapters, which follow our discussion of the defenses, we shall see many examples of such alterations in the formation of neurotic and psychotic symptoms. At this point it will be helpful if we present and partially dissect a nonsensical manifest dream reported during therapy by an intelligent patient.

The patient. A thirty-four-year-old married business man had been in analytic treatment for about a year when he reported the dream that follows. He was suffering from a character disorder, with chronic dissatisfaction over his work, diffidence in social contacts, and timidity in

[13] Freud, S., *A General Introduction to Psychoanalysis* (trans. J. Riviere). Garden City, N.Y.: Doubleday Permabooks, 1953.
[14] Lewis, H. B., "Organization of the self as reflected in manifest dreams," *Psychoanalysis & Psychoanal. Rev.,* 1959, *46,* 21–35; Beigel, H., "Mental processes during the production of dreams," *J. Psychol.,* 1959, *43,* 171–187.

the presence of women other than his wife. He had three children. His own personal history was not remarkable, excepting that his mother had always dominated the home, while his father was passive and shy. The patient had only one sibling, an older sister. She and his mother had always seemed strong and self-assured; they had treated him and his father as though they were of no importance.

The manifest dream. There were two very large naked women in a forest, half-turned away from him. They looked like Greek goddesses in a Renaissance painting. One of them gave him a bow and arrow to shoot her with. It seemed she had done something of the kind herself before. She was confident and contemptuous. He seemed to have shot at her and missed, although he could not remember this happening in the dream. One of the women had disappeared, but the one who had given him the bow and arrow said something about making herself so big that he could not miss. She swooped past him and he shot her in the abdomen with an arrow or a javelin. She had not turned toward him, and he could not recall actually doing this, but somehow he knew he had. Then there was a man facing him at a distance, partly doubled up ("like a martyr") and moving sidewise, with a javelin in his mid-abdomen, and blood flowing from the wound. It seemed that a woman had done it to him. The man clawed at what looked like a window sill, as high as the patient's head, leaving blood marks followed by a message cut into the wood of the sill, in the form of dots and dashes.

The patient felt guilty about the man's death (although the dying appeared in the dream as something that had already happened). He became furtive and watchful. He went around, trying to wipe the blood from things, but without success. Then he was in a mixed group and a woman was offering drinks. He asked for milk because that would make him seem incapable of killing someone.

Then he was in a house with the widow of the killed man, and he felt uncomfortable about her husband's death. But now it seemed that it was her son who had been killed, and she was a widow, with only a daughter left. The patient's guilt disappeared. The son who had been killed seemed to be himself. There was now a "sort of architect" present who knew all about the widow's house, and seemed to have built it. This man said, "Isn't it beautiful!" and asked if the patient had seen the barn. The patient said he hadn't, and at that moment he was back in the widow's house squeezing through a narrow passage toward a disarranged kitchen. He awoke with palpitation and colicky pain.

Some of the patient's associations. A manifest dream as long as this and as complex cannot be thoroughly explored in forty minutes, or even in as many hours. There are a few signs of childhood remembrances which the patient did not himself contribute. These were the enormous size of the women — as adults appear to little children — their being naked, the childish bow and arrow, the patient's being the only person to get milk from a woman, and his finding the window sill at the level of his head. His own associations follow.

Both of the women seemed to be his mother. If so, this would illus-trate another characteristic of the primary process, not so far men-tioned, that of *emphasis by duplication*, a device also used in ancient temples to indicate the importance of a deity. His mother had always treated him with good-natured condescension, as though she and his sister were superior beings. He had owned a bow and some rubber-tipped arrows in childhood, and had gotten into trouble for shooting at other children. He felt "there was something sexy in the atmosphere" of the dream.

Because of the abdominal pain, he felt that the house which the "sort of architect" seemed to have built was his own body, and that the architect was his father who, in the dream, seemed to know all about it. (The architect might also have been himself, although he did not say so, because he was meticulous about his appearance and vain.) The disarranged kitchen made him think of menstruation and his mother again, or perhaps, he said, his sister. His sister had worked in a telegraph office before automatic keys and teletype had come in.

The theme of being alone in the house with the widow of a man he had killed needed little translation. This woman also seemed to be his mother; and she had a son and a daughter, as his mother had. The victim seemed to be the patient's father; and since the guilt faded to mere sympathy as soon as the son seemed to have been killed, it must have been the patient who killed the father, or at least wished him dead. There is primary process maneuvering here. The primary process can-not express negation, and it can tolerate contradictions. It was a woman who killed the man, therefore it was not the patient, even though it was he who a moment earlier had held the arrow or a javelin. Further-more, even though the widow's son had been killed — who the patient felt was himself — and the widow was left with a daughter, it was he himself who was left with the widow in the dream.

Later therapeutic work with this patient threw more light on the primary process displacement and condensation in this dream. The patient had envied his sister in childhood, because she seemed self-assured and because she was openly preferred by his mother. Toward the end of this dream, "the widow with only a daughter left" meant what it depicted: his mother widowed and left alone with him in the preferred position that his sister always had. The wounded, dying man seems also to have represented his sister, since she was the only person he knew who could make messages in dots and dashes with her "claws."

A further reference came out still later in therapy. The patient had a repressed childhood belief, still unresolved, that birth took place through a "cut in the abdomen," or through the umbilicus, he was not sure which. He retained this belief in spite of knowing the facts about childbirth. This retention of two contradictory interpretations, without either affecting the other, is again characteristic of the primary process. Here we see a common childhood fantasy coexisting with adult knowl-edge, as though both were components of the primary process and had once been a part of the id. Actually, as we have seen, this kind of thing happens in fantasies, conflicts, daydreams, and other ego organizations, if they are repressed and come into functional relationship with the id.

There is also confusion of sex role in the manifest dream. A huge arrogant naked woman gives the dreaming patient the means for shooting her in the abdomen, as if he were Dan Cupid himself. It is somehow implied in the dream that she has done something like the shooting herself. Then she swoops near him avowedly to make a target of herself that he cannot miss, since it is implied that he has previously missed. Yet what next appears in the manifest dream is a dying *man* with a bleeding wound where the patient's childhood fantasy placed childbirth. The primary process confusion is compounded by the patient's sex identity confusion, of which, up to the time of the dream, he seemed not to have been aware.

The confusions multiply. The man dying of a javelin wound was killed by a woman, but it is the patient who is furtive and guilty. The guilt disappears as soon as it seems to be not the husband but the son who has been killed. Yet the patient felt that he was the son; and in contradiction to all this, the dream leaves the woman a widow (in reality no one in the family had died), and cancels out the death wish expressed against the father by a death wish against the son. But, as only the primary process can do, it allows the original fantasy of possessing the mother alone to triumph, at least until the "architect" appears. Nothing more childish can be imagined than this dream solution of the edipal conflict, nor than its representation of the inverted edipal complex at the same time — for the dying man seems to have represented the patient himself, as well as his sister and his father.

Nothing so far has been said about the primitive symbolism in the dream. The bow and arrow has been used for milennia as a symbol of sexual love. The javelin as a phallic symbol is also worldwide. A bleeding wound of the kind depicted by the patient usually means the female genitalia. The house is a universal symbol of the body; and the patient experienced the house in the dream as somehow his own body, with his father as its architect. At this point we shall leave the dream, even though it contains a great deal that has not been touched upon here, and pass to the fragments of another person's manifest dream which show obvious residues of the day preceding it.

The day's residues in a manifest dream

To illustrate further the way in which the primary process works in forming a manifest dream, we shall present here some fragments which the writer recently dreamed. These were written down immediately upon awakening, along with the previous day's residues related to them. Each dream fragment will appear first in italics, followed by the day's residues from which it seems to have been derived.

(1) *My wife and I were exploring a new country.* We had been discussing our plans to travel soon after the book was to be finished.

(2) *Someone said something like, "They always give you pesetas and piastres which you can only spend in Spain."* We had talked about currency restrictions in Spain; and I had remarked that the Andalusians say, "Health and pesetas!" — "May you be well and have money!" The word *piastres* sounds ridiculous, since this is Turkish currency, not Spanish. But one of our friends had been telling us on this day, preceding the dream, that he had lived in Turkey for several years. We had not mentioned *piastres,* but in my childhood I had collected Turkish postage stamps with that word on them.

(3) *We were starting out at dawn.* This is actually contrary to our custom, but I had told friends the day before that I would resume my writing this book at dawn, which I had actually been doing for several months.

(4) *There were strange birds with intense black and white markings.* At our friend's place in the country we had seen and talked about many birds, strange to us, which came there to feed. Some of them actually had intense black and white markings, though none of them like the ones appearing in the manifest dream.

(5) *The flowers would not fade.* A man working for us had brought us some beautiful flowers from his own garden on the day preceding the dream. Later the same day we had also visited the house and grounds of other friends in the country whose flowers were fading because the friends were away on vacation, as we would like to have been also.

(6) *It was agreed that I would not shout unless I saw a lion.* Just before going to sleep I had been reading an extraordinary book about a lioness, Elsa, in which the writer expressed concern about the roaring of lions.[15]

In presenting these fragments, I have omitted many personal references for personal reasons. Even so, an astute person, versed in the interpretation of dreams, will detect the expression of previously unconscious wishes, fears and conflicts. The reason for including this section is to offer examples of the use that the primary process makes of the previous day's residues for its own expressive purposes.[16] We may now summarize what we have been saying about the id and the primary process, before going on to discuss the ego.

Summary of the id and the primary process[17]

The id is an abstraction which represents what is probably the mental organization of neonates and very young children. Some such organization

---

[15] Adamson, J., *Living Free.* New York: Harcourt, Brace, 1961.

[16] Pine, F., "Incidental stimulation: a study of preconscious transformations," *J. abnorm. soc. Psychol.,* 1960, *60,* 68–75.

[17] A lively exposition of primary and secondary process thinking is to be found in the original account of Freud, S., *The Interpretation of Dreams.* (1900), Standard Edition, 1953, vols. 4 and 5. There is also a one-volume reprint published by Basic Books, Inc., New York. Both are translations made by J. Strachey. Early translations have been criticized as often misleading and erroneous.

persists throughout life, governed by drives for immediate gratification, and operating in a primitive manner which we call the primary process. Early childhood fantasies, conflicts, daydreams and other organizations, if they are repressed, may join the id and be subjected to the primary process. When we fall asleep and dream, whether we are neurotic or normal, we regress to some such level. We lose some of the differentiation into id, unconscious ego and preconscious ego, and re-experience perceptions from the previous day mixed up with childhood fantasies and, presumably, new perceptual or cognitive creations.[18] All this material has been worked over unconsciously by the primary process, during the day as well as at night, and what we experience as the manifest dream is an end-product, just as a neurotic symptom is.[19]

The energy of id drives or "instincts" is known as *drive cathexis* or *instinctual cathexis*. We believe that it is derived from physiological energy, although a great many others believe that it is best conceived of as a closed psychical system. Id cathexes are mobile; and they give rise to many irrational phenomena, including displacement and condensation. (These also appear in conscious symbolism and in works of art.) There is no such thing as negation in the id; the most that can be done to express negation is disappearance, absence, or the appearance of an opposite.

Contradictions exist side by side in the id, however, without modification or compromise. All drives push toward expression or discharge without regard for consequences or logical reflection. Emphases are expressed by size, repetition and duplication. Primitive symbols appear which if not actually universal, are at least apparently universal in Western culture. They have been ascribed to prehistorical thinking; but they can also be explained in terms of the primitive experiencing of contemporary infants and small children.[20]

We cannot observe the primary process directly; but we can infer some of its properties, thanks to Freud's insight, from a study of preconscious thinking that has been subjected to the primary process during a regression. Ordinary sleep is such a regression. The interpretation of dreams and the study of neurotic symptom formation provide the necessary opportunities. A nonsensical manifest dream has been partially interpreted, that is, traced to some of its unconscious origins, as an example of the way in which the primary process works; and fragments from another dream have been presented, along with happenings of the preceding day, in order to give examples of the way in which the primary process makes use of the day's

[18] DeMartino, M. F. (Ed.), *Dreams and Personality Dynamics.* Springfield, Ill.: Thomas, 1959; Stein, M. I., and Heinze, S. J., *Creativity and the Individual: Summaries of Selected Literature in Psychology and Psychiatry.* Glencoe, Ill.: Free Press, 1960.
[19] See Sharpe, E. F., *Dream Analysis.* London: Hogarth, 1937; French. T. M., *The Integration of Behavior. Volume 2: The Integrative Process in Dreams.* Chicago: Univ. of Chicago Press, 1954.
[20] Moriarty, D. M., "Some observations on animism," *Psychiat. Quart.,* 1961, *35,* 156–164.

residuals in construcing a manifest dream. We are now ready to consider the other half of the original *id-ego nucleus, the ego.*

The Ego and Secondary Processes

The ego is an organization of mental systems which arise out of inter- action with external and somatic reality. Freud at one time conceptualized the ego as a modification of the surface of the id where it was exposed after birth to the impact of reality. Later he conceptualized the ego as probably a differentiation from an original id-ego nucleus, again because of the impact of reality. Both conceptions are in current use. In both, the *ego* is regarded as an organization of mental systems arising out of interaction with somatic and external reality, and it is regarded as lying functionally between the id and reality.

Conscious, preconscious and unconscious ego systems

The division of ego systems into *conscious, preconscious* and *unconscious levels of operation* follows in general the division already described under *levels of motivation* in Chapter 4.

Conscious. Only a relatively small proportion of experience can be con- scious at any moment. Freud compared conscious awareness to the illumi- nation of a circumscribed area by a searchlight. He pictured the act of making something conscious as being something like the function of a special organ of perception. At any given moment we are aware of doing, feeling, remembering, imagining or thinking something; the next moment this may fade into the preconscious background, while we become aware of some- thing else. Such a change in focus may result from a shift in the environ- ment, from a shift of a person's attention, while the environment remains the same, or from both a shift in the environment and a shift in attention.

Preconscious. The scope of the preconscious is vast.[21] It includes the effects of present and past perception, feeling, action, recall, imagining and thinking. It includes the representations of objects, events and relationships, which have been internalized as a result of the impact of external and somatic reality. It also includes representations of the id drives and of pressures from the superego or its precursors. As we pointed out in discussing motivation, there is a vast reservoir of *readily available preconscious experience* upon which we can draw at will. Only the limitation imposed by the narrowness of consciousness prevents our being aware of this experience. There is also a great deal of the preconscious which is *not readily available.* We defend

---

[21] Cf. Kris, E., "On preconscious mental processes," in *Psychoanalytic Explorations in Art.* New York: Internat. Univ. Press, 1952.

ourselves against becoming aware of some of this through such maneuvers as denial, isolation, rationalization, intellectualization, reaction-formation and ritual. Some of the preconscious includes material which once was conscious or readily available, but has since been reshaped and assimilated so as to make it *ego-syntonic,* that is, acceptable in terms of social approval or the image a person has of himself.

Unconscious. Most of the unconscious ego has also at one time been conscious or preconscious. It is barred from direct representation in conscious and preconscious ego systems by the action of defense mechanisms, most of which are also unconscious and belong to the ego organization. Repression is the most important of these mechanisms. The varieties of organization found in the unconscious ego cover a wide spectrum.

At one end of the scale the organization appears to be logical. Normal examples can be found among habitual daydreams, which remain unconscious. We find pathological examples in the logical structure of delusions, which are projected from the unconscious, denied, and misinterpreted as the actions, attitudes and intentions of other persons. The extreme of this kind of operation has been described as the *paranoid pseudocommunity,* a projected delusional organization in which the interrelationships imputed by the paranoid person, even though grossly misinterpreted, are nevertheless realistically conceived.[22] At the other end of the scale, the organization of the unconscious ego approaches that of the primary process in the id.

It is helpful to recognize from the start that the relationships between *unconscious ego* and *id representations* fluctuate a great deal. Id derivatives sometimes are integrated into relatively logical, or at least prelogical, dynamic organizations; and unconscious ego elements are usually subjected to the primary process so that they may become fantastically illogical. In manifest dreams, for example, there may be derivatives from both extremes of the unconscious ego, as well as from the preconscious ego and the superego. All of these may be subjected to the primary process of the *dreamwork,* and projected as a preconscious manifest dream. The differences in organization of manifest dreams seems often to be related to the depth of sleep during the dream, that is, to the depth of regression.

The pleasure principle and the reality principle

In contrast to the id, with its primary process and its mobile cathexes, most preconscious and conscious ego systems are realistically organized. Even the preconscious ego systems, and some of the unconscious ego systems, which *appear unrealistic in terms of adult perception, feeling, remembering, imagining, thinking and action,* were at one time *realistic* during childhood development. In other words, they represent the products of some inter-

[22] Cameron, N., "Paranoid conditions and paranoia," in S. Arieti (Ed.), *American Handbook of Psychiatry.* New York: Basic Books, 1959, pp. 508–539.

action with external or somatic reality at an immature level of interpretation.

We have said that the id operates in accordance with the *pleasure principle.* It seeks immediate gratification or discharge of all its wants and tensions, no matter how contradictory they may be, and no matter what the consequences may be to others or to the person himself. The only concern of the id is that of maintaining an optimal level of internal energies. The moment its tensions rise above this, the id presses toward discharge. It is not organized in such a way that it can tolerate delay, frustration or conflict. It cannot make compromises or consider consequences. It is impulsive, driving and irrational.

Preconscious and conscious ego systems, and some of the unconscious ego systems, operate according to the *reality principle.* They are able to bind cathexes into stable organizations. In fact, the mere organization of an ego system absorbs energy. We have called this *the energy of organization.* Its importance will become obvious when we come to the study of regression.

The ego is capable of organizing experience and behavior in ways that are rational, precise, practical, and appropriate to the human environment.[23] The ego systems that contrast most sharply with the primary process of the id are the mature realistic perceptions, emotions, thinking, and action of adults. Their organization in relation to external and somatic realities sets them apart from the id, with its insatiable upthrust toward immediate gratification. The ego can also organize abstractions whose component parts are internally consistent, even though these components may not correspond point for point with any realistic environmental structure. Theoretical systems and mathematical constructions belong in this group.

We lump all such realistic and logically consistent ego organizations together as *secondary processes,* that is, *processes which have developed secondarily under the impact of external demands.* The ego, with its secondary processes, does not mature fully until adulthood has been reached, and even then it is subject to frequent revision.

Adult ego systems, even the most mature ones, often include a great deal that does not follow exact logical reasoning or realistic action. It is the illogical, unrealistic component of ego functioning that allows for playful, imaginative, poetic and creative activities. Without these an adult is a dull fellow, chained to a slab of concrete fact. But, however fanciful they may be, the daytime performances of a normal adult are a far cry from the almost mindless primary process of the id, with its tumultuous mobile cathexes and its irresponsible drive toward immediate gratification. Even when the ego uses such id-like maneuvers as *displacement, condensation* and *symbolization,* which it often does, they are used in an organized manner that has little resemblance to the helter-skelter primary process of the id.

The major goal of the realistic ego is still the same as that of the id. The ego seeks gratification and a reduction of tensions to optimal levels. The

[23] The ego organization *represents* reality; but it need not have the same structure as the reality it represents, any more than a valid mathematical expression need have the structure of the reality it represents.

difference is that, whereas the id is impulsive and irrational, the ego at its best takes into account the realistic demands of the situation, the consequences of gratification and discharge, the overriding need to preserve the integrity of the psychodynamic system, and the opportunities there may be to relieve id and superego pressures, as well as to reduce those generated within ego systems themselves.

The preconscious ego, as an organization of systems, is sometimes pictured as harassed, hemmed in, and threatened from all sides with disintegration. This is really the picture of an ego organization on the verge of being overwhelmed, and not of the everyday preconscious ego. Most of the time the ego seems to operate like a computer, whose performances may be dazzlingly complex and enormously active, but whose integrity is far from fragile. Nevertheless, the strain of reality adaptation does appear in the periodic need for a flight into sleep, which occupies about one-third of every twenty-four hours. During much of this period of withdrawal into sleep the reality principle no longer rules.

Before leaving the subject of the reality principle, it must be said that the realities of a person's environment, the capabilities and limitations of his body, and the organization of his ego at the time, need not be at odds with one another. Neither, for that matter, need be the pressures from the id and the superego. One of the major functions of the normal ego is that of preserving optimal tension throughout the *entire psychodynamic system*. It is obvious that, since the id is forever pressing toward discharge as its tensions rise, the ego must forever be finding ways of handling id tensions, by binding them in its own organizations, by using them in its unconscious defense mechanisms, by repressing them or by discharging them. Otherwise a general psychodynamic equilibrium could not be maintained.

The ego controls perception and cognition. It commands all of the avenues of discharge and the means of gratification. When it blocks or contains id discharge it acts as the opponent of the id. But whenever it allows its facilities to be used for id discharge, which is very often the case, it acts as the id's most obliging servant.

Inborn patterns and realistic action

The myth of the *tabula rasa,* the empty slate of the mind at birth, has long been discredited. More recently the similar notion, that we begin postnatal life with nothing but a bundle of reflexes, has also suffered a widespread decline. There seem to be many inborn patterns of behavior and experience which are "released" under appropriate conditions.

We do not have far to go to find an example of the release of an inborn pattern of complex realistic behavior. The nursing of a neonate is a realistic perceptual and behavioral performance which emerges in direct relation to an outside food source. Nursing has to be carried out in accordance with the *reality principle,* that is, in accordance with what the infant needs, what the environment actually offers, and what the body actually can do.

Infant hunger and the availability of a nipple act together to "release" a completely patterned, realistic activity. The satisfaction of hunger comes about through a coordinated bodily effort (suckling), in direct relation to an object or "partial object" (nipple).[24] If the infant is not hungry, the nipple does not call out suckling.[25] If the infant is driven by hunger, but there is no milk-yielding nipple available, the nursing pattern may begin, but it almost immediately disintegrates into generalized restlessness, squirming or flailing, and crying. Although hungry crying acts as a signal to the mother that feeding is needed, crying appears *at first* as nothing more than a part of general tension discharge.

It goes without saying that infants usually require maternal help at first in finding the nipple, and they need comfortable support while they suckle. It is also obvious that learning takes place. The nursling learns to perfect the coordinations involved in holding on to the nipple, suckling, swallowing and breathing at the same time.[26] With practice he shows rapid improvement in nursing skill. But the important point is that the initial act of nursing depends upon the pre-existence of an inborn patterned organization, ready in advance for suckling. Without such an inborn pattern, there could be no learning, because there would be no initial hunger-driven, nipple-directed act to improve upon.

Adaptations to need through the use of pre-existing adaptive organizations are actually not new in the organism's history. In discussing embryonic development, in Chapter 2, we mentioned the fact that such organs as the heart and the gastrointestinal tract develop, and even begin to perform their characteristic functions, before there is anything useful for them to do. It is true that they will not as a rule continue to develop indefinitely unless they acquire a function; but their initial development does not come about because their function is needed at the time.

Something of the same kind happens in the perceptual-motor activities of an infant's mouth, eyes and hands, which we also discussed in Chapter 2. These externally directed structures are continually active for a long period before the infant becomes able to deal orally, visually and manually in an intercoordinated way. There may be other ego organizations, maturing later, which help to account for the almost universal appearance of the edipal complex in close-knit family units, just as there must be inborn patterns responsible for the appearance in adolescence of appropriate mature sex behavior and experience.[27]

---

[24] The nipple is called a "partial object" because it is only part of what will later become the infant's love object, his mother.

[25] What is called "pleasure-sucking" of thumb and fingers is qualitatively different from nursing. Its postural head and neck patterns are also different. Sometimes it seems to have been practiced *in utero.*

[26] Cf. Fraiberg, S., *The Magic Years.* New York: Scribner, 1959; Winnicott, D. W., *Mother and Child.* New York: Basic Books, 1957.

[27] Nobody questions the inborn potentiality in the female infant to assume years later a body conformation quite unlike that in early childhood, or the inborn potentiality in the male infant for the growth of a beard in adolescence. What we are discussing here is no more mysterious than this.

This readiness of the human organism's integrative structures to engage in complex behavior and experience, under certain conditions, seems to be just as basic for human development as the human being's tremendous capacity for learning. Both are necessary for realistic ego adaptation and mastery.[28]

Differentiation of the ego systems

Ego systems develop as a result of interactions with external and somatic reality.[29] We have just used the nursing performance as an early example of realistic ego adaptation. The infant, driven by his hunger, reaches beyond his body to work on an outside partial object that can bring satisfaction of his hunger. Each time his hunger recurs it is satisfied by the same partial object (nipple), and through the same suckling activity. Such patterned activity, which the central nervous system makes possible, leads to specific changes in the patterning of the central nervous system itself. The external expression of these changes we see in the improvement of the skilled action. The internal changes, which we cannot observe, lay the foundations for expectation, for secondary processes, and for basic trust.[30]

We assume that in infants, as in older children, there is some central representation or imagery of the whole act and its perceived consequences. This central representation, or *imagery*, would include the partial object (nipple), as the child experiences it, his feelings of hunger, of fulfillment and satiation, and the whole spectrum of his oral perceptions. It would include the experience of hungry searching, the contact with the nipple and its incorporation, the suckling sequences, and finally letting go the nipple and sinking into oblivion. The growth and integration of such organized central representations is a major part of the growth and integration of the ego. These results are unmistakably different from the primary process. They are among the earliest ego systems to arise out of specific abilities to bring satisfaction to id needs.

Earlier we extolled the wealth of diversified experience which the mouth can yield. We know that this complex, self-contained oral system plays a

[28] Frankiel, R. V., *A Review of Research on Parent Influence on Child Personality.* New York: Family Service Ass. of America, 1959; Bishop, B. M., "Mother-child interaction and the social behavior of children," *Psychol. Monogr.,* 1951, *63,* Whole No. 328; Chess, S., Thomas, A., and Birch, H., "Characteristics of the individual child's behavioral responses to the environment," *Amer. J. Orthopsychiat.,* 1959, *29,* 791–802; Tuddenham, R. D., "The constancy of personality ratings over two decades," *Genet. Psychol. Monogr.,* 1959, *60,* 3–29.

[29] By *somatic reality* we mean the body and its functions as a person experiences them. Although difficult to put into words, the experience seems familiar to everyone that his body is a thing, an object of mental observation, as well as of the observation of other people. The body and its functions certainly belong to a person, but they are never identical with his experience of them nor with his concept of them. It is for this reason that we formulate the body and its functions as a special form of reality, and call it *somatic reality.*

[30] Cf. Loewald, H. W., "Ego and reality," *Internat. J. Psychoanal.,* 1951, *32,* 10–18; Loewald, H. W., "On the therapeutic action of psychoanalysis," *Internat. J. Psychoanal.,* 1960, *41,* 16–33.

leading role in contacting, experiencing and incorporating many kinds of external and somatic reality. It serves as the model for incorporation experiences in other perceptual modalities. The mouth adapts realistically to what it wants; it masters the nipple, for example, and successfully milks it. For many months at the start of life it explores endlessly whatever it can mouth. These explorations, as well as the feeding experiences, exert a profound effect upon early ego organization patterns. The earliest ego organization is often called a *mouth ego* to emphasize this dominant influence.[31] Of course, all of the perceptual systems are contributing something to this early ego organization; it is only a question of which contribution is most concentrated.

As ego systems organize through interactions with external and somatic realities, they come to represent, not only these realities, but also derivatives of the drives themselves, and of other contributions from other ego systems. Functionally, the ego occupies a position between the id and reality. Thus, long before an infant is capable of distinguishing between himself and others, between his own body experiences and what he imagines, between drive derivatives and his acts of satisfying them, he is busily engaged in laying down *the foundations for such distinctions* in his rapidly growing ego organization. This he does through his overt behavior and its feedback, through his internal experiences with reality and his wants, through his comforts and discomforts, and through the imagery that his experiences create and his needs reactivate.

(*a*) *Differentiation through organization.* The dramatic change that occurs when a hungry, diffusely squirming, crying infant is put to the breast, is only one example of the contrast that appears between the wild, demanding pressure of total want, and the goal-directed, realistic action of an internally organized system. It symbolizes the contrast between *id representations*, pushing for diffuse action in all directions, and an *ego integration*, which adapts to reality, begins to master it, and organizes imagery that can represent all the components of the integrated act of nursing. It symbolizes also the beginning of a process of channeling and controlling drive-derivatives to form stable ego systems. Such systems lead eventually to reasonable demands upon the environment, and they provide the means of controlling both the demands and the environment.

This factor, *the organization of experience and behavior in realistic terms*, is one of the chief sources of differentiation between ego and id. If they are to be able to operate at all, the ego systems must be capable of excluding any id derivatives that tend to disrupt them. The integrity of ego systems depends upon their maintaining themselves separate from the id and the primary process. We know that when boundaries can no longer be maintained, the derivatives of id drives invade ego organizations on a massive

[31] Hoffer, W., "Mouth, hand and ego formation," *Psychoanal. Study Child*, 1949, 3/4, 49–56.

scale, and realistic ego functioning disintegrates. We shall find examples of this in panic states and in psychoses.[32]

(b) *Differentiation through defense mechanisms.* A factor of the greatest importance in differentiating the preconscious ego from the unconscious ego and the id is the development of specific *unconscious ego defense mechanisms,* such as *repression.* These we shall discuss in some detail in Chapter 6. Many of them are especially designed to contain id activity and limit the scope of the primary process. They become the bastions which consolidate ego boundaries. They make it possible for preconscious ego systems to develop more and more realistically, with fewer and fewer disruptive intrusions from the id and the repressed unconscious ego which becomes associated with it.

(c) *Differentiation through reality-testing.* A third differentiating function of the ego is that of distinguishing between something one is imagining and something perceived in external reality or in the body. Reality-testing is lost in the dreams we have while asleep; what we are imagining as the manifest dream appears to be happening in external or somatic reality until we awaken. Reality-testing is also lost in delusional and hallucinatory states — whether these are part of psychotic regression or are induced by intoxication or by sensory deprivation. We shall discuss reality-testing further, toward the end of the chapter.

(d) *Maturation of the preconscious ego.* A really clear separation of the preconscious and conscious ego from the unconscious ego and the derivatives of the id is not achieved for many years. It is normal for a small child to be impulsive and inconsistent, intolerant of delay and frustration, and self-contradictory in what he expects and demands. These are all signs of his ineffectual control over the primary processes characteristic of the unconscious ego and id-derivatives. His preconscious and conscious ego performance are still showing the influence of primary process intrusions.

Even after years of experience with realities, children are still notoriously unrealistic. The pre-edipal child has innumerable omnipotent fantasies and irrational fears. He cannot always distinguish clearly between what he fantasies and what he experiences or recalls. His "tall tales" reflect this genuine confusion. The edipal child, who has mastered and is daily mastering so much, is still driven by irresistible and incompatible derivatives of id impulses. These, as we have seen, make him anticipate sexual and aggressive relationships which are illusory and impossible, doomed from the very start to failure.

Neither the realities of his body, nor the potentialities of his environment, justify the edipal child's expectations. They are as irrational as an adult delusion, and for the same reason: the upthrust from the drives is more than

---

[32] See, for example, the cases of William T. and of Joan N. both listed alphabetically in the general index, under *Cases.*

the ego can control. Drive derivatives appear in the preconscious and they are projected on to suitable persons in the surroundings. Both the edipal child and the delusional adult imagine themselves doing what their drives urge them on to do. When they face failure, because what they fantasy is unrealistic, both are apt to feel unfairly treated, and even persecuted by people who may actually love them.

As a child resolves his edipal complex, he internalizes aspects of his parents as *ego* and *superego introjects*, and he uses repression and other ego defenses on a massive scale. The separation of his preconscious ego from his unconscious ego and id-derivatives now becomes clearer than ever before. The unconscious ego is barred as much as possible from further *direct* participation in personality development and personality functioning, although its *indirect* derivatives often participate in both.

The repressed unconscious ego retains a host of active, dynamic infantile fantasies and daydreams, infantile wishes, hopes, expectations and fears, conflicts with ambivalent loves and hates, gross misinterpretations of external and somatic reality, and especially the infantile experiences and feelings that at one time were related to parental figures.[33] Material from the unconscious ego and the id appears in dreams, neuroses and psychoses, as well as in drug intoxications and sensory deprivation.

During latency, the long years of realistic experience further consolidate a differentiation between preconscious and unconscious processes. During adolescence, however, there is often some regression, with a stormy invasion of ego systems by id-derivatives. This sometimes revives some of the irrational passions of the edipal period, although in a different form, and appears as ambivalent "acting out," in which the adolescent may alternate turbulently between gross sensuality and asceticism. But as adolescent turbulence subsides, the ego boundaries are re-established on a still firmer basis, and the adolescent moves on into adulthood. Secondary processes regain their ascendancy and form organizations that show little trace of unconscious processes during the daytime hours when the person is awake. In the end, however, there is never complete and absolute separation of the ego from the id. Normally, they always function in relation to one another, no matter how good the ego organization becomes, or how strong the ego defenses are.

The nearest thing to complete separation between ego and id appears, not in normal behavior, but in obsessive symptoms. Here isolation and intellectualization are utilized defensively to produce a colorless existence. The id-derivatives are not mastered in obsessions; their reality is simply denied, and as a result the ego systems appear to lose their vitality.[34]

In normal adult life the id-derivatives and unconscious ego functions,

---

[33] This infantile material is sometimes given a place in the id, rather than in the unconscious ego. We prefer to include it in the deeply repressed ego because of its organization, and because it originated in interactions with external and somatic reality at one time.

[34] Examples are given in the section on obsessive doubt and rumination in the chapter on obsessive compulsive neuroses.

channeled and controlled by the defenses and by preconscious ego systems, contribute much that is emotionally enriching, much that is playful, inventive and inspirational, much that defies logic, and yet in the end may prove to be valid.

Delay, frustration and conflict in ego development

The inevitability of delay, frustration and conflict. Every infant must inevitably experience delay, frustration and conflict. No mother, however devoted she may be, can possibly eliminate such experiences from her child's life; and if she were able to, the product would be an automaton without an ego. Infancy and childhood are not only phases of living in their own right; they are also preparations for ultimate responsible independence. The realistic world around us, and the physiological limitations of our bodies, demand the growth of an organization which is capable of dealing with delay, frustration and conflict.

Delay is inevitable because it takes time to prepare to satisfy infant need, even when a mother understands and has nothing else that she has to do. Often there are other things a mother must do before she can attend to him, and sometimes she does not understand what it is he needs. Delay is often inevitable because it is not to the best interest of the infant, or of others around him, to satisfy his need the moment he feels it.

Frustration is inevitable because delay in satisfaction is often experienced as frustrating.[35] But there are additional sources of frustration. One is that, especially during the first year of life, perception is far ahead of motor development. The child is certain to experience many wants which he cannot satisfy without the help of someone else; and many of them he cannot satisfy at all. Often the means of satisfaction are at hand, as well as the perception that has given rise to the need; but someone or something bars the way to the child's attainment of satisfaction. In addition to all of this, a child's imagination, which may help him endure a delay, can become itself a source of continual frustration. Because his comprehension of realistic limitations is still poor, a great many eagerly fantasied gratifications must always be beyond his reach. The edipal tragedy, which we discussed in Chapter 2, is only one instance of hopeless frustration because of an unrealistic, impossible wish.

Conflict is inevitable for many reasons. The nature of id drives is such that many demands may appear at once, whereas the realistic situation permits the satisfaction of only one. Id demands are often mutually contradictory, so that the satisfaction of one involves the denial of another. To these conflicts of interest within the primary process must be added the realities of the limitations of the body and of the environmental structure. Demands made upon a child, even by his protective loving mother, often run counter

---

[35] Triandis, L. M., and Lambert, W. W., "Sources of frustration and targets of aggression: a cross-cultural study," *J. abnorm. soc. Psychol.*, 1961, *62*, 640–648.

to his impulsive desires. This faces him with a conflict situation in which the satisfaction of his need, which would otherwise be unobstructed, is denied him by someone whom he also needs.

Delay and ego development. A delay between the appearance of a need and its satisfaction is necessary if ego systems are to be organized at all. When the need is not overwhelmingly intense, a delay allows imagery to arise which is related to previous experiences of need and satisfaction. This imagery during the delay, which we have already said is not merely a picture, marks the beginning of central representation. It lays the foundation for later developments in which pondering, remembering, imagining, reflecting, thinking and reasoning can take the place of immediate action. The anticipation thus organized, in relation to a goal that is not immediately attainable, can be extended further and further, as a child matures, until eventually he may gain satisfaction out of fantasying something which he knows he cannot actually experience for many years.

In all situations of delay, the person — no matter what his age — must be able to find a reasonable degree of satisfaction in imagining the achievement of what he wants. This is what Freud was referring to when he wrote about the hungry infant "hallucinating the breast," and about adult dreams which enable a person to go on sleeping because he pictures for himself the satisfaction of the need giving rise to the dream. Because of the interpolation of a delay between need and satisfaction we also develop a capacity for creating imaginary satisfactions while we are wide awake. We develop imaginary ways of achieving our ends, an ability to keep a goal in view almost indefinitely, and eventually the ability to be content with certain imaginary satisfactions. These last go to make up habitual daydreams; they make it possible for a person to find satisfaction in abstractions; they leave room for the substitution of different goals, and of other means of attaining them. A reasonable ability to tolerate delay, an ability to remain undisturbed when a need cannot be quickly satisfied, is one of the most significant marks of maturity and of stable psychodynamic equilibrium.

Frustration and ego development.[36] We speak of *frustration* rather than simply of delay when a person experiences some obstacle, real or imagined, between him and his goal. Certain effects of frustration upon ego development are obvious and have been well-studied. One is the reaction of increased *aggression.* Another is the increase in the *variety* of goal-directed activities, the appearance of indirect, substitute means of problem-solving, which is significantly related to the development of secondary processes. If frustration is experienced too intensely, or if the situation appears hopeless, *apathy* or *withdrawal* may appear instead of aggression.[37] Sometimes previously effective adaptation is then replaced by regressive nonadaptive behavior.

[36] Lawson, R., and Marx, M. H., "Frustration: Theory and experiment," *Genet. Psychol. Monogr.*, 1958, *57*, 393–464.

[37] Sweetland, A., and Childs-Quay, L., "The effects of emotionality on concept formation," *J. genet. Psychol.*, 1958, *59*, 211–218.

A less obvious result of frustration is one that is highly significant for ego development and ego differentiation. This is the *internalization* of some part or aspect of a frustrating person or situation. It can be witnessed most dramatically in normal adults who are mourning someone lost through death or separation. Characteristics of the lost, loved person show up in the appearance, the behavior or the private experience of the mourner. They may be experienced as *introjections (symbolic incorporations)* or as *identifications.* Such internalizations also appear as symptoms in psychotic depressions and some schizophrenias, as we shall see.

Frustration is believed to play a leading role in the introjections and identifications that stimulate early ego formation. The experience of *introjection* is modeled after that of oral incorporation although (as we pointed out in Chapter 2) visual, auditory and manual incorporations also appear very early in infancy. *Identification* is modeled after imitation, but not necessarily conscious imitation. The aims of identification are to be like the other person, to be in some respect the same, to take his role and perform his functions.

We have seen what an important part identification with the frustrating parent plays in precipitating the edipal complex. The small boy identifies so strongly and completely with his father, his rival, that he expects to usurp his father's place as the man of the house. The small girl identifies strongly enough with her rival, her mother, to picture herself as mistress of the home and her father's wife. Declarations of this kind are accepted as routine matters in most nursery schools and in some homes. They are usually made with conviction. The opposite-sexed parent also frustrates the child, though less intensely, by refusing to treat his declarations as seriously as they are intended. A certain amount of identification results from this frustration also.

Introjection and identification are by no means always the products of frustration. They account for a large part of the correspondence between parental and filial orientations, folkways, tastes, customs and standards. Much of this appears to be adopted wholesale from the prevailing family subculture, rather than taken on bit by bit in fragmentary learning situations.

We saw how, in the symbiotic mother-child unit, the child is able to participate directly in the mother's abilities and activities. This is probably the zenith of complete identification in normal childhood.[38] At the same time, experiences of actual incorporation lead to introjection of the necessarily frustrating mother. As the symbiotic unit dissolves, the child retains much of what it has been sharing with the mother, thus organizing *ego introjects* which have many of the mother's characteristics, as the child interprets them. As dissolution of the symbiotic unit proceeds, the child has greater opportunity than before to introject and identify with the father. Rivalry with the like-sexed parent will favor a stronger identification than will love of the opposite-sexed one.

[38] Ritvo, S., and Solnit, A., "Influences of early mother-child interaction on identification processes," *Psychoanal. Study Child,* 1958, 13, 64–91.

Conflict and ego development. Conflict is responsible for delay to the extent that it prevents immediate satisfaction of incompatible demands, holding them in abeyance pending a solution. It is therefore responsible for a great deal of pondering, wondering, fantasying, imagining and prelogical thinking in small children. Conflict is also a source of much frustration. It therefore leads indirectly to increased aggression, to variation of response, to introjections and to identifications.

Apart from these indirect effects, conflict inevitably leads to choice and decision-making, ego functions which also involve giving something up which is also desired. It marks an advance in ego organization when, instead of swinging from love to hate, a child can remain ambivalent. To remain ambivalent is to remain in conflict, to want something or someone and not to want that thing or person, both at the same time. This already means ego structuring, a suspension of final action, and at least the opportunity for considering the desirable and detestable aspects of a thing or a person.

It marks a further advance in ego organization when a child is able to renounce one thing in order to have the other. But to choose one thing and renounce the other effectively means to be able to give up wanting the thing renounced. The most primitive way in which children do this is by *denying* their desire for what they give up, while at the same time they are experiencing it. For example, a frustrated child may give up something angrily, saying that he hates it, when this is only partly true, or only true of the person who compels the child to choose.

A more advanced maneuver than denial is that of *repression*. That which the child chooses remains accessible to awareness, while that which is given up becomes inaccessible, although still present in the unconscious ego. As far as the repressing person is concerned, the repressed has ceased to exist. Unless he suffers a regression which reactivates the conflict, he may remain unaware of the repression and of any influence from the repressed.

A still more advanced technique is that of really giving up what one is obliged to renounce in order to have what is preferred. This can be achieved only if the conflict is really resolved, that is, if a person experiences the implications of a choice adequately in imagination, and finds full gratification in what he chooses.

In progressing from the least to the most mature ways of handling conflicts, every person leaves some residues of his early contradictory, ambivalent, denied or repressed hopes, fears and desires. When a child resolves his edipal complex, somewhere between the fourth and sixth years, he exerts a massive repression which blots out most of his early experience. The early experiences, however, are not necessarily destroyed. This means that whatever conflicts remained still active at the time, whatever ones were still important and still unresolved, were repressed while they were still conflicts. These may persist as active components of the unconscious ego which can exert determinative influences upon conscious and preconscious experience and behavior, without a person's being in the least aware of them. Later conflicts of the same kind tend to reactivate these repressed edipal and pre-edipal conflicts. This reactivation is one source of irrational behavior and experience in adults, since what they do, say or think, is predetermined by a source which lies outside of their awareness.

If the growing child develops an increasing tolerance for conflict, he becomes better able to deal constructively with his contradictory trends. It is only while he is suspending action that he can make a realistic choice between conflicting desires. By suspending action in a conflict situation, a child gives himself the chance to make some choice, or effect some resolution, which might not have occurred to him when the conflict first arose. Such tolerance for conflict requires a certain amount of emotional distance in order that a choice is not made simply in the direction of the greatest emotional pressure. This in turn calls for adequate emotional control, and for the ability to maintain ego boundaries sufficiently intact, so that a person can feel the need and still be free to make a decision.

The autonomous ego and the conflict-free sphere

In psychodynamic theory, attention has been focused upon the prime importance of delay, frustration and conflict in stimulating ego development, and particularly the development of secondary process thinking. One result of this has been a relative neglect of the role played by the maturational sequences of adaptive behavior.[39] The early perceptual-motor coordinations which we discussed briefly in Chapter 2 are obvious examples of progressive adaptation to the realities of the surroundings and of the body's structure. This kind of adaptation depends mainly upon maturation, use and learning, with little evidence of the influence of delay, frustration and conflict. Such perceptual-motor organizations — and they are innumerable — make up what is called *the autonomous ego*. Because they are not necessarily products of conflict, and do not seem to involve conflict in their operation, they have been grouped together as the *conflict-free sphere of the ego*.

The autonomous ego and the conflict-free sphere include the well-known maturational sequences of motor coordinations,[40] the development of perception of the body and of the surrounding world, the maturation of emotional and motivational components, and the growth of the cognitive structures which make all kinds of secondary integration and abstraction possible. They also include all the unnoticed preconscious processes that contribute to our orientation and to our automatic skilled activities in everyday life. Examples of these are the use we make of the perceived environment all the time in orienting ourselves, without noticing it, the myriad coordinated movements that make up our everyday work, play and relaxation, and even the details

[39] Hartmann, H., *Ego Psychology and the Problem of Adaptation* (trans. D. Rapaport). New York: Internat. Univ. Press, 1958.

[40] For detailed accounts of maturational sequences see Gesell, A., and Ilg, F. L., *Child Development.* New York: Harper, 1949. See also Stone, L. J., and Church, J., *Childhood and Adolescence.* New York: Random House, 1957.

of our ordinary problem-solving. In short, the autonomous ego and the conflict-free sphere include most of what constitutes the subject matter of psychology and the other behavioral sciences.

Many of these things are learned at first with conscious effort, even though the details of the learning may not themselves ever enter awareness. Conscious effort may again be needed to improve them. But once mastered, most of them remain automatic, smooth-running and unnoticed throughout life. In fact, ease and skill often depend upon one's remaining unaware of the details of perception, cognition and action. The typist or pianist who, for any reason, becomes aware of the individual movements that go to make up the skilled performance is likely to lose ease and skill.

A previously autonomous, conflict-free function may be dragged into symptom formation. This we shall see with special clarity in conversion symptoms and compulsions. In some of the psychoses, for example in manic excitements, there may be little autonomous ego organization left; almost all behavior and experience seems to have regressed in the service of a childlike, previously unconscious ego.

Ego adaptation and mastery

By now it is clear that ego adaptation involves more than a passive adjustment or conformity. Adjusting to and conforming with the realities of one's body and one's environment are essential parts of ego adaptation. But initiative, enterprise and mastery, which may reshape the environment, are also essential components of normal ego adaptation. They are the components most vulnerable in childhood to adult interference and domination.

We see mastery develop even in the nursing situation; we see it in the continual perceptual-motor explorations of early infancy; we see it in the mastery of space and locomotion that comes as soon as a child can get to his feet alone. Ego adaptation, maturation and mastery together form rising spirals. As a child matures, he increases the effectiveness of his ego adaptation; as he adapts and masters more and more, he matures faster; and as he matures further, his ego adaptations and mastery take on new dimensions and new complexities. The gratifications that once came only with direct discharge now come from the performance of complex maneuvers itself. The end may become less important than the way in which it is achieved. This is obvious in children's play and in many adult rituals.[41]

In many activities and many imaginings both children and adults often seek an *increase* in tension and effort. In play and recreation we seek tension and effort that goes far beyond what is necessary for mere adaptation. Children and adults come to enjoy the build-up and the energetic use of something which they have mastered.

---

[41] Marshall, H. R., "Relations between home experiences and children's use of language in play interactions with peers," *Psychol. Monogr.*, 1961, 75, Whole No. 509.

Ego adaptation and ego defense

In normal ego functioning it is often difficult to differentiate between adaptation and defense. For example, the overall ego defense against disintegrating is at the same time adaptive in character. As we shall see in Chapter 6, this is one of the major functions of regression, that it permits ego systems to remain organized, even though at less competent levels. We shall postpone a detailed discussion of the ego defenses until we take them up in Chapter 6. Meanwhile there are some general principles which deserve mention here.

The newborn, we have seen, remains for some time unreactive to most of the potential stimulation in his environment. Freud postulated the existence of an inborn *protective barrier,* the forerunner of ego defenses. We pointed out, in Chapter 2, that the newborn is also protected by the rudimentary state of his perception, the physiological immaturity of his brain, and the poverty of his repertory of coordinated movements. Most of the complex perceptual patterns that the human environment arouses in adults do not exist for the neonate. They make no demand upon him whatever. He is defended by a shell of perceptual inadequacy which protects him from even having to try to perform the coordinated acts of which he is incapable.

We adults are also familiar with the use of a *protective barrier* when we are bombarded by stimulation and do not react to it. Our ability to daydream or read in the midst of extraneous activity depends upon our erecting a barrier of unreactivity. Whenever we become deeply engrossed in doing something, we experience the same kind of oblivion toward anything that might interfere with it. We do the same kind of thing in falling asleep and staying asleep in noisy surroundings.

Ego adaptive systems also involve *defense* in that they must automatically exclude anything that might disrupt them. This is an ego defensive function which protects its own organization, one that enables it to persist as a system. Thus, for example, ego systems must not only adapt to external and somatic realities; they must also defend their organization from the disintegrating effects of the impact of *too much reality.* This defense becomes most evident when it breaks down, as it does in many traumatic experiences, in panic reactions, and in some of the psychoses.

Ego systems adapt to unconscious strivings and defend against them. They find ways of discharging tensions, sometimes through the use of their own versions of primary process *displacement, condensation* and *primitive symbolization,* much like what we see in manifest dreams and in neurotic symptoms. Ego systems also bind id cathexes in secondary process organizations, as in normal thinking, problem-solving and realistic imagining.

An ego function which is especially significant in psychopathology is both adaptive and defensive. This consists of depriving id-derivatives of their primitive sexual and aggressive cathexes. The function is known as *neutralization* and its products are called *neutral* or *neutralized energy.* These terms do not imply that the neutralized energy is any less energetic, but only that it has been desexualized or de-aggressivized. *Desexualization* is best represented by *sublimation*. Sex drives or their derivatives are used in nonsexual ways that achieve complete satisfaction. *De-aggressivization* (a monstrous word) takes many forms. Initiative, enterprise and regulated competition are all common expressions of primitive aggression that has been tamed by ego action, and is available for activities which may be energetically constructive or creative. Ego defenses, such as repression, use deaggressivized energy derived from the id.

The use of id cathexes to form ego systems which then serve to control id cathexes sounds more paradoxical than it is. It is actually no stranger than the use of water power to construct and maintain a dam, whose function is that of holding the water back, and which may be thus tamed and channeled into other activities (running a mill or a dynamo) which are not aquatic in character at all.

Finally, preconscious ego systems must adapt continually to superego guidance, especially in moral and ethical matters. They also defend against superego pressures when these become too intense or too disturbing to preconscious ego functions. Some common results of these pressures are the *pangs of conscience*, which may become conscious, and the *sense of worthlessness* or *inferiority*, which also become conscious, but have unconscious superego roots. *Unconscious guilt* also belongs here, as we shall see later in the chapter, when we come to a discussion of the superego.

Three worlds of ego function

We have already objected to the notion that realistic thinking cannot be organized without the advent of language. It is a matter of everyday observation that young infants learn to interact realistically in terms of their bodies and their surroundings, even though they are still wordless. Older children tell us of imagery which they find difficult to put in words; and we assume that imagery must organize much earlier than this, probably from the moment of birth. For many years, children go on realistically interacting while their language equipment is far less adequate than their direct adaptation, and far less rich and competent than their imagination. In short, a child learns to interact in terms of his surroundings and his body, and he gains a workable, more or less realistic central representation of both — of the physical properties and the behavior of things, people and himself, long before his language systems are logically organized.[42]

This gives us at least three worlds of ego operation, which we shall sketch briefly here: (1) *the world of somatic and external reality;* (2) *the world of imagination;* and (3) *the verbal world.* There is a great deal of evidence

---

[42] Braine, M. D. S., "The ontogeny of certain logical operations: Piaget's formulation examined by nonverbal methods," *Psychol. Monogr.*, 1959, *73*, Whole No. 475; Fowler, W., "Cognitive learning in infancy and early childhood," *Psychol. Bull.*, 1962, *59*, 116–152.

that these three worlds, even though they interact in everybody's ego, can be differentiated from one another. Their differences are significant for an understanding of psychopathology.

(1) *The world of somatic and external reality.* There is a world of objective reality which can be photographed and otherwise impersonally recorded. We all accept it as something which exists independently of individual experience, as something which was there before we were born and will be there after we die. People also agree that most of what is recorded is experienced and treated approximately the same by everyone, at least by every normal adult in our culture.

The body is included as external reality, that is, we all look upon the body, and even its internal organs, as *objects.* In some ways somatic reality occupies a special place in our experiences of reality. It is always present; it is peculiarly our own; it is tied up with our sense of personal identity. It yields all kinds of experiences that are private. Some of these we can communicate to others, if we want to, but many of them we cannot. The experiences that we cannot, or do not, communicate to others or formulate in words, remain freer to interact with nonverbal imagination. Such interactions need not follow the conventions of the spoken word. They can more easily be subjected to the primary process than language can.

Hereafter, for the sake of simplicity, we shall take it for granted that when we speak of *external reality* we are including most of our experiences of *somatic reality*. We shall mention somatic reality only when it needs special emphasis.

In spite of general agreement as to the objective world, there are many differences in orientation toward it. Boys see the objective world differently from the ways girls see it; a man's world is different from a woman's world. These differences are a function of basic differences in anatomy, physiology and private experience, as well as of differences in social expectations and social roles. The urge to master, especially to master things beyond family life and family organizations, seems to be a masculine perspective everywhere. A narcissistic cathexis of the body and its adornment, and a pervasive interest in the care of children, seem to be feminine perspectives which transcend cultural and historical changes.[43]

[43] Cf. Colley, T., "The nature and origins of psychological sexual identity," *Psychol. Rev.,* 1959, *66,* 165–173. The human being is, however, as plastic with regard to sex role orientation as to other influences. *Cross identification* has been discussed in Chapter 3, and will again be taken up in Chapter 19, where parental wishes will be seen to be determinative in many cases. The rare case of *genetic male* who, because of embryological defect, fails to develop external male genitalia and, for some as yet not understood reason, develops a female body form at puberty, also seems completely oriented in feminine directions because of having been reared as a female. See, for example, Money, J., "Components of eroticism in man: I. The hormones in relation to sexual morphology and sexual desire," *J. nerv. ment. Dis.,* 1961, *132,* 239–248; Money, J., Hampson, J. G., and Hampson, J. L., "Imprinting and the establishment of gender role," *Arch. Neurol. Psychol.,* 1957, *77,* 333–336.

The external world, even though objectively the same for all, is differently structured by different men in accordance with their different interests and different social roles — for example, the farm laborer, the machinist, the white collar worker, the executive, the soldier, the physician, the lawyer, the aviator and the artist. Each experiences a differently organized world of external reality from that of the others. It is not only that they *do* different things; their different worlds also *look* different to them. Some of these differences go back to congenital differences in perceptual, central nervous system and motor equipment, which can create external realities with different emphases. But many of them are also products of individual experience, of chance opportunities and accidental occurrences.

(2) *The world of imagination.* Many of the differences just mentioned, in perceiving the world of somatic and external reality, are reinforced by a person's imaginings. It is generally believed that the world of imagination in early infancy is a world of fleeting imagery. As an infant matures his imagery (or central representation) comes more and more under the influence of realistic experiences, but it does not lose altogether the influence of id-derivatives. The world of imagination never becomes a completely realistic representation of external and somatic reality. It remains in many respects less useful and less logically organized; but in other respects it is richer, warmer, more colorful and more vivid.

Most of the great scientific, practical and artistic advances made by mankind have appeared first in some individual's world of imagination. It is only later that they have been translated into an objective reality which others could share. We need only mention the vast changes in architecture that have developed over the ages.

Many preconscious and conscious fantasies actually contradict the facts of existing external or somatic reality. They may rise above reality or fall short of it; they may extend reality and imbue it with new meaning, or distort it and deprive it of some of the meaning it originally had. The world of imagination ranges in organization all the way from the faithful reproduction of something actually experienced in objective reality to the unrealistic jumble of primary processes, such as we experience in manifest dreams and witness in psychotic symptoms.

Among the major preconscious ego functions must be counted that of differentiating between *objective external* and *somatic reality* and *the fruits of the imagination.* This function we call *reality-testing.* Its forerunner is the perceptual-motor exploration of preverbal infants, which begins by establishing the limits and characteristics of the body. We express this primacy by saying that the first ego is a *body ego.*

Reality-testing enables a child, as he matures and grows in experience, to behave and to experience the world around him and his own body more and more realistically. It also enables him to utilize the special properties of his world of imagination. Imagination can serve creative and recreational purposes, especially as it escapes many of the restrictions imposed by stern objective reality. It can, for example, transcend space and time, change monotony into adventure, picture escape when one is doomed, daydream of a future time in which all difficulties are miraculously surmounted and happiness is complete. For the mature adult it remains a refuge from the world of facts, a world into which he can retire when objective reality becomes too drab.

When reality-testing is underdeveloped, as it is in children and sometimes in adults, the result is confusion. This is of relatively little importance in childhood because there are adults present who can help the child, and because society expects children to be somewhat unrealistic.

Reality-testing is of the greatest significance for *psychopathology* when for any reason it breaks down. We shall see some of the most striking examples of disturbance in reality-testing when we come to the chapters on psychoses, personality disorders and brain disorders. Here the patient may be unable to keep the realities of his body and its environment apart from his world of imagination. The enormous potentialities of imagination then turn reality into a nightmare.

If secondary processes are still effective, one of the most successful means of reality-testing is that of sharing one's experiences with another person through communication. It is a case of "Do you see what I see?" This brings us to our third world of ego function, the verbal world, the one that begins with making playful sounds and ends up by creating an intricate organization of social communication, with its own special rules.

(3) *The verbal world.* The verbal world is peculiar to man. It comes late upon the scene of childhood development, and it requires years of practice before it can represent imagining effectively, or serve as a satisfactory substitute for action. Every child begins to babble spontaneously long before he can speak or understand speech. The speaking of others around him, and their reactions to his babbling, seem to have an especially stimulating effect upon him. Since infant babbling at one time or another includes every sound that is made in all the known languages of the world, it seems to be a matter of selection and reinforcement that makes a child speak the language of those who rear him. The other sounds present in an infant's repertory disappear.

Nevertheless, children do not learn to speak by a word-by-word method. The first thing that shows up is an *expressive jargon,* a meaningless pattern which reflects the intonations and inflections of the language he hears. At a distance this sounds like the real thing. Out of it the child differentiates favorite phrases, and certain "words" which actually function as whole statements. Eventually the child learns to speak and understand the language of his environment, whether or not he ever learns about its rules.

Language always begins in socially shared situations where the babbling, wordless child has an older companion who speaks, and who rewards the child in some way for making similar sounds. The sounds that a child learns to make in the presence of something he can also learn to make when that something is absent. Children soon develop a running commentary on what they and others are doing or have done, and this commentary can be repeated afterwards as a report of things past or an expectation that something will be repeated. This is a way of *keeping something verbally* after it has otherwise disappeared, and of *making it come back again* when it has been absent. Many small children entertain themselves when they are alone by talking to themselves, just as earlier they entertained themselves by babbling. Gradually a child's language takes on more and more conventional forms.[44]

Language has a structure of its own, its own grammatical rules and conventions, and its accepted modes of formulating and expressing experience. Society is organized to a considerable extent in accordance with communication among its members, and language is far and away the most flexible and reliable instrument of communication. Nevertheless, the verbal world is not identical with either the external world of reality, including the speaker's body, or the inner world of imagination. It takes many years of constant practice and continual inquiry (actually another form of *reality-testing*) to master the correct verbal equivalents for what happens in reality, in the body and in imagination.

There are vast areas of experience which can never be adequately verbalized, experience in external and somatic reality as well as in the world of imagination. One need only mention the complex feelings — evaluative as well as sentimental — aroused by paintings, sculpture and music, especially in its contemporary forms, the feelings aroused by looking at landscapes, buildings and people, by sunrise and sunset, by leavetaking and homecoming and all the interactions of lovers and of parents, the hope and despair in life, the loving, hating and fearing, the loneliness and closeness.

There are specialized systems of communication other than language, of course, but these are mainly for specialists. For the ordinary man or woman in everyday life, there are just these three worlds — external reality, including the body, imagination and the verbal world — each differently organized from the other and only imperfectly interchangeable.

The verbal world has special importance for psychopathology. In the first place there is the fact that a great deal of social organization is codified in language.[45] Even private thinking tends to become organized conventionally along verbal lines, as well as in terms of directly experienced external reality, the body, and the imagination. As a result of this conventional organization,

[44] Cf. Cofer, C. N. (Ed.), *Verbal Learning and Verbal Behavior.* New York: McGraw-Hill, 1961; Church, J., *Language and the Discovery of Reality: A Developmental Psychology of Cognition.* New York: Random House, 1961; McCarthy, D., "Research in language development: retrospect and prospect," *Monogr. soc. Res. Child Develpm.,* 1959, *24,* 3–24; McCarthy, D., "Language development," *Monogr. soc. Res. Child Develpm.,* 1960, *25,* 5–14.

[45] Cf. Luria, A. R., *The Role of Speech in the Regulation of Normal and Abnormal Behavior.* New York: Liveright, 1961; Wertheimer, M., *Productive Thinking.* (2nd ed.) New York: Harper, 1959.

language can be made to represent and communicate many experiences which would otherwise remain forever private, forever unknown to anyone else. It is also used to an enormous degree vicariously, to experience, through speech or reading, millions of things that a person cannot experience directly. Without the ability to communicate in speech, and to experience vicariously through language, no one can participate fully in the life of his society.

The acquisition of language also introduces certain difficulties. It provides everyone with two different ways of experiencing both external reality, including the body, and internal reality, the world of the imagination. There is the *direct perception* of what seems to be happening, and there is the *verbal formulation* of what seems to be happening. The two systems are not identical; they do not always operate according to the same principles; they are not always interchangeable. Each system may be inherently consistent without corresponding point for point with the other system.

One of the commonest difficulties arises when the verbal world is made to appear pre-eminent. Logic is widely considered to be more realistic than direct experience. This appears most clearly in intellectualistic defenses, in obsessions and in paranoid reactions. But it is also prominent in the normal worship of *the word*, that is, in the belief that the verbal world is somehow more real than direct experience. We see samples of this attitude in the use of verbal rituals to attempt to control realistic events. All of these examples, normal ritual as well as pathological defense, are particularly interesting because they confuse the perception of external reality with the imagination.

Another difficulty arises from the ease with which the verbal world disintegrates when a person undergoes a general disorganization. In some *brain disorders* the verbal world all but disappears, and with this change the patient loses most of his active participation in the life of his society. In many *schizophrenic disorders* (as also in manifest dreams and in sensory deprivation) the verbal world appears to be subjected to the primary process. The product is often a jumble of words which, however, has meaning, even though this meaning does not follow the rules of verbal logic. It is condensed, displaced and syncretic, like the language of small children.[46] Some schizophrenic patients seem to reverse the process by which they acquired language; they treat words concretely, as though they were things.[47]

The incompleteness even of conventional, secondary process communication becomes especially clear when one listens to a person while he is thinking out loud and paying minimal attention to the direction of what he says. This is the situation in therapeutic *free association*. Under these circumstances, a great deal is expressed that goes far beyond the speaker's intention, and seems to escape his understanding. If one listens not only to what is being

[46] The language of regressed schizophrenics, however, is not the same as that of children. A comparison of the two under similar conditions is included in Cameron, N., "A study of thinking in senile deterioration and schizophenic disorganization," *Amer. J. Psychol.*, 1938, *51*, 650–665.

[47] Searles, H., "The differentiation between concrete and metaphorical thinking in the recovering schizophrenic patient," *J. Amer. Psychoanal. Ass.*, 1962, *10*, 22–49.

said, but also to the emotional undertones, the general drift, the choice of imagery, the condensations, repetitions, substitutions and omissions, free association becomes communicative at more than the conventional level. At the same time that the speaker is expressing something conventional, in secondary process terms, he is also revealing the participation of other preconscious thoughts and feelings, and the contributions made by fantasies from the unconscious ego and derivatives of the id. It is obvious that even conventional, secondary process thinking carries with it many derivatives of unconventional and even of primary process origin. Such speech may be conventionally communicative; but it is also *symptomatic* for anyone who can recognize the symptoms expressed in it. We shall defer further discussion of the symptomatic aspects of the ego until we come to the chapter on symptom formation.

Summary of the ego and secondary processes

The ego is an organization of systems arising out of interaction with external and somatic reality. Repeated performances in any perceptual-motor modality produce changes in central nervous system organization. These changes are expressed overtly in improved skill and in greater comprehension and variability of behavior. Internally they appear as central representations which, for the sake of convenience, we call *imagery*. These central representations correspond to external and somatic reality, past or present, but they do not necessarily mirror what they represent. In time there develop interactions among central representations which may lead to entirely new internal mental structures. Examples of these appear in the omnipotent and fearful fantasies of young children, and in the playful and creative fantasies, daydreams and artistic productions of children and adults. Manifest dreams and pathological symptoms also belong to this group.[48]

Functionally, preconscious ego systems occupy positions which separate the unconscious from somatic and external reality. They also lay the foundations for later distinctions between one's imagination, one's body and external reality, between the drive derivatives we call needs and the act of satisfying or controlling them. These distinctions, which are part of the process of reality-testing, are achieved through overt behavior, through internal experiences with realities and wants, with comforts and discomforts, and through the imagery which experiences create and needs reactivate. The organization of experience and behavior in accordance with the reality principle, and the development of ego defense mechanisms, most of which operate unconsciously, help to differentiate the preconscious and conscious ego from the unconscious ego and the id.

[48] See the accounts in Bruner, J., *et al.*, *A Study of Thinking*. New York: Wiley, 1956; Bartlett, F., *Thinking: An Experimental and Social Study*. New York: Basic Books, 1958.

The separation of the preconscious ego from the unconscious ego and the id takes many years to perfect. The small child normally shows primary process contamination in much of his experience and behavior. During the pre-edipal phases this is obvious in a child's unrealistic and sometimes omnipotent hopes and fantasies, and in his often groundless fears. During the early years, while he is learning to deal realistically with his surroundings and himself, he still betrays at times a surprising inability to distinguish clearly between external reality, somatic reality and the imagination. As he begins to master language, the child adds a verbal world to his previous worlds of reality and imagination. The task of differentiating between the three worlds of the ego — external and somatic reality, imagination and language — and of finding a valid equivalent in one world for experiences in the other, extend the process of reality-testing beyond its preverbal limits.

Even the edipal child is still driven to absurdly unrealistic sexual and aggressive fantasies and expectations, like a delusional adult, and for similar reasons. When he *resolves his edipal complex,* he *internalizes parental objects* in his imagery (or central representation), *differentiates a superego organization,* and *develops massive repression.* This resolution, which may take two or three years to work through, eventually excludes much of the infantile material from further participation in personality development, without necessarily destroying it or even reducing its strength. Such repressed material makes up a good part of the unconscious ego and unconscious superego, both of which interact with the primary process of the id, and contribute to the formation of manifest dreams and symptoms.

Latency, with its years of realistic experience relatively undisturbed by emotional crisis, allows further consolidation of the differentiation of the preconscious ego from the unconscious ego and the id. The physiological upheavals, emotional crises and social pressures of adolescence disrupt some of this consolidation. Sometimes there are invasions of preconscious and conscious ego systems by previously unconscious fantasies and id derivatives. Such invasions revive edipal and pre-edipal struggles, but in disguised forms and with a different outcome, since the adolescent is powerful, competent and equipped with highly organized defenses. As the adolescent upheaval subsides, the functional boundaries between preconscious and the unconscious, as also between the ego and the superego, and between reality and imagination, are all of them clearer than ever, and at the same time increasingly more flexible. Secondary processes continue their advances within the limits of the individual's capacity.

The separation of the preconscious ego from the unconscious ego and the id never becomes complete and absolute. Each level functions in relation to the other. The upward thrust of id derivatives and the products of these and the unconscious ego never cease to influence adult experience and behavior, during the day as well as at night. From these unconscious sources comes a great deal of the warmth, color, passion, playfulness, creativity and unpredictability of what would otherwise be a too realistic, monotonous existence.[49]

Delay, frustration and conflict are not only inevitable in ego development; they are essential for the growth of realistic organization. It is the delay between need and satisfaction that allows imagery or central representation to be interpolated, and begins the development of secondary process thinking. Frustration not only increases aggression and, if not too severe, increases the variability of behavior; it also invigorates processes of introjection and identification which play important parts in organizing the ego, and later on, the superego. We see examples of such processes in older children and even in adults when there is identification with a feared aggressor or with a hated rival, especially when there is little prospect of realistic aggression.

It is generally believed that introjection and identification are much more active early in life than they are after repression has become the dominant defense. The presence of conflict already announces an ability to tolerate suspense, to be at least ambivalent, and eventually to be able to make choices and achieve complete satisfaction in a decision. The residues of infantile conflicts, like the residues of infantile frustration, rage and love, go to make up a large part of the repressed unconscious. We have already indicated the influence of unconscious processes upon the preconscious and conscious life.

There remain to be mentioned the autonomous ego and the conflict-free sphere. As the ego develops, it gains control of perception, cognition and action. To the extent that what it controls is the product of maturational sequences and conflict-free interaction with the environment, or with other maturational organizations, it is regarded as making up *the autonomous ego* and *the conflict-free sphere of operation*. Such conflict-free functions can, of course, become secondarily involved in conflict and in the expression of conflict, as we see with exceptional clarity in conversion symptoms and in the obsessive compulsive neuroses. Neither of these becomes intelligible, however, until we understand the operation of the *superego*.

The Superego and Its Precursors

The superego is an organization of mental systems whose major functions are those of scanning ego activity at all levels, of supplying approval and disapproval, self-criticism and self-esteem. It carries out these functions in relation to internalized moral and ethical standards, and to an *ego-ideal* which is the superego's measuring stick. The superego differentiates from the ego, crystallizing out of the ego as a separate organization, during the resolution of the edipal complex, that is, during the third to the fifth or sixth years.

Normal adults speak of their *conscience*, the conscious part of their super-

[49] See the discussions in McKellar, P., *Imagination and Thinking: A Psychological Analysis.* New York: Basic Books, 1957; Getzels, J. W., and Jackson, P. W., *Creativity and Intelligence.* New York: Wiley, 1962.

ego, as better, stricter, less corruptible and more idealistic than they are themselves. They may react to it with humility and docility, or with resentment and rebellion, for all the world as though it were not really an integral part of themselves, but a separate person — a guide, a judge, an accuser or a self-righteous tyrant.[50] In compulsive neurotics and in psychotically depressed patients we shall witness derivatives of the superego acting out tyrannical roles in concrete, primitive and sometimes dangerous ways. In psychotic paranoid patients, we shall see precursors of the superego projected as imaginary persecutors. All of these are exaggerations of what the public calls a guilty conscience.

Conscience and the superego

When we say that a person has a guilty conscience we do not really mean it. What we really mean is that his conscience is making him feel guilty. The guilt is felt and the anxiety experienced in a person's preconscious or conscious ego, or in the self, but not in the conscience. The conscience has an unpleasant way of always being in the right. A particularly clear example of this appears in the compulsive case of Sally J., where a vindictive conscience seems to be enjoying the process of punishing the ego of a cringing little girl.[51]

It would be more accurate and truer to life if we said that a person had "a guilty ego" or "a guilty self," and if we recognized that this guilty ego or self is anxious because its conscience disapproves of it, threatens or despises it — in short, because it withholds superego love which is the fountain of self-esteem. This is just as true in normal persons as in neurotic and psychotic patients. The adult is rare, as well as unfortunate and abnormal, whose deeds, words and thoughts are not to a considerable extent scanned and guided by an ever-present and usually silent conscience — a semi-independent system of moral values and ideals, with its own hierarchies of good, better and best, and of bad, worse and worst.

When people speak of *conscience* they refer to a *conscious* moral or ethical judgment. Sometimes it seems as though the moment we face a moral choice, up pops our conscience from nowhere to confront us with the moral implications of the situation. It feels almost as if a wiser, more mature and more righteous personage had been awakened to judge us, to approve or to criticize us, to dictate how we ought to act or speak or think. Once the conflict of interest has been settled, and after an approved choice has been made, the righteous giant seems to go to sleep again.

What really goes on is different from this surface appearance. The righteous giant sleeps rarely and he sleeps lightly. Some say he never sleeps. Most of the time, perhaps all of the time, everything we do or say or think

---

[50] Cf. Miller, D. R., and Swanson, G. E., *Inner Conflict and Defense.* New York: Holt, 1960.

[51] Listed in the index, under *Cases.*

is being scanned for its moral or ethical implications, and for the relation it bears to the ego-ideal.

This scanning, evaluating process, however disturbing it may be at times, is an indispensable stabilizing factor in adult life. Without it, we should be forever dependent upon our own momentary whims or, like little children, dependent upon getting somebody's approval for everything we do or say or think. With a superego, we have a built-in stabilizer, an organization of systems that reflects the moral and ethical standards of our society, as these have been transmitted to us through our parents and other authority figures. The superego is by no means infallible. Because of its childhood origins, it sometimes reflects parental distortions, overemphases or omissions. Sometimes it reflects childish misinterpretations, or the influence of authority figures in latency, adolescence and young adulthood which are a liability rather than an advantage. But even a defective superego is far better than none at all.

The superego also includes our *ego-ideal*, an unrealistic standard against which everything we do, say or think may be measured. Because guilt plays such an important part in psychopathology, as well as in normal life, we tend to emphasize the critical, punitive aspects of the superego. It is well to remember that our superego, with its ego-ideal, also provides us with large quantities of self-approval, self-love and self-esteem.

Conscience represents only the conscious fraction of a far more extensive superego which, like the ego, has vast preconscious and unconscious domains. By itself, the superego means nothing, just as by itself the brain is meaningless. The superego always interacts with the ego. It is also responsive to id derivatives and unconscious ego processes, through interactions at an unconscious level. As with the ego, we learn most of what we know about preconscious and unconscious superego operations through the effects they have on experience and behavior. Superego effects show up in manifest dreams, in neurotic and psychotic systems, and in personality disorders. All of these bear the imprint of childhood experiences. We shall first recount a manifest dream which includes a superego representative, and then go on to discuss the origins and precursors of the superego.

A manifest dream which includes representation of the superego

A patient near the beginning of her analysis expressed anxiety concerning what might be brought to light. That night she had the following manifest dream:

> She was with her analyst in a deep hole dug in the ground. Somebody had a spade and they had just struck an iron lid that was covering what lay beneath. Then there was a woman up above, on the edge of the hole, all dressed in white. She was pointing upward and calling down a warning not to dig any further. The patient felt uneasy when she awoke.

The patient's associations showed that the dream had more than one meaning for her. What mystified her most was the fact that the woman in white, who called down the warning, seemed to be herself, even though she was somehow also involved in digging at the bottom of the hole. She also felt when she awoke that there was something very dangerous under the iron lid, which she described as like the hinged doors that covered the farmhouse cellar in the house where she was born. To her analyst the woman in white seemed to represent her superego which was more aware of what further digging might release, especially if the iron lid of her defenses were to be forcibly raised. It was some time before she was able to reduce her anxiety sufficiently to go deeper with her analysis. In short, even though the woman in white mystified her, she obeyed the injunction not to dig further and help lift up the lid. There are other obvious meanings in the dream, but they only serve to reinforce the warning.

The origins and precursors of the superego

The superego that crystallizes out of the ego during the resolution of edipal conflicts is by no means the first sign of internal moral control. The earliest precursors of the superego are most likely included in very early *ego introjects* and *ego identifications*.[52] Studies of many kinds of regressive states all suggest that at first these ego introjects and identifications are experienced neither as internal nor as external.[53] This implies that in early infancy, ego boundaries have not yet been established that make it possible to distinguish between inside and outside, between ego and object.

We see what seems to be a revival of this early situation in the weird shifts and transformations that we all experience in manifest dreams, and that some patients experience in psychoses and brain disorders while they are awake. Even though the distinction between self and object may disappear, the feeling of good or evil, the sense of warning, threat and sometimes reassurance, seem to be directly experienced, without the interpolation of secondary process logic. This is undoubtedly true of infant experience with *good* and *bad*.

It is generally believed that infants experience good and evil in some such direct way as soon as they can distinguish the *good mother* and the *bad mother* which they internalize. We know that small children, when they have learned to speak a little, report such experiences. It is most unlikely that the acquisition of speech introduces a child for the first time to feelings of what is good and what is bad. For the very young infant, the good is the pleasurable, and the bad is the unpleasurable. Later on, he adopts the prevailing attitudes around him, as to what is good and what is bad. These

[52] Ritvo, S., and Solnit, A., "The relationship of early ego identifications to superego formation," *Internat. J. Psychoanal.*, 1960, *41*, 295–300.

[53] Cf. Loewald, H. W., "Internalization, separation, mourning and the superego," *Psychoanal. Quart.*, 1962, *31*, 483–504.

are the attitudes of his society and culture, as interpreted for him by the adults with whom he lives.

In the second year, during the phase of self-assertion and sphincter control, children develop *reaction formations,* which further regulate their general behavior in terms of their society, that is, in terms of those who rear them. These *reaction formations* are attitudes which are diametrically opposed to forbidden impulses and activities, especially the sexual and sadistic ones. The reaction formations are expressed in words and demonstrations by parent figures, who call what is forbidden *bad, dirty* or *cruel,* and act out at least in grimace and gesture the contrast between good and evil. The child, who has committed the bad, the dirty or the sadistic, thus learns to imitate in childish fashion the adult words and demonstrations of the good, the clean and the kind.

In doing this, the child internalizes good, clean and kind attitudes which, reinforced by his need for love and approval, hold the forbidden impulses in check. Through such maneuvers a child gradually becomes good, clean and kind to the best of his ability. He learns to express and to feel shame, disgust, pity and compassion in accordance with social expectations. He does not, however, completely *give up* their opposites. He keeps them in the form of forbidden alternatives; and when he forms a postedipal superego they may simply be repressed, and remain permanently in his unconscious ego and superego organizations.

These are some of the precursors of the superego that crystallizes out as edipal conflicts are resolved. The attitudes that are repressed and become unconscious seem never to die. When an adult regresses, they may be reactivated in his experience and behavior. Then we get the chance to see what they are like.

It is a favorite cliché that a psychotic, drugged or drunken person reveals his "real personality." This is untrue. What he may reveal are impulses which he overcame when he was a little child, but which he only succeeded in repressing, as they then were, in his unconscious ego and superego. In the unconscious, the repressed seems to flourish and ramify, like the hidden roots of a tree. When it escapes repression later in life it takes on an adult form.

The case of Joan N. shows elaborations of sadomasochistic fantasies which, even though they were still unrealistic and childish, were not just the fantasies of a little girl. They had been transformed into something more complex and more adult in content. They were also rich in obvious sex conflicts related to a sadistic father image. The case of Charles G. shows projections in the form of a systematized delusion of persecution, which was immune to logic or demonstration, but was still not the fantasy of a little boy. It represents an adult version of being threatened by terrible punishment for his aggression and his aggressive fantasies, by people around him (parental figures) from whom he felt that he could not possibly escape.[54]

[54] Both cases can be found under *Cases* in the index.

Edipal conflicts and the postedipal superego

The final form of the superego, which replaces most reaction-formation and the direct control by other persons, is a product of the resolution of edipal conflicts. The edipal situation, as we have seen in Chapter 2, is a hopeless one for both the boy and the girl. It is solved by renouncing its unrealistic hopes and expectations, the sexual impulses toward the desired parent of the opposite sex, and the hostile impulses toward the feared parent of the same sex. What the edipal child does is gradually to take over control of his own impulses by internalizing the rival parent and repressing his desire for the other one. In other words, he identifies with the rival as a dangerous parent, and then treats his own forbidden impulses as such a rival would. He also identifies, but to a lesser extent, with his opposite-sexed parent who has punished or made light of his sexual advances and forbidden his aggressions.

As the superego differentiates from the ego, it takes on many controlling and evaluative functions besides those arising directly from edipal conflicts. Eventually, it comes to include many systems and many hierarchies of goodness or cleanliness and superiority, of badness or dirtiness and inferiority. It is finally organized as an internal overseer, the judge of thoughts, words and things, the internal source of love and self-esteem for good behavior, and of hatred and self-condemnation for bad.

Since it is situated within the psychodynamic system it cannot be escaped. It can exercise a constant surveillance over everything that goes on within the system, including even unconscious impulses and conflicts. If it is a healthy superego and reasonably mature it can be much more effective in regulating experience and behavior than any outside agency or person. If it is unhealthy or defective, it can produce a severely inhibited or distorted personality, such as we shall meet in the personality disorders, or a person who may function normally, with perhaps more effort than usual, but who is vulnerable all his life to neurosis or psychosis.

It is essential to bear in mind the fact that the ego begins as that of a small child, who is in direct relationship with nonverbal and early verbal reality, but is full of misinterpretations as well as wisdom. The preconscious ego systems evolve over a period of years before the massive repression that gives final form to the postedipal superego. Successive childhood organizations, precursors of the superego, may all persist in the unconscious, with all their conflicts and many of their infantile perspectives, including some of their primary process derivatives. When an adult regresses, as he does in sleep or in a mental illness, we see some of these early organizations reactivated, from oral, from pre-edipal and from edipal phases.

Some of the *precursors* of the postedipal superego that result in striking examples of adult superego pathology arise during the pre-edipal, sadomasochistic phase of development, the phase of self-assertion and sphincter control. The cruelties of a small child's sadism may be preserved into adulthood as primitive superego structures which interact with reciprocal masochistic tendencies in a repressed unconscious ego. It is this pre-edipal organization which we shall see revived with special clarity in compulsive disorders, where patients sometimes actually punish themselves sadistically, are often incredibly preoccupied with conflicts over cleanliness and dirt, and occasionally show open concern with fecal contamination and sexual fantasy. When regression leads to a psychotic depressive illness, as we have mentioned earlier, there is danger that the sadistic superego may drive the masochistic ego to actual suicide. Sometimes, as in one of the clinical cases we shall describe, obsessive compulsive symptoms appear when a depression clears up, suggesting that there may be a fundamental relationship between depression and compulsion, since in both there is the same overwhelming sense of guilt.

The ego-ideal and its origins

The ego-ideal is an unrealistic part of the superego which has its origin in a narcissistic overevauation of the self and an idealization of parental power and perfection. During the infantile period when the self and others are still imperfectly distinguished, the ego-ideal is probably experienced as a participation in some kind of imaginary omnipotence. For some reason, the ego-ideal escapes the less optimistic modifications which mold the ego in accordance with the reality principle. It evolves with the aid of more abstract ideals and values into an unattainable standard within the superego, which the rest of the superego uses as the measure of what the ego actually achieves.

Adults usually recognize that their ego-ideal is unrealistic; but they retain a wistful picture of what they might have been if they had managed somehow to live differently. The ego-ideal is one of the major sources of dissatisfaction with life, since its goals are perfectionistic, require omnipotence, and are therefore unattainable excepting for the rare genius. It is in the creative genius that one sometimes finds a childish delight in the perfection of what he achieves, an unaffected pleasure in being what everyone else would like to be. It is hardly surprising that with this delight may also go an intolerance of criticism that borders on the fanatic. The ego-ideal remains childish even when it is realized. Among ordinary persons who are by no means geniuses, the ego-ideal is responsible for a great deal of achievement. Like a fond mother, it keeps faith in a person's potentialities when everyone else has given up.[55]

The pathology of the ego-ideal is the pathology of narcissism. It can lead to crippling incapacities when it renders a person incapable of settling for

[55] Howard, R. C., and Berkowitz, L., "Reactions to the evaluators of one's performance," *J. Pers.*, 1958, *26*, 494–507; DiVesta, F. J., "Effects of confidence and motivation on susceptibility to informational social influence," *J. abnorm. soc. Psychol.*, 1959, *59*, 204–209; Beloff, H., and Beloff, J., "Unconscious self-evaluation using a stereoscope," *J. abnorm. soc. Psychol.*, 1959, *59*, 275–278; Rogers, A. H., and Walsh, T. M., "Defensiveness and unwitting self-evaluation," *J. clin. Psychol.*, 1959, *15*, 302–304.

anything short of perfection. It can also lead a person seriously to over-evaluate his achievements, so that he feels chronically neglected and un-appreciated, because he considers himself more unusual than he actually is. This opens the way for paranoid reactions. The ego-ideal is involved in depressions, especially in psychotic depressions, where no matter what a person accomplishes he considers himself a failure. This is sometimes the product of a severe, punitive superego; but it may also be the result of an unrealistic, infantile ego-ideal that makes every achievement seem trivial and unworthy when it is compared with the mangnificence of infantile fantasies. The ultimate in narcissistic extravagance is to be seen in manic excitements, with their acting-out of power and perfection, and among schizophrenic patients who harbor delusions of grandeur.

The Body-Image, the Self-Image and Social Roles

The body-image

The body-image is the central representation of body parts and of the body as a whole. It enters into the representation of the self-image and of social roles. It influences what a person does and does not do, his atti-tudes and opinions, even more than a realistic image of his body.[56]

The body-image is not the same as the body as others see it, or as it might be photographed. People are often surprised by a realistic depiction of their bodies. This appears more commonly among women than among men, both because their body narcissism is normally greater than men's, and because their body conformation is more striking. It is usual for a woman who is trying on a dress in a store to comment openly, sometimes with pleasure, sometimes with dismay, upon the figure she sees in a three-way mirror. Her body-image is obviously different from her external ap-pearance.

The body-image of the contents of the mouth is distorted in both sexes. Teeth which seem so small to a dentist that he needs magnifying glasses to see their details appear enormous to the person who owns them. This is in part a product of the perceptual sensitivity of the tongue, but not entirely so, because the eyes are also exceedingly sensitive. It is probably in part the result of the huge importance of the mouth in early childhood, including the teething period, when some of the most important active experiences with external reality and with the body were oral, and when the first ego to form was a *mouth ego*.

56 Fisher, S., and Cleveland, S. E., *Body Image and Personality*. New York: Van Nostrand, 1958; Fisher, S., "Extensions of theory concerning body image and body re-activity," *Psychosom. Med.*, 1959, *21*, 142–149; Fisher, S., "Prediction of body exterior *vs.* interior reactivity from a body image schema," *J. Pers.*, 1959, *27*, 56–62; Calden, G., Lundy, R. M., and Schlafer, R. J., "Sex differences in body concepts," *J. consult. Psychol.*, 1959, *23*, 378. The rather extensive older literature on the body image will be found in the bibliography and discussion in Fisher and Cleveland's book, cited above.

It is not rare for a pretty woman to consider herself ugly, a body-image distortion which may have deep unconscious roots. It is not unusual for a small man to picture himself as much larger then he actually is; and occasionally a large man pictures himself as being small. Studies of phantom limbs in amputees have provided objective evidence of the disparity of somatic fact and wishful fantasy, even in otherwise normal adults.[57] Among the neuroses, conversion reactions show the greatest distortions of the body-image. They include a variety of neurotic compromises which find visible expressions as symptoms.

The self-image

The self-image, like the body-image, has an external social aspect as well as an internal private one. The two perspectives interact to produce the self-image, or concept of the self, which is not identical with either, and may vary as external and personal circumstances vary.[58] People are sometimes unexpectedly pleased or shocked to learn how others regard them. The picture they have of themselves evidently does not correspond to the more objective but less complete picture that others have of them.[59] The self-image is usually narcissistic because of its origins in the ego-ideal. Sometimes it is chronically self-depreciatory and reveals the baneful influence of a perfectionistic ego-ideal and a demanding superego.

In psychotherapy and psychoanalysis it is sometimes a major task for the patient to remold his self-image so that it approximates the image that others have of him. This can mean an upgrading as well as a downgrading. The self-image of a neurotically depressed patient is characteristically inferior to what others see in him. The hypomanic, on the other hand, has an unrealistic self-image that is overoptimistic and narcissistic, while the psychotically manic patient reflects the extravagances of his infantile ego-ideal in irresponsible adult behavior. Distortions of the self-image are common in schizophrenia and in personality disorders, as we shall see.

What has been called *self-identity, ego-identity* and *self-actualization* belongs to the central representations of the self or the self-image. They have their crises, as we have already discussed them in the course of personality development, and certain additional ones, such as a woman's changed identity after marriage, and the identity changes which each sex experiences in senescence and senility.

[57] Witkin, H. A., *et al.*, *Personality Through Perception.* New York: Harper, 1954.
[58] Cf. Piaget, J., *The Origins of Intelligence in Children* (trans. M. Cook). New York: Internat. Univ. Press, 1952; Piaget, J., *The Construction of Reality in the Child* (trans. M. Cook). New York: Basic Books, 1954.
[59] Lowe, C. M., "The self-concept: fact or artifact," *Psychol. Bull.*, 1961, *58*, 325–336; Akeret, R. U., "Interrelationships among various dimensions of the self-concept," *J. counsel. Psychol.*, 1959, *6*, 199–201; Perkins, H. V., "Factors influencing change in children's self-concepts," *Child Develpm.*, 1958, *29*, 221–230; Prelinger, E., "Extension and structure of the self," *J. Psychol.*, 1959, *47*, 13–23; Engel, M., "The stability of the self-concept in adolescence," *J. abnorm. soc. Psychol.*, 1959, *58*, 211–215.

Social roles and external reality representations

A social role is what a person *is* in relation to his society. It is not normally something that he plays at being. The general outlines of the social roles are provided by the organization of society. The individual performance of them — the particular way that a person occupies his social role — fills in the details and gives a role the personal touch. Society provides men with a great many different roles, besides those of husband, father and head of the household. Society provides less variety for women. The vast majority of women, no matter what their social status or their education, are primarily homemakers, mothers of new human beings, and caretakers of the young, the feeble and the sick.[60]

Although women who evade the essentially feminine roles, and compete successfully with men, are usually praised for it, their choice is often the result of an inability to fulfill a woman's socially prescribed role, rather than a sign of superiority. There is no evidence that men are intellectually superior to women; but there is every evidence that, even though a woman can do a great many things that a man can do, she has powerful inborn needs that cannot be satisfied in our culture unless she accepts the feminine roles of homemaker, wife and mother.

Abnormalities in social role performance carry us into all areas of psychopathology, wherever social expectations and social taboos are in conflict with irresistible individual wants and expectations. It goes almost without saying that such conflicts can occur only in human beings, since no other being has developed an intricate, logical verbal world with which to face an enormously complex, imaginative private world. This is not to say that human conflict is essentially a verbal matter. On the contrary, a great deal of human conflict is never verbalized, and some of it probably never will be. But the ability that man has to symbolize almost everything imaginable makes him able to picture the impossible as possible, and even as something that has happened. It is the imagined adoption of imaginary or real social roles that goes to make up a great many delusions; and these may be expressed logically in words as well as experienced in imagination.[61]

It has often been said that social roles form a bridge between the inner or psychic world and the world of external reality. This is true; but it is not exceptional. There are many kinds of organization in the external world that correspond to organizations within our private world; and a great deal of the representation of the body also corresponds to somatic reality. The bridge between inner experience and the external world is not the social role but man's behavior. We try out the veracity of our imaginations in

60 Bennett, E. M., and Cohen, L. R., "Men and women: personality patterns and contrasts," *Genet. Psychol. Monogr.*, 1959, 59, 101–155.

61 There is a well-organized, logically written account of delusions by a distinguished jurist who at the time he was writing was still having delusional and hallucinatory experiences, and believing thoroughly in them. See Schreber, D. P., *Memoirs of My Nervous Illness* (1903) (trans. I. Macalpine, and R. A. Hunter). London: Dawson, 1955.

some relevant action. This is what is expressed in the term *reality-testing,* that is, acting in such a way as to test the validity of what we imagine or think we perceive.

Summary

We can best summarize what has been implied in this section by saying that the psychodynamic system (pds) includes not only the id, the ego and the superego, but also the central representations or images of external reality that we harbor, and the representations or images of our bodies, our selves, our social roles, and of the bodies, selves and social roles of others.[62] Just how we can best conceptualize all these representations, and where they ought to be located, are still matters of controversy. Some writers place all representations within the *ego,* insofar as they are realistic, and within the *ego-ideal* of the superego insofar as they are unrealistic or unattainable. Others give them a separate place as object-representations and self-representations. The choice is not between two established facts but between two possible ways of conceptualizing the facts, that is, the choice of which seems more promising and useful.

There is something to be said for giving to *external reality representations,* to *the body-image, the self-image* and *the image* or *representation of social roles* a separate status from that of the ego, even though they could never have been constructed without ego function. This is a relatively flexible arrangement. It allows for interactions between the ego, or for that matter the superego, and the representation of objects, the body-image, the self-image, and our representation of our own social roles as well as those of other people. It also simplifies the problem of realistic *versus* unrealistic aspects of our representation of external objects, the body, the self and social roles. All four of these are intimately related to the ego, the superego and even to derivatives of the id; but all four are often realistic representations with which ego, superego and id-derivatives may interact by shifting cathexes.

To give just one example, when a dreaming, delirious or paranoid person denies and projects what has escaped repression in his own unconscious ego and superego, he gets rid of what he projects in the sense that what might have threatened from within now appears to be on the outside. What actually happens, however, is simply a shifting of cathexes, so that previously unconscious ego or superego functions *seem* to be exercised by reality-representations and by the representations of the social roles of other people.

This maneuver is essentially a reshuffling of energies or cathexes. Nothing actually leaves the psychodynamic system of the dreaming, delirious or

---

62 There is a comprehensive literature on psychodynamic conceptions of the self and reality, reaching back more than half a century. A relatively recent account, with a bibliography, is given by Jacobson, E., "The self and the object world," *Psychoanal. Study Child,* 1954, *9,* 75–127.

paranoid person. It is like transferring money from one bank to another without expending any. Sexual and hostile aggressive cathexes are shifted from ego and superego to representations of a fantasied world. This fantasied world lies within the psychodynamic system of the person who is dreaming, delirious or paranoid; but he experiences it as belonging to the world of external reality.

We witness here a regressive return to phases of development when external reality had not yet been clearly separated from internal reality. The regression is a reaction to stress — in the dreaming and the delirious person a state of relative cerebral incompetence, in the paranoid person a failure to develop mature superego structures. The developmental level at which the regrouping takes place when a person regresses will depend upon his childhood fixations. The childhood fixations, in turn, depend upon childhood stresses, including childhood conflicts. Fixation, conflict and regression are closely related phenomena, as the next chapter will show.

6

Conflict, Regression, Anxiety
and the Defenses

Up to this point we have discussed personality development, the
drives and motivation, the psychodynamic system and its constituent parts
— the id, the ego, the superego, and representations of the body, the self
and the object world. Before going on to the clinical chapters, we shall
review briefly the problems of human conflict and regression, as these appear in the psychodynamic system, and the central position of anxiety in
relation to the major defenses.

Most of our information about internal conflict and regression, about
anxiety and the defenses, comes from the study and therapy of the neuroses,
the psychoses and the personality disorders. A good deal also comes from
the study of dreams; and, especially within recent years, there have been
increasing contributions from students of child development, hypnosis, experimentally induced intoxication and sensory deprivation.[1]

---

[1] Many studies of children are reported in *The Psychoanalytic Study of the Child.*
New York: Internat. Univ. Press, 1945–1963, vols. 1–17. The works of Gesell *et al.,*
and of Piaget, J., cited elsewhere in the book, should also be consulted. See Gill, M.,
and Brenman, M., *Hypnosis and Allied States.* New York: Internat. Univ. Press, 1959.
References to studies of *experimental* intoxication will be found in the chapter on brain
disorders. The significance of *sensory deprivation* is discussed in Miller, S. C., "Ego
autonomy in sensory deprivation," *Internat. J. Psychoanal.,* 1962, *43,* 1–20. Many references are given there. See also Solomon, P., *et al., Sensory Deprivation.* Cambridge,
Mass.: Harvard Univ. Press, 1961.

Conflict

In the preceding chapters, we have discussed conflict frequently, because it comes up inevitably in any account of personality development, of need, drive and motivation. There were the conflicting drives of the primary process, out of which the ego in part developed. There were the intensely emotional edipal conflicts, which terminated after a few years with renunciation of edipal desires, freedom from edipal fears, and the development of the superego. There was the pre-edipal conflict over the need for self-assertion and the persistent dependency needs. There were conflicts over sibling rivalry and many others.

External sources of conflict

There are innumerable external situations which make conflict unavoidable for all human beings in their everyday life. At a physiological level these arise because the human organism and the human environment are differently organized. The human environment offers a great many opportunities for the satisfaction of human need, many frustrations and not a few dangers. The human organism has many built-in devices for maintaining a physiologically steady state, called *homeostasis*, which varies only within relatively narrow limits. The continual disturbances of homeostasis, which result both from environmental changes and from physiological changes within the organism, continually call into play the homeostatic functions, which return the organism to an optimal equilibrium, ready for the next disturbance. This kind of automatic internal adaptation should be remembered when we come to study the defenses, which perform similar functions at psychic levels.

At a behavioral level, conflict is also unavoidable, and we all have acquired techniques for reducing the impact of conflict, for avoiding it, and for choice and decision-making which actively accept one thing and give up the other.[2] Conflicts may be resolved in many different ways. Some of them are never settled; yet they wane and disappear with time as conditions change and as new interests make them no longer important. Many of these are suppressed before they disappear, often with the help of consciously adopted reaction-formation attitudes; and some of the most important disappear from consciousness and the preconscious through the defensive action of repression, but remain with all their power in the unconscious. Many conflicting desires are sublimated. They lose their original sexual or aggressive cathexis and become socially approved activities and fantasies which utilize neutralized energy.[3] Many conflicts are resolved through identification, even

[2] Miller, D. R., and Swanson, G. E., *Inner Conflict and Defense.* New York: Holt, 1960.
[3] Buss, A. H., *The Psychology of Aggression.* New York: Wiley, 1961; McNeil, E. R., "Psychology and aggression," *J. Conflict Resolution,* 1959, 3, 195–293.

without full neutralization. The doll play of girls is one example of this. Long after the girl has apparently resolved her edipal conflicts, she rehearses endlessly her mother's role, often taking great pleasure in caring for a doll in every way possible as though it were her baby.

Many external conflicts, which also have internal representation and internal counterparts, are displaced, or their mode of expression is tamed. The small child may attack an adversary with flailing fists, with kicking and biting. In time, however, he learns to attack an adversary verbally, to argue with him, tease or belittle him, or to compete with him in games. So well disguised are these aggressions that adults often do not consciously know that their arguments, teasing, belittling and competing serve the function of attack. Sexual conflicts also find many substitute solutions. Men and women get full social approval for making themselves attractive to the opposite sex, even after they are married, and this can be carried as far as mock courting and flirting, provided the marital partner feels secure, and there is sufficient distance maintained between the persons playing at courting and flirting.

The mere fact of group living ensures that there shall always be external as well as internal conflict. The needs and desires of different persons, living in close proximity, and living out different sexual and social roles, makes for continual multiple conflict of interests. Our society has elaborate traditions, customs and rituals for reducing these conflicts, for making them bearable, for allowing us every now and then to express them openly without retaliation. They are, nevertheless, always with us as the price we pay for our overwhelming need for interdependence with other human beings.[4]

Another major source of inevitable human conflict, and one that will lead us directly to the psychodynamic system, is the human capacity for symbolizing. From a very early age, perhaps from the moment of birth, every human being is able to represent to himself in symbolic form the experiences he has with his body and with what will become external reality. This seems at first to be representation in the form of imagery, probably the kinds of imagery we all experience in dreams. As time goes on, and ego functions grow in complexity and richness, more complicated, more abstract, more continuous and more logical representations are added to the original imagery. Eventually, everyone acquires the language system of his society, a system with its own structure and its own arbitrary rules.

Conflict is inherent in all symbolization because it is the representation of internal, somatic, external and interpersonal realities in forms that are not identical with the original experiences, and, especially in the case of language and mathematics, cannot be in the form of what has been experienced. In both language and mathematics, symbols can be manipulated

---

[4] A detailed discussion of *conflict* as the mutual interference of reactions at a behavioral level is contained in Cameron, N., and Magaret, A., *Behavior Pathology*. Boston: Houghton Mifflin, 1951, pp. 246–275. Experimental studies and clinical examples are cited there.

in ways that correspond to nothing in nonverbal or nonmathematical experience. Sometimes these symbolic manipulations greatly increase man's mastery over reality; sometimes they contradict realities; sometimes they merely express something which does not correspond to realistic experience. Even when what we say or write contradicts reality, it can still contribute richly to imaginative enjoyment and lighten the burden of human living. It can also contribute significantly to human psychopathology, as we shall see.

The potentialities for conflict in nonverbal, nonmathematical imagination — in imagery, feeling, recall, interpretation, fantasy, belief, suspicion, nonverbal pondering and the like — are too well known to need special emphasis here. The thing to remember is that a small child will represent an experience to himself — symbolize it in his imagery — not as it would have appeared in a moving picture with a sound track, but as he himself experienced it, with all the small child misinterpretations, misunderstandings, ambivalent feelings, omissions, passions and distortions intact. This is what he symbolizes to himself; this is the way he will remember what he experienced; and this is what will be reactivated in his adulthood if he regresses — in forming a dream or a symptom, or perhaps in creating something artistic which others can enjoy because of their own reverberations.

Studies of childhood symbolization, such as Piaget has been making over a period of forty years, reveal the extraordinary confusion and perplexity of thinking, fantasy, conception and communication which still persist long after the child has mastered language forms — even up to the ninth or tenth years.[5] Piaget's innumerable protocols of the thinking of normal school children show an almost incredible degree of unrealistic representations, with the most glaring contradictions, impossibilities and illogical conclusions. Yet, in spite of all this, these children manage to live a reasonably well-ordered existence. Probably it is the presence of more logical and more realistic adults that makes life possible for human children, even as late as the latency period.

For our later consideration of psychopathological developments, it is important to bear in mind something that Freud always insisted upon, and Piaget rediscovered, namely, that the old infantile and childish ways of perceiving, conceiving and remembering do not just disappear when something more realistic replaces them. The primitive imagery, the infantile and childish wishes, fears, fantasies and guilt, all leave their mark. They continue, as Freud said, like the remains of an ancient civilization, under successive layers of later civilizations, but with all of them to some extent alive and active. Thus we have to take into account, not only the conflicts of our

[5] The many volumes by J. Piaget give innumerable protocols in which verbal absurdities and obvious contradictions appear side-by-side with normal direct manipulation of reality. See especially *Language and Thought in the Child* (trans. M. Gabain). London: Routledge & Kegan Paul, 1926. See also the more recent books, Piaget, J., *The Origins of Intelligence in Children* (trans. M. Cook). New York: Internat. Univ. Press, 1952; and Piaget, J., *The Construction of Reality in the Child* (trans. M. Cook). New York: Basic Books, 1954.

adult life — in wish, feeling, thought and action — but also the repressed conflicts of our adolescence, our latency, our edipal and pre-edipal phases of development, and even the conflicts that existed in the symbiotic period and what led up to it. We shall return to this last in a moment, when we recall the conflicting impulses of the primary process.

The point is that each adult experience may start up some reverberation in a forgotten, repressed, unconscious experience persisting from his years of adolescence, latency, edipal or pre-edipal phase, or even from experiences earlier than the pre-edipal. If he is awake and reasonably healthy, the earlier reverberations may have little effect and elicit no recall. At most, they may increase his sense of identity — by giving continuity to his experience — and perhaps add some extra warmth or satisfaction, or introduce some playfulness into his action. If he is asleep and dreaming, these early experiences, with their unrealistic symbolization and their inappropriate conflicts, may team up with some of yesterday's experiences to find satisfaction and discharge in a nonsensical manifest dream. If he is neurotic or psychotic, or suffers from a personality disorder, the early experiences and their conflicts will find expression in symptoms even when the adult is fully awake.[6] This brings us to the place of conflict in the psychodynamic system.

Conflict and the psychodynamic system

We have just seen that the distinction between external and internal conflict breaks down the moment we come to symbolization. Every human being internalizes his external conflicts along with everything else. Even the most trivial conflict, such as we face hundreds of times a day in making simple choices, is symbolized or "represented" in one way or another within the psychodynamic system. The enormous volume of our daily transactions in itself guarantees that not every trivial, fleeting conflict shall leave permanent traces. Only those conflicts having special significance for our individual personality, and especially those related to unresolved emotional conflicts of the past, will leave their enduring trace. This they will do because of the organization of the psychodynamic system, with its multiple intrasystemic interactions, its semipermeable barriers, its capacity for sustained reinforcement and its indelible infantile experiences. Our purpose at this point is to review some of the ways in which the psychodynamic system, by its own modes of functioning, gives rise to far-reaching conflicts, and the ways in which it operates in such manner as to resolve conflict.

Conflict and the primary process. The earliest source of conflict within the psychodynamic system lies in the nature of the primary process of the

---

[6] An interesting discussion of conflict in relation to early experience will be found in Kubie, L. S., "The fundamental nature of the distinction between normality and neurosis," *Psychoanal. Quart.*, 1954, *23*, 167–204. Kubie's approach is somewhat different from the one given here.

id. Here, we have assumed, there is an insistent push on the part of contradictory impulses for immediate discharge or immediate expression. If this assumption is correct, it means that conflict between competing impulses exists from the very start within the psychodynamic system, even before there have been any transactions with what will become somatic or external reality.

The earliest signs of ego function, the beginnings of what has been called the *mouth ego,* include attempts at organizing some of these competing and contradictory energies in the service of realistic action. This shows up in the suckling activities of neonates. As we have seen, within a few days, sometimes within a few hours, the neonate has organized anticipation, searching, oral grasping, holding and swallowing. Such an organization, primitive as it may seem, is nevertheless highly complex. It calls for the regulation of several drives in direct relation to one another. It involves, for example, the elimination of such primitive conflicts as those between the need to swallow and the need to breathe, the need for food and the need for infant sleep, a kind of dozing. That such conflicting needs exist is shown by the "preference" which some neonates have for sleep over feeding, so that adult interference is required to make them feed.

In spite of all the ego and superego organization that supervenes, the relationship between the primary process and conflict continues to be significant throughout life. All the evidence that we have from dreams, intoxication, hypnosis and sensory deprivation confirms this. To take the single example of the *dreamwork,* we find that every adult is still engaged in attempting to solve new and old conflicts by means of primary process maneuvers — for example, through displacement and condensation in ways that defy secondary process logic. This apparently goes on during the daytime as well as at night. Much of the dreamwork goes on unconsciously while we are awake, even though we are not aware of it, and even while we are at the same time engaged in secondary process thinking.

What is true of the creation of the *manifest dream* is true also of the creation of the *manifest symptom.* A major difference is that the symptom, which is an expression of internal conflict, comes through during the day when the patient is wide awake. The distinction between the normal and the abnormal person is not merely one of operating according to the primary process or the secondary process. All of us operate according to both primary and secondary processes, while we are awake as well as while we are asleep. The distinction — and it is an important one — is between those persons whose primary process products are limited and more or less under ego control, and those persons whose ego has lost control over some primary process product, which shows up as a *symptom.* Putting it another way, the normal adult confines his primary process maneuvers in such a way that their derivatives appear only in dreams, in jokes, in slips of the tongue and in other parapraxes. The psychopathological person, as we shall see, shows all of these manifestations and, in addition, suffers from symptoms which vary all the way from a neurotic compromise, such as a phobia, to un-realistic chaotic experience and behavior, such as one witnesses in some of the psychoses.

Conflict and the synthetic function of the ego. At a psychic level, the multiplicity of simultaneous human needs goes far beyond those of the primary process. The psychodynamic system requires some kind of systematic regulation to protect it internally from the stress and strain of continual conflict. The chief regulator, of course, is the ego. The ego gains control over the pleasure principle and operates most of the time in accordance with the reality principle. It has immediate access to perception, secondary process thinking, organized feeling and coordinated action. It is the site of most of the defensive systems.

As the preconscious ego differentiates more and more from the unconscious ego and the id, during infancy and childhood, it renders behavior and experience more and more stable, predictable, complex and adaptive. By regulating the discharge or expression of drives and unconscious infantile impulses, the ego greatly reduces the occasions for internal conflict. This regulatory function is further strengthened when the superego matures; but, as we shall soon see, the formation of a superego also adds new dimensions to internal conflict, since it establishes a representative of society within the system itself.

The regulation of internal stress and strain, which includes the reduction of conflict and an increase in general integration of the psychodynamic system, is part of what is called *the synthetic function of the ego.* It is sometimes compared with *physiological homeostasis.*[7] However that may be, the synthetic function of the ego is nothing more than an expression of the more general law that the prime function of any organism is to remain organized, as a separate system, in an environment which is differently organized. In the case of the ego, the reduction of internal conflict through its "synthetic," integrative function, makes for optimal conditions within the psychodynamic system as a whole. Whenever the ego loses its synthetic function, as it does every night when we fall asleep, and as it does in various ways and to different degrees in neuroses and psychoses, the psychodynamic system falls back to an earlier or more primitive organization. We shall have more to say about this in the section on regression.

The ego and the id. We assume that the ego differentiates from the id, or from an undifferentiated id-ego nucleus, through interactions with somatic and external reality. As we have just seen, one of the earliest ego functions seems to be the regulation of competing id impulses in such a way that realistic feeding activities can be carried on. Although such regulation

---

[7] Cf. Hendrick, I., *Facts and Theories of Psychoanalysis.* (3rd ed.) New York: Knopf, 1958; Grinker, R. R. (Ed.), *Toward a United Theory of Human Behavior.* New York: Basic Books, 1956.

allows maximal gratification of certain id impulses, it also delays or suppresses the gratification of others. Here, once more, we find conflict built into the psychodynamic system. The ego, from the very start, is in conflict with some of the id impulses, while it allows and even abets the gratification of others. When the situation changes, and another activity becomes dominant, the pattern of ego-id conflict also changes. Different id impulses are then suppressed and others allowed or abetted. This conflictual relationship between ego and id persists throughout life.

As an infant grows older, the somatic and external realities come to have increasing significance for his ego functions. The ego itself grows in strength and complexity as it introjects and identifies with what it experiences. It takes into itself, internalizes, whatever aspects of the powerful people and things around it that it can. It operates more and more in terms of the realities of its body and its surroundings, including the symbiotic relationship which it develops with the mother. The id, meanwhile, remains unrealistic, and thus it comes more and more into conflict with the increasingly realistic ego.

Without the mother's constant help the ego would be in continual danger of being overwhelmed by id impulses. This is what we meant when we said in an earlier chapter that the infant needs adult protection, not only for survival, but to enable the ego to defend itself without having to overuse introjection and identification. The powerful id drives — the kinds we see unleashed in night terrors and in panic — have traumatic effects upon the infant, not unlike the traumatic effects which helplessness in the face of extreme danger has upon adults. It is presumably this that accounts in part for the acute anxiety that appears in some neurotic and psychotic persons when id derivatives and unconscious ego processes threaten to break through the ego defenses. The anxiety is justified, as we shall see in the clinical cases, since id-derivatives and unconscious ego processes can invade secondary process organizations and make them disintegrate.

We have said, in another connection, that for some time every mother has to act as her helpless child's temporary ego. Here we see the other side of the coin. At first, the infant ego begins to gain control over his previously irresistible id impulses through the use of the mother image which he has introjected and with which he has identified. If the infant ego receives adequate maternal protection from the extremes of internal and external stress, which he cannot handle, he will go on to develop a defensive system which has as its keystone the mechanism of *repression*. This development takes a long time, and seems not to near completion until the resolution of the edipal phase. It is possible, in view of the wide use of *reaction formation* during latency, that a mature defensive system does not develop until after adolescence.

In the beginning, however, the infant ego makes use of maternal introjects and identifications to suppress whatever id impulses his mother seems to suppress, and to permit expression of those impulses which his mother allows expression. As soon as he begins to connect, however vaguely, his experiences of being overwhelmed by id drives with his mother's absence, he will show unmistakable signs of *separation anxiety*. When his mother leaves him alone he will greet the first sign of inner need as though it were already a disaster. We shall return to this when we discuss *anxiety* later in the chapter.

One of the hazards of suppression, and later on of repression, is that if a conflict seems particularly dangerous, the ego will try to dispose of the whole conflict just as it is, unsolved and infantile. As *consciousness* and the *preconscious* differentiate from the *unconscious*, these unsolved infantile conflicts will become themselves unconscious, and therefore inaccessible to the normal processes of maturation and development in the preconscious ego. This is what frequently happens during faulty resolution of the edipal complex. The edipal conflicts, with their infantile desires, fears and misinterpretations, are repressed much as they originally were, ready to break through whenever the defensive organization weakens. We shall find examples of this breakthrough among the clinical cases.

To a minor degree, everyone harbors some unresolved unconscious conflicts which were originally open conflicts between the infantile ego and the id. These do not disrupt adult preconscious and conscious processes because of the defensive system which hold them in check. The advantage of a maturely organized, effective ego defensive system is that it protects adult preconscious and conscious organizations from intrusive primary process id-derivatives and from whatever primitive ego material has been repressed along with them. In short, even though there may be repressed infantile ego-id conflicts beneath the surface, the normal adult ego suffers no disturbances from them as long as he remains awake and reasonably healthy.

Conflict, the superego and the ego-ideal. We have already pointed out the advantages of having a superego and an ego-ideal. A mature superego differentiates from the ego during resolution of the edipal complex. It begins as a personalized representation of parental figures, or whatever other authority figures may have charge of the child. But this is really only a precursor of the superego, the representation which comes to life again in paranoid psychoses, and seems to the projecting patient to be an external persecutor, or a whole community of external persecutors.

The mature superego that supersedes this early personalized form — without, however, completely eradicating it — is something much more abstract, a codification of moral and ethical principles, with many systems of hierarchies. The mature superego is to a large extent representative of the society in which a person lives. Since it is an integral part of the psychodynamic system, it is in a position to scan and evaluate everything that goes on within that system, whether at conscious, preconscious or unconscious levels. It amounts to the presence of society's moral representative, not only right in the home, but right in one's most private, personal experience. This presence, at its best, guides a person's life along socially approved lines. It gives stability and predictability to a person by preventing his being dominated by any asocial or antisocial trends which may still be lurking at some level of experience or behavior within him.

It is obvious that the establishment of superego systems also makes for conflict. Even the most mature and well-intentioned adult has his moments of guilt, remorse and moral struggle. The source may be in something done, said or thought; it may be in something merely contemplated. The superego is always there, with its internalized authority figures, its hierarchies of good and evil, its patterns of social approval and disapproval. The man is rare who escapes all superego censure and can live without superego approval. He is not only rare; he is also pathological, unpredictable, and unacceptable to others. We shall see some of the syndromes of underdeveloped superegos when we come to the personality disorders.

Overdeveloped superegos are also pathological. Because they tend to make a person conform to the dictates of society, the pathology may not be obvious. In fact, people with hypertrophied superegos are sometimes admired for their righteousness or their rigid conformity. If conformity or righteousness comes from anxiety, that is, from the pressure of an unrelenting, domineering superego, it is pathological, no matter how much it may be approved. We shall see clinical examples of anxiety that come from an overdeveloped or distorted superego when we study the compulsions and the depressions, where the superego contribution to the pathology is exceptionally clear. Superego defects appear, however, in almost all psychopathology.

In Chapter 5 we pointed out that only a small portion of superego function, the portion that we call our *conscience,* goes on at conscious levels. By far the most important and far-reaching functions take place at preconscious and unconscious levels. This means that most of our *conflicts* about right and wrong, good and evil, the approved and the condemned, also occur at preconscious and unconscious levels. Moreover, in many persons it is some immature form of the superego, often one of its infantile precursors, that is engaged in the preconscious or unconscious conflict.

Conscience is so strongly entrenched in our thinking as *righteousness* that it is difficult to conceive of any of its unconscious counterparts, or its still active precursors, as being malicious or corrupting. Nevertheless, we all know that superego persecution can make a person commit suicide; this is neither a righteous nor usually an intelligent influence. A persecuting superego can also be projected, as it is by most psychotic paranoid persons, and this may lead to homicide — also hardly to be classified with virtuous acts. The superego, like the ego, may be or may become defective; and when this happens the psychodynamic system is thrown out of balance so that psychopathology develops.

We have already said, in Chapter 5, that the *ego-ideal* is generally considered to be a part of the superego, or at least an organization which the superego uses in evaluating experience and behavior. The ego-ideal is always unrealistic, and to the extent that the superego uses it as a standard of ego achievement, the result is bound to be a conflict. The ego-ideal has its constructive side also, for within limits it can lead a person to become better than he is, and it can hold out hopes when everyone around a person feels that he is hopeless.

The pathology of the ego-ideal, we have said, is the pathology of narcissism. The ego-ideal grows out of the omnipotent fantasies of infancy and childhood, and like them it has little foundation in objective fact. The conflicts that it engenders are most apt to be conflicts over one's attainments or one's goodness in contrast to the perfection of the ego-ideal, which the superego uses as its measuring stick. The origin of the ego-ideal in magical experiences, where everything seemed possible, or where the little things a child could do were blown up into miracles, leaves it with an aura of infinite possibilities. Sometimes a patient's ego-ideal turns out to be little more than an infantile, enormously exaggerated picture of what his parent was like, a picture that has survived the contradictions of subsequent reality. Sometimes it is a magical picture of the patient himself, which has mushroomed from experiences of infantile magic, so that every real achievement seems insignificant by comparison. Origins such as these, when they are combined with a punitive or a ridiculing superego, help to explain the psychopathology of many persons whose considerable accomplishments bring them nothing but self-contempt.[8] The pathology of the ego-ideal, like the pathology of the superego, sometimes appears *overtly* where everyone can see it; but when this happens it is nearly always the product of a pathological regression. Let us turn next to a discussion of regression.

Regression

Regression is not in itself pathological. In the form of sleep, it is a regular nightly experience, without which no one can hope to function normally. After about sixteen daytime hours of maintaining behavior and experience at realistic levels, most people are ready to sleep and dream. They shut out as much stimulation from their surroundings as they can, abandon their structured ways of daytime interacting, let slip the anchor of external reality, and drift into oblivion and unrealistic fantasy. This is the normal nightly regression that refreshes us and makes us ready for another sixteen hours of realistic interaction. Because every person goes to sleep every night, this gives us a good starting point for a discussion of regression in general.

Regression and dreaming

"A dream," Freud wrote in 1938, "is a psychosis, with all the absurdities, delusions and illusions of a psychosis."[9] The process of dreaming gives all

---

[8] This is the place to point out that many patients are still unable to remedy their condition completely even after they gain full understanding of its origins. The same is true of physical defects. Knowing everything about their origin — even their embryological origin — does not remove the defects, although it often makes them more endurable and less distorting to the general personality.

[9] Freud, S., *An Outline of Psychoanalysis.* New York: Norton, 1949.

of us the chance to be unrealistic for a few hours every night. It allows us to express things which we are forbidden to express during the daytime. It lets us re-experience some of the pleasures of infancy and childhood, exposes us to childish fears, and reactivates unconscious conflicts which we have failed to master in our immediate and remote past.

Apparently it is essential that we dream. Recent experimental evidence indicates that everyone has three or four periods of dreaming every night, even though few of us remember the vast majority of our dreams. If sleep is interrupted before sufficient dreaming has gone on, an extra dream period may be slipped in when a person goes to sleep again.[10] In other words, we all have to indulge in a little psychotic experience each night in order to be normal the next day.

The few dreams that we do remember in adulthood are usually confused and superficially meaningless. Sometimes they are impressively weird. Occasionally they are so frightening that we are glad to wake up and realize that what frightened us was only a dream. The regressed, sleeping ego seems to merge again with derivatives of the id. It seems to produce something akin to the undifferentiated id-ego state of early childhood. Now, however, many of the remnants of later childhood, of latency, adolescence and adulthood may appear which, of course, the infant and young child do not have.

When we adults regress in normal sleep we give up the clear distinctions between fact and fantasy which we have to maintain during most of the time that we are awake. We easily pass irrationally from activity to passivity, or from passivity to activity, as in the dream which was cited in Chapter 5. We may lose the boundaries between external and internal reality in our dreams, and even the boundaries between ourselves and others. Sometimes our body-image undergoes grotesque distortions. Conflicts and anxieties come to light which belong to an earlier phase of life, but they usually also include some fragments from the preceding day's experience. Even time is of no importance in dreams; recent and remote past are intermingled freely.

Freud called the dream the royal road to the unconscious, which it certainly is. It is also the royal road to each person's childhood and infancy, not necessarily as things were objectively, but as the infant or child experienced them. In the *manifest dream* — the dream as we recall it upon awakening — we see only the *product* of the *dreamwork*, which is itself unconscious, and operates to a large extent in accordance with the primary process. We also see the results of whatever defensive maneuvers were still operating during sleep, and of superego pressures as well.

The dreamwork is laid bare by analyzing the dream, that is, by finding

[10] Dement, W., and Kleitman, N., "The relation of eye movements during sleep to dream activity: an objective method for the study of dreaming," *J. exp. Psychol.*, 1957, *53*, 339–346; Dement, W., and Wolfert, E. A., "The relation of eye movements, body motility, and external stimuli to dream content," *J. exp. Psychol.*, 1958, *55*, 543–553; Schiff, S. K., Bunney, W. E., and Freedman, D. X., "A study of ocular movements in hypnotically induced dreams," *J. nerv. ment. Dis.*, 1961, *133*, 59–68.

out what latent thoughts the dream seems to have been expressing when the person who had the dream lets down his guard and free-associates. It soon becomes clear that the dream expresses many things at once, some of them mutually contradictory, some of them condensed and some of them irrationally displaced. Dreams sometimes express things which are decidedly ego-alien, including mutilation, murder and incest. It was said more than two thousand years ago that the good man dreams what the bad man does. All of this provides unmistakable evidence that even as adults we still engage in primary process and unconscious, asocial infantile thinking. Our great achievement as adults is that we can keep this material unconscious while we are awake, and in this way engage in the logical, realistic thinking, feeling and action which characterize secondary processes.

Regression and split-level functioning

Dreaming takes place only under special conditions. We are asleep when we dream; therefore we cannot act out weird and sometimes antisocial fantasies. But there is more to it than this. Our dreams are prepared in part during the daytime while we are fully awake and realistic.[11] They come from the forbidden, unrealistic and often infantile processes which our daytime activities stimulate, but our defenses keep for the most part unconscious. Fragments of these unconscious processes occasionally appear in the daytime as fleeting fantasies, as slips of the tongue and other parapraxes, or as jokes which escape repression because they are not intended to be taken seriously.

Incidents such as these, and the still more convincing products of free association, make it clear that during the daytime we are engaged in *split-level functioning*. At one level we are dealing with realities, as reasonable, logical adults. At other levels we are operating simultaneously in unconscious, primitive and even primary process modes. Sometimes, when fully awake and while experiencing ourselves as responsible adults living in a realistic world, we are also engaged surreptitiously in trying to resolve unconscious infantile conflicts. When we fall asleep, when external reality seems to vanish and the boundaries between preconscious and unconscious grow vague, our previously unconscious fantasies become our preconscious realities, and primary process maneuvers rule the night.[12] In short, what had been going on surreptitiously during the day may come out into the open when we are asleep.

The same general result comes about quite differently from two other situations. One of them is intoxication; the other is sensory deprivation. Intoxications of many kinds can weaken our ego defenses, and when this is the case the ego is flooded by previously unconscious, irrational processes.

[11] Cf. Fisher, C., "Construction of dreams and images," *J. Amer. Psychoanal. Ass.*, 1957, 5, 5–60; Fisher, C., and Paul, I. H., "Subliminal stimulation and dreams," *J. Amer. Psychoanal. Ass.*, 1959, 7, 35–83.

[12] Isakower, O., "A contribution to the pathopsychology of phenomena associated with falling asleep." *Internat. J. Psychoanal.*, 1938, 19, 331–345.

A delirium is the usual result, with delusions, hallucinations and sometimes grotesque distortions of the body-image and of external reality. Sensory deprivation involves only reduction of the normal perceptual intake and, as a rule, some restriction of movement. Yet for some persons this relative loss of reality contact induces a marked regression, with the emergence of delusional and hallucinatory phenomena comparable to dreams.

To sum up what we have been saying, our dreams at night show us that mature adults still utilize primary process thinking; they are still preoccupied with infantile desires, fears and conflicts. The fact that these dreams are in part prepared during the daytime suggests that both primary processes and unconscious fantasies are going on while we are fully awake. The products of free association, of intoxication and of sensory deprivation confirm this suggestion. From all of these quite different sources we get evidence of a split-level functioning. The rational, preconscious or conscious process seems to have an irrational, unconscious accompaniment, which only our defensive structure keeps out of our secondary process organizations.

Fixation and regression

Regression does not always carry us to the same level of function. Unless we are dealing unconsciously with some specific trauma all the time, our dreams are not simply repetitious. We dream one thing one night and something else another night. Sometimes the manifest dream deals with current events. We repeat a daytime situation in some weird way, and try to solve conflicts in our dreams which we are also aware of when awake, but cannot solve. Sometimes a dream is childish. It represents pleasures, fears or conflicts that belong to our early years. Sometimes when we dream we seem to be in a symbiotic or an objectless world, where the lack of perceptual organizing can be frightening. Often we pass through several such phases during a dream, or we mix together the characteristics of several phases simultaneously.[13]

What this means is that we all have more than one point of fixation at which regression may halt for an episode of dreaming. These fixation points are specific for each individual. They represent constellations that light up when a person regresses in sleep. In part they are determined by the experiences of the preceding day, which stimulate us at unconscious as well as at conscious levels. In part they are also determined by something in our childhood past which has remained unsolved, and was repressed unsolved, most often at the beginning of latency. As we have said, unless we are struggling continually to master the same trauma or the same conflict, as happens, for example, in the so-called traumatic neuroses and in battle dreams,[14] the

[13] Although dreaming is used here as the example, much the same applies to intoxication, sensory deprivation and, as we shall see later on, to the neuroses.

[14] Grinker, R. R., and Spiegel, J., *War Neuroses*. Philadelphia: Blakiston, 1945; Grinker, R. R., and Spiegel, J., *Men Under Stress*. Philadelphia: Blakiston, 1945.

dreams we remember vary in content and feeling considerably from night to night, or even within a single night.[15] Ordinary dreams vary in their motivation, just as we shall see that symptoms do. Some are motivated by the desire for an infantile pleasure which a person has never outgrown. The regression of sleep gives the opportunity for another infantile *indulgence*. Some dreams are motivated by the need to *master* infantile or childhood conflicts which a person has repressed without mastering.

Whatever the situation, the regression of sleep carries a person to some point of immature fixation. What does this imply? It implies that for some reason he has suffered an arrest of development in that phase of his personality growth. Usually there are points of arrested development in several phases. The arrested development, the *fixation*, as we have indicated, may be the result of overindulgence during some phase of childhood which makes future maturing seem unattractive to the child at the time; or it may be the result of unusual fright or frustration in some phase of development which makes a child retreat to an earlier phase and entrench himself there. It goes without saying that regression during ordinary sleep, even though it reveals unresolved infantile conflicts, does not result in psychopathology. It may be a person's protection from psychopathology, his opportunity to express unconscious fears and conflicts, and thus to gain relief. Sometimes a dream is itself a symptom, a sign that some unrecognized psychopathology lies near the surface.

Fixation and regression in psychopathology

The most dramatic examples of pathological fixation are to be found in the otherwise apparently healthy *autistic child* and *symbiotic child*. The *autistic child*, first described by Kanner,[16] remains fixated emotionally in what is essentially a presymbiotic state. He never succeeds in developing a normal interpersonal relationship with another human being; he never develops a *basic trust*. He may make use of other persons as though they were things, as though they were mechanical devices for satisfying his needs.

> An autistic boy, aged six years, would pull a person's hand over to something that needed adjusting as though the hand were a grasping tool. He would climb upon a person to reach something that he wanted in the same way that he climbed upon a chair. He gave no evidence that he recognized the person as a human being with whom he could interact, as something in any way different from an inanimate object.[17]

[15] Alexander, F., "Dreams in pairs and series," *Internat. J. Psychoanal.*, 1925, *6*, 446–452; French, T. M., *The Integration of Behavior: Volume 2: The Integrative Process in Dreams.* Chicago: Univ. of Chicago Press, 1954.

[16] For a detailed review of the *autistic* and the *symbiotic* child, see Ekstein, R., Bryant, K., and Friedman, S. W., "Childhood schizophrenia and allied conditions," in Bellak, L. (Ed.), *Schizophrenia, a Review of the Syndrome.* New York: Logos Press, 1958, pp. 555–693.

[17] For an account of this case I am indebted to Dr. E. S. Cameron, whose patient the autistic child was.

The *symbiotic child*[18] appears to be fixated at the developmental phase when he had formed a symbiotic unit with his mother, as described for normal development in Chapter 2. His personality development seems to be normal up to this point; but he does not develop reality-testing that establishes himself as a separate being with his own internal psychic organization. His self-image remains fused with the mother image. Both the autistic child and the symbiotic child are results of a grossly defective parent-child relationship during infancy.

A less dramatic and much less disabling case of fixation is that of the abnormally dependent child, who develops reality-testing to the point of recognizing that he and his mother are separate individuals, but remains dependent upon a parent figure for every new move. Some of these children never become emotionally independent, but remain attached to their original edipal object all their life. Many of them continue to live unmarried in the parental home, with a partially sublimated but still intense attachment to the mother or the father. Sometimes a fixated, dependent person succeeds in transferring his dependency from a parent to a marital partner. This outcome is commoner among women than among men, since women are expected to be somewhat dependent in the marital relationship, whereas men are expected to take the initiative and establish the independence of the new family unit.

The chronically dependent person is likely to be defective both in his ego identifications and his superego identifications. His *ego identifications,* and perhaps his ego introjects as well, fail to provide an internal representation of himself as an adequate, autonomous individual. He can only imagine himself as an auxiliary of some other adult and never as a person in his own right. On the other hand, he cannot fully reciprocate by giving adequate emotional support to the person upon whom he depends. The chronically dependent person lacks adequate ego identifications and ego introjects with which to build a stable, mature postedipal *superego.* If he has developed an extreme idealization of a parent in childhood, either because this ideal was forced upon him or because he took refuge from his rivalry and hatred in reaction formation, he may harbor a perfectionistic ego-ideal. This perfectionistic ego-ideal will make him always feel inferior and unworthy, no matter what he achieves.[19]

This discussion of childhood fixations illustrates well the importance of the developmental phase, the level of maturation, at which the pathology first appears. Whereas the *autistic child* is not given the chance to form any meaningful emotional relationship with another human being very early in life, the *symbiotic child* is allowed to merge with his mother but not to emerge as an autonomous individual. The *overdependent child,* on the other hand, is encouraged to become a separate individual with definite childhood re-

[18] Mahler, M., "On child psychosis and schizophrenia: autistic and symbiotic infantile psychosis," *Psychoanalytic Study of the Child.* New York: Internat. Univ. Press, 1952, vol. 7, pp. 286–305.

[19] See, for example, the case of Ernest F., listed in the general index under *Cases.*

sponsibilities, but he is not allowed to take the initiative or to rebel. The mothers of all three types of fixated children do not want, or cannot tolerate, an emotional relationship with their child which permits him to progress toward full maturity.

Nevertheless, the product is different in each type. The most pathological and hopeless is the earliest to develop. Overdependent children usually grow to be overdependent adults, partly because of their early experiences of maternal domination, partly because this experience is likely to be continued throughout childhood. It is one of the many pathological pictures that is likely to be praised. The overdependent child is a conformist and often a devoted child. Girls are more likely than boys to grow into acceptable adults when they have had an overdependent childhood, since they can more easily find a social role that values subordination.

There are many other childhood fixations of prime importance in psychopathology. One of these, which may begin with early childhood overdependence, is fixation in the latency phase, at least as far as sexuality is concerned. This results in a perpetually boyish or girlish adult who is unable to enter the turmoil of adolescence and to seek a marital partner. Such an adult may show initiative in nonsexual spheres and lead an otherwise responsible, mature life. The root of such avoidance of adolescent turmoil may be in unresolved edipal conflicts which have been repressed as such, but not eliminated. Some of these adults may become homosexual, some seem to be asexual, some manage to sublimate their sexuality successfully in a career which keeps them in meaningful contact with other persons.

Still other fixations suggest the unconscious or partially conscious collusion of an abnormal parent. Studies of both parent and child, within the past decade or two, have revealed many instances of unwitting seduction of a child to commit antisocial, delinquent acts, or to develop cross-identification with a parent who appears not to recognize what he or she is doing, even though it is obvious to the trained observer.[20]

Special vulnerability to psychosis originates in an early fixation. The ground is laid by a failure in infancy or childhood to resolve some of the basic conflicts. The child represses or otherwise defends against recognition of his conflicts, and proceeds to mature while keeping them out of his preconscious and conscious organization. If in adulthood he is exposed to extreme or prolonged stress, which he cannot withstand, he will suffer a sweeping subtotal regression to the general area of his unresolved conflicts. The subtotal, psychotic regression then lays bare the early fixations. These may have been well compensated up to the moment of subtotal regression, but they now dominate the adult's experience and behavior.

We shall give accounts of such regressions to early levels of fixation when we come to the chapters on psychotic depressions, on mania, on paranoid psychoses, and on schizophrenia. If an adult has managed his life reason-

---

[20] References to this work will be found in the chapter on personality disorders, especially in the section on sex deviations.

ably well up to the time of a psychotic regression, he has a good chance of recovering with the aid of psychotherapy, whether or not he needs hospitalization to protect him. If he has never been successful in compensating for his defective early development, his outlook is much poorer.

Fixations and regressions are also of prime importance in the neuroses; but the regressions are typically partial, whereas in the psychoses they are typically subtotal. In the *anxiety reactions* there are usually edipal and pre-edipal conflicts not far from the surface. Their threat of breaking through into preconscious and conscious life arouses almost intolerable anxiety in the patient without his being able to recognize what is inducing it, and without his being able to see the relationship between current conflicts or anxieties and those of his past.[21] The *phobic patient* manages to crystallize his anxiety in an irrational fear which, while it does protect him from anxiety most of the time, also conceals from him the dangers from his own impulses.[22] The person with a *conversion symptom* — which has become uncommon in urban areas but is still common in backward rural areas — uses some part of his body to symbolize his conflicts and thus gain relief by expressing what makes him anxious. Usually the conversion symptom expresses edipal sexuality; but sometimes it symbolizes hostility, and sometimes it represents regression to much earlier fixations.[23]

Perhaps the clearest neurotic regressions are to be found among the *compulsions.* In the classical handwashing compulsion, for example, the patient exhibits strong, ambivalent conflicts over cleanliness and soiling, and equates them to the conflict over good and evil, much as a two-year-old child might do. In addition, the compulsive handwasher also expresses regressively a connection between soiling and sexuality. What seems to happen in the life history of such a patient is that he becomes fixated as a child at the developmental level where there is special interest in toilet training, a strong tendency toward conflicts over sadomasochism, and concern with goodness and evil. If the child is traumatized during this period, as our patient was,[24] and the conflicts are repressed without being worked through or lived through, he is likely to remain vulnerable to an obsessive compulsive regression. Under conditions of adult stress, especially sexual and hostile aggressive stress, he may regress to his chief level of fixation, and encounter some such childhood conflict as that between the urges to soil and to be clean, with all the overwhelming childhood anxiety. The spontaneous attempt at self-cure then consists in falling back upon *reaction formation.* Perpetual handwashing appears, with a good deal of sadomasochism mixed in. Therapy, as in the other neuroses, is directed mainly toward an understanding of the conflicts and their origins, and not toward combatting the symptoms.

[21] See the case of Walter A.
[22] See the case of Agnes W.
[23] See the thoughtful discussion in Rangell, L., "The nature of conversion," *J. Amer. Psychoanal. Ass.*, 1959, 7, 632–662.
[24] See the case of Sally J.

Drive regression, ego and superego regression

By *regression* we mean *a return to a less mature, less realistic level of experience and behavior.* The regression lights up or revives conflicts belonging to the chief level of fixation; or, if the regression is sweeping and profound, it revives psychodynamic organizations belonging to symbiotic or presymbiotic phases of development. The latter is especially characteristic of severe schizophrenic regressions.

It is convenient to distinguish between *drive* or *instinctual regression, ego regression* and *superego regression,* because in some clinical cases, as we shall see, the regression is more obvious or more significant in one of these three than in the other two. In practice, however, there is seldom regression in one part of the psychodynamic system, or in one of its functions, without regressive disturbances in the others.

The compulsive handwasher, about which we have just been concerned, is a good example of *drive regression.* Here a predominantly sexual conflict in adult life precipitates regression from a genital to an anal level Both our patient and the therapist recognized this without resort to theoretical preconceptions. It showed up in the adult development of the symptoms without disguise. At the same time, however, the compulsion and all that went with it was involved in conflicts over good and evil. These were expressed at a pre-edipal level, as conflicts over being clean and soiling, and therefore also represented precursors of the superego. In other words, there was not only drive or instinctual regression but *superego regression* as well. *Ego regression* was involved in the childish rituals which were carried on in attempts to ward off the consequences of indulgence in soiling, badness and sadism. In the end, we see that the whole psychodynamic system had regressed; but because the regressive involvement was restricted to a relatively small part of experience and behavior, we call the regression partial, and the result a neurosis.

In contrast to this, we may take the case of a person who has also regressed to a pre-edipal level, but who utilizes mechanisms of *denial* and *projection.* The result is a *paranoid psychosis* with delusions of persecution. Here the balance of forces within the psychodynamic system is different. Although sadomasochism is certainly a prominent characteristic, since the patient experiences himself as persecuted and his projected superego precursors as persecutors, intent upon torturing and killing him, the most impressive thing is the *superego regression.* The pre-edipal level to which such a patient regresses included in actual childhood the supervision of the child's behavior, and punishment for wrongdoing, by outside persons. What seems to have happened in such cases is that a normal, mature superego has never been firmly established. When the patient experiences severe stress, his superego at least in part regresses, and his realization that he has done something wrong, or even that he has had evil impulses, puts him in fear of retaliation from actually nonexistent persons. Here the emphasis is upon superego regression, although the rest of the psychodynamic system also shows regressive disturbances.[25] The *ego*, for example, is now devoted exclusively to the task of defending against dangers that do not exist, and to fantasying about them and trying to work out ways of escaping from them. The whole clinical picture is a childish one; but to the regressed patient it appears as a matter of life or death.

Anxiety

Like regression, anxiety is not in itself pathological, and to a certain extent it is unavoidable.[26] It is also the cornerstone of all psychopathology. The most important symptoms in neuroses and psychoses are attempts to defend against anxiety, attempts to discharge its intolerable tensions, or signs that the threat of anxiety has already been realized and the ego has at least in part disintegrated. Anxiety is directly involved in producing *psychosomatic disorders*.[27] It is a major factor, as we have already seen, in structuring early personality development. If it is allowed to become too intense, too early in life, it can lead to serious *character distortions*. At its worst, anxiety can precipitate and perpetuate terrifying ego disorganizations, in which the grown-up patient experiences something like the objectless world of infancy, but as an adult. At its best, anxiety can make a person alert, sensitive, perceptive and more spirited than he usually is, better prepared to meet a crisis than if he were relaxed and inattentive.

Normal anxiety

We call anxiety normal when its intensity and character are appropriate in a given situation, and when its effects are not disorganizing and maladaptive. Normal anxiety, as we have just implied, has useful functions. It increases a person's readiness for prompt and vigorous action; it adds spice to pleasurable anticipation; it is often the root of laughter and enjoyment. The moderately anxious person, as a watcher, is more apt to be vigilant, cautious and reaction-sensitive to slight stimulation than a complacent one. Moderate anxiety can actually increase endurance during an emergency. Sometimes, under the influence of intense anxiety, people perform feats beyond their ordinary powers, and show a degree of courage outside their ordinary range.[28]

Anxiety is even courted as recreation. Pleasure parks and county fairs

25 See the case of Charles G. listed in the general index under *Cases*.

26 Cf. Freud, S., "Inhibitions, symptoms and anxiety," (1926), Standard Edition, 1959, vol. 20, pp. 75–175; May, R., *The Meaning of Anxiety*. New York: Ronald, 1950; Stein, M. R., Vidich, A. J., and White, D. M. (Eds.), *Identity and Anxiety*. Glencoe, Ill.: Free Press, 1960.

27 Schur, M., "The ego in anxiety," in Loewenstein, R. (Ed.), *Drives, Affects, Behavior*. New York: Internat. Univ. Press, 1953, pp. 67–103.

28 Buskirk, C. V., "Performance on complex reasoning tasks as a function of anxiety," *J. abnorm. soc. Psychol.*, 1961, 62, 201–209.

usually have special contrivances for making people anxious, and people wait in line and pay for this privilege. Television, moving pictures and theaters provide anxiety for millions of willing spectators. So also do competitive sports, horse-racing and auto-racing, circuses, air shows and more recently the daring flight of astronauts. The appeal of adventure stories, murder mysteries and spy thrillers lies in large part in their ability to raise vicarious tension and anxiety in readers. Children enjoy heightening their own anxieties, not only in conventional games, but in original games which they invent themselves, and in the stories they like to hear and the television shows they watch. The only limitation seems to be that the anxiety must not grow too intense or last too long.

Normal anxiety also has its drawbacks. If there is nothing that a person can do about a situation which justifiably makes him anxious, he may become diffusely tense, preoccupied and expectant, to no purpose. In the end this kind of reaction is fatiguing and depletes a person's resources.[29] Even if anxiety readies the normal person for quick and efficient action, it meanwhile sacrifices his freedom and flexibility. He may have to restrict his activities and interest to a wary search for the source of possible danger, to a taut readiness to react, and to an avoidance of being caught off guard. There is always the possibility that someone whose anxiety is justifiably heightened, so that he becomes tense and reaction-sensitive ("trigger-happy" or "hair-trigger"), will respond as if the danger had already materialized, when actually it has not. This, we shall see, is close to the situation in neuroses and psychoses.

Traumatic anxiety and traumatic neurosis

One of the most important functions of normal moderate anxiety has not yet been mentioned. This is the defensive preparation that it affords a person who faces a probable or certain assault. Anyone who is completely lacking in anxiety may be as badly off as the person who is too anxious. The anxious preparation often takes the form of rehearsing the anticipated danger, so that when it finally materializes a person has already organized his defenses in advance. This was an important factor in preparation for surgery in the cases reported by Janis.[30] In other instances, even momentary anticipation appears to act as a protection against being overwhelmed by a sense of helplessness. The anxiety aroused then seems to function as a generalized protective barrier.

The terms *traumatic anxiety* and *traumatic neurosis* refer to the shock

[29] Sweetland, A., and Childs-Quay, L., "The effects of emotionality on concept formation," *J. gen. Psychol.*, 1958, *59*, 211–218.

[30] Janis, I., *Psychological Stress*. New York: Wiley, 1958; Maddi, S. R., "Affective tone during environmental regularity and change," *J. abnorm. soc. Psychol.*, 1961, *62*, 338–345; Hardison, J., and Purcell, K., "The effects of psychological stress as a function of need and cognitive control," *J. Pers.*, 1959, *27*, 250–258.

effect of a traumatic experience — or a series of mild but erosive traumatic experiences — upon a person who feels helpless to protect himself because he lacks adequate defenses. Those who have worked with military personnel in combat areas point out that circumstances can become such that a traumatic neurosis falls within the normal range of reaction.[31]

In extreme cases, such as those occurring during military combat, the traumatic event leads to aimless, dangerous wandering in combat zones, to apathy, to reckless assault or to headlong flight. The aftereffects include general irritability, anxiety attacks, depression, insomnia, and terrifying dreams in which the traumatic event in some form is re-experienced. This last is apparently an attempt at mastering the anxiety by reliving it, an attempt which usually fails. Therapy in some of these cases is successful when the patient is encouraged to relive his experiences under partial narcosis, but in the presence of his therapist, who is thus able to enter into the situation and to make use of it.[32] The common aftereffects in the inadequately prepared surgical cases are loss of self-confidence, and attitudes of distrust and resentment toward persons who, the patient feels, should have protected him.[33]

Pathological anxiety

We consider anxiety to be pathological in adults when there does not seem to be adequate justification for it, when it is exaggerated or unduly prolonged, or when it gives rise to defensive maneuvers which interfere seriously with the enjoyment and effectiveness of a person's life. Anxiety is pathological when it represents tension that demands immediate diffuse discharge in hyperactivity, which is a regression to the infantile situation, or when it results in poorly controlled aggressive or sexual behavior which disturbs interpersonal relationships.[34] Anxiety is also pathological when it demands excessive repression or suppression, so that a person loses his spontaneity and becomes generally inhibited, guarded or apathetic. It is pathological when it leads to the disorganization of experience and behavior, as we shall see in the regressive symptomatology of the *psychoses*. Finally, it is pathological when it leads to impulsive acts, or to distortions of sexual or aggressive impulses, such as we see in *personality disorders*.

[31] Grinker, R. R., and Spiegel, J., *War Neuroses.* Philadelphia: Blakiston, 1945; Grinker, R. R. and Spiegel, J., *Men Under Stress.* Philadelphia: Blakiston, 1945.

[32] Grinker, R. R., and Spiegel, J., *War Neuroses.* Philadelphia: Blakiston, 1945; Grinker, R. R., and Spiegel, J., *Men Under Stress.* Philadelphia: Blakiston, 1945; Kardiner, A., and Spiegel, H., *War Stress and Neurotic Illness.* (2nd ed.) New York: Hoeber, 1947.

[33] Janis, I., *Psychological Stress.* New York: Wiley, 1958; Titchener, J. L., and Levine, M., *Surgery as a Human Experience.* New York: Oxford Press, 1960.

[34] Davitz, J. R., "Fear, anxiety, and the perception of others," *J. gen. Psychol.,* 1959, *61,* 169–173; Cattell, R. B., and Scheier, I. H., *The Meaning and Measurement of Neuroticism and Anxiety.* New York: Ronald, 1961.

Changes in the pattern of childhood anxiety

Since pathological anxiety always involves regression, we shall gain a better understanding of anxiety in psychopathology by reviewing its normal development in infancy and early childhood.

Primary anxiety. The pattern of anxiety which is normal for adults is absent during early infancy. Its precursor in the early weeks is an irresistible need to discharge tension under any stress, which occurs in such activities as crying and generalized hyperactivity. We call this *primary anxiety*.[35] Usually the child is suffering from some identifiable stress, such as that coming from hunger, pain, discomfort, loud noise or rough handling.

Early in life, the tensions arising from stress cannot be tolerated. Their immediate discharge is imperative; and the discharge may continue after the source of stress has been removed. This continuation seems to be a *secondary reaction* to the *experience* of the primary anxiety. Sudden stress sometimes produces a gasp and a vigilant pause before the tension discharge occurs. The gasp and pause resemble the patterns seen in the beginning of adult anxiety, and are presumably innate.

Because it is impossible for someone to be always at hand to anticipate an infant's needs, and because they cannot always be identified, it is inevitable that he be repeatedly overwhelmed by the stress of his needs which he himself is powerless to satisfy. Each time this happens the infant experiences utter helplessness, which constitutes a trauma and is the prototype of future anxiety. It is not necessary to assume that the infant knows or understands what is happening to him, any more than an adult coming out of a general anesthetic needs to know and understand his pain or distress in order to experience it as overwhelming and intolerable. We get some inkling of the urgency of an infant's primary anxiety from the intensity of his discharge and from his mother's intuitive recognition that relief must be provided as quickly as possible. In the psychopathology of adults, as we shall see in the anxiety reaction described in the next chapter, there is apparently a regression to something approaching primary anxiety.

The taming of primary anxiety. As time goes on, the demand for immediate relief from tension, through direct discharge or through maternal help, grows less imperious. The infant seems to gain some control of his tensions; they become less intolerable; a little delay in satisfying them seems less of a disaster. What happens to bring about this change, to tame primary anxiety and give an infant the chance to develop precursors of secondary processes and an independent ego?

An easy overall answer is that the infant develops a psychodynamic system. Many of his early tensions become structuralized at what will

35 Schur, M., "The ego in anxiety," in Loewenstein, R. (Ed.), *Drives, Affects, Behavior.* New York: Internat. Univ. Press, 1953, pp. 67–103.

eventually become unconscious, preconscious and perhaps conscious levels. The structures that he manages to organize absorb increasing qauntities of free energy as their number and complexity increase. A few of the details involved in the taming of primary anxiety will be stressed here, as preparation for a discussion of boundary setting and the defenses.

As everyone knows, the infant gets an enormous amount of help in alleviating the stresses of need to which he is exposed; and he soon learns to anticipate help. He becomes quiet, for example, when he hears and sees preparations being made to feed him, even though nothing has entered his hungry mouth. Whether or not the anticipation involves imagery, it obviously reduces the stress effect of the internal need without satisfying it. An organized expectation takes the place of the previously diffuse, overwhelming tension, and this expectation or anticipation becomes itself an organized response which can absorb free energy.

We adults, when we are injured, in pain, or suddenly taken ill, experience fully the calming effect of anticipating help as soon as we are told that help is on its way. Nothing in the objective situation may have changed, but the unbearable tension from our inner need for help gets channeled into an organized anticipation. The importance of such preparation, which is really an adult form of the infant's *basic trust,* has already been pointed out in connection with surgery.[36]

Something like this experience seems to develop during early infancy as his mother appears and the child's sense of being overwhelmed disappears. There is no need to assume that at first the child recognizes any connection between his mother's appearance and the reduction of stress. The infant's first ego-defense is thus really his mother; his first adaptive mechanism for escaping from his overwhelming tensions is that of crying and becoming hyperactive ("restless," "fussy," "fretting") so that his mother will come. There may be anticipatory imagery involved in the child's growing ability to tolerate delay — what Freud called "the hallucinated breast" — or there may not. It is most probable that some kind of central representation of expected relief develops, and that this is one of the precursors of organized fantasy and of secondary process thinking which fills in the delay. We have already encountered this probability in discussing early introjection and ego organization. All of these processes are intricately interrelated.

As an infant matures perceptually and cognitively, he at the same time develops many motor coordinations which help him to tame his primary anxiety. The things that an infant is able to do need not in themselves be useful; but they are more organized, specific and complex than a primitive, generalized tension discharge. Their very organization, like that of perception and imagery, absorbs or "binds" free energy and thus reduces the sense of being overwhelmed and helpless.

During periods of unrelieved stress, we adults experience something similar

[36] Janis, I., *Psychological Stress.* New York: Wiley, 1958.

when we busy ourselves with some activity or other. Even though we achieve nothing else, the activity soaks up some of the tension engendered by the stress. It helps calm our apprehensions further while we wait for relief. Thus, for example, men pace up and down to no purpose and swear, while women rock and sew or talk.

The child who has a few infantile activities in his repertory is far better off than he was when all he could do was to be restless and cry. For a time at least, he may find relief in sucking, watching, searching, fingering, babbling, playing and imagining, while he waits for the specific satisfaction of some specific pressing need. With these more structured outlets for free energy he can now tolerate delay still better, and fill in the time with ego activity.

A further help in controlling anxiety will come when the infant has matured and developed sufficiently, in perception, in motor coordination and in imagination, to be able to experience *primary identification*, the kind of experience that structures the mother-child symbiotic unit. At first, we assume, the infant cannot experience his own individuality or identity, the kind of individuality that you and I experience as separate persons. Neither can he experience a unity with anyone else, the kind of oneness that we experience in intimate personal relationships and deep emotions, when we seem for the moment to lose our boundaries and merge with others or with the infinite.

The experience of unity appears to come first. The infant at first has developed no boundaries between himself and others. He has no recognition of himself as an individual, and no recognition of others as individuals separate from himself. Therefore it is easy for him to identify with a stable, reliable, trustworthy mother figure. It is easy for him to experience things as his that we recognize as actually his mother's, to experience her achievements, her movements, sounds, warmth, embrace and ministrations as somehow belonging to the fused unity of mother-child.

In some such way, through the lack of separation, through the confusion that we call primary identification, a child's experiences are enormously enriched, and his sense of power and security are greatly enhanced, as long as he has the mother figure within his orbit. He is experiencing in a direct, primitive way the kind of enrichment, the kind of enhancement of security and power that we adults experience at a more sophisticated level when we surrender some of our individuality and identify emotionally with a powerful group or a powerful cause, or even when we share with others some tremendous disaster.

Separation anxiety. There are penalties attached to the enjoyment of borrowed riches, of borrowed powers and security during infancy. One of the most important for psychopathology arises originally from the connection between a mother's presence and the relief of infantile need. If his mother leaves him for long the child loses everything. While he is still in the phase of symbiotic relationship he develops *separation anxiety*. At some level, and in some vague way, the infant apparently equates his mother's absence with imminent danger; and he reacts to the danger as though it had already materialized.[37]

The danger that threatens him comes from his inner needs. These may overwhelm him while his mother is away and he is helpless. After all, he actually is powerless to satisfy most of his needs without help; and his mother is the only person who has become sensitive to his calls for help and can be counted upon to know what they mean. When she disappears and he needs her, the infant apparently regresses and re-experiences the primary anxiety which his mother had originally helped to tame. To him it seems as though he were alone in the world forever, with no one to protect him from being overwhelmed by his own imperious needs. He reacts to the mere threat of danger from his id drives as if these drives had already flooded his ego. As soon as his mother returns to him, the child loses his primary anxiety and is again at peace.

Separation anxiety does not disappear as the infant matures. It remains as a source of disturbance throughout childhood, it is responsible for some of the turbulence of adolescence, and it shows up in one form or another even in adulthood. The study of children in England during World War II established the fact beyond a doubt that separation from their parents, even of half-grown children, proved to be much more traumatic than the noise, destruction and excitement of repeated nightly bombing.[38]

Adults re-experience separation anxiety which threatens to overwhelm them under a variety of circumstances. We see this with especial clearness in mothers who have been separated from a child, even when the separation is for the child's benefit, and it is only temporary. A mother expresses fears about the child which are unjustified and persistent. Because this reaction is familiar we regard it as natural. It is natural; but it is also irrational and regressive. The feelings of a mother who loses her son, whether through his death or through his marriage, often include a sense of being overwhelmed, deserted and helpless. Freud called the loss of a firstborn son a mother's tragic destiny. We often see separation anxiety when marital partners are separated, either intentionally or by the intervention of circumstances. The same thing happens in mourning and, as we shall see, it is one of the chief regressive characteristics of depressive illnesses.

Anxiety over the loss of love. It is not long before a child discovers that even when his mother is present she may not protect him from danger, especially from the danger of his internal needs. As he develops an ego capable of controlling what he does, his mother develops an expectation that he will use that control. If he does not, she lets him know that he has

---

[37] Bowlby, J., "Separation anxiety: a critical review of the literature," *J. Child Psychol., Psychiat.*, 1961, *1*, 251–269.
[38] Freud, A., and Burlingham, D. T., *War and Children*. New York: Willard, 1943.

failed her, by punishing him instead of loving him, or merely by withdrawing her love. Since the child cannot get along without her loving help, the loss of her love has the same effect as separation, even though she is physically present. No one working with children supposes that a child distinguishes clearly between anxiety over loss of love and anxiety over physical separation. He probably equates the two directly and intuitively through primary process procedures. After all, it is only within recent decades that adults have recognized this distinction and experts have formulated it.

Anxiety over loss of love takes its place beside separation anxiety. It has the same general effects, and it may be even more traumatic than physical separation. A mother who is physically present and able to give love seems sadistic to a child when she withholds love, whether or not she also punishes him. The child who is able to speak often calls his mother mean and cruel under these circumstances. The child who cannot speak, or dares not speak out, can still fantasy her as sadistic, as treating him this way because she enjoys it.

Children as well as adults regard love as something to which they are entitled regardless of the circumstances, and regardless of what they themselves do. Realistic experience, however, introduces them to the danger of losing love even without losing the person who has been providing it. Anyone, child or adult, who is dependent for his sense of well-being and self-esteem upon the love of another person, experiences the threat of losing love as the threat of a catastrophe, which it well may be. This reaction is normal for a young child, whether his anxiety is realistically based or not.[39] It is normal for an adult if the threat is a realistic one, and especially so for women, because they are inherently, by training, and usually by circumstance, more dependent than men.

Anxiety over losing love is pathological in both men and women when it preoccupies them without justification or to an unjustified degree. We find it, as a *personality disorder*, in chronically dependent adults who dare not displease a marital partner, a parent or a superior, for fear of the least sign of displeasure. It is also common among the *neuroses* and *psychoses*, in part because of defective ego boundaries, which we shall discuss in the next section. The expression of worthlessness, inferiority and inadequacy in *neurotic depressions* are exceptionally clear examples of the regressive repetition of early childhood feelings, when a parent seemed chronically unloving and the patient as a child seemed to himself unlovable. We shall find anxiety over loss of love in other neuroses also.

In the deep and subtotal regressive picture of the *psychotic depression*, the patient seems to be divided into reciprocal sadomasochistic roles of *cruel, ruthless parent*, and *hated*, but still often *defiant little child*. Both

---

[39] Finney, J. C., "Some maternal influences on children's personality and character," *Genet. Psychol. Monogr.*, 1961, *63*, 199–278; Barnard, J. W., Zimbardo, P. G., and Sarason, S., "Anxiety and verbal behavior in children," *Child Develpm.*, 1961, *32*, 379–392.

roles, in regressing, become repersonalized. In other words, the patient expresses sadistic, hateful attitudes toward himself, and at the same time acts like a person who is hated and deserves humiliating, cruel punishment. Nevertheless, in most depressed persons there is also a contradictory attitude of resentment against the cruel treatment that he says he deserves. The *sadistic attitudes* represent an introjected parent, experienced as sadistic. The *masochistic attitudes* represent the submissive willingness to be punished in a regressive ego which cannot endure anxiety over the loss of love. The resentment comes from a rebellious but also regressive ego.

The *paranoid psychotic patient,* by using denial and projection as his major defenses, manages to escape submission to his regressive superego-precursor. He does not, however, escape the anxiety. The introjected, sadistic parental attitudes are reprojected to the outside. The patient then experiences them as coming from a sadistic persecutor, against whom he feels justified in defending himself. The supposed persecutor is actually a regressively experienced parental figure. It is this that helps account for the emotional paradox often found in paranoid psychoses, namely, that persecutory delusions are projected on to someone whom the patient has previously loved or greatly respected. In such instances, the patient is reacting to an outbreak of his own regressive *anxiety over losing love* by projecting his experience as *anxiety over persecution* at the hands of a parent-substitute. There is good reason to believe that paranoid patients have actually experienced a parent in childhood as unjust and sadistic.

Anxiety and ego boundaries

One of the major achievements in growing up is that of establishing functional boundaries that will protect the preconscious and conscious ego from intrusions which might prove disintegrating. At first, as we have already pointed out, the mother must act as temporary ego to reinforce the almost completely helpless infant ego in dealing with irresistible needs and a hopelessly complex external reality. Behind the protective screen which his mother establishes, and with the help of his own innate protective barrier, the child, like a besieged but well-defended fortress, can carry on the processes of organization which he requires before he is able to grapple with internal and external forces himself. We conceive of the preconscious and conscious ego, within the differentiating psychodynamic system, as developing boundaries which perform such protective functions. We call these the *ego boundaries,* even though they exclude those components of the unconscious ego which have joined with derivatives of the id.[40]

Body-image, self-image and object representations. We have called attention to the difference in fundamental organization between the human organism and the human environment. The effective human environment, in-

[40] The pioneer work in this area is contained in Federn, P., *Ego Psychology and the Psychoses.* New York: Basic Books, 1952.

cluding the existence and role behavior of other persons, is taken care of by *reality representations* within the psychodynamic system. Ego boundaries, which keep external and somatic realities from intruding into preconscious and conscious ego organizations, are formed as the infant and child develops distinctions between body and not-body, between somatic and psychic realities, and between self and not-self, as we have described these processes in Chapter 2. Systems of *body-image, self-image* and *object representations* are slowly established within the psychodynamic system, which in some way correspond to the *body*, the *self* and *external reality, as these are experienced by an individual*.[41] For convenience, we shall lump all of these together here as *reality representations*, even though the body, the self and the external world are different from one another and are differently conceived by the person.

It goes without saying that all such representations or images are continually changing, as experiences change and multiply. The reality representations of a young child are undoubtedly quite different from those of an older child. The reality representations of a child are different from those of an adolescent or an adult. Infantile, childhood, adolescent and adult reality representations differ from one another both because of the maturation and development of abilities and because of the different social roles lived out during each phase. The reality representations of men and women, as well as those of boys and girls, differ because of fundamental differences in body-image, self-image, social role and expectations in the two sexes.[42]

The ego boundaries that keep the environment and its representations from disturbing preconscious and conscious ego functioning in adults are among the most durable of all. This is in part because preconscious and conscious ego organizations change easily and rapidly with reality experience. There is usually little conflict between the two that cannot be resolved through ordinary secondary process procedures (realistic perception, thinking and motor coordination). When these boundaries do dissolve, however, the pathology of experience and behavior that result may be severe, as we shall see when we come to discuss deliria and some schizophrenic reactions.

Id-derivatives and the repressed unconscious ego. Man never achieves a corresponding mastery over id-derivatives, and over the repressed unconscious ego functions which go to join them in the primary process. The best that he can do is to develop defense mechanisms which exclude them sufficiently to prevent their disintegrating secondary process perception, cognition and motor coordination. These defense mechanisms apparently do not prevent a continual interchange from taking place between precon-

---

[41] Cf. Jacobson, E., "The self and the object-world," *Psychoanal. Study Child,* 1954, *9,* 75–127.

[42] Hartley, R. E., "Children's concepts of male and female roles," *Merrill-Palmer Quart.,* 1960, *6,* 83–91.

scious organizations and the unconscious ego and id-derivatives, whose products appear in full preconscious during the night as dreams. We have already said that a night's dreaming is prepared in part during the preceding day, and that it usually includes residues of the day's preconscious and even conscious experiences. We shall devote the latter part of this chapter to a description of the main defense mechanisms, and in the succeeding clinical chapters we shall give examples of the ways in which they work.

The superego and its precursors. Stable self-control is impossible without a superego, and yet the introduction of a superego organization within the psychodynamic system leads inevitably to new sources of conflict and anxiety. In the preceding chapter we discussed the functions of the super-ego, and of its precursors, as internal representations of the parents and other authority figures. To the extent that a child's parents and parent figures are themselves socially organized, and succeed in passing on socially acceptable standards to him, the child will develop his own standards, with their gradients or hierarchies, which help him to structure his experience and behavior in socially acceptable ways.

As a scanning and evaluating system, the superego operates for the most part automatically at unconscious levels. When things go wrong, or we feel in need of moral or ethical guidance, the superego may become conscious and function as our conscience. The rest of the time it is unconscious, but still effectual. As we have said before, the superego makes use of an ego-ideal as its yardstick in evaluating ego performance, including ego percep-tion and thought as well as action. The ego-ideal, unfortunately for some persons, tends to be not only perfectionistic and unrealistic, but also often primitively narcissistic, with infantile components. It can then become the source of much real dissatisfaction and unhappiness, especially if the super-ego exercises punitive parental functions when ego achievement falls short of the narcissistic ideal, or when *ego interests* are also infantile, but far from ideal. We shall see the former with particular clearness in the *neurotic de-pression,* and the latter in *compulsive disorders.*

The superego serves as a watchdog in detecting deviations from socially acceptable standards before they can be put into practice. It reacts em-phatically against attempts of id-derivatives and unconscious fantasies to emerge which might disorganize the preconscious in the daytime. We see what happens at night, in some dreams, when the superego influence is much diminished. Dreams reach the preconscious which may never appear as fantasies while we are awake. The popular expression, "I would never even have dreamed of doing such a thing!" pictures the dream as the limit of one's irresponsibility. Sometimes unconscious fantasies stimulate the superego to intervene even when we are asleep and dreaming. We saw this in the dream of the woman who pictured herself as digging in the dirt, down in a hole with her analyst, while a replica of herself in pure white stood on the rim of the hole and warned her not to continue. This is the kind of thing that presumably goes on during the daytime also, both at regressive infantile and at realistic adult levels (*split-level functioning*).

In spite of all that the scanning, evaluating, moralistic superego contributes to the stability of the psychodynamic system, it can also be the source of intrusions which interfere with the effective operation of preconscious and conscious ego systems. This is particularly true of intrusions from unconscious superego processes, and from unconscious superego precursors which are still active even though they have been superseded by more mature organizations. The same defenses that the ego has developed against id and unconscious ego intrusions are used against the intrusions of the superego and its precursors. Some are barred from reaching the preconscious by repression. Others which reach the preconscious may be counteracted by a *denial of responsibility* which the ego accepts as real. Still others may be denied and projected on to others, not only among paranoid persons, but quite generally, among normal persons, as in the common use of scapegoats, human as well as animal.

Defective ego boundaries and primary anxiety. Primary anxiety seems to arise whenever ego boundaries become defective, the preconscious is invaded by intruders, and regression begins. In the neuroses the invasion and the regression are limited, and some kind of a compromise is sufficient to "contain" the process. We call the compromise the neurotic symptom. It is made up of the intruder and the defense against it, often with a contribution from the superego. Neurotic defenses are never completely effective. Some anxiety is always evident somewhere in the symptomatology.

In the *psychoses,* the ego boundaries prove defective along a wide front, probably because of defects in the early development of the psychodynamic system. Regression is widespread and deep. Anxiety is always present at some phase of the psychotic development, and usually it is severe. Something approaching intense primary anxiety appears in *psychotic depressions,* where the regressed ego plays the role of a hopeless, overwhelmed, guilty little child, against which a chastising, personalized superego makes endless accusations of wrongdoing and utter worthlessness — usually on the basis of unconscious ego trends, fantasies and identifications.

In *manic attacks,* the patient succeeds to some extent in escaping anxiety by his "flight into activity," in which he acts out some version of the role of his own ego-ideal. He can only do this, of course, by a deep regression to an infantile level, where he appears vain, facetious, arrogant and quarrelsome. The manic attack seems to be a reaction against a threatening depression, which occasionally materializes.

In *paranoid psychoses,* as we have seen, the preconscious and conscious ego are invaded by id-derivatives, previously unconscious ego fantasies, and the precursors of the superego. The patient's main defense against this situation is to deny both his unconscious motivation and the regressive superego accusations, to project them, and then to denounce or attack them as the attributes of someone else. This maneuver does not get rid of the regressive anxiety. The most it does is to make it seem to be the consequence of outside persecution, which the patient may then feel free to combat.

Primary and secondary anxiety[43]

In *neuroses* we see a partial ego regression and the revival of something approaching *primary anxiety*, the experience of being overwhelmed and helpless. This will be obvious in some of our clinical cases of *anxiety reaction*, *phobias* and *dissociative reaction*. In the *psychoses*, the regression is so widespread and deep that the patient is in much greater danger of being swamped by massive intrusions from id-derivatives, unconscious ego material and regressive superego precursors. In many psychotic reactions he is actually overwhelmed and helpless; his defensive organization all but disappears; intense primary anxiety results unless the patient withdraws, or for some reason accepts his psychotic material.

Secondary anxiety is a reaction to the disintegrative effects of primary anxiety, which both neurotic and psychotic patients may experience. In *anxiety reactions*, for example, something of which the patient may have been unaware precipitates an anxiety attack — which is a resomatization and a dramatic, infantile discharge — and the patient is then terrified by the attack itself. The latter is *secondary anxiety*. We shall see this happen repeatedly in the case of Walter A. in the next chapter. But the same thing happens in *phobias*, as the case of Agnes W. clearly shows, and in *obsessive compulsive reactions*, and in *dissociative reactions*, as we shall see.

Secondary anxiety is often a potent force in disintegrating the *psychotic patient*. The case of Constance Q. includes strong secondary anxiety, as a reaction to the appearance of regressive primary anxiety and sleeplessness, which hastened her regression by increasing the total stress to which her psychodynamic system was exposed. It is not unusual for a person to sense that he is regressing and beginning to disorganize in a schizophrenic reaction. The primary regressive anxiety that he feels may further frighten him, and make the disintegrative process worse than it had been.[44] In all of these instances the primary anxiety results from a failure of the defense mechanisms to protect the preconscious and conscious organizations from intrusions which partially or subtotally disintegrate them. The secondary anxiety represents a reaction to this failure. This brings us to a description of the major defense mechanisms.

---

[43] See the discussion in Schur, M., "The ego in anxiety," in Loewenstein, R. (Ed.), *Drives, Affects, Behavior*. New York: Internat. Univ. Press, 1953, pp. 67–103.
[44] Rosenthal, D., "Familial concordance by sex with respect to schizophrenia," *Psychol. Bull*, 1962, *59*, 401–421.

The Major Defense Mechanisms

The prime functions of any *organism* are to remain organized, at as effective a level as possible, in an environment whose organization is always different from that of the organism, and if possible to develop and mature according to its own built-in plan. The prime functions of the human *psychodynamic system* are to remain organized at as effective a level as possible, to develop and mature, in the face of stresses arising from interaction with external and somatic realities, and in the face of strains arising within the system itself.

The prime functions of the *preconscious* and *conscious ego* are to remain organized at as effective a level as possible, to develop and mature, and eventually to operate most of the time in accordance with secondary process perception, thinking and action. This must be done in the face of pressures from external and somatic realities, from id-derivatives and the repressed unconscious ego, and from much of the superego, all of which are organized differently.

The preconscious and conscious ego develop and mature slowly. Even with a tremendous amount of adult help, it takes four or five years to establish an effective preconscious ego, one that can operate more or less realistically in accordance with secondary processes while the child is awake. Another five or six years pass before this organization, with its conscious accompaniment, becomes capable of reflecting upon its own activities with *logical justification* — a highly important form of verbal reality-testing.

During two or three years in the adolescent phase a good deal of the ground already gained seems to be lost because of emotional turbulence. The whole psychodynamic system has to be reorganized in such a manner as to give up childish ways and prepare for adulthood. In the end, however, all that has been lost is quickly regained. The adolescent normally moves into adulthood with a greatly enriched and reasonably stable psychodynamic system, ruled during most of the daytime hours by the preconscious and conscious ego.

The so-called *system unconscious*,[45] which includes id-derivatives and the repressed unconscious ego, is still active all of the time in accordance with the primary process, and it is stimulated by what goes on in the preconscious ego and the superego. A certain amount of this unconscious activity seeps through, during the day, to contribute verve and a certain amount of irrationality to normal adult behavior. But the ego boundaries, with their defense mechanisms, keep by far the greater part of unconscious activity silent and unrecognized. The same is true of most superego function, including the activities of regressive superego precursors.

Each night, after about sixteen hours of secondary process functioning, the accumulated stresses and strains call for a period of sleep. During sleep

[45] This was a favorite term of Freud's which will probably survive for a long time.

the psychodynamic system evidently undergoes some dedifferentiation. For whenever sleep is punctuated by manifest dreaming, which apparently happens every night, it is obvious that the sleeping person has regressed deeply, and that the primary process once again dominates his thinking. In his dreams there may be traces of childhood experiences, of infantile wishes, fears and conflicts, mingled with traces of his recent adult waking life. The past and present are no longer distinguished — a typical characteristic of primary process thinking which we shall encounter repeatedly in neuroses and psychoses.

It should be said in passing that a great deal of more or less automatic activity is going on all the time, below the level of awareness, which does not belong to the *system unconscious* and does not operate in accordance with the primary process. This activity goes to make up what is called the *autonomous ego* and the *conflict-free sphere*.[46] It includes most of our skilled automatic acts. Some of these, if they reached awareness, might interfere with normal secondary process operations, as we see them do in obsessive compulsive reactions. Some of them, if deliberately attended to, might themselves disintegrate. Such are the integrated but unconscious activities involved in the process of walking, of driving a car, of typewriting, and even the details of coming to a logical conclusion. In each of these tightly organized activities the very organization of the act excludes whatever would disintegrate it.

The same is true of a great deal of our everyday organized preconscious and conscious perception, thinking and action. Their very operation automatically takes care of most potential threats from external and somatic realities, since our secondary processes have been developed in the course of mastering the body and its environment.[47] All of this takes for granted the physiological integrity and competence of the organism, and particularly of the brain as the chief integrating organ. We see what happens the moment something goes wrong with physiological functioning when we witness or experience a delirium.

To a considerable degree — to a much greater degree than we realized until recently — it is essential to be engaged in realistic perception, thinking and action if we are to keep out intrusions from id-derivatives, the repressed unconscious ego, the unconscious superego and its precursors. This necessity has been reported from time to time by persons who have been isolated from human interaction through accident or in the course of prolonged explorations. They found that the absence of human interaction often led to hallucinatory and delusional experiences, and sometimes these were frightening and disintegrating. Even the ordinary man or woman has known for millenia that keeping oneself active and in contact with others can go a long way

[46] Cf. Hartmann, H., *Ego Psychology and the Problem of Adaptation* (trans. D. Rapaport). New York: Internat. Univ. Press, 1958.
[47] Perloe, S. I., "Inhibition as a determinant of perceptual defense," *Percept. Motor Skills*, 1960, *11*, 59–66.

toward mastering anxieties, unreasonable as well as reasonable, primary anxiety as well as justified apprehension. This kind of influence had never been systematically investigated and verified, as a generalized defense against the emergence of primary process material, until the recent studies of sensory deprivation or perceptual isolation.[48]

It is clear from what has just been said that almost any activity can be used defensively to maintain or to recapture normal daytime secondary process functioning. Even the most irrational fantasies, paradoxically enough, can be effective in staving off primary anxiety, which might otherwise over-whelm a person. Anna Freud has vividly portrayed this in her account of the defensive fantasies of children.[49]

Nevertheless, during the daytime, our preconscious and conscious organizations need special protection against invasions from id-derivatives, re-pressed unconscious ego and superego activities, if they are to function normally. What we are about to describe are certain mechanisms whose functions in the adult are predominantly and specifically defensive. For the most part they *operate unconsciously*, although they do not belong to the *system unconscious*. Topographically, they may best be pictured as belonging to the ego boundaries. They are the major defensive forces responsible for maintaining and restoring the separate identity of the preconscious and conscious organizations, for specifically protecting them against being dis-integrated from within.

There is no general agreement as to the number of defense mechanisms that should be distinguished. A recent account of active, ongoing clinical work points out clearly that the defensive organization of the ego constitutes a *continuum*, and that any attempt to sort out separate defense mechanisms is bound to be arbitrary. On the basis of clinical experience, this study lists and defines twenty-four basic first-order defenses, and fifteen complex or second-order defenses.[50] From this list we have chosen fifteen defense mech-anisms which commonly enter neurotic and psychotic symptom-formation. These are: *introjection, projection, identification, regression, repression, denial, reaction-formation, displacement, turning-against-the-self, isolation, undoing, ritualization, intellectualization, rationalization* and *sublimation*. All that we shall do here is give a brief definition of each defense. In the chapters that immediately follow, we shall expand some of these definitions and describe their operation in actual clinical syndromes.

[48] Cf. Solomon, P., *et al., Sensory Deprivation*. Cambridge, Mass.: Harvard Univ. Press, 1961; see also the panel discussion by Freedman, S. J., Hebb, D. O., Held, R., Riesen, A. H., and Teuber, H. L., "Sensory deprivation: facts in search of a theory," *J. nerv. ment. Dis.*, 1961, *132*, 17–43.

[49] Freud, A., *The Ego and the Mechanisms of Defense*. London: Hogarth Press, 1937; Murphy, L., "Coping devices and defense mechanisms in relation to autonomous func-tions," *Bull. Menn. Clin.*, 1960, *24*, 144–153.

[50] Bibring, G., *et al.*, "A study of the psychological processes in pregnancy and of the earliest mother-child relationship," *Psychoanal. Study Child*, 1961, *16*, 9–72.

Introjection, projection and identification

All three of these defense mechanisms grow out of processes which were originally instrumental in personality development and ego differentiation. *Introjection* is a symbolic incorporation by means of which something *actually outside* the ego is perceived and represented as though it were *inside*. The symbolic incorporation may be modeled after oral, visual, auditory or manual experiences, as we have described these in Chapter 2. Oral incorporation, however, is the most literal and thoroughgoing form, and therefore the most basic for introjection. *Projection* is a symbolic ejection by means of which something *actually inside* the ego, or something gaining access to the ego from the id or the superego, is perceived and represented as though it were *outside*. Although it is the opposite of introjection, it may reinforce introjection by excluding characteristics that contradict introjected ones. Both introjection and projection are presumably practiced in the mother-child symbiosis, where the infant's ego boundaries have not yet been firmly established. *Identification* is originally an inability to distinguish. We have discussed its role in the mother-child symbiosis earlier. Throughout life, but particularly during childhood and adolescence, identification plays an important role in molding and supporting personality characteristics which seem to correspond to those of admired and envied other persons. Identification soon employs imitation as a means of possessing desired characteristics. This leads to a clearer separation of oneself from other persons than in introjection or projection.

Introjection as a defense mechanism. The use of introjection as a defense in adulthood is usually a sign of regression. It occurs in *normal mourning* as an attempt to retain the lost loved one while the work of mourning progresses. It occurs most clearly in *psychotic depressions* where the patient may perceive and represent the characteristics of a loved person as though they were his own. It is often the case that a depressed person regresses to a powerfully ambivalent state, in which he then proceeds to accuse himself, not only of his own actual shortcomings and misdeeds, but also of those of some person whom he both loves and hates.[51]

Projection as a defense mechanism. Projection is used defensively to some extent by everyone. It is the maneuver which makes it possible to perceive and represent one's faults, failings or ego-alien impulses as belonging to someone else. This is the basis of all *scapegoating*.[52] Pathologically, pro-

[51] See the case of Constance Q.

[52] Cf. Murstein, B. I., and Pryer, R. S., "The concept of projection: a review," *Psychol. Bull.*, 1959, *56*, 353–374; Lewis M. N., and Spilka, B., "Sociometric choice status, empathy, assimilative and disowning projection," *Psychol. Rec.* 1960, *10*, 95–100; Peak H., Muney, B., and Clay, M., "Opposite structures, defenses and attitudes." *Psychol. Monogr.*, 1960, *74*, Whole No. 495.

jection appears most clearly in *acute paranoid psychoses* and in some *paranoid schizophrenic psychoses*. Sometimes a patient hears the hallucinated voice of his own unconscious superego accusing him of having impulses which he denies are his own. When projection occurs on such a scale, it also indicates that the patient has deeply regressed. As we shall see, however, the paranoid patient is often paradoxically competent, even though unquestionably psychotic.

Identification as a defense mechanism. Bibring *et al.* distinguish four kinds of identification used defensively. These are as follows:

(1) *Identification with a loved object.* The person models himself according to the characteristics of a loved one, which alleviates separation anxiety or lessens tensions arising out of hostility, if the loved one is ambivalently hated.

(2) *Identification with a lost object.* This corresponds to what we have already called *introjection as a defense.* A person takes on the characteristics of someone or something he has lost in order to lessen or cancel out his bereavement.

(3) *Identification with the aggressor.* Anxiety is avoided through becoming like a feared aggressive person or thing. The aggression is then perceived and represented as though it emanated from oneself and were under one's own control. Anna Freud has also given impressive examples from her study of children.[53]

(4) *Identification out of guilt.* This is also similar to the operation of introjection. It is a self-punishing identification, which arises from hostile aggression felt toward an ambivalently loved person. We shall see examples of this among the *compulsive reactions,* where the patient not only punishes himself but also gloats over the punishment. In one of these cases there was clearly hostile identification of a young woman with her punitive, loving mother.[54]

Regression as a defense mechanism

Regression is used normally every night when we go to sleep. We seek out a situation that will expose us to as little external stimulation as possible, close our eyes, and relax our skeletal muscles as completely as we can. In this way we enter naturally into a situation that simulates the artificially induced sensory deprivation of recent laboratory investigations. We also regress naturally in many forms of recreation, in creative activities, and in sex intercourse. In all of these the regression is controlled; it is in the service of the preconscious and conscious ego. Sleep can be terminated at will by establishing sleep habits or by using an alarm. It is also terminated whenever primary anxiety becomes uncontrollable in anxiety dreams, whose

[53] Freud, A., *The Ego and the Mechanisms of Defense.* London: Hogarth Press, 1937.
[54] See the case of Sally J.

original purpose is to master traumatic experiences which have been repressed while still unmastered. Recreation, creative activity, and sex intercourse are also temporary regressive episodes with natural time limits, after which one goes to sleep or returns to realistic relations with the environment, feeling refreshed.

Regression as a pathological defense is to be found in almost all forms of *psychopathology*. It expresses the same thing that normal going to sleep expresses, namely, an inability to go on functioning at fully mature, secondary process levels. We call pathological regression *defensive* because it preserves the integrity of the psychodynamic system at some level short of complete dissolution.

In the *neuroses*, the daytime regression that permits symptom formation to appear is only partial. Most preconscious and conscious functioning goes on at normal levels. The neurotic defenses bind the intruding impulses and fantasies from id-derivatives, repressed unconscious ego or superego, and thus form the compromise organization which we call the *neurotic symptom*.

In *personality disorders* the situation is somewhat different. Regressive trends do not appear as discrete symptoms in *character disorders*, for example, but rather as distortions of personality structure, comparable to childhood deformities in physical development. This includes the so-called *character-armoring* in which what might have erupted later as a neurotic or psychotic symptom is made into an integral part of the character. A similar situation exists usually in *sex deviations*, where the arrested development may be confined to what is specifically sexual, or may have a limited spread to related functions and identifications. In character disorders and sex deviations, both of which are discussed in the chapter on personality disorders, there may be normal behavior and experience most of the time. Regression to childhood fixation points then occurs during periods of unusual stress, or when the more mature behavior meets with frustration, and primary anxiety threatens to overwhelm the person.

In the *psychoses*, regression can be called defensive as long as it preserves the preconscious and conscious from complete annihilation, which in the vast majority of psychotic persons it does. Psychotic regression, however, is massive and subtotal. Relatively little of the preconscious and conscious ego organization may remain to support an effective interaction with the surroundings.

It is highly important to recognize that some of this organization does remain. In the past, the psychological isolation to which psychotic persons were abandoned — in part because of the anxiety they aroused in their would-be therapists — was responsible for a good deal of the psychopathology observed, for the depth of the regression, and for the generally hopeless outlook. This psychological isolation, which is still meted out to psychotic persons in many places, is comparable to sensory deprivation in its effects.

Special mention should be made here of the often overlooked fact that hallucinations and delusions are usually spontaneous attempts at self-cure, rather than signs of malignant disease. The hallucinating and the delusional patient is often trying to reconstitute his reality representations in such a way as to form a compromise — a compromise between the *impulses* and *fantasies* which are flooding his psychodynamic system and the *external realities* which condemn or contradict them. At the very least, hallucinations and delusions can help keep a patient in contact with reality. The resourceful therapist may then find ways of using these contacts to lead the psychotic patient toward a more realistic level of interaction.

Repression

Repression has been recognized for more than half a century as the keystone of defensive organizations, both in normal and in neurotic persons. Its origins are obscure. It seems to be related to conscious suppression and to preconscious denial; but it operates normally at unconscious levels, as do most of the ego defenses. As we saw in Chapter 2, a *massive repression* occurs normally during the resolution of the edipal complex, so that older children and adults can recall almost nothing of their edipal and pre-edipal phases. The testimony of dreams, myths and symptoms shows that the traces of much infantile experience are still present in the psychodynamic system, although normally unavailable. In *psychoses* some of this infantile experience reappears, not in its pristine form, but with the modifications which childhood and adult experiences impose, and with the transformations resulting from the residual defenses and a regressive superego.

Repression is silent. We only know that something which should be present has disappeared. Repression is apparently developed and utilized at first to "contain" the primary processes of id-derivatives and whatever ego trends prove disruptive or are forbidden by parent figures. Later on, it is used also against the superego and its precursors. In everyone, normal and abnormal, repression remains throughout life the major defense against intrusion from these sources.[55] It is normally the main defense mechanism for maintaining ego boundaries, and thus makes whatever these boundaries exclude into the *unconscious*.

Since repression comes to full maturity rather late in childhood, any regression that is deep and inclusive is likely to impair its effectiveness seriously. When this happens in normal sleep, the effects upon experience and behavior are limited by the simultaneous motor paralysis. It is true that hallucinations and delusions commonly appear in dreams; but they disappear when a person awakens, or, if they are remembered, the healthy ego laughs them off. When deep and inclusive regression occurs while a person is awake, the effects of the previously repressed material, which now invades the preconscious and conscious ego, can be devastating. This is the situation in severe psychoses and in many brain disorders. Normal ego boundaries

[55] Cf. Holzman, P. S., and Gradner, R. W., "Leveling and repression," *J. abnorm. soc. Psychol.*, 1959, *59*, 151–155.

can no longer be maintained, repression fails, and "the return of the repressed" is treated as though it were present fact instead of the expression of an infantile past. The *failure of repression* in dreams and psychoses often calls into play the more primitive defenses of introjection, projection and identification, while at the same time primary processes may once more dominate perception, thinking and behavior.

Denial

Denial plays a defensive role similar to that of repression, but it usually operates at preconscious and conscious levels. Thus adults deny what they perceive, think or feel in a traumatic situation, either saying something to the effect that it cannot be so, or else trying to invalidate something intolerable by deliberately ignoring its existence. Although everyone uses it to some extent, denial is generally considered to be a more primitive defense than repression.

Denial is probably utilized by small children before repression has matured and been perfected. In *psychotic regression* it again comes into use. Delusions are usually projections of something from within, which has gained access to preconscious or conscious ego organizations, but is there denied as being part of the ego, the body-image or the self. Denial by means of fantasy (which represents reality and oneself as different from what they actually are) is a common source of reassurance against anxiety, helplessness or a sense of inadequacy. While such fantasy has been most often reported in the study of children, it is probable that it is also widely used by anxious, unhappy and insecure adults.[56]

Reaction formation

Like *introjection, projection* and *identification, reaction formation* has an active part in early personality development, before it becomes a defense. In Chapter 5, when we were discussing the precursors of the superego, we mentioned the importance of reaction formations in controlling forbidden impulses and fantasies during the second year of postnatal life. The small child assumes attitudes which are diametrically opposed to his forbidden impulses and fantasies, usually in imitation of a parent whose love he needs.[57] In such a way the small child gains control over his impulses to soil and be cruel, and actually becomes clean and kind. These reaction formations are normally superseded by the development of a postedipal superego which establishes parental and societal attitudes as integral parts of the growing child's psychodynamic system.

[56] Cf. Jacobson, E., "Denial and repression," *J. Amer. Psychoanal. Ass.*, 1957, 5, 61–92; Miller, D. R., "Studies of denial in fantasy," in David, H. P., and Brengelmann, J. C. (Eds.), *Perspectives in Personality Research.* New York: Springer, 1960, pp. 43–64.

[57] Peak, H., Muney, B., and Clay, M., "Opposite structures, defenses and attitudes," *Psychol. Monogr.*, 1960, 74, Whole No. 495.

Reaction formation is used as a *defense mechanism by adults* when repression is inadequate and needs reinforcement. It is seen most clearly in *obsessive compulsive reactions,* where soiling and sexuality emerge together in preconscious or conscious experience. This emergence repeats unresolved pre-edipal conflicts which have been carried over by the patient into the edipal phase, and then repressed while still unresolved. Reaction formation is also found as a permanent constituent in *character disorders* where, for example, an exaggerated cleanliness or kindness merely overlays hostile impulses to soil, to be cruel and to destroy. The main defect in such character disorders is their rigidity. Since what is being defended against is an unconscious component of the individual's personality, he cannot afford to reconsider, to reflect or to be flexible, unless he is willing and able to re-examine his own personality organization with expert help.

Displacement

Displacement consists of discharging impulses, or living out unconscious fantasies, by shifting from one object to another. The drive and its aim do not change. We have seen this maneuver as a part of the primary process of id-derivatives and the repressed unconscious ego. According to the primary process conception, sexual and aggressive impulses that are blocked from immediate discharge shift easily to whatever avenue is open to them. Since primary process displacement continues to operate in adult dreaming, it is obvious that this device continues at some level throughout everyone's life.

Displacement as an ego defense amounts to the same maneuver, excepting that the shift involves somatic and external realities as separate entities. It is commonly used to avoid anxiety when to love or to be angry becomes dangerous. The danger may be realistic. It may instead arise from the threat of primary anxiety, when id-derivatives or unconscious repressed ego fantasies are about to invade preconscious and conscious organizations. It may also arise when unconscious superego pressures, or a fleeting pang of conscience, threatens anxiety — either because of rigid, perfectionistic standards, or because the superego is reacting to unconscious forbidden impulses and fantasies that are near the surface. The familiar normal example is the man who, when his employer humiliates and angers him, becomes enraged with his wife or his child over some trivial annoyance, without realizing why he is behaving as he is.

We shall see pathological examples of displacement in the *phobias,* where primary anxiety because of sexual and aggressive impulses is displaced to an irrational fear, which threatens to overwhelm the patient. Other pathological examples will be found among the *conversions* and the *obsessive compulsive reactions. Paranoid projection* usually involves a displacement of intolerable aggressive and sexual impulses on to someone else, even on to a whole pseudocommunity of alleged persecutors. The paranoid process is complicated, however, by the emergence of forbidden sexual and hostile aggressive impulses into the preconscious ego, where they are denied and projected. The projection is itself a form of displacement whenever the impulses or fantasies do not change in the character of their drives and aims, but only in their object. The *drives* and *aims*, still unchanged, are now ascribed to others, while the *object* is changed from others to the self. Such a defensive structure as this illustrates the complex interaction of different defenses, and accounts for the difficulties we all have in singling them out from the defensive continuum where they actually operate in real life.

Turning-against-the-self

This is a special form of *displacement*. Impulses or fantasies directed against someone else are redirected by turning them against the self, without changing their character or aim. The kind of paranoid delusion just described, under displacement, belongs here too. We shall find *turning-against-the self*, used as an unconscious defense, among the *phobias*. Agnes W. began her illness with a wave of justifiable anger against her faithless lover, who had deserted her in a moment of desperate need. But she then irrationally turned her fury against herself with almost fatal consequences. Turning-against-the-self is a common feature of *psychotic depressions* whenever a patient accuses himself of crimes which are actually exaggerations of the infuriating behavior of a loved and hated other person. The case of Constance Q. illustrates the operation of this defense mechanism along with regressive introjection. She was herself a dependable, hard-working, respectable citizen; but when she was overwhelmed by her tension and anxiety she regressed to a psychotic depressive level; and there she used some forgotten lapses as the basis for accusations, which belonged not to her but to her brothers.

What does turning-against-the-self achieve? In *psychotic regressions* it seems to achieve little beyond keeping the psychodynamic system from further disintegration. In some *phobias* and in some *depressions* it may reduce anxiety and help repress conflicts by shifting sexual or aggressive impulses from an ambivalently loved and hated person to oneself. Apparently such patients can more easily tolerate a sadomasochistic attitude toward themselves than the hatred they would otherwise feel toward others. The maneuver has dangerous possibilities in both phobias and psychotic depressions; but, because of the greater regression in the psychoses, the chance that dangerous impulses will actually be carried out is greater in psychotic depressions.

Isolation

Isolation is a defensive misuse of the normal ego processes by means of which different organizations and different attitudes are maintained under different circumstances, for example, by the same man when he is at work and when he is at home. The pathological use of isolation may involve repression of the emotional components of perceptions, thoughts or actions, so that they seem colorless and cannot arouse a person's anxiety. This is a common situation among the *obsessive compulsive character disorders* and *neuroses*.

Pathological isolation sometimes consists of compartmentalization. Different sets of experiences, with or without their emotional components, are unconsciously separated from psychological contact with other sets. This we shall see among the *dissociative reactions* as well as among the *obsessive compulsive disorders*. Less commonly the emotional reaction appears consciously or preconsciously, while the experience to which it belongs remains repressed. This, incidentally, is a common occurrence after ordinary nighttime dreaming; a person wakes up with some feeling hanging over him but cannot recall the dream that called it out.

There is a special form of isolation which Freud called *ego-splitting*, and which he first described in relation to fetishism.[58] It is also found among the neuroses and psychoses. A realistic knowledge of something, usually sexual in character, exists side by side with a regressive, and often absurdly infantile misinterpretation. For some reason the infantile misinterpretation cannot be successfully repressed; it remains more or less accessible to preconscious and conscious thinking, even though it is anxiety-provoking. The patient may behave as if the infantile interpretation were true, even though at secondary process levels he knows that it is not.

In a young woman with a character disorder, who was by no means fetishistic, there persisted along with full adult knowledge to the contrary, a belief that after a woman had given birth to a child her insides might fall out on to the ground. When the patient got around to expressing this belief, much as a small child might, and without any feeling that it might be ridiculous, a simple explanation of the groundlessness of the anxiety was accepted with complete naiveté, as though the patient had never heard of such a thing before. The anxiety and the symptom disappeared. This amounted to meeting the patient at her own regressed level of the moment, and helping her to terminate the isolation, which she did.

Intellectualization and rationalization

These are two preconscious defense mechanisms which are closely related to isolation, but are less primitive. *Intellectualization* transplants all conflicts to the realm of secondary process thinking and talking. Whatever contributes to the emergence of anxiety is repressed. This maneuver uses a method for defensive purposes against anxiety, which is familiar and legitimate in conflict-free spheres of perception, thought, speech and action. When it is combined with an intellectual knowledge of therapeutic measures,

[58] Freud, S., "Fetichism," (1927), Standard Edition, 1961, vol. 21, pp. 149–157.

and even with some experience in using such measures, it can be a formidable obstacle to therapeutic progress.

Rationalization is also more or less intellectualistic. It consists of the justification of otherwise unacceptable, ego-alien thought, feeling or action, through the misuse and distortion of facts and through employing a pseudo-logic. Rationalization is a common device in everyday life where people explain away their own defects, failures and misdeeds, as well as those of persons whom they love or admire — for example, by saying that everyone else does the same thing, or by giving a rationale which they think up after the thing has already been done.[59] It is used in much the same way in the formation of pathological symptoms; it really belongs to the superstructure of symptoms, or to their embroidery.

Ritual and undoing

Once more we meet in *ritual* — and in *undoing*, which is usually ritualistic — forms of behavior and ways of thinking which have many constructive values as well as defensive uses. It is not only man who performs complex rituals. They can be found in many other organisms as an essential, but often unintelligible, part of their behavior. The mating dance of certain birds, for instance, is a thoroughly ritualistic performance. If someone interrupts the dance, the bird is not only incapable of completing sex intercourse; he is also incapable of continuing from the point where he was interrupted. Like some of our obsessive compulsive patients, who have developed a personal ritual in relation to sexual or aggressive impulses, the bird has to begin all over again, from the very start of the ritualistic dance.

Human ritual is one of the earliest forms of gaining control of the environment, of the behavior of other people, and of oneself. It is the basis of exact repetition, and therefore of scientific and technological development. *Ritual* is so important a part of normal human life, in all societies, that it would be absurd to look upon it as always a defense against anxiety. Much the same can be said about *undoing*. It is magical, it is traditional, and it is universal. Penance, our penal codes, and our penitentiaries, are all based upon the conviction that wrongs can be undone through suitable performances or deprivations.

Ritual and ritualistic undoing are used *defensively* when they help a person to solve or at least to avoid a conflict, when they prevent the emergence of primary anxiety, or serve to gain control over it after it emerges. Compulsive ritual is often a caricature of caution. Something has to be done a certain way, which is predetermined, down to the smallest detail. If anything is omitted, done incorrectly, or forgotten after it has been done, the patient is overwhelmed by anxiety. The meaning of the

[59] Bibring, G., *et al.*, "A study of the psychological processes in pregnancy and of the earliest mother-child relationship," *Psychoanal. Study Child*, 1961, *16*, 9–72.

ritual, in obsessive compulsive disorders as well as in ancient cultural practices, may be completely lost — in cultural practices through forgetting, in obsessive compulsive disorders through repression.

Ritualistic performances are retained in *cultural practices* for many reasons. One of them is the enjoyment which they provide, both to the participants and the lookers-on. Another reason is that they may be magical attempts at controlling dangerous forces. In *neuroses* and *psychoses*, ritualistic performances are retained for similar reasons. They differ from social ritual in being individualistic in pattern, and in being directed almost exclusively against the emergence of unconscious conflicts with their attendant anxiety. *Undoing* as an unconscious ego defense consists usually of the ritualistic performance of the opposite of what a patient has just done, in order to cancel out or balance any evil that might have lurked in it. Sometimes it consists of repeating the same performance, which for some reason arouses anxiety, but repeating it with a consciously different attitude. Obsessive compulsive patients are often highly intelligent, sophisticated persons, who recognize the absurdity of their symptoms. They are, however, as powerless to avoid their ritualistic repetitions as the normal person is to avoid having a ridiculous dream.

Sublimation and the concept of neutralization

Sublimation is variously conceived of as the most complete and successful of all defenses, and as no defense at all, but rather the full use of a tamed and channeled drive. In either case, sublimation implies the transformation of what was once direct sexuality into genuine nonsexual love and friendship, creativity and altruism. The development of sublimation does not exclude a capacity for full mature genital sexuality along socially acceptable lines, in relation to an acceptable sex partner. If we recall Freud's early concentration upon the then neglected subject of sex drive or instinct, and his later division of all motivation into the sexual or creative instincts and the destructive or death instincts, the importance of sublimation for the whole libido theory becomes obvious.[60]

Because the term *sublimation* has been used so long to mean deflected or neutralized *sex energy,* there is a reluctance to apply it to deflected or neutralized *aggression.* This reluctance is unfortunate. It has led to the adoption of a terminology which includes such words as *de-aggressivizing,* *de-aggressivized* and *de-aggressivization.* By comparison, the word *sublimation* sounds almost elegant.

As we pointed out in discussing the drives or "instincts," Freud shifted his conceptions to conform to his growing understanding of his material. It was not until late in his life that he made aggression the consort and the

---

[60] For a discussion of the *libido theory,* see Hendrick, I., *Facts and Theories of Psychoanalysis.* (3rd ed.) New York: Knopf, 1958, pp. 108–123; also, Munroe, R., *Schools of Psychoanalytic Thought.* New York: Dryden Press, 1955.

equal of sexuality. He recognized clearly the importance of neutralized aggression; but he never gave it a special title to put the neutralization on a par with sublimation. Within the past decade or two the previous neglect of aggression has given away to a considerable emphasis upon it, especially when it comes to hostile aggression and neutralized aggression. We still lack a flexible terminology that would make conceptions and discussions of aggression more maneuverable. The employment of *neutralization* as a term for both sublimation and de-aggressivization is a step in the right direction, and one which Freud himself introduced.

The facts about neutralized energy are less unclear than the terms describing them. Everyone agrees that, in contrast to normal genital sexuality, *hostile aggression* has a very limited usefulness in our society. Almost everyone agrees that sublimated sexual energy contributes to friendliness among individuals and nations, and that it is essential to creativity in nonsexual areas. *Neutralized aggressive energy* is equally essential for normal initiative, independence, competition and cooperation, to say nothing of ordinary work. It also enters importantly into normal mature sexuality, friendliness and creativity. It has been known for centuries that children who could not control their direct sexual and aggressive drives — the name for this control has varied over the centuries — were unable to learn what they needed to learn and to become what other children became. Like so many other things which have become the subject of courageous, scientific investigation, the problem of the adequate neutralization of drives, unsolved but troublesome, has been somewhere in folklore for milennia.

The topics of sublimation and de-aggressivization bring our discussion of the defense mechanisms to a close. We are now ready to turn to a clinical account of the anxiety reaction.

7

Anxiety Reactions

ANXIETY PLAYS A LEADING ROLE IN EVERY NEUROSIS; BUT WE RESERVE THE term *anxiety reaction* for those neuroses in which diffuse emotional tension and free anxiety clearly dominate the clinical picture, while other symptoms are merely incidental. To suffer from an anxiety reaction is to feel continually apprehensive and to have no idea what the danger is, or from where it comes. Most of the *symptoms* in anxiety reactions represent the patient's efforts to rid himself of excessive tension by direct discharge, in voluntary (skeletal) muscle action or in autonomic activity. The rest of the symptoms reflect the disturbing effects which the tension has upon ego function (*secondary anxiety*). Here are four brief clinical examples which will serve as an introduction.

A young man complained of feeling that something terrible was about to happen to him. For several months he had been continually fatigued. He had had pains in his head, his back and his legs. He suffered from frequent nightmares. Every once in a while he had sudden attacks of cardiac palpitation, in which he thought he was dying. During the course of psychotherapy it soon came out that he hated working for his aggressive, domineering father, but that he felt too afraid and too guilty to face up to the situation and quit his job. When psychotherapy brought this state of affairs out, the young man was soon able to face his father with the fact that he wanted another job and was determined to look for it. It goes without saying that the situation was complicated; but the psychotherapeutic help removed the young man from it, and his anxiety reactions disappeared.

A young woman, whose fiancé has postponed their wedding for the third time, began having bad dreams from which she would awaken frightened and sometimes crying. During the day she felt tense, angry and preoccupied. Her hands and feet became chronically cold and clammy. She developed a noticeable tremor in her fingers. Her menstrual periods became irregular. When, with the aid of psychotherapy, she recognized that her fiancé was afraid of marrying her for his own personal reasons, she was able to handle the situation successfully.

A middle-aged businessman, whose profit margins were progressively narrowing, found himself under pressure to work harder and harder, and to take on more and more responsibility. He grew short-tempered with his family and with his employees. At times he felt as though he would "explode." He found that he could not enjoy recreation. He could not even relax after work. Sometimes he felt that he wavered unsteadily as he walked. He had attacks of dizziness, especially at the telephone, and he could not seem to concentrate or to think clearly. At times he felt as though a "steel band" were compressing his head. He slept poorly, he lost his appetite, and he became relatively impotent. It was interesting that he had never related these symptoms to the increase of responsibility or to his own deep dependency needs. Psychotherapy helped him to make these connections himself, without interpretations by the therapist.

A married woman, whose life was complicated by her mother's living in the home, complained that she felt tense and irritable most of the time. She was apprehensive lest something happen to her mother, her husband, her children, or herself. She had no definite idea what it was that she feared might happen. She suffered from occasional attacks in which her heart pounded and was irregular, and she could not seem to get her breath. Often she broke out in a profuse perspiration. Her mouth seemed always dry, even though she drank a great deal of water, and because of this and her diffuse anxiety, she had nocturia.

All four of these patients believed themselves to be the victims of some organic disease. All four made good recoveries with the help of psychotherapy which treated the total situation, and not just the symptoms.

In Chapter 2 we discussed the anxieties of small children, which arise because of their dependent relationship to adults and because of the relative weakness of their defenses against unconscious strivings. In Chapter 6 we discussed the changes that take place in the patterns of childhood anxiety with the growth of personality organization, and the defects in ego boundaries that result from a failure to master childhood anxiety. As we now turn to a consideration of *anxiety reactions,* we shall find that we are dealing with a regression to infantile reactions, in which apprehension becomes once more diffuse, and in which the reactions become again infantile and inadequate.

Most people relieve their emotional tensions undramatically, as their stress level rises. Emotional storms are unusual. People supplement the relatively few opportunities offered them for a direct consummation of desire, or for directly overcoming obstacles, by finding a great variety of substitute gratifications and substitute forms of mastery. What might have spiraled into violent aggression, for example, is siphoned off through acceptable forms of self-assertion, of initiative and competition, without distorting healthy expressions of aggression and without damaging personal interrelations. What might have culminated in an irresistible sex urge can find many avenues of partial discharge through acceptable forms of affectionate interaction, of creative activity and wishful fantasy, without distorting actual sex expression or injuring love relationships.

Most of us cannot forego permanently and completely the direct gratification of our emotional needs, nor does a healthy society demand such sacrifices from the great majority of its adult members. What the partial and substitute gratifications achieve is a reduction in tension by providing frequent indirect relief. This tames our emotional drives so that we can express them within the limits set by our society and by our own personal ideals.

As we have pointed out earlier, a certain amount of emotional tension and anxiety can serve useful functions. The moderately anxious person makes a vigilant, attentive watcher, who is alert to relatively slight stimulation, and prepared for prompt and vigorous action. Moderate anxiety often increases the pleasures of anticipation. It is a common source of laughter, and a common ingredient of many forms of entertainment. Even intense anxiety can be helpful when it increases one's strength, one's speed, courage and endurance in an emergency.

Neurotic anxiety

The advantages of moderate anxiety disappear when emotional tension grows too great, lasts too long, or underlies too much of one's behavior. The point is finally reached at which tension and anxiety narrow a person's range of perception so much, disturb his thinking and restrict his freedom of action to such a degree, that even routine matters put him under tremendous strain, and ordinary gratifications slip from his grasp. A person's life may then be dedicated to the control of anxiety and the discharge of tension. We see such an outcome in persons who are exposed to realistic danger that far exceeds the limits of their tolerance; and we see it in persons who are experiencing the imminent threat of an upsurge of unconscious impulses and conflicts. The former we have already dealt with in Chapter 6 when we discussed *traumatic anxiety;* the latter we shall deal with now in discussing neurotic *anxiety reactions.*[1]

[1] Cf. Zetzel, E. R., *"The concept of anxiety in relation to the development of psychoanalysis,"* J. Amer. Psychoanal. Ass., 1955, 3, 369–388; Rangell, L., "On the psychoanalytic theory of anxiety," J. Amer. Psychoanal. Ass., 1955, 3, 389–414; Flescher, J., "A dualistic viewpoint on anxiety," J. Amer. Psychoanal. Ass., 1955, 3, 415–446; May, R., *The Meaning of Anxiety.* New York: Ronald, 1950; Janis, I., *Psychological Stress.* New York: Wiley, 1958.

Definition. An anxiety reaction is a state of apprehension, without an apparent object, in which attempts are made to discharge internally generated tension and to reduce anxiety through increased bodily activity. The patient in an anxiety reaction is the victim of a diffuse and nameless dread. He finds himself vigilant and alarmed without being able to understand why — like a frightened sentry on guard who does not know what to do, what to listen for, or where to look. The patient's skeletal muscles are characteristically tense and his autonomic nervous system is overactive. His habitual rhythms of living, including the physiological functioning of his viscera, may be seriously disturbed. He is predisposed to give exaggerated and inappropriate responses upon slight provocation.

Anxiety reactions usually reduce a person's capacity for relaxation, enjoyment and effectiveness, but they are rarely disabling. Judging by the large number of adults who are more or less accidentally discovered to be suffering from pathological anxiety, it is probable that only a small minority of persons with anxiety reactions recognize that something is psychologically wrong and seek psychotherapeutic help. A great many who realize that they are far from being calm or stable simply accept their state as though it were an unmodifiable personality characteristic.

Adaptation. There are persons who manage to adapt themselves to fairly high levels of neurotic tension and anxiety without apparent distortion in their perception of the world, and without serious limitations in their range of action. Some succeed in discharging tensions through continual overactivity in everything they do. Among these are many of the indefatigable workers, tireless enthusiasts, unofficial vigilantes and high-strung critics of daily life. Many reduce their own tension and anxiety at the expense of other people's peace of mind, plunging energetically into personal, family and neighborhood problems, or on a less intimate level waging civic, political or religious warfare. These persons are not so much *led* to action as *driven* to action, driven by an urgent need to master their own anxiety. It is when such devices fail, or when circumstances push tension up to unmanageable levels, that these pathologically anxious persons seek help, though usually what they seek is only help to combat their *symptoms.*

Even though it may be "maladaptive," the *anxiety reaction* is itself a form of adaptation. The adaptation is a costly one. It usually involves a vigilant, unrelaxed attitude which interferes with normal satisfactions and personal interactions. It often includes aches, pains and disturbances of visceral function, because muscles and internal organs are overstimulated during the discharge process. The anxiety reaction is *adaptive,* even though costly, because it acts as a safety valve. By continuously or intermittently discharging excess tension through bodily overactivity, a person manages to preserve the greater part of his ego integration and, excepting for the occasional anxiety attack, he protects himself from being overwhelmed. Without this safety valve discharge, he might well suffer ego disintegration and undergo regression, even to psychotic levels.

Varieties of Anxiety Reaction

Because the anxiety reaction is an attempt to reduce tension and anxiety through bodily discharge, every conceivable combination of voluntary muscle and autonomic nervous system activity may enter into the neurotic patterning. The variety of *complaint patterns*, therefore, is virtually unlimited. All of them show the more or less diffuse, loosely structured character with which we are all familiar through our own experience with normal anxiety.

Varieties in *intensity*, on the other hand, present us with well-defined distinctions. In what follows we shall distinguish three levels of intensity: the *chronic anxiety reaction*, the *anxiety attack* and the *panic reaction*.

(1) In the *chronic anxiety reaction* a diffuse, generalized discharge of tension goes on more or less continuously over a long period of time, often punctuated by acute anxiety attacks. Although the *manifestations* of anxiety are always evident, its *sources* usually remain repressed.

(2) The *anxiety attack* is an acute episode of diffuse tension discharge in which the heaviest burden falls upon the internal organs, especially upon the cardiovascular, respiratory and gastrointestinal systems.

(3) The *panic reaction* is an extremely severe anxiety attack. It is usually the end-result of unbearable, cumulative tension. Panic reactions sometimes lead to a massive eruption of unconscious material, to ego disintegration and a psychotic episode, an example of which we shall give in the clinical material.

Of these three forms of anxiety neurosis the *chronic anxiety reaction* is by far the most common. It will therefore serve as our introduction to the clinical study of neuroses.

Chronic Anxiety Reaction (Anxiety Neurosis)

As the most typical and by far the most common form of anxiety disorder, the *chronic anxiety reaction* conforms closely to the definition of anxiety reaction already given in this chapter. Its details will be only an expansion of that definition. The chronic anxiety patient suffers from an unstructured fear. He usually cannot point to exactly what frightens him. He feels always tense and apprehensive, as though he were waiting for something terrible to happen. He remains physiologically on an emergency footing — strained, expectant and fatigued — ready for a disaster which he cannot specify and which never actually descends upon him. He is almost always unaware that he is generating it himself. He has to make continual efforts to get rid of the tensions and anxieties which continually build up, and he must endure an endless succession of interferences with the normal physiological patterns of his body function which his efforts at discharge entail.

The patient complains openly of his tension, of feeling strained, apprehensive and fatigued. He cannot relax. Almost any unexpected stimulation startles him — the doorbell and the telephone, the noise of an auto horn or something dropped, someone suddenly speaking to him or entering the room unnoticed. He may approach every new task, every little crisis or decision with misgivings — a minor change in work, the prospect of buying something, of employing or letting someone go, of having guests come, or even of going out in the evening. He may grow anxious about such trivial everyday matters as making the right turn in traffic, entering his office or factory, facing his fellow workers, etc.

Housewives who suffer from anxiety reactions face their routine tasks with unreasonable dread, distaste and apprehension. How will breakfast go? How will a mother get her children off to school? How will the little ones be fed, cleaned and kept occupied? The shopping list becomes an immense burden. What shall she do about lunch? How can she do the housekeeping, prepare the evening meal, and keep herself looking well? The little molehills of routine become a great chain of mountains for her to scale each day.

Usually the anxious person *looks* and *acts* strained — in his posture and gait, in his facial expression, in his movements and gestures, in the way he sits and the way he talks. These muscular signs of tension he supplements with complaints of headaches, of a tight sensation around his head, and of aching in his neck, back and legs. There are often tremors in his fingers, tongue and eyelids, and sometimes in his lips.

The chronically anxious patient is apt to be forgetful, unable to concentrate and think clearly, too restless and on edge to stick to any one activity long. He starts reading a story and gives it up. He shifts irritably from one television program to another, from one record to another, or from one page of the newspaper to the next, without finding satisfaction in anything. Poor recall, inability to concentrate and unclear thinking are common direct effects of any excessive tension and anxiety, even in persons who are only temporarily disturbed.

These effects are intensified further by the patient's preoccupation with internal threats and conflicts, coming from the margins of preconscious and unconscious activity, which now begin to interrupt or to invade his thinking. The neurotically anxious person often engages in fantasies about things he fears and dreads — past, present or future. Sometimes a conscious daydream is so frightening that it is enough to precipitate a sudden anxiety attack. The anxiety attack may then be so alarming in itself that it blots out all memory of the daydream that precipitated it. The attack seems to the patient to come from nowhere and to be a sure sign that he has some terrible organic illness or is going insane.

Dreaming at night can become another fruitful source of frightening fantasies. Anxiety dreams and nightmares form part of a general sleep disturbance in anxiety disorders. Often a manifest dream, as the patient remembers it, seems to have started off well, perhaps depicting the frank fulfillment of a forbidden wish. But matters soon get out of hand. Frightening figures appear — like the policemen who appear in real life when one is breaking the law — or there is some transformation in the manifest dream that makes the whole situation seem suddenly horrible, fearful, weird or disgraceful. If the intensity of such developments is great enough the dreamer awakens with all the classical signs of acute anxiety. Here is an example.

A patient dreamed that he was walking through a suburb with an unknown companion. Suddenly he was alone, facing a cemetery, while people were fleeing to his right down a highway away from an atomic explosion which filled the sky. He began running, too, but he ran toward his left and into the atomic blast. He tried to yell. He awoke perspiring and acutely anxious. The situation in the dream included part of the setting of his therapist's office. In approaching it, one actually went toward a cemetery and turned off to the left. The atomic blast in the dream represented the still unconscious dangers which the patient was running into, when he came for his therapeutic hours.

Sleep disorders are almost universal in anxiety reactions; the frightening dream is only the most dramatic complaint. Nearly all anxious patients complain that they cannot fall asleep, and when they eventually do drop off, the least disturbance awakens them. To fall asleep again may then be as difficult as it was at the beginning, and for the same reasons — bodily tensions, fearful anticipations, fantasies, and a dread of letting go, that amounts to a dread of losing control. Thus day and night the anxious person's body seems to be alerted for some danger that never materializes and never disappears.

Manifestations of this constant strain and apprehension can be found in almost any organ or system in the body. The heart may thump, accelerate and skip beats. Breathing is often shallow and irregular, interrupted every now and then by sighing. Appetite suffers. The anxious person may feel queasy, find it hard to eat and to keep his food down. The occasional patient experiences emptiness and instead of losing his appetite, he eats voraciously. The diarrhea of fear and the constipation of tension are both common, well-known symptoms. Glands of internal and external secretion participate in the general emotional disorder. Sexual functions are almost always involved. Relative impotence in the male, menstrual irregularities and frigidity in the female, are the most obvious sexual manifestations.

It is hardly surprising that, with all these emotional disturbances, persons who are chronically tense and anxious begin to doubt the soundness of their bodies. They are among the most susceptible to suggestions of hidden illness made during public health campaigns. "Heart week" finds them with pain in the chest and down the left arm. A cancer drive alerts them to the frightening possibility that they may be victims of this silent enemy. Such preoccupations temporarily serve the same function as genuine phobias. They give some of the free anxiety a definite focus and to this extent relieve the personality system of some intolerable tension. Unlike phobias, however, the anxiety reaction does not crystallize about a single focus; it moves characteristically from one worry to another.

The social life of perpetually anxious people suffers in the same ways that their more strictly physiological and personal life does. If recreation involves highly coordinated movement, for example, the movement loses its fluid character and becomes effortful or awkward. When the anxious man drives his car, he holds the wheel in a tight grip, he is vigilant and apprehensive, he develops aching muscles and tired eyes during what used to be a relaxing experience. If he goes dancing, he holds his partner tightly, makes mistakes, and moves with little grace. If he plays golf he cannot swing freely or maintain a good stance; he tries too hard and is intolerant of his own bad plays. In social conversation he becomes abrupt, and either too self-assertive or too silent, with a general tendency to make irritated and disparaging comments.

In trying to avoid whatever increases his anxiety, the anxious person may make self-protection his main concern, and subordinate everything else to it. This seriously impoverishes his life by cutting him off from many avenues of self-expression, social interchange and pleasure. Even though he may not restrict his activities and contacts as *rigidly* as does the phobic person, his restrictions often cover so much *territory* that his interpersonal relationships are even more seriously curtailed. A case of anxiety reaction will illustrate the operation of many of the factors that we have been discussing.

A case of chronic anxiety reaction (anxiety neurosis)

Walter A., an American oil geologist, aged thirty-two, who had been living abroad for many years, came for diagnosis because of symptoms which he feared might mean that he was going insane. For five or six years he had been having attacks of dizziness, blurred vision, weakness and unsteady gait. For three years he had been suffering from constant "nervous tension," irritability, fatigue, increased sex pace with incomplete satisfaction, inability to relax, poor sleep and frequent nightmares. For a year his restlessness had grown so marked that he could scarcely stand still, sit or lie still. He felt driven to overactivity so that he wore out everyone who worked with him and himself also. He was drinking liquor during the day, "to steady" him, and taking barbiturates at night to sleep.

Soon he began having frequent anxiety attacks. The first came on suddenly while he was dressing to go out for the evening. Something seemed to snap in his head, everything looked unnatural and he felt he was fainting. He lay down for a long time, his heart pounding, his breathing labored, and with the recurring thought, "I'm dying, I'm dying." Other attacks came later. They consisted of "queer head sensations," weakness, sweating, coarse tremor, palpitation and a conviction that something terrible was happening to him. It was his fear of these attacks and of what they might mean that drove him to seek and accept help.

From the nature of the complaints, and the outcome of thoroughgoing diagnostic studies, it was clear that we were dealing with chronic anxiety of long standing. In the course of psychotherapy, in which the patient was seen three times a week for two months, a great many factors emerged to account for the development and perpetuation of his anxiety reaction. On several occasions a great deal of free anxiety appeared during therapeutic sessions in relation to conflictual material. When this happened, Walter always leaned forward on the arm of the chair and performed rhythmic mouth movements which gave an immediate impression of energetic infant nursing. This maneuver, he explained spontaneously, was one that he had discovered as an emergency measure in reducing tension. Twice during therapeutic sessions he had full-blown anxiety attacks. During the first attack he became furious because the therapist did not share his alarm and call in a heart specialist.

Discussion of the case

A brief life history, extracted from the initial interviews and from the therapeutic hours, will give the background of this man's illness. Walter was the youngest of five children, brought up strictly in great fear of committing sin. He was taught to search his conscience every night for "unworthy" thoughts or acts during the day, which might need forgiveness. He suffered from night terrors as a child, and remembered one in which he was being carried off to hell fire. He saw the flames of hell so clearly in this dream that it frightened him even to think of it afterwards.

In his home the sinfulness of sex and the sanctity of marriage were held up as first principles. It came, therefore, as a shock when at fifteen he was told by his mother that she was divorcing his father. He remained with his mother after the separation, but he found he could forgive neither parent for the divorce. He felt that they had swindled him with their fine talk about marriage. His self-righteous mother seemed to him both a sinner and a hypocrite. He concluded that all women were untrustworthy.

After two years at home with his mother this disillusioned young man went off to college. During his first year there, he felt lonely and in continual conflict over the moral and ethical discussions that he heard there. A summer session then threw him with gay, rebellious adolescent companions, whose talk and conduct led him to adopt a new philosophy of life. Everything was now directed toward success and self-aggrandizement. He chose new friends, wangled a good income out of his divorced parents, bought a car, dated freely, and drank heavily. At the same time he despised himself for what he was doing; at times he hated his new friends, and he always felt contempt for the girls he dated. After a year of graduate study in geology, and two more in American oil fields, he accepted a lucrative position abroad.

Walter found his new work taxing, the climate hot, the standard of living luxurious and the social life full of intrigue. The Americans and the Europeans formed a small community in which everyone knew everyone else, and saw a great deal of one another. As an unmarried man, who was not without charm, he soon found himself entangled in a succession of minor affairs with the bored wives of other men. One of these affairs became serious. To escape it the patient asked for a six months' leave, but when he returned he found himself involved with the same woman. This period coincides with the increase in symptoms, listed at the beginning of his account, as appearing three years before he came for therapeutic help.

It was quite clear that Walter did not at the time see any connection between his personal difficulties and his symptoms. Psychotherapy, however, brought out multiple relationships. His simplest conflict arose from the fact that his mistress was the wife of a close friend. At first he told this with the kind of contempt that he had felt toward his "dates" in college. As he became more free to experience other emotional attitudes, his feeling changed to anger, first at his therapist and later at the woman. He now said that she had reinforced his distrust of women, had pushed a normal marriage further from his grasp, and spoiled his friendship with her husband. The limitations of time and psychological understanding prevented an exploration of this triangular situation, beyond the fact that it was related to his own adolescent experiences at home.

The first *acute anxiety attack* began a few weeks after Walter found out that others knew the details of his affair. He now had reason to fear exposure and retaliation. His basically strong sense of guilt, reinforced now by a realistic fear, redoubled his anxiety, and led to his second flight from the situation. This time, however, he fled as a sick man who *knew* that he was sick.

The outcome of therapy, which was of relatively short duration, included a beginning understanding of his own personality limitations and susceptibilities, and some ability to relate his symptoms to their current and their childhood origins. He lost his *anxiety attacks* completely, and he considerably reduced his chronic tension. Four years later he wrote that his anxiety symptoms had disappeared, but his distrust of women persisted. After another six years he sent a message on a Christmas card saying that he had married and felt confident that he had chosen well. Apparently the process of personality maturation, initiated by his therapy, had continued for several years.

In this case the patient was clearly aware of his intense anxiety and of his urgent desire to escape from it. His bodily symptoms — which were his main concern at first — his overactivity, his nightmares and his *anxiety attacks* — all pointed to the compelling need he had to lower his intolerable tension. He formed no stable symptom, but discharged his tensions diffusely through overt and covert behavioral channels. At the same time Walter failed to recognize without help that he was constantly increasing his own anxiety, by getting into situations of real personal danger which were stimulating intense conflict within him. His behavior suggested that he was driven to seek punishment, and that the prospect of meeting it terrified him.

This illness had a background of chronic childhood anxiety in a home that continually emphasized sin, guilt and punishment. In his eyes, the moral standards which Walter had internalized in this home were flagrantly violated by his parents themselves, when they divorced because they did not love each other. What he considered parental deception and sin played a leading part in his own switch to a rebellious, socially irresponsible attitude during his college years. It is an example of adolescent identification. But the fact that he despised himself for what he was doing, hated his new friends, and scorned the girls he dated shows that the old internalized superego standards remained active, even though ineffectual. These conflict-ridden attitudes also expressed his feelings toward his parents.

The contradictory, ambivalent attitudes which he had derived from the emotionally traumatic experiences at home, he carried with him into his work situation abroad. Here he tried unsuccessfully to establish some kind of a life pattern that would gratify his contradictory needs for love and revenge, for security and deceit. In the therapeutic relationship he was able to unravel some of this motivational tangle, to understand what he had been doing and how it affected him, to contrast his life before he was eighteen with life afterwards. He was not able to work out in therapy his basic conflicts regarding his parents, or the distortions which these conflicts repeatedly introduced into his relationships with both men and women. In the light of his marriage ten years later, it seems probable that therapy at least opened the way for further personality growth and learning during the subsequent years.

Anxiety Attacks

Anxiety attacks are acute episodes of emotional decompensation usually appearing in a setting of chronic anxiety, and exhibiting to an exaggerated degree the characteristics of normal fright. The fright usually comes from within, from a sudden upsurge of unconscious material that threatens to disrupt ego integration. The anxiety attack often climaxes a long period of mounting tension to which the anxious person has been progressively adapting, but with ever-increasing difficulty. Finally the limits of tolerance are reached, he can compensate no further, and the continued stress precipitates a sudden discharge into all available channels.

In extreme instances the anxiety attack resembles sudden violent alarm. A patient becomes restless and agitated, his pupils dilate, his face changes color, he breaks out into a sweat and his mouth goes dry. His breathing quickens, he complains of choking or suffocating and tugs at his collar or jerks it open. His heart beats rapidly and develops irregularity. Nausea and vomiting, urinary urgency, and diarrhea are other common features. The patient is often tremulous and may walk or stand unsteadily. He complains of feeling dizzy, faint, or weak in the knees, of hot flashes or chilly creeps. He may be overwhelmed by the anticipation of impending danger, of heart failure, death, insanity or some unidentifiable disaster. He may beg those around him to get help at once, and rail at them for their indifference if they do not share his alarm. This is what Walter A. did in his first attack during a psychotherapeutic session. After a period of from a few minutes to an hour the attack subsides to a comparatively unobtrusive level or it disappears completely.

Anxiety attacks are not always as severe and dramatic as this. Often they are only brief episodes of moderate intensity which are frightening but not disabling. The symptoms vary considerably from one individual to another, depending chiefly upon a person's habitual response patterns to fear or excitement. In some the cardiovascular system bears the brunt of sudden discharge; in others it is the respiratory system, the gastrointestinal or the genitourinary system. People sometimes experience momentary disorientation in acute anxiety, suffer memory distortions or complain of unreality feelings. Some experience disturbances of perception, of various kinds and in various fields, or temporary impairment of locomotion, coordination, speech and thought. Occasionally an anxiety attack is ushered in by what the patient describes as a snapping or an explosion in his head, such as Walter A. experienced, and for which we have as yet no satisfactory explanation.

Panic Reactions

The panic reaction is a maximal anxiety attack, an episode of extreme emotional decompensation. It may be a prelude to violent aggression, headlong flight, ego disintegration, or suicide. The clinical picture is one of uncontrollable fear. Psychotic manifestations are not uncommon, in which the patient may even misinterpret his environment, suffer from delusions of persecution, and experience auditory hallucinations of a threatening, taunting, or reviling character. The duration of *panic* may be brief, lasting a few hours or days, or it may persist for months during which the intensity of the panic fluctuates within wide limits.

The eventual outcome of a panic reaction is difficult to predict, especially when the episode is prolonged or recurs. If the patient is given adequate protection and support, in a situation which allows him whatever degree of seclusion he needs but does not force seclusion upon him, he may recover quickly. However, even in recovering cases, delusions often persist for weeks after panic has subsided, and suspicion may persist for months. In prolonged excessive fright there is always the possibility that some permanent damage to personality organization will result. Sometimes impulses, fears and conflicts, which escape repression and become conscious during acute emotional decompensation, cannot be repressed or satisfactorily disposed of after the acute phase subsides. The sequel to panic is sometimes a chronic paranoid reaction or a schizophrenic disorganization, as the following case will show.

Edgar R., a clerk aged twenty-eight years, was listening at the office to a discussion of sex perversions. One of his fellow workers suddenly noticed that Edgar was blushing and accused him laughingly of "being one of those people." His reaction to the accusation was so exaggerated that he became the target of bantering and obscene epithets over a period of about three weeks. The first change his wife noticed was that he seemed preoccupied and uncommunicative. Then he developed insomnia, lost his appetite, and began harping tensely upon the persecution that he was experiencing at work. Finally he ended up with emotional decompensation in a violent outburst of shouting and threatening which necessitated his immediate hospitalization.

In the hospital, Edgar actively hallucinated voices which accused him of perversion. He believed that his reputation was ruined and his life in danger. He accused attendants of planning to assault him. At one point in a climax of fear, he pulled his cot to pieces and barricaded himself in a corner of the room, threatening to brain anyone who approached him. The psychiatrist in charge treated this episode as the last-ditch stand of a terrified man, and saw to it that no one entered the room without obtaining the patient's permission. Through careful handling the panic eventually subsided, but Edgar remained in a state of chronic schizophrenic disorganization. The office force had come close to the truth. Their merciless teasing had led previously repressed impulses, fantasies and conflicts to break through the patient's inadequate defenses and to become an irrepressible part of his conscious experience.

This panic reaction gives a dramatic picture of the strength of infantile urges, fantasies and conflicts, in a person who had remained partially fixated at a primitive level and was therefore suspectible to a sweeping regression. For more than twenty years the defensive organization of Edgar R. had succeeded in containing or repressing his primitive infantile forces. The fellow worker who noticed that Edgar was blushing inferred correctly that a secret had been uncovered — a secret which at the moment might not have been more than a conscious fear because of unconscious excitement. The malicious teasing which followed, however, had the double effect of further stimulating forbidden trends and at the same time reinforcing superego self-condemnation. Under the combined pressures of realistic accusations from his fellow workers, irresistible forbidden urges from within, and the assaults of a primitive superego, this man's precarious equilibrium disintegrated. His personality organization suffered a sweeping regression in which *denial* and *projection* reached psychotic proportions. He denied his own impulses and projected them to the outside, where they joined forces with the malicious teasing of his fellow workers.

Every so often panic reactions occur that involve whole communities. One of the most impressive of these appeared during the broadcast of a play that represented an imaginary invasion of the United States by men from Mars.[2] Some people who tuned in after the initial announcement that this was a play, accepted the frightening warnings as facts. They rushed out of their houses on to the highways in an attempt to flee. Some carried their belongings with them. The panic was so severe that such broadcasts have been permanently banned. On a lesser scale there was panic in a midwestern

[2] Cantril, H., *The Invasion from Mars.* Princeton, N.J.: Princeton Univ. Press, 1940.

town when someone spread the rumor that enemy agents had released a paralyzing gas.[3] It is true that such rumors may originate with paranoid or schizophrenic individuals; but the spread of panic seems not to be limited to psychotic or near-psychotic persons.

Dynamic and Developmental Background

One reason for beginning our discussion of the neuroses with the anxiety reaction is that it is close to everyday experience. The experiences of neurotically anxious persons, as well as their overt behavior, are like those of normal persons who are in danger and cannot escape it, who are angry but dare not express it, or who are aroused but can do nothing about it.

Another reason for beginning with the anxiety reaction is that excessive tension and anxiety are really basic to all the neuroses.[4] Most of what we shall have to say about anxiety reactions here, especially about their dynamics and development, holds good for other neurotic patterns as well. Their surface appearance may be quite different, but behind their organization of specific symptoms we can always find excessive tension and anxiety.

When *phobic defenses* fail, for example, we witness typical anxiety attacks. It is then obvious that the phobia has been warding off attacks of acute anxiety. The same is true of *obsessive compulsive reactions*. If the repetitive acts or the ritualistic countermeasures are interfered with, acute anxiety will usually come to the surface. Even in *conversion reactions*, where the undisturbed clinical picture is one of bland indifference, the moment a patient tries to work through his neurotic defenses, one finds severe neurotic anxiety behind the bland defensive façade. In short, most of the defensive pictures of other neuroses are defenses against experiencing the tension and anxiety characteristic of anxiety neuroses.[5]

Tension and anxiety in anxiety reactions

As we pointed out at the beginning of the chapter, the neurotically anxious person reacts at the start with an acute tension and anxiety which includes a generalized somatic and emotional discharge. Since his ego organization is for the most part still intact, he succeeds in becoming alert, cautious, and ready to react to danger, just as a normal person does. Unlike the normal person, however, the patient suffering from an anxiety neurosis does not experience a quick reduction in tension and anxiety through his diffuse discharge. On the contrary, tension and anxiety remain high, and they interfere with realistic perception, thinking and action.

[3] Johnson, D. M., "The 'phantom anesthetist' of Mattoon: a field study of mass hysteria," *J. abnorm. soc. Psychol.*, 1945, 40, 175–186.

[4] Freud, S., "Inhibitions, symptoms and anxiety," (1926), Standard Edition, 1959, vol. 20, pp. 77–175.

[5] Many references to the literature on the subject of *anxiety* have already been given in Chapter 6, in the section on anxiety.

Such interference is then likely to disrupt ego integration. As they persist, the symptoms usually rise in intensity. In this way, the symptoms themselves become a frightening focus, thus completing a vicious cycle.

We saw this happen clearly in the case of Walter A., the oil geologist, who lived in constant dread that his symptoms might recur. The end-result was that, for him, the symptoms became the center of his attention. He gave no thought whatever to the interpersonal situations which were continually producing them, situations which he could have avoided if he had been able to recognize them.

The more a patient's tension and anxiety increase, the more imperative it becomes for him to step up his somatic discharge, and the more seriously his perception, thought and coordination are disturbed. It is then no longer merely a matter of *self-perpetuation,* but of a steady *rise* in tension, which even periodic anxiety attacks do not succeed in reducing enough. As time goes on, it becomes increasingly difficult to maintain effective ego integration at fully adult levels. The case of Walter A. illustrated such a progression well.

It should be clear by now that the anxiety reaction is something more than an intense form of normal anxiety. It is a regression to what we described in the preceding chapter as *primary anxiety*. The situations giving rise to it are not just those of environmental danger, or of ordinary anger, or of ordinary arousal. They are situations which threaten to unleash previously unconscious forces.

Sometimes an anxiety attack comes without apparent cause, or a chronic anxiety reaction increases without apparent reason. But even when there is an identifiable excitant — something frightening in the surroundings or a sudden frightening thought — this is not in itself enough to account for the magnitude or the duration of the tension and anxiety which follow. When there is no identifiable excitant — as is so often the case — an anxiety reaction seems to its victim to have no rational explanation and to come from nowhere.

It is because the tension and anxiety seem so irrational to the patient that he so readily attributes his symptoms to organic illness, or fears that he is losing his mind. Actually, no matter how the anxiety begins, it *persists* because the patient regresses, that is to say, because a primary infantile anxiety has been released. In this there are powerfully reactivated a number of infantile and childhood impulses, fantasies, conflicts and frustrations.

As long as the patient's defensive system remains intact, it shields him from becoming aware of what these childhood problems are, problems which if they entered consciousness might be more than he could handle unaided. His defensive system does not shield him, however, from experiencing the tension and anxiety which are being stirred up. He is under an urgent necessity to discharge his tension massively. Such a method of dealing with increased tension and anxiety through a massive, automatic discharge is a regressive, infantile method. It is true that it occasionally appears in the behavior of normal adults when they have an uncontrolled temper outburst;

but temper outbursts are still infantile in pattern, no matter who has them.

In earlier chapters, we have seen that normal infants must rely upon massive, automatic direct discharge — in the form of screaming, yelling and making thrashing movements — because they lack a complex ego organization capable of absorbing tension and thus diminishing anxiety (*energy of organization*). Without this complex type of ego organization, the infant cannot utilize an increase in tension to form perceptual, cognitive or activity patterns, as adults can. He is therefore incapable of suspending action. He cannot deal with threat, as normal adults do, by deliberate observation, evaluation and decision, by a purposeful evasion, or by an aggressive goal-directed action. Rising tensions quickly overwhelm infants and drive them to immediate discharge in violent somatic action.

Many adults behave in some such way when an enormously traumatic situation of objective danger overwhelms them. Battle conditions in actual war, and catastrophic situations in peacetime, have demonstrated this over and over.[6]

The dangers threatening a person suffering from an anxiety reaction come neither from battle nor from an objectively catastrophic situation, but from internal unconscious sources. Accordingly, no amount of violent action can bring more than partial and temporary relief. The frightened neurotic person can find nothing tangible to fight, nothing to evade, and no place to hide.

As an emergency measure, there is no denying the value of an automatic discharge, through general somatic and emotional channels, whether we call it infantile or not. It unquestionably provides temporary relief. Walter A., for example, lived with his anxiety reactions for years, suffering only an occasional anxiety attack and no panic. This is the usual story. Nevertheless, such a method of coping with recurrent problems has serious drawbacks. The immediate discharge takes care of only the immediate need to get rid of excess tension. It does nothing whatever about the *unconscious sources of tension* — nothing about unconscious urges, fantasies, fears, conflicts and frustrations — which keep right on generating the preconscious and conscious tension and anxiety.

What lies behind the symptoms in anxiety reactions

Up to this point we have been chiefly concerned with the neurotic character of the symptoms themselves in the anxiety reaction. Now we shall look behind them in order to understand why it is that they keep recurring even though they are nonadaptive and even though they go unrewarded. We shall see how they distort perception, thinking and action, and how they interfere with the patient's object relationships. More specifically, we shall

[6] Grinker, R. R., and Spiegel, J., *Men Under Stress*. Philadelphia: Blakiston, 1945; Cantril, H., *The Invasion from Mars*. Princeton, N.J.: Princeton Univ. Press, 1940; Johnson, D. M., "The 'phantom anesthetist' of Mattoon: a field study of mass hysteria," *J. abnorm. soc. Psychol.*, 1945, 40, 175–186; Janis, I., *Psychological Stress*. New York: Wiley, 1958.

see that for our patient, the oil geologist, current life situations revived and intensified certain basic conflicts around which his childhood and adolescent personality was organized. And, finally, we shall see that such conflicts can seldom be resolved unless their character is understood, and the way made clear for them to be worked through.

Fixation. Adults who develop anxiety reactions always harbor unconscious conflict systems which are powerfully cathected (energized) and easily re-activated. This is because the conflicts had never been successfully worked through during infancy, childhood or adolescence. In other words, they are examples of arrested development, of prematurely interrupted learning, of *fixation.*

Fixation early in life, at an immature level of functioning, can result from a variety of experiences. At one extreme, we find that an infantile need has been repeatedly aroused but consistently frustrated. It has been denied satisfaction or the child has been threatened with reprisal. At the other extreme, an infantile need has been so intensely satisfied, for so long a time, that it cannot be given up. In addition to these extremes, fixations at pre-edipal levels may result from threatening edipal experiences which make a child retreat from an edipal position before he has been able to consolidate it. Finally, fixation in an infantile mode can result from a fear of regressing into the symbiotic mother-child relationship, in which the child had no genuine independent existence as a person. The patient in this last situation is like a person who has narrowly escaped falling into a canyon, but is still too frightened to go away from it.

In all of these cases the product is essentially the same. A powerful, un-dying infantile need pushes forward continually toward preconscious and conscious expression; but an adult living in an adult environment can never fully satisfy such a need. Nevertheless, even though they may be infantile in organization and goal, these needs have a strength and a tenacity which cannot be overestimated. We see something like them only occasionally in adults who have conscious longings for an impossible degree of love, security, power or revenge — longings that cannot possibly be satisfied, but drive the person on forever.

Defective ego boundaries. These infantile, unconscious conflict systems are easily reactivated — not alone because they are strongly cathected (energized) and have never been succcssfully worked through — but also because of defective ego boundaries. The defensive organization, which should separate conscious and preconscious activities from unconscious ones, is defective. This is sometimes expressed by saying that the neurotically anxious person "lives too close to his unconscious." In other words, his functional boundaries are too permeable. His defenses do not limit ade-quately the influence of potentially intrusive unconscious processes.

Split-level functioning. This is something which is always related to partial regression. We discussed it in Chapter 6. Whenever ego boundaries are defective, there is always the possibility that some current adult situation, with its adult object relationships and experiences, will also arouse infantile object relationships and experiences which correspond emotionally to the adult ones. We have pointed out that this is most obvious in manifest dreams. In both manifest dreams and neurotic symptoms, we find reactivated childhood and infantile impulses, fantasies, conflicts and frustrations, which are much more successful in invading preconscious organizations than in the case of the normal adult who is awake. Split-level functioning is not limited to anxiety reactions. It may occur in any of the neuroses, in psychoses, and in personality disorders.

Symptom formation in anxiety reactions. In anxiety reactions the infantile and childhood versions do not *themselves* appear in conscious experience. The defensive organization succeeds in repressing the infantile impulses, conflicts, fantasies and frustrations, that is, in keeping them unconscious. When they do break through into conscious or preconscious experience, they are usually limited to frightening dreams, irrational impulses, inexplicable inhibitions, apprehensions or anxiety attacks.

The *indirect derivatives* of the unconscious processes, however, including derivatives of the *unconscious defenses* and the *superego,* do get through. Some of these constitute the *neurotic symptom.* For one thing, as we have seen, patients with anxiety reactions are fully aware of being vigilant and exhausted, of being constantly alert for something which they cannot identify and do not understand. The vigilant alertness is a derivative of the high pitch at which the patient's defensive forces are operating; it is also a measure of the pressures being exerted by unconscious ego, id and superego processes. The patient feels exhausted because of this defensive effort, and because of the physical exertion necessary just to work off the internally generated tensions. The alternative to this defensive physical exertion would be that of experiencing a living nightmare, such as Edgar R. experienced in his panic reaction.

The necessity for being alert and vigilant is itself disturbing to ego integration. Even at normal levels, tension and anxiety tend to narrow one's range of perception and cognition, and to restrict or suspend action. Patients with anxiety reactions are also vividly aware of their somatic discharge processes. They usually interpret these as signs of organic disease, or of beginning insanity. And, finally, the simultaneous occurrence of adult experience, along with derivatives of infantile or childhood experiences, is likely to confuse the patient, and to make a good deal of what he does seem mixed up and irrational — as, in fact, it often is.

Our oil geologist patient was painfully aware of his exhausting vigilance, of his frightening somatic symptoms and of his seeming to be irrational and mixed up. He was aware that he could not relax or even sit still, and that every so often he would have attacks in which something terrible seemed about to happen. He knew that he was at times overwhelmed by vague but intense fears of some catastrophe — that he would die, lose control or go insane. His anxiety attacks, which were massive somatic discharges of an infantile character, occurred always during states of consciousness, just as clear as those of a nonneurotic person who faces environmental danger. Our patient was fully aware of their actual violence and of the fright they gave him.

Yet this otherwise intelligent and capable man remained completely unaware, until therapy was well under way, that any of this was related to his mode of living or to his childhood traumas. His defensive forces did not prevent his attempting to act out his childhood conflicts. They did not protect him against experiencing excessive tension and anxiety directly. They did succeed in keeping repressed the infantile processes that generated the tension. Thus his ego defenses kept him in ignorance of the *sources* of the urges which confused and frightened him, and of his superego attempts to oppose and punish these urges. All of this remained unconscious, inaccessible to him. He looked upon it as a sign that he was suffering from some mysterious disease for which he was in no way responsible.

The confusion commonly experienced in anxiety reactions is in part a direct result of the tension and anxiety. Any apprehensive, tense person can become more easily confused than a relaxed and confident one. In part, however, as we have indicated, the confusion represents an actual mingling of childhood motivation with adult motivation, of object relationships and orientations belonging to childhood with those belonging to adulthood. Whenever a current adult situation resembles a basic conflictual situation of childhood, the neurotically anxious adult tries to respond to both at once, although he is conscious only of the current adult situation. Such responses stand little chance of satisfying either adult needs or childhood longings. The anxious person finds himself repeatedly doing things which he thinks he does not want to do, things that defeat his adult ends.

Walter A. showed this confusion in most of his relationships with men and women. As an adult male, he was interested in women and attracted to them; as the resentful son of a deceiving mother, he scorned them and sought only to seduce them, to demonstrate that all women were like his mother. As a person who had been reared to regard everything sexual as sinful, his feelings of interest in women and his attraction to them seeemd wicked and dangerous. As an adult man, he was drawn toward other men as friends; but as the resentful son of an unfaithful father, he tried to spite them all by making love to their wives. Under these conditions it was impossible for him to achieve the security of adult friendship and affection.

A specific emotional trauma in adolescence, such as Walter A. suffered, is by no means the necessary antecedent of an adult anxiety reaction. Adolescence is frequently a critical phase of maturation, during which unresolved edipal and pre-edipal conflicts may be revived and worked through afresh, as preparation for assuming a fully adult role. If a severe adolescent trauma is experienced, the intensity and duration of its effect will depend upon the total situation at the time and upon how well edipal and pre-edipal conflicts had been resolved earlier in life.

The pattern of Walter A.'s neurotic behavior is also not the standard pattern for all anxiety reactions. It is only one example in which the basic symptomatology of apprehension and somatic discharge was exceptionally clear. In a great many cases of anxiety reaction there appears to have been a reasonably well worked-through adolescence and a satisfactory marital relationship. What seems to be a common factor in all cases is a hyper-sensitivity to tension-provoking stimulation and a reaction-sensitivity to respond with diffuse apprehension and somatic discharge. We have discussed some possible origins of such sensitivities in the chapters on personality development.

There are some sources of neurotic anxiety which are more regressive, more infantile, than those we have been discussing. These may not involve guilt because they present reactivations of developmental phases before even a primitive superego precursor had been differentiated. The anxiety seems to come from fears of becoming completely helpless, of being abandoned or even of ceasing to exist. Such dangers arise when regression moves back toward the symbiotic mother-child phase, in which the child had not yet become a separate individual. If this unconscious fear is revived in anxiety reactions, it is only incidental and momentary, because the neurotic defense structure of these patients is strong enough to protect them from profound regression. It may play a leading role, however, in certain of the psychoses, where patients sometimes express the fear clearly and consistently.

Repetition of nonadaptive behavior in spite of failure

The myth is slow in dying that only adaptive or "successful" behavior persists in the long run. The history of magic and ritual has contradicted it for thousands of years. Practices which for aeons have failed to influence natural processes are still carried on today, all over the world, as if their success were unquestionable. Even in our present-day industrial society, with all its science and sophistication, millions of educated persons rely upon magical practices in certain areas of their lives. They engage in ritualistic maneuvers, for example, in efforts at controlling health, prosperity and the weather. Laboratory and field studies have shown that animals, also, perform complex tasks merely for the sake of performing them or, at least, without reinforcement from conventional laboratory rewards. Nevertheless, the repetition of nonadaptive behavior by neurotically anxious patients deserves special comment, since it brings them the extra punishment of intolerable tension and anxiety, which they do not want and do not enjoy.

From all that has been said in the preceding section it is obvious that poorly repressed unconscious forces can introduce strange contradictions into adult attitudes, that they confuse present issues with forgotten childhood issues, and that they sustain the fruitless, self-defeating repetition of non-adaptive behavior. In its futility and apparent senselessness neurotic behavior often shows the kind of dogged determination, the narrowness and the inflexibility that we usually associate with animal instinct. Why is it that neurotically anxious persons get into such hopeless situations over and over? And why is it that otherwise intelligent — sometimes extremely intelligent — adults keep on repeating futile, frustrating behavior when it is doomed to failure?

At first glance it seems as though neurotic patients get into anxiety-provoking situations wholly by accident. A careful study of the life situations of the patient, however, and where possible a study of his dreams, daydreams and fantasies, reveal quite a different picture. Chance does play a part, of course, as it does in the mishaps of everyone. But in addition we find that certain conflictual situations attract these individuals, possess a special fascination for them, of which they are nearly always unaware. They are unconsciously preoccupied with unresolved conflicts, and this preoccupation pushes them into situations that allow their conflicts some degree of expression. In fact, they themselves often help to create such situations out of whatever interpersonal relationships present themselves, as in the case of Walter A. In many cases such a propensity becomes a major therapeutic problem.

Why should an intelligent adult throw himself into conflictual situations, or even help to create them, when they lead only to further tension and anxiety? Why should he go on repeating behavior that always ends in frustration, futility and suffering? An obvious answer is that it is because he does not know what he is doing or why. Usually this is true; occasionally it is not. Sometimes a patient says openly that he knows what he is doing and where it will lead; yet he cannot seem to avoid it. He feels irresistibly propelled into a repetition of the old futile pattern, and it is this irresistible impulse that he does not and cannot understand until he has worked it through in therapy.

Whether or not the patient is able to verbalize what he is doing and what attracts him, the basic situation is the same. He is impelled to repeat his futile, frustrating behavior — in overt action or in fantasy or daydream — because of the relentless pressure of unconscious infantile urges, fears, temptations and conflicts. To these may be added the attractions of more or less conscious daydreams and adult motivational patterns. These pressures and these attractions demand attempts at finding gratification. Adult situations that resemble the childhood conflictual ones rekindle hope and seem to promise satisfaction. But when they end once more in failure there is not only the tension of unrelieved desire to be mastered but also the anxiety aroused by the opposition of a reactivated childish superego.

Thus we see the neurotically anxious person trying over and over to revive childhood object relations with adults in adult situations. These attempts are all regressive in character and they include the participation of primitive superego components. The patient unconsciously assumes an infantile role and yearns for reciprocal role behavior corresponding to his infantile role. Such yearning is foredoomed to be frustrated, since the adult is rare who can derive any satisfaction from meeting infantile needs in another adult. The inevitable frustration of the patient leads to the tensions of infantile rage, and the rage, with its primitive fantasies of revenge, leads to overwhelming guilt and the fear of retaliation. The guilt and the fear sometimes have realistic roots, when the patient acts out the products of his unconscious conflicts, as our oil geologist did. The end-results of all this confusion over motive, emotion and object, are the repetitious, unintelligible behavior on the patient's part, and the anger, irritability or retaliation on the part of the baffled adults around him.

Childhood identification with prevailing patterns

As we saw in the chapters on personality development, early introjection and identification lead to an unconscious adoption of the patterns prevailing in the home. The earliest phase, we said, is that of forming a partial fusion or confusion with a mother image (*symbiotic mother-child unit*). In this the infant shares experiences with his mother within the limits of the opportunities she gives him and in accordance with his ability to utilize them. The later phase is that of dissolving this psychological fusion. The child separates off more or less as an individual. During this later phase the infant internalizes some of the experiences shared with his mother. These experiences become encapsulated within his own ego boundaries as ego introjects and ego identifications. Through processes of identification he continues throughout life to internalize similar experiences as partial identifications, or as modifications of existing identifications.

Anxious attitudes can be internalized as well as secure ones. Anxious adults usually make anxious parents and help create an atmosphere of uneasiness in the home. When this is so, they provide concrete models of anxiety for identification. A child, even before he has formed object relationships, and long before he is able to single out or understand what is disturbing him, may reflect the prevailing insecurity of his home in his own tension and anxiety. We know that babies who are being held by tense, anxious or angry mothers become themselves so tense that they cannot feed; and we know that this situation can be remedied if the baby is handed over to a reasonably relaxed woman for feeding. Even domestic animals develop tension and anxiety in the presence of anxious, tense adults. An apprehensive or distrustful master is likely to have an apprehensive or distrustful dog.

Identification with prevailing patterns never cease to influence individual susceptibilities to tension and anxiety. This was brought out in many dramatic forms during World War II. In the bombing of Britain, for example, adult manifestations were more effective in making children anxious than was the terrific barrage of noise, fire and demolition.[7] Among the military, in American flying and ground personnel, the influence of leaders upon the morale of groups facing the continual danger of death was also found often to determine the prevailing patterns of tension and anxiety in the groups.[8] Identification and the prevailing pattern seem to be especially important determiners of security and insecurity among children and subordinates, among weak, submissive or ignorant persons, in their relationship to adults, leaders, the strong, dominant and well-informed.

In the following clinical illustration we see an anxious, insecure girl grow to womanhood, encounter serious difficulties, and react to them with an anxiety pattern which she had witnessed all her life in her mother.

The patient, a woman of thirty, had seemed nervous and apprehensive as a child. She had slept poorly and cried easily. As far back as she could remember she had lived in daily dread of her mother's sudden death and the loss of her home. The mother, from the time of the patient's birth, had suffered from "heart attacks" and shortness of breath, cause unknown. When upset the mother would often say that one day she would be found dead, "just like your grandmother was." The grandmother's death had made a profound impression upon the patient; her mother's threat never failed to disturb her. This was the specific pattern of insecurity in which she grew up.

At twenty-two she married a stable and responsible older man. He died four years later, a year after they had lost their only child through tuberculous meningitis. Following this the patient nursed her brother through a year of pulmonary tuberculosis until he recovered. During this period she learned of the dangers of contact infection and suspected that her child had died because of exposure to her brother's illness. She found herself thinking that the brother could have kept away from home, or died himself, instead of being the cause of her only child's death. She began hating the sight of her brother, while she was still looking after him, and blaming herself as well as him for letting her child die. In this setting of marked ambivalence and guilt she began having "heart attacks" and shortness of breath. She was now afraid that she would die just as she had feared in childhood that her mother would. She herself realized that her attacks duplicated those of her mother.

Childhood training in anxiety

Children can be *trained* to be tense and anxious by parents who are not themselves especially anxious persons. An overprotective parent, for example, may train a small child to be habitually apprehensive by making sudden protective lunges and by giving continual warnings of danger. Adults

[7] Freud, A., and Burlingham, D. T., *War and Children*. New York: Willard, 1943.
[8] Janis, I., *Air War and Emotional Stress*. New York: McGraw-Hill, 1951.

who, for cultural or personal reasons, are especially alert to strange noises and strange people, or who are too dramatic about ordinary precautions, such as crossing the street when there is traffic, may instill chronic anxiety in a child long before he is able to identify what the danger is about which his mother is warning him. Horror stories, ghost stories and tales of disaster and destruction can have similar effects upon the very young if they open up frightening dangers against which the child feels powerless to defend himself.

Older children are sometimes *taught systematically to ferret out* in imagination every hidden danger that might conceivably lurk in an apparently innocent situation. They learn to think always in terms of the future but never to have confidence in it, to cross bridges before coming to them, and to imagine each bridge collapsing the moment they give it their full weight. By such procedures growing children build into their personality structure tense, uneasy attitudes of anticipation which may interfere with their seeking out the activities they need to become socially mature.

Some parents make the mistake of trying to foster social maturity in their child by *parading adult problems, uncertainties* and *disillusionments* continually before him — doubts concerning food and shelter, financial and business worries, adult social strivings, and parental discord that divides his loyalties and threatens his most fundamental source of security. The child has many difficulties of his own to work out, difficulties that belong to his own age. He needs *protection* from adult uncertainty and adult disappointment so that he may be free to build his security in relation to childhood responsibilities among his elders and his peers. Otherwise a child grows into adulthood prematurely frightened by its threatening aspects and overwhelmed by its burdens. He has learned adult apprehensions before acquiring the strength, social skill and emotional maturity needed to meet and to master the problems of adulthood.

Parental perfectionism can also lead to training in anxiety. Many chronically tense, anxious adults have been reared in homes dominated by incessant demands for better and better conduct, more and more achievement, higher and higher aspiration. They have been led to adopt ambitions and set goals for which they have neither special aptitude nor personal interest. If a person is trained to strive always beyond and above what is possible for him, to expect nothing short of perfection and completeness, he can be certain only of one thing, that no matter what he achieves or what he gets he will never gain lasting satisfaction.

Overpermissive parents, like domineering and restrictive ones, are likely to have anxious children. This is because children need a stable framework within which to develop their behavior. Children often seek out actively the limits within which they may act freely. They feel freer and more secure with parents who set limits for them, who in effect function as their ego substitutes. Self-control has to be learned, just as the control of one's movements have to be learned. The child who finds out where he must stop, who discovers a dependable framework for his freedom, can afford to act and think freely within it.

If a child is allowed to do anything in the world that he can, the world of possibility becomes dangerous, because there are so many dangerous possibilities for action and imagination. One has only to listen to a small child talking with other small children, when imagining becomes competitive, to discover how far this thinking can go in dangerous and antisocial directions.

To have parents who allow a great deal of freedom, but can be depended upon to set limits when necessary, is to have freedom without fear. Even adults find freedom a burden sometimes. The phenomenon of flight from freedom in dangerous and troubled times, such as the present, has been the subject of much fruitful study.[9]

Guilt in anxiety reactions

In most anxiety reactions *guilt* plays a prominent role. Sometimes it is experienced consciously, as having done wrong, as having a bad conscience, or just as being unworthy and inferior. Guilt operates most powerfully, however, at *unconscious levels*, that is, in the form of increased tension between ego and superego systems. Ego defenses protect a person from the full impact of superego aggression. All he may feel is anxiety, tension and fright, without being aware that it is his system of morality, which is a part of his superego, that is exerting pressure, because of what he is doing or saying or thinking.

Superego functioning, like ego functioning, becomes conscious only intermittently; but it operates unconsciously all the time. As we said in Chapter 5, the superego provides an essential source of continual self-control, of prejudging behavior, and of assessing present and past behavior or experience. Without adequate superego functioning at automatic, unconscious levels a person is without dependable, automatic standards of conduct, without a normal capacity for having social perspective and remaining dependably civilized. The superego is close to parental models, but it is also close to everyday action. Its effects are weakest in normal persons during sleep (although, as we have seen, even dreams show superego influences) and in fantasies and daydreams, which frequently provide a welcome release from strict superego standards.

There are numerous ways in which a child can become *chronically guilty*. (1) One of these is to *identify* early in life with a chronically guilty parent, that is, by superego identification. It is normal and necessary to identify with the superego hierarchies of one's parents and other authority figures. But when a person's parents or important authority figures are abnormally guilty themselves, the identification can be a misfortune. When parents seem to violate their own standards without remorse, a child's previous superego

9 Fromm, E., *Escape from Freedom*. New York: Rinehart, 1941; Fromm, E., *The Sane Society*. New York: Rinehart, 1955.

identifications can suffer from serious confusion, as was the case with our oil geologist whose moralistic parents later were divorced.

(2) Another way in which a child can become chronically guilty is through *being punished, neglected* or *depreciated* too much. We have mentioned before that small children feel that a *punished* child must be a *bad child*, not that children are punished because they have done wrong. They also feel that *neglect* means *unworthiness in themselves,* and not irresponsibility in their parents. Children learn to react to themselves and their behavior as *others* react to them. Therefore *parental depreciation* leads almost inevitably to *self-depreciation;* and *self-depreciation,* like unmerited neglect and over-strictness, lead to a *sense of inferiority, worthlessness* and *chronic guilt.*

(3) A third path to chronic guilt is that of being *trained to search one's conscience* for signs of badness. This also appeared in the childhood history of our patient, Walter A. Each night when he was put to bed, he was required to parade his childish fantasies and deeds before his mother and, with her help, to pick out the evil in them. The outcome of such a procedure is to make a child hypersensitive to his own wrongdoing, and to make him anxious when he is on the threshold of sleep and dreaming. As we have seen, it does not ensure a child's growing up into a stable, well-integrated citizen. It makes sure that a person will feel guilty, but not that his life will be a better one than that of persons less sensitive to the evil in them.

(4) Anxiety reactions also arise in persons who, as children, had a *seductive parent.* The usual picture of the seductive parent is that of one who unconsciously tempts a child and then, when the child reacts to the temptation, rebuffs or punishes him, without being aware of having been in the least seductive. The child feels that he is bad because he is punished or rebuffed; he has this experience repeatedly; and he acquires an expectation that he will be treated in such a manner whenever he responds to similar behavior. He thus becomes easily tempted, because of his early exposure to temptation when his self-control was not adequately developed, and he becomes easily guilty because he has learned that he is a bad or punished child. One sees this situation often enough actually in the treatment of children to believe it when it comes up more indirectly during the treatment of adult anxiety reactions. There is also a substantial clinical literature on this situation.[10]

Adult defensive maneuvers in anxiety reactions

Generalized diffuse discharge of tension. Neurotic anxiety reactions develop in persons who are hypersensitive to tension-provoking stimulation, whether this comes from outside the organism or is internally generated.

[10] Johnson, A. M. and Szurek, S., "The genesis of antisocial acting out in children and adults," *Psychoanal. Quart.,* 1952, *21,* 323–341; Litin, E. M., Giffin, M. E., and Johnson, A. M., "Parental influence in unusual behavior in children," *Psychoanal. Quart.,* 1956, *25,* 37–55; Johnson, A. M., "Sanctions for superego lacunae of adolescents," in Eissler, K. R. (Ed.), *Searchlights on Delinquency.* New York: Internat. Univ. Press, 1949, pp. 225–245.

When tension and anxiety become intolerable, and ego disintegration threatens, the patient discharges tensions massively through general somatic and emotional channels. This may take the form of general overactivity or somatic muscle tension, such as we see in the so-called "high-strung" person; or it may take the form of temper tantrums, crying spells and the like. It is easy to recognize the infantile character of these reactions. They are like the paroxysms of rage and fear that are common in early childhood. This similarity is greater in anxiety attacks than in chronic anxiety reactions. The imperious, angry demands for immediate relief which our patient, Walter A., made during his anxiety attacks in the therapeutic situation are clear examples. Even more so were his almost reflex nursing movements which he had discovered gave him some relief. All of this discharge in heightened activity and muscle tension was really infantile and regressive.

The relative lack of symptom structure in anxiety reactions will become clearer after we have seen how phobics, conversion patients and compulsives handle their tension and anxiety. Perhaps patients have anxiety reactions because they have never given up their infantile mode of diffuse discharge under stress. What they succeed in doing is to regress partially, without suffering the *subtotal regression* which we shall witness in the psychoses.

Defective repression. Repression is always defective in anxiety reactions. It is true that the internal *sources* of the heightened tension and anxiety remain repressed and unconscious; but their *effects* are painfully and consciously experienced. Walter A. was incapable of dealing with his unconscious fantasies, unconscious conflicts and unconscious superego pressures, because they remained inaccessible to him. They were all repressed. In spite of its defects, in spite of the fact that the tension and anxiety came through, Walter's repression did protect him from primitive experiences which, if they had come to him all at once and in the absence of therapeutic help, might well have precipitated a sweeping regression into psychosis. As it was, each time that he carried out some activity, or indulged in certain fantasies, he became intolerably anxious without knowing why.

Regression in anxiety reactions. The regression which patients suffer when they experience their symptoms is *defensive* in that it allows them to function in certain respects at a less mature level than they normally would. It allows them to relieve their intolerable tension and anxiety through an infantile discharge, an emotional storm which they characteristically attribute to physical disease. This gives them the chance to get physical care, which can be exceptionally rewarding to a person who has unsatisfied and unconscious dependency needs. There is some danger in regression. We saw this danger realized in the case of Edgar R., who lost his precarious hold on reality and developed a psychosis.

Projection in anxiety reactions. The projection that occurs in anxiety reactions is usually diffuse and nonspecific. This is quite different from the projection in phobias and paranoid reactions, as we shall see. Patients nearly always *ascribe* their tension and anxiety to some unknown danger threatening them from the outside, or else to some bodily disease which they conceive of as being within the organism, but not within the personality system. The *actual* danger to such persons is that of a breakthrough of unconscious forces. Some patients who are suffering from an anxiety reaction do complain that they think they are going crazy; but such a complaint is seldom a recognition of the actual threat of a breakthrough. It is usually a way of describing the inner turmoil and the nameless fear, and it is usually also a bid for reassurance which they may need.

Anxiety reactions are restricted in scope. The regression, the defects in repression, and the diffuse projection, are all restricted in scope in the anxiety reactions, unless a patient reaches a panic reaction. Most of the ego organization remains *conflict-free* most of the time. It does not undergo a general disintegration. Thus, even though the functional boundaries are defective, the defensive organization holds together well enough to prevent a wholesale invasion of secondary process organizations by primary process material. There is no general disorganization, except in the rare panic states, and there are no delusions or hallucinations.

The nearest thing to a loss in reality-testing occurs (*a*) when a patient feels that danger is threatening him from all sides, when actually there is no danger, excepting from his own internally generated tension, and (*b*) when a patient misinterprets his disturbed physiological functioning as the sign of serious illness or the imminence of sudden death. The first relates anxiety reactions to paranoid psychoses; the second relates them to psychosomatic disorders. As we shall see, when we come to consider these illnesses in later chapters, the anxiety reaction is usually a relatively benign process.[11]

Primary gain and secondary gain

In all of the neuroses it is necessary to distinguish between primary and secondary gain. The *primary gain* is the reduction in tension and anxiety which makes it possible for the patient to preserve the greater part of his integration. This is achieved in anxiety reactions, as we have seen, by the direct discharge of tension through general somatic and emotional channels. Such a maneuver is only moderately successful because the defensive discharges themselves disturb the patient. They often increase a patient's anxiety instead of disposing of it. If the patient then experiences a violent discharge in an anxiety attack, he may become still further frightened. The primary gain in anxiety reactions cannot be regarded as a permanent solution, such as many other neurotic compromises are, which construct a stable symptom.

The *secondary gain* in any neurosis consists of whatever advantages the

[11] Cf. Stevenson, I., "Processes of 'spontaneous' recovery from the psychoneuroses," *Amer. J. Psychiat.*, 1961, *117*, 1057–1064.

patient gets out of being neurotic, once his neurosis has been established. The secondary gain is therefore the result of a neurosis and not, as many people suppose, its source. Secondary gain plays a small role in anxiety reactions. The patient suffering from an anxiety reaction remains subject to chronic anxiety, in spite of his discharge processes; he may suffer from acute anxiety attacks as well. What secondary gain does show up in anxiety reactions is generally in the form of demands that other people avoid behavior which makes the patient tense and anxious. This tends to limit the freedom of other people, to make them feel guilty, and thus to give the patient a certain amount of control over them. He may, for example, insist that others agree with him in order to avoid stirring up his anger. He may refuse to be burdened with responsibilities on the grounds that he is too anxious to meet them. But these are small rewards. As we shall see in the chapters that follow, other neurotic patterns are better suited for achieving secondary gains.

Therapy as a way out

Psychotherapy offers the neurotically anxious person certain opportunities which ordinary interpersonal relationships do not. A trained, experienced therapist is able to hear about episodes of anxiety, and to observe them, without himself becoming anxious. He feels no need to offer the patient verbal reassurance, as other persons usually do. He is in a position to determine whether or not the symptoms indicate possible physiopathology or organic disease, as well as an anxiety reaction. He can make intelligent referrals if necessary. Above all, he is skilled in the art of intelligent listening, in knowing when to be silent and when to speak. He can participate freely in the patient's feelings without being drowned in them. He is not tempted to give premature conclusions or to sound omniscient. Whether he is to spend one hour with the patient, a dozen hours, or several hundred hours, the most significant contributions to the therapeutic relationship that a therapist can make will be his specific skills, his understanding, flexibility, self-restraint and mature empathy.

The best hope there is for a patient with an anxiety reaction, his best hope of escaping from it, lies in working through some of his basic conflicts, his repetitious, futile, driven behavior, as this shows up in current situations and in the therapeutic hours. He needs to become desensitized to his frightening symptoms. He can achieve this in part by discovering some of their origins, and thus gaining control over them. He can achieve it in part by unconsciously identifying with his therapist, who accepts the symptoms with quiet interest, instead of trying to counteract them with reassurance, or sharing in the fears that the patient expresses.

In time, the patient should be able to recognize his own maneuvers for what they are, as he attempts to cast others, including his therapist, in roles that seem to promise satisfaction of his neurotic needs. Eventually, the anachronistic and unrealistic nature of these needs may dawn upon him. When this happens, the patient faces the bleak disillusionment of realizing that, no matter how imperious they may seem, his infantile needs can never find full gratification in adult role relationships.

The work of therapy in anxiety reactions, like the *work of mourning*, is likely to proceed slowly. There may be an initial symptomatic improvement; but it seldom lasts. The process of desensitization, of understanding and finally accepting the disillusionment, usually requires a great deal of repetition of the symptomatology, before the obstacles to maturation and new learning begin to dissolve. This kind of work is best begun in a therapeutic relationship. As a rule, such a relationship needs to be continued for some time before the patient is ready to carry on his personality growth alone. What we call *the therapeutic process*, if it is successfully initiated and carried forward, is likely to continue long after the period of actual interpersonal contact has ceased. In our case of the oil geologist it apparently went on for at least another decade. We shall have more to say about the processes involved in psychotherapy when we come to the last chapter of the book.

Anxiety reactions in relation to other neuroses

Tension and anxiety are fundamental to all neuroses. What we have been saying about the dynamic and developmental background of anxiety reactions applies also to the other neuroses. Anxiety reactions are distinguished from the other neuroses by their almost complete lack of a stable symptom organization, one that can absorb or express forbidden impulses, unconscious fantasies, infantile conflicts and superego pressures. These remain unconscious for the most part; but the tension and anxiety are openly experienced. The patient tries to reduce them by resorting to the relatively infantile processes of direct discharge through general somatic and emotional channels.

Clinically, one finds minor symptomatic expressions belonging to one or another neurosis, such as a mild or changeable phobic, conversion, dissociative or compulsive component. The mood may be mildly depressive or mildly elated. But the overall picture is dominated by a conscious awareness of tension and anxiety, and by obvious discharge processes involving both the skeletal musculature and the viscera. Usually, the patient does not recognize the origins of his symptoms in forbidden impulses, fantasies, conflicts or guilt.

As we turn now to a consideration of phobic reactions, we turn from such a relative lack of symptomatic structure to a kind of organized symptom which is often highly effective in disposing of tension and anxiety, as long as certain definite conditions are fulfilled.

8

Phobic Reactions

✛

PHOBIAS ARE SPECIFIC PATHOLOGICAL FEARS. THEY SOMETIMES BEGIN WITH
an anxiety attack; but once this has been mastered, the patient crystallizes
his anxiety around some external object or situation, which he then avoids
as much as possible. Unlike persons suffering from anxiety reaction, the
phobic believes that he knows what arouses his intolerable anxiety, even
though it may seem as irrational to him as it does to others.[1] The phobic
usually does not complain of aches, pains, visceral disturbances or confusion
of thinking. As long as he can avoid the external object or situation to which
he has become sensitized he remains relatively free from tension and anxiety.
His symptoms therefore fall into two general groups: techniques of avoiding
whatever seems to provoke anxiety, and attacks of anxiety whenever his
attempts at avoidance fail, and the anxiety-provoking object or situation
confronts him.

Phobias are so familiar to the general public that we can postpone giving
clinical examples until we take up specific cases in detail. Their dramatic
and sometimes mysterious qualities have made them favorite literary and
journalistic themes. Phobias include the irrational fear of height, of enclosed
places and wide open spaces, of animal life, sharp pointed things, darkness,
wind and lightning, and hundreds of special, personal fears. Logical reason-

---

[1] Panel report, Ferber, L. (reporter), "Phobias and their vicissitudes", *J. Amer.
Psychoanal. Ass.*, 1959, 7, 182–192; Grinker, R. R., and Spiegel, J., *Men Under Stress.*
Philadelphia: Blakiston, 1945, p. 98; Greenson, R. R., "Phobia, anxiety and depression,"
J. Amer. Psychoanal. Ass., 1959, 7, 663–674.

ing rarely helps a phobic to overcome his fear; reassurance does him no permanent good. Even a clear, objective demonstration that a fear is groundless seldom alleviates it; often it only increases the phobia's intensity. For although phobias are usually irrational, they are never actually groundless. Something is really threatening the patient, something from within of which he is unaware. This may not be objectively demonstrable; but neither is a toothache or a feeling of distrust.

Phobia is sometimes called the normal neurosis of childhood. At one time or another almost every little child develops an irrational, more or less specific fear, which persists awhile and then disappears. One day he treats something in his environment with pleasure or with indifference; the next day he may be intensely fearful of it and remain fearful for some time. This can happen at almost any age, early in life, but it seems to be especially common during the period of edipal conflict, that is, during the period when a child is working through his complex emotional relationships with his parents in his fourth and fifth years.

It is often possible to account for the small child's selection of what frightens him, on the basis of some incident or accident.[2] Often, however, this is not possible. Even when it is, the intensity and the persistence of the fear are difficult to explain. We are justified in assuming that other factors, other fears, internally generated and externally projected, must be at work — as we know they are in adult phobias. A great many otherwise normal adults retain some small remnant of an irrational childhood fear, for example, a mild uneasiness while crossing a wide street, or when shut in a small room, some discomfort while looking down from a height even when there is a strong protective railing to lean on, some tendency to pull back from strangers or strange animals, and so on. Seldom can such fears be dismissed as innate; they nearly always have a personal history.[3]

The line is difficult to draw between normal, persistent fears, or between the insignificant remnants in adults of their infantile fears, and the definitely *phobic fear*. There are undoubtedly thousands of adults living in relative peace in spite of one or two minor phobias. We come upon them every now and then by accident, just as we come upon persons with mild anxiety reactions. The minor phobia may restrict a person's freedom somewhat, since he has to avoid whatever seems to be "off limits" for him; but what he has to give up appears to him trifling in comparison with the anxieties

[2] See the interesting and imaginative account in W. E. Leonard's *The Locomotive God*. In spite of its involving fiction as well as fact, this work is often cited as though it were a case report. See also Monsour, K. J., "School phobia in teachers," *Amer. J. Orthopsychiat.*, 1961, *31*, 347–355; Rachmann, S., and Costello, C. G., "The aetiology and treatment of children's phobias: a review," *Amer. J. Psychiat.*, 1961, *118*, 97–105.

[3] For a discussion of innate factors, see Schur, M., "The ego and the id in anxiety," *Psychoanal. Study Child*, 1958, *13*, 190–220, and the bibliography he cites there; Lorenz, K., "The nature of instincts," in Schiller, C. (Ed.), *Instinctive Behavior*. New York: Internat. Univ. Press, 1957; Lorenz, K., *King Solomon's Ring*. London: Methuen, 1952; Thorpe, W. H., *Learning and Instincts in Animals*. Cambridge, Mass.: Harvard Univ. Press, 1956.

he avoids. He is like a person with a specific food allergy who keeps comfortable and well by eliminating something from his diet. It is only when the protective devices in a phobia fail, when fear generalizes and feared things multiply, or when a feared situation for some reason has to be faced, that a person with a minor phobia or a phobic remnant comes for therapeutic help.

Definition. A phobic reaction is an attempt to reduce internally generated tension and anxiety by a process of displacement, projection and avoidance. The displacement and projection take the form of an irrational fear of some external situation; and this object or situation is then systematically avoided.

Phobias persist because they are adaptive; they achieve something, even though what they achieve is neurotic. They are a means of binding excess tension and anxiety, of displacing and projecting, of protecting the patient from having to experience a succession of internally generated anxiety attacks.[4] We call the adaptation in phobias *irrational* because the manifest object of the fear — the conscious referent — is not the major source of tension and anxiety, but only a substitute, a scapegoat. The phobia helps the patient to conceal from himself and to deny his basic conflicts, his shortcomings and his sense of guilt, by the use of mechanisms which focus the blame on something outside him. We shall have more to say about this after we have examined a number of specific phobias.

Varieties of Phobic Reaction

Almost any object, act, situation or relationship can be made the focus of a manifest phobic reaction. Chance may play some part in the selection of the specific focus; but chance is never the whole story. Phobias are always overdetermined. The conscious referent of the phobia — the external something of which the patient is irrationally afraid — always has multiple symbolic meanings that represent the internal, unconscious conflict.

The *dynamic organization* of all phobias, regardless of their different referents, is basically the same. This fact may be briefly summarized at this point as follows. (1) In the background there is always the *danger* that ego integration will be destroyed by internally generated emotional tensions and anxiety. (2) Contributing to this danger is a *defective defense system*, which is incapable of preventing intrusions from unconscious ego, id and superego processes. (3) These intrusions are crystallized in the form of *fearful fantasies*, by the same mechanisms and in the same general way as in the formation of manifest dreams.[5] Finally, (4) these fantasies, usually unconscious and often infantile, are *symbolized as something external*, something that

[4] Cf. Arieti, S., "A re-examination of the phobic symptom and of symbolism in psychopathology," *Amer. J. Psychiat.*, 1961, *118*, 106–110.

[5] Lewin, B., "Phobic symptoms and dream interpretation," *Psychoanal. Quart.*, 1952, *21*, 295–322.

serves as an equivalent for the internal danger — a threatening animal, the brink of a cliff, a storm, mobs, dangerous wide-open or shut-in places. This final displacement and projection completes the phobic symptom formation and gives the patient something tangible that he can avoid.

A list of common phobias

We have said that almost anything, real or imagined, can become the specific excitant for a phobic reaction. This fact has given rise in the past to the wholesale coining of Greek and Greco-Latin terms to designate the excitants. One authority has found over 180 such terms in the literature.[6] In addition to the burden placed upon students of psychopathology, the practice of coining these terms has the disadvantage of stressing the excitant, as though it were the essential ingredient of a phobia, instead of being of secondary importance and sometimes merely incidental. The following list is simply a convenient grouping of common phobic excitants which also gives some idea of their wide range:[7]

1. High places — cliffs, roofs, high windows, airplanes, stair wells, ladders.
2. Enclosed places — small rooms, closets, elevators, alleys, vehicles, shafts, subways, small theaters.
3. Wide-open places — halls, wide streets, squares, fields, parks, beaches, the sea.
4. Animal life — dogs, cats, snakes, frogs, bats, horses, wolves, lions, tigers, spiders, insects, vermin.
5. Weapons — guns, knives, scissors, clubs, picks, axes.
6. Contaminants — dirt, germs, poisons, fishbones, certain foods.
7. Public gatherings — crowds, meetings, lectures, churches, theaters, stadiums, concerts.
8. Vehicles — trains, ships, autos, airplanes, elevators, escalators, buses.
9. Accidents — collisions, crashes, falling trees, bodily injury, mutilation.
10. Natural dangers — storms, wind, waters, lightning, darkness.
11. Strangeness — strangers, unfamiliar places or animals, unidentified sounds and movements, disfigurement, mutilation, blindess in others.
12. Special places, people or situations.

In addition to these objective excitants of phobia there are many imagined dangers which phobic persons cannot actually point out. We have all seen children terror-stricken by nonexistent bogeymen, sandmen and witches, especially during phases of their development when they are experiencing severe internal conflict over sex and aggression. Similarly, adolescents and adults may fear intensely the mere thought of being attacked, trapped, drowned or

[6] English, H. B., and English, A. C., *A Comprehensive Dictionary of Psychological and Psychoanalytical Terms.* New York: Longmans, Green, 1958, p. 388.
[7] There is a certain amount of unavoidable repetition in this list.

buried alive, when there is only a remote danger of such a fate, or no real danger at all. Some persons, because of their phobic attitudes, become irrationally anxious at the mere mention of illness, disease, surgery, bodily injury or death.

Let us now turn to a more detailed description of four representative phobias — fear of height, fear of open spaces, fear of closed places, and fear of animals — in each of which we shall include case illustrations as concrete examples. In each we shall discuss what is feared and why; and then we shall mention the gratifications involved in each phobia. This separation into *the fear* and *the gratification*, although an artificial one, will help us to keep in mind the fact that every phobia combines a promise with a threat, a wish with a fear.

Acrophobia: The Fear of Height

An acrophobic person experiences irrational fear whenever he finds himself on a high place. He may become anxious even when he merely thinks of such a situation. The anxiety varies from a typical *anxiety attack,* such as we have described in the preceding chapter, to an attack of nausea and vertigo, or merely to a mild uneasiness. The acrophobic person avoids going up to high places whenever he can. As long as he is not exposed to his specific fear-excitant he is usually as free from anxiety as a nonphobic person.

The fear

Human beings are not born with an instinctive fear of height. If they were, parents would have an easier time guarding their small children from danger. Nevertheless, almost everyone acquires some fear of height. Children learn through innumerable falls and endless warnings to be somewhat wary of height and to be attentive to their footing. In other words, the pathological fear of high places is related to a realistic danger.

If there were no more to the fear of height than direct learning in concrete situations, fear of height would probably remain a reasonable caution. No pathological acrophobia would develop. But there is another factor to be considered, besides that of concrete learning, and this is the factor of symbolization. Children, as well as adults, are constantly representing things to themselves in symbols — things they see and hear, things they taste, smell and feel, and even such internal changes as shifts in the position of internal organs, and such changes within their personality systems as rises and falls in tension.

Falling in self-esteem and in the esteem of others is also related symbolically with an actual tumble. A child may equate falling on a cement sidewalk with falling, for example, in a beloved parent's favor. The fall in favor is no less painful to him than a physical fall, and he portrays it to himself no

less vividly.[8] With the evolution of more and more mature superego functions, children may find a fall in favor or in self-esteem harder to bear than
a fall from a swing on to hard ground. The fact that the latter is a shared
social episode, and arouses sympathetic responses in others, helps the child
to endure it.

While each of us is learning directly, early in childhood, to avoid the
pain and fright of bad falls, we are also learning indirectly about symbolic
painful and destructive falls from high places. These the child at first
symbolizes and represents to himself as being similar or even identical, in
somewhat the manner that adults symbolize falling from grace or power in
their allegorical speech and writing, in poetry and in caricature. Humpty
Dumpty had a great fall and no one could put him together again. Men
tumble from high places — a workman is demoted, the grocer falls in favor,
a policeman is broken, an official drops in everyone's estimation, a pillar of
the church falls, and so on.

It seems to the child that nobody wants to pick these people up. Adults
often seem pleased with another person's disaster; they even gloat over it.
The child hears of men and women tumbling out of windows, or in front
of subway trains, and learns that they are killed in a terrifying manner. He
hears that a neighbor woman has fallen in the eyes of others who say they
look down on her. Such phraseology is not labeled as metaphorical. It
seems to mean literally what it says. Grownup talk makes it plain that bad
people fall and deserve their fate. We know that, during the early years,
children picture such adult conceptualization quite concretely. It is in part
this primitive concrete imagery — the imagery of allegory, poetry and caricature — which makes up primary process thinking and leads to neurotic symptom formation, as we shall soon see.

Gratifications

So far we have stressed only the painful, destructive side of acrophobia;
but there is also something positive about every neurotic symptom, something
gratifying and attractive. Under certain conditions all normal children enjoy
falling and jumping from a height. Little children love to be thrown into
the air and caught, dropped suddenly from one's knee and safely caught
again, put up on a chair to jump anxiously into daddy's arms. Children have
endless jumping and falling games when they are small, wrestling, tackling
and sliding games. The same child who cries bitterly when he falls accidentally on the way to school will fling himself down on the playground with
glee and abandonment, if this is the game and he does it of his own accord.
Children learn, of course, to limit the distances they jump and fall in accord-

---

[8] Concrete symbol-formation of this kind is most clearly experienced by normal adults
in the visual images of dreams and in the hypnagogic images which appear as we fall
asleep.

ance with the hurts they receive and the degree of excitation they can tolerate
and enjoy. In all of this we see unmistakable evidence of excitement and gratification — giggling, laughing and screaming, insistence upon more and more
— increased tolerance for his anxiety going hand in hand with a child's
intense pleasure.

For adults also there is a thrill in falling and in sailing through the air
that imparts a sense of power and abandon. Normal healthy men and women
travel long distances for the chance to dive into water over and over, or to
make dangerous ski jumps. Millions who cannot do these things delight in
watching others do them on television and movie screens. We need these
reminders of the fascination in jumping and falling if we are to understand
part of the impulse that seizes many phobic persons as they stand on a high
place, part of the impulse that frightens them. For they may be impelled
toward a destructive jump, not alone by archaic, irrational superego pressures, but also by irrational, unconscious fantasies about the powerful pleasures of flight and abandon. Such fantasies in phobias use the same imagery
that motivates high-divers and ski-jumpers; but they may also be linked
with perilous masochistic wishes for self-destruction and the end of everything. A clinical case will illustrate many of these cross-currents as they
actually appear in a phobic patient.

A case of acrophobia or the fear of height

Agnes W., an unmarried woman of thirty, had been unable to go
higher than the second or third floor of any building for a year. Whenever she tried to overcome her fear of height she only succeeded in
provoking intolerable anxiety. She remembered when it all began. One
evening she was working alone at the office when she was suddenly seized
with terror lest she jump or fall out of the open eighth-story window.
So frightened was Agnes by her impulse that she crouched behind a steel
file for some time before she could trust herself to gather up her things
and make for the street. She reached ground level acutely anxious,
perspiring freely, her heart pounding and her breathing rapid.

After this the patient found that as soon as she reached the office
each day her anxiety over height made it impossible to attend properly
to her work. At the end of two months she gave up her position. For a
while she tried unsuccessfully to accustom herself directly to high places.
Finally her need for income drove her to take whatever she could get
within the limitations imposed by her phobia. The result was that she
was downgraded from a confident, well-paid secretary to an unhappy,
poorly paid saleswoman in a store. This was her situation when she came
for treatment.

In therapy it soon came out that Agnes had been deeply involved in
an affair of long standing with a married man who could not, for religious reasons, get a divorce. She found herself caught in a severe
conflict, guilty over her own conduct, too much in love to break off the
liaison, and unable to give up a belief that one day she and her lover

would marry. The crisis came when she was informed that she was pregnant. She told the man that he would have to get a quick divorce and marry her. When he refused she threatened to expose him. A few days before her acute anxiety attack, and the onset of the phobia, she received a farewell letter from him and discovered that he had left town.

Agnes had felt humiliated and angered at having to beg and threaten her lover. His desertion was the final disillusionment. It overwhelmed her with helplessness and hatred. She now concluded that she was no better than a prostitute, and suicide seemed to her the only solution. It was in this setting of shame, fury and abandonment that she became acutely frightened and phobic. She was terrified by her own sudden impulse to leap out of a hopeless situation to her death. When she displaced and projected this fear of suicide to a fear of height she replaced a reasonable fear with an irrational phobia.

The motivation for suicide was multiple. Agnes was impelled to kill herself by a wild desire to avenge herself upon her faithless lover, to punish herself for her sins, perhaps to act out concretely the drama of the fallen woman, and certainly to escape from intolerable anxiety. Instead of giving in to this formidable array of self-destructive impulses, Agnes was able, as we have seen, to mobilize enough realistic ego functioning to flee from the perilous situation to the street. But each time she returned to the office, her intense anxiety also returned. The only way that she was able to avoid it was to stay near ground level. It is noteworthy that she no longer connected her fear of height with her fear of suicide. We saw that in anxiety attacks the patient tends to focus on his discharge symptoms and to ignore what originally aroused his acute anxiety. We now see that in phobias the patient focuses on his fear and ignores what started it. In both cases there is a defensive inability to relate cause and effect.

Phobias are neurotic compromises that partially disable a person but make acute anxiety manageable through the technique of avoidance. By keeping away from heights Agnes kept away from intolerable anxiety and the risk of suicide. She *projected* the danger from her own uncontrollable impulses of self-destruction, of which she was half-aware, on to the impersonal and controllable fear of situations like the one in which she had originally experienced the self-destructive impulse. She *displaced* the upsurge of vengeful hatred toward her lover, which also alarmed her by its force, to a feeling of abhorrence for high places. This feeling of abhorrence, as her therapy brought out, was a mixture of anger and hate, together with an irrational but terrifying fear of superego retaliation.

Phobias have the advantage that, however irrational they may sound, one can admit having them to oneself and to others. This is not true of the impulses, the attitudes and the fears which they conceal. Agnes, for example, could acknowledge her fear of height with only a little embarrassment and perplexity. She could not admit to herself or to others the intensity of her hatred of her lover or her own need for self-punishment. Neither could she accept the fact that she wanted to kill herself, to say nothing of killing the unborn child which she believed she carried. It is not surprising that when she discovered she was not actually pregnant, the discovery did not change her phobic state. The phobia, as we have seen, represented far more than a fear of pregnancy. It represented also her suicidal and homicidal impulses, her feelings of being "a fallen woman," despicable and abandoned, her ambivalent need for punishment and her dread of it.

In such a case as this the reasons for not making a therapeutic assault upon the symptoms are unusually clear. For one thing, this phobia appeared originally as an emergency defense against a situation that not only engendered acute anxiety but also threatened the patient's life. To attempt to remove such a phobia directly, before the patient has begun to deal with her problems, might turn out to be as unwise as to deprive a person in the ocean of his life-belt, before he had learned to float. Therapy should not be directed at destroying neurotic defenses but at working through whatever makes them necessary. In this woman the phobia developed against a background of personality difficulties which were, in the long run, more important than her symptom.

When Agnes learned to recognize and express her ambivalent love and resentment toward her lover, she brought out earlier resentful loving toward other men who, one after the other, had failed her in some way. She shifted her attention from a narrow neurotic symptom and found behind it a broad neurotic pattern of living. It dawned upon her that for more than a decade she had been unable to establish a lasting relationship with any man, even though opportunities had not been lacking. Her curiosity over this personal failing led Agnes quickly into a reconsideration of her life at home.

At home this woman of thirty had been living in the shadow of elderly parents who treated her as an adolescent girl. They expected conformity. When her conduct and opinion met with their approval they gave her warmth and praise; when they disapproved they gave her cold formality and silence. They welcomed the men she brought to the house with courteous hospitality. After a man had come a few times, however, they began pointing out his shortcomings in a gentle, humorous, mocking way, when he had left. Soon Agnes would find herself uncomfortable with him and then ashamed of him. Whatever love-making went on she viewed through her parents' eyes, not through her own. Discomfort and shame soon gave way to a feeling of contempt, and the relationship soon terminated, an outcome which she now began to suspect her parents had always wanted.

Agnes had found that she could avoid this whole pattern, which was really a prolongation of her adolescent conflicts, by seeking the company of men whom she did not have to bring home.[9] She could develop strong and enjoyable attachments as long as her parents were kept in ignorance of them. But now the furtive character of these affairs revived some of her unresolved infantile conflicts and made her feel guilty and afraid. The guilt and fear at the time were fully conscious, but their infantile sources were not. If we add this troubled background of infantile and

[9] The sanctioning of furtive behavior by such parents as these is discussed in Johnson, A., and Szurek, S., "The genesis of antisocial acting out in children and adults," *Psychoanal. Quart.*, 1952, *21*, 323–343.

adolescent conflict to the realities of her supposed pregnancy and her real desertion, we can easily understand why she came close to being swept out of the office window to her death. We can understand also how childish a defense as her phobia, with its multiplicity of meanings, could rescue her from facing such a fate.

Therapy in this case gave Agnes the new experience of being able to talk about her fears, loves, hatreds, conflicts and frustrations to someone who neither praised her nor punished her. The mere presence of an interested unfrightened, noninterfering adult lent her courage. It allowed her the freedom to explore her real and imagined dangers, her desires, ideals, attachments and resentments. Her defenses grew less rigid, and what she was defending against — for example the urge to kill herself and harm her lover — could come to the surface and be mastered. The old conflicts between primitive superego tyranny and her need to be accepted and loved, could be reconsidered and worked through openly in adult terms. The outcome was complete recovery from the phobia, a return to secretarial work and an intelligent dissatisfaction with her emotional immaturity and the home situation that demanded it. She remained mildly depressed over her experience before and during treatment. The personality growth which she was able to achieve with therapeutic help made her ultimate prognosis good.

We have given this case in some detail to illustrate the ways in which phobias speak a symbolic language, just as dreams do. Some of the symbolism the patient understood directly, without interpretation, as her neurotic fears and inhibitions subsided. We do not know for certain why Agnes hit upon acrophobia unless it was because its symbolism best expressed her prevailing fantasies. Had she developed one of the other phobias instead, the dynamic organization behind the symptom would have been much the same.

Let us consider briefly two other possibilities. We know that Agnes shared with most women a strong desire to become pregnant and have a child; but this she also greatly feared. We know that in her predicament, even before she was deserted, she felt trapped, hemmed in on every side. If fantasies built around *these* impulses and fears had dominated her, she might well have developed *claustrophobia,* the fear of enclosed places. On the other hand, Agnes also feared exposure and she feared that her parents would cast her out. She felt consciously that she had been living as a prostitute. If such fantasies and their symbolism had prevailed she might instead have developed an *agoraphobia,* a fear of being alone and unprotected in the open or in the street, with all that these may symbolize. The case of Agnes W. is worth remembering as we turn next to claustrophobia and agoraphobia.

Claustrophobia: The Fear of Being Closed In

The claustrophobic person experiences irrational anxiety whenever he finds himself in an enclosed or narrow place, or whenever he thinks he may not be able to escape from one. In such situations he grows restless, tense, and uneasy; he may sweat and be aware of a rapid heart beat and rapid respiration. He finds he cannot enjoy anything or even think clearly. Sometimes he becomes desperate to escape into the open where all his anxiety symptoms may gradually subside. By avoiding enclosed or narrow places he can often avoid acute anxiety completely. Once more we see a neurotic compromise in which the patient accepts a disability in order to avoid tension and anxiety.

The fear

Claustrophobia is another pathologically acquired fear which, like the fear of height, is related to common realistic dangers. Here the phobic person fears being shut in, trapped, cut off from help and perhaps left to die of hunger and neglect. He may have conscious daydreams of being buried alive, caught in an elevator stuck between floors, or trapped under water in an automobile, an airplane or a steamship. Childhood experiences and stories give form and substance to such fears, while the tales carried by newspapers, illustrated magazines, radio and television reinforce them. A bus plunges into the river, a train into the bay and an airplane into the sea. Everyone aboard is drowned. Children are trapped by cave-ins; adults are left alive to suffocate in mines and submarines. People are cornered and assaulted in narrow alleyways, apartment vestibules or hotel rooms and corridors.

To avoid repetition, let us focus here upon one representative example of claustrophobia, the fear of elevators. An elevator is a tiny steel room which can be so tightly shut that escape is impossible. To be alone in an automatic elevator is to be more completely isolated from human contact and help than anywhere else in ordinary everyday life. For the phobic person it means to be left alone with his dangerous impulses and fantasies, to be deprived of distraction from them and of the freedom to take flight into action. This can be a repetition of his experience of desertion and isolation during infancy, when everyone seemed to disappear, and everything unexpectedly became impersonal and inhuman, and one grew suddenly frightened to the point of infantile panic.

To be shut in alone with an elevator operator means for some phobics to be helpless in the power of an unpredictable stranger or to be in the power of one's own temptations to attack, exhibit or seduce. In a crowded elevator one is surrounded by silent watchers during a period when neither their impulses nor one's own can be controlled or accurately predicted.

Adult patients in therapy sometimes give us a vivid picture of such symbolism. As a patient comes close to his still unconscious conflicts, but is not yet ready to meet and master them, he may suddenly feel trapped and in urgent need to leave. He is aware of nothing but the impulse to get out into the open; and when he leaves he may experience tremendous relief. Actually he is not trapped; he can leave when he likes; no one is threatening him. His therapist makes fewer realistic demands upon him than any other significant figure in his present-day life. In these circumstances the only possible source of anxiety comes from within the organism itself, from the patient's own conscious urges and temptations which the therapeutic process has brought close to consciousness. A brief clinical example in which there is both fear of elevators and fear of the therapeutic situation, will illustrate what has just been said.

Bert C. entered analytic therapy in part because of his fear of elevators. He walked the four flights to his office whenever possible. If he rode in the elevator he was terrified over the possibility of being trapped and of being mutilated or killed in trying to escape. He often pictured these possibilities to himself. As his analysis progressed the fear of elevators was displaced to fear of his therapist's office. It had become clear for some time that Bert was getting close to important repressed material when one day he got up and left the room abruptly before his hour had expired. He explained next time that he had been acutely anxious. Later in the hour he said suddenly, "This room is *flooded* with danger," and again got up and left prematurely. The danger turned out to be a fear that he would assault his therapist and be assaulted in return, or that his therapist would make an unprovoked attack upon him. Long before his transference neurosis had been worked through, his fear of elevators had disappeared.

Gratifications

Solitude, which is so much used as punishment, can also be a highly valued privilege, a condition for freedom from outside interference, an opportunity to be alone with one's fantasies. Some of the most mature and meaningful experiences of adult life depend upon limiting the impact of one's human surroundings to one's own solitary behavior or to that of a chosen companion. Children, as well as adults, like to be able to shut themselves in a room, where they can be free to follow their own impulses without supervision or hindrance. Every normal child invents games in which he is secluded in a small place — a closet, a tent, a cave or simply an enclosure made of furniture.

Many claustrophobic fears originate in situations of infantile and childhood gratifications, situations which may overwhelm a child with excitement and lead to adult discovery and punishment. A child alone, or with another child or two, may be tempted to sexual adventures in the seclusion of a hiding place — under the covers, in closets, bathrooms, basements, attics, cloakrooms, corridors and alleyways. Touching, looking, exhibiting, tussling, and sex play are common incidents in these settings. Moreover, children are almost universally punished by being shut in or locked in bedrooms and small closets. Here they may ease their pain and loneliness by erotic play, but at the same time perhaps increase their sense of guilt. For these and many other reasons the small enclosed place is especially well suited to serve as the symbol for the pleasures of taboo activity, for fears of the intensity of one's own impulses, for the dangers of seduction and the threat of punishment. In the following case some of these symbolic meanings emerge with great clarity, as products largely of the patient's own unaided efforts.

A case of claustrophobia with other phobic symptoms

Kenneth E., twenty-two years of age, could not stay in theaters because they made him feel suffocated and afraid that he would not be able to get out in case of illness or a fire. His fear generalized to elevators, busses and downtown city streets. He sought therapeutic help because his fears were restricting his life without reducing his overall anxiety. In therapy he concentrated at first upon his most recent symptoms and gained his first insight into his phobias.

At the beginning of therapy Kenneth said that whenever he was in downtown streets he felt he might fall ill or be injured in an accident. Since he would be among strangers he might not get the help he needed in time to save his life. There was nothing objective to justify such fears. Later on Kenneth realized that fears of accident and illness were secondary. What he primarily feared was that if he were to "fall in a fit," or be injured, he might lose control of himself and shout something, or talk without realizing what he was saying. Obviously there was something he must hide, something which at the same time he had an impulse to proclaim. This discovery of an impulse to give himself away in public led ultimately to the origin of his phobias.

The onset of his claustrophobic symptoms followed an acute anxiety attack in a theater. The play contained a homosexual theme to which Kenneth was doubly sensitized, by his own trends and by a recent threat to expose them. The anxiety attack was his response to the total stress. When this occurred he became still more frightened that people around him in the theater would notice his agitation and guess its cause. As soon as the curtain fell for the intermission he staggered out, feeling weak, tremulous and nauseated. After this, he could go to the theater only if he sat near an exit, and even then he felt so anxious that he lost all pleasure in being there. The phobia generalized to places where he was thrown with strangers under crowded conditions.

Kenneth's experience in the theater had merely dramatized his current conflict and made him for the moment vividly aware of it. His phobias appeared as defensive devices which moved his conflict from the center of the stage and put a group of expanding fears in its place. What he was basically afraid of was not the theater, elevators, busses or downtown city streets. It was not accident or illness in the ordinary sense, or even the danger of not getting medical attention in time. These were all secondary rationalizations used to explain away the otherwise unintelligible anxiety.

What Kenneth feared basically was the upsurge of his own forbidden impulses, his powerful urge to behave homosexually and give himself away in public. His phobias shielded him from situations which aroused these impulses, offering him the neurotic compromise of freedom from anxiety in return for restricted activity. The neurotic compromise in his case eventually failed because, as with many severe phobias, the situations continued to generalize and the restrictions became impossible to meet. Therapy was successful to the extent that Kenneth was able to explore the larger background of personality distortion from which he suffered and to cooperate with his therapist in working out a solution.

Agoraphobia: The Fear of Open Places

The person suffering from agoraphobia becomes irrationally frightened whenever he finds himself in an open field, in a park or plaza, or at the beach. The term is also used to include neurotic fear of crossing a wide street, and even fears of beings in the street.[10] The anxiety that develops varies from an acute severe attack to mere alertnss and discomfort.

The fear

Like acrophobia and claustrophobia, the fear of open places is derived from realistic dangers. This time the danger is that of being exposed in the open without protection or shelter. It is an exaggeration of normal prudence. The prudent person, when he finds himself in dangerous territory does not cross an open field or a plaza if he can skirt it; he does not walk the streets if he can stay at home. To the agoraphobic person fields, plazas and beaches seem filled with danger, a danger which is no less threatening because he cannot explain it.

Kenneth E., discussed in the preceding section, suffered from a typical street phobia with typical fears of exposure and desertion. He pictured himself lying helpless in the open with a crowd looking on which might be indifferent to the possibility that he was dying. Another patient, a woman, saw herself hurrying along the street frightened, with men staring at her dangerously, and women looking haughty and aloof. She combined a temptation to go streetwalking with a fear of it, just as Kenneth did. Such people experience in anticipation the fright of helpless exposure; they try to avoid streets and open public places as though these were radioactive. Some agoraphobics can go about in relative comfort if someone accompanies them, someone to whom they can cling if necessary. This is especially interesting because it repeats the early childhood situation in which to be left alone in public was to feel helpless and abandoned in a universe of unknown dangers, while to have an adult to cling to was to feel safe.

Phobias, we have said, are related to childhood fears and utilize primitive forms of defense, such as displacement and projection.[11] The infantile mean-

---

[10] Sometimes called *street phobias* in the literature.

[11] For a discussion of displacement in agoraphobics, see Katan, A., "The role of displacement in agoraphobia," *Internat. J. Psychoanal.*, 1951, *32*, 41–50.

ings of agoraphobia, including fears of being left alone in the street, give us further insight into the origins and structure of these neurotic compromises. Familiar surroundings, even for adults, provide a stable framework for our orientation. We feel safe and dare do a great deal within them. If they change suddenly or fall away we feel at least momentarily disoriented, even with all our vast adult experience and inner resources. When we find ourselves unexpectedly lost in the woods or in the desert, and when we awaken in a strange room away from home, we sometimes get at least a taste of what the deserted infant and the agoraphobic adult fully experience.

In early childhood it can be frightening to find oneself alone or among strangers. This is an acquired fear. Its sources go back to experiences of being flooded with need tensions at a period in infancy when resources for defense and mastery are hopelessly inadequate. From this repeated trauma the infant is repeatedly rescued by mothering. His need tensions are reduced, he regains comfort, and he learns eventually that rescue comes from parental intervention. The same is true of tensions arising from external stimulation; parental intervention comes to the rescue. Thus loneliness comes to mean the threat of helplessness, of being exposed to overwhelming inner need and outer stress, and to the indifference of unloving strangers. These meanings are imbedded in highly cathected (energized) infantile fantasies which may eventually become unconscious, but are never wholly lost, even in adulthood.

As a child masters speech and locomotion, his horizons expand in all directions and his symbolism is enormously enriched. He also has his first experiences of getting lost — in field, parks and streets, and at the beach — for him all vastly more spacious and unstructured than for adults. He sees and hears about starving animals and hungry abandoned children, about tramps in the streets, about beggars and abandoned women. He learns that what is good in the home becomes bad out of doors, for example, nakedness, exposure, and elimination. His first experiences with genital exhibiting and looking may occur outside, and often these are linked with frightening punishment. As time goes on the growing child learns — and absorbs into his enduring fantasies — that people are thrown into the streets for wrongdoing. He learns that such public, unprotected places as streets, parks and beaches are places where violence and death sometimes occur, and that "walking the streets" can mean hunger, desertion and sexual sin. These multiple meanings enter into common infantile experience and into the unconscious fantasies which form the background of adult phobias.

Gratifications

Much of what has been said about gratification in relation to claustrophobia and acrophobia could be repeated here. To be left alone in the open means not only to be abandoned and in danger; it may also mean to be free from being watched and restricted, free to have one's fling. Thus, along with fears of loneliness, desertion and attack, the agoraphobic may experience a promise of excitement and freedom from restraint. To walk the streets and plazas, to be in parks or at the beach, means to have opportunities to satisfy libidinous and aggressive desires which are never met indoors at home. Thus gratifications, many of them taboo and most of them unconscious, are mingled with the dread of being alone and unprotected, and the fear of what one may feel impelled to do. The agoraphobic symptom serves the double purpose of providing severe restraint while preserving the excitement of the temptation.

A case of agoraphobia

Ethel H., a married woman of twenty-six, had suffered her first acute anxiety attack two years before she began therapy. She was arriving alone by plane from England after visiting her parents there. As she entered the high-ceilinged terminal, where no one met her, she suddenly felt terrified at the huge empty spaciousness. She began "shaking like a leaf"; she could not get her bags through customs without constant help; she had the impulse to tell everyone around who she was in case she went mad. A porter, sensing her anxiety, expressed his concern over her openly and this comforted her. She managed the rest of the trip by train without mishap, but reached home exhausted and unnerved, certain that something awful was happening to her. She told her husband nothing of this when he returned from work because she was afraid of expressing her resentment at not having been met.

During the ensuing two years Ethel felt nervous a great deal of the time, uneasy about driving on parkways and highways, and lonely when walking along strange streets. Then she made another trip to England, intending to stay three months with her parents. As time went on, however, she heard from her husband less and less frequently, while his letters seemed more and more impersonal, until she began to fear that she would lose him. Her fear was confirmed when he finally wrote that he wanted a divorce. Her immediate reaction was to become depressed, to weep bitterly, lose sleep and appetite, and declare that she was alone in the world.

The day after this letter arrived, Ethel was crossing a moor toward dusk when she was suddenly struck by the desolate surroundings. She felt isolated from the world and terribly frightened. She told herself that she might as well be exiled to Siberia as stranded here. Then she became afraid that she would step into a bog and disappear. Her legs were so weak that she could scarcely walk on to the house. Following this experience Ethel could not cross large open spaces anywhere without acute anxiety, unless someone whom she knew accompanied her. She avoided concerts because of the "emptiness" of concert halls. On the advice of a physician friend she returned at once to the United States. At the air terminal she repeated her experience of two years earlier even though this time her sister was there to meet her.

Because of the impending divorce Ethel moved to another city, terminating therapy, which she believed would be unnecessary once the reality situation was cleared up. During the brief period of treatment certain matters of dynamic interest came out. Ethel's feeling of desolation, which now permeated all her thinking, she ascribed not only to her husband's desertion but also to the lifelong neglect of her father. She had always wanted to be close to him but he had never shown a genuine interest in the family. Now, she said, his only concern about her was a worry that her divorce might hurt his professional standing.

Ethel had had earlier phobias which reflected her frustrated unconscious wishes for a father's love. Around pubescence she often dreamed that burglars had broken into her bedroom. She would wake up with the feeling that someone was in the room; she was too frightened then to move, turn over in bed, or even to breathe, for fear of disclosing her position. She was also afraid that somebody was hiding behind the door when she entered a room. She would push the door hard against the wall to make sure before going in. When she was a little girl, Ethel was often frightened that something was in bed with her and was creeping up toward her. Whenever this happened she would run to her parent's room for comfort and insist upon sleeping with them the rest of the night. Thus, although the irrational fears in early childhood and pubescence were different in kind, the phobic pattern of defense against desire and loneliness was one that she had used in one form or another most of her life.

Zoöphobia: The Fear of Animal Life

The zoöphobic person is irrationally afraid, sometimes to the point of helplessness, when he is in the proximity of a certain form of animal life. The fear is usually limited to one or another kind of living being. Horses, wolves, lions and tigers have always been favorite zoöphobic excitants; so also are spiders, insects and vermin. Sometimes the fear is quite specific. Cats are frightening for some people while dogs are not; snakes may be frightening but not frogs or turtles. Zoöphobic children often scream and cringe or run away when the excitant appears. Adults are usually more controlled, but not always; sometimes they too become acutely anxious in the presence of the feared animal.

The fear

Fears of animal life can easily appear reasonable since they involve something that might conceivably attack. Children often learn to be afraid through actual experiences of hurt or fright — being barked at or growled at loudly, falling over an animal that jumps up, being scratched, bitten or knocked down. Children also acquire fears through visiting farms, and zoos, and especially from the frightening warnings that other children and adults give. Picture books, fairy tales, magazines and stories, moving pictures and television, may all add to a child's anxieties about animals. But this sort of thing accounts at most for reasonable caution and the moderate fears which, in most children, soon disappear. It does not explain the persistence or the intensity of animal phobias in the relatively few.

Animals become the focus of phobias, especially for the child, because they are unpredictable, violent and sexually uninhibited. They can therefore easily be made into symbols of frightening primitivity around which infantile fantasies cluster. Domestic animals commit crimes of violence without hesitation including theft, assault, and murder. Dogs and cats kill and eat small, helpless animals while the child's parents encourage and reward them. They mate with their own offspring and siblings without regard to the most relentless human taboos. Yet they prosper and are loved. Sometimes pet dogs eat their pups, and cats their kittens. Parents are likely to be shocked by such cannibalism but they seldom punish the offending animal.

We must remember that small children do not make the sharp distinctions between man and animal that the adult makes. To them it is conceivable that what dogs, cats, horses or cattle do, their own father or mother might also do. Not only do small children express such fears sometimes in words, but their dreams, fairy tales and phobias also express them in unmistakable symbolism. A child can hardly be expected to avoid fantasying that what father animals do his own father may also do, or what mother animals do his own mother might also do. He has before him all the time the keen interest which any normal parent is likely to express in the doings of his pets.

All of these considerations make it easier to understand the existence of incestuous, murderous and cannibalistic fears and fantasies among small children. For small children include household pets and other animals among their objects of identification, with a freedom that is foreign to adult conscious thinking. And because adult preconscious dreams and unconscious fantasies are often based upon the conscious fantasies of early childhood, long since repressed, we can understand why it is that adult dreams and unconscious fantasies often include forbidden wishes and strange fears. The same considerations help us to understand also the violent and persistent phobias which, in an adult, can represent both a person's poorly repressed unconscious desires and the punishment he fears as retaliation for them.

Domestic pets and the animals of farm and zoo are not the only ones around which phobias can be constructed. But the animal kingdom is so vast and varied that there is no space here to do justice to its symbolic potentialities. We shall mention just one other special group, the group of insects, vermin and the like. Phobias attached to such creatures often represent displaced hatred, loathing and destructive fantasies directed at one time against sibling rivals. Their small size, unattractive appearance, bad reputation and large numbers make them ideal for such representation.

This is perhaps the place to repeat what has been said in earlier chapters, that symbols need not always mean what they appear to mean, any more than need our words. Like words and like institutionalized symbols, our private symbols may mean what they say or its opposite, or something far removed from any generally accepted meaning.[12] The symbols used by phobic patients have the same characteristics. Therefore, in every phobia, the meanings represented by the symptom can be determined only through a painstaking study of the individualistic thinking of the phobic patient, without prejudgment as to the symptom's meanings.

Gratifications

It is obvious from what we have been saying that the animal fantasies included in zoöphobia allow a person to symbolize all manner of erotic wish and destructive impulse. Everyone young or old has witnessed the unbridled violence of animal aggression and the unrestrained indulgence of animal sexuality. Animals breed and care for their young openly in every intimate detail. They express the most uninhibited interest in feeding, grooming and elimination. Almost everything that can arouse human excitement, envy, shame and disgust is at some time witnessed or heard about as animal activity. Thus everyone is provided with unlimited symbols of animal gratification which can be worked into the structure of an animal phobia.

A case of zoöphobia

The most famous case of zoöphobia is also the first one ever to be studied dynamically, the case of Little Hans. This boy of five years refused to go out into the street because he was afraid of horses, actually feared being bitten by them. In the course of therapy it turned out that the horses symbolized the hated and feared aspect of his father. The little patient harbored hostile aggression against his only male rival for his mother's love, but at the same time he also loved his father dearly.

Reduced to its simplest terms the phobic solution was about as follows. The love this boy bore his mother was repressed, it disappeared. The love for his father was retained, while the hatred for him was displaced on the horses. This had the added advantage that the horse could easily be avoided, whereas his father could not. In the usual role-reversal of fantasies and dreams, the boy expected primitive retaliation from his father for the primitive hostility he himself felt. This expectation likewise was displaced. It became the regressive oral fear that horses would bite him.

The whole displacement in the case of Little Hans was made easy by certain other partial identities. (a) The father had often played

---

[12] For example, we say, "He's a fine fellow!" when he mean (a) that he is someone of whom we greatly approve, but also (b) when we mean that he is contemptible. We say, "Aren't you the big, brave man!" (a) when we mean to express admiration, but also (b) to mean that a person is a coward. "Isn't she sweet?" can mean that we think she is sweet, or that we are disgusted with her meanness. In current affairs armament measures are called peace measures while peace proposals are regarded as aggression. This kind of double meaning pervades our general conversation, our political thinking, our humor and our slang. It is hardly surprising that it appears prominently in dream meanings and neurotic symptoms.

"horsie" with Hans; (*b*) the horses' bridles reminded Hans fearfully of his father's dark moustache; (*c*) therapy also brought out his wishes that his father might fall and hurt himself, as the boy had seen horses fall, and as his playmate with whom he also played "horsie" had fallen and hurt himself. As a result of therapy this patient recovered from his phobia. It is interesting that, years later when Hans chanced upon the account of his illness and its treatment, all memory of the once vivid phobia had been *completely repressed*. Some of the incidental comments about his parents made him wonder if he could have been this famous little patient, and led him to visit Freud where he found out that he was.[13]

Concluding comment

We have now described four common phobias, illustrated each with case material, and indicated real life situations to which each is related and from which basic fantasies and symbolism may derive. For each phobia we have sketched both the fearful and the gratifying aspects seperately, to show that for every phobic fear there may be a corresponding phobic fascination. It would be possible to carry out this same descriptive procedure for all the other groups of phobic excitants listed near the beginning of the chapter. It seems more important, however, to discuss some dynamic and developmental considerations at this point.

A note on counterphobic measures

There is an especially interesting derivative of phobias which merits our attention before we go on. This is the so-called *counterphobia* or *counterphobic measure*. Children show it most clearly when they act out in play something frightening that has happened to them in reality. A child, for example, acts out a visit to the doctor, a painful injection or a surgical procedure to which he has just been subjected. Often he does this over and over, as if the mastery of the anxiety he has experienced demands many repetitions. In the play situation the child is active, willing and in control of the situation, instead of being acted upon, unwilling and helpless. Adults who have been the victims of traumatic anxiety in combat situations do the same kind of thing when they repeat their terrifying experiences under narcosis and hypnosis or in dreams.

In all of the above examples the child or adult connects his counterphobic acting out with the originally frightening experience. This is an important condition for successfully mastering the original anxiety. Most neurotic counterphobic attempts do not operate with this advantage. The sources of

---

[13] Freud, S., "Analysis of a phobia in a five-year-old boy," (1909), Standard Edition, 1955, vol. 9, pp. 1–149; Freud, S., "Inhibitions, symptoms and anxiety," (1925), Standard Edition, 1959, vol. 20, pp. 77–175.

phobic anxiety are usually hidden from the phobic person by his own defenses. He feels driven to or attracted to dangerous activity without consciously knowing why.

The most common form of counterphobia is *reactive courage*. The phobic person deliberately seeks out situations of which he is afraid because of an unconscious drive to master a specific anxiety. There are also, of course, the contributing factors of excitement and pleasure in the anxiety of phobics and in its relief, which we have already described. Innumerable examples of counterphobic tendencies occur in ordinary life. The most dramatic examples are to be found among acrophobic persons who choose such hobbies as mountain climbing, or such professions as tight-rope walking and aviation. An aviator famous for his daredevil flights in the days of frail open aircraft — the so-called "flying egg-crates" — said that he was too frightened of height to look out of a five-story window without hanging on to something. There are also actors with chronic severe stage fright who need to be pushed onto the stage, but who still actively seek out public performances, experiencing pleasure and relief in each appearance but never mastering their anxiety.

Daredevils are by no means all counterphobic. Some of them have always enjoyed doing what other people fear. Some have at one time been phobic but have overcome their neurotic fear, and now enjoy repeating the dangerous feat with a sense of mastery, just as normal children also do. The counterphobic character of an activity is shown by the appearance of unusual tension, anxiety, symptomatic acts, and anxiety dreams related to the phobia which is being defended against. Counterphobic repetitions of feared situations do not usually lead to mastery of the phobic anixety because the patient's defenses make him unaware of the neurotic fear which he is trying unconsciously to master. The unconscious drive to master anxiety makes him repeat over and over some activity toward which he feels irresistibly impelled without being aware of the reason. The dynamics and developmental background of phobic reactions will help to clarify such apparent contradiction.

Dynamic and Developmental Background

Phobias are spontaneous, unconscious attempts at self-cure. The phobic person, threatened with ego disintegration by an upsurge of tension and anxiety, undergoes a partial regression and re-establishes ego integration at more primitive levels. One effect of the regression is to reactivate childhood fantasies of a fearful character which mingle with, or even replace, the realistic adult fears. The reactivated fantasies are in turn displaced and projected on to suitable objects or situations in the environment which can be avoided. Such a process may take place quickly, as it did in our three principal cases, or it may develop gradually, keeping pace with a gradual rise in unmastered tension.

Phobic symptoms and the energy of organization

Phobias have a more mature structure than do anxiety reactions, no matter how absurd or childish their form appears to be. They are successful most of the time in binding excess tension and anxiety. This is achieved through a regression, not to the early primitive discharge pattern which we saw in anxiety reactions, but to a level where there are perceptual and cognitive structures — images, memories, fantasies and daydreams — capable of absorbing and utilizing large amounts of energy. The dynamic succession of events in phobias is as follows: *(a) an upsurge of emotional tension with increased free anxiety; (b) beginning ego disintegration; (c) automatic partial regression to more primitive levels; (d) ego reintegration at the lower levels,* as the excess tension and anxiety are absorbed in the organization of reactivated imagery, memory, fantasy and daydream.

Since these reactivated, energized structures may initiate another upsurge, and again threaten a breakthrough — with a consequent further regression — the auxiliary mechanisms of displacement and projection are evoked. These two primitive maneuvers make the threat appear to come from the outside, from something external of which the patient feels afraid. This state of affairs permits the phobic person to use familiar techniques of avoidance as a defense against further anxiety.

A major difference between anxiety reactions and phobias is the much greater use of perceptual and cognitive structures in phobias to absorb excess free energy. Images, memories, fantasies and daydreams are in effect interpolated between the internal or external sources of increased tension and the neurotic response. Because these organizations absorb free energy in phobias there is little need for immediate, massive discharge such as occurs in the anxiety reaction. In organizing his irrational fears, the phobic patient gains mastery over the upsurges of tension and anxiety. It is only when the projected symbol, the feared object or situation, appears on the scene to reinforce the internal stimulation from infantile phobic structures, that an anxiety attack is precipitated.[14]

The phobic patient's use of perceptual and cognitive structures introduces us to the general topic of symptom formation and symptom structure. We shall revert to this topic in a later chapter when we bring together some of the facts about neurotic symptom formation which will emerge from our study of individual neuroses. At this point it is enough to say that, in the course of normal development, the growth of perceptual and cognitive organization bestows upon every child a growing freedom from sudden attacks of emotional tension and anxiety.

It has long been recognized that thinking depends upon the appearance

[14] In actual practice, of course, one finds all degrees of transition between anxiety reactions and phobias—such as, anxiety reactions with avoidance resembling phobic defenses, and phobias which include frequent decompensations in acute anxiety attacks.

of a delay between stimulation and response. This delay appears at first as a suspension of activity, before an act is completed, which can be directly observed in the behavior of young infants. The delay is presumably filled in by fugitive perceptual and cognitive experiences; and it is these experiences that are ultimately stabilized in the form of images, memories, fantasies and daydreams. The formation of such perceptual and cognitive structures in turn helps to prolong and to enrich the intervals between stimulation and response, eventually creating an internal mental life with a considerable degree of autonomy. We experience its fugitive, melting, kaleidoscopic qualities as adults in our manifest dreams; we experience its stable, realistic qualities in much of the practical, imaginative and esthetic activity of waking life.

Such structures must become highly organized and complex even during infancy. Their highly complex organization itself requires energy input just to maintain it in an active state. When these structures are reactivated, as they are in any active fantasy, the reactivation absorbs free energy which we have called *the energy of organization*. Neurotic symptoms, such as the phobias, require free energy for their organization and reactivation. The neurotic symptom is only a special case of the more general use of free energy for mental structuring, a case of its employment as a defense.

Defensive maneuvers in phobic reactions

The advantages of the phobic defense over the anxiety reaction are obvious. In the anxiety reaction, as we have seen, the patient must remain continually vigilant because he feels the constant threat of catastrophe from some unknown source. He is forced to rely upon continually discharging energy as it arises — an exhausting process from which there is no escape. Phobic defenses, by contrast, provide an escape by furnishing fearful fantasies whose *organization* takes care of the excess tension most of the time. These fantasies are displaced from their original infantile sources and projected on to appropriate external objects or situations. As long as the feared external object or situation can be avoided the patient may remain in relative peace.

Regardless of the superior protection from anxiety afforded by phobias, they involve unquestionably childish maneuvers, making use of primitive defenses which play little part in anxiety reactions. Two primitive defenses appearing explicitly in the foreground of phobias are *displacement* and *projection*. Both of these are derived from the earliest phases of personality development, from phases which antedate the formation of stable boundaries that separate conscious and preconscious functions from unconscious ones.

Displacement. Displacement, in the sense of transferring energy or cathexis from one object representation to another, is one of the outstanding characteristics of primary process functioning. It takes for granted a carefree equivalence among objects, and among their representations, which is foreign to secondary process logic, that is, to rational thinking. It may even ignore the basic perceptual distinction in adults between inner and outer, and in this it is closely related to the other outstanding phobic defense, projection.

Projection. As it appears in phobias, projection involves the shift from an actual internal danger, the danger of an eruption of unconscious material, to an irrational fear of something external which can usually be identified and avoided. Although projection, like most of the neurotic defenses, is used to some extent by normal persons in everyday life, its use is restricted to such activities as scapegoating, misidentifying the origins of our irritability, and feeling that nature reflects our own personal mood. The kind of projection which the phobic patient carries out is far more specific, more complete and more individualistic than the projection used in everyday life and in anxiety reactions. It points to a basic defect in ego boundaries, a defect which becomes obvious when regression develops under stress. The only normal situation in which the normal person experiences a comparable loss of ego boundaries is that of dreaming while asleep. The prominence of both displacement and projection in phobic reactions can best be understood as a consequence of inadequate repression.

Repression. Repression is inadequate in all neuroses. In phobic reactions attempts are made to get rid of fearful fantasies, which cannot be repressed, by displacing and projecting them. In other words, the ready appearance of displacement and projection in phobias testifies to the insufficiency of repression in the phobic person. There would be nothing to displace and project if repression had been effective in containing the reactivated unconscious fearful fantasies. We must remember that it is the development of repression which normally establishes functional boundaries protecting conscious and preconscious organizations from unconscious interference. Defective repression means defective boundaries; and defective boundaries mean insufficient separation of the preconscious and conscious from the unconscious.

In phobic reactions, as also in anxiety reactions, it is the threat of invasion by unconscious id and superego forces that induces ego disintegration; and it is this beginning ego disintegration that initiates a defensive regression to more primitive levels. The partial regression enables the phobic person to escape being overwhelmed by ego disintegration; this is the gain he achieves in regressing. At the same time, it also brings him more than ever under the influence of unconscious forces. He escapes from this second danger by falling back upon the primitive devices of displacement and projection with which he is more familiar than the average person.

Before going on to discuss the interrelationship between inadequate repression and the primitive defenses of displacement and projection, let us look back at our cases for illustrations of the dynamic forces in phobias. When Agnes W. suffered her traumatic emotional decompensation in the eighth-floor office, she was immediately assailed by erupting unconscious forces which might have driven her to suicide in a mad rush of fury, hate and guilt. She retained enough realistic ego functioning to get her safely out of the building, to deflect her suicidal aim. Even so, Agnes behaved primitively, crouching like a terror-stricken child behind the steel files, and then groping her way out of the building as if the devil were after her, instead of her own homicidal and suicidal fantasies. It was after this frightening experience that she displaced and projected the whole emotional storm from a realistic fear of her own internal impulses to an irrational fear of the situation in which they erupted, that is, to an irrational fear of height. Kenneth E. attempted the same kind of displacement and projection. He was less successful because his multiple conflicts generalized to so many different referents that eventually avoidance became impossible. Ethel H. achieved little by developing her phobia for open places. She only exchanged a definite adult fear, which she would have soon to face in reality, for an irrational infantile fear, which gave her at most a temporary respite.

The inadequacy of repression in neuroses

The fundamental question is the same in all neuroses: *Why is repression inadequate?* The answer to it in all neuroses is probably the same. It must be sought in the developmental background of children who become neurotic adults. The different patterns of neurosis represent different ways of trying to ward off intolerable anxiety, of trying to reduce the tension which arises because of the beginnings of eruptions from the unconscious.

In the chapters on personality organization and the one on anxiety reactions we began the discussion of developmental background. There are the congenital differences found in newborn infants, which give them very different kinds of sensitivity, and which seem to persist as personal characteristics. There are also the later influences — the separation anxiety in its many forms, domineering parents, overpermissive parents and childhood training in anxiety and guilt. There are the innumerable ego introjects, ego identifications and superego identifications with significant persons in a child's environment, through which he builds up his own individualistic personality system. And there is his adoption of prevailing patterns — emotional and esthetic as well as practical and logical — long before he is capable of analyzing them or of reflecting about them. All of these factors, we have said, may make a person especially vulnerable — or especially resistant — to the development of some kind of neurotic reaction under stress.

The pattern of the neurotic reaction is simply the individual's preferred way of handling intolerable anxiety. It too, depends upon similar childhood background factors. In anxiety reactions, as we have seen, the method of choice is that of discharging tension directly through general somatic and emotional channels. Although this usually protects a person from further regression, it becomes itself a source of anxiety, and to this extent it fails. The phobic reaction, as a reaction pattern for handling tension and anxiety, is more successful because it makes the danger *seem* specific as well as external, even though it remains unintelligible to the patient. In the chapters that follow this one, other patterns for controlling anxiety will be taken up. At this point, however, we shall confine the discussion to phobias, so as to keep from getting lost in generalities.

Displacement, projection and inadequate repression

What is peculiar to phobic reactions is not the inadequacy of repression — this is found in all neuroses — but the way in which displacement and projection are used to supplement the weak repression, to achieve what it fails to achieve alone. This use of such primitive defenses suggests two things: (1) that the defensive structure of phobic persons is distorted in such a way as to give unusual prominence to archaic forms of defense; and (2) that the traumatic experiences giving rise to this distortion must have occurred very early in life. The fact that the patient becomes phobic and not psychotic further suggests that he has been successful in building a reasonably stable personality system in spite of the early traumata. The adult phobic is thus a person with effective overall personality integration, who suffers from relatively ineffectual repression, but who is able to withstand threats of ego disintegration through the use of displacement and projection.

Effective repression develops relatively late in infancy. Displacement and projection are among the earliest of all the defensive maneuvers to develop. The evidence we have from the study of adult and child phobias indicate that phobic persons have been compelled as children to master too much emotional tension and anxiety too early in life. Either their emotional drives were exceptionally powerful, or they were unusually sensitive to anxiety excitants, or they received too little adult protection from tension and anxiety when these passed beyond the limits of their endurance. What they could handle through the use of repression they disposed of in this way. The remainder, which early in life would amount to a considerable fraction, they absorbed in their perceptual organizations, as images and fantasies. The images and fantasies which continued to be frightening were treated as *ego-alien*, that is, as not belonging within the personality system, as coming from the outside. This maneuver makes use of displacement and projection.

No matter how involved and irrational such maneuvering may sound it must be kept in mind that the normal man indulges in it freely every night when he dreams.[15] Dreaming is certainly a regressive experience, sometimes deeply regressive, but it is none the less an essential part of the normal

---

[15] Lewin, B., "Phobic symptoms and dream interpretation," *Psychoanal. Quart.*, 1952, *21*, 295–322.

adult's normal life. Moreover, displacement and projection are practiced widely by otherwise normal adults, in relation to their own motivation, when this seems ego alien to them. They ascribe the responsibility or the blame to other persons or to fate or to the will of God, when an objective study of the situation shows that the responsibility or blame lies in their own attitudes or behavior. And, finally, we must remember that displacement and projection are prominent ingredients of psychoses, and that psychoses are among the commonest of all human illnesses.

To return to phobic reactions, we assume that small children who are compelled to use displacement and projection too often and too strongly, before their repressive defenses have matured, may establish these as their chief defenses, and go on using them in situations which should be calling out repression. Like any other dynamic function of the organism, repression will evolve normally only if it is optimally used at the proper time. If it is neglected it will remain underdeveloped; and if the more primitive displacement and projection continue to perform some of the functions usually left to repression, they will be relatively overdeveloped and overused. This seems to be the situation giving rise to severe phobias in childhood and to a special vulnerability to phobic developments in adults.

Defective repression always means defective functional boundaries — between unconscious ego, id and superego processes on the one hand, and preconscious or conscious processes on the other. Preconscious and conscious organizations will not be adequately protected from invasion by unconscious forces in persons whose repressive defenses are underdeveloped. The result of this situation is similar to that described for anxiety reactions. Under emotional stress, adults with such defects tend to give *split-level responses*, that is, they react to current stress in terms of childhood stress. Previously repressed childhood fantasies — representing the residues of childhood emotional crises — erupt into preconscious and conscious functioning and are treated as though they were contemporary. The result of this is a beginning ego disintegration, an automatic partial regression to more primitive levels, and the reactivation of fearful fantasies which are then displaced and projected as phobic symptoms. Formation of the phobic symptom rids the person of his anxiety, but at the cost of some of his freedom, for he must avoid having to face the projected fear in his surroundings.

Defensive form and perceptual content in phobias

We have already seen that the phobic defense is primitive. Displacement and projection, such as we see in phobias, go back to phases of development in which no clear distinction existed between self and external reality or between mental self and body self. This suggests a phase in which some degree of mother-child symbiosis prevailed. In contrast to this, the *perceptual* or *cognitive content* in a phobic reaction may range from the archaic to the edipal or postedipal phases. We encounter phobias in our clinical work that express the most primitive wordless, objectless fears of disappearing, dissolving or sinking into nothingness. Other phobias, using essentially the same mechanisms, express fears of punishment and retaliation which clearly belong to phases of mature superego development. In terms of erogenous zones, we find the same spread of perceptual or cognitive content in phobias, from the earliest oral fears to the latest phallic fears.[16]

Our case material illustrates some of these variations in level or perceptual content, even though all the patients used the same primitive mechanisms of defense.[17] Ethel H. suggests archaic content in her fear of being lost in space. Her fantasies suggested an identity between the huge, empty air terminal and her own boundless, empty body and self — huge and frightening because she had regressed to a phase in which her body and self lacked definite boundaries. Agnes W. was overwhelmed by superego guilt and involved in an affair which, taken together, point to the release from weak repression of edipal wishes in relation to her father. Kenneth E. reflected in his fantasies both the fear of being abandoned and helpless, and the wish to be exposed, together with indications of later negative edipal conflicts, expressed both in these fears and wishes, and in his homosexual activities.

It is often said that diagnosis can be more accurately made on the basis of the defenses used than on the basis of the symptoms expressed. Actually the two are intimately related. In phobias, as we have seen, the *mechanisms* express a primitive functional level, one in which there are perceptual structures but no clear ego boundaries. What the *symptom* expresses, however, is the danger against which the primitive phobic defenses — displacement and projection — are used. This danger, as we have also seen, ranges from primitive, infantile fears of losing one's identity, of being swallowed up and ceasing to exist, all the way through desires to be taken care of, or to be exposed and helpless like a baby — but separate now, as a being among other beings — up to fears of condign punishment for edipal sins and murderous wishes belonging to fantasies in the fifth or sixth years.

To sum up: we can assume on clinical and developmental grounds that adult phobias are based upon infantile phobias, which almost every child seems to experience. Phobic adults have evidently experienced such childhood phobias more severely than the average, since they exhibit such strongly fixated, fearful perceptual organizations. We can agree with the consensus that phobic persons have not yet been adequately protected in childhood from excessive internal or external stress. We assume that the earliest unmastered, traumatic experiences in the childhood of phobic patients come later than those in anxiety reaction patients. In phobias the regression halts at levels of good perceptual organization, whereas in anxiety reactions regression goes back to a more archaic discharge. When the phobic defense fails, the patient regresses promptly to this earlier discharge level.

The dominant fantasies, memories and daydreams appearing in phobic

---

[16] The concept of erogenous zones was given in some detail in Chapter 2.

[17] Perloe, S. I., "Inhibition as a determinant of perceptual defense," *Percept. Motor Skills*, 1960, *11*, 59–66.

symptoms do not necessarily indicate the *origin* of the phobic defense. Instead, they point to the most severe and often the latest childhood crisis in which displacement and projection have been employed. Thus, the edipal child utilizes his primitive phobic defense to solve edipal conflicts, or to ward off edipal dangers, because he lacks something better to use. The primitive phobia, more successful than the archaic discharge in anxiety attacks, is the mechanism available to him in a moment of edipal crisis because it had been forged years earlier and used successfully to defend against more primitive fears then. Just as a soldier who runs out of ammunition may use his carbine as a club, so the phobic who runs out of adequate repression, falls back upon whatever primitive substitutes he still has. A person who faces a *conflict in adulthood*, which resembles an *unsolved edipal one*, may likewise fall back upon a *phobic reaction* in his attempt to solve it.

In this chapter and the preceding one we have discussed two common neurotic syndromes in which patients made, more or less unsuccessfully, attempts to get rid of excess emotional tension and anxiety. In the *anxiety recation* the patient fell back upon crude, archaic discharge processes which are reminiscent of infant yelling, thrashing and temper tantrums. Where a sexual or an aggressive action might have been expected, the anxious person showed only extreme vigilance and intermittent massive, but nonspecific, discharge. In the *phobic reaction* the patient fell back upon fearful fantasies, more organized than vigilance and nonspecific tension discharge, but still primitive and unsuccessful in achieving more than a restriction of acute anxiety to more or less specific excitants. We turn now to a third neurosis, the *conversion reaction,* in which emotional tension and anxiety often seem to disappear, but always at the cost of some major disability.

9

Conversion Reactions

CONVERSIONS ARE CHANGES IN SOME SPECIFIC BODY FUNCTION WHICH EXPRESS an unconscious conflict in symbolic form. In the two preceding chapters we have seen how patients with *anxiety reactions* rely upon massive discharges of energy through increased muscular and visceral activity to rid them of excessive tension and anxiety. We have also seen that in *phobias* the tension and anxiety are crystallized in the form of a specific fear, a perceptual structure, which the patient displaces and projects to something in the external world, and then avoids as much as possible.

In *conversion reactions* the unconscious conflict leads neither to massive discharges nor to displaced and projected fears, nor even to avoidance. Instead, the energies from id and superego impulses, from unconscious images and fantasies, from ego defenses and adaptations, are crystallized in the altered functioning of some specific body part — of a limb, of sense organs or of internal organs. This altered functioning, as we shall see, expresses the components of some basic conflict in the form of a symbolism which we call *body language*. The patient willingly, or at least passively, accepts his altered functioning as the evidence he needs to show that he is now ill or disabled. Here are some brief clinical examples to make our introduction more complete.

A soldier who had recently killed an enemy in combat found that his right arm was paralyzed. It was neurophysiologically normal and the soldier had suffered no injuries.[1]

[1] See Grinker, R. R., and Spiegel, J., *War Neuroses.* Philadelphia: Blakiston, 1945. See also Grinker, R. R., and Spiegel, J., *Men Under Stress.* Philadelphia: Blakiston, 1945. Many cases discussed in the text of the latter book are listed in its index.

An adolescent girl, after being chased in the woods by a strange boy, developed terrifying dreams in which her legs seemed to be paralyzed. The dreams were premonitory. Following a week in bed with the "flu," she actually developed paralysis of her legs, but without any sign of nervous system involvement. She first expressed her unconscious fear in preconscious dreams, and then brought them out overtly in the form of a conversion reaction.

A college student went numb in his hands and arms after failing in his examinations. This cleared up when he found work, but it returned when he took entrance examinations later in another college, and again just before his graduation. The numbness did not correspond in distribution to that of sensory nerves.

A middle-aged woman lost her voice following a long distance call from her mother, when she learned that her father was dying. All medical examinations, including bronchoscopy, were negative. She recovered her voice spontaneously after a period of mourning.

At the age of eighteen, a young man was struck in the eye by a snowball. He was experiencing general unpopularity among his classmates when this happened. He now found that he could not see, and therefore could not study or remain in school. Whenever he sought work, over a period of four years, he would become functionally blind. He mixed well with his friends who were working and, although jobless himself, he seemed contented with his lot. As long as he did not try to work or to study, his vision remained normal.

We have given these examples, as in the chapter on anxiety reactions, to make it clear from the start what kind of symptoms we are dealing with. We shall not discuss these cases further.

The use of body language symbolization, no matter how primitive it may seem, is by no means necessarily abnormal. It occurs in normal behavior also. Here are a few examples from everyday life.

A person who wants to speak out, but who either does not dare to or feels it would be useless, averts his head and shrugs his shoulders. This nonverbal body language clearly symbolizes turning away from something and not caring, even though not a word has been said. A person who cannot bear to see something, which he knows is about to happen, covers his face and shuts his eyes, as if to deny its happening in advance. People try to avoid hearing bad news by putting their hands over their ears; or they may resist its impact by pulling themselves up straight and refusing to respond overtly at all. (The conversion patient facing such situations might go blind or deaf.) A person whose feelings have been hurt stands and looks as though he had been struck by someone's hand. Sometimes a person who hates what he has done strikes himself or asks someone else to punish him. We are all familiar with such body language expressions as the flushed face and erect posture of courage or triumph, the stance and strut of arrogance, the bent passive waiting posture of humility, and the drooped body, loose gait and lined face of defeat. All of these are examples of symbolic body language and all of them are normal.

Symbolizing something in body language becomes abnormal when its expressive, defensive or self-punitive function is lost through repression, and the patient mistakes his symbol for a sign of disability or bodily illness. For example, it may not be abnormal to vomit as a direct, primitive expression of the refusal to accept a repulsive situation. But to go on expressing rejection by chronically vomiting, and to mistake this expression of disgust for a sign of gastrointestinal disease, is without question abnormal. The abnormality of conversion reactions becomes all the more striking if the patient accepts his apparent illness or disability with indifference instead of being troubled by it. Such an apparently unnatural attitude, still called by its French name, *la belle indifférence,* has been recognized for nearly a century as a common attitude in conversion reactions.[2]

Definition. A conversion reaction is a process whereby an unconscious conflict is transformed ("converted") into a body symptom which reduces tension and anxiety by expressing the conflict symbolically. Unlike phobias, which often end in mere avoidance, and unlike anxiety reactions, which are often mere discharge, the conversion reaction means a dedication and a sacrifice. The function of some body part is dedicated and sacrificed to the expression of a forbidden impulse, or as a defense against such an impulse or a denial of it, or as self-punishment for having such an impulse. All of these meanings may be combined in a single symbol. For example a paralyzed arm may express the fact that it is an arm which has killed, an arm which can no longer kill, and the self-punishment of paralysis for having killed. It is guilty, innocent and punished at the same time. If, in addition, the paralyzed arm also expresses childhood sin, denial and penance, as usually it does, then the paralysis is further reinforced by forgotten fantasies, which like forgotten and repressed happenings are influential without becoming conscious. Under such circumstances, to begin using such an arm again would also be to rekindle old fires of early superego self-punishment.

The paralyzed conversion patient in effect wears his arm in a functional sling or cast to keep from using it for sin, retaliation or self-punishment. He acts out the Biblical injunction, "If thy hand offend thee, cut it off!" He cuts his hand off from participation in his own behavior. In blindness as a conversion symptom, the patient similarly makes his blind eye into a living testament of guilt, innocence, self-denial and self-punishment. Conversion blindness is one of the easiest symptoms in which to demonstrate psychological disability in the presence of physiological soundness. There are several devices which demand vision by the functionally blind eye or by both eyes if something projected before the patient is to be read. The conversion patient has no difficulty in reading them provided he does not know about the device. It is important at this point to emphasize that conversion patients are not consciously malingering or practicing deceit.

[2] Grinker and Spiegel found *la belle indifférence* in paratroopers, whose code forbade expressions of fear, but not in others in the air force. See *Men Under Stress,* p. 104.

Adaptation. Conversion reactions persist because, like anxiety reactions and phobias, they are adaptive, they achieve something. They crystallize out a body symptom in somewhat the same manner that the phobic crystallizes out a fearful fantasy. The body symptom binds excess emotional tension in its structure, reduces free anxiety, and protects the patient from the threat of ego disintegration.[3] The symptom expresses openly in body metaphor something which could not otherwise be openly expressed — a forbidden aggressive or erotic drive, unconscious images and fantasies, ego defenses, and the self-inflicted punishment derived from unconscious superego processes.

The meanings of the metaphorical conversion symptom remain repressed; they do not become conscious for the patient. They are able none the less to reduce tension and anxiety, just as can ordinary fantasying and dreaming. As long as the meanings of his conversion symptom are hidden from him, the patient can go on expressing his unconscious conflicts openly with little or no excess emotional tension and anxiety.[4] The tensions of his active but unconscious conflicts, as we have indicated, are continually absorbed in the process of structuring and maintaining his conversion symptom.

There is another factor which, although present to some degree in other neuroses as well, is no where else as plainly evident as in conversions. This is the factor which we call *secondary gain*. In becoming functionally disabled, the patient may discover secondarily that he enjoys his privileged status as an invalid more than he enjoyed the freedom of being well. This secondary gain sometimes constitutes a serious — even an incurable — obstacle to therapeutic progress, as we shall see especially well in the case of the paralyzed ranch girl.

Varieties of Conversion Reaction

Because conversion reactions use body parts and organs to symbolize unconscious conflicts, the potential variety of conversion symptoms is enormous. It is at least as great as the variety of body parts and internal organs, and of their various functions and combinations. A further extension of variety is furnished by the fact that conversion symptoms develop in persons who are physically handicapped or ill, as well as in the physically sound and well. In developing a conversion symptom, the physically handicapped or sick patient may simply exaggerate or distort the symptoms arising from his organic pathology which are already present. He may, on the other hand, complicate everything further by adding some new form of neurotic disability to his organic disorder.

To keep our discussion of case material within manageable limits, we

[3] For cases in which acute anxiety persisted, see Grinker, R. R., and Spiegel, J., *War Neuroses*. Philadelphia: Blakiston, 1945, pp. 6–10.

[4] The individualistic character of the conversion symbolism is evident in one study which reports that not one twin of patients diagnosed as conversion reaction without manifest anxiety ever had a twin with this diagnosis. Slater, E., "Hysteria 311," *J. ment. Sci.*, 1961, *107*, 359–381.

shall focus in what follows upon patients suffering from a major conversion who are physically sound and well. Major conversions are still to be found in any large treatment center, among psychologically unsophisticated persons, and among wartime military personnel, especially among enlisted men. Fifty years ago they were apparently much more common than they are today. While we know some of the reasons for this shift we do not yet know them all. The greater incidence in wartime than in peacetime indicates that the pattern of stress can be an important factor. The greater incidence among enlisted men than among commissioned officers suggests the influence of being in a subordinate, dependent position. It also suggests the influence of education and psychological sophistication.

Education and sophistication enter into the etiology of conversion reactions because a patient must himself be convinced that his conversion symptom is a sign of organic illness or disability if he is to maintain it. Physical illness or disability seems honorable to the average person in our culture today. Neurotic illness does not. This is why acceptance of a conversion symptom, often with an attitude of indifference to its disadvantages, is essential if the conversion patient is to protect himself from the anxiety which brought it into being. The moment a conversion patient begins to realize that his symptom is emotional in origin, and is not a sign of organic illness or disability, he begins to lose his conversion defense and to become overtly anxious.

In our discussion we shall omit the minor conversions, even though these are more common than the major ones. Dynamically and descriptively there is no essential difference between them. The minor conversions, however, are usually vague, transient and mixed with other neurotic symptoms. They are therefore apt to be confusing, difficult to recognize, and unsatisfactory for descriptive purposes. As in most pathology, psychological as well as organic, the best and most clear-cut examples are to be found among the more extreme developments, among the cases which we often misname the "typical" ones.

In the clinical material that follows we shall concentrate upon relatively clear-cut cases of disability on a symbolic basis — muteness, paralysis, skin anesthesia, defects in sight and hearing, disturbances of movement and posture, and disorders of the internal organs. To the uninitiated some of these descriptions may sound incredible. We shall therefore state immediately that even the most extreme symptoms to be described here can be reproduced in normal persons by means of hypnosis. Since the nature of hypnosis is still imperfectly understood this does not, of course, *explain* the major conversion. What it does is to take it out of the pathological museum and place it in the potential repertory of ordinary adults.

Loss of Speech

To lose one's voice under conditions of stress is not necessarily abnormal. There are many everyday situations in which this happens without surprising anyone — a child facing an audience from a platform for the first time, an adolescent boy introduced to an attractive adolescent girl, a clerk standing before a stern executive, a private suddenly addressed by a reviewing officer. Almost anyone can be struck speechless by good news or bad news, by intense anger or intense love, by extremes of anxiety, fright, conflict, injury or disappointment. The normal disability is usually short-lived and incomplete; and it does not bring with it a relief from anxiety. Loss of speech as a conversion symptom is usually both more complete and more long-lasting — although it seldom lasts longer than a few days — and it often bestows upon its victim a welcome relief from anxiety.

Sudden mutism, a loss of the ability to speak, can be an eloquent symptom. It represents a public renunciation of the person's most important means of social communication. It proclaims dramatically to everyone, "I cannot say anything!" or, "I must not utter a word!" or, "I am afraid to speak!" It expresses a disability with maximal display so that nobody can possibly miss it. In a less dramatic manner, stammering, stuttering and the inability to speak above a whisper carry similar symbolic meanings. A brief clinical example of mutism will illustrate the drama of the symptom as well as the use made of it for secondary gain.

A case of mutism as a conversion reaction

John P., a small-town businessman of good repute, found himself suddenly facing prosecution for a major fraud of which he was completely innocent. His business associates, without informing him, had carried through some illegal deals which threatened members of the community with financial ruin. As a member of the board of directors of the firm he was technically guilty. The prosecution persuaded him to turn state's evidence in return for immunity from prosecution. To his initial intense anxiety over the situation was now added a terrible guilt over betraying close friends. He made his decision to do this because that was the only way he could save himself from unmerited imprisonment and his family from poverty and disgrace.

One day he was accosted in the street by two of his indicted friends, out on bail, who accused him loudly of throwing them to the wolves in order to save his own skin. They next tried to give him a beating. Bystanders intervened and separated them. John P. then discovered that he could not utter a sound. Medical examination showed him to be physically normal. He was referred to a psychiatric clinic where he remained mute and unresponsive to therapy, although apparently in good spirits, until some time after the date of the trial. Then he recovered suddenly and went home.

Such a mode of escape from anxiety and from the awful choice between betraying one's friends and betraying one's family may seem childlike and contrived. Yet it was genuine and it was successful. John P. appeared to himself and to the world as the silent, innocent victim of an undeserved assault by guilty men. The forbidden impulse to speak out, to accuse the men publicly who had sullied his reputation, was clearly expressed in his loss of speech, which called everybody's attention to itself. At the same time, his mutism defended him against having to betray his friends actually by word of mouth. The patient retained his immunity from prosecution because he had already agreed to turn state's witness. His muteness appeared immediately following an attack upon him as state's witness; and apparently it was only this which prevented him from carrying out his part of the bargain. Plainly this disability was beyond his control. Incidentally, he also punished himself for his intended treachery by striking himself dumb. Here in one symptom are expressed all the important aspects of a complex conflict.

A further point is that both primary and secondary gain are merged imperceptibly in this conversion reaction. John P. originally *became* mute in response to a frightening assault which his intention of testifying brought upon him. It was this response that he fixed upon as the neurotic solution for his intolerable conflict. All anxiety and guilt then disappeared: that was his *primary gain*. The *secondary gain* consisted in the patient's not having to appear in court; and this latter gain in turn depended upon his remaining mute until the trial was over. In other words, remaining mute was the use the patient secondarily made of his symptom for a purpose that was not its original cause. Such a secondary use of a symptom to avoid responsibility does not necessarily follow its development. In the chapter on dissociative reactions we shall review the case of a man who lost his memory and almost all his speech, soon after he had committed involuntary manslaughter. This man, however, recovered both memory and speech spontaneously in time to make a scheduled appearance at the inquest.

Muscular Paralysis and Skin Anesthesia

It seems almost incredible that a person with physiologically normal muscles, sense organs and nervous system should become paralyzed or lose sensation in his skin. On second thought, however, we realize that neither loss of function is actually rare.

In ordinary life people often develop functional weakness or paralysis. During moments of crisis it is not unusual for a person to become weak in the legs, to be unable to walk normally, perhaps even to sink to the ground. Under these circumstances no one thinks in terms of nerve reflexes or of brain damage. We all know also that things drop out of a frightened or anxious person's hands; his neuromuscular equipment is made incompetent by his emotional disturbance. People are sometimes actually paralyzed by fear, that is, unable to lift a finger or move a muscle when action is essential for safety and even for life.

Loss of skin sensitivity, though it attracts less attention, is even commoner in ordinary life than muscle weakness and paralysis. In the first place it is one of the normal mechanisms of biological adaptation. Such an ordinary thing as being able to sit comfortably in a chair demands that a person become adaptively insensitive to quite heavy pressures and extensive skin distortions. Under unusual conditions of severe stress a person may develop a loss of skin sensitivity as striking as anything experienced under hypnosis. In street fighting, in military combat, and in such crises as fires and panic, people suffer blows, lacerations, penetrating wounds, fractures — sometimes even a mangled hand or foot — without feeling anything at the time.

Facts such as these do not account for paralyses or skin anesthesias as conversion reactions since in the normal person they do not serve primarily a symbolic function. They do, however, demonstrate that both loss of muscle function and loss of skin sensation fall within the repertory of ordinary human beings who are not suffering at the time from muscle, sense organ or nervous system disease.

Paralyses and anesthesias as conversion reactions go farther than these common losses of function. They persist much longer and they also symbolize conflicts in such a way as to express or to call attention to forbidden impulses, to defend against these impulses, and often to provide self-punishment for them. The body part involved is thus exploited by an unconscious conflict, and it is this symbolic use that interferes with the performance of normal perception. In the following case, the exploitation of the body parts and their loss of normal function are brought out clearly.

A case of paralysis as a conversion reaction

Mildred A. was the daughter of a Rocky Mountain ranchman whose means and education were extremely limited. She was in her early adolescence when she lost the use of both her legs. At the time there was an alarming epidemic of paralysis among ranch animals, and it was generally assumed that Mildred was a human victim of the epidemic. This explanation was welcomed by the girl's parents although they knew originally that it was not true.

What actually happened was that Mildred was alone in the ranch house one afternoon when a male relative came in and, after embracing her, attempted to assault her. She screamed for help, her legs gave way and she slipped to the floor. Here she was found unharmed a few moments later by her mother who had just returned from visiting a neighbor. Mildred could not get up, so she was carried to her bed, and waited upon for several days with unaccustomed devotion. Whenever attempts were made to get her up she seemed frightened, her legs buckled under her and she could not stand unsupported. The family physician correctly ascribed her reaction to fright, but he unwisely recommended that she stay in bed until her legs grew strong again.

As it became evident that the girl was not recovering, she was allowed to displace her father in the parental bedroom, which opened into the living room. Here she spent her days in sewing, talking, reading and napping. Neighbors brought her homemade things to eat or to wear. They discussed her disability over and over. As an invalid and a victim she received the best of food and attention. Her mother continued waiting upon her hand and foot, massaged her legs morning and evening, and slept with her at night. Attempts to get Mildred to stand and walk were finally abandoned because the effort required to encourage her and physically hold her up proved too much for the hard-worked family. She never lost the ability to move her legs in bed or to pull things she needed toward her with her toes.

Mildred might never have come to the attention of neurologists and psychiatrists had it not been for the intervention of a newcomer in the neighborhood ten years later. The newcomer recognized that the paralysis might be emotional in origin and raised hopes of a miraculous cure among the countryfolk. Money was collected, arrangements were made, and the girl with her parents journeyed several hundred miles to a general hospital. As soon as they arrived it was obvious that the parents expected something to be done immediately to make their daughter well. It was obvious also that she herself resented the whole move and felt that the examinations and the questions asked were really accusations of dishonesty.

After the preliminary examinations, consultations and laboratory work had been completed, and after a recital of her illness, its onset and its course, Mildred came to the end of her willingness to cooperate. She and her parents gave the same story of the epidemic and insisted that her illness was "like infantile paralysis." That was all. Her mother summed up parental feeling when she declared, "It's you and not her that's supposed to do the curing." In the face of Mildred's sullen resentment and noncooperation, the parents' secrecy, and the powerful background of primary and secondary gain, therapy could not succeed.[5] In a month's time the patient left for home unimproved. It was only later, by chance, that the traumatic onset of Mildred's illness as given above, was disclosed by another member of the family.

As in the case of the speechless businessman, Mildred's conversion reaction began in the setting of a threatened assault which terrified her. Unlike the businessman, she could scream but she could not stand. She, too, faced a problem of betrayal — the betrayal of a close relative toward whom she had strongly ambivalent feelings. Her solution followed the suggestion given her by her own immediate reaction to the fright, paralysis of her legs. This symptom proved capable of expressing in regressive symbolism her ambivalent unconscious impulses, her defense against them and her self-punishment.

Early adolescence is often a turbulent phase of development. In it emotional conflicts which have long lain dormant may be reawakened with startling intensity. Both boys and girls, as they stand on the threshold of adulthood, are likely to be plagued by ambivalent fantasies — conscious, preconscious and unconscious — in relation to father and mother, brothers and sister, chums and rivals. In these one can find admixtures of fear and fascination, love and hate, hostile aggression and sexual desire. We know that Mildred expressed strongly ambivalent

---

[5] Grinker and Spiegel found cases of astasia-abasia often stubbornly resistant to therapy (*War Neuroses*, pp. 31–32). Our patient had received no therapy whatever during the ten years between the onset of her paralysis and her admission to the clinic.

attitudes toward her would-be aggressor after she developed her symptom; and we assume that she had similar attitudes toward him before this.

The paralysis of Mildred's legs made them the center of attention, and therefore a convenient unconscious symbol of erotic display, to which meaning her mother's devotion may have contributed. At a still further regressed level, Mildred was able to enjoy being waited upon and cared for as a baby. The invalidism also expressed vengeful feelings, since it kept alive her family's resentment, as well as her own, over what had precipitated it. Within the family group she appeared as the innocent victim of assault; but the invalidism also punished Mildred by denying her all of the pleasure and freedom of an active life.

Mildred was both a victim and a beneficiary of the conspiracy of silence. She was a victim in that she was forced by it to occupy the role of a helpless invalid; she could not escape from this role with honor. She was its beneficiary in that her invalidism saved her from the drudgery of life on a marginal ranch, both as the daughter of a poor man and as the prospective wife of some other poor man. As it was, Mildred became a community institution, a much discussed wonder, someone who worked neither in the kitchen nor in the fields. Her *primary gain* had been escape from intolerable anxiety and conflict. Her *secondary gain* was the freedom from want and drudgery. She developed her conversion reaction to achieve the first; her family and neighbors presented her with the second because everyone gained by it. Long before she came to the hospital she had become firmly established in the privileged role of a highly respected invalid. It was to this role that she finally returned.

Other conversion paralyses and anesthesias

Conversion paralyses may involve almost any part of the body — an arm,[6] a leg, a foot or a hand, the head and neck muscles (all called *monoplegias*), one side of the body (*hemiplegia*) or, as in our ranch girl, both legs (*paraplegia*).[7] Conversion paralyses may be even more complete than Mildred's was; some patients are just as incapable of moving the paralyzed part as is the victim of infantile paralysis or the victim of a "stroke." In many conversion paralyses the muscles waste away because of disuse, and secondary distortions develop which in time can no more be corrected than in neglected cases of nerve or muscle injury. What begins as a symbolic loss becomes in the end an irretrievable physical loss.

Skin anesthesias sometimes accompany conversion paralyses; sometimes they occur alone. In either case they can be impressively complete. One can stick a needle into the anesthetic arm of a conversion patient and he

[6] Grinker and Spiegel saw two soldiers with paralysis of the right arm following their killing an enemy. They also saw an occasional hemiplegia among invalided soldiers. (*War Neuroses*, pp. 28–30).

[7] Cf. Leonard, M. J., "Fear of walking in a two-and-a-half year old girl," *Psychoanal. Quart.*, 1959, 28, 29–39.

neither winces nor withdraws. He says he feels nothing and his general behavior at the time supports his statement. Here, once again, we are dealing with something that can be duplicated under hypnosis in almost anyone.

Paralysis and anesthesia as symbols

Striking inconsistencies often appear in conversion paralyses and anesthesias which are absent from nerve and muscle disease. One of these has already been mentioned: the ranch girl could use her paralyzed legs in bed but not out of it. In other patients we see shoulder muscles, which are limp and functionless as part of a paralyzed arm, behaving normally in movement of the head and in general postural adjustments of the trunk. Likewise, when a hand becomes anesthetic in a conversion reaction the insensitivity may stop at the wrist (*glove anesthesia*); when a leg is involved anesthesia may cease in a ring above the knee (*stocking anesthesia*); and when half the body is involved there is no overlap at the midline, as there is in organic diseases. All of these inconsistencies show that paralyses and anesthesias in conversion reactions correspond neither to the patterns of nerve distribution nor to those of muscle disease. They are not organized along strictly anatomical lines, but in accordance with the patient's own thinking.

The conversion patient organizes his symptoms unconsciously to express something, to speak the language of body symbolism. To express in body language, "My hand is useless," or "That hand is not a part of me," or "I feel nothing with this hand," he develops paralysis of the hand or loss of feeling in the hand. By "the hand" he means what is ordinarily meant, something that extends from the wrist to the fingertips. This is the conceptual hand, the social hand, the hand of normal language and thinking. It is not a neuromuscular unit; the disability does not correspond to the actual nerve suppy. Ordinary people know nothing about nerve distribution and neuromuscular units. Therefore they do not develop psychogenic disabilities in such terms.

Defects in Vision and Hearing

Our speech is rich in symbolic references to the special sense organs. We say things about them many times a day that are as metaphorical as anything in poetry and dreams. Love is blind and so is hate. A man is deaf to reason. One situation leaves a bad taste in one's mouth; another situation smells. Often we use a mere gesture — covering the eyes or ears, pinching the nostrils, pretending to spit something out. Such body symbolization is vivid and economical; it condenses a whole sentence into one emphatic word or gesture. The conversion reaction goes a step further than this. It represents the expressive sense organ as actually impaired in function. In doing this it is only exaggerating the normal operation of exclusion which is essential to all organized perception and behavior.

Visual disturbances as conversion reactions

To qualify as a conversion symptom, a visual disturbance must be an expression of unconscious conflict in body language. If there is blindness it is usually selective. A person will blind himself to whatever threatens to reactivate a dangerous conflict, to arouse intolerable emotional tension and anxiety. If the blindness is complete it is usually confined to one eye. The blind eye is used to symbolize the unconscious conflict, while the other eye is free to carry on the business of ordinary seeing. Such functional blindness is not only defensive; it is also indulgent. The "blind" eye actually sees things unconsciously in the forbidden way, erotically or destructively. This contradictory mode of functioning is like that of some persons who set themselves up as guardians of morality by reading pornographic literature so that they can censor it. Consciously they are outraged by what they read, unconsciously they enjoy it and never grow tired of it.

The erotic destructive potentialities of looking have been recognized from ancient times to this day. The destructive power of the "evil eye" is still believed in by millions of our contemporaries. Remnants of this once universal belief persist in such phrases of common speech as, "He looked through and through me!" and, "If looks could kill. . . ." The erotic function of vision is expressed clearly in the Bible. "Whosoever looketh on a woman to lust after her hath committed adultery already with her in his heart." Disturbances and destruction of sight as self-punishment also have an ancient history. In Sophocles' play, King Oedipus blinds himself as partial expiation of his crime in committing unwitting incest. The Bible says, "If thine eye offend thee, pluck it out and cast it from thee; it is better for thee to enter into life with one eye than, having two eyes, to be cast into hell fire." These are some of the verbal metaphors which are expressed more concretely in the body language of conversion reactions.

Deafness as a conversion symptom[8]

What has been said of visual disturbances is to a large extent true of deafness also. Patients use selective, partial or complete deafness to express forbidden impulses, as a defense against impulses and as self-punishment. Complete deafness is rare and can usually be shown to have inconsistencies as glaring as those in paralyses and anesthesias. Partial deafness is more common. A patient in analysis, for example, lost completely the hearing of the ear nearest her analyst whenever he made an unwelcome comment or interpretation. Selective deafness is used to screen out what has been forbidden or is unacceptable. It is an exaggeration of normal selective hearing, for even normal persons hear what they want to hear more easily than they hear indifferent and unwelcome things. There is also the adage, "None so deaf as those who *won't* hear."

[8] See cases of psychogenic deafness in Grinker and Spiegel, *War Neuroses*, pp. 27–28, Case No. 11.

Disturbances of Movement and Posture

As conversion reactions, disturbances of movements and posture can discharge many of the same functions that paralyses do. They can express forbidden impulses, represent defenses against these, constitute self-punishment and interfere with normal behavior. Movement and posture are especially well adapted to serve as unconscious gesture language. We shall distinguish four groups: *tremors, spasms, tics* and *postural peculiarities*.[9]

Tremor as a conversion reaction

Tremors occur normally in emotional excitement, in anxiety and in anger. They usually die down slowly and they are apt to interefere seriously with skilled acts. They also occur in fatigue, in convalescence, in intoxication, and following exertion in persons not used to heavy work. Tremor as a conversion reaction usually begins as a part of emotional excitement, anxiety or anger; it persists or recurs because it comes to express an unconscious conflict in body metaphor.

Tremor can express an emotional excitement directly that has otherwise been repressed. It can make a public statement of incapacity — the trembling hand is incapable of skilled acts, the trembling leg is a poor support. It can also punish a culprit, since tremors may bar a person from gainful and pleasurable activities. The following case illustrates a naive use of tremor for secondary gain, after it had served to protect the patient from an intolerable anxiety.

A dull normal war veteran, aged forty, developed a general body tremor when the noncombat area in which he was stationed was heavily bombed. The unexpectedness of it caught him completely unprepared. There were severe casualties, but he himself was unhurt. His tremor proved resistant to available therapy, so the patient was returned to the United States and eventually discharged. The tremor, however, recurred whenever this man tried to exert himself, as he had been doing at the time of the bombing. It consisted of a trembling of his whole body and legs, so violent that he had to hang on to something to keep from falling. During the attack he looked startled and frightened, but at the same time intent upon giving his symptom maximal display. Secondary gains — a pension and his first experience in ruling the roost at home — stood in the way of recovery for this mildly retarded, timid man.

Spasm or cramp as a conversion reaction

Spasms or cramps are higher on the scale of coordinated movement than tremors. They consist of sudden, painful muscle contractions. Men get them normally when they suddenly cool off after heavy work; women often get

[9] A description of tremors, spasms, tics, and postural disorders, as parts of neurological disease, will be found in Grinker, R. R., *Neurology*. (5th ed.) Springfield, Ill.: Thomas, 1960.

them when they change from high heels to low; both get them when swimming in cold water. As conversion reactions, cramps or spasms perform the same general functions and have the same origins as tremors, but they are more convincing because they speak a richer body language. They are usually highly selective, appearing whenever a person tries to do some specific thing, but not when he does something different even though he may employ the same muscles. They represent a disability, an active interference in the performance of a skilled act which symbolizes a conflict.

The aggressive element is more obvious in spasms than the erotic, although both may be present in the focal conflict. The spasm makes impossible for a person to do what he wants to do, or to do what is demanded of him. Its painful character also visits him with obvious punishment for his desire or his refusal. What could be more impressive than painful spasms of the hand in a man who must write for a living or to maintain his reputation? What more disabling than a cramp in a typist's hand, which grows worse when she has been reprimanded, but is absent when she handles knife and fork? A boy is pushed into becoming a violinist, against his wishes, to satisfy his mother's ambition. He loathes the violin and deeply resents maternal domination. A violinist's cramp allows him to express his aggression, to defeat his mother's ambition and safely to resist her domination. Only a tic can be more flexibly expressive than a cramp.

Tics as conversion reactions

Tics are forms of unconscious gesture language. They appear to be useless, involuntary coordinated movements which keep recurring intermittently. In normal persons they are usually called mannerisms — little meaningless movements of hands, shoulders, fingers or feet, grimacing, sniffing, throat-clearing, eye-blinking, head-nodding and the like. Normal mannerisms are often the remnants of a forgotten repetitious gesture which at one time expressed something specific — an identification with someone having a similar mannerism or an organic defect, or with someone who had a conversion reaction, an attitude of disdain, indifference, apology or compliance. Tics continue as an habitual act even though they no longer express anything but a piece of one's past.

As conversion symptoms, tics can be much more versatile in expressing conflict than can tremors and spasms. Sometimes they look to an observer like the sign language people in trains make through a closed window to people they are leaving on the platform — gestures full of an earnest meaning that seldom succeeds in getting communicated. In conversion reactions the unconscious meaning of the tic is a mystery to the patient himself as well as to other people; it is like the fragment of a sentence from some story that he cannot recall. Some patients make a display of their tic but regard it as a meaningless twitch. Others look upon the tic with some concern, seeing it as the possible sign of an organic disturbance but not, of course, as a symbol of conflict. This was the interpretation given his tic by a young physician whose case we shall describe briefly here.

George D. was serving his medical residency when his tic appeared. It took the well known form of *spasmodic torticollis*, a recurrent rotation of the head to one side, while the chin is sharply raised. This movement looks like a reaction of aversion and disdain, but it is usually a result of central nervous system disease. George had good reason to know about its nervous system origin, as we shall see, but in his case there was no organic pathology. The source lay in George's past. His father was an easy-going general practitioner whom George's mother despised. To her he seemed a man without dignity, self-respect, prestige or culture. She herself had come from a family which placed its highest values on appearances, pride and prestige. It had more than one distinguished member.

Under his mother's influence George felt ashamed of having such a father and turned away from his affectionate approaches as coming from an outsider. Until he was eleven or twelve years old he was a mama's boy, shy and withdrawn. Then his family moved to a new neighborhood where circumstances forced him to leave his mother's side and play freely with other boys. Their teasing and bullying led him to turn against his mother who had encouraged both his dependence upon her and his attitude of arrogant superiority. Although he got along well for many years, his internal equilibrium was not a stable one. For he had turned away from his mother without in the least working out his deep attachment to her; and he had identified, not with his actual father, but with an ideal, imaginary physician who bore his father's name. His choice of profession grew out of this fantasied identification, and into it he carried his still unresolved childhood problems.

The crisis came years later. After getting his medical degree, George took a residency in a strange city. Here he worked under a chief who appeared amiable, but who treated him with constant teasing behind which there was an obvious attitude of mild contempt. George found himself in a serious predicament. He could not endure being teased and depreciated; but he could not quit without jeopardizing his career. In this setting he saw a clinical demonstration of spasmodic torticollis by his chief who behaved toward the patient in a friendly but amused, condescending way. Soon afterwards George developed his spasmodic tic. Since it looked like the patient's symptom George assumed that it must have the same organic source. After diagnostic procedures had shown that it was a conversion reaction he agreed reluctantly to try psychotherapy.

George's major problem was a still unresolved identity conflict. His official role was that of an amiable, easy-going physician. This he had modeled according to an idealized version of his father, for whom in real life he felt neither respect nor affection. Behind this official façade there was an entirely different personality, proud, and disdainful like his mother, which had no legitimate outlet.

Goaded by the teasing condescension of his chief, George identified pathologically with the patient and adopted the torticollis gesture as a tic. Now he was able to show disdain and aversion in the grand manner, as his mother might have done. He expressed publicly what he deeply felt, and at the same time he preserved his official role of the amiable physician. As long as he regarded his tic as a sign of neurological disease, and therefore not his personal responsibility, he did not have to face the contradiction in his fundamental attitudes. Therapy soon revealed to George his identity conflict and gave him opportunities to work out his problems to a more mature and realistic solution.

Postural peculiarities as conversion reactions

Posture can speak the same language as gesture. Normal variations in posture often express underlying personality variables. A proud man may have an upright stance, a stubborn man a rigid one, a humble man an apologetic stoop. When a man's stance contradicts his words we tend to suspect double-dealing. Peculiarities of posture can express unconscious conflicts in body symbolism just as can tics. If our young physician with the head-twisting tic had "frozen" in his disdainful attitude he would have shown us a postural conversion instead of a repetitive movement. In either event the meaning would have been much the same. Here is the fragment of a case of postural conversion in a girl. It gives us a clear example of displaced symbolized guilt.

Olivia B. was a small-town shopkeeper's daughter from upstate New York. Her elderly uncle, who was devoted to her and pampered her, walked bent over at the middle because of an arthritic deformity. At the age of eleven she developed her uncle's symptom in an exaggerated form. She could walk normally in an orthopedic cast, but without it the bend at the waist reappeared. In psychotherapy she expressed a belief that her symptom was a punishment for her taking her uncle's cane in her hand and imitating his walk. At another time she complained of his insistent kissing; she called his kisses "wet smacks," made a face and a gesture of revulsion. She went on to describe some sex play with another girl and some boys. This last she told with marked indifference and said that it did not bother her to think about it any more. As soon as her symptom disappeared she was taken home, but a later inquiry from Syracuse indicated that she had been back in the plaster cast again and was once more in treatment.

There were probably two sets of displacement in this conversion reaction — one from early life on to the sex play that she described without conscious guilt, the other to her current conflicts. Her posture obviously symbolized identification with a person who aroused her. It was also an exhibitionistic statement of forbidden impulses and an attempted defense, since the posture called attention to the alliance with her uncle.

We have her own word for it that the bend was punishment for wrong-doing. The plaster cast, about which she did not complain, also punished her at the same time that it prevented her, like a mechanical superego, from indulging in the body symbol of her unconscious fantasies. Resumption of psychotherapy might give her the chance to work out her conflicts in more flexible ways.

Visceral Disturbances as Conversion Reactions

Not all visceral disturbances that have an emotional basis are conversion reactions. If a visceral disturbance is only part of an emotional discharge, without clear evidence of having a symbolic function also, it belongs under the *anxiety reactions* or the *psychosomatic reactions*. This is the case when, for example, vomiting or diarrhea simply represents a direct, primitive expression of anxiety or fright.[10] If, on the other hand, vomiting or diarrhea symbolizes a conflict over acceptance and rejection, if it represents in body language an unconscious sexual or aggressive drive, or if it expresses ego defenses or identifications, then we call it a *conversion reaction*. Visceral disturbances of all kinds can be employed to express unconscious conflicts in nonverbal body metaphor. They can reduce emotional tension and anxiety just as conversions in skeletal muscle and sense organs can. Disturbances of visceral function in these cases result from the use of the internal organ to say something, to express something which is not its primary function. Such an exploitation has effects upon internal organs similar to those it has upon skeletal muscle and sense organ.

Practically all of the viscera, we have said, can take part in symbolic activities. For lack of space, however, we shall confine ourselves to examples of symbolic disturbances of appetite. Eating and drinking always mean more to human beings than mere food intake.[11] From the earliest weeks of life we all experience love and closeness in feeding situations. All through childhood and adolescence we eat and drink in the company of persons whom we usually love and sometimes hate. To be given food and drink lovingly is to be given love; to be denied food and sent from the table is to be denied love and excommunicated. As adults we often eat or drink with others to restate acceptance and affection; we sometimes eat or drink alone to express solace and self-love. To refuse to eat or drink with someone is apt to be interpreted as a personal rejection. In what follows we shall discuss both loss of appetite and excessive appetite in cases which obviously express through body language some deep unconscious conflict over sex and aggression with their related fantasies.

10 This differentation will be further discussed in Chapter 20, "Psychosomatic disorders."

11 For a review of research on food habits, see Gottlieb, D., *Study of the Bases for Changing Food Habits*. Chicago: Univ. of Chicago Press, 1958.

Anorexia as a conversion reaction[12]

Anorexia means loss of appetite. It can signify many different things. Here we shall be concerned with loss of appetite that expresses an unconscious conflict in body metaphor. In the clinical case which we have chosen to illustrate anorexia, the function of eating has more than one meaning for the patient.[13] The refusal to eat is carried so far that finally the patient becomes unable to retain anything that she manages to get down. This combination of refusal and ejection is not rare, and it has a rich symbolic yield.

Betty S. was the immature daughter of domineering, overprotective parents. At puberty she found herself suddenly facing the approach of an adulthood she did not want. She rebelled against her developing womanhood and especially against the prospect of her adult sex role. Her parents had always told her that children must eat if they want to grow up. Therefore she launched her rebellion by sharply reducing her food intake. This engaged her at once in a battle with her parents, who insisted that she go on eating as before.

Betty now had two reasons for losing her appetite — her aversion to becoming an adult woman, with the prospective role of wife and mother, and her resentment at having the parental demands forced down her throat. In earlier years she had done what many children do when they are required to eat more than they want. She had concealed food at the table and later disposed of it. Now she went further. She not only revived this practice but also began vomiting much of what she had swallowed. The battle went on without a decisive trend for almost two years. Then the situation got out of hand. To her growing loss of appetite she added nausea and a positive disgust for food. She could scarcely eat anything without feeling full, and she could no longer keep down what she managed to eat. Eventually Betty had to be hospitalized for vomiting and semistarvation. Psychiatric cooperation was then enlisted.

Once she had learned to trust her therapist she was able to put into words, and to experience clearly, both her aversion to adulthood and her anger over parental domination. As psychotherapy progressed the nausea, vomiting and aversion to food gradually disappeared. Betty's parents, however, reacted to her improvement as Olivia B.'s did, a reaction which is common among domineering, possessive parents. They insisted that she give up therapy. Thus the chance to work through her problems slipped from her grasp. She left treatment with great symptomatic improvement and a better understanding of her conflicts.

[12] Anorexia and inability to retain food can also result from simple starvation, without unconscious conflict. It is possibly for this reason that the official classification places *anorexia* among the nonsymbolic "Psychophysiological Disturbances." Our cases of *anorexia* and of *bulimia* belong obviously with conversion reactions.

[13] Davids, A., and Lawton, M. J., "Self-concept, mother concept and food aversions in emotionally disturbed children," *J. abnorm. soc. Psychol.*, 1961, *62*, 309–314.

What more might further therapy have given Betty? Above all, it might have given her the chance to express her focal conflicts in less regressive ways, to verbalize and experience emotionally more of her adolescent problems and to work these through with someone who wanted her to mature. She would probably have brought out into the open a natural constructive and maturing wish which her symptoms were expressing and denying: the wish to be a mother. In a large proportion of cases such as this fantasies of being pregnant eventually emerge, fantasies which normal little girls at some time consciously entertain and often act out in play.

Here once again we see a patient expressing symbolically both sides of her conflict in a single set of conversion symptoms. The basic function of nausea and vomiting is to reject; we express this consciously when we make gagging noises in response to unwelcome information or opinion. But as every woman knows, nausea and vomiting can also mean the beginning of pregnancy. Betty expressed both rejection and fulfillment in her symptoms. When she gave up her symptoms, without working through her conflict, she was giving up her repressed and repudiated wish to become a mother. Yet in the acceptance of this wish lay her best hopes for growing into a mature womanhood.[14]

Bulimia (overeating) as a conversion reaction

People overeat for a great many different reasons besides that of enjoying food. A person is likely to eat well when he is with people he likes, but he may also eat heavily because he feels lonely in a strange city. In the first example eating is an accompaniment of affection; in the second it is a substitute for affection. Eating can also have direct aggressive or sexual meaning. When we say a man attacks his meal we mean it literally; some treat a juicy steak as though they had just killed it. The best places to witness aggressive eating are at picnics and on camping trips when no one is concerned about appearances. Adults in love speak of wanting to eat each other up, like the praying mantis. A few years ago people spoke of an attractive girl as a "nice dish." Women are sometimes called "confections" and "good enough to eat." Parents may say to a child, affectionately, "I could eat you up!" — a compliment which is unfortunately taken literally by some little children.

Fantasies of eating and being eaten are among the most primitive of all. Myths, rituals, fairy tales and adult dreams do not hesitate to express oral destructiveness and even cannibalism. Adults undergoing intensive psychotherapy sometimes experience waking fantasies of devouring or being devoured. Sexuality as eating is usually expressed less openly in more indirect symbolism; but it can still be recognized. Some children's fairy tales of sudden growth through eating a magical food belong in this category, as

[14] For a review of the literature and protocols of cases, see Bliss, E. L., and Branch, C. H. H., *Anorexia Nervosa: Its History, Psychology and Biology*. New York: Hoeber, 1960.

does the common childhood belief that mother is growing large because of
something she has eaten. Such fantasy was probably central in Betty's case
of anorexia. It is clearly focal in the following case, where excessive eating
(*bulimia*) expresses an unconscious conflict in the language of body symbol.

Mary G. was a domestic science teacher aged twenty-five. Her parents
seemed always to have preferred her younger brother and her older sister
and to have treated Mary as a child of little worth. The brother was
born when Mary was three. He replaced her in the parent's bedroom
and held first place in their hearts. She could always gain praise and
attention by eating well, especially from her father who was a food
faddist. She recalled no particular difficulties during latency excepting
that she seemed always hungry. Before meals she sometimes felt lonely
and deserted; after them she felt heavy and contented. In high school
she took to cooking like a duck to water, and around this she shaped her
future career in domestic science.

Mary entered adolescence as a fat girl. When she found herself
passed up by the boys she tried going on a diet. This went against the
grain with her; but what made it doubly difficult was that her father
acted as though her refusal of food were a mortal sin. He had not
treated her older sister this way. After a heavy meal Mary sometimes
induced vomiting secretly in the woods near home, but this made her
feel as if she "had broken all Ten Commandments."[15] By the time she
got to college she had achieved some loss of weight. But when she went
on dates a new symptom appeared: she could not eat in the presence of
her escort.

This was her confused and inconclusive situation when Mary was
graduated from college and went to spend the long summer vacation
with her now married older sister. The sister was near the end of her
first pregnancy. Mary at once felt intensely jealous and unexpectedly
attracted to her sister's husband. When a baby boy was born she disliked him from the start. She moved back to live with her parents as
soon as she began her new job in her home town. She tried dating, but
found herself angry and bitter toward men and still unable to eat in
their company. When her parents went off on a trip, Mary regaled herself with enormous meals which she cooked and ate alone, completely
satisfied. When they came back she decided to seek therapeutic help.

Therapy provided Mary with the first experience in her life of talking in the presence of someone who was interested in her but not inclined to sit in judgment. Most of what has just been related had never
before crystallized for her into anything meaningful: the compound
meanings of her food indulgences and her guilt over vomiting; her
father's demand that she eat and be fat as the price for his interest in

[15] Cf. also Bruch, H., *The Importance of Overeating.* New York: Norton, 1957;
Fisher, S., and Cleveland, S. E., *Body Image and Personality.* Princeton, N.J.: Van
Nostrand, 1958. (Fisher and Cleveland's work includes a review of the literature
covering more than 50 pages.) See also Fisher, S., "Extensions of theory concerning
body image and body reactivity," *Psychosom. Med.,* 1959, *21,* 1–7; Stunkard, A. J., "Eating patterns and obesity," *Psychiat. Quart.,* 1959, *33,* 284–295.

her; her inability to eat in the company of a male escort and her bitterness toward men; her surprising upsurge of jealousies, affection and dislike in her sister's home where — as in her own early childhood — a baby boy was born; her regression to the point where she felt unloved and could not love, and where she ate enormously when alone. These interwoven themes she succeeded in working through in relation to her current living as well as in relation to her past. After two years of therapy Mary seemed to have good prospects of realizing the career of marriage and motherhood which she wanted.

Dynamic and Developmental Background

Conversion reactions and anxiety reactions. In contrast to anxiety reactions, the conversion reaction seems to dispose of tension and anxiety almost completely. The *anxiety reaction* patient, as we have seen, must remain continually vigilant and uneasy; and every so often he may experience a frightening tension discharge like the emotional storms of infancy. The *conversion patient* presents quite a different picture. He gets rid of whatever excess emotional tension he cannot repress by crystallizing it in a body symptom, which he openly displays as evidence of illness. He usually remains relatively calm. In extreme cases, he seems not only to lack anxiety but to be indifferent to his plight as a disabled person. Sometimes he even seems to relish it. His *compliance* is then not only *somatic;* it is *total.*

Conversion reactions and phobias. There are sharp differences between conversion reactions and phobias too; but there are some interesting similarities. Both *conversions* and *phobias* use mechanisms of *displacement, condensation* and *symbolization* in forming the symptoms, and all three of these are characteristic of primary process unconscious thinking. *Phobias* and *conversions* both have multiple meanings, that is, they are both *overdetermined.* Both also *project* the derivatives of their reactivated unconscious fantasies in attempting to get rid of intolerable tension and anxiety. The *kind* of *projection* in the two, however, is quite different. In *phobias* the fantasies which cannot be successfully repressed are projected on to *external* objects and situations. The danger seems to come specifically from the outside. The phobic symptom appears to make a clear distinction between inner reality and outer reality. The patient relies upon avoiding the external danger, even if this means concealing himself.

In conversion reactions the projection is merely to a *body part,* to some specific organic function. The symptom distinguishes only between inner reality and somatic reality. The conversion patient takes special satisfaction in an exhibitionistic display. No frightening objects or situations threaten him. The catastrophe he might have feared has already happened. There is no danger as long as he accepts his disability. The conversion patient is therefore more successful in controlling anxiety than is the phobic, although he pays a much higher price in loss of body function.

Conversion reaction and behavior organization

Exclusion and inclusion in normal behavior. It is a truism that in both the learning and the performance of skilled acts as much depends upon what is excluded from the act as upon what is included. This holds true whether we consider manual skill, close attention, problem-solving, consecutive speech, logical thinking or comprehensive understanding. To be optimally effective, it is essential that one exclude competing and contradictory tendencies from the act, that they be inactivated, and that irrelevant components be reduced to a minimum.

Merely to sit and read, for example, means to inactivate innumerable responses to both internal and external stimulation. The sense organs to whose activity one does not respond are normal, the corresponding nerves are certainly intact, and there is no question of central nervous system damage or muscular impairment. Yet, as far as the reading man is concerned, there might just as well be no stimulation whatever beyond that which falls within the narrow range of his reading.

The reading man has learned to become, in effect, deaf and selectively blind, insensitive to the irrelevant and competing stimulation that still assails his sense organs. Even distracting fantasies and the recall of things undone must be kept out of his present occupation. If the reading has a strong enough personal appeal, its organization may even exclude the smell of something burning, the discomfort of heat or cold, the demands of hunger and the call to dinner.

The moment that any of this excluded stimulation succeeds in breaking through the normal barriers of behavior organization, the reading becomes ineffectual and may itself be excluded by what comes next. The man's eyes may continue to scan the lines, but for him they begin to lose their meaning. In short, one system becomes dominant at the expense of others; and, for the time being, these others cannot be aroused by stimulation which under different conditions would be fully effective. The comparison of such normal exclusion with what happens in conversion reactions is too obvious to merit further exposition. We shall see its operation in still more striking examples when we take up the dissociative reactions.

Unusual stress may magnify such normal trends. We have already mentioned the disturbances of speech, of vision and hearing, that normal persons suffer when they are excited, frightened or awestruck. We have spoken of the muscular weakness and the skin insensitivity that also appear under extreme stress. During intense emotional experiences of almost any kind it is common for normal people to lose the power of movement and the strength to stand, to have their familiar coordinations disrupted and to lose some form of feeling. One sees this kind of thing in court when startling evidence is produced or a sentence is pronounced. One sees it in catastrophes and even in unexpected joy. For the moment, a normal individual in some such situation fails to see or to hear what is going on around him. He does not feel an embrace, or a hand upon his shoulder. In combat settings or during a panic, as we have pointed out earlier, a person may suffer serious injury without noticing it, or find himself rooted to the spot by muscular inaction when he should be fleeing for his life.

Behavior organization and conversion symptoms. There was a time when clinicians believed that the only conceivable explanation of conversion symptoms lay in some undiscovered lesion of the nervous system. There are a few who still believe this. But this belief has been continually contradicted for more than half a century by the unyielding facts of clinical examination. Conversion symptoms fail to correspond to the known patterns of nerve distribution. They are often inconsistent and shifting. The manner of recovering from them violates all the painstakingly established rules of neurological disease. The patient loses his symptom when he is not supposed to lose it, and often under influences which cannot remedy sense organ impairment, brain damage or neuromuscular disease.

It is easy to understand the exasperation felt by clinicians in the old days who denounced conversion patients as common frauds. It is easy also to understand why the more imaginative clinicians who were able to look beyond their rigorous neurological training, and to recognize conversion symptoms as the symbolization of something repressed, proved a boon to the misunderstood neurotic. It was this recognition, in the latter part of the nineteenth century, that ushered in the modern phase of psychotherapy; and it was the conversion patient who became the focus of the new psychotherapeutic developments.

From a strictly anatomical or physiological standpoint conversion symptoms make no sense. They are irrational and unintelligible. The patient who displays them seems to be pretending to be sick or disabled. From the standpoint of symbolization, however, they are neither irrational nor unintelligible. They use an idiom that is different from the idiom of anatomy and physiology. It is the idiom of words and names, of the perceptual and conceptual things in terms of which we live our everyday lives, scientists as well as ordinary laymen.

The hand that becomes insensitive or paralyzed under stress is therefore not the anatomical hand but the social hand. It is the hand which the patient has normally used as a tool, in his working and playing, in his loving and fighting, in his eating and drinking, in his creating and his sinning. It is the hand to which he can also react as he does to other social objects, in much the same way that others react to it. The same is true of all inactivation in the conversion reactions. Speaking, for example, grows out of social interaction in childhood. It remains always one of the most effective means of social communication.

Eyes and ears help us to build our worlds of internal and external reality from the earliest phases of infancy. They come to participate in human interaction to a degree rivalled only by hand and tongue. Eating and swallowing, regurgitation and elimination, the comforts of body contact and human warmth, the multiple meanings of movement and posture — all these have influences upon personality development and personal functioning that leave their anatomy and physiology as irrelevant to what they symbolize as is the chemistry of a painting. The anatomy and physiology must be understood, taken into account and allowed for; but they cannot be made central to an understanding of the final product, the meaning conveyed.

The meanings in conversion reactions are like the meanings in modern works of art and in ordinary dreaming. They express something that is significant to the person creating them, even though the significance remains partly hidden from him. The satisfaction of an abstract painter with his work may not be shared by others. What he says about it may not clarify his own intellectual understanding; and it may leave others unconvinced. The same is true of many manifest dreams. They seem clear, cogent and powerful to the dreamer, even though he cannot explain why to himself or to anybody else. Conversion symptoms, as we have seen in our case material, are as likely to be misunderstood by the patient who creates them as by the layman who merely sees them. Abstract paintings and sculpture, manifest dreams and conversion symptoms are all modes of expression. Their translation into words leaves out the intensity, the richness, and often the essential violence of what they represent.

Conversion symptoms and the energy of organization

The succession of events in the formation of a conversion symptom is much like that in phobias. There is an upsurge of tension because of increased unconscious forces which cannot be successfully repressed. The upsurge results in increased anxiety and leads to the beginning of ego disintegration because of the excessive tension and anxiety. The threat of ego disintegration brings about an automatic partial regression to more primitive levels. Here a reorganization takes place, as it also does in phobias, in the reactivation of perceptual and cognitive structures — images, memories, fantasies and daydreams — which are capable of absorbing and utilizing large amounts of free energy. In other words, the reactivation of these regressive structures binds excess tension and anxiety, which are necessary in forming and maintaining complex organizations. This is what we called the *energy of organization* when we discussed phobias.

This whole process of symptom formation may be compared to the process of forming normal manifest dreams — something that all of us engage in during normal sleep, when we often express in dream symbols and primitive fantasies what we cannot put into words when we wake up. Displacement and projection are often as obvious in manifest dream imagery as they are in phobias and in conversion symptoms. In dreaming, such primitive processes seem natural and acceptable because we are out of contact with external reality and because our perceptual and cognitive organization is normally much regressed. Thus what we are dreaming appears at the time as if projected upon a screen, the *dream screen*. Here the similarities between symptoms and manifest dreams end. The final product in *phobias* is a projected fear, experienced by a person wide awake. The final product in *conversion* is a change in the function of some body part which has symbolic meaning.

In conversions, as in phobias, the auxiliary defenses of displacement and projection come to the aid of a defective repression. All that has been said in the preceding chapter about the role of the energy of organization applies equally here. The structuring of images, memories, fantasies and daydreams makes it possible to organize and maintain perceptual and cognitive experiences in place of what would otherwise be dissipated in massive discharges, such as occur in anxiety attacks. The last step is taken in conversion when the unconscious processes lead to a symbolization in expressive body metaphor. The conversion patient achieves neurotic mastery over the threatening upsurge of free unconscious energy by crystallizing it in a symptom. The symptom looks like illness or a physical disability, but it is actually a statement in the metaphor of body language.

Somatic compliance in conversion reactions

Our cases have already shown us that the body part selected for such metaphorical expression is well suited to represent the focal conflicts involved. We call the body part that lends itself to such unconscious exploitation *compliant,* and we call the process one of *somatic compliance,* that is, compliance with unconscious needs. Unconscious selection such as this appears to us mysterious. In part this is because our explanations of it are as yet inadequate, in part because it does not operate in terms of our familiar logical thinking but in much more primitive, often more artistic forms. It helps us to accept and try to understand the indisputable fact of unconscious selection when we stop to realize that we all exercise it when we dream. In manifest dream imagery, as in conversion symptom formation, a structure is chosen that can represent unconscious processes springing toward preconscious or conscious expression. At the same time, because the defensive system is still in operation, both manifest dream and conversion symptom are likely to show the influences of ego defense and adaptation, as well as the effects of superego pressures. The conversion process, as we have indicated before, distorts the body image and interferes with the functioning of the selected body part.

We have plentiful evidence that primitive impulses, infantile imagery, fantasies and dreams arise in the daytime activities of normal adults. Normal repression is sufficient to take care that these influences do not disrupt adult thinking and lead to ego disintegration and regression. Only enough escapes normal repression to brighten up the otherwise austere and calculating nature of adult reason, to give it lightness and let it play, to spill over into nonsense and laughter, to allow empathy and feeling which may be quite unreasonable, and let us grieve and mourn when we know what has happened cannot be helped. We owe it to the influence of unconscious processes within us that we can have fanciful daydreams as well as reason, that we can celebrate feasts which can be rationalized but not logically explained, and that we have poetry, drama, decoration and the beautiful, irrational arts.

Conversion symptoms and meaning

To call something irrational is not to deprive it of its meaning. On the contrary, some of the most meaningful experiences in life are irrational in the sense that they cannot be fully expressed in logical terms, and sometimes cannot be communicated at all. The form of any neurotic pattern, we have said, is simply an expression of a person's preferred way of handling intolerable tension and anxiety. Some hit upon the method of massive emotional discharge, or perhaps have never given it up, and these develop *anxiety reactions*. Others displace their revived infantile conflicts, with all the passion, to something impersonal which has a perceptual structure. This structure they drive out, or project, as a symbolic fear which they can then avoid. This, we have seen, is the general pattern of the *phobic reaction*. A third neurotic "style," which we have been discussing in this chapter, is the *conversion reaction*. The anxiety and guilt of the phobic seem to have disappeared. There is marked *display* in place of avoidance or concealment. The symptom is continuously present and it is usually disabling.

The selection of a body part as the site of the symptom poses the possibility, especially attractive to the practically minded, that the symbol means what it says and nothing more. A body part has lost its function — as in the man struck dumb during an assault — or it has become semi-independent in some inexplicable way — as in the girl whose body froze in her uncle's arthritic posture. One was convenient, the other a deserved punishment. To the more imaginative, who are apt also to be more realistic, the likelihood will at once arise that such body language, like the ordinary spoken word, can mean many things it does not actually say. Those who are familiar with the meanings of unconscious processes, through their work with living patients, take it for granted that symbols are always *overdetermined*, that is to say, symbols always have many meanings, whether they are in the form of spoken words, of actions, or of uncommunicated fantasies.

What a body symbol says in conversion reactions needs translation because, like dream imagery, it speaks in primary process terms.[16] Neurotic symptoms and manifest dreams alike are intended as *expressions* of something, not as communications to another person. They are as a rule only

---

[16] S. Isaacs calls conversion symptoms "the most convincing evidence of the activity of fantasy without words." "The nature and function of fantasy," *Internat. J. Psychoanal.*, 1948, **29**, 84.

vaguely communicative. The translation of manifest dream or neurotic symptom must remain vague and tentative unless a great deal is known about its context and its origins from other sources. It is at first only possible to say that this or that fantasy seems primarily sexual or aggressive in character, that it seems to reflect early infantile dependency needs, or that it expresses edipal wishes, fears and conflicts. Certainty and precision of translation, if they come at all, must come from the knowledge and emphatic understanding of what has produced the symptom in each individual case, of what defenses have been used and are now being used, and of what the most pressing emotional drives and needs are. In short, the translation of body language into verbal terms requires insight into the chief strains within the psychodynamic system of the individual conversion patient, including those produced by his superego functions. The complex meaning of body symbolization, and its relation to childhood feeling and symbolic play, are especially clear in the following case.

Deborah W., a married woman, aged twenty-three, complained that whenever she tried to typewrite her forearms became rigid in a half-raised position and her hands became clenched. She had been obliged to give up a position as secretary a few weeks previously because of this symptom. A general medical and neurological examination revealed no organic pathology to account for the disability, which appeared only in relation to typewriting and not in relation to other activities, even when the same muscles were used. Her only other relevant complaint was that for some years she had been dreaming of little boys lying in the street mangled, apparently having been run over by an automobile or a truck. In the rest of the case abstract we shall limit discussion to just three events forming part of the context of the conversion symptom.

When Deborah was four years of age a brother was born, the first boy in the family. She and an older sister were sent to stay with relatives on a farm just before the brother's birth. She remembered taking a violent dislike to the new baby because of the fuss everyone made over his being a boy. She did not recall any aggressive fantasies about him; but the current dreams of mangled little boys suggest strongly that she had had them as a little girl.

The patient did recall that, after the brother's birth, she and her older sister played in secret at being boys by putting some object between their legs so that it protruded. She remembered that this play was accompanied by much giggling and excitement, and that she and her sister openly ridiculed the brother's genitals which they secretly resented. The patient apparently solved her conflict over the brother's birth by attaching herself passionately to her older sister and ignoring her brother's existence as much as possible. This maneuver was so successful that even after several months of intensive therapy no early memories or fantasies about her brother returned from repression.

This young woman had the misfortune to marry an ineffectual husband. Their low income and her own restlessness and dissatisfaction drove her to prepare for work outside the home. She enrolled in a secretarial school while still feeling that if she were allowed to do what her husband was doing she could certainly do it better. Her frustration over her own awkwardness at the typewriter was heightened by the pressure to work harder from the teacher, her parents and her husband. In spite of her feelings of frustration, and her disillusionment in relation to her home life, she completed the secretarial course creditably and secured a reasonably good position. At work she found that she resented having to do what she was doing and often lived out her working day in a spirit of sullen anger. It was in this setting that her conversion symptom appeared. It repeated in a different mode her resentful, envious childhood play with her sister after the brother's birth, it expressed doubly her masculine protest, and in the form of clenched fists it symbolized both her general aggressive hate and her specific unconscious refusal to do work that she despised.

Fixation, regression and defenses in conversion reactions

In most of the cases that we have used to illustrate conversions, the *regression* has developed suddenly and often dramatically, in response to identifiable external and internal stresses. But suddenness and drama are not necessary to produce such regression. The external stress may be relatively slight and difficult to identify. The rise in internal stress may be gradual or in widely spaced steps. The only essential conditions are that emotional tension and free anxiety rise to such a level as to exceed a person's tolerance limits, and that the person have a predisposition to develop conversion symptoms rather than those of some other neurosis. When this rise occurs, ego disintegration begins or threatens to begin. Regression then proceeds automatically and the ego reorganizes at some more primitive level of fixation, where primitive fantasies and primitive drives are reactivated. This reactivation, as we have seen, leads to a secondary breakthrough of unconscious derivatives — because of the defective repression — and the body symptom is organized to express unconscious aims and to contain their energy.

It has been recently emphasized that the *fixation points* in conversion reactions may be multiple, not single, and that they may belong to more than one layer.[17] The fantasies, whose reactivation absorbs free energy and halts the regression, may be pregenital as well as genital in origin. They may express oral and anal conflicts as well as phallic ones. A single conversion symptom thus often represents simultaneously more than one *identity crisis*,[18] more than one critical phase of personality development. The predominant emotional drives involved are usually libidinal but they may also

[17] See especially Rangell, L., "Nature of conversion," *J. Amer. Psychoanal. Ass.*, 1959, 7, 632–662. Also articles in F. Deutsch (Ed.), *The Mysterious Leap from the Unconscious to the Conscious*. New York: Internat. Univ. Press, 1959.

[18] For a discussion of identity crises, see Erikson, E., "Identity and the life cycle," *Psychol. Issues*, 1959, 1, 1–164.

be aggressive. We have seen this multiplicity of meaning in some of our case illustrations already. Let us summarize three of these cases here.

Mildred A., the paralyzed ranch girl, developed her symptom when a sexual assault threatened her. This must have reactivated libidinous edipal conflicts, to which young adolescents are especially susceptible, because of their rapid sexual maturing. We know from clinical experience that erotization of the legs is common in conversion paraplegias, and we can assume that it played an important part in perpetuating this girl's symptom. At the same time Mildred created a situation in which she had to be protected and taken care of like a baby because — like a baby — she could neither stand nor walk. Thus, in addition to the edipal factors, she was able in such a situation also to display her ungratified dependency needs. Her helplessness was similar to that of an infant in an early oral, dependent phase of personality development.

Betty S., with her anorexia, showed multiple fixations still more clearly, She was expressing rejection obviously at an oral level by her repeated vomiting and her refusal to eat. At the same time her extreme obstinacy and her power struggle with her parents — both in her childhood and in her adolescence — were characteristic of conflicts belonging to the anal level of toilet training and the early struggle for independence.[19] Betty was also rejecting adult womanhood by refusing to eat when eating meant growing up to her. The vomiting itself undoubtedly held the meaning of an unconscious wish to be pregnant — as well as a contradictory rejection of pregnancy. These meanings almost always emerge in long-term, intensive therapy with anorexia patients.

We know that Mary G. was expressing pregnancy fantasies in both her *bulimia* (overeating) and her *anorexia* (loss of appetite). She overate because she wanted her father's love; and her father's unconscious wishes made him demand that she be always fat. She lost her ability to eat in the presence of her male escorts, not daring to indulge in something that had acquired sexual meaning for her. She also condensed many levels of desire and guilt when she said that vomiting up food seemed to her to break all the ten commandments. This condensation, arrived at spontaneously by an inexperienced girl, is as creative as poetry or any other work of art. In addition to these edipal meanings, Mary's symptoms also had archaic oral implications. She overate even when she did not want food because, like a baby, she was willing to eat in order to be loved. She prepared large meals for herself and overfed herself when she felt lonely and unloved, thus playing simultaneously the roles of the loving mother who feeds and the greedy child who eats. Needless to say, most of these meanings involve a free-wheeling equivalence that is characteristic of unconscious primary process thinking and dreaming, rather than of adult logic.

If the fixations in conversion reactions are often multiple and go back

[19] The relationship between adult neurosis and anal fantasy will be obvious when we come to discuss the obsessive compulsive neuroses, especially in the case material there.

to different phases of development, so are also the defense mechanisms which help determine the form of the body symbol. We have already discussed *displacement* and *projection* in relation to formation of the symptom. *Repression*, we have said, is both exaggerated and defective. In some cases it seems to dispose of the focal conflict completely, although repression in conversion reactions can achieve this only through the aid of displacement and projection to a body part. Repression is responsible also for the failure of sexual and aggressive elements to appear openly in the symptoms when sex and aggression are focal in the pathogenic conflicts. Repression helps account for the absence of anxiety in many cases (*la belle indifférence*) where the disability would otherwise be distressing or even frightening. In many respects conversion reactions are essentially severe emotional repressions. They go much further than the repression in anxiety reactions, where the source of anxiety is hidden but not the anxiety itself.[20] We have also discussed the importance of overexclusion in the section on conversion reactions and normal behavior organization. Overexclusion may be regarded as the probable precursor and counterpart of repression.

Internalizations as defensive and expressive maneuvers have not yet been mentioned in relation to conversion reactions, but they unquestionably play an important part. Internalization as a primitive symbolic *introjection*, as a taking-in through the mouth, appears clearly in the case of the girl with bulimia. She introjected love when she orally incorporated her food. She also expressed the same meaning of introjection, that is, the meaning of a physical incorporation of love, when she was unable to take in food in the presence of male escorts other than her father. This girl's anorexia pointed to the same kind of refusal to incorporate that Betty, the anorexic girl, also exhibited.

Internalization often takes the form of *identification* through imitation. The *imitative identification*, although somewhat more mature than *introjection*, is still childlike. The girl who walked in a rigid, bent-over manner illustrated an unconscious identification that belonged to an early phase of personality development, when to be *like* another person is to take on as much as possible his outstanding characteristics and the form of his overt behavior.

Conversion reactions and early childhood

Because the conversion symptom represents a body change, it is better adapted than any of the other neurotic symptoms to symbolize concretely the focal conflicts of the edipal phase of development. As we pointed out

[20] E. R. Geleerd, F. J. Hacker, and D. Rapaport, in "Contribution to the study of amnesia and allied conditions," *Psychoanal. Quart.*, 1945, *14*, 199–220, state that there is no anxiety in conversion because the entire conflict has been repressed and transformed into a physical symptom. If anxiety persists, this is because repression is incomplete, and the superego punishment comes through. R. R. Grinker, and J. Spiegel discuss this differently in *War Neuroses*. Philadelphia: Blakiston, 1945, pp. 127–128.

in the chapters on personality development, both pre-edipal and edipal forces may prevent the normal resolution of edipal conflicts. This leaves the individual vulnerable to the later development of a conversion reaction under conditions of pubertal, adolescent or adult stress.

We have already discussed the damaging effects of maternal rejection and neglect, of maternal overprotection by domineering, possessive mothers, of faulty identification and of superego defects.[21] This discussion included the influence upon personality development of ineffectual fathers and mothers, and of seductive fathers and mothers. There remain to be discussed two childhood factors of special importance in the background of conversion reactions. One is the presence of a narcissistic, histrionic parent. The other is the effect of pre-edipal masochistic fantasies.

The narcissistic, histrionic parent. A special role in preparing a child for a later conversion reaction is played by the narcissistic, histrionic parent, usually the mother. A narcissistic, histrionic woman calls attention to herself, her body, and the moody exhibition of her feelings. She provides her child with a dramatic model for identification; but she suppresses similar behavior in the child, both because it seems insincere to her and because it calls attention away from herself. The frustration which the child then experiences is almost sure to arouse his — or her — anger. The anger, however, must also be suppressed.

The effect of this double suppression is to drive the needy, frustrated child into dramatic fantasies and daydreams. These express his infantile fury over the frustration, and they give rise to furious fantasies about the retaliation that he may himself expect. Both his own fury and the danger of the fantasied retaliation frighten him. The pre-edipal fantasies stimulated in such situations are likely to include those of swallowing up, of engulfing and being engulfed, of biting and being bitten, of attacking, soiling, destroying and killing. Along with these go also the forbidden gratifications, which take the form of attention-getting fantasies and daydreams, including those of exhibitionistic display, such as the narcissistic parent indulges in, but does not countenance in the child.[22]

Masochistic fantasies. A further source of failure to solve edipal conflicts is to be found in the pre-edipal overdevelopment of pleasurable masochistic fantasies. These often arise through identification with sick or injured persons, who lead the child to feel that it is necessary to suffer if one is to be loved. Pleasurable masochistic fantasies are also encouraged by unusually punitive parents. It may seem to the child that he is noticed only when he is being punished. The result is that he seeks punishment whenever he wants

[21] See the discussion in Chapter 3 of "Stresses resulting from failure to resolve edipal problems."

[22] Extravagant pre-edipal fantasies appear in more or less undisguised form in the experiences of borderline and of fully psychotic patients. They can often be investigated during therapeutic sessions.

love. The same effect is produced by parents who follow punishing the child with unusual demonstrations of love, because their action makes them feel guilty. Suffering, in each of these relationships, becomes erotized. It is then only going one step further when the child equates love with injury, and expresses his need for love by showing some sign that he is suffering. A body symptom thus becomes a symbol of a need for love.

Resistance to failure. So much has now been said about pre-edipal and edipal failure to master focal conflicts, to establish identifications, and to work out one's identity in childhood, that a word needs to be said on the other side. The influence of parental defect upon a child's development need not be as decisive as our discussion makes it appear. Not every child exposed to parental defects succumbs to them. A child is an energetic, active human organism, with all the potentialities for normal growth and development inherent in human organisms. He is capable of seeking and finding much of what he needs in the way of psychological nourishment even in an emotionally unfavorable climate. He has two parents, one of whom may compensate for what the other lacks. Usually he has siblings and other close relatives. In this chapter, however, we have had to concern ourselves, not with persons who master their major conflicts in spite of difficulties, but with those who at least partially succumb, persons who as adults take refuge in a regression which brings out the defects of their individual past, and even magnifies them.[23]

We shall turn next to a discussion of *dissociative reactions,* which include such weird experiences as *estrangement, depersonalization, massive amnesia, trance states* and *multiple personality.* Up to the recent past, these reactions have been grouped along with *conversion reactions* under the name of *hysterical disorders* or *conversion hysteria.* Dissociative reactions are still discussed in the current literature as conversion hysteria; this is especially the case with clinical and theoretical writers who are most concerned with psychodynamics.[24] One result is that a separate genetic and dynamic background for dissociative reactions has yet to be worked out.

There are similarities between the symbolic disturbances of function that we see clinically in *conversion reactions* and in *dissociative reactions.* The two groups are clinically distinctive enough, however, to merit separate consideration. In the *dissociative reactions* we find a kind of gross disorganization or personality fragmentation that is foreign to *conversion reactions.* Even in the milder dissociative syndromes, such as *estrangement* and *depersonalization,* there are falsifications which are more like mild psychotic

[23] The adult personality frequently related to conversions will be described in the section on narcissistic (hysterical) personality in the chapter on personality disorders.

[24] Rangell has recently pointed out the disadvantages of equating conversion automatically with hysteria. See Rangell, L., "Nature of conversion," *J. Amer. Psychoanal. Ass.,* 1959, 7, 632–662.

episodes than conversions. When it comes to *dream-states*, *massive amnesias*, *fugues* and *multiple personalities*, the closeness to psychotic developments, and particularly to schizophrenia, becomes quite marked. Now that the distinction has been made and accepted in the official classification, it is difficult to understand why dissociative reactions were ever grouped with the conversions.

10

Dissociative Reactions

DISSOCIATIVE REACTIONS CONSIST OF THE SEPARATION OF ONE OR MORE COM-
ponents of the personality system from the rest. This separation begins as an
ego *defense,* as an attempt to isolate something that arouses anxiety, to gain
distance from it. But the separation ends up as an ego *defect,* as a disturbance in object relations.

In the mildest forms of dissociation the patient suffers from feelings that
familiar places, events and even the self have somehow become unfamiliar.
In more serious forms, the external world becomes so strange that the patient
feels himself in a dream world. Sometimes he blots out painful experiences
on such a widespread scale that he forgets his own past and may even lose
his personal identity. The strangeness and the dramatic possibilities in some
dissociative reactions have made them favorites in fiction and on the stage,
as well as in semipopular accounts of actual cases. The most famous fictional
example is Stevenson's *Doctor Jekyll and Mr. Hyde.* The most famous case
history from real life is still Morton Prince's *The Dissociation of a Personality.*
Here are three clinical examples which will serve to orient the reader.

A young woman had episodes of acute anxiety which were followed
by an uncomfortable feeling that people's voices seemed far away, and
that people and things no longer seemed real. At times she also felt
unreal herself and as though it were not she who was thinking her
thoughts. Although the acute anxiety which preceded onset of the dissociation meanwhile disappeared, this patient experienced the strangeness
and unreality feelings as even worse than the original anxiety.

A senior medical student, living in a dormitory, walked in his sleep almost every night, apparently searching for something he could never find. He entered the rooms of other students and rummaged about in their closets, desks and bookshelves, sometimes mumbling to himself. When spoken to, while in this state, he would stare vacantly and grope for words like a drunken person, and then go back to bed. In the morning he had at most only fleeting memories of the sleepwalking; often he remembered nothing of it at all.

A young married woman, chronically unhappy and in conflict over her marriage, occasionally wandered from her home in the daytime and got lost, much as unhappy little children do. She would suddenly "come to" far from home, and with no memory of having left it. None of these three persons was psychotic; none gave evidence of nervous system abnormalities.

In the last chapter we mentioned the fact that until recent years it has been customary to group dissociative reactions with the conversions, under the common name of *hysterical disorders* or *conversion hysteria,* and that this custom is still followed in much of the contemporary literature. We said there also that a separation into the two groups, sanctioned by the official classification, is justified by certain fundamental differences between them. In *conversion reactions,* for example, the unconscious conflicts are typically expressed in symbolic form by some specific body part. The symptom, thus constructed, is displayed publicly by the patient, as evidence that he is ill or disabled. In *dissociative reactions,* as we shall soon see, the patient tries to escape from his conflicts, not to display them, even if his escape maneuvers separate him from his immediate surroundings or from his own personal past. The rare cases of public display that do occur take place where the patient is in a dreamlike state and out of contact with the actual persons around him.[1] Another point worth making here, which will become more apparent as we go into the case material, is that the separation technique used by dissociative patients resembles closely the ego defense of *isolation,* which is characteristic of obsessive compulsive neuroses. Moreover, under test conditions, some dissociative patients reveal a personality organization closer to that of obsessive compulsives than to that of the conversion patient.[2]

Normal dissociation

Mild and temporary dissociation, sometimes hard to distinguish from repression and isolation, is a relatively common normal device used to escape from severe emotional tension and anxiety. Episodes of transient *estrangement* and *depersonalization* are often experienced by persons, neither neurotic nor psychotic at the time, when they feel the first impact of bad news or a

---

[1] See the case of Minnie D. in this chapter.
[2] See, for example, Geleerd, E. R., Hacker, F. J., and Rapaport, D., "Contributions to the study of amnesia and allied states," *Psychoanal. Quart.,* 1945, *14,* 199–220.

catastrophe. Everything suddenly looks strange and different; things seem unnatural, distant, indistinct, and foggy or too distinct and clear. Often the person feels that he himself is unreal, that it cannot actually be he who is hearing, witnessing or feeling what is going on. Examples of normal estrangement and depersonalization can be found at the scene of a terrible accident or at a time when catastrophic news arrives. Sometimes even so commonplace an experience as a long trip by plane or steamer leaves a person with transient feelings of strangeness and unreality, in his own home as well as in a foreign land.[3]

The *dreamlike states* and the *massive amnesias* of dissociative reactions also have their normal counterparts. Sudden anxiety can make a person feel dazed or stunned; he may behave as though he were walking in a dream or in another world. He seems deeply preoccupied; we say he is "not himself." He may also be unable to remember anything about an accident which has just happened, even though he himself is not injured. Soon afterwards he may give a reasonably accurate account of it, showing that during the accident he had been wide awake. Even psychogenic fugues or flights, which seem at first glance so strange, turn out to have something in common with the flights from daily life that many responsible businessmen take each year, when they go off on vacation into the wilderness. Their purpose, so they say, is to get away and forget everything. This is exactly the purpose of the psychogenic fugue. The businessman does not succeed in forgetting everything when he is away, and when he comes back he can tell you all about his vacation. The man who flees in a fugue succeeds only too well in forgetting everything while he is in it, as we shall soon see, and when he emerges from it he can tell next to nothing about what went on while the fugue lasted.

Abnormal dissociation

Dissociation becomes abnormal when the once mild or transient expedient becomes too intense, lasts too long or escapes from a person's control. It becomes abnormal whenever it leads to a separation from the surroundings which seriously disturbs object relations. Feelings of estrangement and depersonalization, we have indicated, develop as a defense against anxiety, as an attempt to put unacceptable or catastrophic events at a distance, or as an attempt to deny their reality. Their weakness is that they may lead to a form of *separation anxiety* which turns out to be worse than the original anxiety from which the patient has managed to escape. He now feels strangely detached from the world of objects and persons which makes up the familiar background of his own behavior when he is normal; or he feels detached from his own past and even from his social self.

Dreamlike states carry the apparent separation further. They create a situation similar to that which can be artificially induced in normal persons

---

[3] The opposite experience of false recognition, the feeling that one has been in a strange place before, or that all that is now going on has been experienced exactly the same at some time previous (*déjà vu*) seems related to anxiety also.

by extremes of sensory deprivation.[4] Massive amnesias, with or without fugues, separate a person from his own past. If the amnesia is complete there may be no anxiety manifest at all. As a rule, however, the patient seems deeply preoccupied and troubled without being able to tell why.

Definition. Dissociative reactions are attempts to escape from excessive tension and anxiety by separating off some parts of personality function from the rest. As we have already seen, (*a*) this may take the form of making familiar objects, places, persons or the self seem strange and unfamiliar (*estrangement* and *depersonalization*). (*b*) It may appear instead as an apparent withdrawal from the external world into a world of fantasy (*dreamlike states*). (*c*) It may take the form of a sweeping amnesia in which most or all of the past seems to be forgotten (*massive amnesias, fugues, multiple personalities*).

The defensive measures used in dissociative reactions are those of *over-exclusion, denial* and *repression,* which relate them to conversion reactions, and those of *ego-splitting* and *isolation,* which relate them to obsessive compulsive reactions. It is sometimes difficult to make meaningful distinctions between dissociative reactions and those psychotic reactions which also include depersonalization and dreamlike states.[5]

Adaptive functions. It will be obvious in the case material that dissociative reactions, in their fully developed forms, are not adaptive in the sense of preserving ego integration and keeping the emotionally disturbed person in effective contact with his surroundings and his past. Nevertheless, this miscarriage of an attempt at adaptation, which often disables a patient as seriously as do the worst conversion reactions, must not blind us to the essentially adaptive character of its beginning. Dissociation is an attempt to preserve ego integration by reducing ego span, that is by eliminating some ego functions in order to bring emotional tension within manageable limits. The process is a pathological form of the common demand of many a normal harassed person who exclaims tensely, "One thing at a time, please!" We have said that it is also a pathological exaggeration of the attempts made by normal persons to lessen the impact of sudden bad news, intolerable accidents and personal catastrophes. The normal person practices dissociation in order to hold off something traumatic, so that he can prepare himself to accept, digest and ultimately assimilate it.

In *estrangement* and *depersonalization* the adaptive attempt miscarries when the strange or artificial appearance assumed by objects, places, persons or the self exposes the patient to a "distancing" or an unreality experience which precipitates him secondarily into a kind of *separation anxiety.* It is impossible even for a stable person to feel secure and confident when he seems

---

[4] Solomon, P., *et al., Sensory Deprivation.* Cambridge, Mass.: Harvard Univ. Press, 1961.

[5] See, for example, Blank, H. R., "Depression, hypomania and depersonalization," *Psychiat. Quart.,* 1954, *23,* 20–37.

to be living in a mock-up world with an artificial self. Adaptation miscarries in *dreamlike states* because the familiar external world seems to be replaced by an unstable fantasy world, with all the unpredictable and unintelligible characteristics of a dream. In *massive amnesias* the attempt at adaptation miscarries because, although emotional tension and anxiety may almost disappear, the loss of memory and of personal identity make it impossible for the patient to maintain his previous level of ego integration. He becomes a man without a past who does not even know his name.

We shall need to remind ourselves of the initial adaptive attempt in dissociative reactions as we now turn to a discussion of their clinical varieties. When this initial attempt miscarries it often leads in these disorders to a degree of pathological functioning that overwhelms the patient. Yet even in our case of John Doe,[6] who lost his memory and his personal identity after committing involuntary manslaughter, the value of his dissociation becomes clear the moment we realize that it gave him three days of relative oblivion for the tragedy in which he had been innocently involved — three days that would otherwise have been spent in anxious, frightened waiting. The adaptive value of dissociation is perhaps least evident in estrangement and depersonalization. This is because the separation anxiety to which they expose the patient is something which everyone in normal life tries as much as possible to avoid.

Varieties of Dissociative Reactions

Because dissociative reactions constitute a relatively new group of neuroses, their arrangement into subgroups is still somewhat fluid. In what follows we shall distinguish three subgroups.

(1) *Estrangement,* which also includes *depersonalization,* is by far the most common. It represents an attempt to exclude the reality, the familiarity, the "belongingness" of things, places, people, events and situations. It may also produce loss of familiarity with one's own body or with one's own self.

(2) *Dreamlike states* are similar in many ways to normal dreaming. They carry the dissociative attempt at exclusion to the point where a person becomes more or less oblivious to his surroundings, as in the common dissociative experience of sleepwalking.

(3) *Massive amnesias,* our third group, exclude a person's own past, and they often deprive him of his personal identity. Occasionally they divide up his personality organization into two or more semiautonomous pseudopersonalities, each of them defective in some respect. We shall begin our clinical presentation with a discussion of estrangement and depersonalization.[7]

[6] The case of John Doe will be given in the section on massive amnesias.

[7] The term *estrangement* is preferable to Mayer-Gross's term *derealization*. Patients often feel that the now unfamiliar thing is still *real* enough, but has somehow become *strange*. We are retaining the term *depersonalization*, with its current meaning of self-estrangement, because of its widespread use in contemporary literature.

Estrangement and Depersonalization

Estrangement is one manifestation of the dissociative attempt to escape from excessive emotional tension and anxiety by creating a separation within the personality system. It fails because it results in a feeling of strangeness and detachment from once familiar experiences which patients find difficult to endure. It merely exchanges one evil for another. Before the dissociation the patient is frightened by feeling too close to familiar anxiety-provoking things; after the dissociation he finds himself frightened by their unnatural distance or their weird unfamiliarity.

If estrangement develops in relation to objects, people, events or situations, we speak of *object estrangement.* If it develops in relation to one's own body, body part or body image, we speak of *somatic estrangement.* If it develops in relation to one's self or self-image, we speak of *self-estrangement,* or, more commonly, *depersonalization.* Some patients suffer from one of these forms of estrangement, some suffer from two, and many suffer from all three at once.

Object estrangement

In object estrangement the once familiar world of ordinary objects — by which we mean things, persons, places, events and situations — seems to have undergone a disturbing and often indescribable change.[8] What once seemed lively and interesting now appears colorless, lifeless and artificial; it may seem unnatural, unreal, too far away, or too distinct and sharply defined like stage scenery.

In attempting to alleviate their anxiety by making the objective world seem unfamiliar, some patients succeed in impairing one of their most important ego functions, that of maintaining *object constancy.* They may, for example, perceive round tables seen from one side as oval tables, and square tables as diamond-shaped. Such perception corresponds to the retinal image perceived; it represents objects as artists learn to represent them; but it fails to correct automatically for the distortions in images upon which object constancy depends.

Estrangement is likely to introduce another source of anxiety secondarily. When the patient tries to describe to someone else what he is experiencing he discovers that no one seems to understand him. To the barrier set up by the experience of strange detachments is now added the barrier of being unable to communicate. This further isolates the patient; it disturbs his object relations in their own right.

The inability of normal persons to understand communications of this kind is in part because they are seldom formulated by anyone. No adequate language for their communication is available. The inability to understand has, however, another source in the listener's own defenses. By being unable

[8] Cf. Bird, B., "Feelings of unreality," *Internat. J. Psychoanal.,* 1957, *38,* 256–265.

to understand, the listener defends himself from having to share the patient's weird experiences and his disturbing anxiety.

Although almost everyone has experienced mild, brief object estrangement at some time in his life, few have witnessed the distress of a full-blown case such as the following abstract presents.

Julia K., a married woman aged thirty-four, entered the clinic because she could not get through an ordinary day's routine without continual guidance. Her dominant complaint was that everything seemed strange and different. She said, "I can't understand it. Things don't seem like they used to. On the way here it was like a foreign country. Is this really Wisconsin? Will I be able to find out why things are so different? Things look out of shape. That table — I know it's straight, but it looks all crooked on the top." (Her gesture showed that she meant to say that there were unexpected angles, i.e., the right angles did not look like right angles from where she sat.) "And the signs on the highway weren't the same. The arrows pointed to places we didn't want to go to."

On the ward Julia conversed normally with other patients, but afterwards she would ask if they really were patients. People, she said, seemed to change their personality in the clinic from day to day. When relatives visited her they looked so different to her sometimes that she wondered if they could be strangers made up to look like her friends, so that she herself would not feel deserted. These feelings, of course, represented fluctuations in her own degree of object estrangement from time to time.

When Julia went for walks outside, the shops and houses looked strange and unreal. People walked as if they were robots. One day she exclaimed, "Look at that little boy! He isn't running the way a little boy would!" She thought that the statue on the university campus could not be one of Lincoln, which it was, because "people just don't sit that way."

As she improved this patient grew more and more skeptical of her earlier misinterpretations, which she remembered well. She said, for example, "Was this all my imagination? I don't feel the way I did (before) at all." When she was transferred to an open ward, she exclaimed with pleasure, "These look like *real* patients!" Later on she commented, "Everything looks normal to me now but I'm scared because it does," i.e., afraid that the change to normal might not in itself be real or might not last. After she had recovered she expressed astonishment that she could ever have thought things had all changed.

All the way through this dissociative illness, which had been precipitated by a real personal tragedy, Julia groped her way about in a make-believe world of distorted shapes, peopled by what seemed imitations of human beings. She accepted her distorted perception as direct evidence that the world of objects, and not her own feelings, had undergone drastic change. This is obviously a poor way of handling intolerable stress, both because it is incapacitating and because it only substitutes one awful anxiety for another. To understand such a development it is necessary to bear in mind constantly that people do not choose such a solution consciously, that they do not know where it will lead them. They select it automatically through the operation of unconscious ego defenses. The dissociative solution represents the best of which they are capable when they suffer regression under stress.

We assume that persons who easily develop severe object estrangement are persons who, for one reason or another, have always been somewhat defective in their object relationships. We assume that their hold on external reality and its objects has always been somewhat tenuous, or that object relationships have always aroused more than an average degree of anxiety. Expressed in another way, these seem to be persons who have experienced more than average difficulty in maintaining object constancy under stress. It should be added that, because they succeed in weathering their dissociative reaction without regressing into a psychosis, we can also assume that their overall ego integration is more stable than that of a psychotic person.

Somatic estrangement

In somatic estrangement it is the body as a whole, or some part of it, or the body image, that seems to have become unfamiliar or unreal. The patient may look with anxiety or bewilderment at his hands, his face, or his body conformation. What he sees or feels no longer appears to be the same as it used to be. It may even seem no longer to be his own.

One patient, for example, complained, "My legs move, but it feels like someone else's legs moving; my arm moves from the paper to my lap, and it feels like another's arm moving and doing what mine actually does." Another patient, a young woman of twenty-two, felt that she looked old and different, although objectively she had not changed in appearance. A third felt that her body had become as light as straw, and that the wind might pick it up and whirl it away.

Somatic estrangement and body image. Often somatic estrangement concerns the patient's body image, that is, the conception a person has of what his body is like, how it appears and how it feels. A brief digression is needed at this point to indicate in what way the body image is involved. Even normally the image which each person has of his own body is never a "true" or objective representation of his body. The body image is significantly influenced by a great many things which do not enter into the making of a photograph or even into another person's conception of what one's body is like. Everyone, for example, has personal experiences with different parts of his body, and with their interaction, and even with his body as a whole, which no one else can share. These experiences are of great importance in forming and maintaining a body image. Every person sees himself differently from the way that others see him. One has only to observe the embarrassment which most people express when they see themselves in a moving picture to realize how different must be their body image from the camera's image.

The body image is also influenced by the varying intensities and the vary-ing clarity of one's perceptual experience with different parts of the body. These variations are often also purely personal in character and have no counterpart in the experience of observers.[9] The body image is distorted one way or another by infantile, latency and adolescent experiences, including those of the growth, maturation and functioning of body parts, which assume a different importance at different times. It is also influenced by adult emo-tional experiences, by anxiety and narcissism, by a person's particular mech-anisms of adaptation and defense, by the effects of illness, injury and ageing, and, in women, by experiences with pregnancy and childbirth. Even the ordinary daily experiences of falling asleep and of waking up often leave strange imprints of apparent body conformation which may definitely affect the body image.[10]

Anyone who suffers severe regression while he is awake may experience a frightening or bewildering somatic estrangement. We see this commonly in febrile illnesses, in intoxications — experimental as well as nonexperi-mental — in hypnosis and in such special states as those induced by sensory deprivation. Some individuals seem to be especially vulnerable to this kind of regressive change. Whenever they pass beyond the limits of their tolerance for emotional tension and anxiety they develop somatic estrangement.[11]

Closely linked to somatic estrangement is the ignoring or the denial of a somatic change that is occurring or has already taken place. This is not rare in normal beginning adolescence. Some adolescents ignore or deny the early development of their secondary sex characteristics because for some reason sexual maturity is unwelcome. Somatic changes in normal ageing and in disease sometimes give rise to similar reactions. If an adult's identity is too closely tied to a narcissistic body image, some involutional or pathological change in his appearance or function may tip the scales in favor of regression, dissociation and denial of the change.

Self-estrangement or depersonalization

In self-estrangement, or as it is usually called, *depersonalization,* the pa-tient seems to himself no longer the same person. He appears to himself to

---

[9] Fisher, S., and Cleveland, S. E., *Body Image and Personality.* New York: Van Nostrand, 1958; Kolb, L., "Disturbances in the body image," in S. Arieti (Ed.), *Amer-ican Handbook of Psychiatry.* New York: Basic Books, 1959, pp. 749–769.

[10] Silberer, H., "Report on a method of eliciting and observing certain symbolic hallucination phenomena," in Rapaport, D. (Ed.), *Organization and Pathology of Thought.* New York: Columbia Univ. Press, 1951, pp. 195–207; Federn, P., "Ego feel-ing in dreams," in Federn, P., *Ego Psychology and the Psychoses.* New York: Basic Books, 1951, pp. 60–89.

[11] A particularly interesting facet of the denial of body change is to be found in the phenomenon of the *phantom limb.* A person who has lost part or all of a limb ignores the loss, or even denies it. Sometimes he speaks and acts as though no loss had occurred. See Fisher, S., and Cleveland, S. E., *Body Image and Personality.* New York: Van Nostrand, 1958.

have somehow changed, to have become unfamiliar, detached or unreal. A person's general reaction to such a change varies all the way from uneasiness and perplexity to extreme distress and fright. Object estrangement and somatic estrangement often accompany depersonalization, but sometimes it occurs alone. The depersonalization we meet in neurotic dissociations is only partial. The patient recognizes that he actually is the same person even though he feels inexplicably different.

Depersonalization and the self-image. In depersonalization there is a basic disturbance in a person's *self-image,* that is, in the conceptual matrix which he uses as the internal frame of reference for himself. The conceptual matrix has become unstable; it is no longer constant and dependable (*loss of self-constancy*).[12] A few words need to be said at this point about the self-image. In normal as well as in neurotic persons the self image is more inclusive than the body image. The self-image is a product of an infinite number of interactions with other human beings. These interactions have in the past led, and go on leading, to internalizations of the experiences of interaction as *ego identifications* and as *superego identifications.* The identifications, modified or transformed by the ego or superego organization into which they enter, also interact with each other within the personality system. Among other things, the self image represents one's status as an organism, as a unit in a series of social systems (family group, neighborhood group, school, religious and work groups), as a person toward whom, within the different social systems mentioned, other people have many different and conflicting attitudes, and toward whom the person himself has his own complex attitudes.

Into the formation of the self-image the early hierarchical systems of value judgments of mother, father, siblings and other close associates enter, in relation both to ego functions and to superego functions. Thus moral and esthetic elements are a part of its dynamic structure almost from the start. The small child's introjections and multiple identifications form overlapping nuclei of self-images until, some time during latency, the unit of the *self-image* and of *self-identity* begin to crystallize.[13] The child, as he matures biologically and socially, comes to know with greater assurance what kind of a person he is. He operates in terms of increasingly stable hierarchies of motivational values, to know what he likes and does not like, what he can and cannot do, what he will or will not do, what he wants to be and expects to be.[14]

The self-image is indispensable for everyday living, but it is by no means invulnerable. As we all know, intoxication and head injury can seriously

[12] C. Fisher, cited in Spiegel, L., "The self, the sense of self and perception," *The Psychoanalytic Study of the Child.* New York: Internat. Univ. Press, 1959, vol. 14, pp. 81–109.

[13] See Erikson, E., "Identity and the life cycle," *Psychol. Issues,* 1959, *1,* 1–171, for a somewhat different presentation.

[14] The fantasy of being an adopted child is related to this.

disrupt it. The police are continually running across drunken men who are still able to navigate fairly well, but who have no clear idea of who they are, what they do and where they belong. Patients suffering from head injury often pass through a phase during which they cannot identify themselves or recall their status as individuals or as members of social groups. As the intoxication and the effects of head injury clear up the self-image usually re-establishes itself much as it had been before.

Emotional stress alone can have similar effects. In mild cases of dissociation under emotional stress the patient knows who he is and where he belongs; but he feels himself to be changed in some indescribable and usually painful manner. He is not the same person, he says, he no longer feels anything as he once did, something strange seems to be happening to him.[15]

One patient, who experienced depersonalization most acutely when she awakened in the morning, expressed it as follows: "I don't know who I am when I wake up in the morning. I seem to need someone to help me get things straight. My mind seems to be on a sort of precipice, and I'm not sure which way it's going." She was also expressing an as yet unconscious fear of regressing into something approaching personal nonexistence. This kind of experience has been described as not uncommon among women concentration camp victims while they were fully awake during the day.[16] It is also apparently not unusual among small children during their mother's absence.[17]

Severe emotional stress in a vulnerable person can disrupt the self-image almost completely, leaving him disoriented in a world he cannot fathom. He may wander about aimlessly in familiar territory as though he were lost in a jungle. According to World War II studies, soldiers who were stunned, not by shell fire, but by a close companion's death, sometimes stumbled around fearlessly because they had no conception any more of who they were, where they were, and that there was imminent danger that they would be killed.[18] As we turn to a discussion of *dreamlike states,* we shall witness the disorientative effects of still more severe disruptions of the self-image. Later on, when we come to the section on massive amnesias, we shall deal finally with the dissociation of personality which Freud called the extreme of depersonalization.[19]

[15] Cf. Jacobson, E., "Depersonalization," *J. Amer. Psychoanal. Ass.*, 1959, 7, 581–610; Berman, L., "Depersonalization and the body ego," *Psychoanal. Quart.*, 1948, *17*, 433–452; Peto, A., "On the so-called 'depersonalization'," *Internat. J. Psychoanal.*, 1955, *36*, 375–378.

[16] E. Jacobson reports that women prisoners in concentration camps awoke at night with experiences of somatic estrangement, and during the day suffered frightening depersonalization. See her "Observations on the psychological effects of imprisonment on female political prisoners," in K. Eissler (Ed.), *Searchlights on Delinquency*. New York: Internat. Univ. Press, 1949, pp. 341–368.

[17] Fraiberg, S., "A critical neurosis in a two-and-a-half-year-old girl," *The Psychoanalytic Study of the Child.* New York: Internat. Univ. Press, 1952, vol. 7, pp. 173–215.

[18] Grinker, R. R., and Spiegel, J., *War Neuroses*. Philadelphia: Blakiston, 1945.

[19] Freud, S., "A disturbance of memory on the Acropolis," (1936), in *Collected Papers*. London: Hogarth Press, 1950, vol. 5, pp. 302–312.

Dreamlike Dissociative States

As with estrangement, so with *dreamlike dissociative states*, there are certain common forms with which we are all familiar, and others which occur with relative infrequency. Sleepwalking or somnambulism is something which we have all seen and some of us have experienced, at least as children. Somnambulistic attacks, psychogenic trances and stupors, on the other hand, are uncommon and strike everyone at once as pathological. Yet the familiar and the unusual forms have many things in common. In all of them the person typically has his eyes wide open and shows that he can avoid obstacles, but he is obviously not in normal contact with his environment. His lack of adequate grasp of his environment sometimes gets him into dangerous situations with which he cannot cope, as we shall later see. The sleepwalker, after he awakens, can sometimes tell something about what it was that he was trying to do while he was walking in his sleep. Often he remembers nothing about it at all. Patients who have been in a psychogenic trance or stupor usually cannot give a spontaneous account of their dreamlike experiences. In exceptional cases they can, with or without the help of narcosis.[20] Information gathered from the latter sources make it clear that experiences in trance and stupor resemble those of the ordinary sleepwalker.

Sleepwalking or somnambulism

Ordinary dreams, without sleepwalking, are dissociative experiences in which a person has already withdrawn from his surroundings and regressed into sleep. They characteristically express conflicts in some form, often a forbidden wish distorted beyond recognition by ego defenses and superego pressures. As we have said, experimental studies indicate that everyone dreams every night, whether he remembers having dreamt or not.

The person who gets up and walks in his sleep, the somnambulist, is exhibiting a special kind of dreaming. His motility is more or less at the service of his dream fantasies, so that he acts them out to some extent, and his eyes are open so that he can carry out complex acts before he wakes up or returns to bed. Walking about with eyes open does not happen in ordinary dreaming.

The sleepwalker, without awakening, goes in search of something about which he has been fantasying in his dream, or he tries to work out a conflict, or he attempts to escape from something he has been imagining. The wishes, conflicts, and fears expressed are often related to daytime matters of the present — as in the famous sleepwalking of Lady Macbeth — but they also represent in some form a revival of childhood fantasies.

Although sleepwalking is commonest in childhood it is by no means rare among adults. Most of us who have lived in dormitories or barracks have seen it. The successful somnambulist gets up without wholly waking, his eyes

[20] Grinker, R. R., and Spiegel, J., *Men Under Stress*. Philadelphia: Blakiston, 1945.

open and his movements are reasonably well coordinated. He rummages about, sometimes asks incoherent questions or gives strange answers to what an awakened person asks him.[21] He may dress and go out, or go out half-dressed as he is, walking down corridors, down flights of stairs, into other rooms or into the street. Eventually something awakens him or he just goes back and continues sleeping. In either case he may remember nothing coherent when he wakes, or he may recall a manifest dream in which some of the events from his sleepwalking episode can be identified.

Performance such as this, as we have said, can lead a person into danger. Sleepwalking soldiers in wartime service have more than once been fired upon for not responding to a sentry's challenge.[22] Not long ago a sleepwalker climbed out of the second-story window of a college dormitory and was seriously injured. Sleepwalking children and adults get out on ledges and roofs, or walk in front of moving vehicles or fall downstairs. Sometimes a sleeping person gets up and walks or runs because he is impelled to escape from the dangers threatening him in his dream life. The dangers in the dream may pursue him after he is up on his feet, and the dream has too strong a hold on him to let him wake up. Here are three examples.

A girl aged four years began walking in her sleep at a time when serious marital discord between her parents was smouldering near the surface of their life and she herself was in the edipal phase of her own development. One night she was walking along the upstairs hall, in a somnambulistic state, when a ghost seemed suddenly to come out of her parents' bedroom. She rushed to the stairs, ran down them at top speed, and near the bottom tried to jump the rest of the way. Fortunately her parents, who were still downstairs, heard her and her father was able to catch her as she jumped. Back in bed she asked openly that her mother go away, and persuaded her father to stay with her until she fell asleep again. According to her mother, the child remembered the whole episode, including the ghost, as something that had really happened. There were other related dreams which need not detain us here.

An adult in therapy recalled that when he was seven years old he found himself out on the fire escape one night, with one leg over the railing, five stories above the street. He had been dreaming that the apartment was ablaze and that he was fleeing from it in panic. The vividness of the dream, and the settings in which he again and again recalled it during therapy, suggested that he had been trying to escape from the fires of an early childhood conflict, in which passion, hatred and the fear of retaliation each played a part.

Another adult in therapy awoke one night to find himself running downstairs in the hotel where he was staying during a business trip. All that he could remember was that somebody was terribly in need of help and that he was running to the rescue. Similar dreams without sleepwalking soon made it clear that the "somebody" was himself. It was

---

[21] Such a case has been briefly described at the beginning of this chapter.

[22] Sandler, S., "Somnambulism in the armed forces," *Ment. Hyg.*, 1945, *29*, 237–247.

apparently his absence from the therapeutic help he needed that had pre-cipitated the sleepwalking dream.

The chronic sleepwalker demonstrates that he is less able to keep his dream life and his waking life apart than the average person can. The boundaries between sleep and waking seem to be somewhat blurred. Perhaps sleep-walking is commoner in childhood than in adulthood because the functional boundaries separating fantasy from objective reality are much less clearly marked early in life than they are later on. It should be noted, however, that even though sleepwalking places perceptual, cognitive and motor sys-tems at the dream's disposal, it can be found among adults who otherwise show no signs of personality dissociation. It gives us, therefore, a more or less normal foundation from which to understand the definitely pathological somnambulistic attacks, the trances and stupors, the fugues and dissociated personalities.

Somnambulistic attacks ("hysterical convulsions")

The somnambulistic attack, which used to be called an hysterical fit or hysterical convulsion, is actually not one of the convulsive disorders. This has been recognized for almost a century. It is a little drama, as we shall see, in which a person becomes suddenly oblivious to his surroundings while he acts out some fantasy which he has up to then been repressing. During the attack, the socially shared world exists as little for the patient as it does for an ordinary sleepwalker. When he comes out of his somnambulistic state he has no memory for what happened in it. Sometimes he behaves as though nothing out of the way had happened at all. Sometimes he seems a little dis-oriented for a short time. Sometimes he goes into a passive dreamlike trance state, as the following case of somnambulistic attack will show.

Minnie D., an unmarried woman aged twenty-three was brought to a psychiatric in-patient service on a stretcher by the police. The admitting officer stated that she seemed to be having a generalized atypical convul-sion. The day after admission she appeared normally alert and willing to talk about herself. Everything went well until she told of a sexual assault she had suffered which, she said, had led her mother to drive her out of her home. As she spoke about this, Minnie's account grew vaguer and vaguer. She seemed preoccupied and confused, like a person going into a stupor. Suddenly she slid from the chair to the floor, let out a scream and began her somnambulistic drama.

Her behavior was clearly not that of someone in a generalized convul-sion at all. It was a melodramatic piece of unconscious acting in which she gave a vivid pantomime of a woman being assaulted. Minnie seemed to be engaged in a violent struggle with an invisible assailant who ap-peared finally to overcome her. She screamed at the beginning as if in fright, she struggled and fought throughout her fantasied attack, she screamed in outrage when she finally gave up the struggle, and she sobbed afterwards without shedding tears. This solitary drama she repeated over and over, each performance separated from the next by a period of rest. While resting, Minnie rolled her head from side to side, breathed heavily, knit her brows, and sobbed occasionally in what might have been only a discharge of tension, but which had the sound of outrage.

The somnambulistic attack just described came as an immediate sequel to the verbal description of an assault. It was as if Minnie had said, "Let me show you what happened!" But the act was not really intended as a communication. It was a sudden dissociation in which a previously half-suppressed memory returned to dominate her behavior completely, even to the exclusion of her human environment. When Minnie slipped on to the floor she slipped into her fantasy world. She slipped out of the shared realistic world to which her verbal description up to that moment had belonged. She was to repeat this performance many times during the ensuing weeks. Whenever she recalled or reconstructed this past event she lost her hold on contemporary social reality and regressed to a traumatic memory, which she was then compelled to act through again and again. Here we have a fantasy, based upon a memory, which is being played out overtly before our eyes, instead of remaining in partial repression.

This patient ended each series of attacks, which sometimes lasted many hours, by going into a deeply preoccupied trance state, which lasted as much as a day and a half. Although we shall not discuss *trance states* until the next section, it will be useful to describe what Minnie did in hers at this point. Her trance behavior, in contrast to what went on in the attacks, was passive and subdued. She stood or sat wherever she was placed. She went wherever she was led. At the same time, she avoided obstacles normally, went upstairs and downstairs without stumbling and without help, and waited for doors to be opened for her. She took food and drink only when it was put to her lips; she chewed and swallowed like a stunned, grief-stricken person. Her facial expression was sorrowful and perplexed. Occasionally she shook her head slowly from side to side, as if to say, "I can't believe it." But she neither spoke a word spontaneously nor responded verbally to anybody's speech.[23] Although she seemed to be in a dream she lacked entirely the initiative of a sleepwalker. Once the trance state had terminated, Minnie appeared normal again; but she could recall nothing of what she had so recently acted out and nothing about her trance state.

Minnie turned out to be unresponsive to psychotherapy. For one thing, she was poorly educated and of limited intelligence; and for another, she was in trouble with the police whose presence for some time in the background was evident. An additional factor was that the somnambulistic attacks were a form of unconscious display which must have brought her gratification in itself. They also brought her secondary gain. When she was lonely, especially in the evening when

---

[23] R. R. Grinker and J. Spiegel describe a similar trance in *War Neuroses*. Philadelphia: Blakiston, 1945, p. 34. Their patient also had to be led about in a "twilight state," or trance state.

things were quiet, she would sometimes let out a startling scream and begin another series of attacks. Other patients crowded sympathetically around her, expressing openly their concern. For a day and a half after the attacks ended Minnie received special attention from nurses and attendants, since she was helpless in a trance state. Although there is no reason to doubt the genuineness of these attacks, it is interesting that they decreased in frequency sharply when the patients were instructed not to go near her when she had them, on the grounds that excitement made her worse.

Therapeutic sessions had eventually to be abandoned, since they invariably precipitated a somnambulistic attack followed by another trance state. Instead, Minnie was given a program of light housework and allowed ground privileges on condition that she had no attacks. Within four months after her admission she was discharged symptom-free. Two years later, under similar circumstances, she was readmitted with similar somnambulistic attacks and again discharged after symptomatic recovery.

Relatively rare cases such as this give us rare insights into the dynamics of dreamlike states. Minnie could be precipitated into a dissociative attack almost at will, by a stimulus situation that could be predicted. The form of the fantasy acted out had obvious meaning; it referred to a life experience which was known. Finally, and perhaps most important, once Minnie entered into her dreamlike state she could not leave it until she had acted through her melodrama many times. Neither could she cut short the protracted trance state that followed the attacks, in which she seemed to be a helpless, grieving automaton. In other words, this was not a conscious play acting, put on to gain sympathy and escape punishment. It was an unusual process of dissociation, occurring automatically when the patient was frightened, lonely or in the midst of recounting her traumatic memories. It was a regression into an individualistic pattern of fantasies, which the human environment could encourage or discourage, but which, once begun, followed an undeviating course controlled by unconscious processes.

The patterns of somnambulistic attack are highly individualistic from patient to patient, varying greatly in complexity, duration and repetitiousness. Often they give the superficial impression of deliberate theatrical display, as in the case of Minnie D. They differ from mere display, however, in becoming automatic and uncontrollable once they have started, and in the fact that patients are usually amnesic for the period of the attacks, as well as for the trance state, if there is one.

Trance state ("twilight state")

Trance states have also been called twilight states. Trance patients seem to be living in a kind of half-light, between clear reality and dark fantasy, like a person who is stunned or lovesick. They move about in an objective environment where there are other human beings, but they remain deeply immersed in regressive preoccupations which they cannot express in words or share with others.[24]

It is unfortunate that most persons who experience a trance cannot tell us about it at the time or recall it afterwards. Nevertheless, the trance state is as genuine as the everyday dream and usually much better structured. We know something of this from direct evidence. Occasionally a patient is able to talk about what he is experiencing while he is in a trance, or to describe it after it is over.[25] We also have indirect evidence of the power of unconscious or partially unconscious processes in determining mood and action from the study of dreams and fantasies in normal, neurotic and psychotic persons.

What is the relationship between the *trance* and *sleepwalking*, which we have just discussed, and what is the relationship between the *trance* and the *massive amnesias*, to which we shall soon turn? In both instances the relationship is a close one; and the dynamic differences between them are relatively minor.

Sleepwalkers are easily awakened — although they should not be — whereas people in dissociative *trances* are not. Both may follow instructions in a dreamy way, and even answer questions in more or less incoherent phrases, although the latter is unusual in trance states. The person in a trance or twilight state is as a rule more withdrawn than sleepwalkers are. He is not asleep. He is held in bondage by fantasies which are normally unconscious.

Amnesic patients, as we shall see, are less dazed than is the patient in a *trance state*, less passive, and more able to navigate without help. Amnesic patients maintain a surface integrity of behavior by almost completely repressing their otherwise disruptive fantasies. The trance patient's behavior is poorly integrated because his repression, and the separation of his repressed functions in his ego organization, are less complete. The patient in a trance seems not to be quite of this world; the amnesic patient seems to be of this world whereas actually he is not. Both trance states and amnesias result from the use of archaic defense mechanisms. The regression in both is deep; but whereas repression in trance states is insufficient, in the massive amnesias it is excessive.

Psychogenic stupor

Psychogenic stupor looks at first like an attempt to escape from the anxious confusion of a trance state by flight into apathy and inaction.

---

[24] A description of behavior in a deep trance has just been given in the case of Minnie D.

[25] R. R. Grinker and J. Spiegel give an example of a soldier plunged into a trance state. See *War Neuroses*. Philadelphia: Blakiston, 1945, pp. 9–10.

Stuporous patients sit motionless, except for an occasional shift in position, or they lie with eyes closed as if in a deep coma, without overt response. If they do respond it is only because their stuporous fantasy has been interrupted by some insistent outside stimulus or by some powerful inner urge.

It takes little clinical experience to discover that the patient in psychogenic stupor is neither as apathetic nor as inactive as he looks. He may perceive a great many things going on around him which he later recalls and talks about, once the stupor has lifted. Like the person in a trance, he is deeply preoccupied with previously unconscious fantasies, which have become conscious or preconscious because of his regression. This also we learn from the occasional patient who is able to give us a retrospective account, either spontaneously or under narcosis. Psychogenic stupor, in short, utilizes wholesale repression in massively inhibiting expressive and adaptive behavior. It is much less successful, however, than it may seem. Like the trance state, the stupor experience has a nightmarish quality in which anxiety is often painfully felt.

Massive Amnesias

The *dreamlike states,* which we have just been discussing, form a bridge between the more limited dissociative states seen in *estrangement* and the more sweeping dissociation characteristic of the *massive amnesias.* We shall distinguish three main varieties of massive amnesia: (1) *massive amnesia without fugue;* (2) *massive amnesia with fugue;* and (3) *dissociated personality.*

Massive amnesia without fugue

When massive amnesia enables a person to escape bodily from a situation and to forget all about it we call the flight a *fugue.* This we shall discuss in the next section. Massive amnesias also occur without an actual flight from the situation; the patient simply wanders aimlessly about because he has forgotten who he is and where he belongs. It is not unusual for such an amnesia to clear up suddenly, after lasting two or three days, as we shall see in the following clinical case.

A young man, dressed in working clothes, appeared at the main entrance of a general hospital one Saturday morning with the complaint that he did not know who he was. He seemed dazed. There was nothing on his person by which he could be identified. On the emergency service he was found not to be intoxicated, there was no evidence of bodily injury, and he was not medically ill. He was admitted to the psychiatric in-patient service under the name of John Doe.

There was nothing evasive about this man. He kept asking earnestly, though laconically, for help. He could remember nothing about himself — who he was, where he lived, what work he did, and who his relatives and friends were. Most of the time he sat staring at the floor with his head in his hands, as though deeply preoccupied. Every now and then he raised his head and shook it slowly and sadly, or he looked up at someone and said, "Can't you help me?" Hypnosis was tried with no effect. Narcosis only put the man to sleep. To avoid the publicity which such cases as this arouse no alarm was sent out about him; the staff heard nothing about a missing man over the radio. He spent Saturday and Sunday on a closed ward, going about the usual routines without any noticeable change in his clinical picture.

On Monday morning John Doe awoke in great distress. He demanded to know why he was in a hospital. He told the nurse who he was. He insisted that he must leave at once in order to appear at a coroner's inquest.[26] Here is his story.

At dawn on Saturday morning the patient was driving his produce to the vegetable market. On the outskirts of the city an elderly man stepped from between two parked cars directly in his path. There was no time to put on the brakes. The truck ran over the man and killed him. The police who arrived at the scene seemed convinced that John Doe was not responsible. They released him on condition that he send a report of the accident at once to the Commissioner of Motor Vehicles and appear at the coroner's inquest the following Monday.

Much shaken, John went to the home of friends in town where he filled out a form for reporting accidents which the police had given him. His friends succeeded in alarming him. They appeared to think that he would be found to blame and might go to prison for committing manslaughter. They finally left for work, and John went out alone to send off his report, leaving his wallet in his friends' home. The last thing he remembered was the act of dropping the report into the mail box. It was learned later that a stranger, who probably saw how dazed he was, led him to the door of the hospital and then departed.

The precipitating factors in the case are obvious — the terrible accident at dawn, the police, the shadow of the coroner's inquest, the frightening friends. John Doe had signed a report which amounted to a confession of manslaughter, as his friends had pointed out, and he had mailed it. There was something irrevocable about dropping the letter into the box. The patient reached the limit of his emotional tolerance. Regression and a massive amnesia then shut everything out. He became literally a man who was not responsible. He made no attempt at flight. All that the amnesia gave him — and it was quite a lot — was two days of freedom from a clear recognition that he had killed someone and might be held responsible for it.[27]

Lesser amnesias than this are common. We see them after accidents in which there has been neither bloodshed nor head injury. We see them in

[26] R. R. Grinker and J. Spiegel report a military case with abrupt spontaneous recovery like this. See *War Neuroses*, pp. 9–10.

[27] Similar cases are reported in Geleerd, E. R., Hacker, F. J., and Rapaport, D., "Contributions to the study of amnesia and allied states," *Psychoanal. Quart.*, 1945, *14*, 3; Rapaport, D., "Consciousness: a psychopathological and psychodynamic view," in H. Abramson (Ed.), *Problems of Consciousness*. New York: Josiah Macy, Jr., Foundation, 1951, pp. 18–57.

situations of personal tragedy and of extreme guilt, and in the wake of a general catastrophe. Survivors often remember only fragments of an experience they have just been through. They may recall trivial incidents and not the main current of events.[28] The selective recall of trivial incidents, with amnesia for the major trauma, is probably related to the trivial recall which is characteristic of screen memories and manifest dreams.

Massive amnesia with fugue

In many cases of massive amnesia the patient tries to escape from his intolerable stress by forgetting everything and running away. It is customary to call such an amnesic flight a *fugue*, the name under which it was originally described in French. The patient carries out literally the wish that many a harassed normal person expresses when he says, "I'd like to get away from it all, just go away and forget everything!" The fugue is the kind of literal acting out that our sleepwalker exhibited when he tried to get help for his inner turmoil by going out of his hotel room toward the street. Instead of simply wandering about in a daze, as our John Doe did, the man in a fugue takes to the road, like Launcelot Gobbo in *The Merchant of Venice*, or he rides freight trains like a vagrant. Here is a case illustration.

Samuel O., a graduate student, impoverished and far from home, was invited to dinner at the home of an instructor whom he had known when they were socio-economic equals in another town. He accepted the invitation because he was lonely and hungry, but he regretted it almost at once because his clothes were shabby. He thought, in retrospect, that the instructor had seemed condescending. That evening he left his rooming house in plenty of time for the dinner, but he failed to show up at the instructor's home. Two days later he was picked up by the police in a neighboring state. He could remember vaguely having ridden a freight train, talking with strangers and sharing their food; but he had no idea who he was, where he had come from or where he was going. The contents of his pockets identified him and he was fetched by relatives.

Later on, this young man was able to remember the events leading up to the fugue and something of what went on during it. He had started for the instructor's house while still in strong conflict over going there. He was ashamed of his appearance, resentful over the condescension, and afraid to express what he felt and call the dinner off. On his way he was held up at a grade crossing by a slowly moving freight train. He had a sudden impulse to board the train and get away. When he acted on this impulse he apparently became amnesic. He retained enough ego integration, however, to be able to carry through complex coordinations, to converse with others and to get food. Nonetheless, he was much less in contact with people than anyone suspected until the police began to question him.

This is almost all that we know for certain about our fleeing graduate

[28] Sargent, W., and Slater, E., "Acute War Neuroses," *Lancet*, 1940, Part II, 1–2.

student. But from studies of others like him we can assume that through-out his dissociative flight he was deeply preoccupied, caught in a web of conflictual fantasy.[29] Before his encounter with the patronizing in-structor an emotional turmoil had probably been seething beneath the surface. The dinner engagement was only a precipitating factor which increased the turmoil and brought its components into sharper focus. This then made flight irresistible once the impulse to flee clearly emerged. Flight under such circumstances, however, is a turning away from realities — from social responsibility, job and future. This kind of turn-ing away, and the regression that makes it effective, can also seriously disturb an already unstable inner equilibrium, and awaken the shades of dormant conflicts to new life.[30]

Dissociated personality

The dissociated personality is the star performer among the dissociative reactions, the most dramatic, the favorite of stage, screen, television and the newspapers. It is relatively rare but it does actually occur. Descriptions of genuine dissocated personalities have appeared for at least a century. Freud regarded this clinical state as an extreme form of depersonalization. We have found it convenient from a dynamic standpoint to distinguish two main varieties: (1) *alternating personality;* and (2) *double* or *multiple per-sonality.*

Alternating personality. This variety consists of two or more ego-superego organizations which have become more or less completely dissociated from one another. One such system dominates all conscious perception, thinking and action for a time to the virtual exclusion of its rival or rivals. Such organizations may *alternate* in dominating the situation as often as several times a day, or as seldom as once in several years.[31] The alternating per-sonalities are actually incomplete organizations; each one suffers from massive amnesia for characteristics of the other or others.

Sometimes these ego-superego organizations contrast with one another strongly. In one personality, for example, a person may seem shy, timid and overconscientious, while in the other he is bold, enterprising and even unscrupulous. A fictional account of this kind of contrast, exaggerated for dramatic purposes, is given in the famous *Doctor Jekyll and Mr. Hyde.*

Real alterations of personality seem themselves to be exaggerations of the

---

[29] For other cases, see Fisher, C., "Amnesic states in war neuroses: the psycho-genesis of fugues," *Psychoanal. Quart.,* 1945, *14,* 437–468. Some of Fisher's cases travelled hundreds of miles in a fugue during wartime conditions.

[30] Easton, K., "An unusual case of fugue and orality," *Psychoanal. Quart.,* 1959, *28,* 505–513; Berrington, W., Liddell, D., and Foulds, G., "A re-evaluation of the fugue," *J. ment. Sci.,* 1956, *102,* 280–286.

[31] In a military case, an infantryman "alternated" during the course of psychotherapy. See Grinker, R. R., and Spiegel, J., *War Neuroses.* Philadelphia: Blakiston, 1945, p. 9.

normal differences that we see every day in the attitudes and behavior of ordinary persons as they turn from one to another of their social roles. There is, for example, the hard-boiled businessman driving a bargain, who shows little or no consideration for the feelings of others, and the same man at home, an easy mark for everyone in the family. He may keep these two roles separated so strictly that he has little or no recall for his prevailing behavior in one while he is in the other. Unlike the victim of personality dissociation, however, the businessman can make himself remember both roles if it becomes essential.

Occasionally an alternating personality begins with a fugue that does not clear up for years. Suppose our graduate student, who ran away and lost his memory on the way to a dinner, had failed to recall his pre-amnesic life, had carried no identification, and had escaped detection as a vagrant. His massive amnesia robbed him of his present identity and of his personal history. Without these a person cannot nowadays hold a job for long, which means that he cannot pay for food and shelter. What can such a man without a present or a past do?

The solution which people with lasting massive amnesia hit upon is that of inventing a past, and of building it up as they go on living in a community through more and more inventions. In time they believe their own confabulations, just as many of us think we recall a childhood which is actually quite different from the childhood we really lived. Sometimes the name a person chooses, to orient himself in his amnesic state, reveals an identification with some adult belonging to his forgotten life. Men have invented a past under such circumstances, settled down in a new kind of work, married and reared children. Then one day somebody comes along who recognizes them, or they see a picture in a newspaper, and the real past comes back to eclipse the fictional one — and usually to ruin both. If there is another wife and other children in the background, the man is lucky who is not indicted for bigamy. Even if he escapes indictment, he still must deal with the fact of bigamy and illegitimacy, usually in an atmosphere heavy with suspicion of fraud.

Double or multiple personality. In this variety there is no real alternation. One comparatively mature and realistic ego-superego organization dominates nearly all the time, while one or several other relatively incompetent organizations may occasionally take over in a somewhat childlike way.[32] The dominant personality in double or multiple personality is as a rule completely amnesic for the subordinate one or ones. On the other hand, at least one of the subordinate systems appears to have access to what goes on in the more mature, more realistic dominant organization. The classic example is still Morton Prince's *Dissociation of a Personality*. In the actual dissociated reaction, there were fragmentary, subordinate systems that spied

[32] Rapaport, D., *Emotions and Memory*. Baltimore: Williams and Wilkins, 1942, pp. 197–224.

upon and persecuted the dominant personality, finally driving it into therapy and almost driving it to suicide.[33]

One is struck by the close resemblance of such rare cases of dissociation, with their open warfare between partial personalities, to the common struggles in normal conflict and ambivalence and to the less obvious relationship between unconscious motivation and conscious knowledge. They resemble in some ways also the open warfare which goes on in some cases of obsessive compulsive neurosis, as we shall see clearly when we turn to them in the next chapter.

Dynamic and Developmental Background

Earlier in the chapter, when we were stressing the adaptive achievements of dissociative reactions, we said that an attempt was made in dissociation to preserve the overall ego integration by reducing the total ego span, that is, by eliminating some ego functions. This elimination varies all the way from denying the reality or familiarity of something perceived to the splitting off of large segments of socially integrated personality functions, as for example in the dissociation of a personality.

As we have also pointed out, all the dissociated states have their normal counterparts. This is easiest to demonstrate in the common experiences of sudden estrangement and depersonalization. Normal adults have such experiences in mild or transient form under conditions of extreme stress, external or internal, and under conditions of extreme monotony or deprivation. They also have them when they undergo an abrupt change in surroundings, even though the change in itself may be pleasurable, as in going on a vacation or when returning home from a foreign country.

The fact that dissociative reactions all have their normal counterparts does not, of course, make them normal. It only makes them acceptable as variants within the repertory of human behavior. It gives us a basis for understanding them as pathological exaggerations and ineffectual uses of defense mechanisms that every human being has in his unconscious ego organization. We shall discuss in a moment what defense mechanisms are most characteristic of dissociative reactions. Before doing so, it will be helpful to re-examine some of the basic similarities and differences between the conversions and the dissociations.

Dissociative reactions and conversion reactions

Similarities. The most obvious similarity between conversions and dissociations is their exaggerated and pathological use of processes of *exclusion*.

---

[33] Prince, M., *Dissociation of a Personality.* New York: Longmans, Green, 1908; Thigpen, C. H., and H., and Cleckley, H. M., *The Three Faces of Eve.* New York: McGraw-Hill, 1957; Lipton, S., "Dissociated personality: a case report," *Psychiat. Quart.,* 1943, *17*, 35–56.

It will be recalled that in our discussion of the dynamic and developmental background of conversion reactions we began with a section on exclusion and inclusion in normal behavior.[34] We said there that the learning and the performance of skilled acts depend upon excluding all competing and contradictory tendencies from participation in the act. This principle holds good, not only for skilled acts, but also for perceptual structuring, for close attention and for problem-solving, consecutive speech, logical thinking and intelligent understanding. We also made comparisons between the automatic utilization of *exclusion* in normal organized behavior and experience, on the one hand, and its exaggerated and pathological utilization in conversion reactions, on the other.

All of this discussion is as relevant to the dynamics of dissociative reactions as it is to conversions, even though the disturbances in function in the two groups result in quite different symptomatic pictures. Both conversions and dissociations have their origins in a grossly defective repressive function which fails to prevent eruptions of unconscious derivatives into preconscious and conscious organizations when the patient is under unusual stress. The inevitable regression to more primitive levels, common to all the neuroses, leads both the conversion patient and the patient who dissociates to exaggerated and pathological processes of exclusion. Some segment of reality, internal or external, gets separated off from the rest of the personality organization.

Differences. The dynamic differences between dissociative reactions and conversion reactions become obvious in the form taken by the manifest symptoms which follow the overexclusion. In conversions the patient unconsciously creates the symbol of a conflict, and then treats the symbol as a sign of illness or of disability. In dissociations the patient does not create symbols in this way, but instead pathologically denies the reality or the familiarity of something which is already present in his preconscious or conscious organization. We shall restate these differences in a little more detail.

In *conversion reactions,* as we have seen, a circumscribed disturbance or loss of function appears in some body part, the part used for symbolic expression. This disturbance or loss may go as far as paralysis or anesthesia. The rest of the personality — which is to say nearly all of it — remains little affected by the functional change. In some instances the patient even seems to be satisfied at being ill or disabled (*la belle indifférence*). The conversion symptom itself gives unconscious symbolic expression to more than one facet of the focal conflict which may have been involved in precipitating the neurosis. This expressive function of the symptom can have the value for the patient of a creative act.

In *dissociative reactions* it is only in experiences of estrangement that the

---

[34] See the section entitled *Conversion reaction and normal behavior organization,* in the preceding chapter.

presenting symptom is restricted to some object or to some body part, e.g., to something that now seems unreal or unfamiliar. And even when there is such restriction the act of overexclusion in dissociative reactions does not dispose of the anxiety, as conversions often appear to do, but tends rather to increase it even to the point of extreme fright.

With this exception, in certain cases of estrangement, the dissociative reaction typically involves large segments of external or internal reality. Often, as we have seen, the estrangement or depersonalization is sweeping; the patient reports that everything seems strange or that he is not the same person as he was. In dreamlike states the dissociation leaves the person so ineffectual that he stands in need of constant protection. In massive amnesias, especially in fugue states and in dissociated personality, the patient may deal with external reality in a remarkably effective way — considering the extent of his dissociation — but he does so at the cost of losing contact with whole areas of experience that identify him as a certain social person.

Fixation and regression in dissociative reactions

The process of symptom formation in dissociative reactions follows the same general pattern as that in other neuroses. Increased internal or external stress brings about a decompensation in the ego defense system which can no longer contain unconscious id and superego forces. An upsurge of derivatives of these forces threatens to destroy ego integration and raises the anxiety level to the point where it can no longer be tolerated. A partial regression then occurs which makes it possible for ego integration to be reconstituted with more primitive components. There is a major difference between the outcome of this regression and that which characterizes phobias and conversions. This difference can be summed up by saying that in dissociations the regression reactivates earlier and more primitive ego organizations than in phobias and conversions. It revives processes of primitive denial and ego-splitting which were used in infancy before mature repression had developed.

The major fixation points in dissociative reactions toward which regression leads are multiple fixation points belonging to more than one phase of personality development.

In *somatic estrangement,* for example, the patient undergoes a partial regression that revives archaic problems related to formation of the *body image,* as well as to its incorporation in the image of the self. Patients who complain that some body part has become unreal or has changed in some way often stare at it as though it were not a part of themselves. This reaction is not found elsewhere in the neuroses; but it does occur in toxic psychoses, in schizophrenia, and occasionally in experimentally induced sensory deprivation.[35] It also seems to repeat early infantile experiences, before the body

[35] Solomon, P., *et al., Sensory Deprivation.* Cambridge, Mass.: Harvard Univ. Press, 1961.

image has been constructed and used. A mouth ego, a visual ego and a hand ego seem to evolve separately, with little or no regard for one another. Thus, when the hand happens to stray across the visual field, the infant stares at it attentively, as though it were some strange object, and without any evidence that the eyes and the hand are interrelated.[36]

In *object-estrangement* and in *depersonalization* the regression revives archaic problems related to the distinction between a *self* and the *notself* or environment, between one's sense of identity and one's sense of the separate existence of other things and persons. Sometimes it seems to be the *self-image* that is chiefly affected; sometimes it seems to be the object world, while the self appears relatively whole; most often both self and object world are involved in the estrangement, since self and object are actually reciprocal constructs.[37]

Estrangement and depersonalization form a bridge between the relatively stable, symbolic conversion symptom and the dreamlike or amnesic dissociations. In mild estrangement and depersonalization the patient is far from being overwhelmed by his symptoms. The strangeness of his experience may make him uneasy or anxious at the moment; but the estrangement or depersonalization may provide a separation from something traumatic which adaptively lessens its immediate impact. On the other hand, in severe estrangement or severe depersonalization, as in dreamlike states and massive amnesias, the patient is often overwhelmed by his symptoms, thrown into a world of weird unreality, engulfed by a world of fantasy, or cut off from large segments of his own personality organization. In these states the patient does not gain control over the situation, as he often does in conversion reactions, but loses control of it and often of himself as well.

Ego-splitting in dissociative reactions

In all the varieties of dissociative reaction we find examples of pathologically sharp or pathologically exclusive cleavages in the personality organization. That is to say, the dissociations are not diffuse or haphazard, but involve more or less orderly separations into suborganizations which may or may not interact with one another. Such cleavages illustrate a process which has been called *ego-splitting*, that is, separation of the ego organization into two or more autonomous parts.

The universal normal form that ego-splitting takes is the division into an observing and an observed function. Everyone develops the capacity during early childhood of looking upon his person, his feelings, acts and thought, in somewhat the way that he looks upon other persons and that others look upon him. The most significant permanent splitting of the ego occurs in the

---

[36] Piaget, J., *The Origins of Intelligence in Children.* New York: Internat. Univ. Press, 1954, vol. 9, pp. 75–127.

[37] Jacobson, E., "Self and object world," *The Psychoanalytic Study of the Child.* New York: Internat. Univ. Press, 1954, vol. 9, pp. 75–127.

process of forming a mature superego, which then functions in such a way as to approve and love or to disapprove and punish the rest of the ego organization. We shall see striking exaggerations of this split into ego and superego in the obsessive compulsive neuroses and in the depressions. But exaggerations also occur in the dissociative reactions, as for example in the apparent loss of superego control in the graduate student, who went off in a fugue instead of facing a dinner engagement, and in Minnie D. who slipped into her rape fantasy and acted it out in public without shame.

Most of the ego-splitting in the dissociative reactions is not simply an ego-superego split. In estrangement and depersonalization the splitting seems to be motivated chiefly by an attempt to gain psychological distance from something traumatic or from something which demands too abrupt an adaptation. In dreamlike states the chief split seems to be between orientation with respect to one's fantasy life and orientation with respect to one's surroundings. It is obvious in all dreamlike states, from ordinary sleepwalking to psychogenic stupor, that the fantasy orientation prevails, and that orientation to external reality is maintained only to the extent that it is necessary for acting out the fantasy. In massive amnesias the ego-splitting develops along other lines. To a large extent the orientation to external reality remains fairly adequate, especially in fugues and dissociated personalities. The split seems to separate the present day personality from its past identity. It is obvious that such highly developed skills as one's communication — the use and understanding of language — are unimpaired in most cases. (Our case of the amnesic John Doe is an exception; it was part amnesic, part dreamlike). Other skills and a general understanding of one's complex culture are not lost in even the most severe massive amnesias.

The reason that dissociative reactions lead to ego-splitting and not to ego diffusion is that ego development does not begin with combinations of reflexes or of sensory or perceptual elements. The most elementary grouping, which seems to be that described by Piaget as mouth, hand and eye organizations, still embraces in its earliest form an exceedingly complex integration. The interaction of mouth, eye and hand organizations lead very early to a stable and unitary ego organization which becomes incapable of breaking down into its components without a general disintegration. What we are witnessing in dissociative reactions is not a disintegration but the forcible separation of functions, a separation which makes such heavy demands upon the defensive system that it cannot as a rule be long sustained.[38]

Defenses in dissociative reactions

The regression and the ego-splitting already discussed belong among the chief defensive maneuvers in dissociative states. By themselves, however,

[38] E. Jacobson makes this point in relation to depersonalization. It also applies to our own cases and to those of R. R. Grinker and J. Spiegel (*Men under Stress; War Neuroses*).

they do little more than describe what happens when a fully mature ego integration cannot be maintained. To understand the phenomena peculiar to the dissociations it is essential to understand the role played by denial and repression in them.

Denial as a defense.[39] Denial as a defense is older than repression. It operates early in childhood, before functional boundaries have been firmly established between ego and id, between ego and external reality, and of course long before there is a recognizable, autonomous mature superego. Denial operates before there is adequate distinction between what will become unconscious and what will become preconscious and conscious. It consists originally, perhaps, as a separation from the rest of the emerging personality organization of that which hurts or is unpleasant or heightens anxiety.

Denial is the antecedent of repression, the model for the development of repression, and ultimately a relatively minor auxiliary defense which is never given up.[40] Normal adults use denial chiefly as a defense against something which they perceive, something which has already gained access to the preconscious but may not yet have become conscious. It is possible to avoid a great deal of anxiety through denying the possibility, the approach and even the immediate presence of danger;[41] but of course denial is apt to leave the denier exposed to harm which he could have avoided. It is the mythical ostrich sticking its head into the sand when danger threatens. Denial is a contradiction of something known or perceived. In the young child the reality that is contradicted or split off from the rest of the personality organization is perceptual reality. Something actually *perceived* is treated as though it *did not exist*.

This is quite different from mature repression. In denying something that is known or has been perceived, a person is actually admitting its existence; he only denies its effectiveness. In repressing something perceived or known, a person eliminates it from all consideration. It becomes to all intents and purposes as though it did not exist and never had existed. Where denial only separates something off, repressing seems to destroy it, to push it out of the known and perceived world and keep it out.[42]

Denial and repression in dissociative reactions. In the dissociative reactions it is denial that comes to the rescue when repression fails. It supplements the inadequate repression and, especially in the amnesias, it provides large areas of preconscious functions for a secondary act of repression. In what follows we shall touch upon the regressive uses of denial and repression

[39] B. Lewin gives a thorough account of denial as a defense in *The Psychoanalysis of Elation.* New York: Norton, 1950.

[40] Jacobson, E., "Denial and repression," *J. Amer. Psychoanal. Ass.*, 1957, 5, 61–92.

[41] Cf. Janis, I., *Psychological Stress.* New York: Wiley, 1958.

[42] This statement ignores the fact that what has been repressed may remain effective through the action of its *derivatives* which escape repression.

in each of the major varieties of dissociative reaction, and indicate where possible the role they play in the ego-splitting which develops.

(a) *Estrangement and depersonalization.* Even in the mildest case of estrangement and depersonalization there is an obvious disturbance in object relations. Something which a person certainly perceives is experienced as strange or unreal. He stares at it, as a child stares at what arouses uncertainty or anxiety; or he refuses to give it a place in his perceptual and cognitive organization. He ignores it as a small child may ignore what he does not like.

The same is true if what is perceived is part of one's own body or one's self. The first step in separation is that of experiencing the body part or the self as strange or unreal. The ultimate step is that of denying it completely, even to the point of losing one's identity; but this comes only in massive amnesia. In object estrangement, somatic estrangement and depersonalization, what has actually undergone distortion is the patient's feeling, perception and cognition of something; but patients usually *project* this distortion, so that it is the object, the body or the self that seems distorted.

The distortion — the separation off of something as *ego alien* — is introduced in the first place as a primitive defense, as a regressive attempt to reinforce an insufficient repression. It is the revival of a device successfully used in early childhood before repression was well developed. As we have pointed out, things which could not be handled by the weak repression of childhood were simply denied admission to the dominant ego organization of the moment. They were then perceived as alien; and often their emotional aspects were eliminated, much as an obsessive compulsive eliminates emotional aspects of his experience by isolation.

The weakness of this maneuver, as we have said, is that it leads to a form of separation anxiety which sometimes frightens an adult patient more than whatever gave rise to the defense in the first place. The small child who uses such means can turn to his mother, his partner in infantile symbiosis, for the renewal of his confidence. The adult who uses it must stand alone.

(b) *Dreamlike dissociative states.* These, it will be recalled, include sleepwalking, somnambulistic attacks, trance or twilight states, and psychogenic stupor. In all of these the split is between fantasy and external reality. The fantasy life in all of them has become dominant; it has escaped repression; it is not denied. The person acts out his fantasies, with as little regard as possible to external reality, or else he passively experiences his fantasies with so much denial of external reality that he must be protected if he is to survive.

The somnambulistic attacks of Minnie D. give us the most clear-cut, and at the same time the most pathological, example of the denial of external reality and the acting out of a personal fantasy. Each time this patient came to a traumatic memory she regressed to the point where she excluded her surroundings almost completely, and slipped into her fantasy of rape, which had much that she desired as well as feared. This is the epitome of neurotic acting out instead of remembering and verbalizing. Minnie was overwhelmed by her fantasy material; the best she could do was to deny her surroundings so that she could give way to it.

The much commoner and less pathological sleepwalking has some of the same defensive and adaptive properties. The sleepwalker has already regressed normally in going off to sleep. But while he is sleeping some of his previously unconscious conflicts emerge and create their own active ego organization by invading the preconscious and activating part of its organization. The attempt is then made to act out or to find a solution to the conflict while remaining asleep. It should be stressed that such activity as sleepwalking could not be carried on without denial and exclusion of the actual environment of the sleepwalker. Neither could it be carried on if the sleepwalker were unable to perceive anything in his environment, for then he would simply bang into something or fall over something and wake himself up. He accepts the unconscious fantasies, which have now gained access to the preconscious because of his regression into sleep, and he denies whatever in the perceived environment contradicts his fantasies, i.e., the totality of the environment and the fact that he is sleeping. There are many points of similarity between the state of sleepwalking and the state of partial drunkenness.

In trance or twilight states and in psychogenic stupors the patient gives the impression of being either like the sleepwalker, able to make use of his surroundings as long as they do not interfere with his fantasies, or almost entirely out of contact with what goes on around him. Even in the latter case, as clinical evidence repeatedly shows, the denial of the environment does not prevent patients from perceiving a great deal of what is going on, and in some cases does not prevent their recalling it after the trance or stupor has passed.

The general impression that all dreamlike dissociative states give is one of being swamped by fantasy material which would normally be repressed. The patient tries to handle what might be a chaotic situation by denying what he cannot afford to face. Because of the depth of regression in dreamlike states this means denying much of external reality, and experiencing the intrusive fantasies with as little general disorganization as possible.

(c) Massive amnesias. The regressive development of massive amnesia has its counterpart in normal childhood. It has often been pointed out that all of us have massive amnesia for events of the edipal and pre-edipal phases of development, even though these phases include experiences of great vividness and emotional involvement. A part of this amnesia can be accounted for by the fact that a child's poverty of verbal expression hinders both the registration of early events and their adult recall. Nevertheless, there still remains the fact that all of us do remember much that is trivial and unemotional from our childhood, while we cannot remember the vivid and

significant events in which we took part during those same years. This massive amnesia for the events of early childhood seems to be a necessary result of the development of repression through which functional ego boundaries are formed and maintained. In intensive psychotherapy and psychoanalysis, for example, it has been found that the ability to recall edipal and pre-edipal events and fantasies with great ease and emotional fullness is often not a sign of good ego integration in an adult, but rather a sign of poor ego boundaries.

The pathological massive amnesias of dissociated adults point to a similar insufficiency of ego boundaries which quickly shows up during regression. The patient is at first overwhelmed by the upsurge of unconscious derivatives of id and superego activity and of unconscious conflictual fantasies. If this state of affairs should persist, the result will be what we witnessed in our John Doe, who had just committed involuntary manslaughter. The person continues in his massive amnesia without making much use of his environment but without going into a dreamlike state. He remains dazed and stunned as if by grief but with no memory for what has happened and for who he is. This is a sweeping denial of the tragedy and of his own participation in it. It is probably also a sweeping repression of all that had been denied. The denial takes place first, with respect to material already preconscious or conscious; and the repression follows it, making inaccessible and unconscious all that has been denied.

In cases of fugue and in many dissociations of personality the patient retains or regains mastery over his environment to the extent that is necessary to prolong the massive amnesia. Our graduate student, who went off in a fugue like a vagrant, certainly had to execute complex coordinations to ride hundreds of miles on freight trains, which must usually be boarded and left while the train is in motion to escape the notice of railroad personnel. He engaged in conversations with strangers and obtained food without money. In other words, the denial of reality which characterizes dreamlike states and estrangement seems not to play a leading role in fugues and dissociated personality. It is rather the selective denial of one's identity and one's personal past.

It is easy to see how this denial and repression are maintained. By denial the patient has dissociated or split off all that connects him with what he cannot tolerate. By subsequent repression he has made all of this unconscious. In this way he loses every clue to his own identity, every clue to the fact that he is the person who had or was having the intolerable experience, the person who faced danger or humiliation.

Denial of responsibility and the repression of one's identity must involve dissociation of much that we attribute to superego function. Nevertheless, even in massive amnesia there does not seem to be complete loss of superego function, but rather a split in the superego, into areas denied and repressed, and areas which go on operating more or less normally.

Our case of John Doe showed deep preoccupation with trouble, in spite of the fact that everything connected with it had been denied and repressed. The denial and repression in dissociated states seem to be maintained because to accept and remember means to the patient to bring back the flood of intolerable feelings which initiated the regression and the massive amnesia. While the great majority of massive amnesias clear up spontaneously within a few days, there are some which last for weeks, months or years. We have no ready explanation for this difference.

Childhood background of the defenses used in dissociative reactions

Mild and *transient* experiences of *estrangement* and *depersonalization* are so common that, as we have indicated earlier, they can be regarded as modes of defense which are available to almost everyone in the face of stress. They are *defensive* in the sense that they lessen the impact of a traumatic experience, and they give a person both time and psychological distance for the process of preparing to withstand shock and sudden change. We have pointed out that *denial,* which is responsible for feelings of estrangement and depersonalization, is one of the earliest ego defenses to develop. It is also a defense which practically all adults utilize to some extent when they face unpleasant, dangerous or anxiety-provoking situations — situations which have already become preconscious or conscious. The denial results in *ego-splitting* because part of the ego organization, something actually perceived, is treated by the rest of the ego organization as something alien to it.

Severe estrangement and *depersonalization, dreamlike states* and *massive amnesias* are not modes of defense available to almost everyone. They are available only to those who readily dissociate when they deeply regress. They, too, may protect a person from being overwhelmed by immediate intolerable stress; but they involve a degree of dissociation which becomes in itself in the end overwhelming. The dissociation results from an extensive utilization of denial in a primitive form. This happens because the repressive defenses have been inadequately developed and denial has been overdeveloped.

The excessive use of primitive denial in adulthood, when repression fails and a deep partial regression occurs, points to *an excessive use of denial before repression had developed into the key defense.* This in turn implies that *early in childhood* the person who later dissociates readily must not have been sufficiently protected by others at a time when his ego had not reached sufficient maturity to provide itself with protection. He must have been exposed repeatedly to unpleasant, dangerous and anxiety-provoking situations which demanded immediate effective defense at a time when *denial* was his best means for providing it.

Before *repression* has matured and before firm functional boundaries have been established between ego and id, unconscious and preconscious, internal reality and external reality, *denial* of what cannot be kept out of preconscious ego function is a major defense. It is, as we have said, the forerunner of repression and the model upon which repression is built. The small child, for example, uses *denial in fantasy* to a far greater extent than does the average adult, and far more successfully. When he feels unprotected and faced by more danger than he can handle otherwise, he may fantasy himself the leader of a powerful gang or the owner of a powerful animal, and thus unrealistically deny his helplessness by providing himself with imaginary defenders.[43]

One reason why the small child is able to utilize *denial in fantasy* successfully as a defense is that as yet he has not made a clear-cut distinction between external reality and imagination. He is in the same state much of the time that we occasionally experience when we are not sure whether something we recall was a dream, a waking fantasy or something which really happened, that is, something which happened in objective reality. This difficulty in distinguishing imagination from objective reality in early childhood is itself also the product of inadequate ego boundaries and of inadequate boundaries between unconscious and preconscious. The child experiences imaginary dangers as real and defends against them by creating imaginary defenses. He also makes the same use of fantasy, when the need arises, to defend himself against intolerable situations in external reality, which for him is not yet really a separate realm.

We assume that the overuse of fantasy as an escape from danger, unpleasantness and anxiety makes it more difficult for a child to arrive at a normal distinction between fantasy and external reality than its moderate use. We assume also that such overuse leaves a person, after he has grown to adulthood, more vulnerable to regression into fantasy and to denial of reality than the ordinary person. In other words, the child who overuses denial and does not distinguish between imagination and external reality as early or as fully as he should is the child who, when he becomes an adult, will be more vulnerable to the development of dissociative reactions than will others.

A disturbance in object relations is obvious in all dissociative reactions. When these disturbances are severe or prolonged they imply a defective ego integration in the same sense that the overuse of denial does. Since a major source of early ego integration lies in the development of identifications with significant persons in a child's surroundings, a failure to develop strong ego integration means *a failure to establish strong early identifications*. Actually, of course, object relations and identifications early in life are in a reciprocal relationship with one another. In order to be able to identify strongly with a parent, for example, a child must be able to establish that parent as a safe internal object. This demands, in turn, that the child be able to experience the parent as a safe, protecting external object.

There is thus an interaction between external and internal objects which goes on for years before external and internal have become distinct realms for the child. If all goes reasonably well with this interaction, strong, stable,

[43] Freud, A., *The Ego and Mechanisms of Defense*. New York: Internat. Univ. Press, 1946.

secure identifications are constructed within internal reality; and at the same time strong, stable, secure *object relations* are established with respect to external reality. An integrated person interacts with an integrated world.[44] We assume that adults who dissociate readily under stress have not been successful in setting up effective, stable identifications and object relations in early childhood.

Dissociative reactions and psychoses

Major disturbances in object relations and the overuse of denial are characteristic of psychoses. Why, then, should not the dissociative reactions be grouped with them rather than with the neuroses? The answer to this question gives more weight to tradition and convenience than to basic psychodynamics. The dissociative reactions have until recent years always been grouped with conversion reactions as hysterical disorders or as conversion hysteria; and no one doubts that conversion reactions should usually be included among the neuroses. Occasionally a conversion reaction borders on the psychotic or develops into a psychosis, which is most often a schizophrenic disorder. Often a dissociative reaction borders upon the psychotic and in many cases of dreamlike states it is doubtful if the distinction between neurosis and psychosis can be maintained. Moreover experiences of estrangement and depersonalization are common components of psychotic reactions of all kinds.

In mild or moderate estrangement and depersonalization there need be no sign of delusion formation or hallucination, two of the chief forms of so-called *restitutive processes,* whereby the psychotic person tries to rebuild the objective world that he has lost. The same is true of most massive amnesias; they do not involve delusional or hallucinatory restitutional processes. In fugues and personality dissociation the patient usually retains enough ego synthetic function to invent a plausible past to replace the past that he has lost through denial and repression. In other words, he responds appropriately to the demands of his human environment that he give an account of who he is and what his past has been. The fact that the account he gives is a confabulation does not make him psychotic.

The delusional and hallucinatory processes invented by psychotic persons are not confabulations made in response to the demands of other persons, and they rarely vanish spontaneously as dissociations so often do. Delusions and hallucinations appear and persist in spite of the determined resistance to them which the human environment puts up. They are distortions of reality which become essential to the psychotic person because of the distorting pressure of unconscious derivatives.

The dissociative patient usually does not need restitutive processes, such

[44] Corresponding developments take place in the construction of a mature superego and of its predecessors. This topic has been deferred until a later chapter in order not to complicate the account here unnecessarily.

as the delusions and hallucinations, even though he has lost his identity and his past. The psychotic cannot get along without them even though his memory is reasonably intact and he can tell you who he is.

As for severe estrangement and severe depersonalization these may be looked upon as transitional states between neuroses and psychoses, the issue depending upon how far the falsification of reality is carried.[45] We have already said that dreamlike dissociative states are also transitional. Sleep-walking, for example, hardly deserves to be called psychotic, even though object relations are ludicrously distorted and external reality denied. On the other hand, the somnambulistic attacks of Minnie D. hardly deserve to be called neurotic; they might as well be characterized as schizophrenic episodes. The same is true of many trance or twilight states and psychogenic stupors. Some of these similarities and differences will become clearer when we discuss the psychoses in more detail.

Dissociative reactions and obsessive compulsive reactions

Superficially regarded, there is little resemblance between dissociative and obsessive compulsive reactions. Obsessive compulsive patients never develop dreamlike states, go off into fugues or suffer the kind of personality dissociation decribed under massive amnesia. The obsessive compulsive neurotic seems in continuously close contact with external reality and with persons around them. His ego integration seems, if anything, too tightly held together.

Beneath this superficial difference, however, there lie many deeper similarities. In the first place, *denial* is closely related to obsessive compulsive *isolation*, so closely related that many regard them as two aspects of the same basic defense. In the second place, the close contact with external reality is more apparent than real, for the obsessive compulsive patient is actually engaged in attempts to find solutions to infantile problems in an adult world. These attempts, as we shall see, are as doomed to failure as are the attempts of persons to solve their problems while they remain dissociated. Finally, ego-splitting and a split between ego and superego are as common in the obsessive compulsive neurosis as they are in dissociative reactions. Let us take up next the clinical and dynamic aspects of obsessive compulsive neuroses.

[45] See, for example, Blank, H. R., "Depression, hypomania, and depersonalization," *Psychiat. Quart.*, 1954, *23*, 20–37.

11

Obsessive Compulsive Reactions

IN THE PRECEDING CHAPTERS WE HAVE SEEN HOW SOME PATIENTS ATTEMPT to reduce emotional tension and anxiety by direct discharges of energy (*anxiety reactions*), how others displace and project internal dangers so that these are experienced as coming from the outside (*phobias*), how still others reduce anxiety and discharge tension in forming body language symbols (*conversions*), and finally how some use denial and ego-splitting to separate themselves from their sources of tension and anxiety (*dissociative reactions*).

As we turn now to *obsessive compulsive reactions* we shall encounter additional forms of neurotic behavior and defense. Unconscious conflicts here are expressed openly in apparently senseless repetitive acts, words or thoughts, in rituals and ceremonials, in endless doubting and ruminating. The major conflicts deal with problems of love and hate, right and wrong, cleanliness and dirt, orderliness and disorder. Sadism and masochism find free expression; and, as we might expect, strong feelings of guilt appear, sometimes rivalling the overwhelming guilt in psychotic depressions. Magical thinking and superstition appear more clearly than in the manifest symptoms of any other neurosis. And, finally, the patient usually is conscious of being in conflict, even though he may not understand what the conflict is about. A few brief clinical examples will illustrate the wide range.

A boy of twelve years suffered from sudden impulses to call his parents obscene names. He managed to control these impulses by saying to himself out loud, "Stop it! Stop it!" Sometimes he swore at himself for having such impulses.

A man with irresistible impulses to utter blasphemies actually taped up his mouth at times, both to control and to punish himself.

A middle-aged woman occasionally had so strong an impulse to choke her husband while he slept that she would have to get up and leave the bedroom.

A young woman, in conflict over erotic fantasies, developed the need to think of a different person with each separate act she performed. If, for example, she thought of the same person twice while walking along the same street, she felt sure that something terrible would happen.

A senior engineering student was afraid that if he just looked at people they might die. He was a modern example of the superstitious belief in the "evil eye." He knew rationally that if someone at whom he had looked should happen to die, this would be pure coincidence; but he could not get rid of the feeling that he had a deadly power in his eyes, or of the awful guilt that went with this feeling. We shall have more to say about the boy of twelve and the young woman later in the chapter.

Normal counterparts of obsessive compulsive symptoms. Obsessive compulsive symptoms are exaggerations and often caricatures of normal human trends. This does not make them normal, but it does make them more intelligible and acceptable. It is not always recognized that repetition and ritual, magic and superstition, enter into our everyday living in a great many ways. Some of these are basic to our most highly prized customs and social institutions.

If we examine compulsive ritual dispassionately, we find that it springs from the same roots as do the rituals which have given rise to the evolution of modern society — the rituals of the practical skills, of science, politics, social customs, art and religion. Unless we recognize that the relationships between normal and abnormal in this area are more than superficial resemblances, that both go deep into human nature, we cannot begin to understand obsessive compulsive behavior. We will not recognize neurotic devotion to exact repetition, rigid uniformity, strict taboo and severe self-punishment, as pathological variants of universal human trends.

These trends are clearly expressed in children's games. If you watch a group of little girls playing hopscotch in the street, you will be impressed at once by the insistence upon inflexible rules of procedure, exact repetition, fixed formula and precise ceremonial, down to the most minute detail. It is obvious here that variations are not to be tolerated. Instead they appear to be transgressions which call for penalties and even for ostracism from the active play group. It is true, of course, that the patterns and rules of such play are transmitted culturally from older to younger children. But this fact in itself cannot account for the intense moral indignation that sweeps the group if one child inadvertently changes or omits a step in the traditionally fixed sequence — stands on the right foot instead of the left, or turns one way instead of the other, even though one seems objectively as good as the other. The child who is playing actively at the moment is being watched closely by every other child in the game to see that she conforms rigorously to the established pattern. It is clearly not alone the outcome that counts but also the precise repetition of every step in the ritual.

When children improvise new games among themselves they show the same intense concern over repetition, rule, formula and ceremonial. Nor are these attitudes confined to play. Children also insist upon hearing a familiar story read or told by an adult without a change. Here, too, they may greet the most trivial omission or alteration with passionate and irritated outcries. Innovations or gaps in the recital of a story seem to interrupt the expected, familiar sequences. This frustrates the child because it cheats him out of his anticipated experience of closure, i.e., the experience of having the story fulfill his expectations as a rounded out, familiar whole. It frustrates him because the story loses its predictability for the child and seems to him to be out of his control. The old ways, the orderly completed ways, are sacred to a child in their own right. They fulfill his expectation and satisfy a compelling need.

The normal adult also shows a passionate insistence upon maintaining inflexible, arbitrary rules. He jealously preserves ritualistic forms for centuries after their direct relevance has passed. One has only to look at the archaic language of contemporary law to realize the power of ritual for ritual's sake in human affairs. Thousands of contracts are executed between ordinary persons every day worded in a jargon belonging to an ancient language which hardly anyone today can understand. The same is true of ritual and ceremonial in other areas. Some special virtue attaches to uniformity, exact repetition, uncompromising procedure and unvarying sequence. These are among the most primitive forms of mastery, and they are also basic to the most advanced forms of scientific inquiry and practical skill.

In courts of law any man capable of raising his right hand, in swearing to tell the truth, would be barred from the witness stand and might be held in contempt of court if he insisted upon raising his left hand. Why? Suppose a man has the signing of his will witnessed by two persons, not knowing that in his state the law is exceptional and calls for three. The will may be declared invalid even though no one doubts that it represents the true intent of the deceased.

In politics and in custom it is the same. If a man hopes to achieve a certain thing in the public interest, he must proceed meticulously, step by step, in accordance with the established rules. Never mind how urgent the need may be for speedy action, he must not omit a single station, or someone will make him start his pilgrimage all over again. This compulsive trend helps to build bureaucracies which only the bold genius can circumvent, and even he not often or for long. If a bride wishes to have a formal wedding she must on no account walk down the aisle with the man she is about to marry, even though she expects to walk beside him throughout the rest of her life.

There is no doubt that, whatever its origins, man's devotion to order, repetition and ritual has played an essential part in the evolution of modern civilization. We tend so much to emphasize change in the history of science and the arts that we often lose sight of the equally important role played by man's ability to repeat things exactly without change, to establish uniformities in what he does. Scientific, artistic and ethical advances have always depended upon the repetition of successful techniques, upon preserving their continuity and building them through cultural transmission into a lasting tradition, a human heritage.

In the course of transmitting cultural traditions it has happened over and over that man has evolved techniques intended to predict and control long before he was able to understand thoroughly what he was doing. Nevertheless human beings demand explanations and cannot resist giving them. The result has been that plausible hypotheses about prediction and control have again and again been adopted in which the accidental and irrelevant have not been distinguished from the essential. Many discredited hypotheses still flourish in the form of magical practice and superstitious folklore, even in our own highly advanced technological civilization.

Thus, for example, the hotels in which executives, scientists and government officials stay are unlikely to have a thirteenth floor because too many people consider it unlucky. This is true also of some of our most advanced, scientifically run hospitals. It is all right to have the thirteenth floor called *twelve-B* or *fourteen*. All kinds of charms, signs and amulets are worn today to bring safety or good fortune. A rabbit's foot, if it has been gnawed off by a rabbit in escaping from a trap, is esteemed by some adults, and even carried in the pocket as a safeguard and a good luck charm. Magic formulas, often containing meaningless words, and a thousand other superstitious tricks, are used everywhere today to influence events in the objective world. This is the cultural background against which compulsive repetition, compulsive order, ritual and penance, compulsive magic and superstition must be viewed.

Obsessive compulsive procedures often appear to be caricatures of some of these normal practices. Their goals are similar to normal goals. Sometimes they are attempts to increase one's control over events, or over one's conduct, by observing absolute conformity. Sometimes they represent highly personal methods of anticipating danger and of warding it off. Sometimes they express a belief that misdeeds can be undone, and freedom from guilt can be gained, through private rituals and self-imposed penalties. Obsessive compulsive reactions thus take their place beside other neurotic behavior as exaggerations, distortions and inappropriate uses of ordinary human trends. Behind the symptoms, as we shall see, there lie the familiar unresolved conflicts with their threat of disrupting ego integration.

Definition. Obsessive compulsive reactions consist of apparently useless but irresistible repetitious acts, words or thoughts, whose aim is to reduce tension and anxiety, (a) by indulging in something forbidden, (b) by deny-

ing such indulgence or guarding against it, or (c) by punishing oneself for having had the impulse to indulge. All three aims, no matter how contradictory they may be, are often included together in the symptomatology of the same obsessive compulsive reaction.[1]

Obsessive compulsive symptoms vary in complexity from ordinary trivial little acts — such as tapping, counting, snapping the fingers, saying a set word or phrase over and over, imagining some prescribed sound or scene — to the most complex ceremonials which are carried out in fixed, unvarying sequences. Some symptoms seem superficially absurd or ridiculous; some seem humiliating, horrifying or disgusting; some appear to be dangerous; some are limited to abstract doubting, ruminating or speculating, in which there is no feeling.[2]

What makes the obsessive compulsive reaction especially illuminating is that in it one can often witness the elements or the direct derivatives of an unconscious conflict being acted out as manifest symptoms in plain view. We have already seen that in *conversions* the components of a focal conflict are often condensed into a single somatic symptom which symbolizes everything at once, just as a piece of sculpture may. In *obsessive compulsive symptoms* the conflict does not lead to such a static result; it is performed actively as in a drama or a puppet show. Hostile or erotic impulses may appear openly upon the stage of conscious experience and behavior, with the meanings and origins thinly veiled. Sometimes countermeasures against unconscious or preconscious impulses emerge among the visible symptoms with little or no disguise.[3] Self-punishment, carried out under the influence of an archaic, retaliative superego, may be so obvious that a person would have to be functionally blind to miss its meaning. Sometimes, especially in obsessive doubt and rumination, all feeling seems to be replaced by a cold intellectual detachment.

Adaptive function. Obsessive compulsive patients vary greatly in the degree to which their maneuvers actually reduce emotional tension and anxiety. Some of them are tense and anxious most of the time in spite of utilizing their defenses. Some become tense and anxious only when there is interference with their indulgence or with a countermeasure. Some show little anxiety and seem mainly perplexed and ashamed of their symptoms. Some seem to lose all tension and anxiety; they appear to look upon their manifest symptoms as an objective scientist is supposed to look upon his data.

Incidental unimportant obsessions and compulsions are common. We run across them clinically by accident. From this fact it is fair to assume that a great many people succeed in reducing their tension to manageable pro-

---

[1] This was also true of conversion symptoms, as we have seen.

[2] The distinction often made in textbooks between *obsessions*, as thoughts, and *compulsions*, as words or acts, is largely a matter of tradition. In the current literature the two terms are often used interchangeably. Obsessions are sometimes called *compulsive thoughts*, which of course they are.

[3] See especially the cases of Ramona M. and Sally J. in this chapter.

portions by the use of minor obsessive compulsive defenses — repetitious little acts, rituals, penances and ceremonials — without attracting particular attention, and without significantly distorting their general life pattern.

There are some persons who utilize obsessive compulsive trends to make their work or their play more effective and enjoyable. Among these may be mentioned the activities of some librarians, bookkeepers, statisticians, chartists, theoreticians and systematizers, as well as a host of hobbyists, e.g., collectors and classifiers, chess players, amateur designers, organizers and architects. Obsessive compulsive trends may enter into almost any activity that involves meticulous detail, extreme orderliness or disorder, exact repetition or systematic doubting, rumination, speculation and superstition.[4] It is worth mentioning here that work involving arbitrary demands that others conform to one's will in every detail also attracts persons with irresistible compulsive needs to control themselves. This they in part satisfy by controlling others, children or dependent adults.

For the average obsessive compulsive patient an indulgence in his symptom brings only temporary relief. The tension and the anxiety, coming as they do from internal instability, soon become intolerable again. It is then necessary to repeat the symptom to regain relief. With the passage of time obsessions and compulsions often tend to generalize. They may grow into more or less stereotyped methods of meeting all emotional tension and anxiety, whether internally or externally generated, and whether related to the original conflicts or not.[5]

Compulsions and phobias. Compulsions often appear combined with phobias. Some obsessive compulsive persons displace and project in such a way as to make over fear of an internal conflict into fear of some external object or situation. This means the development of a phobia. Such a patient may repress the origin and meaning of what threatens him, just as ordinary phobics do. He is more likely than phobics to remain continually aware of his ever-present danger, to guard against it or try to undo it. The obsessive compulsive who is also phobic suffers much more from conscious guilt than does the typical phobic patient. One of our major cases in this chapter will present us with the picture of a woman, Ramona M., pursued by terrible irrational fears, who organized rituals with which to fight them, and whose life was so filled with her fears and her rituals that she drove everyone around her, as well as herself, to desperation.

Varieties of Obsessive Compulsive Reaction

No one has yet come up with a classification of these complex, multiform disorders which everyone else accepts. Some, for example, have tried group-

---

[4] This is not to say, of course, that all such interests indicate an obsessive compulsive neurosis, any more than it is true that all aviators and test pilots are counterphobic.

[5] The case of Sally J. illustrates such a stereotyped generalized use clearly.

ing them on the basis of the varieties in overt behavior. This has the advantage of simplicity and directness; but it underplays the leading role of regression, of the superego, and of the defenses characteristic of obsessive compulsive reactions.[6] Others have tried to maintain a strict separation between obsessions, as thought disorders, and compulsions as symptomatic words and deeds; but this creates an artificial distinction between thinking and speaking or doing. In practice, compulsive speaking and doing are always accompanied by compulsive thinking, and all of the dynamic characteristics of one can be found in the others.

In the clinical material that follows we have not attempted to create a strict classification. Instead, we have formed three clinical groups which represent an ascending scale of complexity. Each group will highlight a different facet of the obsessive compulsive reaction. At the end we have added obsessive doubt and rumination which do not fit into this arrangement. The groups are as follows:

(1) Attempts to handle intolerable tension and anxiety through *regression, displacement* and *isolation*. These are unconscious defensive techniques with which we are already familiar. *Regression* we have met with in all of the neuroses. We were introduced to *displacement* when we studied the phobias. *Isolation* is closely linked to what we called denial and ego-splitting in the dissociative reactions; it may even be only a variant of the same general process.

(2) The overt use of one neurotic maneuver as a *countermeasure* in an attempt to offset the effects of some other neurotic maneuver. This technique is present to some extent in most obsessive compulsive reactions. In the case of Ramona M. we shall see a phobia, combined with compulsive rituals, and used together in an attempt to hold in check a frightening urge to kill — an urge that at one time flashed into consciousness by accident.

(3) We next add to the previous defensive measures the use of *reaction formation,* ritualistic *undoing* and openly *sadomasochistic self-punishment*. A classical handwashing compulsion will serve to illustrate all these processes.

(4) Finally we come to *obsessive doubt* and *rumination*. Here a great deal of the emotional aspect of obsessive compulsive reactions has been repressed. The result is what we have called caricatures of magical, scientific, artistic and religious practice. Obsessive doubt and rumination may almost paralyze a person by suspending all decision and by replacing action with speculation.

Regression, Displacement and Isolation

All three of these maneuvers are evasive. In obsessive compulsive reactions, *regression* replaces a current sexual or aggressive conflict with problems belonging to a pre-edipal level, where the patient may feel stronger or

[6] See, for example, Cameron, N., *The Psychology of the Behavior Disorders.* Boston: Houghton Mifflin, 1947, Chapter 10.

more at home. *Displacement* is used throughout obsessive compulsive reactions to shift the focus from current conflicts to infantile problems, or
from a dramatic struggle to a colorless action — a chess game in place of
a battle. *Isolation* is also used to separate opposing aspects of a conflict or
to eliminate emotional components from compulsive symptoms. If this is
successful, isolation prevents the genuine confrontation of opposite attitudes.
Its effects, as we have indicated, are similar to those achieved in dissociative
reactions by denial and ego-splitting.

All three maneuvers are employed because repression is defective. They
are defensive in that they make it possible for a patient to escape further ego
disintegration. It is true that, following the regression, part of an obsessive
compulsive person's functioning proceeds at more primitive levels; but the
rest of it usually goes on more or less normally. Through the use of these
maneuvers the obsessive compulsive patient is enabled to continue functioning at a neurotic level; he does not regress further into a psychosis.[7]

In the three cases that we shall use here to illustrate obsessive compulsive
regression, the displacement and isolation will appear simpler and less
dramatic than the ones to be presented in later sections. Their relatively simple unconscious ego defenses have been successful; no further elaboration
of symptoms was necessary. With the help of displacement and isolation, a
great deal of an unresolved childhood conflict, which had been regressively
revived, could still be held in repression. Only fragmentary signs of the
repressed conflict appear in conscious and preconscious ego organization.
These are largely expressions of hostile, sadistic impulses from pre-edipal
levels; some of them betray also sexual conflicts.

> Horace N., aged twelve and an only child, is the boy whom we
> mentioned early in the chapter as having impulses to call his parents
> obscene names. He controlled himself by saying out loud, "Stop it! Stop
> it!" At the beginning of his adolescence, in the face of increasing emo-
> tional tension, he had reacted by regressing to a level of ego-superego
> development similar to that at which he had tried to resolve the same
> general problem in childhood. By this maneuver he was able to displace
> his disturbance over his own adolescent sexuality on to the sexuality of
> his parents — without in the least recognizing what he was doing. His
> obscenities were early adolescent expressions of the angry resentment
> that a child of two or three years might feel with regard to parental in-
> timacy and his own sense of frustration over being excluded.
> This case is especially instructive because at twelve Horace felt no
> resentment or anger toward his parents, but only anxiety and humilia-
> tion because of his obsessive symptoms. This switch is clearly the work
> of his unconscious ego defenses. The obscenities seemed to Horace to
> be automatic intrusions, without feeling, which he could not begin to
> understand. He had not only *displaced* his own rising tide of sexuality
> on to his parents; he had also *isolated* all emotional tone from the
> obscenities that emerged against his will.

[7] This relationship between obsessive compulsive reactions and depression will appear in the case of Sally J.

When Horace said, "Stop it! Stop it!" to himself, he was repeating actual parental commands which he had heard in his own childhood. This was, in other words, an attempt to control his own thinking by the use of parental injunctions, which he had internalized early in his life — the precursors of his own superego.

A further instructive aspect of this case is that, in swearing at himself for wanting to say obscene things, Horace was giving a classical example of the way in which forbidden impulses often come through into consciousness as part of the defense. He used obscene language to prevent himself from saying obscene things. Horace was like a policeman who must use violence to preserve the peace. The unconscious impulse to say forbidden things gained its expression in his obscene self-reproach.

Our second case is that of Doris I., a young mother who sought help because of what seemed to her a senseless, dangerous impulse of brutality toward her infant daughter. The impulse seemed to well up within her suddenly every so often without any apparent provocation. She said, "I'm looking at my little baby, so sweet and precious, and then I get the feeling I might choke her or drown her!" Aside from these isolated sadistic impulses she felt nothing but love for her child.[8]

In the course of therapy no hatred toward the baby came to light. But this young mother had a younger sister, born when Doris herself was four years old. Doris reacted to the birth of her sister, as many little children do, by persistently soiling and wetting. For this she was severely punished. She loved her baby sister as a living doll, a baby such as she herself wanted; and she hated her as a rival for her mother's love, and probably as a constant reminder that her mother could have babies while she herself could not. She never succeeded in resolving this early childhood conflict. The best she had been able to do as a child was to buttress her inadequate repression with a reactive over-solicitude toward her sister (*reaction formation*).

The sister grew up to be prettier and more popular than Doris. She was married sooner and already had two sons before Doris had her first child. Doris had wanted a boy. When she gave birth to a girl the whole bitter competition with her younger sister was rekindled. She unconsciously cast her baby daughter in the role of her sister as a baby. The hatred that welled up toward her daughter expressed unconscious resentment at two levels: the old hatred for the baby rival of her childhood, and the current bitter envy over this same rival sister having two boys, while she was given a girl. As therapy progressed, the irrational hatred for her sister emerged from behind her exaggerated solicitude for her. As this was worked through the homicidal fantasies of killing her own baby disappeared.

Our third case is that of Oscar E., an unmarried man aged forty-two, whose widowed mother was slowly dying at home. He was shocked when he experienced sudden waves of hatred toward her and had the conscious wish that she would hurry up and die. These experiences repeated themselves at intervals without warning, sometimes when they had been gazing tenderly at each other. The rest of the time he felt himself to be,

[8] G. Gero and D. L. Rubenfine state that this impulse is not uncommon. "Obsessive thoughts," *J. Amer. Psychoanal. Ass.*, 1955, *3*, 222–243.

as he had felt all his life, her devoted and self-effacing son. These sudden symptoms were not only distressing but they seemed to Oscar to make no sense at all.

Oscar was the unwelcome child of his mother's middle age and by far the youngest. She fastened him to her with a domineering, possessive, love. Throughout his childhood she infantilized him in one or another way. Oscar, for his part, loved his mother when he was a child as the source of all good and all affection; and he hated her because she was self-willed and frustrating. The only serious rebellion that he could recall took place during his phase of toilet training. They would sometimes spend an hour or more in a contest of wills while she tried to compel Oscar to move his bowels. Eventually she always won because if he did not give in she gave him an enema which excited and infuriated him.

Now on her deathbed she was weak and helpless. Sometimes she soiled. Her approaching death loomed as the final frustration for Oscar. She was about to leave him alone in the world, with no one to depend on, after she had monopolized his affection all his life. Following her death he developed a severe depression for which he had to be hospitalized.

In all three of these cases we see sadistic impulses breaking free of repression — to call one's parents dirty names, to choke or drown one's baby, to hate one's loved mother and wish her dead. None of them makes complete sense in terms of the patient's current life situation. All of them make sense the moment we realize that the patient has *regressed*, that he has reactivated early childhood conflicts, and unwittingly *displaced* them on to corresponding adult relationships. In the first two, the pubescent boy and the young mother, *isolation* of the emotional component, the affect, was present. In the third, Oscar E. did not isolate the emotional component; on the contrary, he felt his hatred vividly. But he *isolated* this feeling in *time*. Accordingly, he alternated between brief moments of conscious sadism and long periods of clinging love. When in the end Oscar began to mourn his mother's death, he could no longer sustain his defence of isolation; infantile hatred and love combined to force him into still further regression until he became psychotically depressed.

Obsessive Compulsive Countermeasures

The patients discussed in this section also use regression, displacement and isolation in trying to handle their execessive emotional tension and anxiety; but in addition they employ some overt obsessive compulsive *countermeasure* in their attempts to control dangerous or unwanted impulses. In other words, not only will we see the overt expressions of strong unconscious impulses appear, but the forces used to oppose them, the *countermeasures*, will show up also, transforming the original repressed conflict into a full-dress public performance. The first case to be given sounds childlike and simple; the second case mingles phobias and compulsions together in a complex and desperate struggle.

Frances P. was an unmarried typist, aged twenty-four. She was trying to control erotic fantasies which she could not repress. Her countermeasures put into practice, in a compulsive way, the advice often given to adolescents who are struggling with sex problems, "Think of something else!" Walking to work was an activity that permitted erotic fantasies to emerge easily. So each time Frances stepped on or off the curb at a corner she made herself think of a different person. This kept her mind busy preparing for the next intersection. If she ran out of persons she allowed herself to change streets and start the list over again.

This obsessive countermeasure cost Frances time and effort. As it became entrenched, it made her shun company to avoid having to explain her preoccupations and her zigzag course as she changed streets. She needed to concentrate upon the task of having names ready in time for the next block. The device failed, however, to eliminate all her erotic fantasies, it tended to sustain rather than to reduce her anxiety, and it kept her from the benefits and pleasures of sharing in the company of others.

In time the countermeasure generalized to other activities. As Frances dressed and undressed she found that she had to think of a different person with each article of clothing that she put on or took off. Later this became necessary for each mouthful of food, and for each act in washing dishes, doing laundry, and other housework. It began creeping into her office work, as she opened or sealed envelopes, filed away or got out letters, inserted paper and carbon in her typewriter, etc. Ultimately the countermeasure had to be applied to the details of typing — a different person at first for each new page, then for each new paragraph and line, and finally for each word. The girl had to give up her job.

Frances had a passive, defeated attitude toward her symptoms. She said, "For a long time I couldn't break it; and now it just seems easier to go on." She was speaking as much of her drift into uncontrollable erotic fantasy as of the generalization of her tyrannical countermeasures. Her outlook for recovery was poor.

The next case is far more complex and more dramatic. It consists of the interweaving of apparently senseless fears with strict obsessive compulsive countermeasures to ward off what was feared. The momentary flash of a murderous impulse is the most important clue that we have to the meaning of whole systems of compulsive safeguards against killing others. Without this clue the woman's symptoms might have remained as unintelligible to us as they were at first to her and to her intended victims. The patient herself knew of the occurrence of this impulse before entering therapy, but she had never connected it with her neurotic illness. She had kept the knowledge isolated.

Ramona M. was the forty-two-year-old wife of a Minnesota business man and the mother of three children. Her symptoms appeared suddenly.

She was serving the family dinner one evening when she dropped a dish on the table and smashed it. The accident appalled her. While clearing up the fragments she was seized with an unreasonable fear that bits of glass might get into her husband's food and kill him. She would not allow the meal to proceed until she had removed everything and reset the table with fresh linen and clean dishes. After this her fears, instead of subsiding, reached out to include intense anxiety over the possibility that she herself and her children might be killed by bits of glass.

The patient's fears and defensive rituals did not stop with this. Ramona developed an irresistible need to examine minutely every piece of glassware that she handled. If anything had the slightest chip in it she threw it away; and she had to carry it to the trash can herself to make sure that it went out of the house. Then she would hunt for the missing chip which, of course, she could rarely find. She had read somewhere that copper pots and aluminum pots were not safe for certain kinds of cooking. Her worries now included their use. She remembered that her wedding ring had some copper in it as well as gold. First she took it off whenever she cooked or washed dishes; then she lost it.

Meanwhile she heard about other things which raised new fears and touched off further compulsive countermeasures. These included the danger of a spread of virus disease from toilet to kitchen, the dangers of lye and pesticides, and of the chemical and organic fertilizers used on the lawn. Eventually all potential poisons of every kind had to be isolated from cooking utensils and dishes by storing them in the garage — even the cleaning fluids and scouring powders needed for everyday washing and cleaning.

These endless precautionary rituals drove the family almost frantic. Yet they brought Ramona no lasting peace. Her list of potential dangers kept growing until she simply did not have enough attention to bestow upon them all. If she was not certain that she had or had not done something in a certain way, she would have to rehearse her steps to make sure, or else begin all over again.

One of the hardest things for her to endure was that she could not control what the others did or convince them that her precautions were essential. She tried to make someone stay beside her to help keep track of every move she made; but when they did they proved to be not nearly as meticulous or concerned as she was. She found herself watching her husband and her children furtively for signs of ill health. In the end the whole situation became too much for her and the family to handle. Ramona had to give up housekeeping and seek fulltime therapeutic help.

What was the meaning of this network of fears and precautions? Why did this ordinary housewife act as though her husband and children might be treacherously murdered in their own home, like medieval princelings? It came out in the course of therapy that Ramona was protecting everybody from herself. Eventually she recognized the source of her dangerous hostility. Some time before the breaking of the glass dish she had discovered what she considered to be certain evidence that her husband was having an affair. This humiliated and angered her, but she said nothing about it. What appalled Ramona when she smashed the dish was the momentary conscious hope that he would eat glass and die, a homicidal wish that her carelessness would kill him. She immediately denied and repressed the wish; but from that moment all her obsessive compulsive countermeasures were directed against the possibility of some new accident in which she might inadvertently carry out her unconscious wish.

In this case, as in many obsessive compulsive cases, the symptoms were very versatile. At the same time that her cleansing and isolating rituals protected Ramona from acting out her homicidal impulse, they also served to frustrate, restrict and exasperate beyond endurance the object of her hostility, her husband. Meals were never ready. They took forever to serve. Cleaning was going on all the time everywhere. Ramona's revenge thus came through deviously in her precautionary symptoms. She held the family as prisoners in the protective custody of her neurosis. She punished them in such a way that — since she herself was neurotically ill and suffering — they could not even complain about seeming heartless to themselves.

Ramona also was punishing herself. Her dangerous impulses forced her to devote all of her waking life to defensive measures. She was like someone on a dyke with the flood waters threatening to break through in many different places. She kept finding weak places in her defenses while she had to keep constantly on guard to see that the old ones did not crumble. In the end she herself collapsed.

This case illustrates clearly the marked ambivalence toward loved ones which is so common among obsessive compulsives. Ramona experienced a momentary death wish toward her husband whom she also loved. Her endless defenses against committing involuntary homicide can only be accounted for by assuming that unconscious impulses to kill must have persisted after the momentary conscious flash. Ambivalence was not completely new in the patient's adult life. She had always had mixed feelings about her husband, hating him at times even though she loved him deeply — a pattern which she had transferred to him directly from her feelings for her father. Regression to a compulsive level only increased the contradiction and lit up her sadistic trends until they broke out as overt symptoms.

We have seen that Ramona was overwhelmed by fantasies of contamination — from feces in the toilet, from organic fertilizer, which is dried feces, and from all kinds of potential poisons. A preoccupation with contamination or soiling is especially characteristic of obsessive compulsive reactions. It is usually taken as evidence of a regressive reactivation of pre-edipal fantasies which belong to a phase of development when little children are struggling with conflict over bowel control and over parental demands in general.[9]

In the next section the relationship between contamination and feces no longer remains at a level of inference; the patient makes the relationship

[9] In this case oral fixation is also represented by the strong preoccupation with food and oral poisoning.

manifest in her own symptoms. As with Ramona, so also with our next case, the cleansing rituals are used by an archaic superego to carry out self-punishment relentlessly and, from a normal adult point of view, senselessly. Impulses to contaminate mingle overtly with ambivalent hate and love. The same activities that are used for defense are used to indulge in something forbidden and as self-punishment for having the forbidden impulse. In both cases the whole regressive struggle is carried on openly; we see the neurotic conflict acted out before our eyes.

Reaction Formation and Undoing

The patient who will be the center of our discussion in the present section gives us clear evidence of regression to a pre-edipal level, just as the patients did whom we discussed in the two preceding sections. She also uses *displacement* and *isolation* prominently among her defenses. Her compulsive handwashing is just as much a *countermeasure* as were Ramona's cleansing and precautionary rituals. What she adds to our account so far of obsessive compulsive reactions is the unusually vivid use of two other characteristic techniques — *reaction formation* and *undoing*.

Reaction formation. (a) Normal reaction formation. By reaction formation we mean the use of some impulse or attitude for the purpose of keeping in check an opposite impulse or attitude which is not being successfully repressed. Reaction formation is used to some extent by everyone throughout life. Adults encourage reaction formation in children who are too young to be able to repress undesirable trends. If a little child goes on being messy when he is considered capable of keeping reasonably clean, or if he is cruel to pets or a younger sibling, adults impress upon him the socially or personally acceptable cleanliness or kindness, usually with a concrete demonstration. During a transitional stage a child may verbalize the acceptable behavior but act out its opposite. Eventually he finds pleasure in being clean and kind; and repression becomes effective enough to mitigate his impulses to soil and be cruel. Reaction formation becomes necessary only when temptation is greatly increased or when frustration unleashes cruel aggression.

(b) Abnormal reaction formation. Reaction formation becomes pathological when a person has unusually strong sadistic impulses which he can neither express nor repress. If the threatening impulse is to soil, directly or symbolically, the person may insist upon being so meticulously neat and clean that even laymen suspect his behavior of being a defense against something he fears. If the threatening impulse is to be cruel, a person may unconsciously fall back upon becoming excessively gentle and passive, to counteract his otherwise uncontrollable aggression, so that he is incapable of being even normally aggressive when he should. Infantile aggression, especially

during the pre-edipal phase of toilet training, is closely allied with impulses to soil. We have already pointed out that the same symbolic equivalence is to be found in the vulgar speech of all Western cultures, not only among therapists and their patients, but among children and adults who know nothing about psychological theory.[10]

Undoing. (a) Normal undoing. The other mechanism to be stressed in this section, *undoing,* is an example of magical thinking which all of us use normally in one form or another. When, for example, a small child falls and hurts himself, his mother may kiss the hurt place and say, "Now that will make it all better again!" She uses the magic of her love to undo the pain. If her magic works the hurt child's crying is modulated to a whimper. He feels now a litte grief instead of fright and anger.

Apologies among adults often follow similar principles. You say you did not mean something when sometimes you know you did, and the other person knows it too. Nevertheless, your disavowal may magically undo the evil. Undoing also appears in the practice of sending a conciliatory gift. A person tries to *undo* a quarrel by an offering of flowers or a present — anything that symbolizes his humility and esteem in the wake of some meanness or anger.

Modern society shows some of the same kind of magical thinking in its legal codes. It demands that an offender undo or expiate an offense by submitting to degradation and the loss of all affection for a specified period. American society even calls its prisons "penitentiaries," that is, places for penitence. They are places where offenders are expected to undo an evil deed by an amount of suffering which is supposed to cancel out his crime and leave him guiltless again. The period of penitence is made longer for evils considered to be greater. This practice is an institutionalization of the talion principle, an eye for an eye, a tooth for a tooth. Although many legal experts consider it an ineffectual system, we still live by it every day.

We all use *symbolization* in our practice of undoing. What is more, we often symbolize both guilt and innocence in the same fantasy, the same word, action or symbolic object. The cross, for example, signifies to Christians both the burden of their sins and their redemption from their sins, their inevitable guilt and their eventual innocence. When they gaze religiously upon the cross, their fantasies may be a blending of sin and forgiveness or an alternation between the two.

For a billion human beings, of many different creeds, washing rituals have the same symbolic elements. They are an acknowledgment of sinfulness, of having been an unclean transgressor, and at the same time a statement of newly acquiring cleanliness or innocence. The contamination of dirty thoughts, of evil deeds and bad intentions are ritualistically washed away by a symbolic act.

---

[10] Nursery school children express hostility or contempt by calling other children by whatever name is used in their own home for feces or bowel movements.

No believer tries to justify such thinking through an appeal to verbal logic. No one thinks of asking for a scientific study of the cleansed person and the cleansing agent. Religious behavior belongs to a different realm of experience. For thousands of years the public ablution has been used as a visible, tangible ritual to serve notice upon others and upon oneself that sins have been committed and are now in the process of being undone. The act is literal and physical, but its target is symbolic and spiritual. What the evil thought or intention has been may never be revealed to another person. Yet washing can still signify the desire to regain innocence or to reassure oneself of being guiltless.

(b) Obsessive compulsive undoing. In turning now to *neurotic undoing* we are not turning to something completely new and strange, but rather to the maladaptive use of techniques that are familiar, universal and ancient. Obsessive compulsives often use undoing in forms which seem more primitive, more childlike and magical than normal rituals. This is in part because the obsessive compulsive ritual is likely to be personal, inventive and unfamiliar to others. It is also in part because the patient regresses, and in regressing he reactivates and releases unconscious fantasies or their derivatives. These belong to his early edipal or pre-edipal childhood, to a phase in which primitive magical techniques were among the child's chief resources.

The regression often brings into the open also an early, primitive precursor of the mature superego, as described in Chapter 5. This transforms what was once parental strictness into a sadistic gloating cruelty. A whole system of unconscious thinking, never extinguished and always to some extent present in adult behavior, now comes forward to dominate the neurotic situation. It is especially clear, as we would expect, in matters of love and hate, cleanliness and dirt, moral right and wrong.

The case of Sally J., which we are about to present, forms an interesting contrast to our previous one. Sally was at least the intellectual equal of Ramona M. Culturally and educationally she was superior. Yet her hostility was crudely expressed in frank physiological symbols; and her handwashing ritual followed a monotonous, primitive pattern. Her preoccupation with soiling showed little of the defensive displacement through which Ramona was able to focus upon chipped glassware, lye, cleaning fluids and scouring powders. And whereas Ramona tried to head off her unconscious hostile impulses by means of elaborate protective devices, Sally openly expressed her hostility, and only afterwards turned to her magical washing ritual to undo the evil and punish herself.

A case of obsessive compulsive handwashing

Sally J. was an attractive unmarried state employee in her twenty-seventh year. She came for help because her symptoms had forced her to break off an engagement of three years' standing. She complained of ungovernable outbursts of rage against her fiancé, of continual thoughts about contaminating others, and of irresistible impulses to wash her hands over and over. Once again we find here a familiar obsessive compulsive trio: *intense emotional ambivalence* (hating a loved one), *preoccupation with contamination*, and the use of *defensive countermeasures* (handwashing against soiling).

Childhood background. Sally's childhood throws a great deal of light upon her neurotic illness. She was an angry child. As an infant she had frequent breath-holding spells in which she would go purple with rage. Temper tantrums continued right through childhood into adulthood. Sally grew into a demanding, willful little girl with a strong edipal attachment for her father. She made such a terrible fuss over his leaving her that sometimes he had to sneak out of a side window to get to work. Her father never spanked her, but her mother did and Sally never forgave her for it. She remembered sitting alone in a corner on the floor as a child, weeping over her mother's treatment of her.

Great difficulties over bowel function seem to have begun in infancy and to have extended into adolescence. The mother, a practical nurse, was most exacting. Sally appeared always to be getting constipated; and to this challenge her mother responded by giving the child enemas, just as we saw that Oscar E.'s mother also did. Sally remembered watching the preparations in helpless rage. The contest of wills often ended with Sally messing up the bathroom which, in later years, she had to help her mother clean. She recalled how peaceful it seemed when the storm was over and everything had been put away.

Sally had a vivid memory of sitting on a log in the backyard with her father, waiting for something. She was then three and a half years old. The something was her baby brother's birth. She had known for some time that her mother was "going to be sick." Sally had said then that she could look after herself; but after Billy was born everything got worse. He was clearly the favorite of her father no less than of her mother. All through the rest of her childhood she felt herself compared unfavorably with him. At first she used to say to her father, "Put him down! Take your *own* baby!" She remembered brooding over this preference for her brother, feeling terribly jealous of him and resentful toward her parents.

In time, however, Sally gave up expressing hatred toward Billy. She adopted instead a protective attitude toward him of tender loving care. This change was a product of *reaction formation.* The hate was still there not far from the surface; for whenever Billy teased her, she responded with violent temper outbursts.

Sally also used reaction formation in her attempts to handle her conflicts over bowel function and soiling. Around the age of five years she became fastidious in the extreme. Her own person had to be meticulously clean, her hair smoothed out, and her dresses without a crease or a speck of dirt. She always sat down carefully, like a woman in a party dress, smoothing her skirt and watching to make sure that it did not wrinkle. There was a big row over an expensive hat that Sally wanted when she was only six. She got it.

She identified with her mother in an ambivalent admiring, hating way. According to Sally, her mother had been a beautiful woman who devoted much silent attention to her own appearance. Sally boasted about her mother to her little friends, but at home she always treated her mother with disdain. She went on trying to win back her place as her father's favorite without success.

As long as she could remember, Sally had suffered from an absurdly guilty conscience. Almost anything could arouse it. If something at home was missing she felt that she was suspected of having made away with it. Even when she was sick in bed she felt that she was only pretending. Her parents impressed upon her a strict sense of moral responsibility from the very start. She never lost a fascination for unpardonable sin and the fate of sinners. Her childhood dreams sometimes turned into nightmares; but when they did it was to her mother, not to her father, that she went for comforting when she awoke.

Another thing that went back to early childhood was an insatiable curiosity about sex. Her baby brother's genitals caught Sally by surprise, but her parents would not allow her to speak about them. She decided that there was "a surface way of living and a hidden life." Later on she discovered that it was safe to discuss such things with her girl friends.

Between the ages of ten and twelve Sally had occasional episodes of mutual masturbation with other girls. She felt wicked at the time but developed no serious manifest conflict. When she was ten a boy showed her a picture of an embryo in a mother's womb and said, "That's how babies are made. Want to try it?" She felt more humiliated than frightened. She had always been shy with boys, preferring distant hero-worship to a date. She did not go out on a date until she was twenty.

Adolescent symptoms. The first frankly obsessive compulsive symptoms appeared when Sally was twelve or thirteen, well after she had given up her exaggerated neatness and cleanliness. For several months, in early adolescence, she found herself continually counting parked automobiles and passing automobiles in groups of seven. She had to keep the count of parked cars completely separate from the count of passing cars (*isolation*). Otherwise something terrible would happen —she was not sure what. The parked cars, she said, seemed to her more like girls and the passing cars like boys. At this time she was also haunted by abstract uncertainties over right and wrong. She engaged in anxious rumination about God's will, and how she could ever be sure what it was.

In high school, in business school and at work Sally developed a variety of obsessive compulsive doubts, repetitions and rituals concerning numbers, equations, balancing accounts, filing systems, indexing and the like. These seemed to rise and fall with the rise and fall of difficulties over interpersonal relationships. At home she grew generally more and more irritable, she slept poorly, she had temper outbursts and occasional crying spells. This gives us a sketchy picture of the tense, uneasy situation in which Sally developed her acute illness.

Guilt and mild depression. When she was twenty Sally began dating and going steady with a dignified, reserved man of thirty-five. Her parents disapproved of him on religious grounds. She found herself getting more and more tense with him as time went on. Finally, after nearly two years, she flew into a rage one evening and told the man she never wanted to see him again. She never did.

Her second serious interest in a man, six months later, ended disastrously for her. One evening her escort unexpectedly began sex play. Sally reacted with a violent upsurge of anxiety and guilt, returned home at once, and went immediately to her mother for comfort, just as she had done after her childhood nightmares.

This episode of sex play brought out into the open a long struggle with sex and hostility which Sally had been trying to wage secretly and alone. She made a series of abject confessions to her mother, passing quickly from the evening's petting to focus upon her sex play with other girls in preadolescence, and upon her solitary masturbation before that. She told her mother in a spirit of self-abasement that she had sinned against God and that her hands were unclean. No handwashing occurred at this time.

In the weeks that followed Sally talked a great deal to her mother about right and wrong, about being sinful and unworthy, about being different from others because of all that she had done. She said that for years she had been troubled by what she called "sensual sensations." These occurred especially when she was sexually aroused, when she was constipated or had a full bladder, and whenever she indulged in "evil thoughts." She thus tied together her sexual, bowel and urinary functions with evil thinking.

Her trouble with men, Sally said, was that they stirred up these "sensual sensations" until she could not stand it. Then she would have a violent temper outburst and feel relieved; but with the outburst she often had orgasm, and this led to a new build-up of guilt and tension. We see here the confusion of love and hate in an adult, and the linking of this sexual-aggressive experience with bowel function, which was to precipitate a classical handwashing compulsion.

For several months Sally remained subdued and mildly depressed. She managed to stay at work, but she ate and slept poorly. She went out with no one, and there were no temper outbursts. Then she took advantage of her summer vacation to obtain a ninety-day sick leave. She spent this period resting on a farm which took "paying guests," and which had only an outhouse toilet supplemented by commodes in every bedroom. It was here that Sally replaced her mild depression with an obsessive compulsive disorder.

The handwashing compulsion. Sally attributed the onset of her compulsive handwashing to the haphazard way in which the commodes at the farm were collected and redistributed. She became obsessed with the unreasonable fear that she might contaminate others and even be responsible for somebody's death. This was a combination of guilt, hostility and an infantile overvaluation of the powers of her excreta. The only way that Sally could relieve the tension of this obsession was to wash her hands — a particularly irrational, magical remedy, since washing her hands did nothing to the "dangerous" commodes. Each time she thought of contaminating others she had to scrub her hands. She began using yellow soap and a nail brush, and she scrubbed her arms up to the elbows. The farmers used lysol, which contains carbolic acid and liquid soap, so she sometimes added a little of this to her washing water.

Sally returned home in good spirits but with a fully developed hand-washing compulsion which did not go away. She soon had an ugly, painful dermatitis. Her hands and forearms became red, tender and swollen; sometimes there was a crack in the skin which oozed serum. But ugly and painful or not, the hands and forearms had to be scrubbed every time Sally went to the toilet, and every time she had a "sensual sensation" or thought about contamination. If she resisted the impulse to wash and scrub she had an anxiety attack. Her heart would pound, she would break out into a sweat and feel panicky and breathless — "as if something were pressing the life" out of her, she said.

The obsessive compulsive reaction soon generalized. It seemed to Sally that she contaminated everything she touched. Towels and under-clothes had to be laundered after a single use; dresses had to be cleaned after one wearing. Her bureau drawer became filled with discarded brushes, combs, powder puffs, gloves and handbags which, she felt, might contaminate others. They were dangerous to use and too dangerous to throw away. A streak of omnipotence, an unconscious fantasy of being the foul fiend, lurked behind this primitive, regressive belief. At the same time, as might be expected, there was a marked increase in reactive orderliness at work. Sally was more than ever repetitious, uncertain and ritualistic at the office.

When she was twenty-four Sally fell in love with a man of whom her family approved. She soon became engaged, but all the old difficulties arose again and new ones appeared. Just being in her fiancé's company gave Sally "sensual sensations." This made her feel guilty and resentful, and at the same time frustrated, neglected and unappreciated, much as she had felt in early childhood. Every so often the situation would get beyond her control and a violent temper tantrum would erupt, something like her childhood response to her brother's teasing.

Two new elements entered the situation: actual soiling and penitential sadomasochism. Sally's temper outbursts now culminated in the physiological act of passing traces of urine, gas or feces, which to her meant a deadly assault upon the man she loved. She had to change her clothes immediately and scrub her hands and forearms. Sally began to feel pleasure in hurting herself. While she was using the nailbrush, and wincing, she would tell herself under her breath that she had it coming to her. Something in her seemed to gloat when the pain made her wince and whimper. Her remorse over her now open hostility toward her fiancé added fuel to this sadistic attack upon herself. When the ritual was over she felt relaxed and gratified. In therapy, it reminded her of the peace that had always followed after her mother had given her enemas as punishment in childhood.

A homoerotic component also appeared in the clinical picture, but only in Sally's manifest dreams. One dream she related as follows, "I was kissing a person. I can't remember — maybe it was a girl. I can't remember. Maybe one of the girls at work or one I know in the neighborhood. At least the girl had that girl's dress on." Another dream she had repeatedly. In it she seemed to be walking down the street with another woman, each of them with an arm around the other's waist. The pressure of the other woman's arm would begin to squeeze her — an awful feeling as if something were closing in upon her, as though she could not bear it, as though her breath were being taken away. She associated this repetitive dream with her mother, and also with the anxiety that came whenever she resisted handwashing, "as if something were pressing the life" out of her. In this dream, with its associations, Sally's childhood love, her fear, and the "sensual sensations" were brought together.

The now well-established cycle — hostile and erotic thoughts, token soiling, scrubbing and final relaxation — generalized further to all kinds of situations. Whenever Sally heard somebody else praised and her old inadequacy feelings came back, like the ones she had experienced in relation to her little brother, this was enough to start off the cycle. The same thing happened when she compared herself with anyone she admired, and whenever she felt neglected or unfairly treated. Any erotic, jealous or angry rumination was enough to do it. Even standing on line, when she could not move forward fast enough, started off the cycle — angry thoughts, token contamination, handwashing and then peace. In spite of her tensions and rituals, the engagement with her fiancé lasted two and a half years. Then there was a temper outburst, the engagement was broken, and Sally sought psychotherapeutic help.

Therapy began, as usual, with what the patient herself first provided. Broadening and deepening of this material developed slowly as the interviews progressed. What has just been told as a consecutive, unfolding story actually emerged in a more or less scattered order. The fragments emerging were themselves a product and a part of the treatment. Sometimes things seemed to emerge out of context, as things often do in dreams; but they were not really out of context with Sally's focal conflicts and fantasies. Some fantasies and conflicts appeared consciously in the form of ritual and magical thinking. Improvement came with the new insights and perspectives which Sally was able to work out. Her tolerance for anxiety increased, so that she could face things which she had formerly repressed, and her obsessive compulsive behavior became much less tyrannical. She was still far from complete recovery when she terminated her treatment. It was learned a few years later that she had married and borne a child.

Discussion of Sally J. This case has been presented in some detail because it expresses openly many characteristics which often can only be inferred in obsessive compulsives. While it is still fresh in our memory we shall discuss some of its dynamic and developmental background, even though this anticipates the general discussion of obsessive compulsives at the end of the chapter.

Perhaps the most striking pathological characteristic that Sally showed was her *ambivalence.* As a little child she hated her little brother whom she grew to love. She hated her mother but admired her and turned to her for comfort and forgiveness. She resented bitterly her father's desertion in favor of her brother; but she never gave up trying to win him back. She was meticulously clean and neat at the same time that — during a decade of childhood struggling with her mother for independence — she was messing things up with her excretions. As an adult she was an attractive, well-dressed, ladylike young woman; yet she was using soiling, flatus and wetting whenever she became tense or angry. And whenever she began to love a man she flew into violent temper tantrums.

This ambivalence itself rested upon *defective repression.* If it is true that we unconsciously hate a little those whom we love much, it is also true that our little hatred remains most of the time repressed. We have no need to become aware of it and express it. The process of maturing consists in part of the mastering of such disturbing and self-defeating trends. They must become subordinated so that emotional experience can include wholehearted love or hate, and in such a way that one's behavior in either case falls within the limits of social and superego regulation. This process of maturing Sally had never carried through.

One of the chief signs that repression is chronically defective is the overuse of *reaction formation* as a defense. The child who becomes too good, too clean or too obedient is usually a child who has not been able to come to terms with his unconscious impulses in the opposite directions. He must lean over backwards to be able to keep his balance. In Sally's case, reaction formation was used far beyond the range of normal variation; and, even so, its use was not enough to enable repression to hold hostile and erotic impulses within normal bounds.

The *regressive* nature of Sally's behavior appears in many ways. Openly hating loved ones, messing while being clean, liking pretty things and soiling them, expressing love and hate through bowel and bladder functions — all these belong more to a two-year-old level than to adult maturity. So also, of course, does the use of reaction formation to buttress the defenses when repression is still underdeveloped.

Sally's magical thinking was also regressive. It expressed childlike omnipotence clearly. She was frightened that her excreta might kill, and she dared not throw away things that she had used for fear of what they might do to other people. Even her thoughts about contamination seemed potentially dangerous to Sally. This is not the logical reasoning of a sophisticated adult, which in other respects the patient was, but the prelogical, primary process thinking of a confused little child.

Much the same can be said of the purifying handwashing ritual as the patient used it. Handwashing might have been in part a return to the reactive cleanliness which Sally abandoned when she was twelve; but, if so, its use in adulthood was also in her case a return to ritual magic. Her fear, as we have seen, was that she might harm others through her thoughts of soiling. Yet it was her own hands and forearms that she scrubbed. In this symptomatology Sally neither distinguished clearly between herself and others, nor recognized the everyday logic of cause and effect. Her attempt to undo her magical harm to others by washing herself was on the same general level as the ritual practice of rattling dry beans in a gourd to make the rains come. Sally's purification ritual, like her fear of exercising omnipotent evil, belongs to prelogical, primary process thought.

Outstanding in the clinical picture is also an *archaic precursor of the superego,* a sadistic monitor and punisher. This superego precursor goes far beyond her mother's sadism by carrying retaliatory self-punishment to cruel extremes. Sally's mother used enemas to subdue and punish her in childhood. Sally, as an adult, used laundry soap and water on her hands and forearms. She scrubbed them with a nailbrush and sometimes added lysol. All this she did, not only to undo magically her dangerous contaminations, but also to give herself savage punishment.

Sally gloated vindictively as she gave herself pain. Her own words were, "A part of me seems to gloat." At the same time she sometimes whimpered out loud like a cruelly treated child. Thus she brought to light her immature superego identifications which belong to a period when parental punishment is experienced as torture and the parent as a relentless tormentor. These superego identifications Sally used immaturely, as an archaic superego struggling with a partially regressed ego. Instead of an interaction between two aspects of a unitary personality, we witness here a punitive mother image and a suffering daughter-image, both viewed from the perspective of a confused, sadomasochistic little child.

We shall turn next to forms of obsessive compulsive neurosis which contrast sharply with the vivid drama present in the case of Sally J. These forms have similar dynamic roots, but in spite of this the life seems to have gone out of the struggle. What remains of it seems to operate entirely upon an intellectual plane.

Obsessive Doubt and Rumination

Doubt and rumination are among the commonest obsessive compulsive symptoms. Some of the patients whom we have been discussing were beset by continual uncertainty and concern over what they had or had not done, or over the efficacy of their countermeasures and rituals. There are also cases, however, in which doubt and rumination are the chief and even the only manifest symptoms. The French had a name for this. They spoke of *la folie de doute,* "the madness of doubt." Obsessive doubt can literally be maddening.

Obsessive doubts and ruminations have been, as a rule, unconsciously *displaced,* from something forbidden or highly conflictual on to something apparently senseless, harmless or merely intellectual. The feelings which originally belonged to the forbidden and the conflictual have been *repressed* or *isolated.* The result is that whatever doubts or ruminations appear in consciousness as symptoms seem to be nothing more than meaningless preoccupations or speculations about reality, existence or morality. These preoccupations may seem unrelated to anything else or, as in the case that follows, they may seem directly related to some practical aspect of what the patient is about to do.

Eliot H., a college student, went to a telephone booth to call up a wealthy girl whom he had recently met, to ask her for a date. He spent an hour there, anxious and indecisive, unable to put the coin in the slot and unable to give up and go home. Each time his hand approached the telephone he anxiously withdrew it because he felt that telephoning her might ruin his chances with her. Each time he withdrew his hand he seemed to be throwing away a golden opportunity. Every positive argument for telephoning her he matched with a negative argument for not doing so. He went into all the ramifications of his ambivalent motivations. He imagined to himself what the girl and the members of her family — whom he scarcely knew — might think of his attentions to her; and then he had to picture to himself what they would think if he neglected her.

His whole future seemed to Eliot to hang on the outcome of this little act. Had he any right to put his coin in? If he did so would the girl respond favorably? If she did, what would happen next? Eliot fantasied every conceivable consequence as he sat there sweating in the booth, consequences to him and to her, on and on into remote contrasting futures. He was helplessly caught in an obsessive dilemma, as he had been caught before hundreds of times. The more he tried to be sure of what he did, the more things he imagined going wrong, any one of which might ruin everything. In the end he gave up the anxious debate and went home, exasperated and worn out. Later he became convinced that in not making the call at that particular time he had missed the chance of a lifetime for winning security and happiness.

This absurd little episode sounds like the mere exaggeration of a shy suitor's hesitancy, but it was much more than this. It was a condensed symbolic expression of an intensely ambivalent personality, one that was volatile, impulsive and unpredictable. Almost every enterprise upon which Eliot had embarked since early adolescence had involved similar obsessive rumination. Into each decision he funneled all of his ambivalent conflicts — conscious, preconscious and unconscious — and then he found himself unable to follow through to a decision. The same thing unfortunately happened to his search for therapeutic help. He began with despair, switched quickly to great optimism, and then got bogged down in endless doubting and rumination over whether to continue. In the end he withdrew from therapy without ever becoming really involved in it.

Obsessive doubting such as this often turns from indecision over some specific action to a more general fruitless, abstract speculation. The patient may ruminate about the same problems that have occupied some of the greatest thinkers. *What is time? What is space? What is eternity? What is man? What is God? Where are we all going? What is justice? What are right and wrong? What is the meaning of life?* And so on. In the obsessive patient these questions are not what they appear to be but symptoms of unconscious conflict and indecision. As in dreams, so also here, it is not alone what appears in preconscious and conscious thinking that matters. It is also the repressed, displaced and isolated background, the genesis of the doubt and rumination, and what these are expressing at regressive levels as well as at adult ones.

In obsessive doubt and rumination there is the same degree of regression as in other obsessive compulsive reactions, regression that reactivates unsolved infantile conflicts belonging to the second and third years of life. This period is normally one of intense ambivalence. Final commitments to many basic attitudes have not been made. The little child is still indecisive about basic social roles, at times even believing that he has to choose in matters, like that of his sex role, which were decided for him before he was born. At primitive levels he may still be indecisive about whether to hate or to love a parent, whether to preserve what he loves or destroy it, and even whether or not to preserve what he loves by consuming it — an obvious analogy with eating what one likes.

To this phase of normal development belong also the uncertainties about which parent the child shall turn to and for what. How much shall he identify with each and what will happen to him when he does? With what characteristics and functions shall he identify? Shall he or she play the man's part or the woman's?[11] Or shall he or she play something of each in different social roles? Behind these lie still older and more basic uncertainties. *Where did I come from and how was I made? Where did mother carry me and how was I born? Or did father carry me?*[12] And so on.

The adult thinking of an obsessive patient understands the answers to early childhood questions such as these. But his unconscious regressive thinking does not understand them; and it is from these regressive levels that his obsessive doubt and rumination spring.

No matter how sophisticated and intellectual obsessive rumination may sound, it is actually primitive and pseudo intellectual. It represents an extreme of *displacement* and *isolation,* in which logical processes and abstract speculation are carried out in the service of magical, primary process fantasy — just as they are in fairy tales, myths and dreams. Some of the basic perplexities of early childhood are expressed in questions such as the following, all taken from the words of obsessive adults: *Why am I here and not somewhere else? Why is a ball round, water wet, grass green and summer hot? Why do I have two ears, eyes, nostrils, arms and legs? Why do some doors open inward and others outward? Why does water run downhill? Why do we have four seasons and four directions on the compass instead of three?* Each such obsessive question must be regarded as a dis-

[11] See Searles, H., "Sexual processes in schizophrenia," *Psychiatry,* 1961, *24,* 87–95.
[12] A normal nursery school boy said, "I take after my father, not my mother. so I must have come out of him."

placed symptom, as a preconscious or conscious expression which — like a manifest dream — may have condensed in it a multitude of deeply personal meanings not evident at first glance.

Freud called the obsessive compulsive neurosis a private religion. It has elaborate rituals and ceremonials. It has symbols of good and evil, protective words and gestures, self-denials, indulgences and penances. It may have whole systems of conscious, preconscious and unconscious faith and hope. But above all it is saturated with principles of good and evil, right and wrong, the clean and pure versus the dirty and impure. Thus we find endless obsessive rumination over the ageless problems of sin and redemption, directly or deviously expressed, but on a neurotic basis. In this the patient reflects the deep involvement of his regressed archaic superego precursor, which is exceeded in primitive harshness and cruelty only by the depressive superego. Let us now turn to a summary of the dynamic and developmental background of obsessive compulsive reactions.

Dynamic and Developmental Background

In this chapter, more than in any of the preceding ones, we have discussed dynamic and developmental factors while presenting the case material. The case material was actually organized around these factors. Here we shall need only to summarize the salient features of the regression and the defenses in obsessive compulsive reactions, and to bring into prominence what we have been calling an archaic superego precursor, which we shall meet again in the psychoses.

We said early in the chapter that repetition, formula, rule, ritual and ceremonial are not in themselves necessarily obsessive compulsive. Neither are magic and superstition. All of them can be found in the repertory of normal adults. They show up in one form or another among everyday customs, in practical skills and artistic experience, in science, politics and religion. Many magical and superstitious beliefs of today are the residues of yesterday's exact science; many scientific precepts of today will leave magical and superstitious residues in the the beliefs of tomorrow.

The artistic qualities of repetition, rule, formula, ritual and ceremonial in the play of children and the everyday life of adults are too evident to require further comment. Were it not for these qualities, and were it not for magic and superstition, the dramatic, poetic, visual and plastic arts of the world would be left mean and impoverished.

Even highly intelligent, sophisticated adults fall back upon magical and superstitious rituals when they find themselves unable to cope with an upsurge of dangerous threat or insoluble conflict. We are accustomed to recognize these trends in religious behavior; but they are just as much the characteristics of conflicting political ideologies. We are witnessing today on an international scale the growth of political rites and ceremonials, taking place in an emotionally charged atmosphere, with all the publicity, the credos and the denunciations of evil in others, which used to belong to religious creeds. There is magic and there is superstition in these political rites and ceremonials, but there is nothing that can be called artistic or spiritual. We shall turn from these normal phenomena to the fixation and regression of the obsessive compulsive.

Fixation and regression in obsessive compulsive reactions

The single most revealing thing about obsessive compulsive symptoms is that they represent a deep partial regression to pre-edipal levels of fixation. This regression reactivates the angry frustrations of a small child who has not yet succeeded in establishing his personal identity, who has not resolved the conflict over his need to remain dependent and his need for self-assertion. The struggle revived in obsessive compulsive adults is an infantile power struggle. It was originally carried on in an atmosphere of toilet training, at a time when bowel products and bowel control were among the child's paramount interests. Because of unusual difficulties during this phase of development the child remained partially fixated at this level. The characteristics reappearing in adult obsessive compulsive patients, as we have already seen, reflect derivatives of the childhood fixation.

The child in the phase of toilet training is normally a stubborn, rebellious, ambivalent child. He normally vacillates between loving and hating, between his pleasure in messing and his pride in being clean, between his need for approval and his need for independence.

When a small child courts love, approval and cleanliness — when he tries to be a "good" child — he feels himself moving toward conformity with what his parents seem to want. If he has already had serious difficulty in gaining independence, in breaking away from the symbiotic union with his mother, conformity may have frightening connotations. It may appear to mean losing one's identity and sinking back into nothingness.[13]

When a small child hates, messes and asserts himself — when he indulges in being a "bad" child — he feels himself gaining in independence, that is, in daring to do what is forbidden when he wants to do it.[14] If he has had serious difficulty in breaking away from the symbiotic union with his mother earlier in life, the child may experience his own obstinate rebellion as a life-and-death struggle, as a struggle to preserve his identity in the face of a dangerous encroachment.

Under such circumstances, when a child is struggling to preserve his identity and gain independence, he is likely to experience firmness or wilfullness in a parent as harsh, arbitrary and sadistic treatment. The merely insistent parent seems a relentless persecutor. A determined parental face,

[13] This threat is consciously experienced and expressed in psychotic and borderline psychotic cases, as we shall see.
[14] Such a conception of independence can be found also among juvenile delinquents, in sociopathic disorders, and in adult "acting out."

seen by a small child who is filled with fury and frustration, may be seen as the cruel face of a monster.[15] It is clear that the angry child himself contributes to the hostility that he experiences. The parental contribution, however, is often much greater than the parent realizes. In some of our cases the parental contribution was decisive.

The adult who develops obsessive compulsive symptoms under stress has in his make-up focal conflicts whose major points of fixation are at these levels. He carries within him systems of unresolved infantile conflicts over angry self-assertion, over deep needs to be dependent and deep fears of letting himself be dependent, over order and disorder, cleanliness and soiling — all expressed from time to time in some derivative form, concretely or symbolically. When such an adult regresses he revives some of these infantile, pre-edipal struggles and attempts to work them out in imagination and in overt behavior. At the same time he also revives whatever edipal conflicts remain for him unresolved and carries them back also to pre-edipal levels.[16]

To regress in this sense does not, of course, mean to become once again a child. The adult neurotic utilizes his adult skills when he regresses, carrying them back with him also. His language is the language of an adult; his use of logic and number, even though in the service of regression, remain adult in form. Part of the forcefulness often seen in obsessive compulsive behavior comes from the expression of powerful infantile needs by a powerful adult.

We shall defer discussion of certain characteristically obsessive compulsive symptoms, for example, sadism and emotional ambivalence, consciousness of the conflict and the regressive use of secondary process thinking, until after we have summarized the typical ego defenses.

Defense in obsessive compulsive reactions

The regression in obsessive compulsive reactions can be considered a defense on the same grounds that regression in other neuroses can. It prevents ego disintegration and permits reorganization at more primitive levels. It also determines the general character of the defensive structure. The *defective repression* is here buttressed by such auxiliary mechanisms as *reaction formation, isolation* and *undoing,* as well as by the more familiar *displacement.* The obsessive compulsive patient relies more heavily upon *magical thinking* and upon *rigid ritual* and *ceremonial* than do other neurotics and normal adults. Most of this has already been sufficiently discussed in the clinical sections of the chapter. Let us review them swiftly.

Defective repression. We assume that anyone who develops an obsessive compulsive reaction has suffered from defective repression all his life. He may have managed to remain clinically well, however, because his defective repres-

---

[15] This is the parental image which many borderline patients and some neurotic patients retain from early childhood.

[16] Edipal conflicts were especially obvious in the case of Sally J. and her father.

sion has always been buttressed by some of the auxiliary mechanisms just mentioned. Repression, in spite of being insufficient by itself, is still the keystone of the defensive organization, just as it is in normal adults. In most cases of obsessive doubt and rumination, as we have seen, repression is excessive in disposing of all affect in relation to the symptoms; but it is inadequate in failing to handle the derivatives of unconscious conflicts. These derivatives appear in consciousness as the obsessive doubt and rumination, colorless, often senseless, but imperishable.

As a rule the auxiliary defenses used by potentially obsessive compulsive persons do not attract special attention to themselves as long as the defensive organization, with repression as its keystone, succeeds in preserving ego integration. Other persons tend to look upon signs of reaction formation, isolation, undoing and magical or ritual rigidity, as incidental personality characteristics. Such and such a person, they will say, is too fussy, too careful, too neat, or messy, disorderly and reckless. The obsessive compulsive defensive system may be cumbersome but it often works well. It is then only when emotional stress precipitates regression, by providing an overload which the defensive system cannot handle, that the auxiliary defenses rise to prominence and contribute to the formation of obsessive compulsive symptoms.

Displacement. In many obsessive compulsive neuroses the forbidden id impulses, unconscious fantasies or superego retaliations which escape repression are merely displaced and isolated. We made this the topic of our clinical section, *Regression, displacement and isolation*. In the case of Doris I., described there, the poorly repressed impulses to kill her rival baby sister emerged as impulses to kill her own baby. They were thus not experienced at conscious levels in relation to their original object, her sister, but irrationally *displaced* in relation to her own daughter.

Ramona M., used as an illustration of countermeasures, also showed irrational *displacement*. She displaced hostile impulses to kill others on to the danger of involuntary killing through the use of all kinds of noxious substances. At the same time she also displaced her homicidal impulses of vengeance on to a sadistic attempt to control her family and spoil all their pleasure.

Sally J., on the other hand, did not displace her hostile impulses to contaminate. She acted them out, and actually became frightened of her supposed magical power for doing harm. This is what compelled her to keep washing her hands.

The displacement in obsessive doubt and rumination often makes the symptoms appear abstract and intellectual. In spite of this appearance, they have their sources in the same regressive infantile conflicts that give rise to the other forms.

Reaction formation. This, we have said, is the use of some act, attitude or thought — the opposite of one threatening to escape repression — in an effort to deny a place in consciousness to the one threatening to emerge.[17] We have discussed it in our clinical section, *Reaction formation and undoing*, and stressed the problem of unrepressed hate in our discussion of the case of Sally J.

Some persons who maintain that they cannot be anything but kind, gentle, passive and clean, under circumstances that call for combative aggression and indifference to dirt, are exhibiting reaction formation. They owe their rigidity not so much to a powerful inner conviction as to a powerful inner need to defend themselves against their own hostile, sadistic impulses to injure and contaminate, which they cannot otherwise keep in repression. When such defensive characteristics become structured as obsessive compulsive character traits, which can then often be maintained with little anxiety or guilt, we have what is called an *obsessive compulsive personality* or *character*.[18]

Isolation. This is a process which separates two opposing aspects of an ambivalent conflict, or eliminates emotional components from obsessive compulsive symptoms. It is related to *ego-splitting* and *denial*, as discussed in the preceding chapter on dissociative reactions. If isolation is successful no meaningful confrontation of contradictory attitudes, actions or thoughts can take place. It is thus a source of ego disintegration since it prevents an integrative fusion of opposing trends. In its more concrete form isolation prevents the patient from making contacts which to him seem somehow dangerous. It is also utilized in magical ways to avoid some imaginary contact or influence.

Sally J. employed isolation in her early adolescence. She separated in her mind small groups of passing automobiles from equal groups of parked ones. This seemed to be a magical form of symbolic protection against ideas of what might happen if boys and girls were allowed to mingle. Ramona M. spent most of her waking life in trying to isolate food from all dangerous chemicals and fertilizers — a magical orderliness designed to protect others from her unconscious homicidal impulses. Horace N. tried to render his obscene impulses meaningless and harmless by robbing them of their emotional component. They seemed to be actually an adolescent revival of childhood resentment and jealousy, but Horace experienced only anxiety and shame. We have seen how isolation operates in connection with reaction formation to make obsessive doubt and rumination seem colorless and impersonal.

Undoing. Undoing is the use of an act, attitude or thought to annul or "make up for" something that has *already* been done, felt or thought. Sally J. washed her hands *after* a contaminating act, attitude or fantasy. She tried

---

[17] Cf. Peak, H., Muney, B., and Clay, M., "Opposite structures, defenses, and attitudes," *Psychol. Monogr.*, 1960, *74*, Whole No. 495.
[18] We shall revert to a discussion of this in the chapter on personality disorders.

symbolically to undo something which she had already done or fancied. Superstitious undoing rituals appear in such common practices as knocking on wood after one has boasted or claimed good luck. Institutionalized undoing in the form of penance, retributive justice, pilgrimages and penitentiary service can be found in most modern societies. It plays a prominent part in ideological "brainwashing."[19]

Sometimes obsessive compulsives practice magical undoing by repeating the forbidden thing itself, but this time "with a different attitude," i.e., if a forbidden thing has been done with an evil attitude it can be undone if it is repeated with a "good" attitude. Even such an irrational practice as this has its normal parallel in the ritualistic killing of a murderer called *capital punishment*. This second killing, because it is done by an employe of the state who has a "different attitude," not only cancels out the first killing but is also supposed not to reflect upon the official executioner. It is significant, however, that executioners usually conceal their identity because the public still regards them as killers.

Rigidity. This is perhaps too general a characteristic of obsessive compulsives to merit the name *defense*, but it does deserve special mention. Rigid systems and rigid methods of doing, saying and thinking have appeared in our case material already. The fact that they are also essential to logic and scientific method, as well as to magical practice and religious ceremonial, does not make them any the less pathological when they are used by a neurotic person for neurotic purposes.

The rigidity of the obsessive compulsive has the same general aim as that of institutionalized strict regulation. The patient seeks to avoid intrusion and contamination, to ensure a favorable outcome, to reduce temptation, and to increase his own security, integrity and control.

As might be expected from their sadistic attitudes, obsessive compulsives often use rigidity as a means of punishing others and of punishing themselves. A compulsive housewife, for example, would not allow the family or visitors to use the living room unless it was subjected afterwards to a rigidly supervised ritual of thorough housecleaning in which the family was obliged to participate. Because of this the family of five persons spent all their evenings in a bleak and crowded kitchen. Ramona M. utilized her rigid precautions against potential poisons in a similar sadistic manner. In both cases one is reminded of the rigid and sometimes pointless protocol which must be followed in business conferences and official meetings and dinners.

Ego regression and the archaic superego

We return now to the study of regression in obsessive compulsive reactions in order to stress some peculiarities not already stressed, and to introduce the

---

[19] Lifton, R. J., *Thought Reform and the Psychology of Totalism: A Study of "Brainwashing" in China.* New York: Norton, 1961.

archaic sadistic superego which we shall meet again in studying the psychoses. We have already indicated that obsessive compulsive regression revives an ego-superego relationship which reflects the patient's pre-edipal phase of development when he was preoccupied with conflicts over dependence and self-assertion, conflicts which often found clearest expression in the area of toilet training.

Obsessive compulsive reactions are often called *guilt neuroses* because the anxiety most openly expressed by the patient is concerned with being good or being bad. As we have seen, the topics of good and evil, right and wrong, helping and harming, cleanliness and contamination, seem to preoccupy every obsessive compulsive patient in one form or another. The problem here is really one of approval-disapproval; it takes the form of cleanliness versus contamination so often because the pre-edipal phase to which regression carries the patient is that of toilet training. The case of Sally J., to which we shall revert later on, is only more obvious than most cases; it is not unique; it is not even rare.

In Chapter 5 we pointed out that when we say a person is suffering from a guilty conscience we do not really mean it. We mean that he is suffering from guilt and that it is his conscience which is making him suffer. In terms of ego, id and superego, this can be restated to mean that superego disapproval or condemnation is experienced by the ego or the self as a special kind of tension and anxiety — the kind that we describe popularly as guilt, remorse, shame, self-condemnation and the like. Keeping in mind what has already been said in this section about fixation, regression and defense in obsessive compulsive reactions, we can arrive at a formulation of guilt and the regressive superego which will prove useful throughout our later discussions of the psychoses.

What seems to happen in obsessive compulsive neuroses is that whenever there are impulses to do, say or think something forbidden, these impulses arouse an overwhelming superego reaction. The resulting tension and anxiety threaten to disintegrate ego function still further. The defenses against disintegration help produce the familiar symptoms. All of this takes place at a regressed level to which the patient has already been carried by the eruption which occurred when he exceeded his limit of tolerance under stress. The impulses are primitive, the unconscious ego is partially infantile, and the superego — which is after all only a differentiation within the ego organization — is also partially infantile. In what follows we shall ignore for the most part the well-established fact that both ego and superego operate at adult levels when they are not dealing with the focal conflicts and their direct derivatives. It will be simpler and clearer to confine the discussion to the part of the ego-superego organization which has regressed and helps produce the obsessive compulsive symptoms.

We have said, in the section on defenses, that repression is always defective in obsessive compulsives. Under stress, repression becomes obviously insufficient and the auxiliary defenses are stepped up in an effort to preserve ego integration. In spite of this increase in auxiliary defense, the obsessive compulsive defensive organization does not succeed in containing id impulses or their derivatives in unconscious fantasy. Neither does it succeed in blunting or deflecting the intolerable pressure from a regressed superego. The end-result is that both id impulse and superego pressure must find outlets if the ego integration is to be maintained intact. What we have been calling the symptoms are ego attempts at such expression. All of this might be dismissed as mere speculation if it were not for the fact that patients actually do express these forces in their overt symptomatology as openly as normal children express them in their play. This is the chief importance of obsessive compulsive neuroses: that they demonstrate the interplay of forces which in other neuroses remain for the most part hidden, and which in the psychoses are often mixed with such bizarre behavior as to discourage confidence.

The obsessive compulsive regression results in the revival of an ego-superego organization which contributes certain specific characteristics to the obsessive compulsive picture. Among those not already taken up are: (1) sadomasochism, (2) consciousness of conflict, and (3) use of secondary process thinking.

1. *Sadomasochism.* Regression in obsessive compulsive reactions reactivates an early archaic precursor of the mature superego. For the sake of brevity we shall call this the *archaic superego,* even though many workers in the field object to using the term *superego* for anything but postedipal super-ego.[20] The archaic superego is the remnant of some of the earliest attempts made by the infant to gain self-control. This remnant persists to some extent in all of us; but in most of us its expression is confined to dreams and to whatever preconscious fantasies manage to escape repression during intoxication or febrile illness. Otherwise it remains repressed; we know nothing of it.

Because of fixations at pre-edipal levels these remnants of archaic superego function seem to be better preserved in persons subject to obsessive compulsive neuroses. They probably lie closer to the preconscious than in other persons; their derivatives play a more important role in adult superego functioning; and when regression occurs they are expressed sadistically as superego attacks. At the same time, there are reciprocal areas of ego functioning which are also regressed to the same levels, and these contribute the reciprocal masochism which we saw so vividly expressed in the symptomatology of Sally J. This is, in effect, a revival of the primitive pre-edipal ego-superego relationship in which precursors of the mature superego were already discharging punitive, controlling functions in relation to precursors of the mature ego. The appearance of sadomasochism in obsessive compulsive neuroses is actually the reappearance of an infantile relationship.

[20] For a lucid discussion of this concept, see Weissman, P., "Ego and superego in obsessional character and neurosis," *Psychoanal. Quart.*, 1954, *23*, 529–543, and also his "Characteristic superego identifications of obsessional neurosis," *Psychoanal. Quart.*, 1959, *28*, 21–28.

We have seen that Sally J. repeatedly flew into a rage with each of her suitors in turn, as her sexual tension and frustration grew to be more than she could bear. This always ended in her driving them away which, as far as she was concerned, meant destroying them. According to her own account, she tormented some of them with a capricious willfullness as long as they and she could endure it. This might have been a repetition of her capricious, willful behavior as a frustrated little pre-edipal and edipal girl who, it will be recalled, created such a furor over her father's going to work that he sometimes had to crawl out of a window to escape her. In her handwashing compulsion, Sally obviously identified with a sadistic rendering of her mother, about which we shall have more to say later, as well as with herself as a whimpering, helpless little child. Our other cases showed similar identifications, but less clearly.

2. *Consciousness of conflict.* In most obsessive compulsive reactions the patient is fully aware that he is in active conflict, even though the form taken by the conflict may wear a defensive disguise. As a rule there is a pervasive sense of guilt; and often anxiety is openly expressed. This presents a very different picture from the concealment practiced by conversion patients, who display their symptoms only after the conflict has been condensed into a body symbol which they do not themselves understand.

Horace N. experienced consciously his struggle against conscious impulses to call his parents obscene names, and he used his infantile cries of "Stop it! Stop it!" with conscious intent.[21] Doris I. was consciously battling with a conscious urge to choke or drown her own child. Oscar E. knew about his death wishes, and he paid for them later with a psychotic depression which put his life in danger. Ramona M. was taking deliberate precaution against involuntary manslaughter; she even remembered the flash of a conscious death wish which started off her neurosis. Sally J. was fully aware that her soiling was hostile, and that she was fighting contamination through compulsive handwashing. Eliot H. had an acute experience of conflict as he sat in the telephone booth, even though he was not fully aware of its sources. All of these patients were openly waging a regressive war in which they were both hero and villain, the superego white knight and the id or ego dragon.

3. *Secondary process thinking.* We have said that even though obsessive compulsives regress partially to the level of little children, and become preoccupied with problems of good and evil at the level of toilet training, they are still actually adults. They all use adult language, not baby talk, and they employ adult secondary process logic in addition to their infantile symbolism. The rituals, countings, groupings, symmetries, equations and even complex systems which appear in their symptomatology are far beyond

---

[21] Hollander, R., "Compulsive swearing," *Psychiat. Quart.*, 1960, *34*, 599–622.

the capacities of a small child. Obsessive doubts and ruminations some-times rival the complexities of professional philosophical speculation.

These are examples of the use of secondary process forms in the interest of primary process aims. Artistic creativity has been formulated as regression in the service of the ego.[22] We can similarly formulate obsessive compul-sive symptoms as regressive thinking in the service of maintaining a neurotic equilibrium. This thinking is in reality being used by the patient prelogically and syncretically,[23] regardless of the outward form it takes. It utilizes de-based conceptualizations as primitive tools, something like the use of a digital computer to hammer in a nail.

The secondary process thinking of obsessive compulsiveness becomes erotized and aggressivized when they regress, that is, it is infused by primitive sexual and aggressive forces contributed from both id and super-ego. Erotic components are mixed with cruelty; aggressive components are obviously erotic. Such confusions as these belong also to the level of fixation to which the obsessive compulsive patient has regressed.

The childhood background of obsessive compulsives

From the study of adult patients, and from studies of normal and ab-normal little children,[24] what can we conclude about the probable child-hood of persons who are susceptible to obsessive compulsive reactions in adulthood under stress? We have said that in obsessive compulsive regres-sion there is revived an ego-superego relationship that reflects the patient's own pre-edipal life. This does not mean that what happened during the pre-edipal phase is faithfully reproduced by the regression. What seems to be revived is some part of the original situation *as experienced by a little child*, with whatever changes that later experiences may have induced in the un-conscious and preconscious imagery and cognitive structure.

The small child in a pre-edipal phase is too helpless and far too ignorant to be able to evaluate the situation objectively. To become objective at all, a small child has to work through his crises of identity-formation and his often seething edipal problems. If, for example, a pre-edipal child feels at the time oppressed by self-righteous, persecuting figures, this is the experience that his regression will revive. He will relive in his neurosis the misunder-standings and distortions of his early childhood, along with some actual parent-child relationships during pre-edipal phases.

[22] Kris, E., "On preconscious mental processes," *Psychoanal. Quart.*, 1950, *19*, 540–560.

[23] For a discussion of syncretic thinking, see Piaget, J., *Language and Thought of the Child* (trans. M. Gabain). London: Routledge, Kegan Paul, 1926; Wolff, P. H., *The Developmental Psychologies of Jean Piaget and Psychoanalysis. Psychol. Issues*, 1960, *2*, No. 1 (Monograph 5).

[24] For a detailed account of obsessive compulsive neurosis in a neglected two-and-a-half-year-old child, see Fraiberg, S., "A critical neurosis in a two-and-a-half-year-old girl," *The Psychoanalytic Study of the Child*. New York: Internat. Univ. Press, 1952, vol. 7, pp. 173–215.

Ego-superego in the case of Sally J. The regressive ego-superego struggle that Sally J. exhibited as her obsessive compulsive symptomatology gives us an example of such a revival of childhood experience. To what extent were these experiences based upon actual parental cruelty during Sally's struggle for self-assertion and her battles over toilet training? To what extent were they products of infantile distortion and misunderstanding?

The evidence indicates that Sally was treated with unnecessary severity by self-righteous parents. They were still strict and self-righteous when Sally had grown to adulthood. It is improbable that anyone was deliberately cruel to her, although deliberate parental cruelty is not unknown at any level of society.[25] Sally probably distorted and misunderstood the severity and implacability so that to her it seemed gloating and vindictive.

Sally internalized her strict, severe, religious parents as ego identifications which laid the basis for her archaic superego. She identified with her parental aggressors as they seemed to her to be. In this way she distorted what must have seemed to her a sadistic, relentless parent figure, and built it internally into something inhuman and savage. To this sadistic internal object she reacted, as we have seen, with masochistic ego attitudes and behavior — the reciprocals of the superego sadism. Sally whimpered like a little child when she punished herself; and she punctuated her behavior from time to time with equally childlike angry self-assertive outbursts and token soiling.

The reappearance of this whole complex in her obsessive compulsive regression means, of course, that Sally had never succeeded in mastering this pre-edipal phase of personality development. We had other indications that led us to believe that she had probably been struggling with unconscious anal-sadistic conflicts during most of her life. Regression threw these up to the surface where they appeared vividly in her neurosis; and therapy apparently enabled her to embark on the task of mastering some of the conflicts.

Parental figures and the archaic superego. The *archaic superego*, precursor of the mature superego, as we see it in operation in obsessive compulsive patients, is clearly a neurotic rendering of parental figures from the patient's own pre-edipal childhood. It is, we have said, a reproduction of the way the patient experienced his parents when he was two or three years old. If we were to assume that his experiences reflect objectively what actually went on during this phase of development, we would have to conclude that the parents were indeed overdemanding, relentless and sadistic. We would have to conclude that they threw their irresistible will into a power struggle over conformity, cleanliness and obedience, and that they actually enjoyed wielding unrestrained power and seeing their child coerced into an anxious, resentful obedience. How much truth is there in such a

[25] Niederland's article on Schreber's father gives startling evidence of this. See Niederland, W. G., "Schreber, father and son," *Psychoanal. Quart.*, 1959, *28*, 151–169.

portrayal of parental attitudes and actions as the foundation for adult obsessive compulsive reactions?

The truth, as far as we can ascertain it, seems to be as follows. A minority of obsessive compulsive patients have had at least one sadistic parent who could enjoy coercing a child and witnessing his outbursts of helpless rage. A much larger number seem to have had parents who were not consciously sadistic, who would have preferred to avoid the outbursts of rage, but who simply could not themselves tolerate a normal degree of soiling in their child, or could not endure the headstrong negativism of infant self-assertion. This latter group of parents is pushed into a battle of wills with their children because of their own uncontrollable anxiety and counteraggression. Clinicians encounter both types of parents often enough — during periods when battles over self-assertion and bowel control are actually being waged in the home — to indicate that those parent-child relationships are unfortunately not rare.[26]

Such parents are often themselves compulsively clean, conforming and perfectionistic. They may be demanding no more of the child than they demand of themselves. But they are adults with adult resources and adult pleasures, whereas the child is still an infant with limited resources and primitive infantile pleasures. The demands made upon him that he curb his self-assertion and keep clean may be at least premature. The child is often physiologically incapable of genuine bowel control. He may not yet be psychologically ready to give up the infantile privilege of soiling whenever and wherever he wishes. Such a child needs not only to understand and accept parental demands that he be punctual, orderly and clean; he must also have other resources and other pleasures to which he can turn, other kinds of mastery that he spontaneously enjoys.

It takes time for a child to acquire these resources, to gain an understanding and genuine acceptance of parental demands. It depends upon a certain degree of maturing, upon crystallizing the personal freedom to assert oneself along socially acceptable lines. A tolerant, loving parent will encourage the negativistic child — when the child is not being negativistic — to acquire more mature forms of self-assertion as the child's inner resources and his mastery of the environment grow. No major battle lines will be drawn at the level of negativism and sphincter control.

May an obsessive compulsive adult have had parents in his childhood who were not themselves unusually coercive, hostile or compulsive? It is certainly possible. There are at least four other factors in childhood development to consider.

(1) In the first place there may be inherent characteristics of the child himself which favor fixation during the phase of dawning self-assertion and

[26] Littin, E. M., Giffin, M. E., and Johnson, A. M., "Parental influence in unusual sexual behavior in children," *Psychoanal. Quart.*, 1956, *25*, 37–55. Cf. Maccoby, E., Maccoby, N., Romney, A. K., and Adams, J. S., "Social reinforcement in attitude change," *J. abnorm. soc. Psychol.*, 1961, *63*, 109–115.

bowel control. This is a period in which children are normally obstinate, negativistic, anally oriented and sadistic. Whatever individual differences tend to accentuate this phase of development might favor the development of an archaic superego with strong pathogenic potentialities. In that case, regression under stress in adulthood might lead to obsessive compulsive reactions independently of pathogenic parental influences. We would have to add the effects of early illnesses, suffered before the beginning of the pre-edipal phase, as possible early sources of obsessive compulsive predisposition, particularly those involving bowel function.

(2) Children with only moderate fixation in their pre-edipal phase may be driven back upon it because their later edipal experiences are too frightening. They fail to work out edipal conflicts at edipal levels, and they retreat or regress while still little children to try working edipal conflicts out at pre-edipal levels. Such children, grown to adulthood, are likely to do the same kind of thing again. An adult sexual or aggressive crisis reawakens their poorly repressed, unresolved edipal conflicts, and they regress as adults to pre-edipal levels carrying their conflicts with them. In some of these cases — the man in the telephone booth is an example — the primitive sexual or aggressive character of the regressive processes is kept under repression. Only abstract, pseudointellectual doubt or rumination appears on the surface.

(3) It is well known that fixations may develop during any phase of development because of overemphasis rather than frustration. Parents who overemphasize bowel control, cleanliness and punctuality — because of competition with other parents or because of unwise advice — may lend an exaggerated importance to these things which they had not intended. Thus, for example, parents who overemphasize self-control, when a child is still only able to be negativistic, may influence him to develop his automatic opposition as his substitute for a more mature independence.

(4) Finally, a child who develops an obsessive compulsive reaction when he grows to adulthood may have received too little patience and affection during the phase of bowel control and self-assertion because his parents were preoccupied with other problems. Whenever a child has to endure weaning of any kind, a determining factor in the outcome is always the compensation he gets in the form of loving encouragement from his parents. Even adults who are called upon to suffer temporary loss of privilege in order to learn something new, will do it more gladly and with less pain if they are treated with patience and affection.[27] The small child is in the special situation that he is dependent for all of his comfort, security and love upon the very persons who are denying, coercing and teaching him to accept the weaning process. It is essential that he have a reasonable degree of patient understanding and affection from them if he is not to develop a pathological degree of resistance and hate.

[27] This is especially important in the rehabilitation of amputees and cases of poliomyelitis.

Obsessive compulsive reactions
and neurotic depressions

As we turn now from obsessive compulsive reactions to neurotic depressions we turn from one kind of *guilt neurosis* to another. In both neuroses the patient reactivates pre-edipal conflicts when he regresses in the face of adult crisis. In both neuroses a severe, unloving superego precursor emerges. In both a regressed, ambivalent ego struggles openly with infantile conflicts over being good and being bad. Attempts are made in both to resolve pre-edipal conflicts by means of overt defensive behavior. In both, the regression affects only a part of the personality; the patient maintains relatively good object relationships and remains able to handle most reality situations satisfactorily. These are some of the chief similarities between the two *guilt neuroses*. There are many obvious differences.

Only a few essential differences need be mentioned here. The rest will be reserved for discussion in the chapter that follows. *Obsessive compulsive* patients are usually *action-centered*. They try to "go it alone," using rituals, countermeasures, reaction-formation, isolation and undoing. They are self-assertive, openly hostile and oriented toward gaining independence — all these, of course, at a regressive level. *Neurotic depressives* are *other-person centered*. Their basic drive is to be taken care of, like a helpless infant; but at the same time they are frightened by the danger of becoming helpless and perhaps losing their identity. They are oriented, in other words, toward gaining infantile dependence. They try to exploit others to give them comforting reassurances to offset their overwhelming sense of being *inferior* and *unworthy* — the neurotic depressive's major expression of unconscious guilt. They conceal frustration and hostility behind complaints of being unloved and unlovable.

Whereas obsessive compulsives are typically obstinate, overtly negativistic and self-sufficient, the neurotic depressive is typically tenacious, clinging, overtly compliant and sometimes parasitic. The regressed ego of neurotic depressives seems much weaker in relation to the archaic superego than is the case with the regressed ego of obsessive compulsives. Ego and superego in obsessive compulsive reactions seem about equally matched, even though one represents the child and the other a caricature of the parent. The neurotic depressive ego, by contrast, seems more infantile; it relies more upon complaining and clinging, and less upon acting and counteracting, than the obsessive compulsive does. Let us see what the depressive complaints are and how they are utilized defensively.

12

Neurotic Depressive Reactions

✠

THE NEUROTIC DEPRESSION APPEARS TO BE PRIMARILY A MOOD DISTURBANCE. It is a reaction to loss or threatened loss, to failure, discouragement or disillusionment. The basic symptoms are self-depreciation, dejection and appeals for reassurance. The neurotically depressed person no longer finds interest in people, things or activities; he gives up initiative; he expresses over and over his feelings of inferiority, unworthiness and hopelessness. He does not, however, withdraw completely from effective interaction with his environment. His regression may be deep but it is only partial, that is to say, its *extent*, what it includes, is limited. Most of his ego integration remains intact. In short, the neurotically depressed patient maintains the greater part of his hold on object relationships. For this reason he does not become psychotic.

Neurotic depressive reactions are among the easiest to understand. Rises and falls in mood without apparent cause are normal and common. We all have happy days and unhappy days, days that seem interesting and worthwhile and others that seem dull and purposeless. Some nights we go to bed feeling pleased with life and with ourselves. Other nights we go to bed feeling that life is a bit empty or futile, and sleep seems a welcome escape. When morning comes the mood may have shifted again. Although we seldom make a systematic effort to find reasons for the shift, if a systematic effort is made we can often find them.

In addition to such apparently spontaneous rises and falls in mood, nearly everyone gets discouraged, dejected or disillusioned from time to time on the basis of identifiable, objective conditions. When things go wrong, almost anyone may feel that he has been a failure and suspect that he may not be much good. When this happens a temporary indulgence in gloomy, self-depreciatory daydreams, and even in some mildly depressive complaints, still falls within the range of normal behavior.

If a loss is heavy and irreparable, as in the loss of a loved one, a depressive reaction may go fairly deep and last a long time, without incapacitating the grieving person. In such a case, we speak of *normal mourning*. Mourning is a process which is usually necessary for a grieving person to go through before he can reach a new stable equilibrium.

Gloomy self-depreciation becomes a neurotic depressive reaction when a person grows chronically preoccupied with complaints of unworthiness, failure or hopelessness, when he remains dejected in spite of everything, loses initiative and interest, and lapses into repetitive expressions of futility which his actual situation, objectively considered, does not justify. Somatic symptoms may appear which are very much like those we described as *anxiety reactions*. The mood, however, is not merely one of apprehension but one of despair.

Definition. Neurotic depressive reactions are mood disorders in which tension and anxiety are expressed in the form of dejection and self-deprecia- tion, somatic disturbance, and repetitive complaints of feeling inferior, hope- less and worthless. Guilt plays a prominent role in neurotic depressions, just as it does also in obsessive compulsive reactions. There is, however, a fundamental difference in the way that guilt is handled in the two neuroses.

The *obsessive compulsive* uses displacement, isolation, reaction formation, undoing, and various countermeasures, in his attempts to *deny* his guilt, or magically to *counteract* it. The *neurotic depressive,* on the other hand, *ex- presses* his guilt only a little disguised as inferiority, hopelessness and worthlessness. These insistent complaints coincide with his mood, but they also are adaptive in the sense that they call forth reinforcements from other persons.

Adaptive functions. Neurotic depressions are adaptive in the sense that they keep a person in effective contact with his environment and prevent an even deeper regression. They are also adaptive in that they supply him with outside aid in his struggle against his destructive superego attacks. By his incessant complaints, the neurotic depressive patient stimulates his rela- tives and friends to counterbalance his feelings of inferiority, unworthiness and hopelessness by providing reassurances and protests that he is not at all inferior, hopeless or unworthy.

This process of stimulating others to reassure and protest is the neurotic depressive's chief defensive maneuver against his superego attacks. The patient is not consciously aware either of the superego attacks nor of his use of his complaints to combat them. As in other neuroses, the symptoms appear to the patient as signs of illness. He does not single out some of them, as we do, and call them defenses.

Unfortunately, the reassurances and protests of friends and relatives, which the patient seeks and urgently needs, can bring him at best only partial and temporary relief. This is because he has suffered partial ego-superego regression. An infantile ego — even more infantile than that of obsessive compulsives — is now under attack by an archaic superego, something which we shall see still more clearly when we come to psychotic depressions.

The neurotic depressive patient, feeling the supergo attack unclearly as a sense of gloom and worthlessness, reaffirms his dejection and self-depreciation, thus stimulating other people to go on protesting and trying to reassure him. But the superego attacks continue, the patient keeps on complaining of his inferiority, worthlessness and hopelessness, and so the cycle keeps going, until finally his comforters lose patience and begin to upbraid the patient. When this happens, the impatience and the reproaches of others seem to the neurotic depressive to *confirm* what he has been saying all along, that he is no good and beyond hope. It is at this point that patients usually seek therapy or are pushed into it by others. Let us turn now to a clinical discussion of neurotic depressions.

Clinical Aspects of Neurotic Depressive Reactions

Neurotic depressions appear in many forms, depending in part upon the many different ways in which depressed persons communicate their feelings of dejection and futility, in part upon the character of the somatic involvement, and in part upon the intensity of the reaction. As was also the situation in anxiety reactions, the variations in depressive pattern are so great that no satisfactory division has yet been made into identifiable varieties.

Even the differentiation into chronic, acute and hyperacute, which we recognized among anxiety reactions, cannot be made here. For when a depression becomes acute and severe, the patient loses his grip on object relationships and suffers so sweeping and deep a regression that he usually requires hospitalization or its equivalent. It is customary to call such a depression *psychotic* and to discuss it as a separate entity among the psychoses. For the sake of convenience and clarity we shall follow this tradition and take up severe depressions later in a separate chapter.

In the discussion which follows we shall take for granted the many variations in the pattern of neurotic depressions, even though we do not always spell them out. All the varieties have certain symptoms in common — dejection and self-depreciation, loss of interest and initiative, somatic disturbances, and repetitive complaints of inferiority, unworthiness and hopelessness. They also have certain common precipitating factors which, while often present in other neuroses, are especially characteristic of neurotic depressions.

Precipitating factors

Neurotic depressive reactions are precipitated by deprivations and frustrations which exceed the limits of individual tolerance. Depressive persons are especially vulnerable to anything that destroys or seriously threatens the satisfaction of their deep dependent needs, and to anything that lessens their self-esteem. The commonest precipitating factors are: (1) loss of love or emotional support; (2) personal or economic failures; and (3) new responsibilities or the threat of new responsibilities. To such factors the patient reacts with a partial regression; and this regression reactivates infantile conflicts, infantile ego attitudes and defenses, and an archaic superego.

1. *Loss of love or emotional support.* The adult who becomes neurotically depressed is one who has always needed a great deal of emotional support to shore up his own sagging self-esteem. To lose love, or even to be threatened with its loss, is for him to experience an attack upon the most vulnerable part of his personality system.

The death of a loved one is a potentially dangerous form of such loss because the depressive person, like the obsessive compulsive, is strongly and primitively ambivalent in his love relationships. On the one hand, he may irrationally resent being deserted through death, and even hate the one he loves for dying and deserting him. On the other hand, he is likely to identify powerfully with the dead person whom he has loved. At one level or another — conscious, preconscious or unconscious — he will then experience love, hatred, resentment, self-condemnation and identification with the dead.

Love can be lost, of course, without a death. A patient may have been scorned, deserted or divorced. A leader may lose his followers. A loved one may go away emotionally without leaving physically. Some married couples, for example, scarcely speak to one another over a period of years. For a chronically dependent, self-disparaging adult such experiences as these can become completely demoralizing. So also may disillusionment with respect to a loved one: weakness appears where the patient had expected strength, failure where he had counted on success, irresponsibility where he had counted on integrity. These losses, desertions and disillusionments disturb profoundly a dependent person's internal equilibrium. They arouse in him dejection, hostility and guilt. The dejection is usually experienced consciously; hostility and guilt appear as a rule at unconscious and preconscious levels.

2. *Personal and economic failure.* Failure strikes at the heart of the security systems with which dependent persons try to surround themselves. Losses in power, prestige, property or money may cut a person off from important sources of moral and material support. The same is true of waning strength, health, youth or beauty. Many potential depressives cannot get along without these sources of support to counterbalance the internal

weakness and hunger of their personality organization. Personal and economic privilege for them are not mere resources as they are to normal adults. They are the symbolic realizations of their most urgent unconscious needs — to be loved, taken care of and babied. Without them the depressive feels deserted, worthless and unloved.

3. *New responsibilities.* New responsibilities, or even their prospect, can set off a neurotic depressive reaction. In some persons the success of being advanced in position itself arouses unconscious guilt; it represents to the neurotic some forbidden triumph related to his early childhood.

This last is particularly true of many so-called *promotion depressions.* A business man sees his efforts finally crowned with an important advancement. He is consciously proud and delighted; but he becomes depressed. One explanation for such a strange contradiction is that the competitive victory represents unconsciously a triumph over a father figure or a sibling figure whom the patient is supplanting. Another is that the prospect of increased responsibility pushes away farther than ever the fulfillment of an unconscious longing to be dependent, loved and protected. It is something like the victory gained by a general who loses his favorite son in battle.

From what has just been said it should be obvious that not all potentially depressive persons are overtly weak, passive, or dependent. Many of them actually reach and sustain high levels of attainment. As long as they are well they may show exceptional courage and initiative. Their exceptional dependence upon approval and success does not become apparent unless they lose their emotional support. We read in the newspapers every now and then of a sudden and sometimes tragic depression that has overtaken a strong public figure when he has lost power or prestige.

Onset of neurotic depressions

We all have limits to the amount of frustration from losses and failures that we can endure, regardless of whether the stress comes suddenly or rises step by step. Everyone finally reaches a point at which he begins to lose courage and self-confidence. He is likely then to suffer a temporary depressed mood, with perhaps some feeling of inferiority or remorse. But with normal persons such reactions do not go deep or last long. If loved ones provide reassurances and affection the discouragement and self-blame quickly disappear.

Neurotic depressive reactions are provoked more often than not by something that would upset anyone. The difference is that the depressive patient fails to recover his lost equilibrium as normal persons do.

The onset of a neurotic depression is sometimes in the form of a *sudden decompensation.* Up to a certain point the patient has preserved a personality organization which, although internally it is in precarious equilibrium, has appeared superficially adequate. The balance of internal strains, however, is not stable enough to withstand a severe external stress. Neither is the defensive organization. With the occurrence of sudden loss or failure, and the frustration of dependent needs, the patient develops a deep partial regression, and his depressive illness appears.

The more usual onset is *gradual*. Either there has been a steady building up of emotional tension and anxiety over a long period, or else a succession of minor crises has occurred, each leaving in its wake some increased tension. Then the loss or failure, and the frustration of dependent needs, finally trigger off the depression. The precipitating factor may seem objectively trivial; it is the last push that starts the landslide.

During the period of incubation, which usually precedes the appearance of an outspoken depressive picture, we find many of the familiar products of rising tension and anxiety. The patient complains of headaches and backaches, of diffuse aches and pains in his legs, of chronic fatigue and poor sleep. There are changes in appetite and in gastrointestinal functioning; and there are sexual disturbances which range from impotence, or frigidity and menstrual irregularities, to increased sex pace without lasting satisfaction. Often there are angry outbursts, periods of bitter sulking, gloomy daydreams and nightmares. Suicidal fantasies are nearly always a part of the depressive picture; sometimes open threats of suicide are made.

Clinical course

Signs of deepening preoccupation now appear. The patient may begin to express more and more openly his worries and misgivings about his physical health and his personal competence. As these preoccupations grow his decline in interest and intiative pick up momentum. He complains of having lost whatever pleasures he had formerly derived from work and recreation, from his family, his home and his friends. He becomes withdrawn, irritable, lonely and short-tempered. He may demand that he be given more consideration and fewer burdens. This last, of course, is the sign of a regression toward infantile dependence, a slipping away of the enjoyment of adult responsibility.

Closely related to the preoccupation and partial withdrawal are the common complaints of being unable to concentrate, to remember, to understand what is said and to think clearly. Patients also complain of mild experiences of estrangement and depersonalization ("unreality").[1] All of these complaints have some basis in fact. Anyone who is deeply preoccupied, worried and anxious, whether he is depressed or not, will suffer a reduction in his general efficiency and in the effectiveness of his contact with the world around him, that is, his object relations.

Many patients focus their attention, at least for a time, almost exclusively upon body overconcern. Some insist that all their difficulties stem from a

---

[1] *Estrangement, depersonalization* and *feelings of unreality* are discussed in the clinical section of dissociative reactions, **Chapter 10.**

hidden physical illness. They may refuse to consider any other possibility and demand that their physical symptoms be given direct treatment. The physical health of most of these patients is reasonably good. What their complaints express is in part the loss of a sense of well-being, an intensification of what everyone feels when he is downhearted, and in part an increased sense of personal inadequacy. The patient translates his feeling that he is inferior — based as we shall see upon unconscious guilt — into a belief that his body is inferior. "I am no good" becomes "My body is no good." Having made this translation unconsciously, the patient then accepts his somewhat infantile metaphor in its literal adult meaning. He accepts the body metaphor, "My body is no good," because it appears to him to give his irrational complaints a rational basis. This also accounts for his determined resistance to any other interpretation.

Neurotically depressed patients, whether or not body overconcern is their major focus, complain that they have lost all interest, pleasure and initiative. They feel gloomy, worried and disgruntled. Nothing seems to reach them emotionally — other people's joys or sorrows, what they read in the papers and what they see on television or at the movies. Things which they used to undertake with pleasure now leave them cold or fill them with aversion. They get no satisfaction out of anything they do; they may go through the same motions but nothing feels as it once did. Everything becomes a burden. Ordinary routines call for more effort than they can muster. The mere thought of adding anything new, even as recreation, seems intolerable.

Self-depreciation is the neurotically depressed person's most striking symptom, as well as dynamically the most important. He calls himself no good, a failure and a burden to others. He says that he is not what he used to be, that he "can't take it any more." These statements, apparently so simple, are the irrational products of deep unconscious conflicts, of ego defense and ego adaptation, of superego pressure and appeals for outside aid. The original sources of depressive self-depreciation, the sources that defeat all attempts by other persons to reassure and to reason, lie in a state of ego-superego tension which we call *unconscious guilt*.[2]

In plain words, the neurotically depressed person hates himself but does not know it. When he says that he looks down upon himself he is telling more dynamic truth than he realizes. A part of himself is looking down upon another part of him, as though the two parts were two persons. For convenience we say that an *archaic superego* is looking down upon — rejecting, despising, attacking — an *infantile, regressed ego*. But this terminology is only a system of notation, a technical shorthand. What it describes is a process by which the patient rejects, despises, looks down upon himself, in much the same way that he felt his parents rejecting, despising and looking down upon him when he was a disobedient, disappointing, unwanted or "bad" child.

---

[2] In psychotic depressions, which we shall take up in a later chapter, the feeling of guilt is no longer indirect or unconscious. It is expressed spontaneously and repeatedly, often with savage insistence.

As a neurotically depressed adult, the patient revives this feeling in relation to other adults. He complains of feeling lonely, lost, deserted, abandoned — these are the actual words chosen by depressed persons — more
like what a little child feels when his parents seem to hate him than what
an adult experiences in a realistic world. Such irrational attitudes toward
himself are the fruits of regression; they are characteristic of the reactivated
archaic superego. The patient's overreaction to these attitudes belong to his
reactivated infantile ego.

Since the patient unconsciously hates himself, he is justified in saying that
he feels unloved and unlovable. He also realizes that he does not feel the
love for others that he used to feel. Neurotically depressed persons usually
go further than this; they behave cruelly to those whom they would like to
love and go on loving. If, as a result, they suffer from remorse, the remorse
is fully justified. Each curt answer or sharp protest, each temper outburst,
each quarrel leads to an increase in realistic guilt; and each increase in
realistic guilt brings an increase in the hostility of the archaic superego.

The neurotic depressed patient's anger and sadism succeed in isolating
him further from persons whose help and affection he needs. This in turn
increases his sense of loneliness, desertion and hopelessness. One reason for
his being so angry and sadistic is that he has regressed; but another is that
he needs an infinite amount of reassurance and affectionate support for an
indefinite time. Nobody can give him this. It is only given to babies. When
he tries resentfully to *force* people around him to give him affectionate
support, to counteract his overwhelming sense of worthlessness, the sadistic
way he treats them defeats his ends. It only makes him feel more guilty and
more unloved than ever. The intensity of his need and his regressive behavior
drive people away. This is the self-defeating cycle that we shall witness in
the following case of neurotic depression.

A case of neurotic depressive reaction

Complaints. Ernest F. was a thirty-year-old married bus driver, the
father of two small children. Chief among his complaints were the
following. He felt tired, discouraged and unfit for work all the time.
He slept badly and spent part of each night roaming around the house
downstairs. His legs and ankles ached. He had backaches, especially
at work. His head ached and his eyes smarted; sometimes while driving the bus everything would blur. He had no appetite, he was constipated, sex desire was infrequent, and part of the time he was impotent.
He took no pleasure in anything any more.

What worried Ernest most was his incompetence on the job. He had
always been a dependable, steady worker who prided himself on leaving
and coming back from each bus trip on the dot. Now he was having
difficulty in remembering the schedules. Whenever he was shifted to a
different route he would skip some of the stops. Once, to the passengers'
consternation, he went the wrong way. He was now growing irritable
with passengers and with vehicles that blocked his way. He made angry
jerking stops and starts. To the passengers' protests he gave angry

retorts. They reported him to the company. When the starter told Ernest about the complaints the best he could do was to say he guessed he was no good and had better quit. The starter would then tell him that he was the best driver they had ever had, that he ought to take it easy and not let those so-and-so's get him down.

At home Ernest felt lonely, irritable and aloof. He lost his temper with his children and quarreled with his wife. Each time this happened he hated himself for it and called himself all kinds of humiliating things. He was a no-good, run-down bum, he said, and a failure in life. He was getting too old to be a good bus driver, and soon he would have to give up work. Then they could all go and live with their in-laws who were so much better than he was.

Ernest had entertained suicidal thoughts — his wife and children knew it — but he said that he did not have the guts to do anything to himself. No one understood him, he said, and nobody sympathized with him. His wife had lost patience with him and every time he tried to say anything to the children they began to cry. The in-laws sneered at his illness and ridiculed him to his face. Everyone appeared to agree on one point, even the patient himself, that if he were a man he would snap out of it.

Childhood. Ernest had a long history of unsatisfied dependent needs. He was the third of four children. A brother was ten years his senior, a sister eight years, and another sister two years his junior. The two older siblings always treated him as a know-nothing and a weakling. His younger sister was the family pet. His mother gave him a mocking kind of affection which made him feel ridiculous and left him hungry for the tender love his sister got. He had wet his bed until he was six years old, bitten his nails until he was fourteen, had frequent nightmares, and was noted for his fits of angry sulking. Ernest's mother encouraged him to tell her about his troubles, his failures and his longings. She would give him a little hugging and then push him away, telling him what a big boy he was and that he was acting like a baby.

Ernest's father was energetic, brusque and hard. His one affectionate interest was his auto repair shop. He treated his children, with the exception of the youngest, as nuisances. The older brother was allowed to do some tinkering at the shop in his early adolescence; and when he turned sixteen he went to work permanently with his father. Ernest was never welcome in the shop. Whenever he tried to hang around the place his father or his brother told him bluntly to go home, which he remembered doing sometimes in tears.

In spite of the frustrating character of his life at home Ernest disliked leaving it. He often helped his mother with her housework on Saturdays instead of going out to play. She paid him for this chore, but she also laughed at him publicly for being "a better daughter" to her than his younger sister. He made few close friends. Usually he had a chum older and stronger than himself who extracted a certain amount of subservience from him in return for a patronizing kind of protection. In high school he got on the school paper in a minor capacity. Whenever he was chosen as an officer in anything it was always as secretary, which meant that he got the work without the glory.

Work. At seventeen, after a short intensive course in automobile mechanics, Ernest also went to work for his father. He was eager to please his father, he said, and to show his brother, who had never had any formal training, what he could do. But all he ever seemed to get was criticism. They took tools out of his hands and finished jobs which he felt he could do better than they could. (Even depressed as he was he told his therapist that he was a better mechanic than his brother ever would be.) Whenever he tried to show either of them something that he had learned at school they jeered at him and called him Einstein.

The patient finally gave up hope and apparently went into a mild neurotic depression. He became sullen, resentful and unhappy, slept and ate poorly, and felt himself to be a total failure. He confided in his mother that he felt useless and unwanted. She comforted him enough to whet his appetite for affection, and then spiritually dropped him on the floor, saying that he was old enough to stand on his own feet and not to go around whining all the time.

Leaving home and marrying. Military service gave Ernest his chance to break away from home and to recover from his mild depression. There was a shortage of auto mechanics, and he was assigned to repair work which he liked and could do well. While in the service he read in a magazine about life in a western town. He persuaded a buddy to go there with him to live when they were discharged. His buddy opened a garage and filling station, and tried to talk Ernest into joining him as a junior partner. Instead, he took a job on a milk route. Soon afterwards he met his future wife and, he said "married her in the teeth of her family's objections."

The father-in-law had a managerial position with the local bus company. He persuaded Ernest to take a job as bus driver. The pay was not quite as good but the hours were much better. Four relatively peaceful years followed during which two children were born. The in-laws were critical of Ernest's lack of ambition and compared him unfavorably with another daughter's husband in public. He saw a great deal of Buck, his army buddy, now also married, and whenever he did, Buck asked him when he was going to join him at the filling station, which was always shorthanded. Ernest was reluctant to give up a job in which it seemed so easy to please people.

Precipitating factors. Two crises upset everything. They had to move and then Ernest lost all his teeth. He was strongly attached to the home they had to give up. He had put in a lot of work on it after hours. But the street was being integrated into a truck highway and this made it too dangerous for the small children. They moved into a larger house next door to his wife's parents who owned it and let him have it at a nominal rent. It had modern conveniences that delighted Ernest's wife. The secret clause in this apparently generous arrangement was that the in-laws were going to supervise their daughter's home life and billet friends and relatives with them, sometimes practically without notice.

The billeting was a serious nuisance to a man who loved his home and liked a schedule that he could count on. But the interference with his private affairs — amounting at times to quarrels as to who had jurisdiction over his own children — exasperated him beyond the power of words. He grew angrier and angrier, but there was nothing he could say, since his wife was torn between him and her domineering parents. When he tried to vent his anger against them she became upset and began defending them. He felt alone, as he had in his childhood, surrounded by critical people, with no one to comfort him and take his part.

The climax came when Ernest lost his teeth. It was a painful experience but, as he soon discovered, one that brought him little genuine sympathy. He found himself the target of a sadistic kind of humor, which the Germans call *Schadenfreud*, joy in another's suffering. The in-laws had a field day. They called him "grandpa," made jokes about his food and mimicked his defective speech — all in good fun, of course. Ernest missed the good fun because he looked through it and saw the cruel humiliation intended. His wife, he said, protested against their teasing him; but she did it laughingly. At work he met a more benign form of the same teasing which spoiled the beginnings and ends of his runs. His new teeth hurt him, made him gag and dulled his sense of taste.

The depression. Ernest thought he could have weathered the dental crisis if his home life had not turned so sour. As it was, he no longer looked forward to going home. Some of his days off he spent with Buck who gave him profane advice which he did not have the courage to follow until some time later. Meanwhile the depressive symptoms began to show up — dejection, insomnia, headaches, backaches, aching legs and ankles, eye-strain and blurred vision, constipation, no appetite and no sex desire. He was tense and irritable; and the terrible loneliness of his childhood returned. He lost pleasure in everything and felt that he had no love and no future. His work became almost more than he could face, especially now that complaints were coming in about him. Each time he turned in the fare money he thought with anger that this was helping pay the manager, his father-in-law.

Ernest's in-laws saw that he was slipping. They told him so; and they told him that he was making a big fuss over nothing. If he were a man, they said, he would snap out of it. Ernest began harping on his physical decline, telling his wife over and over that he was growing old before his time and everybody knew it. He called himself "a dental cripple" and wished out loud that he were dead. It might be easier for her and the children. She could find another husband any day who was better than he was; and the children would have a decent father. Then he opened up on his own worthlessness as a person. His father-in-law was right, he said, he never would amount to anything, he had always known that he was really no good. What could he do? A bus driver all his life, and now not even good enough for that! He could hardly stand himself. And so on, over and over, on and on.

For a long time his wife tried to combat his endless complaints and self-depreciation with endless reassurances. She reasoned with him. She took issue with him over his unrealistic self-condemnation, meeting argument with counterargument, over and over, on and on, sometimes far into the night. But it was useless. In the morning he would be as gloomy and sullen as ever; and in the evening the whole thing would start over again. She tried to keep her parents out of the home, get the children to bed early, and have the place quiet and peaceful for him.

Nothing worked. The endless repetitions finally wore her down and made her break out into fits of exasperation. They quarreled. She told him to buck up for his children's sake even if he cared nothing for her. Sometimes she agreed angrily with his self-accusations. Then he would say, "See? That's what I've been trying to tell you! It's true!"

The payoff came at the funeral of the wife's grandmother. Ernest had a crying spell which he could not stop. After everything was over there was a solemn family dinner at which the father-in-law made a caustic remark to someone in the patient's presence about his tears. Ernest astonished everyone by flying into a rage and telling the whole crowd exactly what he thought of them. Some of the language he used came from Buck and his military service. The in-laws were speechless. His wife told the therapist that at the time she had been secretly proud. Ernest left the place for Buck's shop, had another crying spell, and took Buck's advice to go the next day for therapeutic help.

Therapy: Anger. In the initial interview Ernest was gloomy and tearful. He said grimly that he had messed up his life for good. There was a mix-up in his next appointment. The social worker said that he had looked angry; but he only said that it didn't matter and he apologized for giving her so much trouble. A medical checkup was arranged for the same afternoon. It gave essentially negative results.

Ernest broke the next appointment and came to the third with a sheepish grin and further apologies. He had trouble in talking. He frequently interrupted a silence to ask, "Where are we getting?" or "What good is this doing?" The next time he talked about his failure in life and the hopeless future a bus driver had. They used him more as a "jumper" than they did anyone else, that is, he was put on fill-in runs during rushes or when other drivers failed to show up. He often felt pushed around. He would get to work and have to wait around for a bus. They couldn't get away with this with the other drivers, he said. He got paid for his time all right; but he was treated as if he was always the one they could push around. At home it was the same. He could come home from work and there would be guests — the in-laws' relatives or friends — supper an hour late, and his wife too rushed to notice him.

The therapist said that it must have made him angry to come here and have to wait around for nothing. He said, no, that it hadn't at all, that he was glad to get the medical checkup. They would probably find out what was wrong with him. "That woman will tell you I wasn't mad," he said. After awhile he remembered that, yes, he had been angry; but he knew it wasn't that woman's fault. Everybody treated him fine here. He had no right to be mad, etc. At the end of the hour he asked irritably, "Where is this getting us?"

Resentment. There were other opportunities for working on this angry man's resentment. When he had to wait an hour on another occasion he had meanwhile gained enough confidence and insight to be openly hostile. He asked the secretary who we thought he was and said he couldn't wait. He did wait, however, because he wanted to tell off the therapist, which he proceeded to do.

This led him into new paths. In his childhood everybody else came first. His mother was too busy with the baby sister. The older sister and the brother, being much older than he, exercised freely their rights of superior strength and know-how. The father let it be known that he was supporting the whole show and that nobody had better bother him.

Ernest returned to this theme more than once in later sessions. It came up in relation to his life. After their first child was born, nothing that Ernest wanted mattered until after the baby's wants were all satisfied. It was not as bad with the second child's arrival, because Ernest had learned that he did not count when there was a baby around, and besides now the older one had to wait too. At this point he stopped his tirade suddenly to say, "I felt like taking the bottle out of the baby's mouth. Some father, huh? Some —!"

Need and guilt. It cost Ernest a great deal of work to bring out and recognize how much he needed to feel preferred above everybody else. To be loved, for him, meant to be first in line for handouts. He had to find out that he was chronically angry because these needs were never really gratified, and that they never could be, as long as they were pitched so high. He had to find out, too, that his guilt over his suppressed fury made him give up the ordinary rights he should have had — like his bus schedule and the privacy of his home, which he now called his father-in-law's "motel."

Improvement. As therapy progressed, Ernest became for a while more aggressive and less angry. The body symptoms waxed and waned. They appeared often enough in relation to home and work situations to make him suspect their emotional origin without admitting it. In time they became negligible. The self-depreciation also had its ups and downs. Sometimes a phase of self-assertion was followed by further self-disparagement —" "no good," "a heel," "a drifter," "no guts," "no future." But in the absence of reassurance or condemnation, self-assertion finally gained the upper hand and held it most of the time.

On the job the patient's irritability disappeared. But he could not seem to regain the pleasure he once had in greeting the passengers, in serving them and in making model runs. He himself attributed his indifference to the complaints the passengers had formerly made about him, but it is probable that the effects of his therapeutic work were responsible. He no longer needed to be incessantly courting everybody's favor, being paid in advance by them for everything he did, being the Number One Person on the bus, or earning a pat on the head from the starter six times a day. He now began having arguments with the starter which resulted in fewer shifts for him, but a cooler and less friendly relationship.

His angry outburst against the in-laws after the funeral made it easy for Ernest to bring the discussion of them into therapy, once his guilt and self-disparagement had weakened. In the process he ventilated a lot of resentment against his wife; this, in its turn, allowed him to take the initiative in insisting that they move out of his father-in-law's house. He had a rough time of it; but when it was over, and they were settled two miles away, his wife found herself as relieved as Ernest was. It was like starting life over again in their own home.

Ernest gave up his driver's job and went to work for Buck, even though it was not clear exactly what his status there was to be. He still had some important things to work out about himself. He needed and received further therapy; but he was no longer clinically depressed.

What this case has shown us is a pattern of life that is made up of infantile pleasures, smothered angry resentment, demands upon the human environment which cannot be satisfied, and the practice of self-depreciation. On the positive side, we see a person who is capable of loving others, who reaches out for affection, enjoys being kind, and is conscientious. The patterns of loving needed to become more maturely masculine, so that the patient could enjoy caring for his family as husband and father, enjoy being kind without having to be rewarded with the kind of approval a little child craves, and perhaps could restructure his conscientiousness so that it was motivated by a more mature pride. The strength that burst forth under the stress of the sadistic treatment which Ernest endured from the in-laws gave the patient a good prognosis, since this was done without the support of a therapist, and in the teeth of what seemed to Ernest overwhelming, unanimous opposition to him.

It is essential that one understand the smothered anger and resentment that lead to depression if one is to understand both the cruelty which depressed persons show to others and the much more dangerous sadism they exhibit toward themselves. The depressed person, we have said, is often an angry person as well as a sad one. The sadness relates depression to normal mourning; the anger relates it to compulsions. As we turn now to discuss the dynamic and developmental background of neurotic depressions, we shall make these relationships clear.

Dynamic and Developmental Background

The neurotic depressive reaction forms a natural bridge that connects the neuroses with the psychoses. It involves only a partial regression, so that the neurotically depressed person is nearly always able to continue with his daily work, just as most obsessive compulsives are. The partial regression, however, goes very deep — deeper than that of any other neurosis. This is why a great deal of what we shall have to say about the dynamic and developmental background of neurotic depressives will be found to apply also to the more disabling and potentially dangerous psychotic depressions. An understanding of the relatively circumscribed neurotic depression, in which the patient retains good contact and can effectively communicate with others around him, will provide us with an easy transition to the more sweeping psychotic disorders, in which object relationships are distorted and communication becomes difficult or impossible. Let us begin with a review of the similarities and differences between neurotic depressions and obsessive compulsive neuroses so as to describe one span of the bridge.

Neurotic depressions and obsessive compulsive reactions

Neurotic depressives and obsessive compulsives both regress to pre-edipal levels where the focus is upon being good or being bad. In both there is an infantile ego facing an archaic punitive superego. Attempts are made in both disorders to meet the conflicts by resorting to overt behavior in the form of active symptoms. Both are *guilt neuroses,* although the expressions of guilt in the two take very different forms.

We have already said that there are many differences between neurotic depressions and obsessive compulsive reactions. The most obvious one is that the neurotic depressive seems dejected; the obsessive compulsive does not. The obsessive compulsive is also action-centered; he uses primitive defenses and magic, but he tries to "go it alone." The neurotic depressive turns outward; he looks to other people for emotional support. Whereas obsessive compulsives, with the exception of the withdrawn doubters and ruminators, are typically self-assertive, the neurotic depressive does not want to assert himself. He wants to be taken care of like a helpless baby. He is oriented toward becoming more dependent than he is, but he is also frightened by what infantile dependence might entail. This is part of his basic conflict.

Obsessive compulsive patients are notoriously obstinate, negativistic and at least superficially self-sufficient. They even try to force others to conform to their ways, to obey them, to do as they direct. Neurotic depressive patients, by contrast, seem to be clinging, compliant persons who are sometimes almost parasitic. They do not demand conformity or obedience; they do not try to direct what others shall do. Rather they demand special privileges and affection; they reproach others for not giving them enough.

We have called both neurotic depressions and obsessive compulsive reactions *guilt neuroses*. The obsessive compulsive usually reveals his unconscious guilt through his ritualistic precautions and his penitential self-punishment. He is often aware of feeling guilty and may express this feeling openly. Neurotic depressives sometimes express guilt feeling also, but usually they are unconscious of their guilt. They express it in such disguised forms as feelings of inferiority, of worthlessness and hopelessness, of feeling that they are unloved and unlovable. There is a great deal of hostile aggression behind these disguises, of hatred and frustration as well as a longing to be loved. We shall have more to say about the complaints and what lies behind them as we go on to discuss the fixation and regression, the defensive structure, and the ego-superego relationships in neurotic depressive reactions.

Fixation and regression in neurotic depressive reactions

The regression in neurotic depressions, we have said, goes deep. It reactivates fantasies and conflicts belonging to a pre-edipal phase of development even earlier than the phase revived in obsessive compulsive reactions. There we witnessed the revival of an infantile power struggle, the struggle against an archaic superego which the patient as a child had internalized, during the phase of toilet training and obstinate self-assertion. Here we witness something still more infantile. The adult who develops a neurotic depression when he regresses is one whose major points of fixation belong to a phase of development when dependent needs were more powerful than needs for self-assertion. We assume that, as a child, such an adult had unusual difficulties in separating himself emotionally from the protective custody of his mother. His need to be taken care of as a baby was either left ungratified or else it was gratified in such a way that only feeble impulses toward mature independence could emerge. What we see in the symptomatology of neurotic depressive adults are derivatives of an early dependent infantile fixation.

Before the phase of self-assertion and toilet training, early childhood is normally a period of profound dependence. Almost everything pleasurable that an infant gets must come from those who normally love him. During the earliest months he must derive his most intense pleasures from the receptive experience of nursing and from being held, supported, warmed, moved, cuddled and loved.[3] This phase of oral dependence upon others is

---

[3] Although much of the literature on this topic appears to take breast-feeding for granted, bottle-feeding is actually a common procedure in our culture. If bottle-feeding is performed perfunctorily by the mother, the infant must get whatever pleasure he can from his own activities during the feeding, and he must get the enjoyment of being held, supported, moved, warmed, comforted and loved at other times.

normal and inevitable for all human beings at the beginning of their life as separate organisms.

Nursing, of course, is not the suckling infant's whole existence. He has innumerable tactile experiences. He has feelings of warmth and cold, and of pressure, tickle and pain, in which perineal stimulation plays an important part. Visual and auditory experiences contribute to the total picture, and so do being moved about and actively moving, especially the activities of the hands.[4] Feelings of many kinds undoubtedly well up within the infant. Internal organs provide a larger proportion of direct stimulation than they do in the adult because the infant cannot respond to the immense variety of things and events that have meaning for adults. The gastrointestinal tract is particularly important, with its mouthing and swallowing, the comforts of filling and retention, the distress of distention and regurgitation, and the pleasures and pains of peristalsis and excretion.

Nevertheless, the mouth remains the major focus of every infant's earliest intense coordinated activity. Around its activities and experiences he must crystallize his first object relationships. We have reason to assume that all infants symbolize their early major experiences in oral terms — that is, in some kind of primitive oral imagery — whether the experiences symbolized are actually oral ones or not. This means that sucklings tend to transform any kind of gratification, as well as any deprivation, frustration or aggression, into primitive oral symbols. For the time being this is every infant's major symbolic orientation to his still undifferentiated world of self and object.

We have no direct evidence that sucklings make these transformations into oral imagery and little hope of ever getting direct evidence. Neurophysiology is completely inadequate in this area; and infants during their first year cannot speak. Three sources of indirect evidence, however, make the assumption tenable.

One is the observation that sucklings use their mouths much as adults use their eyes. With their lips and tongue they learn to examine, explore, test, accept, reject and otherwise experience things. They hold things with the mouth and let things go. Taking something in and swallowing it may have immediate comforting or distressing results. Rejecting and regurgitating things orally must also leave impressions of some kind. We do know from the direct testimony of older children and adults that oral experiences normally play a leading part in a wide variety of behavior and leave their vivid traces in normal memory.

Another source of indirect evidence is that adult language, although heavily loaded with visual and auditory metaphors, still transforms a vast number of nonoral experiences — even including things ethical and scien-

[4] Cf. Hoffer, W., "Mouth, hand and ego integration," *The Psychoanalytic Study of the Child.* New York: Internat. Univ. Press, 1949, vols. 3 and 4, pp. 49–56. Also the separate origins of mouth, visual and manual planes of perception, and their observable interaction, in Piaget, J., *Origins of Intelligence in Children.* New York: Internat. Univ. Press, 1952.

NEUROTIC DEPRESSIVE REACTIONS

tific — into oral symbols which are often crude and pungent. Here are a few examples from the thousands which are current: I cannot swallow his explanations. Their opinions made me want to vomit. I could not stomach it. It left a bad taste in my mouth. He mouthed his words. His words bit deeply. Put teeth into the law. Revenge is sweet and remorse bitter. Life has lost its savor. His paintings have a nineteenth-century flavor. Man tastes of death but once. He drank in what he heard. I'll make him eat his words — and so on for a thousand more, some of them almost unprintable.

A third source of indirect evidence comes from the manifest dreams of adults and from psychotic symptoms. These are often incredibly primitive and concrete. Both dreams and psychotic symptoms can express desires of every kind in oral terms. They can represent all kinds of fears and dangers as oral fears and oral dangers — of being bitten or swallowed or engulfed, of having swallowed something dangerous which now seems to be inside. We shall hear more about these last when we come to psychotic depressions and schizophrenia.

All infants eventually are weaned from their phase of oral dependence — gradually if they are fortunate, abruptly if they are not. They are usually allowed to be somewhat oral and somewhat dependent; but they learn to derive great pleasures from nonoral modes of experience and they learn pleasure in doing things for themselves.[5] During the period of being weaned from the pleasures of suckling and of being almost completely dependent young children experience many complex difficulties in addition to those of simple adaptation. They often feel an unwillingness or a fear of going forward. Independence is often hard to distinguish from loneliness and desertion. There are also fears of slipping back or being drawn back into their former state of helplessness. Sometimes a small child feels strongly tempted to give up his dawning independence. One sees these conflicts reactivated when a baby sibling appears and the older child experiences vicariously the joys of his lost infancy. We assume that it is during this period that primitive oral fantasies are formed, full of longing, fear and conflict, which in later childhood undergo repression.

The adult who develops a neurotic depression under stress is one whose major points of fixation lie somewhere in this period of weaning from an oral infantile dependence toward a dawning independence. He carries within him some infantile conflicts which are like those of obsessive compulsives, particularly the basic conflict over dependent needs and the fear of becoming helplessly dependent. Unlike obsessive compulsives, the neurotic depressive is not usually self-assertive and he does not express his guilt as a conflict over being clean or soiling. Instead, he expresses his usually unconscious sense of guilt in the still more infantile forms of feeling unloved

[5] Even normal adults still take pleasure in their orality and in their relative dependence upon other people. They enjoy eating and drinking, mouthing, chewing, kissing, talking, singing and whistling. Most of them cannot resist smoking, or at least having a pipe in the mouth, even though smoking is thought to be dangerous, and no one has ever considered an empty pipe a source of nourishment.

and unlovable, inferior, worthless and unwanted. In his regression he is somewhat like the small child who has a sibling rival. He does not wet or soil, as small children often do when they feel unloved, but he does complain of the same things in adult terms and he tends to cling.

It is necessary to make a preliminary distinction at this point between neurotic and psychotic depression since they are in fact closely related. The major distinction is that neurotic regression is only partial whereas psychotic regression is subtotal. The neurotically depressed person manages to keep his hold on external reality. He can usually go about his daily work with only some loss in efficiency. The psychotically depressed person tends to lose his hold on external reality almost completely, to restructure the world around him in regressive terms of desertion and impending disaster. He can seldom go on with his daily work. He is too apprehensive or too slowed up, he suffers from severe disturbances of thinking, and he is in considerable danger of suicide. The neurotically depressed person, in spite of the depth of his regression, has preserved most of his defensive organization intact.

Defenses in neurotic depressive reactions

The regression that occurs in neurotic depressive reactions can hardly be counted as a defense. By allowing the emergence of infantile fears and longings it carries the patient back to a phase of development during which he felt helpless in the face of overwhelming dependent needs. It is only because the regression remains a partial one that he manages to retain effective contact with the realistic world of things, events and people. When a regression as deep as this becomes practically complete the patient loses effective contact with external reality and develops a psychosis. The neurotically depressed person owes the partial preservation of his ego integrity, as we shall see, to certain auxiliary factors that help to keep his defensive organization intact. The three most important constituents of neurotic depressive defense are *repression, projection* and the use of continual complaining to extort from others the narcissistic supplies the patient needs.[6]

Defective repression. We have seen in the other neuroses that defective repression seems to be a precondition for their development. The same is true for neurotic depressions. The neurotic depressive owes his escape from a psychotic depression to his ability to maintain his repressive defense at a reasonable level of effectiveness. This he achieves, as we shall see later, by the use of projection and by complaining in such a way that he gains allies in his struggle against internal assaults upon his own self-esteem.

The repression in neurotic depressive reactions is aimed in two directions

[6] By *narcissistic supplies* we mean such things as reassurance, praise, reward, esteem, pride and self-esteem.

and is defective in both. It is aimed at the control of id impulses, in whose derivatives there are oral dependent longings for love mingled with hostile resentment because these longings are not fulfilled. Repression is also aimed at the control of attacks by the archaic superego. This latter is the most significant repression in neurotic depressions. When superego aggression is dominant a sense of guilt threatens to become conscious. It usually does not become conscious, partly because repression is automatically increased, partly because projection also appears, and partly because the complaining brings to the patient increased narcissistic supplies. What does emerge is chiefly a feeling of inferiority, worthlessness, self-disparagement and hopelessness — chief among the cardinal depressive symptoms.

Neither of these repressions is successful; some derivatives of each appear as symptoms. The unconscious guilt emerges, not only as inferiority feelings and self-disparagement, but also as a vague sense of feeling responsible for something or ashamed of something. The referent, the "something," is often displaced, and its intensity is always diminished. The oral dependent longings emerge in derivative form, as demands for narcissistic supplies, and as passive-dependent acting out. The hostility appears in the form of insistent complaining, accusations of neglect, and threats of suicide or physical disability. In all of these derivatives, which we call "symptoms," we see the participation of other defense mechanisms. Among these we shall pay particular attention to the characteristically depressive use of complaints to gain needed narcissistic supplies.

The defensive use of complaints. The manifest complaints of neurotic depressives give us the key to an understanding of the whole defensive structure. These are the continual complaints — often exasperating to relatives and close friends who continually hear them — of being inferior, unworthy and hopeless, of being unloved and unlovable. To some extent these are actual discharge processes; they provide an outlet for the hostile superego attitudes with which the patient's ego is bombarded. They are also urgent appeals for help from outsiders against the sadistic attacks of the archaic superego. Because of the relatively good object relationships which the neurotic depressive maintains, he is able to utilize the reassurances, protests and contradictions of other people as narcissistic supplies, and in this way to offset superego sadism. The complaints thus represent attempts to restore an internal equilibrium, by expressive discharge and by stimulating others to give narcissistic supplies, and to make good the loss which originally precipitated the neurosis.

Two factors render these attempts unsuccessful. One is that other people eventually weary of having to give constant reassurance; the other is that the unconscious archaic superego attacks continue indefinitely. When, as in the case of Ernest F., everyone becomes eventually exasperated with the patient and gives up reassuring, he must either find other sources of emotional support or sink deeper into a psychotic depression. Ernest F. found emotional support of a different kind when he turned to Buck and to his therapist. We shall discuss the defensive use of complaints further under four headings: (*a*) *maintaining good object relationships;* (*b*) *ensuring narcissistic supplies;* (*c*) *discharging superego aggression;* and (*d*) *discharging ego aggression* or *id aggression.*

(a) Maintaining good object relationships. Neurotic depressive complaints, for all their seeming ineffectuality, do help materially to keep the patient functioning at a realistic level in a realistic field of interpersonal relations. He does not slip into the abyss of psychotic depression. Even though the patient unknowingly plays an unrealistic game — in stimulating others to contradict his archaic unconscious superego — he plays the game in deadly earnest and manages to recruit the aid of real persons. The archaic unconscious superego of the neurotically depressed person represents an originally introjected parental figure, which was experienced in early childhood as dangerous and destructive. The reassuring other person in adulthood, in the case of Ernest F. his wife, takes the role of a kindly supporting parent who battles without knowing it against the introjected parental figure. If everyone turns his back on such a patient, so that he is really deserted and alone with his archaic superego, he may lose his hold on external reality and regress further to psychotic levels. We shall see how much more dangerous such a regression can be when we come to discussions of the psychoses.

(b) Ensuring narcissistic supplies. We have indicated earlier, in a footnote, that the term *narcissistic supplies* refers to such emotional supports as reassurance, praise, reward, esteem, pride and self-esteem. The term is a convenient shorthand for this whole class of supports, practically a piece of technical slang. It must be clear already that neurotic depressives are seriously lacking in wholesome pride and self-esteem, while they are sick or all the time. The lack of healthy pride and self-esteem is an important factor in keeping the neurotic depressive dependent upon others to an infantile degree.

The complaining of depressed adults is like the crying of a hungry baby. It is an expression of urgent need and a means of stimulating someone to meet it. Narcissistic supplies, like food, can have only a temporary effect; the need for more comes back. But without them survival may become impossible. The neurotic depressive is repeatedly overwhelmed by the tensions of unconscious guilt. Anything that reinforces self-esteem will tend to decrease guilt. He is distinguished from the psychotic depressive by his responsiveness to other persons. His continual complaining, even when it sounds like angry argument and rejection, is a crying out for narcissistic supplies. With their help he manages to keep afloat.

(c) Discharging superego aggression. Everyone recognizes the insistent self-depreciation of neurotic depressives as a value judgment passed by the

patient upon himself or, as we find it more convenient to say, passed by his superego upon his ego. When a patient gives voice to this judgment, he not only stimulates others to contradict it, but he also discharges guilt tension at the same time by externalizing his superego condemnation. One could say metaphorically that some of the superego hate is funneled out through the expression of verbal symbols.

The repeated self-accusations are symbolic equivalents of a continued superego offensive. They relieve internal stress in the same way that public confession often does, in the same way that confessions to a loved and trusted person do. They temporarily satisfy the need to accept a little self-punishment in exchange for a little self-forgiveness. Each self-depreciatory repetition acts as a safety valve. As the superego builds up the pressure, self-accusation lowers it again. The complaints are seen once more to perform a defensive function.

(d) Discharging ego and id aggression. The unconscious hostility that creates the intolerable tensions of guilt, in neurotic depressions, comes as much from unconscious ego and id sources as from superego sources. Oral dependent persons, in particular, are forever being frustrated by people around them. They can never be fed enough, taken care of, comforted and protected enough. Their experiences of frustration go deep and generate violent archaic hostility. This archaic hostility is basic to the tensions of depressive guilt because it stimulates superego counteraggression. Hence, if some of this hostility can gain direct expression there will be a corresponding decrease in superego attack.

Because the patient makes inordinate demands upon his loved ones, they are most apt to be his frustrators. This is why we find him tormenting them with his disturbing self-depreciation, with statements about his incompetence which threatens their security, with thinly veiled threats of suicide, and with accusations of being badly treated, that, is, unloved, unwanted and despised. Such discharges of id and ego aggression serve the same dynamic purpose as does the superego discharge. It lowers for the time being the overall tension of depressive guilt.

Projection. We have now seen that unconscious guilt is the kind of anxiety which arises in the neurotic depressive ego when it is assailed simultaneously by strong unconscious id and superego aggression. We have seen also that tension and anxiety can be reduced by the discharge of hostile id and ego aggression through attacks upon loved ones, and by the discharge of superego aggression in self-depreciation and self-condemnation.

A further important defense in neurotic depressions consists of the *projection* of superego aggression into external reality, that is, the ascription of one's own superego attitudes to other persons. Loved ones are insistently accused of holding the patient in contempt, of sensing his unworthiness, of finding it impossible to go on loving, respecting or emotionally supporting him. In this way a pseudocommunity of disdainful and unloving superego figures is organized by the patient, who utilizes whatever real and imagined behavior of his loved ones he needs for the purpose.

The advantage to the patient of doing this is twofold. It allows him to protest openly, as he may have done in childhood, that he is unloved. This expresses symbolically, and discharges, some of the unconscious tension in a semirealistic way. It also enables him to enlist the aid of these superego figures against his own attacking superego. They protest against the unloving, disdainful role which the patient ascribes to them and thus, as we have seen, provide him unwittingly with the narcissistic supplies he needs. Their protests at first give him love from superego figures outside him to counterbalance his own infantile superego hate.

Eventually these persons find they cannot keep the process up. They may then actually adopt the attitudes which the patient has been projecting on to them. They grow disdainful and then become exasperated and angry. In the end the patient thus gets from the superego figures around him what he originally ascribed to them. What was at one time false projection becomes finally actual fact. This is the same thing that happens in paranoid projection, as we shall see, and it forges another link in the chain connecting neurotic depressions with psychoses.

It is interesting that, even when the neurotic depressive person has turned people against him in this manner, he may be better off dynamically, even if he is worse off socially. When loved ones become hostile, the patient can keep on projecting his superego hostility on to them with less guilt. The now more realistic bad treatment which the patient gets may give him the chance to discharge further ego and id aggression in hating and resenting those who have turned against him. The now hostile others become targets for simultaneous id, ego and superego tension discharge by way of objective interpersonal relationships. This is what we saw in the case of Ernest F. After he had goaded others into expressing genuine contempt, he was able to burst out with righteous indignation, and then to accept the help of a neutral therapist in reaching a more stable equilibrium. The now reasonable complaint, "I hate them because they hold me in contempt!" replaced and obliterated the original irrational complaint, "I am no good! I hate myself!" — the last being unconscious superego aggression.

To sum up what has just been said: Neurotic depressives project symbolized functions which belong historically to their own infantile object world, symbols which were consciously experienced in infancy as parental disapproval, dislike, contempt and condemnation. The adult patient ascribes such attitudes to persons who may not actually have them, or who have them unconsciously and to a minor degree. In this way, by his projections, he stimulates others to contradict the unconscious attacks being made by his own superego. While this situation lasts, his relatively feeble regressive ego receives external reinforcement in the way of narcissistic supplies from other persons, who thus act as superego substitutes. Thus an archaic, infantile conflict situation is transformed by the defensive organization into a current, contemporary representation. The chief disadvantage of the transformation is that eventually it may turn everyone against the patient. The final outcome will depend upon what outside help is available and to what extent the patient is able to make use of it.

Ego and superego regression in neurotic depressives

Ego and superego functioning are for the most part normal in neurotic depressions, just as they are in other neuroses. This is what enables neurotic persons to keep in effective contact with their surroundings. The partial regression, however, revives infantile processes which the patient cannot control. In each neurosis regression leads to a different pattern. The infantile pattern reactivated in neurotic depressions reflects some of the earliest desires, fears and conflicts which human beings experience — those involving helpless dependence. Infants can enjoy helpless dependence as long as their needs are dependably met. When an adult partially regresses to infantile dependence no one can meet his unreasonable needs. This is what happens in neurotic depression.

The regressive ego functions in neurotic depressions, as we have described them, include unconscious wishes to satisfy infantile needs which were imperfectly met in childhood or were too strongly developed. These needs appear in disguised form as demands for less responsibility and more emotional support. The demands are so great, however, that the neurotically depressed adult never finds them satisfied. The result is that the longings to be as dependent and irresponsible as an infant are certain to meet with frustration. Anger and resentment toward loved persons, or toward superiors, who might conceivably provide infant care, are therefore almost inevitable. These, as we have seen, are prominent symptoms in most neurotic depressions. The pre-edipal, unconscious ego and id desire, fear and anger reach consciousness in the more or less disguised form of appeals for greater consideration and more love. The anger and resentment over frustration of these needs are usually obvious parts of the neurotic depressive picture; but the original infantile forms have been disguised by the defenses.

To the adults who are the targets of angry resentment it seems as if nothing they do is ever right. They are playing blind man's buff with the patient's infantile unconscious and do not know it. In his own way the patient feels consciously and preconsciously the same way; but he has to find justification for such emotional attitudes, since in their original form they are repressed. This justification is what we see included in his symptoms, which come also from the archaic superego, the complaints that he must be no good, worthless and unlovable. He is also sad and hopeless because he sees no prospect of ever gaining satisfaction for his infantile longings. This despair is usually realistic. The infantile id and ego longings cannot be fully met in an adult world.

The regressive superego in neurotic depressions is at least as archaic as the superego in obsessive compulsives; but apparently regression and projection are more effective, since patients are able to use their complaints in such a way as to keep the archaic superego activities unconscious.[7] Nevertheless, the archaic superego hostility succeeds in making the patient feel irrationally inferior, deserted and unloved. His partially regressed ego is incapable of resisting the archaic superego attack, just as his ego was in actual infancy; and the patient turns to other persons for help, just as in actual infancy he turned to others to protect him from external dangers. He does this, as we have seen, by projecting upon others whatever components of the superego attack he cannot repress, and thus stimulating them to contradict and reassure him, to protest against his self-depreciation, and in this way to oppose his superego.

We can picture this as a battleground within the ego. A feeble infantile ego faces mammoth internal objects, the products of early introjection of "bad objects" and of identification with them.[8] The narcissistic supplies which the patient procures from other persons by his complaints and accusations serve as reinforcements for the beleaguered ego. Their contradictions, reassurances, protests and reaffirmations of love are used unconsciously by the patient to ward off the attacks made by the infantile internal objects which go to make up the archaic hostile superego.

To sum up: In neurotic depressions the regression revives an infantile struggle between an abnormally dependent ego and an abnormally critical superego, the latter made up of introjected hostile objects and infantile identifications with aggressive parental figures. The patient keeps what he can of this critical superego under repression. The rest he projects upon other people, especially upon loved ones, whom he recasts unconsciously in the role of parents. He complains against them in such a way that they give him exaggerated reassurance, praise and love. These narcissistic supplies reinforce his infantile ego, and he uses them in his internal combat with his archaic superego. As long as this process continues the patient may be able to maintain his neurotic depressive equilibrium. In time, however, the adults upon whom the patient depends for narcissistic supplies become exasperated and rebel. They refuse to give him any longer what he needs; and they may unwittingly join forces with the depreciating superego by upbraiding him. When this happens the added frustration may lead to one of two common results.

(*a*) The frustration and apparent abandonment may sharply increase the hostility of the archaic superego. The patient may then give up his dependence upon external help, including that still offered by loved ones,

---

[7] In psychotic depressions the archaic superego activities are more nearly preconscious and conscious, as we shall see. This creates a much more painful and dangerous situation for the patient.

[8] These "bad objects" reappear in psychoses and are sometimes vividly described by borderline psychotic patients.

and regress further into a sadistic psychotic depression. We shall describe this situation further when we discuss psychotic depressions.

(b) The added frustration may instead increase ego aggression sufficiently to enable the patient — usually with the help of an emotionally neutral person who is a therapist — to counterattack and come out of his depression. This is what we saw Ernest F. do. It is more likely to occur spontaneously in neurotic depressions than in psychotic depressions because of the relatively good contact which the patient maintains with his external environment during his illness. Sometimes a neurotic depression seems to "run its course," like normal mourning. But the danger of regression into a psychotic depression is real enough to make therapeutic help always advisable.

The childhood background of neurotic depressive reactions

We have pointed out several times that neurotic depressives have their major fixation points in an infantile phase of oral dependency, a phase of pre-edipal development still earlier than that of self-assertion and power struggle to which obsessive compulsives regress. The neurotic depressive shows anger and resentment, as obsessive compulsives also do, and he expresses deep dependent needs along with fears of becoming helplessly dependent. But the conflicts which his regression revives do not focus upon cleanliness and soiling or upon abstract problems of right and wrong, but rather upon the desire to be loved and treated like a baby and the conviction that he is unlovable and unwanted. Such conflicts arise in the transitional period of infancy during which weaning stimulates increased dependent needs at the same time that it raises the fear of slipping back or being tempted back into symbiotic helplessness.

The unconscious sense of guilt that prevails in neurotic depressions is not expressed directly or experienced consciously as guilt. Instead, it appears in derivative form as complaints of being unloved and unlovable, of being worthless, unwanted and inferior. Anger and resentment, although close to the surface most of the time, are usually denied. They show up in the tone of the patient's complaints, in an occasional outburst, and when therapy allows them to find free expression.

The neurotic depressive does not lose his hold on external reality in the way that psychotic depressives do. He preserves his defensive organization more or less intact and he continues to be able to communicate effectively with other persons. In short, he is more infantile than the obsessive compulsive and less infantile than the psychotic depressive.

Here, then, we have a personality matrix which differs in emphases and combinations from the matrices of all other neuroses and psychoses, one in which *good object relations* are maintained in spite of *deep oral dependence, self-depreciation* and *unconscious guilt*. It remains now to point out the most probable childhood background of persons who develop neurotic depressions when they regress under stress.

Deep oral dependence. All human adults enjoy a variety of oral gratification — in eating and drinking, kissing, smoking, talking, singing and whistling — and everyone is dependent to a significant degree upon at least one other person. Moreover, we can still find in ordinary adult metaphor and in adult unconscious and preconscious fantasy the oral receptive symbolism which we ascribe to suckling infants.

It is generally assumed, on the basis of much clinical and observational evidence, that an oral orientation is the dominant mode during the first months of every infant's life, and that the earliest ego is primarily a mouth ego.[9] According to this view, the suckling experiences his universe primarily in terms of passively receiving food which he then actively takes in or rejects. If we group with these experiences the related ones of body care, of being held, warmed, moved about, and comforted, and of being lovingly watched over, we have most of the overt contributions to an infant's wellbeing which we call his *narcissistic supplies.*

To say that a fed, cared-for, comforted, warmed and loved child is *valued* or *esteemed* is to say the obvious. But it may not be as obvious that such experiences are also the foundation of what is called *basic confidence* or *basic trust* in infancy, and of what we have been calling self-esteem. To be free to love oneself normally, to have self-esteem, it is necessary to have had infantile experiences of being fully loved. Not to have had this experience consistently in infancy and early childhood is to lack the foundations of normal self-esteem. Once basic trust or basic confidence has been established, the child is free to go on building up the foundations for his self-esteem in his relations with others.

Fixation at the level of deep oral dependent needs is always pathological. It implies one of two opposite conditions. Either the patient as a child enjoyed excessively deep gratifications from early nursing experiences — including what we have grouped as infantile narcissistic supplies above — or else he was denied adequate oral and related gratifications. In one case the fixation is the result of extravagant indulgence; in the other it arises from frustration.[10] In either case the fixation paves the way for the enjoyment of dependent, submissive, subordinate roles, as well as for periodic rebellion against being dependent, submissive and subordinate. It may also lay the foundation for later adult declarations of being helpless, unworthy and inferior, and even for a lifelong desire to be treated like a baby. After

[9] Piaget, J., *The Origins of Intelligence in Children* (trans. M. Cook). New York: Internat. Univ. Press, 1952; Hoffer, W., "The mutual influences in the development of ego and id: earliest stages," *The Psychoanalytic Study of the Child.* New York: Internat. Univ. Press, 1952, vol. 7, pp. 31–41.

[10] The fact that the same fixations may be produced by opposite extremes becomes less surprising when one realizes that a person may become avaricious because he has once been rich or because he has always been poor.

all, a baby is helpless and subordinate; he can easily be made to feel unwanted and unloved which, without self-esteem to counteract it, is the same as feeling unworthy and unlovable.

Self-depreciation and unconscious guilt. Self-depreciation is not only the expression of a lack of normal self-esteem but also the product of archaic superego attack. This means, we have said, that during pre-edipal phases of development the child has introjected his experiences of severity or neglect in the form of enduring sadistic internal objects. And it is, of course, such internal introjects that go to make up the precursors of the later mature superego, the precursors which we have been calling the *archaic superego*.

Much of what is experienced during infancy becomes later unconscious when repression develops functional boundaries that differentiate experience into conscious, preconscious and unconscious. The archaic superego, with its good and bad internal objects, is among the early experiences that undergo a sweeping repression and become unconscious. This does not mean that it ceases to exist. It may, however, have no appreciable effect upon adult behavior and experience. It is when the archaic introjects persist unconsciously in an unusually active state, and when repression is inadequate, that they produce in conscious and preconscious experience a persistent feeling of being inferior, unworthy and unloved. This result is especially likely if during the rest of a child's development he experiences a continuation of the same kind of treatment as that which led him originally to introject a severe archaic superego. We have discussed this situation in the chapter on early personality development under the topics of maternal overprotection and overindulgence,[11] sudden traumatic weaning, parental inconsistency, parental anxiety and parental guilt.

Another source of unconscious guilt, which may result in preconscious and conscious feelings of being inferior, unworthy and unloved, lies in suppressed feelings of angry resentment over being frustrated. There may be infants who, because of their congenital organization, are more easily enraged than average, just as there seem to be congenitally anxious infants.[12] In any case, if parental sanctions against expressions of forbidden desire and forbidden aggression call out severely angry infant and child behavior, this may lead to still stronger parental suppression, leaving the child full of suppressed rage which later undergoes repression. Anything that reactivates the archaic sadistic superego is likely also to reactivate unconscious infantile id and ego counteraggression. The conscious or preconscious sign of this, as long as repression holds, would be a sense of being for some unaccountable reason hateful, unlovable, unworthy or inferior.

[11] It is well to repeat here that the term *maternal* refers to a set of functions usually carried out by mothers. Maternal overindulgence may come also from father, a sibling, a foster parent or other mother substitute — even from a part of the social system.

[12] This has been described in Chapters 2 and 8.

It should be said that there are parents who actually do not love their child and cannot hide it. And there are children who actually face the threat of emotional starvation unless they comply with what their parents demand of them in every detail. Parental love in the former case cannot be obtained. In the latter it is made conditional upon complete submission and sometimes submergence of the child's individuality. This is seen more commonly among adults who become psychotic than among neurotic depressives.

Good object relationships. Why is it that neurotic depressives, in spite of deep oral dependence, self-depreciation and unconscious guilt, still manage to maintain good object relationships — often better than those in other neuroses? The responsibility for this redeeming quality, which protects the patient from becoming psychotic, rests partly with the parents and partly with the patient as a child.

Parents who demand submission to an unusual degree may give the child a great deal in return for his submission. Within the frame of a powerfully dominant-submissive relationship there can be many opportunities for freewheeling expression and for identification with parental characteristics which build good object relationships. A domineering father or mother presents the child with a strong model for identification if he can find channels for expression that do not go counter to the domineering parent's will. It is better, for example, to have a colorful domineering parent than a wish-washy permissive parent as far as the development of internal richness is concerned. Parents who encourage infantile dependence are often themselves able to give and receive a great deal of affection without breaking down the ego boundaries of their dependent child. A child growing up under these conditions should be well equipped to maintain good object relationships in spite of becoming depressed.

The child's contribution to his ability to maintain good object relationships comes from his flexibility within the framework of dependence which limits what he can do and what he may express. Instead of fighting off encroachment, as obsessive compulsives do, the child of domineering parents may learn to exploit parental domination in such a way that he gets more than average attention, solicitude and opportunity. We are all familiar with exploitative persons who, in spite of having infantile oral trends, manage to attract and to gratify others who enjoy acting as patrons and protectors. These represent extremes of the kind of reciprocal behavior with which orally dependent adults are equipped to contribute to interpersonal relationships.

Therapy in neurotic depressions

Therapeutic intervention can be attempted in neurotic depressions with a high probability of success as long as one bears in mind that therapy aims at improvement and not necessarily at cure. A permissive therapist who has ego strength to spare can become the basis for a new introject within the patient which shifts the internal balance within the patient's superego, rendering it less sadistic and less dangerous. This may not only reduce the original archaic superego hostility but make the superego less hypersensitive to ego aggression and to forbidden id impulses. Superego attitudes may become conscious in therapeutic sessions, particularly if technical jargon is rigorously avoided, and they are then much more accessible than while they remain unconscious. The same kind of thing may happen if unconscious ego hostility toward loved ones and toward the self penetrate into preconscious and conscious organizations in recognizable form. Unconscious feared dependent needs may be dealt with at more integrative adult levels.

The relationship of the depressive complaints and the repetitive act of complaining to the unconscious sense of guilt may emerge. It will not emerge healthfully under the influence of exorcism, name-calling or badgering, unless the therapist has a maturely empathic understanding of the patient which is at least in part reciprocated by the patient. As the patient's ego needs become less urgent, he will become less likely to resort to coercive, exploitative methods when he is anxious. In the end, some restructuring of the personality system may result, with an internal equilibrium that is more stable and therefore less dependent upon external forces to sustain it. This is not, of course, a task to be undertaken by amateurs.

Neurotic depressions and psychotic depressions

Neurotic depressions are not merely mild forms of psychotic depression; they involve a qualitative difference in object relationships. The regression in neurotic depressive patients is to deep oral dependent levels but it is only a partial regression. Object relations remain fairly intact; the defensive organization is well preserved; and genuine communication can be maintained with other persons at more or less realistic levels. This resistance to regression seems to be a function of maintaining adequate object relationships, since ego development and the evolution of external reality are only different aspects of a single integrative process. Stimulating others to contradict, reassure and protest is in itself a defensive technique that limits regression. It involves active commerce with the surroundings and it provides channels for the dischage of ego, id and superego hostility.

Psychotic depressions, as we shall see in a later chapter, represent a subtotal regression to deep oral levels. Thanks to a strong ego-superego at these levels the psychotic depressive is saved from slipping back into the kind of ego fragmentation that one often sees in schizophrenia. Nevertheless, the psychotic depressive is much less able to engage in genuine communication with other persons than are neurotic depressives. He repetitiously and monotonously makes his statements of doom, of self-condemnation and self-hatred, without paying more than passing attention to whatever reassurances, contradictions or protests other persons offer. He has obviously regressed beyond the point where he can make dynamic use of anything that other people do or say. He has become delusional; his defensive organization has crumbled; and he may be incapable of surviving outside of a hospital. It is obvious from a psychotic depressive's behavior that he is locked in a struggle which is actually going on within his own personality, but which he misinterprets as objective reality. In other words, he has lost his hold on external reality and is attempting to reconstruct it in accordance with his own delusions.

This distinction in the character of object relations holds true not only as between neurotic and psychotic depressions but also between neuroses and psychoses in general. This is to say, in neuroses there is relatively good preservation of object relationship, ego regression is only partial, and the defensive organization remains intact. Abnormalities of behavior represent largely attempts of the patient to deal with his experiences on a realistic level in spite of partial regression. In psychoses there is always a substitution of delusional reality for objective reality. Since, as we have observed, ego and object are different aspects of the same processes, ego integration also suffers serious distortions in the psychoses and so does the defensive structure. Before going on to deal with psychotic disorders we shall bring together what has already been said about symptom formation in the various neuroses and summarize it in the chapter that follows.

13

Symptom Formation

It is time now to interrupt our recital of the symptomatology of the neuroses and to consolidate what we have learned about the general process of symptom formation. The variety of symptoms encountered in psychopathology is endless. We have already described some of the most typical ones in the preceding six chapters, but we have by no means exhausted the list. In the chapters still to come — on psychoses, on psychosomatics, and on personality disorders — we shall encounter new ones. And even after all this has been covered, there will still remain a vast array of more or less individualistic symptoms which we shall not have described.

In addition to this array of individualistic symptoms, there are innumerable combinations which cut across the classification of neuroses. In clinical experience we seldom find cases as clearcut as the ones we have described to illustrate the various neuroses, and to point out id impulses, superego pressures, unconscious fantasies, ego defenses and ego adaptations. In almost every neurosis there is some degree of contamination by incidental symptoms which complicate the clinical picture. Symptoms belonging to one neurosis appear in the structure of another neurosis; or one finds in a neurosis some more or less incidental symptom belonging to a psychosomatic, a psychotic or a personality disorder.

It will be remembered that we described *anxiety reactions* as in many ways the simplest and most unstructured of the neuroses. Yet even in relatively clear-cut anxiety reactions one can nearly always find some phobic admixture, or a conversion symptom or an obsessive compulsive symptom. Depersonalization and unreality feelings appear in many neuroses, and so do psychosomatic components or mild depressive manifestations.

Our case of the oil geologist, Walter A., even though a typical anxiety reaction, showed many contaminations. He had somatic complaints, for example, that would be difficult to distinguish from those characteristic of psychosomatic disorders. These were physiological discharges which seemed devoid of symbolic function. He also suffered from minor phobic symptoms which we deliberately slighted in our presentation in the interest of clarity.

We did discuss in this case, however, the important role played by guilt. It was the pathological development of guilt in childhood that predisposed Walter to develop pathological anxiety under stress; and it was his pathological guilt in adulthood that helped precipitate the first anxiety attack. It is highly probable that, if he had not received therapeutic help in time, he would have developed a guilt neurosis, most likely a neurotic depression. We saw that he became very subdued and solitary following the separation of his parents, and that a few years later, while he was away in college, he apparently escaped into what looked like a hypomanic state of overactivity and aggression. We know that during his trip back from abroad, just before he began psychotherapy, Walter was isolating himself from everyone, even to the point of having his meals served to him alone. This might well have been the prelude to a depression.

When we turn to the *phobic reactions* we find that what phobic patients are trying to avoid through their symptoms is an anxiety attack. Whenever they fail to avoid the feared object or situation they actually suffer acute anxiety which is indistinguishable from an anxiety attack. Something the same is true of *obsessive compulsives.* They avoid acute anxiety by their repetitions, rituals, doubts and ruminations. If they resist indulging in their compulsive symptoms, or if someone else prevents their indulging, they may have a typical anxiety attack. Persons with *conversion reactions* are usually better defended against experiencing conscious anxiety than are phobics and obsessive compulsives. Yet it can be shown that they, too, are warding off potentially intolerable anxiety. One of the chief obstacles to therapy in conversions is the fact that, to achieve any substantial improvement, it is necessary to mobilize painful underlying anxiety in a patient who has been escaping it through his symptoms. In *dissociative reactions* there is usually manifest anxiety — clearly evident in estrangement and depersonalization — and where anxiety is absent, as in some dreamlike states and massive amnesias, a great deal of ego-superego functioning is also absent. *Neurotic depressives,* as we saw in the preceding chapter, are nearly always manifestly anxious, in spite of all the help they provoke by their complaining.[1]

There are many other interrelationships among the various neuroses, as

[1] Freud, S., "Inhibitions, symptoms and anxiety," (1925), Standard Edition, 1959, vol. 20, pp. 77–175.

well as between them and psychotic, psychosomatic and character disorders, which complicate the clinical picture further. We witnessed the intermingling of phobias and compulsions, for example, in the case of Ramona M. The *tics*, which we grouped with conversions, are often called obsessive compulsive. The confusion of dissociative states with conversion reactions, on the one hand and with beginning psychotic reactions, on the other hand, gives us still another example of the complexity of symptom structure.

In a great many instances there seems to be a kind of layering of neurotic façades. A compulsive neurosis may be guarding against an intolerable phobia, while the phobia is defending the person at unconscious levels against attacks of naked anxiety. Conversions often perform a similar service. Behind the conversion lies an unconscious phobia; and behind the phobia there is always the threat of frightening anxiety attacks. Neuroses may also serve to defend a person from the threat of a psychosis — a vitally important practical consideration in treatment — but we shall leave this for discussion later in the chapter.

In spite of all this variation and complexity in neurotic symptoms, they are all fundamentally similar in dynamic structure, and in the way that they are formed. The formation of neurotic symptoms has its origin in a disturbance of psychological equilibrium. This may come suddenly, as it did in most of our cases, or it may come gradually, step by step, over a period of years. It may result from the frustration of strong needs, from the loss of important gratifications or of self-esteem, and from the lighting up of conflicts through external circumstances or increased internal drive.

The essential thing is that the development of neurotic symptoms is part of an attempt at adaptation, an attempt to cope with adult situations which arouse powerful unconscious infantile need.[2] If we bear in mind throughout that neuroses are always made up of admixtures of adult and infantile experience and behavior, and that the defensive measures take place at unconscious irrational levels, it will not be difficult to understand the sequence of events that leads to neurotic symptom formation.

Neurotic Symptom Formation

To each of our patients, or to their relatives and friends, the neurotic symptom seemed unintelligible, an intrusion of something irrational into an otherwise normal existence. Or else the symptoms were misinterpreted and accepted as signs of physical illness and disability, or as evidence of overwhelming guilt. The complaints of each patient were based upon experiences of genuine distress or disability, they were inescapable, and yet in themselves they made no sense. Let us review some examples from our own cases as an introduction to the process of neurotic symptom formation.

[2] Earle, A. M., and Earle, B. V., "Early maternal deprivation and later psychiatric illness," *Amer. J. Orthopsychiat.*, 1961, *31*, 181–186.

Review of cases

The oil geologist, Walter A.,[3] was actually provoking his own intolerable anxiety by defying the standards of conduct which he had internalized during his childhood. He was trying to act out his adolescent conflict — whether to hate his beloved mother or to hate his beloved father — by seducing the wives of his friends in a series of little dramas which cheated both the women and the men. In the end he met his match in a woman who refused to let him drop her. It was her insistent attachment, coupled with Walter's fear of discovery, that drove his tension and anxiety out of bounds, even after he was safely back in the United States. He returned here to get rid of his terrible symptoms, as well as to escape from a dangerous situation. But he achieved more than either of these when he was able to revive and face his earlier conflicts, and to work them through to an apparently successful final solution.

Edgar R., the patient who was taunted by his fellow workers, developed a panic reaction in which he actively hallucinated voices which seemed to accuse him of perversions and to threaten his life. Although this is a psychotic reaction, and belongs to a later discussion, it serves to illustrate at this point the dramatic intensity of infantile urges, fantasies, fears and conflicts, which a person may be successfully repressing without even needing to know of it. This patient had been apparently symptom-free for twenty years before the taunting campaign began at his office; and it seems likely that he might have gone on successfully repressing or containing his infantile impulses and the archaic superego which erupted into frightening projected voices.

The woman who developed a phobic fear of height, Agnes W., was defending herself primarily against an impulse to commit suicide. This alone justified her anxiety since it is a fact that many persons in her situation have killed themselves. Her defensive phobia, however, concealed this impulse from her. It also concealed impulses to avenge herself upon her faithless lover and upon the unborn child which she had been told she carried. There were other motivations involved which were discussed in the chapter on phobias. This patient overcame her neurotic symptoms, not by attempting directly to master the fear of height, but by revealing to herself the infantile pattern of her adult life and by working through the unresolved conflicts which held her in bondage under the supervision of her parents.

The man who feared riding in elevators quickly transferred his phobia to fear of his therapist's small office and then to fear of the therapist himself. Through this series of mutations it became unmistakably clear to the patient that elevators and small closed places were not the underlying causes of his intolerable anxiety, but something to do with being alone with other persons.

[3] The cases are listed alphabetically in the index, under the general heading *Cases*.

A similar constellation appears in the symptomatology of Kenneth E., who began with a fear of being in theaters and ended up by being pathologically afraid of many different situations in which he might conceivably be trapped or might expose his homoerotic trends. Once phobic fear was established in this man's internal neurotic equilibrium, it generalized so widely that he was finally forced to seek therapeutic help if he was to go on earning a living. Once more, it was not the constellation of specific fears which the patient directly overcame, but the infantile and adolescent conflicts, fears and impulses which had been reactivated by the decompensation of his unconscious ego defenses. We shall skip over the other cases of phobia, which merely present similar unconscious problems in different conscious guise, and review a sampling of the conversions.

The Rocky Mountain ranchman's daughter, Mildred A., reacted in her early adolescence to an aggressive attempt at sexual assault with a disability that paralyzed her. The unconscious multiple meanings of her symptoms have been discussed in some detail with the description of her case. It was infantile in more than one sense. It kept the patient as helpless as an infant, dependent upon others for everything, and encouraged by her family's sanctions to remain helpless and dependent. Her parents even compared her state with infantile paralysis, even though they were told that this was a false comparison. The patient also utilized her invalidism for secondary gain, becoming through it a distinguished person who enjoyed many privileges. Nevertheless, this young woman was not consciously malingering, and under the circumstances the symptom was outside of her awareness as something over which she could regain control. It was the symbol of something that had once happened to her, a primitive acting out in place of a recall.

The medical resident, George D., who developed a complex tic involving his head and neck, was also symbolizing something that he could not otherwise express. The external circumstance which precipitated the conversion symptom was the behavior toward him of his clinical chief who, it will be remembered, teased and goaded him while he was in a defenseless position as the chief's subordinate. Through a pathological identification with a patient, whom his clinical chief had demonstrated, George was able to express openly the angry contempt that he felt for someone who was depreciating him. In this he was also identifying, at an infantile level, with his arrogant mother, while at the same time he preserved his almost equally infantile identification with his easy-going physician father. The symptom attempted the solution of an adult conflict, over being unable to identify with a physician who belittled him, by resorting to an infantile unconscious identification, amounting to little more than an imitation of a patient. This man's task was to work through a complexly immature identity problem which had its roots in early conflicts over parental discord.

The domestic science teacher, Mary G., overate all her life in response to an unverbalized demand on her father's part.[4] The fact that she equated refusing food with mortal sin, and regurgitation with "breaking all ten commandments," indicates that she recognized at unconscious levels the fundamentally sexual character of the demand, as well as her incapacity to resist it. Intertwined with this edipal conflict was her hostility toward her younger brother, and the fact that the birth of her sister's boy was intolerable to Mary because of this unexpressed but deeply felt hostility.

So much of what occurs in the dissociative reactions falls between neurotic and psychotic symptomatology that we shall make mention here of only two examples: *sleepwalking* and the *somnambulistic attack*.

Sleepwalking is of particular interest to the student of symptom formation because it occurs under conditions of what should be normal regression. To fall asleep is to allow oneself to regress. The sleeping person normally lets go of the reality of his surroundings and sinks into a more or less inactive state which seems to be punctuated by dreaming. One of the major requirements for sleeping is that motility be excluded along with most of the effects of sensory stimulation. In sleepwalking we see motility activated and sensory stimulation responded to sufficiently to save the sleepwalker from injury most of the time. It is, in effect, a demonstration in normal or near-normal persons of the potential power of unconscious and preconscious motivation.[5] A person who should be resting, and who is more than half-asleep, walks about, rummages through things, perhaps dresses and goes out, talks more or less incoherently, and often gives the distinct impression that, like Lady Macbeth, he is trying to work out something belonging to his waking life that he cannot express satisfactorily when he is fully awake.

The somnambulistic attack shows all this with still greater clarity. Minnie D. literally slid into her dramatic *acting out* whenever she approached the topic of sexuality and conflict with her mother. Each attack was the expression of a dominant daydream in action, a daydream in which there were intermingled feelings of desire, temptation, helplessness and fear. Each trance state that followed her attacks seemed to express feelings of being stunned, disillusioned and remorseful over what had happened. The failure of therapy to help Minnie has been ascribed to her limited education and intelligence. It was also suggested that Minnie derived enough gratification from the unconscious or preconscious display to outweigh the disadvantages of being ill. Finally, in this as in all other therapeutic failures, one must be aware of the inevitable limitations of therapy and therapists.

[4] Litin, E. M., Giffin, M. E., and Johnson, A. M., "Parental influence in unusual sex behavior in children," *Psychoanal. Quart.*, 1956, 25, 37–55.

[5] For recent reviews of *motivation*, see Young, P. T., *Motivation and Emotion: A Survey of the Determinants of Human and Animal Behavior.* New York: Wiley, 1961; Brown, J. S., *The Motivation of Behavior.* New York: McGraw-Hill, 1961; Hall, J. F., *Psychology of Motivation.* Philadelphia: Lippincott, 1961; Olds, J., *The Growth and Structure of Motives.* Glencoe, Ill.: Free Press, 1956. Also see the *Annual Review of Psychology* which reviews the current literature each year. For several years there have been symposia on *motivation* at the University of Nebraska, under the editorship of M. R. Jones. These will be found listed in the *Psychological Abstracts* annually.

In our chapter on obsessive compulsive reactions we grouped the cases in accordance with the defensive maneuvers that each illustrated best. Here we shall need only to emphasize certain aspects of their dynamics.

The twelve-year-old boy, Horace N., is a good example of the reactivation in early adolescence of methods of control that were used by his parents when he was a small child. His increasing sexual drive disturbed him, which is not unusual, but it also drove him to displace his adolescent sexuality on to his parents and to think obscenely about them, which is unusual. In the end his own sexual conflict became a conflict over hostility toward his loved parents, a conflict that should have been better resolved during his edipal phase. His regression carried him back farther than his edipal phase to one in which angry resentment could only be controlled by his taking the role of a parent and telling himself "Stop it!"

The young mother, Doris I., who had impulses to kill her baby, was also regressing to a pre-edipal level, where she repeated her own early childhood hatred of her baby sister, but directed the hostility toward her own baby without knowing why. When she was able to revive the hatred for her sister, hidden by repression and reaction formation, the irrational impulses to kill her own baby girl disappeared.

The Minnesota housewife, Ramona M., gives us a clear example of compulsions magically guarding against an outbreak of phobic anxiety. Here we have defensive systems layered one above or outside the other. We also encounter murderous id impulses and unconscious fantasies which keep the symptoms alive, and superego self-punishment which adds a sadomasochistic note that will be echoed in a different key when we come to psychotic depressions. The endless preoccupation with contamination, and the endless rituals and obsessive precautions to guard against it, suggest immediately a regression to the pre-edipal level of toilet training and concern over feces.

The relationship between compulsive cleanliness and soiling becomes unmistakable when we come to the case of Sally J. So also is the pre-edipal confusion over bowel movements and sadomasochism. Sally gloats over her own real suffering as though a part of her were a cruel vindictive relentless mother figure. She herself found the relationship in her primitive thinking between sexuality and soiling, between soiling and possibly killing others, between sex thoughts, increased sex tension and the undoing ritual of washing and scrubbing her hands. There is drive regression here, from mature genitality to immature, pre-edipal hostility toward the men she wanted to love. There is ego regression from meticulous orderliness, which was a little abnormal, to compulsive orderliness punctuated by outbursts of soiling, which was definitely pathological. Finally, there was superego regression in her sadomasochistic drama which she reenacted every time she washed and scrubbed her hands, at the same moment whimpering like a baby girl and gloating like a little girl's conception of a severe punishing mother, and perhaps like real unconscious attitudes that her mother may have had.

We shall end our review of cases by returning to Ernest F., the man who developed a neurotic depression when his dependency needs were severely frustrated — when he lost his home, his teeth, and the undivided loyalty of his wife. Although Ernest was no coward, and eventually reacted to his father-in-law's goading with a startling temper outburst, his partial regression laid bare a passive, dependent, infantile level of fixation, more infantile than the aggressively hostile levels to which Ramona M. and Sally J. regressed when they developed neurotic symptoms. The archaic superego that was unconsciously revived in him had nothing of the savage, sadistic quality which dominated the archaic superego of these other two. Ernest seemed to become a rather pathetic, complaining, self-depreciating person, much as he apparently had been in his own childhood. The regression in neurotic depressions seems to revive phases of dependent infantile attitudes that belong to earlier periods of development than those of any other neurosis. It is the kind of regression which, if it were to become general instead of remaining partial, would end up with a depressive psychosis.

Reaction sensitivity and the predisposition to neurosis

In discussing each of the neuroses we have assumed that certain persons are predisposed to develop neurotic behavior under stress by the kind of internal, psychological equilibrium which they establish during their first five years. This may have its roots in a congenital hypersensitivity to anxiety-provoking stimulation. It certainly has its roots in early environmental experiences, particularly those having to do with interrelationships with other persons.[6]

This assumed predisposition consists of the residues of unresolved infantile conflicts, the failure of repression and other defensive maneuvers to contain them, and a tendency throughout life to react in terms of these infantile conflicts whenever something similar to them is experienced. Thus a person such as Walter A., with his early training in seeking out guilt and his traumatic experiences of early adolescence, will tend to react with guilt in many more situations than the average person would, and even to seek out situations in which he can re-experience guilt. Likewise, a person with unsatisfied infantile dependent needs, such as Ernest F., will react to all frustrations of his dependent needs with an exaggerated demand for satisfaction, or by withdrawing into lonely isolation when he should be taking aggressive action. Finally, a person with unresolved ambivalent emotional attitudes

[6] Emmerich, W., "Parental identification in young children," *Genet. Psychol. Monogr.*, 1959, *60*, 257–308. For a review of the literature on separation anxiety, see Bowlby, J., "A critical review of the literature," *J. Child Psychol. Psychiat.*, 1961, *1*, 251–269. See also Cattell, R. B., and Scheier, I. H., *The Meaning and Measurement of Neuroticism and Anxiety*. New York: Ronald, 1961.

over soiling and keeping clean, being hostile or being loved, as in the case of Sally J., will find conflicts revived whenever she is in adult situations which arouse her sexually, make her angry, or threaten to destroy orderliness.

Thus we assume that the person who reacts to frustration, anxiety or guilt with anxiety attacks has had emotionally traumatic experiences in early childhood which differ in kind and in timing from the traumatic experiences of persons who cover their anxiety with phobic defenses. We assume that persons who cover both their anxiety reactions and their phobias with a conversion or an obsessive compulsive reaction have suffered emotional traumata early in life that differ from these others and from one another. Finally, we assume that the early childhood experiences of orally dependent persons, who develop a neurotic depression, must have differed from those suffered by persons who react to increased drive, to frustration or to loss with some other kind of a neurosis.[7]

These *reaction sensitivities* — these readinesses to react with one rather than with another neurotic pattern — may determine not only the neurotic pattern that develops, but also what precipitates it. We have spoken several times of the so-called *split-level response*. Adults whose defensive structure is defective will react to many adult situations simultaneously at two levels: at an adult conscious level, and at an infantile unconscious level. Any situation that resembles a traumatic emotional situation of early childhood will call out a repetition of the childhood response at the same time that it calls out the adult response. The adult response is likely to be direct and overt; the childhood response is likely to be covert and derivative. It is the mingling of different levels of experience that all of us witness in our own manifest dreams, and that the neurotic person lives through while awake. It may lead only to an exaggerated reaction which is otherwise appropriate. It may also lead to ambivalent feelings and ambiguous behavior. Finally, it may lead into symptom formation. When this last is the case, the form of the symptom will depend both upon the person's specific vulnerability and upon the situation which disturbs his internal equilibrium.

The adaptive functions of neurotic symptoms

From a dynamic point of view the neurotic symptom has three essential aspects: (1) It is a sign that the balance of forces within the personality system is disturbed. (2) It is a sign that infantile conflicts have been reactivated. (3) It is itself an attempt at spontaneous cure, that is, an attempt at adaptation. We have already discussed these aspects of the neurotic symptom at some length in discussing the dynamic background of each neurosis; and we have discussed them further in the review of cases just

---

[7] Cf. Holzman, P. S., and Gardner, R. W., "Leveling and repression," *J. abnorm. soc. Psychol.*, 1959, *59*, 151–155.

finished. Here we shall add a few more words to introduce the sequences that constitute the process of symptom formation.

We conceive of the normal personality system as a system of forces or energies which are maintained in a reasonable state of equilibrium. This is a fluid and not a static equilibrium. The forces are constantly shifting. One of the main ego functions is that of maintaining an optimal balance of these forces, not only within its own organization, but also in relation to id impulses, superego pressures and external stimulation.

An optimal balance among such forces is one that enables the personality system to carry on its activities with a reasonable degree of satisfaction. To achieve it there must be, among other conditions, a continual redistribution of energies among ego, id and superego organizations, and among unconscious, preconscious and conscious levels of function, as well as a more or less continuous discharge of tension. When ego functions of energy redistribution within and tension discharge without do not work well the personality system is in for trouble. Untamed id impulses and unconscious ego fantasies threaten to gain expression in preconscious and conscious ego organizations, thus initiating a certain degree of disruption or disintegration. Superego pressures mount, partly in response to the threatening id impulses, partly because of beginning ego disintegration which makes ego boundaries less effectual in all directions. Unconscious ego fantasies and daydreams enter preconscious ego organizations, ego tensions accumulate and anxiety rises to intolerable heights.

The total organism, as we all know, is continually adapting to continual change. At physiological levels a vast number of adaptive responses keeps the body's systems in optimal balance with one another, for example, in the respiratory and cardiac cycles, in the maintenance and recovery of postural equilibrium, in compound hormonal interrelations, in the rapid production and destruction of cellular elements in the blood, and in a thousand other ways.

The personality system, as a part and a product of organism-environment interaction, has the same fundamental problem, that of maintaining an optimal balance of forces, and that of recovering equilibrium when this has been disturbed. In a person who is symptom-free the shifts and changes, which go on continually as a part of normal mental activity, are in part regulated by the various defense mechanisms, many of which we have discussed in their exaggerated forms as they operate to maintain a neurotic equilibrium. The stresses that develop within the personality system, in normal as well as in neurotic persons, lead at once to the automatic activation of the ego defense mechanisms. These then play a leading role in controlling the new tensions, in discharging them energetically, or in redistributing them to form a new equilibrium within the personality system.

Symptoms are formed, as we have seen, when the balance of forces within the personality system is disturbed, when infantile conflicts are reactivated, and when ego organizations are threatened with disintegration.

We have already discussed some of the possible congenital factors predisposing a person to develop unusual stress in the course of everyday living; and we have discussed some of the experiences in early childhood which leave a person with ego defects that make him vulnerable to both internal and external stress. When ego adaptation fails, either because the external stress is excessive or because the internal balance is precarious, the formation of a neurotic symptom may represent the best adaptive maneuver of which a person is capable at the time.

Neurotic adaptations are usually inferior adaptations. They are likely to be tortuous and clumsy, with childlike and even dreamlike qualities, which make them often irrational and costly. Sometimes the patient is worse off with his neurotic adaptation than he was without it. There are two general reasons for this: (1) the defense mechanisms responsible for maintaining and for recovering equilibrium are unconscious and need not operate in terms of conscious logic; (2) the revived infantile conflicts, which become powerful factors in symptom formation, introduce serious distortions in ego function. Let us now turn to the sequence of events which ends with neurotic symptom formation.

Sequence of events in neurotic symptom formation

In describing the sequence of events in neurotic symptom formation we shall take as our model the relatively sudden developments that occur in the face of sudden stress, since these give us the most clear-cut picture. Neurotic symptoms which develop over a period of years do not present clear phases. It should be borne in mind, however, that even in rapid neurotic developments there may be much overlapping and interaction of different phases, just as there often is in the development of organic disease.

We shall present the phases of neurotic symptom formation in the following sequence: (1) increased tension and anxiety because of frustration, loss, threat, danger or increased drive; (2) threat of ego disintegration; (3) partial regression to main levels of fixation; (4) reactivation of infantile conflicts and return of the repressed; (5) defensive transformation and secondary elaboration within the ego; and (6) final emergence of the symptom.

1. *Increased tension and anxiety.* Everyone experiences at one time or another an increase in tension and anxiety in the face of frustration, loss, threat, danger or increased drive. It is only necessary to think of normal adolescence to have in mind a period during which most persons in our culture have to cope with all of these factors. Sexual and aggressive drives rise to new heights, frustrations appear because experience and opportunity are still inadequate, the pleasures of childhood and its security are lost, new and unknown dangers seem to threaten. Both the external situation and the internal equilibrium of forces appear unstable. There are usually signs

of increased tension and occasional periods of heightened anxiety. The early adolescent superego, perhaps stimulated by the increased id drives, tends to be strict and rigid.[8] The average adolescent meets his critical situations, one way or another, masters them and grows into a normal adult. During his adulthood he will, of course, experience many recurrences of increased tension and anxiety, but for the normal adult these lead only to transient disturbances which are soon overcome.

Some adults and adolescents are not successful in handling their increased tension and anxiety under conditions of external and internal stress. In spite of their efforts to discharge tension, and in spite of the unconscious mechanisms which should redistribute energies within the personality system, tension and anxiety mount until they become intolerable. This is particularly the case if repression has always been inadequate, if ego boundaries have never been firmly established, and if infantile conflicts are easily reactivated. In persons with such defects, adult anxieties are reinforced by infantile anxieties, adult conflicts arouse simultaneous infantile conflicts, and the irrational influence of an archaic superego makes unreasonable demands and invokes strong auxiliary defenses to buttress the inadequate repression. This is the internal state of affairs that results in intolerable tension and anxiety.

2. *Threat of ego disintegration.* There is a limit to everyone's tolerance of tension and anxiety. When that limit is passed something has to change. In normal persons the threat of ego disintegration, posed by the heightened tension and anxiety, is met through an increase in coping behavior and in the use of whatever unconscious ego defenses are available, especially of repression. Changes in the external situation — in work, in love relations, in domicile, in recreation, in personal welfare and personal health — cooperate with changes in the internal economy to enable the person to weather his storm and emerge with a new equilibrium.

The person developing neurotic symptoms is not successful in his attempts, no matter how hard he tries. His repression and the rest of his defensive organization are defective, his ego boundaries are pathologically permeable, derivatives of infantile conflicts muddy the picture or completely distort it, archaic superego pressures continue to impinge upon ego function, and the threat of ego disintegration turns into a reality. The disintegration of the ego — and usually of the superego also — is always incomplete in the neuroses. Most ego-superego functioning goes on at fairly normal adult levels. Secondary process thinking and adaptation are not swamped by primary process material, as they are in the psychoses. Most object relations remain relatively normal, as we have seen in our cases, and contact with external reality is maintained without serious distortion. Delusion and hallucination, for example, are absent. Nevertheless there is a

[8] Mohr, G. J., and Despres, M. A., *The Stormy Decade: Adolescence.* New York: Random House, 1958.

partial ego-superego disintegration and this leads to a partial regression.

3. *Partial regression to main levels of fixation.* A threat of ego-superego disintegration cannot remain indefinitely without evoking an internal adaptation. Since integration cannot be maintained fully at the current level a partial regression ensues which carries part of ego-superego function back to less mature levels. Or, to put it more accurately, a partial regression revives certain ego-superego functions which represent in adult terms certain fixations in infantile conflict. This kind of thing has already been described in direct relation to concrete case material.[9]

Regression in itself is neither necessarily pathological nor even unusual. All of us regress when we go to sleep. All of us experience to some extent in dreams the confusion of yesterday's adult happenings, usually modified or distorted, mingled with the residues of things from our more remote past. Sometimes the product seems absurd or weird; sometimes we develop anxiety that wakes us up. If we have the need and the opportunity to do so, any of us can discover that underlying some of these confused manifest dreams are the still-unresolved conflicts, the wishes, fears, superego pressures and unconscious fantasies, which are rooted in our own childhood.[10] The regression that occurs in neuroses occurs while the patient is wide awake; but it does not compare in completeness or in weirdness with many an ordinary dream. Nevertheless neurotic regression is in itself pathological and leads to further pathology in a continued attempt at adaptation.

The fixations in neuroses are also pathological. They represent, as we have previously pointed out, areas of arrested development, areas in which childhood frustration or childhood overindulgence has prevented a normal weaning process to go to completion. Our neurotic depressive patient remained fixated in oral dependence; he accepted and enjoyed being passive or receptive as long as this was allowed him. Our obsessive compulsive patients showed unmistakable evidence of fixation in phases of conflict over being good and being bad, in the sense that small children experience such conflict, and in choosing between soiling or being reactively clean.

Fixations are not only pathological in neuroses; they are also defensive. They provide a person with strong points to which he can regress and around which he can reorganize in such a way as to remain at a neurotic level — that is, remain for the most part in effective adult contact with the world around him. For there is not just one alternative to neurotic regression; there are two. One is that the patient might have remained normal if his defenses had held; the other is that he may regress still further and become psychotic.

Therapists have to keep in mind this possibility that a neurotic patient may become psychotic, if he is deprived of his neurotic defenses, while

[9] See the sections on the dynamic and developmental background in the six preceding chapters on the neuroses.

[10] DeMartino, M. F. (Ed.), *Dreams and Personality Dynamics.* Springfield, Ill.: Thomas, 1959.

they are treating him. It sometimes appears that a patient's neurosis is actually protecting him, through the strength of his fixations, from regressing further. When this is so, the question arises as to the wisdom of risking a psychotic development in an effort to help a patient overcome his neurosis. The risk, like any surgical risk, must often be taken in good faith; but it is always well to recognize the possibility that it may be present.

4. *Reactivation of infantile conflicts and return of the repressed.* When we say that neurotic regression *reactivates* infantile conflicts, at the main levels of fixation, we are not always being absolutely accurate. Infantile conflicts, in persons vulnerable to neurotic regression, have often been active all along, active enough to call for greater unconscious defensive effort than in normal persons.[11] What we really mean to say is that neurotic regression *intensifies* infantile conflicts, and thus paves the way for their eruption into preconscious and conscious organizations, where we then can find derivatives of unconscious fantasies, id impulses and superego pressures — including those from the archaic superego.

These infantile conflicts have their own strength. Abnormal fixation, we have said, can result from a variety of infantile conditions, ranging from almost total frustration to gratification that is so intense or so seductive as to interfere with maturation. Extreme frustration often leaves the residues of an indestructible wish for the denied infantile gratification. We often see derivatives of such a wish in the extravagant plans a parent makes for his child to reach some goal which once was his own goal. Extremes of gratification, especially when coupled with seduction, leave residuals belonging to a phase of infantile mastery which may have included experiences of great power and pleasure.

The strength and potentialities of unconscious infantile fantasies are easier for a normal adult to understand if he compares them to his own regressive conscious memories and fantasies about some important mastery in his own youth. These memories and fantasies may seem trivial and uninteresting to others. But for the adult who feels defeated and unhappy they are often a strong fortress into which he can retire and gather courage to go on.

The unconscious infantile fantasies of neurotic persons perform similar functions. When they have been intensified through partial regression, however, they are not only powerful. They are also in a state of unstable equilibrium. Because the defensive organization of potentially neurotic persons is chronically defective, the reinforcement of infantile fantasies, with their conflicts, their id and superego components, leads to an immediate crisis. The previously repressed and otherwise defended against material

---

[11] A great many persons, deprived in early childhood, overcome the effects of their early deprivation in later life. These have not been specifically studied. Cf. Clarke, A. D. B., and Clarke, A. M., "Recovery from the effects of deprivation," *Acta Psychologica, Amst.*, 1959, *16*, 137–144. (Only abstract available.)

begins to break through into preconscious and conscious organizations once more. This phase we call *the return of the repressed.*

5. *Defensive transformation and secondary elaboration.* What eventually breaks through into preconscious and conscious organizations is not the naked drive or the untamed archaic superego. It is not even the infantile unconscious fantasy. As soon as the breakthrough begins, or even as it threatens, the relatively intact ego automatically calls out auxiliary defenses, just as it does in dreams. What remains of repression now works in cooperation with the reinforced auxiliary defenses to produce *transformations* of whatever manages to escape from unconscious sources. Just as the manifest dream represents a compromise — in which id impulses, archaic and mature superego pressures, ego defenses and ego adaptations all play a part — so also does the manifest neurotic symptom represent a compromise and with much the same components. It is this *compromise,* usually as unintelligible to the patient as his manifest dreams, which will appear as his neurotic symptom.

We have already documented sufficiently such interplay and such compromise products in discussing the clinical material of each of the neuroses. We have seen, for example, what the patient suffering from an anxiety reaction is neverthless successfully warding off, when we chance upon someone like Edgar R., who fails to form organized fantasies at neurotic levels, succumbs to his excessive tension and anxiety, and goes into a panic reaction. Here the id impulses and a projected archaic superego overwhelm the mature ego-superego organization and disintegrate it. We see clearly the imprint of displacement and projection in the phobias, the fusion of drive, defense and superego in the conversions, and the alternation of drive satisfaction with superego punishment in some of the obsessive compulsives, most clearly in the case of Sally J. The insidious influence of an archaic superego is often not easy to demonstrate directly in neurotic depressions, where the complaints of inferiority, unworthiness and hopelessness may not seem at first altogether unwarranted. Nevertheless the effect of psychotherapy usually points to such an influence clearly; and even if this were not the case, the unmistakable operation of such an archaic superego in the overt symptoms of psychotic depressions would unmask the origins of such complaints.

Meanwhile the compromise formations emerging into preconscious organization may also undergo secondary elaboration which often make them appear to be either signs of well known disease or disability, or else the product of genuine secondary process thinking, which they actually are not. This process bears comparison with the secondary elaboration of the manifest dream. Dreamers usually elaborate or revise their manifest dreams in such a way as to make them sound more and more like waking experience. This is, of course, an unintentional process. If the dreamer tells his dream to two or three different people during the day its form is likely to undergo successive changes, each change moving away from the primary process and toward the secondary process structure.[12]

One of the clearest examples of secondary elaboration occurs in the development of obsessive compulsive symptoms. Even the most primitive obsessive compulsive symptoms exhibit a primitive logic, an organization in space and time that is foreign to primary process functioning. Obsessive doubt and rumination go perhaps the farthest of all in making use of the forms and the machinery of secondary process logic to rationalize their conflicts and to conceal them. The logic used may actually be pseudo logic; but it succeeds in transforming undoubted primary process material into secondary process form. It achieves a distancing when it substitutes apparent intellectual speculation for the infantile emotional tangle in which the patient's conflicts lie.

Another clear example is the use made of denial in the dissociative reactions. Here repression does not succeed in keeping something unbearable from being perceived. Denial comes to the rescue and separates off recognition of the perception. In some instances, as we have seen, this leads to estrangement and depersonalization; in others it produces dreamlike states; in still others it cuts off whole areas of experience by inducing secondarily a massive repression of what has been denied. The denial itself, however, seems to take place as part of a process of secondary revision.[13]

Many other examples could be cited; but we shall mention only two. In the development of a *phobia*, once the process has reached preconscious levels, it may mushroom into a mammoth defensive structure which, on the surface at least, may seem quite justified. In the many forms of conversion reaction which mimic organic disease we are dealing with *secondary elaboration*. This is essentially the same as the secondary elaboration which most manifest dreams show. They are reorganized in such a way as to make them more acceptable to the patient and to those around him. We witnessed this, for example, in the case of Mildred A., whose paralysis became for the patient and her family a part of an epidemic of horse-encephalitis, which everyone could accept. An important difference, of course, is that the secondary elaboration occurs in the conversion patient while he or she is fully awake, whereas at least part of the secondary elaboration of manifest dreams takes place while the person is still asleep.

6. *Final emergence of the symptom.* The symptom that finally emerges is usually contained in the patient's complaint or in the complaints of those around him. Like the manifest dream it seldom reveals its origins to the patient. What emerges, as we have said, is neither naked drive nor untamed

---

[12] When a person writes down a visually experienced dream, immediately after awakening, he has to revise it in order to translate it into words. If he writes it again a few hours later, without referring to his first written edition, he will usually find that it has meanwhile undergone further revision. Cf. Bartlett, F., *Thinking, An Experimental and Social Study.* New York: Basic Books, 1958.

[13] Jacobson, E., "Denial and repression," *J. Amer. Psychoanal. Ass.*, 1957, 5, 61-92.

archaic superego, nor even the unconscious infantile fantasies from which the symptom may have sprung. The still relatively intact ego, with boundaries that are only partially defective, and with a defensive organization backed up by more than one level of superego functioning, shows itself capable of creating manifest symptoms which may at first be acceptable to everyone. The form of the symptom — whether it resembles well-known disease or disability, whether it seems only exaggerated fear, estrangement or a repetitive ritual, or whether it consists only of depressive complaints — can somehow be made to appear reasonable. There is still enough adult ego adaptive function to maintain good object relations, excepting in some of the dissociative reactions. There is still enough adult superego functioning to enable the neurotic person to operate according to prevailing standards, to provide at least a modicum of self-esteem, and to protect him from self-neglect and self-injury.

There should be no mystery about the unintelligibility of most neurotic symptoms. Like dreams, they are not primarily intended as interpersonal communication. Almost all of the processes entering into neurotic symptom formation are themselves unconscious. We see only the end-product. The released id impulses and the unconscious fantasies driving toward expression, together with their regressive reinforcement, are all unconscious. Patients usually know nothing whatever about them; and even the clinician may recognize them only through a process of sophisticated inference. Most of the *ego defenses* responsible for transformations, disguises and elaborations are also unconscious. The patient is as ignorant of them as he is of the mechanisms operating to form his manifest dreams. Superego interventions and pressures, whether archaic or relatively mature, also work at unconscious levels. And, as we have seen, the regression that starts off the whole reactivation chain is no more conscious than is the process of suddenly falling asleep. It cannot be surprising that the final end-product, the neurotic symptom, seems to the patient to be devoid of conscious meaning.

There remain still to be discussed the problem of neurotic gratification through fantasy and the distinction between primary and secondary gain.

Neurotic gratification through fantasy. Unconscious wishes gain a certain amount of gratification through fantasy, and are expressed ambiguously in neurotic symptoms, even though they are never clearly recognized for what they are. We have discussed many examples of this. There was, for example, the patient who feared height. She also was greatly tempted by fantasies of falling, by the punishment falling might also bring her, and by the revenge it might represent against her faithless lover. The patient with bulimia was acting out her pregnancy fantasies by eating. Her irrational superego reaction against her refusal to eat and her attempts at regurgitation brought this out clearly. Each of the several guilty neurotic patients — whether their symptoms came through as anxiety attacks, phobias, conversions, dissociations, obsessive compulsive reactions or depressive complaints — was guilty because of some fantasied forbidden gratification for which he felt the need for self-punishment.

Unconscious fantasies have been demonstrated so regularly in neuroses during psychotherapy that their presence is no longer seriously doubted. We saw in the case of Ramona M. — the compulsive patient who was also phobic about contamination — that there was abundant evidence of her having entertained homicidal impulses toward her husband, and of her gratifying these impulses in homicidal fantasies. In fact, it was the sudden breakthrough of these fantasies, when Ramona broke the crockery, that precipitated the irrational phobias and the no less irrational compulsive measures taken against harming loved ones. In the case of Agnes W., with her phobia for height, and of Kenneth E., with his phobia for theaters, elevators and downtown streets, the unconscious fantasies in modified form spontaneously emerged; and as therapy progressed the symptoms based upon them disappeared. Among the conversion reactions, unconscious fantasies became more or less clear in the cases of George D., Olivia B., and Betty S. George D. overcame his spasmodic torticollis; but Olivia gained only temporary improvement in her postural deformity and Betty S. retained her eating problems because the therapy of both girls was interrupted. In the case of Ernest F., with his neurotic depression, the unconscious wishes for infantile dependence became much less urgent as he worked them through in relation to his adult situation.

How can fantasy alone bring gratification? The answer to this question can be made through an appeal to everyday experience. Everyone knows from personal experience that fantasies of a better world, a more adventurous or richer and more secure world, can afford the fantasier a great deal of gratification. For millions of normal persons such fantasies are major sources of a serene outlook upon a sorely troubled world. Fantasies of revenge, of "getting even," however childish and impractical they may be, can nevertheless have a soothing and pleasurable effect in many normal adults. Anyone who reads stories, attends plays, watches television or enjoys "comic strips" should be able to understand the strong appeal of gratification through unrealistic and often irrational fantasy. One gets a measure of the strength of such appeals when a story is unexpectedly interrupted, a television set shut off, a play canceled, or a paper not delivered that carries a favorite "comic strip."[14]

These examples are all of conscious fantasies; but most of them share in the unreality and extravagance that are characteristic of unconscious and infantile fantasy. Many of them even owe their power to the unconscious fantasies which they succeed in stirring up. As a matter of fact, one of the major contributions to our present-day understanding of normal emotional behavior and experience has been the recognition of the enduring power of unconscious fantasy in the life of neurotic patients. As we have frequently

[14] See, for example, the discussion of *expressive styles* in Miller, D. R., and Swanson, G. E., *Inner Conflict and Defense*. New York: Holt, 1960.

pointed out, the experiences of neurotic patients are not completely different from many of those of normal persons.

Primary gain and secondary gain. Before turning from neurotic symptom formation to the closely related psychotic symptom formation, we shall repeat the distinction made earlier between primary gain and secondary gain in neurotic symptoms.

(a) Primary gain. In all neurotic symptom formation the primary gain lies in the mastery of otherwise overwhelming tension and anxiety. Tension and anxiety initiate the threat of ego disintegration which leads automatically to partial regression; and the symptom as a rule confers upon the now neurotic patient a certain degree of freedom from tension and anxiety at the cost of some reduction in effectiveness. It is true, as we have seen, that some neurotic patients in the end are worse off than they were when their neurosis began; but this is due usually to complications which the patient does not anticipate.

We can sum up the question of primary gain by saying that, thanks to the ego defenses, a new equilibrium is established which, even though pathological, succeeds in minimizing the newly created internal stresses. The key factor in this new neurotic equilibrium is what we have been calling *the symptom.* And this gives us at once a therapeutic insight: that in many of our patients it is the *symptomatic compromise* that is holding them together. The neurotic equilibrium which they have unconsciously achieved, and which is expressed in the symptom, is usually an effective equilibrium, and sometimes it is the best equilibrium of which the patient is capable. The competent therapist does not lead his patient to get rid of his symptom until he is prepared to substitute something more effective for it.

(b) Secondary gain. The secondary gain is never the source of a neurotic symptom. It is always a more or less incidental result of symptom formation. The patient succeeds in his primary gain; he lowers or gets rid of excess tension and anxiety. Afterwards, or during the process of forming his symptom, he discovers that there are advantages in being neurotic quite apart from tension reduction. He may find that he need not work any more, or that he can demand exemption from responsibility, from punishment or from domination by other people. The most exaggerated example we have given is that of Mildred A., the paralyzed ranch girl, who not only escaped the drudgeries of being a poor man's daughter and of becoming a poor man's wife, but gained prestige and honor in her community, where she lived a life of unrivaled ease and comfort.

Secondary gain is by no means a necessary result of neurotic symptom formation. A great many neurotic persons are much worse off after developing their symptoms than they were before tension and anxiety precipitated them. The cases of Walter A., the oil geologist with anxiety attacks; Agnes W., the secretary who could not stay in the office where she earned a good living; Ramona M. and Sally J., with their slavery to compulsive ritual; and Ernest F., with his miserable depressive unhappiness — all show clearly how ineffectual neurotic symptoms can be in bringing satisfaction to a person. Nevertheless all of these persons were better off with their neurotic symptoms than they might have been had their defenses proved still more defective under stress so that they developed a psychosis. Let us turn now to a brief consideration of psychotic symptom formation before proceeding to a study of paranoid reactions.

Psychotic Symptom Formation

What is a psychotic reaction and how does it differ from the neuroses which we have been discussing? A psychotic reaction is a sweeping personality disintegration with major fixation points still earlier than those in neurotic reactions. The most obvious difference is that the average psychotic person is far less able to deal realistically with his surroundings and with himself than neurotic persons are.

It is true that neurotics also behave irrationally — the phobic has irrational fears, the compulsive has absurd rituals, the conversion patient uses his body to express archaic symbolism. But their areas of unreason are limited, and their regression is only partial. Outside of these limited areas even a frankly neurotic person can participate satisfactorily in the life of his social community. He is likely to seem normal to most of his associates. One can communicate realistically with a neurotic person and enter into reasonably good interpersonal relations with him. He seems to share one's general orientation toward everyday life. He can distinguish his own private fantasies from social reality and his emotional expressions are appropriate. At conscious and preconscious levels he does not confuse the present with his own childhood past, or confuse his own person with what is going on outside him.

In all these respects the frankly psychotic person is defective. His areas of unreason include a major part of his overt behavior. As those close to him can plainly see, he has lost interest in real happenings, in realistic hopes and fears, in real objects and real people. He has become preoccupied instead with matters which superficially seem unrealistic, trivial, absurd or fantastic. The interest that he had previously invested in the socially shared adult world he now invests in imaginary situations.

Under these conditions no real interchange is possible. Effective communication breaks down. The psychotic person sees everything from his own distorted private perspective, while everyone else around him shares in the perspectives of social reality. He cannot see things from others' points of view and they cannot see things from his. The patient becomes desocialized — that is, the process of socialization by which he came to be an integral part of society is at least partly undone.[15] It becomes impossible for him to engage in his usual everyday activities because his perception and cognition are swamped by primary process fantasies. His social role organizations and his role expectations disintegrate. Even his socially elaborated self, in certain instances, may all but disappear.

This is the psychotic person's dilemma: that he must face a world of adult demands when his conscious and preconscious organizations are shot through and through with active infantile impulses, fantasies, conflicts, fears and attitudes. He may act like an adult and speak like an adult; but his basic attitudes express overtly the unsolved problems of his early infancy.

It is this revival of infantile dynamics that forms the core of every psychosis. Infantile ways of experiencing are once more dominant — in thinking and feeling, in defending and perceiving, in ego and superego adaptation. In many cases traumatic anxieties, such as normal and neurotic adults experience only in night terrors, now visit the psychotic person while he is wide awake. And when this is so, the terrified patient no longer has available the mature defenses and the adaptive maneuvers which other adults have. He must meet these waking nightmares with his available archaic forms of defense, such as massive projection, introjection and denial. His loss of reality-adaptation leaves him unable to control and manipulate his environment as other persons do.

There are exceptions to the above. In clinical work we come across psychotic persons, all of them with delusions and some of them hallucinating, who still manage somehow to operate at reasonably competent levels as business men and women, as professional persons, or as wives and mothers. Some of these are talented, some are average, some are dull.[16] On the other hand, as we have already seen, there are many neurotic patients who are barely able to keep going without hospitalization or its equivalent. Nevertheless, the average psychotic patient is much more incapacitated than the average neurotic, and for reasons which reach down into the dynamics of psychoses.

Comparison of sequences in neurotic and psychotic symptom formation

At this point, as a general introduction to the psychoses, we shall attempt a comparison of each step in neurotic symptom formation with what happens or does not happen in psychotic symptom formation.

1. *Increased tension and anxiety.* Psychotic reactions develop in relation to frustration, loss, threat, danger or increased drive, just as neurotic re-

[15] For a more detailed account of desocialization in psychosis, see Cameron, N., and Magaret, A., *Behavior Pathology.* Boston: Houghton Mifflin, 1951, Chapter 16, "Desocialization." See also Moriarty, D. M., "Some observations on animism," *Psychiat. Quart.*, 1961, *35*, 156–164.

[16] Stein, M., and Heinze, S., *Creativity and the Individual: Summaries of Selected Literature in Psychology and Psychiatry.* Glencoe, Ill.: Free Press, 1960.

actions do. In fact, psychoses often begin with a prodromal period in which typical neurotic symptoms prevail. When these fail to hold the line the patient regresses further into psychosis. The distinguishing feature here is the instability of neurotic fixations and the strength of earlier levels of fixation in persons who become psychotic.

It is only within recent decades that such relationships in psychotic reactions have been demonstrated and accepted by clinicians.[17] Today there persists a certain amount of uneasiness among the rank and file of clinicians when it comes to accepting a psychodynamic origin for psychoses. An active and vocal minority still continues in the older tradition which maintained that psychotic reactions were constitutionally determined, or were the direct products of biochemical disorders, and in either case lay outside the realm of psychodynamics and psychotherapy. Why?

There are several understandable reasons for the reluctance to accept psychoses as having dynamic relations comparable to those established for neuroses.[18] We shall mention three.

(1) Psychotic reactions are often *stormy* and *unpredictable*. They may arouse fear, sometimes not without reason.

(2) Some psychotic symptomatology, as we shall soon see, has a *strangeness* about it that is sometimes compared to the weirdness of manifest dreams. This strangeness arouses anxiety in most observers, especially in the inexperienced, because it tends to stir up primary processes in them and they may not know how to handle these themselves. We witness such anxiety in the course of training clinicians. There is also evidence of it in the laughter which psychotic manifestations often provoke — a reaction which at one time was also given to disabled and deformed persons, as the social history of western civilization clearly shows.[19]

(3) Psychotic patients are often extremely difficult to treat by psychotherapeutic means. Their symptoms, which often represent a last ditch stand for them, may not yield to more mature maneuvers for a very long time. For these reasons therapy in the psychoses is still often carried out on an empirical basis. All kinds of shock treatment are used, frequently with dramatically rapid improvement, especially in the depressions. These treatments still lack a sufficient rationale, but their efficacy in many cases is beyond question.

One of our patients, a severely catatonic man who had not spoken in years,

[17] For an historical account of this evolution, see Cameron, N., "The functional psychoses," in J. Mc.V. Hunt (Ed.), *Personality and the Behavior Disorders.* New York: Ronald, 1944, pp. 861–921.

[18] In a relatively recent review of the literature on the pathology of schizophrenia, for example, the statement is made that "no specific change in any tissue or system of the body has been demonstrated that can account for the clinical syndrome of schizophrenia." See Dastur, D. K., "The pathology of schizophrenia: a historical survey," *Arch. Neur. Psychiat.*, 1959, *81*, 601–604. Fifty years ago there was a similar and more widespread reluctance to accept psychological origins for neuroses also.

[19] Blindness still arouses so much anxiety in some people that they become angry and reproachful when a blind person approaches them.

made a startling recovery when he fell downstairs, suffered a concussion, and was hospitalized on the neurosurgical service. He spoke freely, interacted normally with other persons around him, took a normal degree of initiative in following hospital routines as soon as he was up, and seemed emotionally well. The recovery, however, did not last. Within three weeks the patient had drifted back into his catatonic state; and neither insulin nor metrazol shock made any difference

In spite of widespread lingering prejudice and the unquestionable success of shock therapy in many psychotic depressions, there has been a decided shift toward accepting a psychodynamic origin for psychoses and a psychodynamic interpretation of their persistence. The evidence in favor of such a shift has grown impressively within recent years.[20] We may sum up the situation with regard to tension and anxiety by saying that the same kinds of precipitating factors resulting in neurotic reactions in some persons produce psychotic reactions in other persons. The chief differences in symptom formation seem to arise from the different character of the regression in psychoses and in the different defensive transformations.

2. *Threat of ego disintegration.* Repression has never been adequate in persons who develop psychoses. Auxiliary defenses — especially projection, denial and introjection — perform much of the work ordinarily handled by repression. Ego boundaries are never secure. In psychotic decompensation they sometimes appear to dissolve. The patient may then be overwhelmed by primary process material and lose his ability to distinguish between internal and external reality. Derivatives of infantile conflicts, id impulses, archaic superego and ego functions may take over the functions usually performed by a mature ego-superego structure. Object relations suffer severely. Reality-testing is largely replaced by reality distortion or reality reconstruction. The threat of ego disintegration may be met initially by a neurotic regression and neurotic symptoms, but eventually these give way to the products of deeper regression.

3. *Subtotal regression to major fixation levels.* We have already pointed out that neither regression nor fixation is in itself necessarily pathological. We all regress when we fall asleep, we regress briefly in normal sex relationships, and we regress whenever we create. In our manifest dreams we sometimes show where our major levels of fixation lie, what our auxiliary defenses are like, how partial repression works,[21] and even the influence of our archaic superego. Once in a while a normal adult has an unmistakably archaic manifest dream, one that mystifies him or makes him laugh, or one

[20] Bychowski, G., *Psychotherapy of Psychosis.* New York: Grune & Stratton, 1952; Bychowski, G., "An approach to psychotic anxiety," *Amer. J. Psychother.*, 1961, *15*, 409–415.

[21] Complete repression leaves no trace whatever.

that portrays some desire, fear or punishment that seems completely foreign to his nature when he awakens.

In psychotic reactions both regression and fixation are pathological. Regression is characteristically subtotal rather than merely partial. Most of the mature ego-superego organization undergoes primitivization, leaving little for realistic interaction with other persons and with interpersonal events, even sometimes with inanimate and impersonal things.

There may be a certain amount of adaptive value even in psychotic regression. The best examples of this can be found in paranoid projection and in manic reactions. It has long been known that the construction of a paranoid pseudocommunity can protect a patient from losing all contact with his surroundings. A paranoid coloring may give a schizophrenic picture a better prognosis than it might otherwise have. Manic reactions appear to be primarily defensive.[22] Although usually manic reactions end in recovery, there are exceptional instances in which they are replaced by a more dangerous depression or even a schizophrenic disorganization, from which the elation seemed to have been protecting the patient.

Fixations are defensive in psychoses only to the extent that they protect a patient from a still deeper regression and still greater disorganization.[23] From this point of view a moderately severe paranoid reaction is better than a moderately severe psychotic depression, at least in terms of suffering and of danger to the self. Similarly, a moderately severe depression is better than a moderately severe schizophrenic reaction, because in the latter the regression is often abysmally deep. A severe schizophrenic regression leaves the patient almost defenseless.

4. *Reactivation of infantile conflicts and return of the repressed.* What has been said of infantile conflicts in persons who develop neuroses holds true also for psychotic persons: they have usually been defending against eruption of infantile conflicts most of their lives. Because the regression in psychoses is subtotal, rather than merely partial, and because the fixation points that are reactivated are more archaic than those of neuroses, psychotic experience and behavior appear more primitive. Either an archaic, impulsive ego dominates the scene, making behavior unpredictable and difficult to understand, or else an archaic superego emerges. In psychotic depressions one sees frequently an archaic ego in a life-and-death struggle with an archaic, cruel superego. This is the same phenomenon that we witnessed in obsessive compulsives, most clearly in the case of Sally J.; but the level at which the struggle is carried out in psychoses is much more primitive and the dangers to the patient are correspondingly greater. *The return of the repressed* occurs in psychoses,[24] as it also does in neuroses, but the repressed which returns

[22] Cf. Lewin, B., *Psychoanalysis of Elation*. New York: Norton, 1950.

[23] For a discussion of disorganization in psychoses, see Cameron, N., and Margaret, A., *Behavior Pathology*. Boston: Houghton Mifflin, 1951, Chapter 15, "Disorganization."

[24] Waelder proposes *return of the denied* for psychoses. See Waelder, R., *Basic Theory of Psychoanalysis*. New York: Internat. Univ. Press, 1960.

is more archaic and the ego-superego organization to which it returns is much more chaotic.

5. *Defensive transformation and secondary elaboration.* Because of the depth and extent of regression, there remains little mature ego defensive organization to deal with whatever escapes repression and appears in preconscious and conscious life. The psychotic patient is thrown back upon such primitive defenses as massive projection, introjection and denial.[25] He lacks the advantages of the better organized neurotic compromise. Whatever secondary elaboration takes place, during the filtration of primary process material through the residual ego-superego structure, is likely itself to be archaic and more like a manifest dream than like waking reality.

As we shall see in the succeeding chapters, the most characteristic symptom of psychoses is the delusion. The delusion is one of the most remarkable pathological products. It represents not only a distortion of external reality but also a defensive reconstruction of external reality.[26] As a matter of fact, it is through his delusions that a psychotic person may maintain his contact with the world of people and things around him. Since, at the same time, the delusion often represents the satisfaction of a deep unconscious need, it is easy to understand a patient's unwillingness and even his inability to give it up. We shall have more to say about delusions as reconstructions of reality in the next chapter. Suffice it to say at this point that the delusion, like the neurotic symptom, is always a spontaneous attempt at self-cure, and that inexpert attempts to remove it may be dangerous to the patient.

6. *Final emergence of the psychotic symptoms.* What emerges as symptom in psychoses is much closer to naked drive, untamed archaic superego and infantile fantasy than what emerges in neuroses. Psychotic symptoms show a wide range in variety and complexity. We shall postpone detailed discussion of them until we come to describe actual psychotic cases, so that the discussion may have an immediate connection with actual events. In psychoses, unlike the situation in most neuroses, there is often a catastrophic destruction of object relationships, of self-esteem and of the machinery for self-protection. Psychotic symptoms are much more difficult to make intelligible than are neurotic symptoms. Indeed, until the rise of dynamic interpretations, and their confirmation through the study of infantile behavior and the intensive psychotherapy of psychotic patients, psychotic symptoms seemed capricious, unintelligible and more chaotic than they actually are.

[25] Stone, A. A., and Eldred, S. H., "Delusional formation during the activation of chronic schizophrenic patients," *Arch. gen. Psychiat.*, 1959, *1*, 177–179; Miller, D. R., "Studies of denial in fantasy," in David, H. P., and Brengelmann, J. C. (Eds.), *Perspectives in Personality Research.* New York: Springer, 1960.

[26] Cf. Kaplan, B., "An approach to the problems of symbolic representation: nonverbal and verbal," *J. Commun.*, 1961, *11*, 52–62.

Once clinicians were able to recognize that psychoses were the products of profound, subtotal regression, they were encouraged to attempt an understanding of them in ontogenetic terms, that is, in terms of primary process and infantile defenses. Once they realized that delusions were basically attempts to regain reality relationships, that they were attempts at reconstructing what had been lost through a disastrous regression, there began studies of delusion as a form of psychotic compromise, analogous to the neurotic compromise that goes to make up neurotic symptoms.[27] Advances were first made in relation to paranoid delusions under the influence of these new insights. It is, therefore, appropriate that we should begin our study of the psychoses with *paranoid reactions,* where the delusion is plainly to be seen.

Precipitating factors common to all psychoses

Before going on to consider paranoid reactions, it will simplify our later discussions if we list here five situations to which persons who develop psychoses are especially vulnerable. These constitute stress situations for all persons, normal and neurotic as well as prepsychotic; but certain adults because of their childhood background find them intolerable. These are the persons who regress subtotally, when they are exposed to such stresses, and develop one or another psychotic reaction. The five situations to which they are especially vulnerable are as follows:

(1) *Loss or threatened loss of a major source of gratification.* This may result from death, desertion or disillusionment. It may come from humiliation or neglect. It may follow a loss in status or a decline in health. The effect of any of these losses is to reduce or eliminate a person's available *emotional outlets.*

(2) *Loss or threatened loss of basic security.* This may come through personal failure, lowered status, economic loss or the pressure of new or increased demands. Such factors reduce or eliminate a person's available *emotional support.*[28]

(3) *An upsurge of erotic or hostile drive.* This becomes a precipitating factor when no adequate discharge is possible. It may also become a factor when an opportunity for discharge presents itself, but leads to behavior which the person himself then cannot control. This latter includes a person's

[27] Modell, A. H., "An approach to the nature of auditory hallucinations in schizophrenia," *Arch. gen. Psychiat.,* 1960, *3,* 259–266; Nash, H., "The behavioral world," *J. Psychol.,* 1959, *47,* 277–288.

[28] Cf. Hilgard, J. R., and Newman, M. F., "Evidence for functional genesis in mental illness: schizophrenia, depressive psychoses and psychoneuroses," *J. nerv. ment. Dis.,* 1961, *132,* 3–16; Brown, F., "Depression and childhood bereavement," *J. ment. Sci.,* 1961, *107,* 754–777; Schwartz, D. A., "Some suggestions for a unitary formulation of the manic-depressive reactions," *Psychiatry,* 1961, *24,* 238–245.

poorly repressed unconscious impulses if these provoke anxiety or a rebuff in other persons.

(4) *A sudden increase in unconscious, preconscious or conscious guilt.* This may come about through an erotic or hostile upsurge, which arouses an exaggerated *superego* reaction, or an exaggerated reaction from regressive *precursors of the superego.* It may also come about because of an accusation,[29] because of having forbidden fantasies, or because of a forbidden reality experience.

(5) *Reduced general effectiveness of the defensive organization.* This we see in cases of unusual stress or shock, in physical and mental exhaustion, in exposure, severe organic illness, accident, intoxication, brain damage or cerebral degeneration.

In turning now to a discussion of *paranoid reactions* we shall need to bear in mind that these precipitating factors may be present in the clinical course of the paranoid psychosis.

Attention should also be called at this point to the fact that a parent, who might himself or herself otherwise become psychotic, guards against this unwittingly by having a child act out the psychotic trends, or by unwittingly fostering a deviant role in a child. Sometimes we find clinically that one member of a family seems to have been "chosen" to be the psychotic or deviant member, by an often unverbalized and unrecognized general consent. Occasionally, the patient recognizes this scapegoat role consciously, after it is too late to avoid it. We shall refer to these phenomena again in the chapter on personality disorders and in the chapter on therapy. The evidence is particularly clear for such family influences in studies which bring all or most of a family into therapy simultaneously.

[29] The case of Edgar R., who developed a panic reaction and then a psychosis, gives us a clear example of this.

14

Paranoid Reactions

PARANOID REACTIONS ARE GROUPED WITH THE PSYCHOSES. THEIR CHIEF characteristic is the presence of persistent organized delusions, which are usually persecutory, but are sometimes jealous, grandiose or erotic. The prevailing mood is in keeping with the dominant delusions, being hostile in delusions of persecution and of jealousy, erotic in erotic delusions, and exalted in delusions of grandeur. There is no general personality disorganization in the paranoid reaction such as we see in schizophrenia. Paranoid persons usually remain in relatively good contact with their environment, much better than most schizophrenics do, and better than do most manics and psychotic depressives. Because of this good contact, the paranoid reaction forms a bridge between the *neuroses* and the *psychoses*.

Normal thinking and delusional thinking. Paranoid reactions also form a bridge between *normal* and *delusional thinking*. It is common knowledge that attitudes of belief, confidence and expectation — or their reverse — are a part of the context of every normal person's thinking, just as they are in paranoid reactions. We are all continually acting in accordance with such attitudes, even in such simple matters as approaching a door to open it, waiting for the evening paper to arrive, or driving to work. We take a lot for granted in all such ordinary matters. We assume that the door will open, that the evening paper has been composed and printed, and that we are among those destined to receive it. We assume that when we drive to work the place will still be there and that our services will still be in demand. None of these assumptions is absolutely trustworthy. In short, we act most of the time upon anticipations which are based upon incomplete information.

In perception it is the same.[1] We usually see only parts of things, the mere beginnings of some complex series, or only its end-product. From such fragments we continually make assumptions that enable us to act confidently, as though the whole thing or every step were there in front of us to see. We seldom have either the opportunity or the patience to wait until all the evidence is in before we act.

Cognitive processes likewise involve inductive leaps. We have indicated earlier that the normal child does not slowly collect evidence and then draw logical conclusions about the things that interest him. He takes it for granted that he understands things even when he does not; and he himself expects others to understand his explanations even when, as a matter of fact, they are unintelligible.[2] Adults use logical reasoning only when they need to, and when it suits them. Often they use logical reasoning to justify an intuitive or an irrational judgment after it has already been made. Even the creative scientist makes bold leaps which carry him beyond the evidence, and only then does he put his intuitive conclusions to the logical test. In other words, to make inferences on the basis of incomplete evidence, and even to leap to conclusions which may turn out to have been unwarranted, are not necessarily abnormal procedures. It is only when the inferences and the conclusions become fixed, adamant, inflexible, and untouched by contrary evidence, that we begin to speak of delusional thinking.

A great deal of ordinary communication also has this fragmentary character. We say, or hear, only parts of a sentence. We assume the rest either from the context or on the grounds of general familiarity. We know in what sense to understand something that is said, or how to communicate something potentially ambiguous, by the inflection of certain words, by using emphasis, by facial expression and by gesture. A mere word or a sound may be enough to convey complex meanings and start off a program of action, or to stop one. Something left on a table, or something missing from it, may indicate some conscious or unconscious intention of communicating. The way a person dresses, walks, sits or stands can likewise display attitudes not otherwise expressed. When it comes to personal interaction, all of these factors are normally taken into account, and usually at preconscious or unconscious levels.

In whatever we do, whether it is an anticipation, a response to some fragmentary stimulus, an intuitive induction, or an attempt to communicate, we

[1] Cf. Witkin, H. A., *et al.*, *Personality Through Perception*. New York: Harper, 1954; Allport, F., *Theories of Perception and the Concept of Structure*. New York: Wiley, 1955; Tagiuri, R., and Petrullo, L. (Eds.), *Person Perception and Interpersonal Behavior*. Stanford, Calif.: Stanford Univ. Press, 1958; Solley, C. M., and Murphy, G., *Development of the Perceptual World*. New York: Basic Books, 1960.
[2] This was first pointed out in the studies of Piaget, J., *Language and Thought in the Child* (trans. M. Gabain). London: Routledge, Kegan Paul, 1926.

all depend heavily upon hidden meanings, special significance, and intuitively experienced evidence.[3] Our daily activities are almost all based upon probabilities, upon attitudes of belief and confidence, or of disbelief and distrust. We see a shadow near a corner where there has recently been a holdup, and immediately we perceive a threatening figure where actually it is harmless. We look out of the window and see a brilliant star, but even the most superficial check-up shows it to be only a street lamp. We pass a group of strangers just as everyone in it bursts out laughing. The laughter has nothing whatever to do with us, but there are times when for a moment we are unsure. We see and hear many things that we want to see and hear, even though they are absent. We miss seeing and hearing many things that we do not want to see and hear, even though they are visible and audible.

Recall has many of the same characteristics. What we remember is rarely a simple repetition of what we have experienced. It has nearly always been edited. Everyone who has gathered testimony from eyewitnesses knows this. Each witness, no matter how honestly and intelligently he reports, will give an account of the same happening that differs in some respect from the account of each other witness. In short, to remember is not simply to recall. It is rather to reconstruct, even sometimes to create, to express oneself through the medium of telling something.[4]

In all of what we have been saying there is a determinant which we have so far not mentioned by name. This is our *feeling* about what we perceive, anticipate, reason about or communicate, our *feeling* about what we experience intuitively, recognize or recall. If, for example, we are frightened, we experience everything differently from the way we experience it when we are serene. When we are in love, the whole world seems a more lovable place than ever before, including even the landscape and the city streets. When we are filled with hate, the whole world seems to be filled with hatred. When we feel jealous, we can find all kinds of things to be jealous about, which before had not seemed significant. When we grow suspicious, we are more apt to notice things that justify our suspicions than when we are trustful.

All of this leads up to the question of distinguishing between *delusional* and *nondelusional thinking*. The way we all have of acting on the basis of fragmentary information, of interpreting signs and signals, of depending heavily upon hidden meanings and intuitions, of reconstructing what we "recall," and of being always subject to shifting emotional influences, makes a clear distinction exceedingly difficult to formulate. At the same time, such examples help us to recognize that delusional thinking has normal counterparts, and that paranoid reactions can best be understood if we bear this fact in mind.

[3] Cf. Maddi, S. R., "Affective tone during experimental regularity and change," *J. abnorm. soc. Psychol.*, 1961, 62, 338–345.

[4] Bartlett, F., *Remembering, a Study in Experimental and Social Psychology.* Cambridge, England: Cambridge Univ. Press, 1932; Bartlett, F., *Thinking, An Experimental and Social Study.* New York: Basic Books, 1958; Kamano, D. K., and Drew, J. E., "Selectivity in memory of personally significant material," *J. gen. Psychol.*, 1961, 65, 25–32.

Definition. *Paranoid reactions are attempts to escape from tension and anxiety through processes of denial and projection, which result in more or less systematized delusions.* These delusions, we have said, are usually persecutory, but sometimes jealous, erotic or grandiose; and the emotional component is in keeping with the delusion.

The term *delusion* itself needs to be defined. *A delusion is a fixed belief which persists even though social reality contradicts it.* Delusions are characteristic of paranoid reactions; but they are found in other psychoses also. As we shall soon see, it is the delusions from which psychotically depressed and manic persons suffer that render them socially incompetent. The schizophrenias are also delusional disorders; but schizophrenic delusions are as a rule poorly systematized, and often they are extraordinarily bizarre.

It would not be difficult to make a case for the presence of delusions even among normal persons.[5] The full acceptance of a belief, and its indefinite persistence, even though it contradicts all the objective evidence, is not uncommon in ordinary life. When this is true, however, the belief is one that is shared by others in the same culture. It is a belief that depends, not upon objective evidence, but upon group identification.

Paranoid reactions and phobias. Phobias depend upon beliefs that contradict the objective evidence available; but they are much more individualistic than group delusions, and they do not stem from group identification. Phobias either exaggerate a common fear beyond all reason, or else they represent a fear that almost no one else can share. In the latter case, as we saw in Chapter 8, something harmless is responded to as though it were dangerous, and this irrational fear persists in the face of clear demonstrations that it is unjustified.

Phobic and paranoid patients are alike in denying and projecting their internally generated tension and anxiety in order to get rid of them. Yet the symptomatology of the two disorders is very different. The phobic patient regards his projected fear as something unreasonable, peculiar or even absurd. It seems foreign to him, or, as we say, it is *ego-alien.* He would gladly be rid of it entirely; and he typically turns to a therapist in order to gain this end. The paranoid person accepts his delusions wholeheartedly. He sees nothing unreasonable, peculiar or absurd in his complaints. He believes implicitly in the reality of what he projects. It does not seem foreign to him. On the contrary, it is *ego-syntonic,* that is, something which seems to him a genuinely experienced piece of reality. Paranoid persons often try to convince others of the objective reality of their delusions, and sometimes they succeed. If they fail, they are likely to suspect a skeptical person of being a possible party to the "conspiracy." They appeal to a therapist, not to

---

[5] "A delusion must be considered a definitely abnormal phenomenon, even though a normal individual may hold it." English, H. B., and English, A. C., *A Comprehensive Dictionary of Psychological and Psychoanalytical Terms.* New York: Longmans, Green, 1958, p. 143.

get rid of their symptoms, but to help ward off the persons who seem to be threatening them.

Another outstanding difference between phobias and paranoid reactions is a difference between impersonality and personal involvement in the symptomatology. Phobic patients typically focus their fear upon animals, things and situations, or upon man-in-general, as in the fear of crowds.[6] Paranoid patients, in striking contrast, always focus upon persons and interpersonal relationships. They do not feel threatened primarily by dogs, insects, closed rooms or height, but by the hatred of some person or the "plot" of some pseudocommunity. It is obvious that paranoid persons are suffering primarily from a disturbance of personal interrelationships, a defect in understanding and trusting other people, while the phobic person is not.

Adaptation. We know that neuroses are attempts at adaptation. The neurotic symptom is a compromise. If it is successful it will discharge or express something which the patient cannot repress. As the same time it will repudiate what it expresses, and perhaps inflict punishment upon the patient for expressing it. In a conversion reaction, for example, the clenched hand in a symptomatic spasm expresses both a hostile wish and a disability which makes it impossible to carry out the wish. The disability also punishes the patient by crippling him.

The areas involved in such a neurotic compromise are usually limited. Regression is only partial. Aside from these limited areas the neurotic patient may seem normal to others. He may be able to participate satisfactorily in the life of his social community and to share its general orientation toward life. His emotional expressions fit into this general orientation. He can distinguish between private fantasy and social reality, between the adult present and his childhood past, and between his own person and what is going on around him.

Psychoses are also attempts at adaptation, but the attempts are rarely successful in the sense that neurotic compromises are. Psychotic regression is deeper than neurotic and it involves much greater areas of ego-superego functioning. The psychotic patient reconstructs large areas of social reality to make them agree with his regressed beliefs, fears and orientations. These reconstructions appear as delusions and hallucinations which are, in spite of their pathological character, spontaneous attempts at self-cure. To understand a psychosis one must go behind the delusion or the hallucination to find what the situation is that necessitates it. This is not always possible, and even when it is, the result is not always to hasten recovery.

Paranoid reactions, even though psychotic, are more often adaptively successful than are other psychoses. They lack the desocialization and disorganization of schizophrenia, and they do not show the profound mood changes that we see in psychotic depressions and in manias. We have sug-

---

[6] Cf. Arieti, S., "A re-examination of the phobic symptom and of symbolization in psychopathology," *Amer. J. Psychiat.*, 1961, *118*, 106–110.

gested elsewhere[7] that paranoid reactions may be a combination of neurosis and psychosis. The psychotic element appears in the fixed, inflexible delusional development and in the distortion of social reality, the formation of a pseudocommunity, to rationalize the delusion. The neurotic element appears in the good residual object relations which, in many cases, allow the patient to carry on a comparatively normal life as business man or woman, as professional person, or as wife and mother, in spite of the delusions.

Incidence. Paranoid reactions seem to be common in the general population, but their number cannot be accurately estimated. For one thing, mild paranoid trends appear in otherwise normal and neurotic persons without disabling them; for another, they are often disguised as caution, aloofness and snobbishness. The chief paranoid defenses, denial and projection, are present to some extent in everyone. If such trends are dominant in a person's makeup, if regression occurs with exceptional ease under stress, and if delusional beliefs tend to persist in spite of contradictory evidence, then we are justified in speaking of paranoid reaction. At the same time, we must leave room for the many irrational beliefs which groups of normal people hold without supporting evidence, or even in the face of contradictory evidence.

A final source of difficulty in estimating the incidence of paranoid reactions is that mildly and moderately delusional persons do not usually seek therapeutic help. They consider their suspicions, jealousy, erotic attachments or grandiosity to be objectively justified. Their relatives, friends and business associates regard them only as cautious, suspicious, jealous, seductive or narcissistic persons. Some paranoid patients, even with marked delusions, manage to lead a relatively normal life. Occasionally, one of them becomes a leader because others enjoy following his extravagant ideas.

Data on heredity, sex and marital status, and on social milieu, obtained from hospital records, fail to show any relationship to the development of paranoid reactions. One study,[8] for example, found that only eight out of four hundred cases, showing marked paranoid trends, had paranoid ancestors, and only forty-four of the four hundred had ancestors who had suffered *any* kind of nervous or mental disorder. Hospital records are not, of course, ideal sources for such data; but in the absence of other data, and within these limits, the figures are impressive.

The question of age incidence is controversial. It is generally agreed that paranoid delusional psychoses without deterioration appear most often in later maturity. One investigator feels that this represents the age period in which paranoid trends become intolerable to others, and not the age at which they develop. But the fact that the paranoid form of schizophrenia

---

[7] Cameron, N., "Paranoid conditions and paranoia," in S. Arieti (Ed.), *American Handbook of Psychiatry.* New York: Basic Books, 1959, pp. 508–539.

[8] Tyhurst, J. S., "Paranoid Patterns," in Leighton, A. H., Clausen, J. A., and Wilson, R. N. (Eds.), *Explorations in Social Psychiatry.* New York: Basic Books, 1958, pp. 31–76.

occurs on the average a decade later than other forms of schizophrenia throws doubt upon this interpretation. The prevalence of paranoid disorders chiefly in the fourth, fifth and sixth decades may be, of course, the artificial product of our system of classification. We restrict the diagnosis *paranoid reaction* to persons with well-organized delusions who show no deterioration. This automatically rules out the relatively disorganized schizophrenics, who become ill usually in the second and third decade, the period of adolescent and postadolescent stress; and it rules out cerebral arteriosclerotics, who go under because of vascular disease in later life.

There are, however, sources of anxiety, frustration and conflict during the fourth decade and later, which are peculiar to this phase of life. Among them must be reckoned waning youth and waning attractiveness, reduced vigor and reduced flexibility, increasing neglect by the younger generation, and a clearer recognition than before that one's life span is limited. As a person grows older, it becomes increasingly difficult for him to make or even to plan fundamental changes, because of his commitments and because he has already invested so much time, energy and training in his way of life. The disillusionments and disappointments which are almost everybody's lot often accumulate with age. A person with paranoid trends grows less and less able to compensate for them. The upshot may be the development of a frank persecutory delusion, although sometimes there develop delusions of jealousy, erotic or grandiose delusions instead.

Varieties of Paranoid Reactions

In what follows we shall recognize four varieties of paranoid reaction: (1) *paranoid delusions of persecution;* (2) *paranoid delusions of jealousy;* (3) *paranoid erotic delusions;* and (4) *paranoid delusions of grandeur.* To these four clinical varieties we shall add brief discussions of *classical paranoia,* an extreme form of delusional systematization, and of *folie à deux,* a special situation in which a suggestible person takes over the delusions of a dominant paranoid person.

It should be said at the outset that, just as a pure neurosis is rare, so pure paranoid reactions are rare. Almost all paranoid reactions include some neurotic symptoms. Many of them have at least a trace of schizophrenic thinking, but without disorganization. Some paranoid persons are mildly depressed or mildly elated; but we call them paranoid because the delusional aspect is more striking than the mood. A great deal of what we shall have to say about the emotional drives, the ego defenses, the ego adaptations, and the delusional reconstruction of reality, will be found to apply also to cases of psychotic depression, mania and schizophrenia.

Persecutory paranoid reactions are by far the most common form. We shall therefore devote most of our discussion to this variety, treating the others as relatively minor variants.

Persecutory Paranoid Reactions

Even normal people, when they are acutely anxious, badly frightened or shocked, cannot reason well at first about a suspicion or a fear. Their greatest need under these conditions is to be able to check the validity of their observations, to be able to look at the situation from more than one angle, and to question their own conclusions. For these vital procedures three things are necessary: (1) *trust in others*, an ability to put faith in someone else even when one is frightened and suspicious; (2) *tolerance for suspense*, an ability to stem the tide of emotional reasoning so as not to be swept away by it into premature action; and (3) *skill in shifting role perspectives*, an ability to take the role of a detached observer for a few moments under stress, even to take the role of the feared or suspected person. In these borrowed roles, and with final judgment suspended, a person can reconsider his situation from different angles, and perhaps arrive at different interpretations.

An ability to tolerate suspense and shift perspectives is the product of mature ego-superego development. In an emotional crisis this ability may be lost even by a maturely organized adult. When such a loss occurs, a person's only salvation lies in his being still able to share his fears and suspicions with somebody who is less emotionally involved and can be trusted. The shocked or frightened adult can then treat a trusted confidant as his temporary *substitute ego-superego*, making use of his confidant's reality-testing, social skills and detached perspectives. Through some such maneuver he experiences the enormous comfort of sharing his anxiety with someone who is concerned but does not get upset. He gains the advantage of seeing things from cooler, more objective points of view.

Personality background

Trust in others, a readiness to tolerate suspense, and skill in shifting role perspectives under stress, are exactly what paranoid personalities lack. They seem for some reason to have been denied the protection from excessive tension and anxiety early in life which every infant and child requires for normal ego maturation. They have not developed infant trust or confidence; and as a consequence they have never mastered their primal fears. Some of them have obviously gone without the experience of consistent parental love, as our case presentations will show. They have not been able to build the conception of a stable, friendly, dependable world. In short, they lack the behavioral foundations and the ego-superego organization for making safe, close interpersonal relationships.

The paranoid person is equipped with a chronic expectation that others will treat him badly or deceive him, and with a readiness to react aggressively whenever he feels badly treated or deceived. In many cases, the patient has actually been treated sadistically during infancy or early childhood, with the result that he has internalized sadistic attitudes toward himself and others.[9] This is a well-known infantile process, sometimes referred to as *identification with the aggressor*. Because he has been reared in an environment that he has never learned to trust, the paranoid person is always watchful; he has learned to live on guard against sudden deception and attack. Above all, his experiences in early childhood and his sadistic identifications make him exquisitely sensitive to the smallest traces of hostility, contempt, criticism or accusation in the attitudes of other people.

Paranoid hypersensitivity to the unconscious attitudes of others. The trouble with this hypersensitivity is that it always finds something on which to feed. All of us harbor minute traces of hostility even in some of our most favorable attitudes toward others. Most of us at times feel indifferent toward everyone, especially when we are preoccupied. These traces are usually unconscious and the periods of indifference unimportant. Sometimes they are momentarily conscious — a passing resentment toward a good friend, a temporary annoyance with someone whom we love, an occasional feeling of aloofness that we may not always recognize. Nearly all of us manage to get along, without suffering serious disturbance, in a social atmosphere that has its negative components and negative moments in its overall friendliness.

Not so the paranoid personality. He detects our contradictory traces clearly and consciously, even when we are totally unaware of them ourselves.[10] They disturb him because he experiences them as though they were conscious, dominant and intentional in our thinking and our feeling. Because of his selective hypersensitivity to slight, resentment or rejection, he greatly magnifies what he perceives. He may make a molehill of momentary dislike into a mountain of eternal hatred. Because of his intolerance for suspense, and his inability to imagine the roles of other people and their feelings realistically, he takes it immediately for granted that the traces of hostility or indifference, which he detects, are clear, dominant and conscious in the thought and feeling of others. Even hostility that is aimed at someone else is apt to be picked up by the paranoid person and misinterpreted as hostility aimed at him.

This hypersensitivity to unconscious traces or momentary moods, their tremendous magnification, and the assumption that what seems clear to the paranoid person must be equally clear to others, create a pervasive atmosphere of misunderstanding, questioning, distrust, uneasiness and resentment. Such an atmosphere usually follows the actively paranoid person wherever he goes.

[9] Bychowski, G., "General aspects and implications of introjection," *Psychoanal. Quart.*, 1956, 25, 530–548; Jacobson, E., "Contributions to the metapsychology of psychotic identifications," *J. Amer. Psychoanal. Ass.*, 1954, 2, 239–262; Bychowski, G., "Struggle against introjects," *Internat. J. Psychoanal.*, 1958, 39, 182–187.

[10] Everyone who has treated an intelligent, communicative paranoid person has had the experience of having his own unconscious or preconscious hostility pointed out to him by his patient.

Paranoid insensitivity to their own attitudes. There is still another disturbing factor in the paranoid personality. Along with this exquisite sensitivity to the unconscious trends in others goes an equally striking unawareness of the hostile, contemptuous, critical and accusing attitudes which the paranoid person has himself. This unawareness is unfeigned. It is an important product of denial and projection which operate at wholly unconscious levels. One trouble with these unrecognized attitudes is that they stimulate avoidance and dislike in others; and this seems to the paranoid person objective evidence that his expectation of being discriminated against was justified.

Such is the background which a paranoid personality brings with him into an emotional crisis. He is exquisitely sensitive to traces of hostility, contempt, criticism and accusation in others, but blind to their presence in himself. He is forever questioning other people's motivation; but he is incapable of questioning his own. He is always suspicious of what might lie behind neutral and friendly appearances. He lives in the expectation that someone will sadistically belittle or attack him, just as he felt belittled or attacked in childhood.

Paranoid reactions and sexuality. As a rule, paranoid personalities feel secretly inferior in their sexual development, whether or not such a feeling if justified by their performance.[11] The inferiority has its roots in poorly repressed sexual identity confusions from their early life, in the conflicting fears and wishes of childhood which they never succeeded in working through. Sometimes a low level of overt sex drive adds objective evidence of relative sexual inadequacy, as one of our cases will demonstrate. Sometimes homoerotic and pregenital trends are present in the preconscious, and are denied and projected with great difficulty and incompletely. Occasionally, homoerotic trends are openly expressed and made the basis for a homosexual way of life.

Even when a paranoid personality manages to reach an adult heterosexual level, he may have difficulty in maintaining mature genitality. Many respond to heterosexual invitation as though it were a challenge to prove themselves. Many approach sexual relationships with an expectation of being rebuffed, disparaged and rejected. This last probably comes from experiences in early childhood, of being belittled and rejected when they were longing for love. Now, as adults, their feelings of love revive the infantile expectations of unkind, depreciatory treatment, which are poorly repressed and vividly reactivated. The result is that they approach the heterosexual situation, not only with these expectations, but also poised to retaliate with behavior that is certain to provoke rebuff. Failure in sex relations is all but certain under such conditions, and failure is the one thing that the paranoid personality cannot tolerate.

[11] For a review of the literature on homosexuality in relation to paranoid reactions, see Cameron, N., "Paranoid conditions and paranoia," in S. Arieti (Ed.), *American Handbook of Psychiatry.* New York: Basic Books, 1959, pp. 508–539.

Some paranoid personalities are selectively hypersensitive to traces of unconscious homoeroticism and other pregenital trends in persons around them, reacting as though these traces were major, conscious attitudes.[12] This is the same kind of reaction as that which we have discussed in relation to hostility. Such a response becomes especially serious when a social isolate is pushed into close contact with others, as, for example, in military barracks. The minimal unconscious and sublimated homoerotic expressions of other people seem to the frightened paranoid person to be actual threats of seduction or assault. This situation may precipitate a psychotic episode.

It is noteworthy that, even in frank delusional developments, the paranoid patient can go on defending himself against recognizing his own deviant trends, through vigorous denial and projection. He seems normal to himself, but he feels surrounded by perverse persons who make outrageous insinuations about him. He remains angrily innocent.

The minimal erotic cues to which hypersensitive paranoid personalities respond are not invented by him, of course, any more than minimal signs of hostility are. All adults have traces of genital and pregenital traits in their everyday social behavior. Kindness and friendly interest can have erotic components without being pathological; and so can teasing, argument, unkindness and even indifference. Everyone now and then expresses some little infantile interest, such as curiosity, looking, exhibiting, inflicting insignificant injuries or seeking them, making regressive oral or anal comments (especially in slang expressions), even sometimes showing semierotic competitiveness. To any of these a hypersensitive paranoid person may respond as though a full-blown, overt erotic intention were being expressed. If at the time his psychodynamic system is in a state of precarious balance, this may be enough to precipitate an unconscious breakthrough and produce a psychosis.

Lack of self-esteem. Although the paranoid personality rarely recognizes it, he suffers seriously from a lack of healthy self-esteem. He does not even trust himself. This lack of esteem and self-distrust are easy to understand if the patient lacked *basic trust* during early infancy, and if he made hostile or untrustworthy ego and superego identifications. For the same infantile reasons, there is a powerful undercurrent of unconscious guilt in the paranoid personality. This he is obliged to ward off through denial and projection, since his repressive defenses are inadequate. The paranoid person usually holds grudges like the proverbial elephant. He never forgets an injury, and he always takes it for granted that others know how he feels about them and why. It is a relatively small step from such ingrained attitudes to the development of frank delusions.

---

[12] Klaf, S. F., "Female homosexuality and paranoid schizophrenia: survey of 75 cases and controls," *Arch. gen. Psychiat.*, 1961, *4*, 84–86; Klaf, S. F., "Evidence of paranoid ideation in overt homosexuals," *J. soc. Ther.*, 1961, *7*, 48–51.

Precipitating factors in paranoid reactions

At the end of the preceding chapter we listed five situations which find adults who develop psychoses especially vulnerable. These are as follows:

(1) *Loss or threatened loss of a major source of gratification,* which deprives a person of his accustomed emotional outlets.

(2) *Loss or threatened loss of basic security,* which reduces or eliminates a person's available emotional support.

(3) *An upsurge of erotic or hostile drive,* which either finds no adequate discharge or leads to unacceptable behavior.

(4) *A sudden increase in guilt,* because of superego reaction or because of the accusatory attitudes of other persons.[13]

(5) *Reduced general effectiveness of the defensive organization,* because of any one of a number of circumstances, internal as well as external.

To all of these situations the paranoid person, like all other prepsychotic persons, is more vulnerable than normal and neurotic persons are. His special sensitivities, however, and his excessive use of denial and projective discharge, place a greater emphasis upon some aspects than upon others, and give to the clinical picture of paranoid reactions its characteristic delusional patterns. When he is comparatively well, the paranoid person lives in a state of unstable psychodynamic equilibrium. Whatever seriously disturbs this equilibrium, and forces him to step up his defenses of denial and projective discharge, is likely to precipitate a paranoid psychosis.

In addition to the five precipitating factors listed above, which are common to all psychoses, there are still others that especially favor a *paranoid reaction.* These are as follows:

(1) Anything that confirms the chronic expectation of receiving sadistic treatment, and therefore increases a readiness to retaliate.

(2) Anything that increases suspicion and distrust, thereby confirming a lifelong expectation of deception and betrayal.

(3) Whatever increases vigilance and at the same time tends to isolate a person from social interchange with others.

(4) Anything that increases envy and jealousy, thereby arousing resentment, hatred and a sense of inferiority.

(5) Whatever lowers self-esteem, thus encouraging superego attack, and necessitating vigorous denial and projection.

(6) Anything that stimulates a person to see his own defects in others, thus increasing his anxiety, and demanding more denial and projective discharge to overcome it.

(7) Situations combining idleness with isolation, which leave a person free to ruminate over probable meanings and motivations, when he has less than average chance for valid social reality testing. For one of our paranoid patients, a teacher, mere isolation in the library "stacks" was enough to

[13] The case of Edgar R., who developed a panic reaction and then a psychosis, gives us a good example of this.

light up dormant suspicions, so that they quickly became frank delusions.

Most of the seven precipitating factors just given, and the five listed before them, will be illustrated and discussed further in the case histories, and in the section on dynamic and developmental background.

Onset. When frustration from any combination of these sources exceeds the limits of what he can tolerate, the patient turns away from the frustrating situation, and turns inward to solitary rumination. He may then suffer ego disintegration and undergo a deep and massive regression. Unconscious fantasies and conflicts are now reactivated at infantile levels. They escape repression and press toward preconscious and conscious expression. The mature repressive defense structure crumbles, while projection and denial — alway overactive in persons vulnerable to paranoid reactions — now take over repression's major defensive functions.

The symptoms that emerge bear the distinct imprint of paranoid conflicts, fantasies, sensitivities, and primitive defenses. They are drive-organized rather than reality-oriented. The patient then tries to deal with his environment in true psychotic fashion. He attempts to reconstruct reality so as to make it correspond with his reactivated fantasies. This is the restitutive attempt which results in the organization of a paranoid pseudocommunity.

We can distinguish three clinical types of onset in the paranoid reactions. (1) *Sudden and dramatic;* (2) *Sudden clarification preceded by an incubation period;* and (3) *Gradual and insiduous.*

(1) *The onset is sudden and dramatic.* The patient meets with a sudden internal or external crisis which overwhelms his adaptive and defensive systems. Or else, there is a prolonged period of steadily increasing stress, until the adaptive and defensive systems abruptly decompensate. In either case, there is a sudden upsurge of primary process material from unconscious sources into preconscious and conscious organizations. By vigorous denial and projective discharge the patient succeeds in preserving some ego integration; but the result is a delusional system which contradicts reality.

(2) *The onset is preceded by a well-marked period of incubation, terminating in sudden clarification.* The patient reacts to stress at first by partial or complete withdrawal and regressive fantasying. He tries privately to figure things out, i.e., he seeks a unifying "explanation" which will serve as a focus for aggression. Because he suffers from defective social reality testing, his solution will usually be a premature crystallization. Everything seems to the patient to become suddenly "clear," and he feels free to act. In one of our cases, as we shall see, the sudden clarification occurred in a dream.

(3) *The onset is gradual and insidious, without a sudden crystallization.* The patient progresses slowly from being a paranoid personality to becoming a paranoid psychotic, over a period of many months or years. He

may cross and recross the vague boundary line before finally taking up a definitely delusional position. His progressive "adaptations" include more and more deviation from realistic solutions. Social reality is gradually replaced in his thinking by delusional reconstructions.

Clinical course

The paranoid person, even when he is not ill, is a vigilant person. He lives uneasily in a dangerous world, a disparaging hostile world, in which it may seem wise to keep one's distance from others. The personality of such a person is in a chronic state of precariously held, unstable equilibrium. He walks through life on a tightrope.

Early phases

Whenever his unstable equilibrium is threatened, the paranoid person's immediate reaction is to heighten his vigilance and to increase his psychological distance from others. He discharges as much aggressive energy as possible by stepping up his processes of projective discharge. He denies as much as he can keep in denial. He binds as much as he can by crystallizing out fantasies. The fantasies are intended to "explain" the situation and reduce the suspense. When these maneuvers fail and tension continues to rise, the patient eventually passes beyond his limits of tolerance, and the paranoid psychotic process begins.

We have already said that it is difficult even for mature adults to feel secure and trusting in an emotionally disturbing situation. The more a situation stirs up unresolved personal conflicts the more difficult security and trust are to achieve. Paranoid persons rarely feel secure with others; they cannot put their full trust in anyone. Therefore in an emotional crisis they are thrown upon their own inept resources to keep afloat as best they can alone. They may at first share their suspicions with another person; but their basic defects nearly always trip them up. When they are emotionally aroused, they can assert convictions and pile up evidence, but they cannot endure doubt or disagreement, they cannot tolerate suspense. Once started they must go on. Another person's doubt or disagreement seems only an obstruction to the patient's forward thrust. It is experienced as frustration, and the frustrator becomes an opponent. Accordingly he is classed with other opponents as another enemy.

Now the patient faces his emotional crisis all alone. With no one to rely on but himself he falls back on the basic processes of inquiry common to the higher mammals: alert, tense, solitary watching; inferences limited by drive organization, by fear and mistrustful expectation; finally closure and attack or flight. Like a detective, or like a man wanted by the police, he watches everything and suspects everyone. The more he watches, listens and ponders, the more his suspicions grow. Because he has always lived in expectation of hostile aggression his sense of danger grows greater and greater.

An emotional crisis sharpens the patient's wits; but it also narrows the range of what he perceives, how he makes interpretations and what he does. It makes him more than ever selectively hypersensitive. Because he is a human being he ponders, ruminates and makes hypotheses; but because he lacks the basic social skills he needs, he cannot put his hypotheses to a realistic test. If the inferences of a paranoid person confirm his suspicions he accepts them; if they do not he rejects them. He then goes on, with the same inflexible perspective and the same inept techniques, to make further observations of the same kind, and come to similar conclusions. He hunts for evidence that will support his suspicions, his fears and his wishes, and with this attitude he always finds it.

The human environment is full of little movements, gestures, looks and signs, by which human beings consciously, preconsciously and unconsicously orient themselves. From this inexhaustible mine of meanings it is easy for a person to dig up apparent confirmation for anything he suspects or fears, especially when he is anxious, insecure and socially inept. The most circumstantial, flimsy kind of evidence is all that a one-track mind requires to build his case. The paranoid person, having little skill in reality-testing even when things are going smoothly, becomes incapable of validating or invalidating his conclusions the moment he is emotionally upset.

When a disturbed paranoid person makes an inference it becomes for him at once a fact, an unchangeable fact. He selects and interprets the evidence, without knowing what he is doing, to fit his growing delusional system. When he reaches a conclusion he considers this as proof and a valid basis for his next step. He builds up chains of inference, usually interspersed with actual observations. But he does not make clear distinctions between what he sees and hears, and what he merely thinks. He recalls selected incidents from the past, reshaping them to fit his present needs (retrospective falsification); and thus he uses distorted memories to buttress his unsound beliefs.[14]

To a normal listener, who does not know which things have been actually observed and which only inferred, the chains of logic may sound irrefutable. This is why an intelligent and earnest paranoid person sometimes convinces relatives and friends, and occasionally even juries and the public, that his delusional convictions are social fact.

It is not the force of reasoning that determines this inexorable march from fear or suspicion to delusion. Paranoid reasoning is sick; its logic is

---

[14] To a much lesser degree we all falsify what we remember so that it fits in with our dominant beliefs. See Kamano, D. K., and Drew, J. E., "Selectivity in memory of personally significant material," *J. gen. Psychol.*, 1961, *65*, 25–32; Paul, I. H., "Studies in remembering: the reproduction of connected and extended verbal material," *Psychol. Issues*, 1959, *1*, No. 2. Also see Bartlett, F., *Remembering: A Study in Experimental and Social Psychology.* Cambridge, England: Cambridge Univ. Press, 1932; Bartlett, F., *Thinking: An Experimental and Social Study.* New York: Basic Books, 1958.

not strong but weak; only the onward march is strong. The force of this irresistible forward movement comes from id impulses. Delusional reasoning is drive-organized. It is propelled forward by libidinal and aggressive pressures. Its directions are determined by previously unconscious motivation which has come to take charge of thinking.

An emotional crisis, or a series of emotional disturbances, reactivates unconscious conflicts in paranoid reactions. Because of defective repression these escape into preconscious and conscious fields. Here they dominate perception, thought and action; and they may arouse intense superego guilt. This immediately intensifies defensive denial and projection. The result is that the ego is flooded with tension and anxiety which, because of the denial and projection, is perceived as external danger. The basic paranoid drive organization gives this danger a sadistic character.

The drive-organization of perception, thought and action, the flooding of the ego with intense guilt, and the intensified use of denial and projection, help to explain why paranoid delusion formation goes on so irresistibly to an impulsive climax in attack or flight. Merely to imagine something, when primary process thinking is in the saddle, is to have it magically happen. To fear something is to make it appear. To be filled with hatred is to be immersed immediately in a sea of hate.

Finding a focus: preliminary crystallizations

We must not forget that, for all its social ineptness, delusion formation is a serious attempt at *restitution* — an attempt to *reconstruct reality* so as to bring it into harmony with an irresistible drive organization and with previously unconscious fantasies. In persecutory paranoid restitution the patient tries to reconstruct his environment in such a way that it serves his need for acting with hostile aggression. In his early life, the person who is to experience paranoid persecutions as an adult, is dominated by an expectation of sadistic treatment and by a readiness to meet such treatment with counterattack. It is this infantile pattern which the paranoid psychotic reactivates when he regresses, and it is this pattern that he projects on to his adult environment.

The frightened solitary patient, who lacks the basic skills he needs for social reality-testing, is like an unskilled and inexperienced man who gets lost in a jungle at night. He appears suddenly to become the focus of a hostile, living environment, obscure and unintelligible. Now everything he sees and hears seems to threaten him personally. It is his own vigilant anxiety that binds together trivial and unrelated things going on around him into a great net from which he can see no escape. His projected fears become predatory animals, and he becomes their prey. His tension may eventually become so intolerable that he must take action even though action threatens to kill him.[15]

[15] Davitz, J. R., "Fear, anxiety and the perception of others," *J. gen. Psychol.*, 1959, *61*, 169–173.

Being aggressive as well as frightened, the acutely paranoid person faces his danger with hostile vigilance, like a patrol expecting an ambush. He smells a plot, and he feels certain that he is its focus. He cannot stand suspense. He feels impelled to find out quickly what it is all about.

Vigilant suspense is hard for anyone to bear; and the more anxious a person is the more urgently he needs to end it. The need for relief from suspense leads even normal people to take serious risks. Sometimes it seems easier to go out to meet death than to sit and wait for it to come, knowing that it is near.

We have said that the paranoid person, even when he is well, is intolerant of suspense. Now that he has regressed and become psychotic he seems driven by his irresistible aggressive impulses to take violent action. It is actually his own pent-up hostility that threatens to destroy him as a person. His need for closure is tremendous, but he cannot experience closure through aimless activity, no matter how vigorous it may be. He must find something definite, a focus upon which to discharge his intolerable hostility, with the feeling that he has destroyed the danger before it can destroy him.

Finding a focus: the paranoid pseudocommunity

It is this irresistible need for a tangible target that drives the psychotic paranoid person to find culprits and to uncover plots. He begins by attributing a malicious intent to the actions of real persons in his environment, and of other persons whose existence he merely infers. The actions themselves may be trivial and unrelated. Through his drive-directed interpretations he organizes these real and imagined persons into a community of plotters. To him their supposed activities seem unified in a single hostile purpose, all directed against him.[16]

The community which a paranoid person thus builds up to meet his own irresistible needs does not correspond, of course, to any organization of persons that exists in social reality. It usually does include real people and their actual behavior, along with the imagined persons and their inferred behavior. But the patient misperceives and misinterprets even the actual behavior; and when he recalls it later he falsifies it. He ascribes motivation to the real and imagined people, a unity of purpose against him, which does not exist except in his own thinking. In short, he organizes a pseudo-community with which to bind together his projected fears and wishes, to justify his own hostile aggression, and to give it a tangible target.

The paranoid pseudocommunity is a reconstruction of reality. It organizes the observed and the inferred behavior of real and imagined persons

---

[16] This tendency to interpret all kinds of irrelevant things as having specific reference to oneself makes up what is called self-reference, sometimes *delusions of reference*. It can be found in many acutely anxious normal people, as well as in those who are psychotic or borderline psychotic.

into a conspiracy, with the patient as its focus. This organization of a hostile pseudocommunity does not comfort or reassure a paranoid person, but it does satisfy his overwhelming need for closure. He finds out "what it is all about." He feels that he now has some idea of what he may expect. He knows whom he must watch and why. The formation of a pseudocommunity may even increase a patient's fright, but at least the obscurity has gone. The fright is no longer a nameless, formless terror. It is organized now and has a focus.

In most paranoid reactions the pseudocommunity has a principal person or two. Patients do not choose their pseudocommunity leaders at random. The significant person is usually well suited for some special reason to act as the symbol of a patient's major conflicts. He may be a stranger — some-one in authority or someone prominent in public life — a politician, an actor, an industrialist, a scientist or a criminal. Sometimes he is an un-suspecting friend, a neighbor or a fellow worker, who happens to have characteristics or connections that fit him for the imaginary role of chief watcher, slanderer and persecutor — the embodiment of a patient's projected hostility and guilt. Sometimes the significant persons are close to the patient; and the reasons for their selection are obvious.

Useful functions of the pseudocommunity

As a reconstruction of reality the pseudocommunity may have useful functions. These we can sum up as follows:

(1) The pseudocommunity is itself a hostile aggressive organization. By merely functioning it absorbs a great deal of the patient's destructive energy (*energy of organization*).

(2) In particular, it absorbs denied and projected guilt ("superego anxiety") which the regressed psychotic can no longer repress. It is "they" who want to torture and to murder. The patient feels that he himself is innocent.

(3) The pseudocommunity provides a definite target which includes real people. Against this target the patient's hostile aggression can be con-tinually discharged. The aggression stirs up little guilt, since "they" provoke it and therefore deserve what they get.

(4) It gives a unified and apparently logical explanation for the sudden traumatic anxiety which comes with the unconscious breakthrough in the psychotic regression. All human beings are comforted by explanations; even a wrong one sometimes seems better than none at all.

(5) Although the pseudocommunity is strictly delusional, and is the prod-uct of drive-organized behavior, its superstructure entails much highly organized secondary process thinking. This is utilized, of course, in the service of the id; but it is still secondary process thinking, often well pre-served and intelligently used.

(6) The imagined maneuvers of the pseudocommunity have to be met by countermaneuvers, and this, in turn, means further high level secondary

process thinking. We see this in the counterattacks and the flights across country which paranoid persons carry through.

(7) Because he has to "recognize" the supposed pseudocommunity maneuvering and counteract it, the patient keeps in contact with real people and their real social interaction. This keeps avenues to reality-oriented behavior open, which would be closed if the patient's delusions involved only fantasy, as they often do in manic, depressed and schizophrenic patients who are comparably regressed.

Paranoid action

Notwithstanding these useful functions, the organization and formulation of a pseudocommunity often speeds up the elaboration of further delusions, much as a new scientific explanation speeds up research. Unless therapeutic intervention changes the situation the pressure for hostile discharge remains high. Pseudocommunities, like real communities, tend to expand and to include new persons, new actions and new dangers. If this expansion continues, a point may finally be reached at which the patient can no longer tolerate the apparently growing threat. He is likely then to burst out into violent action and thus to run afoul of the real or social community. When this happens, it brings about actual intervention or actual counteraggression. It is true that intervention may save a patient's life and make it possible for him to get well, as we shall see. But the patient is fortunate who gets expert help promptly and is able to profit by it.

Intervention sometimes makes matters worse instead of better. If it includes counteraggression — a violent struggle or police action — the immediate effect is always bad. But even under the most favorable conditions some paranoid psychotic persons never recover fully. Some of them remain permanent patients in a hospital. Some live in the community as suspicious, aloof, angry eccentrics. Some are able to return to relatively normal living, but with delusions which are still active, even though concealed. Among these last belong the litigious paranoid persons who continually seek reaffirmation of their injured rights and proof of their innocence in courts of law. It goes without saying that no court of law can absolve a paranoid person's unconscious guilt which he is projecting. Let us turn now to a clinical case of persecutory paranoid reaction.

A case of persecutory paranoid reaction

Charles G., a bachelor of forty-nine, became involved in a furious quarrel with "bookies," men who place bets on racehorses. They insisted that he had not put money on a certain winning horse, which had unexpectedly won, and he insisted that he had. He was superficially a pleasant, reserved person, but on this occasion he worked himself into a towering rage. Fortifying himself with a few drinks at a nearby tavern, he returned to the "bookies," demanding the payoff, shouting threats and insults at them, and inviting them into the street to fight. When he found that this was ineffective, he returned to the hotel where he lived, still furious.

Later on, as he pondered over the injustice and his rage, Charles began to worry over the possibility of retaliation against him. He recalled that "bookies" were supposed to have gangster protection. With these thoughts his fury changed to fright and his recklessness changed to vigilance. The next day he noticed strangers loitering about the hotel lobby. They seemed to be watching him and making little signs which referred to him. An automobile full of men stopped in front of the hotel entrance. He now felt sure that he would be kidnaped, tortured and killed. He barricaded himself in his room and arranged by telephone with a relative to flee the city the next morning. His relative accepted the patient's fears as facts.

As Charles thought over his plan that evening, he suddenly "realized" that the telephone wire had probably been tapped by the gangsters. So he fled alone in his car during the night, to outwit the imagined pseudocommunity. We shall see this sequence of confiding and then anticipating betrayal again in his behavior pattern. We know from other evidence that this sequence had been repeated over and over by Charles in the past. It was probably basic in his personality organization and had its roots in his early childhood.

In his long flight across the country he kept seeing signs that he was being trailed. He could not possibly doubt them. He decided that he would never be caught alive. When he reached the home of relatives a thousand miles away they at first believed his story. When, however, they found poison and a razor concealed in his clothing, and he admitted that he was planning suicide, they brought him to a psychiatric hospital to preserve his life.

Charles was courteous and pleasant in the hospital, but he always chose solitude when he could. Although he obviously wanted to confide in his therapist, and several times started to do so, he could never bring himself to talk about anything but trivialities and the plot. He persuaded a local pastor to visit him in the clinic. He then arranged a later meeting which was to be kept secret from the clinic. There was something in his past, he said, that he wanted to confess. As soon as the pastor had gone, however, Charles "realized" that he had made a terrible mistake. The pastor was dark-skinned. Therefore he must be a foreigner and a gangster in disguise. Charles made a suicidal attempt, and when this was unsuccessful, he insisted upon transfer to a Veterans Hospital, for which he was eligible. In view of his lifelong asocial modes of life and thought, the most that could be expected of therapy was that it would enable him to return to his solitary mode of living, and perhaps give him something more to occupy his time.

Discussion. An outburst of frustrated rage marked the onset of this psychosis. Charles could neither endure his furious hostility nor adequately discharge it. When he turned from reality to fantasy he turned suddenly from an angry aggressor into a frightened victim, who was threatened with death by a pseudocommunity of gangsters. How did Charles achieve this result? He denied and projected his own violent aggression, as he had always denied and projected his fears and suspicions in the past, and this made it possible for him to see himself as an innocent, persecuted man. In this delusional process, he escaped guilt and self-accusation completely. It was not he who was violent and threatening but "they," an imaginary gang of persecutors. The price for this immunity from guilt was that of living in such extreme fear that he planned to kill himself.

It goes without saying that even a towering rage is not in itself enough to precipitate a paranoid psychosis. Charles certainly had other serious personality problems. Since he could not bring himself to confide in anyone, we can only guess at what they might have been from his mode of living and from the nature of his fears and suspicions. In what we did know of his past, he presented what has been called, "the paranoiac pattern of the 'haunted man' whose fate is fleeing from one city to another."[17] It is striking that he took no realistic steps to test the validity of his delusional interpretations, even though he was in good enough contact with his environment to plan and carry through a long, complicated flight. It was as if murderous pursuers were less dangerous than the volcano of his own wrath; from pursuers there is the possibility of escape but from oneself there is none.

When a paranoid patient regresses and thinks delusionally, as Charles did, his superego regresses to its archaic form. The hostile functions of such a superego precursor are distributed among real or imaginary people around him. The patient then feels guiltless, and unjustly attacked by these other people, much as a small child may feel that he is the victim of unjust attack from parents and siblings. We shall come back to this problem of superego regression when we discuss the dynamic and developmental background of paranoid reactions. Meanwhile let us review briefly some less common forms.

Delusional Paranoid Jealousy

Jealousy is never wholly rational. Even when it deserves to be called normal it arouses unconscious and preconscious fantasies which are not in the service of the conscious ego, and usually make the jealousy seem disproportionate to the objective situation in which it originates. Jealousy is most commonly precipitated by a fear of the loss of love or loss of status, by hostility toward both the rival and the loved one, or toward the origin of the loss, together with a painful blow to one's narcissism which takes the form of a severe loss in superego self-esteem.

Delusional jealousy is not just an exaggeration of normal jealousy. It is a psychotic reconstruction of reality which falsifies and invents "facts" in order to be able to rationalize the feeling. It shows the typical paranoid characteristics of inflexibility, of the exclusion of everything that might

17 Bak, R. C., "Masochism in paranoia," *Psychoanal. Quart.*, 1946, *15*, 285–301.

contradict the delusion, and of the inclusion of trivialities and distortions that seem to support it. Primitive defensive forms of denial and projection dominate the dynamic picture. Delusional jealousy has the same tendency to expand, to feed upon itself, that persecutory delusions have. Let us begin with a clinical case which brings most of these characteristics to light.

A case of paranoid delusional jealousy

Infancy. Alan K, was the youngest child in a matriarchal household. He had two sisters, one six years older and one eight years older than he. His mother was a strong-minded, independently wealthy woman who ruled the roost. The father played a subordinate role, moderately successful in business but an insignificant figure in the home. "She treated him like a servant," Alan said of his mother and father. "She enjoyed humiliating him in front of us."

Alan felt that his father's attitude toward him was one of amused detachment, tinged with mild contempt. He in turn looked down upon his father as a passive, ineffectual man. Toward his mother he had always felt a passionate mixture of loving admiration and exasperated hate. "I'm devoted to her," he said as an adult, "because she's a great woman; but I can't stand being near her."

The patient's mother told him that he had been a fearful and stubborn baby from the very start. He never felt soft and relaxed in her arms as the two girls had. He stiffened and cried when she held him. He was afraid of the dark, of being alone, and particularly of strangers and of animals. His mother was determined to make him into a manly man, she said, "not like your father." To this end she avoided "coddling" him and ridiculed his fears. He was plagued by nightmares from which he often awoke screaming.

Fits of rage also plagued Alan. Everybody teased him. He remembered his mother talking to him animatedly in Italian, which he did not understand, until he got so angry that he would beat her thighs with his fists. He felt that she enjoyed seeing his fury and encouraged his attack as a show of masculinity. It is possible that she took pleasure in driving the little boy into his futile rages, just as she seems to have enjoyed humiliating her husband.

This gives the picture of a tormented childhood. It had one saving grace: Alan was not directly punished for his angry outbursts. If they got out of bounds he was shut in a room alone to cool off; but he was not forced to suppress all his rage and adopt a passive, compliant attitude in this kind of situation. It is probable that his freedom to be furious when he was teased and frustrated is what allowed him to grow into an angry paranoid adult instead of a compliant schizophrenic, which might have been worse.

There was much ambivalence in Alan's attitudes toward his two sisters, just as there was toward his mother. They also teased him when he was small by mischievously hiding his things and following him about as he tried to find them. According to Alan they enjoyed taking care of him as a baby, treating him as a living doll, feeding and diapering him, dressing and undressing him, and fussing over him so much that his mother often had to intervene to protect him. As he grew older, but while he was still small enough to be enticed or coerced, his sisters continued the same sort of thing as a game, making him play the baby when they played house. All this must have given him further experience with dependent gratifications, erotic stimulation and frustrating restraint.

Alan described his sisters as haughty and superior. He secretly envied them their self-assurance and their pride in their appearance. He felt "shabby and small" beside them. There is a parallel between his feelings of insignificance in relation to his sisters and his father's shabby unimportance in relation to his mother. Such feelings help to form patterns that may determine a child's later conception of himself.

Childhood. As he grew up, Alan had his friends and chums; but he was unpopular and he was often excluded from group games. He recalled having been a stickler for rules, penalties, fairness and equal rights. Sometimes when he lost an argument over a decision he would shun everyone for several days, indulging meanwhile in vengeful fantasies that kept him feeling "hot all over." Alan was always fascinated by accounts of murder, torture, imprisonment and execution.

In first talking about himself to his therapist Alan said that during latency and adolescence he had little interest in sex. When he had gained more confidence he modified this statement significantly. He was actually much attracted to girls, he said, because they seemed worldly, self-assured and "all in one piece." When he was in their presence he became tongue-tied and timid. He felt that they looked down upon him. During his junior year in engineering college he had a blow-up with his fraternity brothers when they teased him about never going on dates. He moved out of his fraternity house and experienced great relief at being alone. Alan defended himself by saying that his studies "left no time for girls." He said that he "fought off" masturbation by regular workouts in the gymnasium. Whenever he gave in he felt "weak and degraded."

Career. Alan had his heart set on becoming an architect, but his mother persuaded him to follow a career in automotive engineering because it would give him more security. He graduated with honors, but the economic depression held him back until he was twenty-eight. When a state of national emergency was declared he found his engineering talents in demand. He made a good start but he did not progress, evidently because he was a serious personnel problem. He criticized his fellow workers and expressed contempt for his superiors. He welcomed newcomers as friends, but soon grew jealous of them. Thus he was forever making and losing friends. Each new boss was "a great relief" from the previous one; but then difficulties would soon accumulate and the old tension would return.

Early in the war Alan was deferred from military service as an essential worker. Later on he was exempted on psychiatric grounds for which he felt that he never got a satisfactory explanation. He suspected that his firm had given derogatory information about him in a conspiracy to keep him with them. At the first opportunity he changed jobs. He was taken aback when his old boss seemed cheerful about his leaving. On thinking the whole thing over he "realized" why. They must have heard in some way that he knew what they had done, and were relieved to see him go.

This has so far been the story of a paranoid personality which has been crystallizing out in an atmosphere of ordinary business competition. The psychotic reaction is yet to come.

Marriage and parenthood. When he was twenty-nine the patient married on impulse a registered nurse of twenty-five. There were sex difficulties right away. Alan was not wholly inexperienced, but he found himself anxious and embarrassed. Bessie, his wife, seemed to him to accept sexuality too readily. He began wondering how naive she really had been. As time went on, and his passivity seemed to increase, Bessie changed from "a meek little thing" into a decisive woman who gradually took charge, as Alan's mother had done in his childhood home.

The couple had two boys and then a girl. Alan was jealous of their first baby when it came, but he soon discovered that he enjoyed looking after it. He liked it when Bessie went out of an evening and left them alone. During his wife's third pregnancy he began an affair with a woman in the neighborhood which played a part in his later delusions of jealousy. When a girl was born to Bessie he was disappointed. He could not fully accept his new daughter. "I'm just the opposite of my father," he said. "He always liked my sisters better than me."

Psychotic reaction. When the patient was thirty-nine his wife became actively interested in community affairs. It was this that led indirectly to his developing delusional jealousy. Bessie was put on a welfare committee with one of Alan's factory superiors, Ralph D., whom Alan described as "an attractive bachelor." The committee met weekly in rotation at the various members' homes. Each time it met at Bessie's house, Alan would retire upstairs with the children when the members arrived — "like a nursemaid," he said. This situation made him feel publicly humiliated before his wife and before his factory superior. A teasing cliché, something about Alan's being "a good mother," which one member repeated each time, made the patient furious.

One evening he telephoned the home where the committee was supposedly meeting only to be told that it was not there. He drove at once to Ralph's apartment. The lights were on there, but no one responded to his ringing and knocking. Bessie came home late and explained that the meeting had been held at a roadside inn so that they could discuss a member in his absence. Alan was beside himself with rage. He accused her bluntly of infidelity, and she retaliated with counteraccusations, citing his diminished potency as evidence. He felt doubly injured, first by her attack on his virility and second by her accusations. It did not help matters that both were based upon fact. From this point on the two were estranged and the children sided with their mother.

Soon after this the firm asked Alan to work evenings while they redesigned some engines. When he saw Ralph leaving at the usual time he felt sure that he was being "rigged." He began a systematic campaign of spying on his wife and Ralph, often leaving work suddenly to check on their movements. He discovered nothing. This did not make him doubt his convictions; it only made him more certain and more angry. Obviously, he felt, someone at the factory was tipping them off when he left. The more he brooded over the situation the clearer the picture seemed to become, and the more things he could recall from the past that fitted into the plot. He saw himself as the stupid victim of a transparent conspiracy which was making him ridiculous in everybody's eyes.

The patient's vigilance and his suspicions multiplied. While he was with his mistress he noticed noises over the telephone and in the wall. These he interpreted at once as signs of wire-tapping and of hidden dictaphones. Now apparently people were spying on him. He complained to the telephone company and got polite reassurances. This sounded to him like complicity. He began tapping on the walls until he located solid places where he felt sure the dictaphones must be. He could not persuade his mistress to let him crack open the plaster and disclose them. She insisted that the sounds came from steam pipes which had always been there. Her obstinacy and apparent anxiety — she was probably getting alarmed at his delusions — convinced him that she also was a party to the plot. He left her abruptly without a word, too frightened even to start a quarrel.

The climax came when Alan half awoke one night to see his wife standing at his bedside with a syringe in her hand. He struggled hard to awaken fully but only went back to sleep. He decided afterwards that he must already have been given an injection. In the morning when he awoke he found small brown specks on his arm which he was sure were the marks of previous injections. He flew into a rage, accusing his wife of trying to kill him and threatening to kill her and Ralph instead. Bessie told him he must be crazy and persuaded him somehow to go for psychiatric help. He was frightened enough to agree to enter a hospital, but he did so on the express condition that no one else whom he knew should come into contact with the psychiatric staff. He was openly afraid of further conspiracy against him.

Therapy and recovery. In the clinic Alan was suspicious of everyone he saw, even of the maintenance men. He was especially vigilant during visiting hours and on walks outside. Progress in therapy began when he recognized that he had had serious problems long before the supposed plot of Bessie and Ralph. At first he would talk of nothing but the plot. He was preoccupied with vengeful fantasies of killing the pair and himself. A change came when he admitted to himself that his vision of his wife with a syringe at his bedside, ready to kill him, might have been a dream. His therapist had early expressed this possibility casually when he said that it sounded like a dream. Although the immediate effect of this comment had been to make Alan distrust the whole clinic, it succeeded in penetrating his delusional armor, and it helped provoke the change.

Alan now narrowed down the blame to Ralph. He said, "If I could just go and kill that man I'd be so relieved I wouldn't care what they did to me. At least I'd be able to sleep again. To keep from doing it all the time uses up my strength. It gives me an actual all-gone weakness."

On several occasions Alan quarreled with another patient over trivial matters, a patient who had strong but well-defined latent homosexual trends. He was alarmed at having fantasies of killing this man also. He saw spontaneously a connection between these fantasies and his thoughts about Ralph, although he said nothing about the connection until much later.

Alan remarked one day that he guessed we all thought that he was "a homosexual," adding, "and I guess subconsciously I am." He went on to tell something he had not mentioned before: a fascination with the male body. He said that in his college days his favorite recreations were those of exercising in the gymnasium, watching others exercise and attending boxing and wrestling matches. He had come to the conclusion that his fascination might somehow be related to perversion, which he abhorred. The mere possibility frightened him, he said. Having verbalized and met this fear, and finding himself none the worse for it, he went on to talk about the meaning of homosexuality to him, and to speak with greater frankness about his own sex worries.

In early adolescence the patient had tried mutual masturbation twice with chums. He had enjoyed the close contact, but afterward he had been overwhelmed with guilt and shame. The fact that his own level of sex desire had never seemed powerful to him made him feel inferior and incomplete. He was puzzled by the strength of his erotic fantasies which seemed to contradict what he said. His marital life had been marred by his inability to measure up to his wife's sex needs, which he regarded as unreasonably demanding.

Although nothing dramatic came out of these discussions, their effect was to ease up noticeably the patient's tension and suspiciousness. The quarreling on the ward stopped and the therapeutic atmosphere was freer. Alan used his first chance to go out alone as an opportunity to make a surprise visit to his home. He said afterward that he had done it to check up on his wife. The reception that his wife gave him convinced him that she was through with him. After he had digested this experience, with therapeutic help, he took the initiative in getting himself transferred to another of the company's plants. The critical shortage of engineers made this easy to accomplish.

The patient left the clinic still suspecting that there might have been something between his wife and Ralph, but no longer afraid that anyone was plotting against him. He expected his wife to divorce him and marry the other man. It is unknown whether this prediction was justified or not because the clinic never heard from him again.

The therapeutic result achieved was recovery from a paranoid psychotic reaction, with some improvement in a basically paranoid personality, and with increased tolerance for latent homosexual trends. If such an improvement is consolidated the likelihood of further psychotic reactions is correspondingly reduced. In the discussion of paranoid reactions that follows we shall have more to say about the dynamics of this case.

Erotic Paranoid Reactions

In erotic paranoid reactions the patient has the delusional belief that someone loves him or her but dares not make an open avowal because of other commitments or because of embarrassment. With his hypersensitivity to unconscious attitudes and his practice of selecting whatever supports his delusions, the paranoid person interprets all kinds of irrelevant actions as disguised signals of the other person's love. These reactions are most common among women and among passive men. The delusions usually focus upon a prominent public figure of the opposite sex. Many persons with such delusions act upon them. They approach their supposed lover in private or in public, or send letters, urging that the love between them be acknowledged before the world. Their victims are likely to appeal to the police for protection from possible scandal.

One of our patients was an unmarried woman of thirty-six who had been attending a series of popular lectures on the history of art. She became more and more attracted to the lecturer, and then began to notice all kinds of little signals that he was emitting to let her know that he loved her. The situation came to a head when she approached him, after one of his lectures, and insisted that he declare publicly the love she felt sure he felt for her. He was wise enough to call for a conference, which included the patient, himself, members of her family and a psychiatrist, so that she was able to get help without police intervention. She did not succeed in giving up her delusion, but she at least renounced her original goal of having the lecturer declare his love.

The love expressed in erotic paranoid reactions is usually a narcissistic love projected on to another person. When this is the case the sex of the supposed delusional lover seems to be unimportant.[18] Sometimes the delusion is a defensive maneuver which secondarily substitutes a heterosexual attachment for a denied or repressed homosexual one. Freud has formulated this for men as follows: "I don't love *him*; I love *her* because she loves me."[19] For women this would become, "I don't love *her*; I love *him* because he loves me."

Some patients with erotic paranoid reactions feel themselves to be persecuted by love and make indignant protests. Others treat the situation with a narcissistic pleasure which is similar to the normal pleasure felt over being loved, except that it is delusional and goes unsatisfied. Erotic paranoid reactions which elicit pleasure in the patient are generally considered to be

---

[18] Fenichel, O., *Psychoanalytic Theory of Neuroses*. New York: Norton, 1945, pp. 432–433.

[19] Freud, S., "Some neurotic mechanisms in jealousy, paranoia and homosexuality," in Standard Edition, London: Hogarth, 1955, pp. 221–232.

untreatable. If, on the other hand, the patient feels persecuted by love, the situation is similar to that in other persecutory paranoid reactions and calls for similar therapy.

Grandiose Paranoid Reactions

Delusions of grandeur are also much less frequent in paranoid reactions than are the common delusions of persecution. They are commoner in severe cases than in mild ones, probably because a more primitive, transparent denial is required to sustain them. As also in the case of persecutory delusions, the most prevalent themes are derived from the surrounding culture, including its folklore and popular stories. The patient may picture himself as immensely talented or irresistibly attractive, as of noble birth or of rich heritage, a powerful leader, an inspired genius, a saint, a prophet or even a god. He may feel that he has secret knowledge or that he has been chosen to perform a great mission.

We shall see similar grandiose delusions in schizophrenia, but in schizophrenia they are poorly organized, vague, mystical and shifty. Grandeur also characterizes mania, but the manic expresses his delusions garrulously and he can be easily distracted. It is only in the paranoid psychoses that delusions seem stable, persistent, earnest and well organized. These characteristics give further evidence that paranoid persons preserve and use complex secondary processes of thinking in the service of the id.

Complex secondary process thinking appears in the grandiose delusions of paranoid "inventors," "scientists" and "mathematicians." Some of these have specific plans — often worked out in minute detail — for solving industrial problems, overcoming natural barriers, transforming one substance or force into another, changing the calendar, or setting up new systems of numbers and symbols. Some are conceived on a huge scale, involving schemes for saving or destroying the world, and for manipulating planetary systems. With the rapid advance today of scientific systems for destroying the world and for interplanetary travel the problem of distinguishing between paranoid and scientific planning becomes more and more difficult. It is not rare, for example, to find that a paranoid patient has already taken out a patent on his delusional idea. From a dynamic standpoint, it seems highly probable that a preoccupation with inventive, scientific or mathematical logic or pseudologic may defend many a paranoid person from ego disintegration.

Politics, being an area in which everyone fancies himself something of an expert, is especially attractive to paranoid schemers. Few government activities have not received earnest and insistent advice from persons with obvious delusions of grandeur. In both political and religious fields one is likely to meet paranoid persons who believe themselves to have been chosen to perform a great mission, usually to save others, sometimes to destroy them. The origin of such "missions" lies in a tremendous need which the patient has to save himself or to discharge hostile aggression. Occasionally an inspired paranoid person crystallizes his delusions into a belief that he is a Messiah or, in time of war, a great strategist, a leader, Joan of Arc or Napoleon, someone who can bring universal peace or universal destruction. The situation in which the world finds itself today makes it of more importance than ever to be able to recognize the potential threat, which such trends might constitute, in a person who seems better integrated than he actually is.

Classical Paranoia

Classical paranoia is only an extreme, complex paranoid reaction which may grow more extensive with time but does not diminish. The patient performs the difficult feat of building and expanding a systematic delusion while maintaining good object relations. In contrast to schizophrenia there are no hallucinations, there is no disorganization and there is little desocialization. Patients with classical paranoia have been known to continue with their business or professional work. This is also true of a majority of persecutory paranoid reactions, but the degree of delusional development in classical paranoia makes it more remarkable. The explanation seems to lie in an encapsulation of the delusional system which leaves the rest of the personality free to operate with relative normality. Classical paranoia is extremely rare.[20]

Apart from its severity, and its position in the history of psychopathology, there is no reason for giving classical paranoia a separate place among paranoid reactions. The form of the delusions and their content are the same, except that there is usually greater emphasis upon grandiosity. The paranoic often considers himself a great genius, and occasionally other people accord him the same status, especially if he represents their own unconscious, infantile megalomaniac trends. Once in a great while a gifted paranoic person enriches human experience with his delusional productions, and leaves behind him a heritage of good or evil.

Classical paranoia reminds one of obsessive doubting because of its rigidity, its tendency to expand, and its concern with speculation. There is, however, much more manifest passion in paranoia. It is infused with much direct primary process; it is much less a product of defensive isolation. Whereas obsessive speculation vacillates, and stops short with doubts, classical paranoia goes on from one "certainty" to another, building speculation into a delusional organization which seems to the patient to have greater reality than the world as others see it. The patient characteristically expresses hauteur and contempt for any reasoning that contradicts or questions what he believes.

It must be remembered that all paranoid structures are defenses against ego disintegration. Classical paranoia is only an extreme development of

20 *Mental Disorders.* Diagnostic and Statistical Manual. Washington, D.C.: Amer. Psychiatric Ass., 1952.

such defenses. To give up a paranoic delusion would very likely be to give up ego integration. This is probably why the condition is usually found to be untreatable.

Folie à Deux

Folie à deux is difficult to place in the current classification. Its delusions may simply be paranoid, or they may be accompanied by unquestionably schizophrenic symptoms, such as frank hallucinations. We include them at this point because it is convenient.

Folie à deux presents the interesting picture of two persons sharing the same delusional beliefs. One of the two is usually a dominant paranoid person with more or less fixed delusions. The other is likely to be a suggestible, dependent person who takes over the dominant one's delusions intact, but gives them up easily when he is separated from the dominant person and given therapeutic help.[21]

Most of the delusions reported in *folie à deux* have been persecutory, as we might expect from the general prevalence of perscutory delusions in paranoid reactions. The classical articles on this topic are those of Gralnick.[22] He found that in most cases the two sick persons had been living in close contact for a long time. His clinical report of 103 pairs lists the following combinations in their order of frequency: two sisters, 40; husband and wife, 26; mother and child, 24; two brothers, 11, brother and sister, 6, father and child, 2. The greater susceptibility of women than of men may be the result of the relatively passive, dependent, submissive roles that women assume in our culture, and to their more limited opportunities to assume roles demanding dominance and initiative.

A relationship of dominance and submission, according to Gralnick, is probably always involved in *folie à deux*, even though the participants in it may not be aware of such a relationship. H. Deutsch considers the assumption by the more dependent person of the dominant one's delusions to be an attempt by the dependent person to recover a lost object through identification. This identification may be with the dominant person or only with his delusional system.[23] Any two persons living in close communication are likely to have unconscious bonds between them. A delusion shared in common may be an expression of such bonds. In the final reconstruction of reality, which constitutes the *folie à deux*, the two participants will share a common pseudocommunity. The dominant paranoid person is its major

21 When three or more persons are involved, such terms as *folie à trois*, etc., are sometimes employed. The principle remains the same even when delusions are embraced by a whole community. See Pulver, S. E., and Brunt, M. Y., "Deflection of hostility in *folie à deux*," *Arch. gen. Psychiat.*, 1961, 5, 257–265. (Includes review of the literature.)

22 Gralnick, A., "Folie à deux: the psychosis of association," *Psychiat. Quart.*, 1942, 16, 230.

23 Deutsch, H., "Folie à deux," *Psychoanal. Quart.*, 1938, 7, 307–322.

architect, while the dependent person does little more than agree with the delusional reconstruction.

Dynamic and Developmental Background

At the beginning of the chapter we pointed out the close relationships between normal and paranoid thinking. We said there that belief, confidence and expectation play a tremendous role in everyday experience and behavior. All of us must be continually acting upon the basis of fragmentary information, in which inferences, assumptions and probabilities determine what we do, and how we feel and think. Fear and desire can influence anyone's perception and cognition.

It is only with great difficulty that even a logically disciplined normal adult manages to think objectively, as a scientist would, when it comes to something that moves him emotionally as a human being. Most of the time his thinking about personal matters will drift along intuitive paths, which are at least in part laid down by traditional and personal feelings. The important thing about the normal adult is that, when the need arises for logical thinking and an impersonal perspective, he can usually meet the need.

Paranoid thinking does not succeed in becoming objective where it should. It tends to treat impersonal things and events as though they were personal. It is much less susceptible to correction than is normal thinking. These defects come from a lack of development of *basic trust*,[24] and from defects in the defensive organization about which we shall have more to say in a moment.

When the paranoid person believes that he can identify the persons and activities "responsible" for what he is experiencing, he acts as though his inferences and suspicions were established fact. Because of his lack of *basic trust*, he cannot share his inferences and suspicions with somebody else. Above all, he lacks skill in imagining himself as being in another person's situation, in taking the other person's role and seeing things from the other person's perspectives. In a personal crisis, the paranoid person trusts no one but himself. He lacks the means for reconsidering his conclusions. For him they have become irresistible facts.

Fixation and regression in persecutory paranoid reactions

The adult who develops a persecutory paranoid reaction is fixated both at neurotic and at psychotic levels. His regression, as he becomes ill, carries part of his organization to neurotic levels, and part of it to deeper psychotic levels, in both instances to his major fixations.

Neurotic fixation. The neurotic character of some of the paranoid fixations — to which paranoid patients regress — appears in the relatively good

[24] Finney, J. C., "Some maternal influences on children's personality and character," *Genet. Psychol. Monogr.*, 1961, *63*, 199–278.

object relationships that the patient preserves. The delusional persecutory fears involve real persons and real situations. Paranoid delusions *distort* social reality, and they often lead to tragic results, but the object relations which the paranoid patient maintains are superior to those of any equally ill manic, depressed or schizophrenic patient.

Psychotic fixation. In spite of what has just been said, the paranoid patient is also fixated at psychotic levels. His denial of reality, the projection of his fears and wishes, and the sadomasochistic character of his emotional drives, all combine to form a delusional picture quite unlike anything to be found among the neuroses. Thus, while a paranoid patient is able to interact with people and things more successfully than other psychotic persons can, *he makes use of his interactions* to act out primitive, infantile fantasies, which do not even distinguish between his own regressed, sadomasochistic drives and the intentions of real people in his social environment. The "dangerous people," some of them real and some of them imagined — but still realistically imagined — are experienced by the patient as sadistic persecutors. To him they often seem united, as a delusional pseudo-community, whose major function he imagines as that of sadistically persecuting him. In the case of Charles G., we saw this projective organization carried to the extreme of delusional cruelty. Solely on the basis of his own imaginings, the patient expected in the most real and vivid sense to be tortured and to be murdered.

Such expectations must come from somewhere, and they must have some reason for emerging. As we shall see, they come from the patient's own sadism, which he denies and projects on to other people. They emerge because of the patient's defective defensive organization. The paranoid patient is unable to repress completely the impulses and fantasies which to a large extent represent infantile cruelty and the hostile persecutions of his superego precursor (or *archaic superego*). He is also unable to distinguish between his own intentions and the intentions of other people around him. Thus, as we saw in the case of Charles G., it was he himself who had flown into a furious rage and threatened other persons. Yet, as he regressed, the "dangerous people" (which were in reality his own dangerous, projected impulses) seemed to be cruel and threatening, while he became their innocent intended victim. As we turn now to consider the defective defenses in paranoid reactions, we shall find that some repetition is unavoidable, simply because all of these defects are interrelated.

Defenses in persecutory paranoid reactions

Regression as defense. The neurotic fixation and regression in paranoid reactions, as we have just seen, allow relatively good object relationships and a continued interaction with the real environment of the patient. Even the psychotic fixations and regressions at least protect the patient from further disintegration — from the deeper regression that we see in schizophrenia. Both the neurotic and the psychotic regressions can be considered as *defensive* in the sense that they are spontaneous attempts at maintaining some degree of ego-superego integration, even if this must be at primitive levels. In short, regression to primitive levels of organization, that is, to early infantile fixation levels, defends the patient against the imminent threat of still further disintegration.

Defective repression. The paranoid person is one who has had to compensate throughout life for defective repression. This compensation includes the overdevelopment and overuse of denial and projection. It is probable that the overdevelopment and overuse of denial and projection in the beginning actually interfered with the development of normal repression. That is to say, primitive denial and projection were called into action to such a degree (because of excessive tension and anxiety early in life) that they became established as major forms of defense before repression took over as the keystone of the defensive organization.

Repressive defenses, more than any others, are directly responsible for maintaining a functional barrier that separates unconscious from preconscious and conscious organizations. This separation is a vital one because unconscious processes are differently organized from preconscious and conscious systems. Unconscious processes operate according to different principles, the so-called *primary process,* and are much more immediately responsive to primitive asocial urges, needs and fears. One of the greatest of all human achievements is the containment of the primary processes, their channelling and their creative use. Without their containment, we would not be free to evolve our characteristically human ways of thinking and acting — the subordination of primitive drives and needs to the demands of social reality, the development of realistic logical thought, the control and channeling of emotional expression, the evolution of reciprocal role behavior and of a self, even the organization of human society.

Repression cannot operate effectively unless there is a relatively mature ego organization. During psychotic regression, with its ego disintegration, there is a progressive weakening of repressive defenses. The functional barrier which has "contained" the unconscious system begins to disappear. Previously unconscious processes now invade the preconscious and conscious organizations on an increasing scale. This invasion itself has the effect of rapidly weakening the barrier, much as waters rushing through defects in a dam hasten the dam's destruction. This invasion also further disintegrates the preconscious and conscious systems, and thus prevents restoration of the repressive defenses, in somewhat the same way that flood waters destroy a community that might have been able to restore the dam. By the time regression is halted in paranoid reactions, and reorganization at more primitive levels has begun, repression has become so defective that only the overuse of denial and projection can save the patient from deep ego disintegration.

Denial in paranoid reactions. We have said earlier[25] that denial as a defense is older than repression. Denial operates early in childhood before ego boundaries have been established and much before a mature superego has materialized. Denial operates before there is a clear separation of unconscious from preconscious and conscious organizations. It is, in effect, a defense against something that is perceived or felt, something that has not been repressed or has escaped repression. Denial is overdeveloped in paranoid persons. When, therefore, the defective repression allows a breakthrough of primary process material in a paranoid reaction, it is denial that defends the psychotic person from having to admit potentially disintegrative trends as coming from himself.

Denial can be successfully used by normal and by neurotic persons to ward off anxieties from sources which cannot be avoided or repressed. Denial alone is not sufficient, however, to dispose of threatening disintegrating forces in paranoid reactions. The fears, suspicions and accusations which erupt in persecutory paranoid reactions have to be disposed of in some way if the patient is to escape further disintegration. Since repression is inadequate to dispose of them the patient is forced to supplement denial with projection. He not only denies but he disowns; he not only disowns but he attributes what he denies to someone else.

Projection in persecutory paranoid reactions. The person who develops a persecutory paranoid reaction is basically a hostile person who feels surrounded by hostility, and whose major ego and superego identifications have been sadistic. When such a person regresses under stress he becomes overwhelmed by his own sadistic impulses and by corresponding fears. He denies and projects the sadistic impulses which then appear to come from someone else.[26] We saw this development in the case of Charles G. He worked himself up into an ungovernable fury over losing a bet. The moment that he became frightened of retaliation he denied his own furious hostility and projected it upon his originally intended victims, as their sadistic intent. In this way, the vengeance which he would have liked to visit upon his frustrators seemed to him to be threatening his own life. His regression led at once to an exaggeration of the danger, barred him from sharing his fears with others, and made the projected violence seem to follow him wherever he went.

The manner in which denial and projection operate. As we have just seen, the paranoid patient must rely mainly upon denial and projection in dealing with the massive eruption of unconscious material which constitutes the onset of the paranoid psychosis. In these circumstances, denial and projec-

---

[25] In Chapter 10 on dissociative reactions.

[26] Cf. Murstein, B. I., and Pryer, R. S., "The concept of projection," *Psychol. Bull.*, 1959, *56*, 353–374; Peak, H., Muney, B., and Clay, M., "Opposite structures, defenses and attitudes," *Psychol. Monogr.*, 1960, *74*, Whole No. 495.

tion have to do the work usually performed by repression, in addition to their own work. The patient makes use of paranoid reasoning to organize his pseudocommunity and shape his strategy. Aggression is his chief weapon. His infantile sadistic, and often homoerotic, conflicts can no longer be repressed. They are recast in the form of a contemporary drama, which is acted out in adult dress on a stage that is part social reality, part private imagination.

In this drama, the patient assigns the leading role to himself. The paranoid play revolves around him. In it, he is represented as a righteous, innocent, indignant and justifiably angry victim. He is angry and indignant because he feels threatened, persecuted, tempted and slandered. By a process of sweeping, psychotic denial, he purges his role of everything evil and contemptible.

This is actually a remarkable defensive feat. We must bear in mind the fact that the patient is actually swamped by cruel, sadistic, homoerotic and murderous fantasies. With a great part of his repressive functions gone, he cannot possibly keep this terrifying material from becoming preconscious and conscious, in crude, barbaric forms. What can he do about this situation?

The answer, we know, is that he can deny and project. Regression has already produced a partial dissolution of the boundaries between fantasy and social fact.[27] The patient has lost his function of social reality-testing — which is a disaster — but he has at least gained a greater ease than ever in projecting. Whatever is evil, whatever is contemptible and guilt-provoking in his fantasies he now not only denies as being his own, but projects on to other persons, real and imaginary, to form his paranoid pseudocommunity.

The patient's persecutors, pursuers, tempters and slanderers are the embodiment of his projected fantasies. He selects real and imagined persons unconsciously on the basis of their fitness to play the delusional role he assigns to them. Their fitness depends upon the feelings they arouse in him, and often upon their resemblance — in appearance, behavior, status, role, etc. — to significant persons in his own childhood. Some of them represent his projected fears of sadistic, murderous or sexual attack. Some represent corresponding urges and wishes which he both denies and projects. Some represent his diffuse projected superego aggression, the source of the unconscious guilt.

Projection as a defense suffers from the fatal defect that it actually gets rid of nothing. A patient projects his fearful fantasy, and he is faced with a frightening person no less real. He denies and projects a sadistic, murderous, or homoerotic urge, and he seems immediately threatened by sadism, murder, or homosexual advances from other persons. He projects his superego aggression and, while he does get rid of overwhelming guilt, he faces threats, accusations and slander from which he cannot escape.

[27] Spilka, B., and Lewis, M., "Empathy, assimilative projection, and disowning projection," *Psychol. Rec.*, 1959, 9, 99–102.

In all of this, it is his loss of clear boundaries between private fantasy and social fact, and between object-representations and self-representations, that makes projection easy. But this same lack of clear boundaries makes it inevitable that whatever is projected will return as embodied danger. If you cannot be sure what is imagination and what is not, if you are not certain what is yourself and what is somebody else, you can never tell what is your fantasy and what is somebody else's real intention.

It is clear that paranoid projection settles nothing. It replaces a real internal danger with a fictitious external one. Against this fictitious danger the patient directs his real denials and external counterattacks. He denounces his accusers, slanderers and persecutors. He uses up tremendous amounts of energy in espionage and counterespionage, in elaborate precautions, in attempts to outwit his imaginary opponents, to throw them off his trail and keep on theirs. He formulates and reformulates the plots against him and his own counterplots. He gathers evidence to prove their persecution and to establish his own innocence. And often, as we know, he finally resorts to violent threats and action.

The obvious question is: If these defenses and all this laborious work and thought get the patient nowhere, why does he keep it up? There are three answers. (1) The first is an old familiar one: this is the best solution of which the patient is capable without expert help. (2) The second is that, by means of his delusional activities, the patient remains in contact with some kind of reality — a restitutive or reconstructed reality. He does not disintegrate as a personality, and the road to further contact is still open. This we have already discussed in relation to the pseudocommunity. (3) The third answer is that all this activity — including even the senseless violence — performs the vital function of binding and discharging an excess of aggressive energy which threatens to destroy the psychodynamic system.

Binding and discharging aggressive energy. The greatest danger to which a regressed paranoid is exposed comes from within. It is that his psychodynamic system will disintegrate completely under the impact of a flood of free aggressive energy let loose within it. This flood comes from several sources: (1) from disintegration of organized preconscious fantasy systems (energy of organization); (2) from regressive deneutralization of ego adaptive energies, previously used up in reality relationships; (3) from the countercathectic energies released when mature defenses dissolve during regression; (4) from the reactivated unconscious fantasies and conflicts that emerge as repression dissolves; (5) from the superego aggression which is an immediate reaction to these forces; and (6) from the energy of superego organization, as the superego partially disintegrates in the process of regression.

This destructive flood must be discharged or bound if the personality is to escape disintegration. To a large extent paranoid symptomatology is an expression of the methods used in disposing of excess aggressive energy.

Some of these methods are: (1) to form elaborate new preconscious fantasy systems, which are extremely hostile, by an intensive use of secondary process thinking, (energy of organization, used in making inferences and complex interpretations and in forming hypotheses and delusions); (2) to increase perceptual vigilance, muscular tension and strenuous activity — watching, checking, investigating, gathering "evidence," taking elaborate precautions; (3) greatly to increase primitive defenses, especially denial and projection, and to keep up an incessant, aggressive projective discharge; (4) to keep one's own behavior (perception, thought and action) perceptually organized in relation to a restitutive reality, which one must also keep organized by his own efforts — the two forming a highly complex pseudocommunity; and (5) to burst out into hostile talk and violent action. Even if all these procedures did nothing more than bind and discharge destructive energy, they would justify themselves.

Reactivation and reorganization at infantile levels. In paranoid psychoses, regression comes to a halt when fixation points are reached which correspond roughly to revived experiences of the second and third years of life. This general level is indicated by the dynamic structure of the paranoid pseudocommunity which adult patients organize — with its fears of external persecutors and accusers, its primitive defenses, the prominence of sadism and pregenital elements, and the way guilt is denied and projected. For the child of two or three is still subject to more or less arbitrary parental control in matters of right and wrong. His superego is rudimentary and diffuse. Primitive defenses such as denial and projection are active, while repression remains weak, and pregenital, sadistic interests prevail.

Regression stops at this general level, of course, because it is here that nuclear unconscious structures are fixated and stable — preserved almost unchanged from early childhood. Around these reactivated stable nuclei a new ego organization next begins to crystallize. In this new ego organization the previously repressed urges, fears, fantasies and conflicts will escape repression and remain dominant as long as the psychosis lasts.

Return of the repressed and the formation of symptoms. Paranoid regression goes deep but it does not sweep everything away. An ego defensive structure still remains in which projection and denial play leading roles. There is still an ego adaptive organization, with many of its perceptual and coordinative skills intact. There are even active secondary process operations. They show damage but they are by no means ineffectual. Charles G., for example, could still telephone, drive a car along strange roads, get meals and lodging, and converse normally. Alan K. could walk alone to a psychiatric clinic, arrange his own admission and conduct himself on the ward with at least surface normality. In other words, the released energies that flood the psychodynamic system in paranoid psychoses, and the unconscious conflicts and fantasies pressing forward toward expression, meet a residual ego organization which is still capable of binding energies and moulding infantile material. In short, the return of the repressed in paranoid psychoses may be an eruption, but it is rarely an explosion.

Nevertheless, when this eruption merely threatens, the paranoid patient experiences tremendous signal anxiety; he feels unbearably apprehensive; he is surrounded by danger. When the unconscious breakthrough actually comes, his signal anxiety becomes traumatic anxiety. The danger is no longer anticipated; it is realized. The patient's preconscious and conscious organizations are flooded with free energy — especially aggressive energy. They are invaded by unconscious infantile fantasies and conflicts, and they are disorganized by primary process contamination.

The immediate result is intense confusion and a sense of impending destruction. This the patient experiences as the danger of external assault and death, but we recognize it as the danger of internal personality disintegration and death of the self. It is now impossible for him to distinguish clearly between private fantasy and social fact, between what threatens him from within and what is happening around him. And, as we have seen, a paranoid person is unable to trust anybody else. He cannot turn to a confidant who might be able to serve as his substitute ego, and do his reality-testing for him.

The paranoid psychotic keeps in contact with his surroundings. In his emergency the patient automatically increases his favorite defenses, projection and denial, which are still intact. They will produce the characteristic paranoid picture. As a matter of fact, the patient begins to increase projection long before regression comes to a halt. The same projective operation that makes danger seem to threaten from the outside also makes him turn to the outside to meet it. In doing this he re-establishes contact with his environment, piece by piece, almost as quickly as he loses it. The new contact, of course, is on a delusional basis, since perception and interpretation are now dominated by the revived infantile fantasies and conflicts. The replacement is thus a replacement of realistic interpersonal relationships by unrealistic ones.

This early vigorous use of projection in his psychosis is one factor that enables the paranoid person to keep in better contact, and to make better use of his environment than other psychotics can when they are equally disturbed. Another factor is his lifelong vigilant readiness to counterattack. To a paranoid person the surroundings have always seemed hostile, so he has always had to face outward and watch them. The onset of a paranoid psychosis, we know, is marked by increased vigilance and an aggressive attitude, both of which also force the patient into an active orientation toward his environment.

A third factor is the habitual use of secondary process thinking in the service of drive-organization. Everyone uses reasoning to some extent in support of emotional prejudice and in defense of personal weakness.[28] But the paranoid person does this with extraordinary zeal and persistence. His reasoning is notoriously defensive, obstinate and partisan. We assume that when an unconscious breakthrough occurs, and there is a sudden hyper-cathexis of secondary process thinking, the paranoid does not find the experience seriously disruptive. For him it is only an intensification of something familiar to him. In any case, paranoid thinking seems more logical, and in better contact with reality than it actually is, because it somehow retains its formal organization in spite of primary process contamination.

Ego-superego regression in persecutory paranoid reactions

We have said that ego-superego regression is not merely *partial* in paranoid reactions, as it is in the neuroses, but *subtotal*. This means that the greater part of ego-superego function operates at a more or less infantile level. This statement needs to be amended. In spite of the delusional distortion present, good object relations are retained in paranoid reactions, much better than in comparatively severe manic, depressive and schizophrenic reactions. This, we have already pointed out, indicates that a neurotic regression is involved as well as a psychotic regression. The dynamic picture in paranoid reactions therefore has three characteristics: (1) preservation of more of the mature ego-superego organization than in other psychoses; (2) regression to neurotic fixation levels where, for example, one also often finds sadomasochistic relations with other persons; and (3) deep psychotic regression which necessitates delusion formation if object relations are to be preserved. In other words, the mature ego-superego that persists in this psychosis allows relatively well-organized ego adaptation — the patient handles his environment well — but at the same time there is a deeper regression which compels delusion formation. If we recall the social character of the pseudocommunity, its concern with other persons and its organization, we shall see at once that both in perception and in action the patient is not nearly as desocialized as are other psychotic persons.

The psychotic regression seems to rest upon a lack of basic trust or confidence. Adults who are especially vulnerable to paranoid psychoses have not been adequately protected from excessive tension and anxiety in early infancy. Such protection requires that a mother-figure furnish the buffering action which later on will be furnished by the child's own maturing ego. Without such a *substitute ego*, in the form of a protective and providing mother-figure, a child must somehow develop an ego of his own, with what-

---

[28] Cf. Kamano, D. K., and Drew, J. E., "Selectivity in memory of personally significant material, *J. gen. Psychol.*, 1961, 65, 25–32; Paul, I. H., "Studies in remembering: the reproduction of connected and extended verbal material," *Psychol. Issues*, 1959, *1*, No. 2.

ever primitive defenses and coping behavior may be available at the time. Otherwise he will not be able to survive because of the disintegrative effect of excessive tension and anxiety.[29]

This is the task facing the paranoid person in his infancy. He meets it by crystallizing a precocious ego organization at a time when denial and projection are available as defenses, but mature repression is not. The infant who in adulthood will develop a persecutory paranoid reaction is an overstimulated, angry, aggressive baby whose parents allow him to express his anger. This freedom to express rage is not the result of permissiveness on the part of the parent or parents. It is the result either of indifference toward the baby's fury or of actual enjoyment of the fury. There is clinical evidence to indicate that the paranoid patient must have experienced sadistic treatment in his infancy, and that he must have reacted to this with ungovernable sadistic rage.

The precocious crystallization of ego organization distorts all later ego maturation sequences. Repression matures late and imperfectly because its early functions are already being performed by the overdeveloped denial and projection. It never reaches the level of supremacy that normal and neurotic repression reach. Thus a normally strong repressive barrier which will contain unconscious processes does not develop.

A normally strong repressive barrier, we have said, makes it possible for preconscious and conscious organizations to develop normally and for secondary process logical thinking to evolve. Such a barrier keeps invasions from unconscious ego, id and superego processes at a minimum. It holds primary processes within strict limits during the daytime hours.

A weak repressive barrier, such as we see in persons who develop paranoid psychoses, sets ineffectual limits. It allows unconscious fantasies and conflicts to invade preconscious and conscious organizations. It permits primary process contamination of logical thought and perception. These influences are obvious in the perceptual hypersensitivities and misinterpretations of paranoid persons.

Early in the chapter, we pointed out that the unreasonable fears of paranoid patients were related to phobias. The fears of paranoid patients, however, are more violent, more personal, and more likely to be organized into delusional pseudocommunities of persecutors. This is a much more serious falsification of reality than one sees in phobias.

The powerful sadomasochistic fantasies and conflicts in persecutory paranoid reactions also relate them to compulsive reactions, as does also the intense ego-superego struggle.[30] But there is a world of difference between the sadomasochistic self-punishment of the compulsive patient and the sadomasochistic projection of the paranoid. The persecutory paranoid patient

[29] We see the results of such failures in the so-called anaclitic depressions of deprived, institutionalized infants, and in the autistic child.

[30] See especially the case of Sally J. in Chapter 11 on obsessive compulsive reactions.

denies his guilt. He represents to himself the superego attack as the plot of other persons to attack him. This brings us to a consideration of the *superego* in paranoid reactions.

The regressively reactivated superego. In all of this one sees a deeply regressed superego which is destructive, highly personalized, but at the same time diffuse. The paranoid superego suffers the same regressive fate as the paranoid ego. This is hardly surprising in view of the fact that the superego originated in childhood as a differentiation within the ego, and that the superego always operates in close relation to the ego. The level to which the paranoid superego regresses is doubly interesting. On the one hand, it reflects some of the basic defects of paranoid personality integration; and on the other hand, it accounts for some of the outstanding paranoid symptoms.

Paranoid regression carries the superego organization to a level just preceding the transfer of moral control from outside agents (parents and others), to moral control by an internalized, unified self-regulating system, the postedipal superego. This transfer is never a complete one, even in the most independent, mature adult. Moral self-control is always responsive to the reactions of other people. But paranoid personalities suffer from an arrest of development which interferes both with their realistic responses to others, and with their ability to exercise mature self-regulation. The ease with which such persons project their own self-criticism, even when they are not psychotic, makes it look as though *superego control* and *control by outside agents* were still interchangeable, that is, still fixated at a level of unstable equilibrium. It looks as though the paranoid superego were not freed from the primitive, personalized images of childhood, and for this reason not freed from interchange with and confusion with external objects.

The small child normally lives surrounded by people who keep watch upon his movements. They seem to know in advance what he will do next, and have an uncanny knack of intercepting and frustrating him. In action, the child is practically powerless against them. If the adults are punitive, they seem to the child to bear down relentlessly, and sometimes mercilessly, upon him. He always finds that in the end he cannot defend himself or escape. Even if he flies into a violent rage he can be easily overpowered. His violence is often met by adult violence.

Translated into adult terms, with adult knowledge about violence and with hostile strangers in place of punitive parents, what is all this but a picture of the situation in which Charles G. seemed to find himself? His furious, violent behavior aroused in him the expectation of pursuit by relentless persecutors. It was his own rage and fright that had driven him into a psychotic regression. He feared extinction. He felt unable to defend himself against attack and unable to escape. There was no one whom he could trust.

What paranoid psychotic regression does is to intensify a weakness that has always been present. A diffusely organized superego is reactivated, in its primitive form, with personalized sadistic images. It is this diffuse, primitive organization which the psychotic paranoid person projects as his pseudocommunity of enemies, critics and slanderers. But even in this, the patient is only intensifying his lifelong tendency to blame failure on others, to feel discriminated against, belittled and disliked. As a small child he was actually no match for his seemingly sadistic parents. When he regresses as an adult, his infantile ego is no match for its sadistic superego; and even when he projects his superego on to others, he finds himself no match for his delusional sadistic enemies.[31]

Delusion formation as reality reconstruction

Regression stops when a new ego-superego organization is crystallized around the nuclear conflicts and fantasies of the major levels of fixation. A place in this organization must be found for the reactivated fantasies and conflicts. Since those reactivated in persecutory paranoid patients cannot be accepted as their own, and since they can no longer be kept in repression, it becomes necessary to deny them and project them. This also requires a reconstruction of one's perception of external reality, in order to give them an intelligible place. When such a reality reconstruction is carried out in a well-organized way, we have the paranoid delusion.[32] The delusion, like the neurotic symptom, is also a compromise, but the distortion of external reality that is required is much greater than that in the neurotic symptom.

Delusions are not only evidence of illness, but also signs of an attempt to work out a spontaneous cure. They are the best the patient can do at the moment in the way of adapting to a situation which places his fantasies on an equal footing with objective reality. The only alternate to such reconstruction under the circumstances would be to withdraw from the confusion into a stupor. It is sometimes of the greatest importance to recognize the appearance of delusions as heralding a new attempt to cope with reality.

Emotional drives in paranoid regression

What persecutory paranoid regression lays bare is the nucleus of primitive rage, love and fear of a deprived, frustrated child, whose resentment may be implacable. The fantasies and conflicts revived, in all their infantile intensity, deal with sadistic impulses toward parental figures, and with retaliation which seems to the patient inescapable. These factors were evident in both the case of Charles G. and that of Alan K. The familiar vicious cycle develops: a fantasy of attacking sadistically; then a frighten-

31 Hesselbach, C. F., "Superego regression in paranoia," *Psychoanal. Quart.*, 1962, *31*, 341–350.
32 We shall see that reality is more distorted in manic, depressed and schizophrenic delusions.

ing fantasy of cruel retaliation; then fantasies of still more cruel revenge; and so on.

Homoerotic fantasies and conflicts also belong to the infantile level to which paranoid persons regress. The question as to whether or not these are *central* in paranoid reactions is still a matter of controversy. The case of Schreber is often cited as positive evidence.[33] This case does not settle anything, because Schreber did not deny or repress his homosexual orientation, but on the contrary emphasized it constantly. Schreber is considered today to have been a paranoid schizophrenic person, rather than a paranoid one. Another difficulty arises from the finding that paranoid psychotic women are characteristically concerned with accusations of being prostitutes, not of being homosexual.[34] Finally, there is an insistence among certain workers in the field that early confusion as to one's sexual identity, rather than homosexual fantasies and conflicts, is basic to paranoid and to schizophrenic reactions.[35]

Summary of persecutory paranoid symptom formation

Paranoid personalities are especially sensitive to certain kinds of frustration for which they have low tolerance. When their limits of tolerance are exceeded, they give up reality, turn inward, and invest unstable preconscious fantasy systems with the energy which is withdrawn from reality operations. Because of defensive defects, the preconscious systems discharge into related infantile unconscious systems, with which they freely communicate, and this lights up the unconscious systems. The latter, in turn, discharge libidinal and aggressive energy into the preconscious systems, making them still more unstable, and setting up a vicious cycle.

In the end, some preconscious systems disintegrate, flooding the preconscious ego with their *energy of organization,* and precipitating a general ego disintegration and regression, in which the superego also participates. The regression comes to a halt when an infantile level has been reached at which powerful fixations make a stable reorganization possible. In paranoid personalities, this corresponds roughly to a period in childhood just *before* the *superego* began to crystallize out. The fixated conflicts and fantasies of this period become the nuclei around which a new ego organization forms; and they dominate the ultimate clinical picture.

In acute onsets the *regressive breakdown of mature defenses,* especially of *repression,* releases unconscious forces which invade preconscious and

[33] Schreber, D., *Memoirs of My Nervous Illness* (1903) (trans. I. Macalpine and R. A. Hunter). London: Dawson, 1955.

[34] Klein, H. R., and Horwitz, W. A., "Psychosexual factors in the paranoid phenomena," *Amer. J. Psychiat.,* 1949, *105,* 697–705.

[35] MacAlpine, I., and Hunter, R. A., "Introduction," and "Discussion," in translation of Schreber, D., *Memoirs of My Nervous Illness.* London: Dawson, 1955, pp. 1–28, and pp. 369–411. See also Greenspan, J., and Myers, J. M., "A review of the theoretical concepts of paranoid delusions with special reference to women," *Penna. Psychiat. Quart.,* 1961, *1,* 11–28.

conscious organizations (*unconscious breakthrough*). Such an invasion may produce traumatic anxiety, confusion and an expectation of attack. Whatever defensive and adaptive organizations remain intact begin to mold the emerging unconscious fantasies and conflicts, and deal with the flood of libidinal and aggressive energy by binding it and projectively discharging it. *Denial* and *projection* are the principal defensive measures, *secondary process organization* is a major source of delusional adaptation, and *hostile aggression* is often the chief weapon.

Restitution consists in the construction of a delusional paranoid *pseudo-community*, in which the patient appears as an angry, innocent victim.[36] All that is evil, guilt-provoking and contemptible is denied and projected, that is, assigned to other persons, both real and imagined. The final outcome may be (*a*) *recovery to something like the prepsychotic level of functioning*, usually with psychotherapeutic help; (*b*) *a chronic paranoid state*, often preceded by an acute outburst; or (*c*) *disintegration secondarily into a chronic schizophrenia*.

Childhood background of persecutory paranoid reactions

When a person decompensates under stress in adult life and develops a persecutory paranoid psychosis, it can be assumed that he has suffered all his life from the following personality defects: (*a*) *a distorted defense structure*, with inadequate repression and strong tendencies to use denial and projection; (*b*) *vulnerability to traumatic anxiety;* (*c*) *powerful fixations in early infantile conflicts;* (*d*) *incompetent reality-testing;* and (*e*) *a poorly integrated, sadistic superego system.*

Some of these defects are usually apparent during his adult life, before a psychosis develops. He may have been a tense, insecure person who easily becomes anxious. Often the anxiety and insecurity are concealed behind a defensive façade. He has found it difficult to trust in anyone. Often he is secretive, suspicious, seclusive, and given to solitary rumination. He is usually inept at understanding the motivations of other people. He is plagued by ideas of reference, too aware of unconscious trends in others, but insufficiently aware of his own. He tends to deny responsibility for his failures, for his inacceptable desires and attitudes, and to ascribe them to others around him. He is basically a hostile person, even though he may appear agreeable to himself and to others.

What factors in childhood development are responsible for such an adult personality? Many answers have been given to this question, not all of them in agreement. It is a difficult matter to reconstruct an adult patient's prob-

---

[36] Stone, A. A., "Delusional formation during the activation of chronic schizophrenic patients," *Arch. gen. Psychiat.*, 1959, *1*, 177–179. There is a discussion of the emergence of reality in Schachtel, E. G., *Metamorphosis: On the Development of Affect, Perception, Attention, and Memory.* New York: Basic Books, 1959.

able childhood; and different factors can often contribute to the same end-result.

There are a few areas of general agreement. It is generally believed, on the basis of several decades of clinical study, that paranoid persons have not been adequately protected from excessive tension and anxiety during their first two years. Consequently, they have not been able to develop a *basic trust* in childhood. They have not had an adequate *substitute ego* at a time when they were already using denial and projection, but had not yet developed adequate repression. On the other hand, they had been allowed to *express* their tension and anger openly. In many instances the paranoid patient seems to have identified with whichever parent appeared to him the more hostile one. This *identification with hostile aggressors* is a wellknown defense even among fearful, nonparanoid adults.

Often what is called *sadistic treatment* of a small child turns out to have been only maternal indifference, coldness, teasing or belittling. These can *seem* cruel to the child. Often, however, a parent has been actually cruel. A sadistic mother, for example, may deliberately provoke and encourage her child to become furious because she enjoys the helpless violence of his rage. This was true of Allen K.'s mother. In such situations, the infant or small child is overstimulated, angry and aggressive. He is allowed expression of his feelings but, while this may protect him from the futility which leads to a schizophrenic personality, it does not allow the child to work through his love-hate ambivalence in a normal way. Sometimes a parent behaves toward a child in ways that *anyone* would call cruel. Later on, persistent interference with a child's freedom of action, through parental domination and control, creates further problems. So does a home atmosphere of watchfulness, suspicion and chronic disapproval.

The period of self-assertion and toilet training, which we described in Chapter 2, is especially important in producing a basically hostile, distrustful person. This is the period of rapid increase in muscular strength and skill, of negativistic self-assertion and independence. At this time a child can easily be pushed into hatred and temper outbursts by a teasing or domineering parent. Normally, parental love and patience soften a child's resentment at being controlled, and lead him to internalize parental controls in forming his own superego.

The superego of paranoid persons seems to have remained fixated at a period when they were still under parental control. They develop a postedipal superego also, but this remains unstable. In regressing, the patient returns to the older pattern. Outside agents, which are his own projections, seem again to be controlling, criticizing and threatening him, as they were in childhood. The "persecutors" are powerful and dangerous, just as his parents seemed to be when he was a small child.

Some paranoid adults give evidence of sexual cross-identification, usually because of a dominant, aggressive mother. They may experience fantasies belonging to the opposite sex. In the case of Alan K., for example, there was the *double contradiction* of identifying with a *mother* who was dominant and sadistic, and with a *father* who was weak and ineffectual. This combination is not rare. When such a child enters the edipal phase, both these identifications may make the choice of a love object seem dangerous. We have already discussed the problem of homoeroticism in paranoid developments. It goes without saying that sex identity confusion is much more likely in the child of parents who themselves show contradictions in their sex roles.

Let us turn now to a consideration of psychotic depressions, in which the dynamic picture is somewhat clearer than it is in paranoid psychoses, but the patient is usually much more helpless.

15

Psychotic Depressive Reactions

✣

PSYCHOTIC DEPRESSIVE REACTIONS ARE MOOD DISORDERS IN WHICH DEJEC-
tion, guilt and organized delusions of self-depreciation dominate a person's
thinking. The prevailing delusions are in keeping with the dejected and
often apprehensive mood. They are usually exaggerations and distortions of
what any normal adult might feel after personal failure or serious loss.
Psychotic depressives lose effective contact with their human environment
to a much greater degree than do comparably ill paranoid psychotics. They
do not, however, suffer general personality disintegration such as we commonly see in schizophrenics. Hallucinations are not a part of the typical
psychotic depressive picture.

When a person develops a severe psychotic depression he shuts out as
much of his environment as possible and withdraws into deep preoccupation. He may do this suddenly or gradually. He becomes absorbed in some
overwhelming conflict over guilt and unworthiness, to the virtual exclusion
of everything else. When he gives voice to his delusions, accusing and
debasing himself, it is soon obvious to everyone that he is ill. Rarely do
relatives and friends take a severely depressed person's delusional statements at face value, as they so often do with paranoid psychotics. The
commonest and most dangerous mistake they make is to underrate the
murderous self-hate in depressions, and so to let suicide take them by surprise.[1] Occasionally, in committing suicide, a depressed person also kills

[1] Weiss, J. M. A., "The gamble with death in attempted suicide," *Psychiatry*, 1957,
17–25; Mintz, R. S., "Psychotherapy of the suicidal patient," *Amer. J. Psychother.*,

loved ones. In spite of the rationalizations which he gives for this, in advance or in suicide notes, it is actually an extension of archaic superego hostility to include other persons, as well as the depressive ego.

It is not as easy to understand psychotic depressions as it is to understand neurotic depressions. This is because of the deep regression and the loss of interest in almost everything in the environment. Discouragement, dejection and disillusionment are not only deeper in psychotic depressions. They are also much more fixed and rigid than in neurotic depressions. Complaints are not made to stimulate others to contradict superego attacks; they are made as statements of fact. Attempts at reassurance are met with stubborn and often angry rejection. Depression has reached a delusional level; it has replaced external reality with an overwhelming internal reality. We shall have more to say about this when we come to the dynamic and developmental background. There we shall find that psychotic depression is closely related to normal mourning and realistic grief. In fact, one could say that normal mourning is a realistic form of psychotic depression, especially when the lost person is resented as well as loved.

Definition. Psychotic depressions are mood disorders in which dejection, self-depreciation and self-condemnation reach delusional proportions. The sense of worthlessness and guilt persists in spite of what anyone else says or does. In fact, when other people attempt to contradict and reassure the patient, they may deepen the depression rather than lessen it. This contrasts sharply with the neurotic depression,[2] in which the patient stimulates others to contradict and reassure him so as to ward off his own superego attacks. The psychotic depressive is moved by contradictions and reassurances to heap up further self-depreciation and self recrimination which are more and more delusional. The deep-seated guilt relates psychotic depressions also to obsessive compulsive neuroses; but the guilt in psychotic depressions is acutely conscious and the depressed patient is interested in almost nothing else. Moreover, he is usually actively suicidal in his fantasies, which is not true of obsessive compulsives, and much less true of neurotic depressives. As we shall see later on, this difference goes deeper than the symptoms. It involves regression to a phase where the sadistic superego seems to be stating facts, and there is little really adult ego operative to resist it.[3]

Adaptation. There is little of adaptive value in psychotic depressions.

1961, *15*, 348–367; Fellner, C. H., "Provocation of suicidal attempts," *J. nerv. ment. Dis.*, 1961, *133*, 55–58; Gottschalk, L. A., and Gleser, G. C., "An analysis of the verbal content of suicide notes," *Brit. J. Med. Psychol.*, 1960, *33*, 195–204.

2 Gutheil, E., "Reactive depressions," in Arieti, S. (Ed.), *American Handbook of Psychiatry.* New York: Basic Books, 1959, pp. 345–352.

3 For a review of the literature on psychotic depression, see Bellak, L. (Ed.), *Manic-Depressive Psychosis and Allied Conditions.* New York: Grune & Stratton, 1952.

They involve such deep regression that the patient can make little use of his environment and, unlike the paranoid person, he does not project his internal hate and fear; or if he does, he considers his fate, as he imagines it, to be a well-deserved one. He takes an actively cruel attitude toward himself and, in those cases which expect torture and death at the hands of sadistic people, the torture and death are felt to be right and just. The superego attitude is one of hatred, cruelty, and gloating — not unlike that of some obsessive compulsives — and the ego response to the superego is a submissive one, even a welcoming one. Perhaps this submissive, receptive attitude helps to account for the fact that psychotic depression is commoner among women than among men. As we have said, the psychotic depressive patient does not make his self-depreciatory statements to stimulate others to contradict him, but only as statements of "fact." Therefore his complaints are neither defensive nor adaptive. The only sense in which the term *adaptive* can be used in psychotic depression is that the patient manages somehow to escape the fragmentation and the abyss of schizophrenia. This is probably related to his much better object relations, when he is well, and therefore to his better organized personality.

Clinical Aspects of Psychotic Depressive Reactions

In discussing *neurotic depressions*, in Chapter 12, we said that when a depression becomes acute and severe, the patient loses his grip on external reality, regresses *deeply* and *subtotally*, i.e., he regresses to infantile levels almost totally, but not quite. He usually requires hospitalization, to protect him from his suicidal superego impulses. Under such circumstances we are no longer dealing with a neurotic depression but with a psychotic one.[4] There are the same numerous varieties of *psychotic depressions* as there are of neurotic ones. Even the precipitating factors may be closely similar. The major differences are that in the psychotic depression the regression goes deeper and includes much more than does the regression in neurotic depressions. We attribute this vulnerability to deep, subtotal regression, in adult psychotic depressives, to personality defects which go back to early childhood.[5]

Among the acute, severe psychotic depressions, we distinguish two varieties: the *agitated depression* and the *retarded depression*. Actually, these are not so much differences in fundamental pattern, or in psychodynamics, as they are differences in the degree of overt activity which the patient shows. The same patient may be *agitated* at first, and later on become slowed up, or *retarded*. Another may begin by slowing up, and only later become agitated.

[4] Arieti, S., "Manic-depressive psychosis," in Arieti, S. (Ed.), *American Handbook of Psychiatry.* New York: Basic Books, 1959, pp. 419–454.
[5] Hilgard, J. R., and Newman, M. F., "Evidence for functional genesis in mental illness: schizophrenia, depressive psychoses and psychoneuroses," *J. nerv. ment. Dis.,* 1961, *132*, 3–16.

Agitated depressions. Many patients begin by developing more and more anxious overactivity, until they grow so restless and tense that they cannot sit still or lie down for more than a few minutes at a time. They may talk incessantly about their despair and their fears; or they may limit their talk to desperate exclamations, or expressions of self-hate. Many of these patients are extremely apprehensive. They seem to expect some disaster to descend upon them at any moment, often without being able to say what kind of disaster they expect. The patient paces back and forth, moans and cries, rubs and picks at his body, wrings his hands and rocks in suffering. Some patients anticipate severe punishment for their misdeeds; some, like the agitated patient we shall present later, demand that they be punished cruelly, and even regard punishment as inevitable in the end. There is often bitterness and resentment about being cruelly punished, even though the patient demands it. We assume that it is the superego that demands it, and that it is the suffering ego which resents it with bitterness.

Retarded depression. The patient in a deep retarded depression looks stunned by grief. His back is bent, his arms hang limp, his eyes are fixed on the ground, his face is immobile and his brow is furrowed. He is the picture of a person who has lost everything in life. When he sits down he slumps and stares. He may hold his head in his hands and look at the floor. His movements are slow and leaden. He has enormous difficulty in initiating activity and in keeping it up. His talk is slow, repetitious and monotonously uninflected. He cannot enter into a conversation. The best he can do is to answer questions briefly, often almost inaudibly. His sentences often trail off unfinished, as if the effort were not worth while. His voice and his words sound like that of a doomed man without hope. He can no more interest himself in everyday activities than can a man actually awaiting execution.

By the time a patient has reached this degree of depression, hospitalization becomes inevitable. His appetite has disappeared and he is usually constipated. Sleep may decrease to as little as two or three hours a night. The patient loses weight, looks careworn, haggard and unmistakably ill. Retarded depressed men usually become impotent. Retarded depressed women become frigid, and their menses grow irregular or stop entirely.

Extreme cases of retarded psychotic depression are often called *depressive stupor.* In these all spontaneous activity stops. The patient becomes almost completely unresponsive and apparently oblivious to what is going on around him. Most of the time he sits motionless, as if in a daze or in shock, saying nothing whatever, his face fixed in tense anxiety or else without expression and immobile. In appearance the stuporous depressed patient may be indistinguishable from a stuporous schizophrenic. He must often be tube-fed and cared for like a helpless baby, if his life is to be preserved. One only learns after he has recovered enough to be able to communicate that, during this apparently vacant period, he has been swallowed up in fantasies of abandonment and despair.

Depressive delusions

Delusional self-depreciation and self-accusation. Patients who begin by calling themselves no good, worthless, a failure and a burden, now say that they are beyond all hope, outside the pale, unfit for decent human company. They are absolutely sure that they will never recover, never be able to work again, never be able to face people. Some accuse themselves of unpardonable sins, say they are degraded and despicable, call themselves fool, thief, liar, hypocrite, degenerate and murderer. Many also project their self-depreciation and self-accusation, insisting that others secretly hate and despise them. Ideas of self-reference creep in to support the projection. To the patient, people seem to look at him with pity, aversion and disgust.

Actual misdeeds, often trivial, are dredged up from the past and their importance greatly magnified. One middle-aged depressed woman, dressed in black from head to foot, including quite inappropriate black gloves, harped continually upon the fact that she had stolen a plum when she was a little girl, behind her mother's back. Such a complaint usually symbolizes childhood sin and functions like a screen memory by representing more serious sinning in a trivial act. Often less trivial misdeeds, which may have caused only temporary conflict at the time, are now recalled with crushing remorse. Still other events are given a delusional reinterpretation and then paraded as further evidence that the patient is really vile. We shall see in both our case illustrations how self-accusation is used sadistically to punish other people as well as the patient.[6]

In all of this, the patient is finding explanations for his overwhelming sense of guilt. We know that the immediate source of this guilt is in super-ego aggression, that its origin is infantile and its intensity irrational. We also know that in a great many instances the self-accusations are taken over directly from the patient's own previous accusations against an ambivalently loved person, now turned against the self. We shall see a clear example of this in the case of Constance Q., who began accusing herself of the irresponsibility which had actually been the behavior of her brothers. Nevertheless, as we shall see, the patient is incapable of recognizing any of these relationships. To him the delusional beliefs are monstrous facts.

Depressive self-accusation is often grandiose. The patient calls himself the *world's greatest sinner* or *criminal*, a *colossal failure*, the *cause of widespread suffering and disaster*. Such delusions are really infantile fantasies of hate and destruction. They are *omnipotent* in the same sense that a small child's imaginings are. A depressed person who pictures himself as the cause of ten thousand deaths by infection — as one of our patients did — is certainly far from humble. He is committing mass murder in fantasy. He

---

[6] Fromm-Reichmann, F., "Psychoanalytic remarks on the clinical significance of hostility," in Bullard, D. M. (Ed.), *Psychoanalysis and Psychotherapy.* Chicago: Univ. of Chicago Press, 1959, pp. 277–282; Buss, A. H., *Psychology of Aggression.* New York: Wiley, 1961.

is full of hatred and resentment. He has regressed to a level where he can no longer differentiate between himself and others, as targets of his hostility. Suicidal acts also express this generalized hostility when a depressed patient tries to take others with him to the grave.

Delusional expectation of punishment. It seems to be a general law of human thinking that guilt must somehow be expiated.[7] Many depressed persons wait in a spirit of hopeless resignation to be punished — often to be killed — feeling that they deserve it. The delusion that they are destined to be punished terribly makes some patients desperate. Some demand that the terrible suspense of waiting for the inevitable be ended — as we shall see in the case of Constance Q. — that they be put on trial, that they be imprisoned, executed or lynched. Some psychotic depressives ask to be beaten, trampled on, starved, degraded, pilloried or mutilated. Some visit punishment upon themselves. It is the unbearable suspense, the frightening expectation, and the absolute conviction of terrible guilt that drive many depressed people to suicide.

Delusions of unreality and estrangement. All depressed persons experience disturbing changes in their own emotional responsiveness. On the basis of their own feelings many of them develop delusions that the world around them is changing or that they themselves are undergoing a transformation. It is not uncommon for a psychotically depressed person to believe that the nurses are not really nurses at all, but only women dressed up to look like nurses, that the other patients are not patients at all, and that visiting relatives are fradulent impersonators. The whole ward, some insist, is not real. The surroundings appear to be as artificial as a stage set. All such beliefs are expressions of the patient's own altered feelings, of his own *estrangement.* They are exaggerations of normal projections, such as those which make it possible for us to speak of a "gloomy morning," or a "lonely landscape."

Nihilistic delusions. Anxious and agitated depressed patients are especially apt to feel that some terrible catastrophe hangs over them, that a desolate loneliness is coming and the end of everything (*nihilism*). In psychotic depressions these delusions are especially common in the middle-aged and elderly.

An elderly woman felt sure that the end of the world was at hand. She went about the house at night, heaping blankets and woolens upon her sleeping relatives to preserve them from the cold. Nothing could symbolize more vividly her own depressive loss of warmth and the impending danger of losing reality, which actually threatened her.[8]

[7] Rado, S., "Psychodynamics of depression from the etiologic point of view," *Psychosom. Med.*, 1959, *13*, 51.

[8] Fromm-Reichmann, F., "Psychoanalytic remarks on the clinical significance of hostility," in Bullard, D. M. (Ed.), *Psychoanalysis and Psychotherapy.* Chicago: Univ. of Chicago Press, 1959, pp. 277–282.

Another depressed middle-aged woman talked endlessly, in a weary monotone, of being condemned to wander over the face of the earth forever. She wanted a steel identification band riveted on her wrist so that future generations would know who she was.

A wealthy man was certain over a period of a year that he was penniless and would starve to death. His accountant and his banker brought him certified statements of his real financial situation; but he called the statements "fakes," and he angrily tossed them aside. His lawyer also tried his hand at demonstrating the patient's financial solvency, but he finally gave up. The patient and his advisers seemed to be talking about the same thing, but actually they were not. He was talking about his bankrupt personality without knowing it; and this personality bankruptcy was a fact which no amount of reassurance or contradiction by accountant, banker or lawyer could actually deny. When this man recovered, he remembered his nihilistic delusions clearly. He dismissed them as "just crazy ideas."

Somatic delusions. A conviction that something is the matter with one's body often develops out of an earlier phase of body overconcern. The regressed, psychotically depressed person who has been worrying about his health without good reason is now convinced that he is physically deteriorating or has a fatal disease.

Another source of somatic delusions is the regressed psychotic patient's experience with estrangement. Actual physiological changes, such as decreased gastrointestinal motility and secretion, may lead the patient to symbolize them in concrete terms, for example, that he has no stomach or no intestines, or that they have turned to wood. One of our patients complained that his head was full of granite, a woman said that her bowels had become stone, and a man thought that his hands were now shaped like claws and were turning black.

Guilt itself gives rise to some somatic delusions. A guilty, depressed psychotic looks in the mirror, sees his lined, haggard face, with the dark rings of sleeplessness and suffering around his eyes, and interprets his appearance, not as that of a sick man, but as that of an evil, depraved one.

Precipitating factors

In Chapter 13, when we were discussing psychotic symptom formation, we stated that all persons who are especially vulnerable to psychotic episodes are hypersensitive to certain general situations. These situations are: (1) *the loss or threatened loss of a major source of gratification;* (2) *the loss or threatened loss of one's basic security;* (3) *an upsurge of erotic or hostile impulses;* (4) *a sudden increase in guilt* — conscious, preconscious or unconscious; and (5) *reduced general effectiveness of ego adaptation or defense.*[9]

[9] These are given in more detail in the section on precipitating factors in Chapter 14.

Vulnerability to depression. The person who is vulnerable to psychotic depressions does not have a normal personality organization, no matter how normally he may live when he is well. He always has to work against certain odds. He is fundamentally deficient in self-esteem because his superego condemns readily and supports reluctantly. He needs reassurance, appreciation, encouragement and approval from others — the so-called "narcissistic supplies" — to help make up his standing personality deficit and to offset his own feelings of worthlessness and guilt.

An adult vulnerable to psychotic depression is not likely to admit, or even to recognize, his need of "narcissistic supplies" as long as he remains well. But his way of living usually reveals it. However mature he may be in other ways, he is always dependent upon others to help him maintain his equilibrium.[10] Losses and failures for such a person — or even the mere threat of loss or failure — may prove dangerously disturbing, and sometimes catastrophic. The danger arises because, after a certain point has been reached, the depressive personality gets only a momentary lift from the love and reassurance which others can offer him. Regression may grow irresistible, and unconscious conflicts may begin to emerge into preconscious and conscious thinking. Once this happens, love and reassurance from the outside are likely to lose their effectiveness.

We may sum this up by saying that the depressive personality is most vulnerable to whatever frustrates his dependent needs, and in particular to whatever gives him the experience of *losing love,* of *losing personal security,* or of *losing self-esteem.* Let us examine each of these sources of vulnerability to psychotic depression.

(a) Loss of love. This may come in the form of a death,[11] as it did in one of the cases that we shall present, or in the form of a disillusionment, as it did in the other. It may also come through separation, desertion, severe disappointment, rebuff, humiliation or neglect. If personal failure, or if a decline in health, status or attractiveness threatens the loss of another person's love, this can also precipitate a psychotic depression. Likewise when forbidden impulses emerge which — if acted out — would threaten loss of love, their emergence alone may be enough to precipitate depression. The death wishes of one of our patients and his sadistic impulses toward his wife give us one set of examples. The hatred our other patient felt toward her brothers, and the murderous impulses that she expressed in her early suicidal plans, give us another.

[10] Gibson, R. W., Cohen, M. B., and Cohen, R. A., "On the dynamics of the manic-depressive personality," *Amer. J. Psychiat.,* 1959, *115,* 1101–1107.

[11] Freud, S., "Mourning and melancholia," (1917), in Strachey, J. (Ed.), Standard Edition. London: Hogarth Press, 1957, pp. 239–258; Abraham, K., "Notes on manic-depressive insanity," in *Selected Papers.* London: Hogarth Press, 1949, pp. 137–156; Ostow, M., "The psychic function of depression," *Psychoanal. Quart.,* 1960, *29,* 355–394; Rochlin, G. R., "The loss complex: a contribution to the etiology of depression," *J. Amer. Psychoanal. Ass.,* 1959, *7,* 299–316.

(b) Loss of personal security. Almost everyone finds deep satisfaction in having friends, possessions, prestige and reputation. These afford emotional support and reassurance in times of trouble. For most people a home, familiar surroundings and habitual ways of living also have the same significance. The loss or threatened loss of such resources is enough to sadden or discourage anybody.

For a depressive personality such losses are equivalent to a loss of love. They are frustrations of imperious dependent needs which leave him feeling deserted, deprived, debased and unloved. To feel unloved and deserted is to be exposed to superego attack which, for a depressive person, is an intolerable situation. The stage is set then for withdrawal and regression to experiences of worthlessness, loneliness and guilt, like those of the individual's own unhappy childhood.

If we are to understand the precipitation of a psychotic depression we must bear in mind that what counts is the intensity and significance of the depressive person's experience, and not the loss or the threat as you or I might see it.[12] Psychotic depressions can be set off by what looks to us like a minor threat or loss. It may even look like a gain or a promise to us, as in the depressions following promotion. In such cases we can take it for granted that the situation has for some reason stirred up deep unconscious dangers. It symbolizes something traumatic in the patient's own individual past; and he reacts as if what it symbolized has actually happened again, or is about to happen.

(c) Loss of self-esteem. We have said that depressive personalities are dependent upon love, approval, reassurance and support from outside sources because they seriously lack self-esteem.[13] It is none the less true that they need all the self-esteem that they can muster. This they derive from the same experiences which contribute to normal self-esteem — the feeling that one has lived up to one's expectations, has acted with integrity and competence, has achieved something in whatever is personally important, that is, happiness, friendliness, a respectable or an enviable status, success, power over others or service to others, and so on.

It is failure in such areas that lowers or destroys the depressive person's self-esteem. Once more we see the depressive reacting to losses and threats that might trouble anyone, but his ease of reacting is greater than average and his way of reacting is exaggerated and long-lasting. Failure to live up to his own expectations, for example, disturbs him at a point earlier than it would a normal personality, and he responds to his disappointment with himself as though he had committed a crime.

One of our depressed patients, a small-town banker, failed to lay in a

[12] Zetzel, E. R., "Introduction to symposium on depressive illness," *Internat. J. Psychoanal.*, 1960, *41*, 476–480.

[13] For an experimental study of self-esteem, see DiVesta, F. J., "Effects of confidence and motivation on susceptibility to informational social influence," *J. abnorm. soc. Psychol.*, 1959, *59*, 204–209.

stock of currency in preparation for a town celebration. When he discovered his lapse he was powerless to remedy it; he then developed delusional fears that the townspeople might lynch him when they found money was not available. Another patient, a rather prudish young woman, committed a minor indiscretion during her vacation. Although she was criticized by few people, she withdrew from work and from her friends, called herself a fallen woman, and expected to be beaten and thrown into the streets. Both of the cases, which we shall soon present, show the same quick and exaggerated reaction to what they felt were moral lapses.

The depressive personality's predicament.[14] We can present the depressive's predicament in this way. His greatest danger comes always from within, from the ever-present threat of an attack by a hostile, unloving superego. Against this destructive inner force he uses three kinds of counterforce. One is the love he gets. Another is the reassurance and support that he derives from status,[15] possessions, friendship, reputation, familiar patterns of living, and the like. A third is his self-esteem which is never enough alone.

A great many depressives reveal their personality defects one way or another, throughout most of their lives, even though they remain clinically well. Some have marked mood swings, from optimistic to pessimistic, and from pessimistic to optimistic, which only their close associates recognize. Some habitually overreact to kindness and unkindness in others, to personal failures and successes, to current events, and to other people's joys and sorrows. Not all of these express their overreactions openly, but they feel them and the feeling lasts. Many betray a depressive personality organization only in habitual self-disparagement or in chronic feelings of being unworthy, guilty or insignificant. All of these signs and symptoms are evidence that a destructive critic lives within, a hostile force which in fair weather creates only mild and shifting mood disturbances, but which in stormy weather can make the depressive personality wallow in the sea of life and founder.

In the lives of some depressive persons it takes something unusual to upset the balance. Then they develop delusions of worthlessness and guilt, and these delusions lay bare their previously well-compensated depressive foundations. In others the precipitating factor, as we have noted before, seems to others a trivial one. In both well-compensated and poorly compensated depressive personalities, a psychotic reaction develops when the patient suffers a serious frustration in his deeply dependent needs. Such an experience weakens the alliance which has previously held his superego aggression under control — the alliance between his relatively weak self-

[14] The characteristics and mode of life of the depressive personality are discussed in some detail later in the chapter.

[15] Fromm-Reichmann, F., "Intensive psychotherapy of manic-depressives," in Bullard, D. M. (Ed.), *Psychoanalysis and Psychotherapy.* Chicago: Univ. of Chicago Press, 1959, pp. 221–226.

esteem and his available external sources of narcissistic supplies, that is, of love, approval, respect and all the rest. When serious frustration of this kind arises the potentially psychotic depressive person makes the fatal move of withdrawing from external reality. This withdrawal paves the way for ego disintegration, under the impact of superego aggression, and leads to an unconscious breakthrough and a deep regression.

Onset of the depression

Psychotic depressive reactions typically occur in the form of an attack. The patient may seem stable and well for many years before his illness; and after recovery he may again seem well and stable. This appearance of stability is deceptive. The patient manages to develop adaptive and defensive systems which work reasonably well as long as he is not exposed to certain losses or threats of loss. Under ordinary circumstances he is able to maintain an effective balance of internal stresses; but if his stress tolerance is exceeded he may suddenly lose his actually unstable equilibrium. Then his regression into a primitive delusional state reveals the basic weakness of his personality organization.

Sometimes the onset is quite sudden. Everything seems to have been going reasonably well until some personal catastrophe plunges a person into a full-blown depression within a few days. Usually, however, the onset is more gradual. In the first place the stressful situation may itself be slow in developing. But even when there is a sudden blow the patient may give little evidence for some time that he is heading into a depression. This preliminary phase we shall call the period of incubation.

Incubation period

There is usually a period of incubation, lasting a few weeks or months, before the depression becomes unmistakable to relatives and friends. During this phase many signs of rising tension and anxiety make their appearance. The patient complains of fatigue and headache, of tightness in the head and neck, of aching limbs and tired eyes. He cannot relax or get refreshing sleep. His appetite falls off, and he may develop indigestion with constipation or diarrhea. He now begins to look as tired as he feels. He suffers an overall slowing down in activity, even though he is at the same time restless, irritable and indecisive. He loses interest in conversation, in going places and in doing things. He is dissatisfied, discouraged, gloomy and preoccupied.

It is not unusual for a depressed person to try to overcome his weariness and gloom by sheer effort, urged on by relatives and friends. This seldom works. Instead he becomes more than ever aware that something is wrong with him. He may grow still more preoccupied and dwell upon his misgivings about his physical health and personal competence.

Many patients focus their major attention upon body overconcern. Some insist that all their difficulties stem from physical illness. They seek repeated medical examinations and resort to all kinds of medication. Their somatic complaints are intensifications of the ones already mentioned — aches and pains, fatigue and poor sleep, inability to relax, changes in appetite and in gastrointestinal functioning, and finally a decline in sexual desire and potency. In women, menstruation usually becomes irregular or stops altogether.

The depression deepens

As his preoccupation grows, the patient's decline in interest and initiative begins to pick up momentum. Life now seems to have lost meaning and purpose. Things the patient used to undertake with pleasure now leave him unmoved or fill him with aversion. He loses his emotional resonance. Other people's joys and sorrows leave him untouched. The same is true of what he reads in the newspaper or sees on television and at the movies.

The depressed person now cannot get emotionally involved in anything outside himself.[16] He may go through the same motions as before, in doing something, but nothing feels the same to him. Even his food actually loses its savor. Everything becomes a burden. Ordinary duties call for more effort than he can muster; each day's routines are almost more than he can face. The mere prospect of adding anything new is intolerable.

Meanwhile thinking difficulties arise to complicate matters. The patient finds that he cannot concentrate without great effort, and that he cannot think clearly or remember. He may not even be able to understand what he hears. Now and then he has fleeting feelings of estrangement — things and people look different or seem far away. All this can be frightening. The patient fears that he is losing his mind and wonders what is happening to him.

It is true that anyone as anxious, worried and preoccupied as this might have thinking difficulties, whether he is depressed or not. But the depressed person is justified in worrying about his growing incompetence. Something actually is happening to him. The world of people and things is losing its meaning because unconscious processes, belonging to another world, are on the verge of breaking through. When they do break through the patient's world of social reality will largely be replaced by an unrealistic delusional world. The patient will then regress to infantile feelings and infantile conflicts, and hate will rule his life.

The patient begins by reacting to his increasing incompetence with complaints that he is no good, a failure, worthless, a burden to everyone. In such depressive complaints there is both self-accusation and an indictment of others. If someone who loves him tries now to reassure him that he is

16 Cameron, N., and Margaret, A., "Depressive disorders," in *Behavior Pathology.* Boston: Houghton Mifflin, 1951, pp. 314–327.

none of these, he simply repeats his complaints and buttresses them, in the face of the other person's obvious pain. His voice is full of vengeance, not of meekness.

To his lost emotional responsiveness the patient reacts similarly. He takes it at once as a sign that he is incapable of loving — which is by now true — and underserving of anyone's love. This, too, is a mingling of an attack upon his loved ones with an attack upon himself. If you listen dispassionately to such a patient, the hostile note comes through. If you watch him telling a loved person these things, over and over, it is impossible to doubt that he is not only suffering pain but deliberately inflicting it upon someone else. We shall see this clearly in one patient's treatment of his wife, and in the other's suicidal plans and her tormenting demands in the hospital.

The depressed person can no longer restrain his cruel, sadistic behavior. He is already too ill. He has regressed to a level of thought and feeling at which infantile conflicts and fantasies begin to emerge as reality for him, while the world of social reality almost disappears. The people in this new regressive world are reduced to the role of players in the patient's private drama — a dark tragedy in which everything is swallowed up in suffering, hate and guilt. Let us now turn to a consideration of two such cases of psychotic depression, one an agitated depressed woman, the other a retarded depressed man.

A case of agitated psychotic depression

Constance Q., a single self-supporting woman, aged forty-eight, found herself facing heavy expenditures to help her two brothers. They had for years been a constant financial drain upon her. She had never received from them either appreciation or repayment in return for her sacrificing her own security and pleasure. Now it became again clear that, even though her previous sacrifices had been in vain, she would again have to make still further ones.

Constance became more and more tense with time, more anxious and more irritable. In the daytime she could not concentrate; at night she could neither relax nor sleep. Her angry resentment grew until she considered killing herself so that her brothers would be left to shift for themselves. Eventually the dreaded family conferences came. When they were over the patient found herself a thousand dollars poorer. There was no prospect of an end to the demands made upon her purse. During a vacation in the country she set out three times to drown herself, but each time she could not take the final step.

In the end Constance went to her old family physician. To him she poured out her angry complaints against her brothers, her own feelings of misery and hopelessness, and even her suicidal plans. He advised her to go to a hospital at once, which was good, but he also added his opinion that, in her own way, she was just as bad as her brothers. The latter comment proved to be a turning point. She was looking desperately for sympathy and love, but what she got was a harsh rebuke. She now turned away from the realistic crisis that faced her, and began attacking herself with accusations which soon reached delusional proportions. It was then that relatives took her to a psychiatric hospital.

Hospitalization brought no improvement. Constance sat staring in front of her, silent, tearful and dejected, wringing her hands, rubbing her forehead and picking at her skin. She was the picture of a woman in profound grief. She rarely spoke. When she did she said that she had no feeling and no thoughts, that she was like a statue, a vegetable, lifeless. To an experienced eye it was obvious that she was deeply preoccupied and in an emotional turmoil. Before long both the preoccupation and the inner turmoil came to light.

Constance began to grow less withdrawn and more aware of her surroundings. As she re-established contact with the hospital environment, her quiet grief gave way to restless agitation, and in place of brooding there were outspoken self-accusations and insistent demands that she be punished. It became clear that she was no longer living in terms of social reality, but rather in terms of a delusional world of her own. The whole hospital, with its patients and personnel, grew to be a stage on which she acted out her fantastic drama of self-degradation and hate.

Now Constance denounced herself venomously as a person steeped in sin, a liar, a hypocrite and a cheat. These were all accusations that she had previously leveled at her two brothers. She confessed publicly an affair she had had with a man many years earlier. She demanded repeatedly, angrily, tormentingly, that she be brought to trial for her terrible crimes, that she be imprisoned for life, that she be beaten and thrown naked into the street. She continually harped on the refrain, "Get it over with!" meaning, "Bring me to trial and punishment!"[17]

The patient's delusions spread. She said that autos were painted yellow and sent past the hospital to advertise that she was a dirty, yellow dog. When a door on one of the nearby houses was painted red, she told everyone that this was to show the world that she was a prostitute.[18] She kept demanding that she be debased, made to scrub floors and do menial work. Her angry insistence, and her way of following nurses and doctors about with her noisy self-accusations and demands, made everyone dread seeing her. She seemed bristling with hostility. Eventually she was transferred to a bleak public hospital which she herself called a prison. Here she managed to work through her depression, recover her composure and return to her previous work.

Discussion. Here we see the psychotic reaction of a woman frustrated by a final disillusionment in her emotional life. She had never been able to

[17] A depressed soldier reported by Grinker and Spiegel kept asking to be sent back to the front lines, to "get it over with." Grinker, R. R., and Spiegel, J., *War Neuroses.* Philadelphia: Blakiston, 1945, pp. 35–36.

[18] This is an obvious example of delusional *psuedo-community* formation, which has the same characteristics as pseudocommunities in paranoid reactions. It is only the profound, overwhelming depressive mood that differentiates it from a typical paranoid reaction.

establish a stable love relationship with a man outside her family. All her life she remained attached to her brothers, loving them enough to rescue them over and over from personal disaster, hating them for always failing her and for neglecting her callously when they were not in desperate need. Eventually she reached a point where she could no longer blind herself to the futility of her sacrifices and the certainty that she could expect nothing whatever in return. When she was so full of unbearable hate that she made plans to kill herself so as to spite her brothers, the last person to whom she appealed for help told her bluntly that she was as bad as her worthless brothers. This was the final frustration that tipped the scales. It focussed all her violent hatred upon her already guilty, ambivalent self.

As we have seen, Constance at first reacted to this final blow by withdrawing into what looked like deep grief. She was stunned. Because of her personality defects, however, the withdrawal led to a deep regression and to hateful self-accusations. In her delusions she now accused herself of her brothers' faults, which were really not her own, and she raised the ghost of an old sin — her long buried love affair — to bear witness against her. She attacked herself sadistically, demanding outrageous punishments, and making everyone around her dread the sight of her.

Can any sense be made of such delusional, self-defeating behavior? Psychotic behavior always makes sense if we understand the personality changes behind it. Under the stress of her frustration, and given her personality defects, this woman suffered a sweeping disintegration and regression. This process reactivated an early phase of her development when the psychodynamic balance was quite different. In this regressive phase her ego integrations were relatively weak; and they were dominated by an abnormally severe, archaic superego. As we shall see later on, such an interpretation helps to make the otherwise absurd, but terribly dangerous, behavior of depressed delusional patients intelligible. In this particular case there is also a certain grandiosity — all the world is interested in her sins — which serves to link it with the paranoid reactions and with manic reactions also.

A case of retarded psychotic depression

Hugh W., a business man aged forty-three, father of four children, was brought to a psychiatric clinic by his wife. She said that he was deeply depressed and could not work, that he felt he was a disgrace to his name and ought to die. He had made no suicidal move; but she was frightened because she knew that if he once made up his mind to kill himself she could do nothing to stop him. His own complaints were as follows: "I'm down and depressed. I've failed everybody. I've lost every bit of self-respect I ever had. I can never face people again. I feel numb but I'm frantic inside. This is worse than being dead."

The patient sat slumped in the chair, his chin sunk on his chest, his eyes fixed on the floor, the picture of dejection and despair. He looked more like a sick man of sixty than a man of forty-three. After his first statements he spoke only when spoken to, his answers were brief, his voice was monotonous and sometimes inaudible. His face was masklike, but his eyes were troubled and his brow was furrowed. Occasionally he spoke with disgust about himself, and when he did he looked bitter and he almost snarled. He agreed to hospitalization with only a nod. He got up heavily and moved off like a man being led to prison.

Immediate background of the depression. Hugh's wife said that he had never recovered from his mother's death five months earlier. When she was found to have incurable cancer Hugh was stunned. Why hadn't it been discovered earlier? He blamed the doctors first and then himself. If he had paid more attention to her, he said, and made her get more frequent medical check-ups, this would never have happened. "She was always so uncomplaining — a saint if ever there was one." He kept repeating, "I shouldn't have let this happen. I shouldn't have let it happen." Sometimes he said, "How could she *do* this to me!"

When the will was read there was a codicil leaving Hugh a larger share of his mother's equities than his siblings got. They were polite but cool. One of them remarked that of course he had stayed close to his mother in recent years. This was true but unjust, since he had always been close to her, and they all knew it.

Mourning becomes melancholia. After the funeral Hugh remained quiet, sad and silent. He ate poorly, toyed with his food, spoke little at meals, and was unresponsive to his family, which had never been true before. He seemed always tired. He would throw himself into a chair immediately after dinner. He went to bed early but his sleep grew worse and worse, until he was reading half the night and getting up for coffee at four or five o'clock. Sex interest disappeared. Hugh's wife accepted all this as the not unnatural mourning of a favorite son. She tried to comfort him but he pushed her away. She persuaded him to get a medical check-up. He was still able to put up a good front away from home, so he got a clean bill of health.

As time went on Hugh did not get better. He got worse. He could hardly drag himself to work. He confessed one evening to his wife that someone at the office had told him he was slipping. He could not remember things or concentrate on his work. Everything worried him. It was as if he were "holding things off." He checked and rechecked his work, but his mistakes were increasing. He said, "I guess I'm getting old before my time." He began calling himself lazy, a "has-been," a drifter and an "also-ran."

His growing silence at the table threw a pall over every meal. Hugh began excusing himself and leaving soon after the meal started. His wife now felt that he was carrying his grief too far. She told him in private how upsetting his behavior was to the children. He was surly at first and then apologetic. He could not help it, he said, and he was beginning to realize the kind of man he was and trying to face it.

He said that he had always been selfish and demanding, that he was neglecting the children just as he had neglected his mother and let her die. He added, "I've lived as if the world revolved around me. I realize now what life must have been like for you and the children all these years."

Following this Hugh seemed to come out of his shell a bit, but he was also more disturbed. He sat through the meals and tried to converse, but his talk was forced and everybody felt uncomfortable. Meanwhile his wife noticed that he was getting hesitant and indecisive, even about little things, like choosing a tie and putting cuff links in his shirt. Sometimes he seemed lost in thought, motionless, right in the middle of dressing. Sentences were left unfinished. Hugh sighed a great deal. On the next trip to his doctor he failed to conceal his despondency. A prescription raised his spirits for awhile, but it also made him more restless and sleepless than before.

The acute onset. One evening at dinner Hugh put down his things and abruptly left the house. His wife followed him and brought him back. They went upstairs together and he told her that he had reached the end of the road, that he could not go on. Now he knew how hateful he was. Look at what he was doing to everyone. His brothers and sister were right — he was as good as a murderer. How could he face his own children with this on his conscience? If they knew what he was like they would not stay in the room with him. He could not go on pretending that he was a decent, responsible man when he had broken every trust he had ever been given. He went on to tell her about a premarital affair. When Hugh's wife told him that she did not care what he had done before marriage he stared at her as though she had struck him. It was then that she called in their doctor and arranged for his admission to a psychiatric clinic.

Behavior in the clinic. Hugh gave a general impression of bovine submissiveness. He took no initiative, he went where he was led, and he accepted hospital restrictions without a word. Most of the time he sat or stood alone. When he walked he moved slowly and heavily, with head bowed and body stooped. He ate only when coaxed. Sometimes he had to be reminded to chew the food he had in his mouth. If he was prodded he sometimes became nasty. He slept only two or three hours a night, and he never wanted to get up to face another day. He rarely spoke unless spoken to, but he often moaned, muttered and sighed. When asked what he was saying he only stared and said, "Nothing, nothing."

During therapeutic sessions Hugh was formal, grave and uncommunicative. He complained that everything was an effort and useless, that his head was "in a vise," that he could remember nothing and concentrate on nothing. "I'm just going downhill," he would say, "and you know it as well as I do." He spoke briefly in a monotone of his failures and his guilt. He was utterly convinced that everything was his own fault. "You'll tell me this is an illness," he would say, "but there's no excuse for being like this. It's just the final failure." His whole life now seemed nothing but "failure and broken trust." He had failed his mother, his wife and his children. He had never really loved anybody in his life and he was unfit to be loved. He paraded all his mistakes. He wished he had a broken leg or a real illness to justify the way he felt. His wife and children seemed to be a thousand miles away. At times he could not picture them at all.

Further delusional development. The patient's most bitter self-reproach now was that he had left his wife to care for their four children alone, that he was selfish, irresponsible and no man. Yet when she visited him he would at first simply stare at her, or look away and say that it was no use, that she had better forget him. As he began to regain contact with his surroundings he grew more cruel. He used self-condemnation and contempt in such a way as to undermine every ideal his wife had ever had of him. He repeated statements that had hurt and frightened her before he was hospitalized. Sometimes he told her to take the children somewhere and start a new life without him. Other times he told her to bring the children with her so that they could see the kind of a father they had. After some of these visits the wife needed therapeutic help herself.

Hugh developed a few delusions of reference. He knew that everybody hated him from the way they looked at him and walked away from him. The patients must know all about him from the doctors. The nurses looked pityingly at him. One of them seemed sad and disappointed when she was with him. If they knew the kind of life he had lived they would despise him. He insisted that he was not sick, but only a quitter. His mother had always said, "No W's are ever quitters!" It was a good thing she was in her grave and was spared the disgrace of seeing him mindless and a quitter.

There was something else that he had been hiding. He had been turning in "dishonest reports" at the office. Hugh expected to be prosecuted for this and sent to prison. He knew it would be found out sooner or later. Were we holding him here until his company could work up a case against him and put him in jail? He would rather face it now, he had no defense. "I've led a Dr. Jekyll–Mr. Hyde life. I've always known about Mr. Hyde, and now everybody else will know." He wrote a letter to his firm, admitting his wrongdoing and offering his resignation, which the firm refused. (There actually had been serious mistakes and omissions in his reports after his mother's death.) Hugh also brought up an old income tax error which had long since been straightened out. He had been expecting every day for weeks, he said, that the government men would come and claim him.

Signs of improvement. The ideas of self-reference were actually signs of improvement. They represented an attempted return to reality relationships by way of *delusional reconstruction (restitution).* The fact that Hugh could talk about them and write a letter, even a delusional letter, was a further sign of a return toward a lost reality.

He had spent many weeks in a fog of psychotic unreality, wrestling with imagined crimes and conflicts belonging to a forgotten childhood. Now he was getting a little paranoid on his way back toward health. Besides, his expressions of guilt and worthlessness had less finality and doom about them than earlier.

There were other signs. Sleep and eating were noticeably better. Constipation, as characteristic of depressions as insomnia, was disappearing. Hugh was talking more and smiling sometimes. Once he even laughed during a movie show, and then looked startled, as if he had been caught laughing at a funeral. He was able to sit and read a bit, and eventually to play cards in a group. Like most depressives, he could not admit improvement until long after everyone else had seen it.

Therapy and recovery. Early in any severe depression treatment is aimed primarily at keeping the patient alive, and keeping him free from the demands of a normal environment which are more than he can possibly meet. Electroshock is commonly employed to cut short the more acute phase and bring the patient back into effective contact. If expert psychotherapy is available, and the patient is able to cooperate in it, some progress can be made toward understanding the personality defects which leave an individual vulnerable to depression, and the kinds of stress responsible for precipitating it. The aim is both to help a person toward a better adaptation after his illness and to decrease the likelihood of recurrence. Nearly all depressives ultimately recover.

While Hugh was in the clinic he gained considerable insight into his own personality problems and their childhood origins. Some of his findings we shall include in the discussion of his family background; but first we shall mention a few specific things about his more immediate past.

Toward the end of his stay in the clinic, Hugh recalled much of his delusional material spontaneously. He found it now absurd; he could not understand how he had ever believed it. He seemed to himself at the time, he said, to be standing before the world as an utterly worthless failure, a man devoid of love, responsible for his mother's death and his family's ruin, with even his name disgraced by dishonesty at work.

He remembered that when his mother's will was read he had felt a glow of pride over her preference for him. This was at once followed by guilt, which received a booster charge from a sibling's remark, as we have seen. He was angry over the remark, but as usual he was not able to retort. This reminded him that he had never been able to get angry unless he lost control. Whenever his sister teased him beyond endurance in childhood, for example, instead of fighting back he would go out to the back porch and spit. He remembered also that when his mother lay dying he had wished her dead for her own sake, instead of praying for a miraculous cure. This had made him wonder how much his love for his mother might have been motivated by secret hopes of profit.

After his mother died Hugh felt angry as well as sad. He found himself making comparisons between his mother and his wife in which his mother came out much the better of the two. His loyalties had always been divided between them, and he had felt double guilt because the two women obviously disliked each other. He recalled slighting things that his wife had said about his mother, which now seemed sacrilegious, and his mother's poor opinion of his wife. He wondered what she would have said if she had known about their premarital relationships. Perhaps now that she was dead she knew. The man was obviously identifying with his lost mother. He began to hate his wife and children.

It was with this background of feeling that Hugh confessed his premarital affairs to his wife. It was a typical depressive confession, always two-edged and usually sadistic. His stunned confusion over what his wife replied — that she did not care what he had done before their marriage — had two sources. Here was a mother substitute saying something that would have outraged his dead mother; and here was his wife in effect sanctioning their own premarital behavior when he was already in conscious guilty conflict over it.

When Hugh got well enough to go out walking with his wife, his children came to see him. He spent a few weekends and paid one visit to his place of business before he was discharged. Afterwards he went with his wife on a vacation, during which he became mildly elated and then mildly depressed, before he settled down. In turning now to an account of the patient's childhood we shall be dealing with a composite picture derived from accounts given by Hugh himself and by his wife and his sister, neither of whom shared his admiration for his mother.

Remote background of the depression. Hugh was the youngest of four children. His sister was four years older than he, his brothers six and eight years older. To his mother he seemed "the flower of the flock." His father was seventeen years older than his mother — an austere, pious, silent man who rarely needed to do more than speak to the children to make them behave. When he punished them he was severe but never angry. He was an antivivisectionist and a member of the antisaloon league. Hugh was always frightened of him. He pictured God as his father's father. His father died when Hugh was twenty.

The description of Hugh's mother came from three sources. Hugh had admired her all his life; his sister had mixed feelings about her; his wife disliked and resented her. Their accounts were not much at variance, but their emphases and interpretations were. She seems to have been as strong-minded as her husband, but affectionate, accessible and talkative. She kept herself the emotional center of the family, while at the same time deferring to her husband whom she revered.

Hugh's sister called her mother strait-laced and idealistic, a woman who never allowed her children to criticize anyone, but who gave her own judgments freely to guide them. She ran things in the home without seeming to do so. She treated her children with affection as long as they conformed to her wishes.[19] She disapproved of all her sons' girls, but once marriage became inevitable she allowed herself to be won over. Hugh's struggle for independence was the hardest of all.

Hugh's wife called his mother self-righteous, a holy martyr, shrewd and possessive, a woman who gave moral opinions with her chin held high. You either agreed with her or you had no standards, she was always in the right, a Puritanical snob. Hugh at his very worst was like her. He never got free from her influence. The mother liked to say, "Love conquers all!" but what she meant was her love. She threw a shadow over their life that was like a religious difference.

During therapy Hugh modified his idealistic conception of his mother considerably, but she still came out rather well. He said at first that he owed all that was best in him to her — his tastes, his feelings, his moral outlook above all. He treasured the knowledge that he had always been her pet, and it took him some time to see that he had paid a price for this advantage. As long as he could remember he had placed her approval before everything else. She had seldom punished him; but whenever he erred she became silent, solemn, hurt and withdrawn. This he could never endure. He always gave in, even when he felt angry and exasperated. She usually referred to herself in the third person — "Mother doesn't like you to do that" — which made her seem more a sacred principle than a displeased woman. Three things she could never forgive: irresponsibility, dishonesty and immorality. Another thing was Hugh's choice of a wife. She gave up open opposition when she realized that she was going to lose, but she never became reconciled to her youngest son's marriage.

With the suffering, hate and penitence of a depression now behind him, with his mother dead and his wife at home with the children, Hugh had a chance to look at his life through different eyes. He could begin to give up his dead mother and turn his affection toward his living wife and children. The shadow of his mother's displeasure was still there and so were his infantile conflicts; but the shadow was lighter and the conflicts less intense. When he was nearly well, Hugh seemed remarkably independent, self-reliant, considerate and kind. His wife said that these were his normal traits. He had evidently regained his previous adult personality structure with a good deal of insight into what lay beneath it.[20]

Summary of the two depressive cases

A single self-supporting woman of forty-eight suffered a cruel disillusionment and a grave economic loss. She was forced to face the fact that her two brothers, whom she had treated for decades as though they were

[19] Fromm-Reichmann, F., "Intensive psychotherapy of manic-depressives," in Bullard, D. M. (Ed.), *Psychoanalysis in Psychotherapy*. Chicago: Univ. of Chicago Press, 1959, pp. 221–226.
[20] Gibson, R. W., Cohen, M. B., and Cohen, R. A., "On the dynamics of the manic-depressive personality," *Amer. J. Psychiat.*, 1959, *115*, 1101–1107; Brown, F., "Depression and childhood bereavement," *J. ment. Sci.*, 1961, *107*, 754–777.

her sons, cared nothing for her and were hopelessly irresponsible. Her immediate reaction was to become anxious and angry. Then she combined hostility toward her brothers with self-hate; she made suicidal plans to spite them. In desperation, she turned to her family physician, complaining of her brothers' callous treatment of her. After he told her that she was no better than they were she vented all her fury upon herself and, not unnaturally, upon her physicians and nurses. She denounced in herself faults which were in reality her brothers'. She also confessed an affair, thought that automobiles and street doors were painted to express evil opinions about her, and demanded angrily that she be brought to trial and imprisoned, or thrown into the street. She finally worked through her depression in a setting that seemed like a prison to her. Eventually she recovered and returned to work.

A married business man, aged forty-three, father of four children, developed a retarded depression in which there were intense ambivalence and guilt. His siblings' coolness when they found that he had been favored in the mother's will aroused resentment at the same time that it increased his guilt. He felt remorse over the pleasure he had experienced when the will was read; and he recalled momentary wishes, when his mother was suffering, that she would die. He slipped from mourning into melancholia, complained of fatigue and worry, lost interest in everything, could not sleep or eat, and found himself unable to concentrate or remember.

The self-accusations and incompetence increased. The patient called his whole life a failure and a succession of broken trusts. In relation to his mother he said that he was no better than a murderer. To his wife he confessed premarital affairs and said he was unfit to be in his children's company. After he was in a hospital he grew still more preoccupied, he spoke little, groaned, sighed and muttered to himself. Ideas of reference appeared — patients "disliked" him and nurses "pitied" him.

Following improvement, psychotherapy threw light upon his childhood background. His father had been an austere, pious, forbidding man, seventeen years older than his mother. His mother had always been the emotional center of the family, a strait-laced, strong, opinionated woman, who gave affection only in return for compliance with her wishes. If opposed by her children, she became silent, hurt and withdrawn. She objected to each of her sons' marriages, but to that of her youngest son, the patient's, the most of all. In the course of psychotherapy, he was eventually able to give up his dead mother, to become once more kind and self-reliant, and to turn toward his living wife and children.

The development of so much hatred and guilt, which both patients showed consciously, is not self-explanatory. Neither is their persistence in the form of outspoken delusions. The woman was in a position that justified both anxiety and anger. The man was in a position that justified mourning, and perhaps a certain amount of remorse and anger. But anxiety, anger, remorse and mourning do not ordinarily lead to a regression as deep or lasting as theirs. Under these circumstances a psychotic depression seems to develop only in persons who are strongly ambivalent toward loved ones and who, early in life, have introjected and identified with sadistic love objects.[21] All the evidence that we have about the woman patient points in this direction; in the case of the man patient the evidence is explicit. Let us turn now to an organized discussion of the dynamic and developmental background of adults who develop psychotic depressions under stress.

Dynamic and Developmental Background

Psychotic depressions are common and usually easy to recognize clinically. Everyone agrees that they involve profound regressions in persons who are more than ordinarily dependent and oral in their personality orientation. Everyone also agrees that psychotic depressions always include delusions of guilt, self-depreciation and self-condemnation. There are still controversies regarding the relation of psychotic depressions to neurotic depressions.[22] We shall follow the prevailing trend, already set forth in the chapter on neurotic depression, according to which the milder forms are called neurotic and the more severe and sweeping forms psychotic.

Denial and distortion of external reality may occur to some extent in neurotic depression, in order to make external reality seem to conform to internally generated fantasies and conflicts. But whenever such denial and distortion reaches delusional proportions, we are dealing with a psychotic reaction. This holds true whether or not the patient is able to compensate for his defective reality testing and to conceal his delusional thinking. The same point can be made in relation to psychotic paranoid reactions, as we have seen, and to psychotic schizophrenic reactions as we shall later show. There are always some patients who, in spite of psychotic delusions, manage somehow to maintain object relations sufficiently to hide the fact that they are at the time psychotic. These last are the patients who seem psychotic to their therapist but to no one else, sometimes not even to themselves. For the majority, however, the psychotic regression renders the patient incompetent to deal with his everyday object relations. It is with this majority that we are here concerned.

Mourning and melancholia

For half a century mourning has been compared with psychotic depression or, as it used to be called, melancholia. In normal mourning, especially if someone has lost a loved person through death, the grieving one goes

---

[21] Klein, M., "A contribution to the psychogenesis of manic-depressive states," in Klein, M., *Contributions to Psychoanalysis.* London: Hogarth Press, 1950, pp. 282–310.

[22] See, for example, Greenacre, P. (Ed.), *Affective Disorders.* New York: Internat. Univ. Press, 1953; Arieti, S., "Manic-depressive psychosis," in Arieti, S. (Ed.), *American Handbook of Psychiatry.* New York: Basic Books, 1959, pp. 419–454; and Gutheil, E., "Reactive depressions," in same *Handbook,* pp. 345–352.

through is a process of gradual weaning.[23] As with other weanings, the process may be exceedingly painful. Day by day, bit by bit, the mourner has to realize that one or another experience can never again be shared with the lost, mourned loved one.[24] Some of these remembered experiences are trivial, some important, but the pain comes in either case with the recognition that the sharing can never come again.

Normal mourning usually involves identification with the person who is being mourned. There is an overwhelming sadness that the lost one should have died, a sense of all the lost possibilities, the hopes and the future which those who are alive possess. But in addition to this, the mourner tends to take over some of the characteristics of the lost one — to act like him, speak as he did, even to look like him and live as he lived. It is as though the mourner were saying to the world, "He lives again in me!" When this is done it is usually done without awareness; it is rarely a conscious mimicry. Friends and relatives notice it before the mourner does. Nevertheless, it seems to be a normal defense against crushing loss, a process of taking into oneself parts of the behavior and appearance of the lost person, so that they are in a sense preserved alive. This process of taking in another person is based upon what we call identification, and in its more basic, primitive form, the process of introjection. Identification and introjection occur in both normal mourning and in melancholia, that is, in psychotic depression.[25]

There are differences, however, between mourning and psychotic depression. Psychotic depression may begin with identification and the kind of introjection which we see in normal mourning; but the sweeping regression that soon develops transforms the clinical picture into a life-and-death struggle between a sadistic superego and a cringing, but also sadistic, infantile ego. The situation is often compared with that in severe compulsive reactions, like those we have discussed in an earlier chapter. There, too, we witnessed the struggle between an archaic sadistic superego and a cringing infantile ego. But the level of regression in compulsives is neurotic. The patient may act out his little drama of ritual and self-punishment, but his fantasies and conflicts do not swallow up the realistic world as they do in psychotic depressions. Let us look at the character of fixation and regression in psychotic depressions.

Fixation and regression in psychotic depressions

In psychotic depressions we see a picture of regression to the earliest levels that we saw occurring in neurotic depressions. The regression re-

[23] Freud, S., "Mourning and melancholia," (1917), in Strachey, J. (Ed.), Standard Edition. London: Hogarth Press, 1957, vol. 14, pp. 239–258.

[24] Rochlin, G. R., "The loss complex: a contribution to the etiology of depression," *J. Amer. Psychoanal. Ass.*, 1959, 7, 299–316.

[25] For a discussion of food aversions in relation to the self-image, see Davids, A., and Lawton, M. J., "Self-concept, mother-concept, and food aversions in emotionally disturbed and normal children," *J. abnorm. soc. Psychol.*, 1961, 62, 309–314.

activates conflicts and fantasies belonging to phases of development much earlier than those seen in obsessive compulsive reactions, to phases of oral dependent relationship in which the frustration of dependent wishes provoke savagery. The patient who regresses to psychotic levels, when he grows depressed, loses the relatively good object relationships which the neurotic depressive manages to retain.

This loss of object relations makes the whole clinical picture different from that of neurotic depressives. In normal and in neurotic life it is the meaningful relationship with external reality that helps keep a person free from being overwhelmed by his own internal reality, with all its primitive fantasies and conflicts, with its primary processes and its lack of stable objects. We all have some experience with this fluid internal world when we regress in sleep and have a vivid dream. The dream then seems to be the only reality there is, even though the shifts, sequences and meanings do not follow the paths of logical thought or objective experience.

Within recent years, experiments in isolating apparently normal adults from most of their accustomed stimulation — so-called *sensory deprivation* — have demonstrated anew the proposition that there is a life of fantasy, in which primary processes seem to rule, that can come to the surface even when a person is awake. For some persons the fantasy experiences thus released grow intolerable; for others they may be only amusing, but still apparently uncontrollable.

Regression in psychotic depression does not reach the degree of abandonment of external reality that regression in dreams and in sensory deprivation does. It is, nevertheless, a deeper regression than that which we witnessed in paranoid reactions where denial of one's own hostility is buttressed by projection of it on to actual or at least possible persons in the human environment. Projection is utilized to a very limited degree in psychotic depression. When the depressed person loses his object relationship he experiences a tremendous upsurge of hostility, just as the paranoid persecuted person does; but because he does not succeed in projecting it, he becomes overwhelmed by it and disintegrates. It is as though a primitive sadistic hostility had escaped from repression with an irresistible rush, disintegrating ego-superego organizations and reducing defenses to infantile levels.

The manifest products of such a regression seem to represent a split into two more or less reciprocal organizations, one of which has been historically equated with the sadistic archaic precursor of the superego, and the other with the archaic infantile ego. Actually the clinical picture is not as distinct as this. What we find is a person who hates, abuses and abominates himself, but who also, as in both our cases, may be hateful, abusive and abominable to other persons around him. His hatred of others is more realistic by far than his hatred of himself. It is true, as we have pointed out before, that a psychotically depressed person is capable of killing loved ones as well as himself; and it is true that this seems an extension of self-hatred to these others. But psychotically depressed persons do not typically call for the cruel, inhuman punishments for others that they commonly do for themselves.

Instead of a mere increase in unconscious guilt, such as neurotic depressives show through their complaints of inferiority, worthlessness and hopelessness, the psychotic depressive experiences overwhelming conscious guilt. Instead of merely feeling unloved and unlovable he feels himself to be vile, hateful and utterly despicable. The violence of his self-hatred exceeds anything seen in neurotic depression; and his actual inaccessibility to objective reality comes out clearly the moment anyone makes an attempt to help him.

In support of the overwhelming self-hatred that he is experiencing the psychotic depressive develops unmistakable delusions. Without his delusions of hatred and destruction the depressed patient would be totally unable to justify his overwhelming feelings. In this sense the delusions are adaptive, even though maladaptive. Through them the patient reconstructs his world in such a way that he can find a place for himself in it. Admittedly, this reconstruction of reality is delusional, is contrary to many facts, and all too often puts the depressed person in jeopardy. He may hate himself so much at this level, and be so cruel and insistent about it, that eventually he kills himself. But this outcome, which if prevented gives way almost always to final recovery, has another alternative which also has its serious perils. The alternative would be to disintegrate still further, to become acutely schizophrenic, and thus run the risk of nonrecovery. About 90 per cent of psychotic depressive patients ultimately recover, whereas only about 50 per cent of definitely schizophrenic patients make a comparable recovery.

One of the most important characteristics of psychotic depressives is that when they are threatened by a loss, or when they have suffered a real loss, they at once accept it as irretrievable and final. Instead of performing the *work of mourning*, the weaning process to which we have already referred, the patient seems to be locked in a life-and-death struggle. The participants in this struggle are divisions of his own personality organization, now regressed to an infantile level where infantile defenses operate, but with the power, danger and logic of a monstrously sadomasochistic adult. The attacking part is certainly derived from an archaic superego, still more primitive than that involved in obsessive compulsive neuroses, more cruel and more dangerous by far. There are signs that the attacking archaic superego here is itself a product of internalized infantile objects, conceived at the time of introjection as sadistic and irresistible. The part attacked seems to be derived from the early infantile ego, from self-reactions which may have arisen in response to the sadism experienced in early life along with love, and most likely mother love, since mother love is for most persons the earliest powerful form experienced.

If we bear in mind the obvious fact that, no matter how deeply a person regresses in a depression, he never acts like an infant or sounds like an infant, we shall find it convenient to characterize the life-and-death struggle of the psychotic depressive as a fundamentally infantile one. It is a struggle between the revived derivative of a sadistic archaic superego, a product of the internalization of the sadistic love objects in infancy, and a sado-masochistic archaic ego, a product of reciprocally developed reactions to the introjected love objects of infancy. The regressive psychotic state is not like anything in normal infancy. Instead it represents the pathological *adult products* of early infantile interaction between the patient as an orally dependent infant and the others around him, as he himself experienced them at that time.

There is general agreement that psychotic depressions seem to appear among certain kinds of adult personalities and not among others. If a person experiences a psychotic depression in full adulthood, first of all he is almost sure to recover, and in addition he is almost certain to have another depression if he falls mentally ill a second or a third time. He will almost certainly recover from a second and a third attack if he is unfortunate enough to have them.[26] It will increase our understanding of the dynamic and developmental background of psychotic depressions if we examine what is known about adults who are vulnerable to them, in other words, if we examine the *depressive personality*.

The Depressive Personality

We have seen that people who develop psychotic depressions have deep-seated fixations toward which they regress when they become ill. The depressive personality is organized around an unconscious sense of guilt because of excessive unconscious hostility. Once in a while one finds a depressive person who, without being psychotic, is nevertheless continually aware of feeling guilty without knowing why. He may express this openly and live a life of atonement and self-denial. Usually, however, the unconscious sense of guilt manifests itself vaguely as chronic feelings of inferiority, insignificance or unworthiness, which may not interfere with a general enjoyment of life.[27]

These feelings are expressed in a variety of ways,[28] not all of them obviously depressive. A depressive person may seem merely humble and chronically self-disparaging. He belittles himself, is apologetic, and compares himself unfavorably with others. He may ingratiate himself with his associates by deferring to them, or by playing the ignoramus or even the

---

[26] Arieti, S., "Manic-depressive psychosis," in Arieti, S. (Ed.), *American Handbook of Psychiatry.* New York: Basic Books, 1959, pp. 419–454.

[27] When these feelings interfere with the enjoyment of life, but do not lead to a *psychotic regression*, we see the *neurotic depression* described in Chapter 12.

[28] Gibson, R. W., Cohen, M. B., and Cohen, R. A., "On the dynamics of the manic-depressive personality," *Amer. J. Psychiat.*, 1959, *115*, 1101–1107; Arieti, S., "Manic-depressive psychosis," in Arieti, S. (Ed.), *American Handbook of Psychiatry.* New York: Basic Books, 1959, pp. 419–454.

clown.[29] He may seek to overcome his feelings more actively by achievement and success, so as to stimulate others to praise him. Some depressive personalities can accept such praise when it comes; others seem forced to reject it, as though praise made them anxious.

Depressive personalities are seriously deficient in their capacity for maintaining a normal, stable level of self-esteem. They can never generate enough to meet their own needs. It is for this reason that they must live forever dependent upon other people to provide them with a stream of narcissistic supplies — of love and esteem — to make good their own deficiencies. The alternative is to feel abysmally unloved, deserted, worthless or guilty, and to run the risk of regressing into a psychotic depression.

It is this lack of normal self-esteem that makes the depressive always especially vulnerable to losses of love and security. Normal personalities are better able to withstand such losses because they can offset the deprivation involved by drawing upon their own resources of self-love. The depressive cannot "go it alone" like this. Just because he is unable to supply himself with esteem he must have external supplies to counteract his own internal self-hate.

Dependence upon others. Depressive personalities are often said to be dependent. This in itself says nothing. Everyone is dependent upon someone else. Every adult needs love or esteem from the outside. The critical point is that when the depressive person's external supply of love or esteem is threatened, he may be unable to preserve his integrity as a social personality. He may lose contact with external reality and disintegrate. He cannot defend himself against his own hostility. He has within him powerful unconscious primitive self-depreciation and self-hate, but he lacks well-developed self-love. Under these conditions, to lose love or esteem from other people is to lose one's personality equilibrium and to be abandoned to destructive forces from within. Narcissistic supplies to the depressive person are as essential as insulin is to the severely diabetic.

This anxious, insecure and sometimes desperate dependence has a life-history. It reflects infantile experiences quite different from those of paranoid personalities. The basic fears of depressives are not of attack and ridicule, but of desertion and loss of love. Their basic defenses are not projection and counterattack, but introjection and appeasement. Depressive dependence shows both a need and a capacity for emotional closeness. It points to experiences of close emotional relationships early in life which must have been rewarding and desired.

On the other hand, the depressive's unreasonable anxiety over losing love — his reaction to the mere threat of desertion as if desertion had already taken place — points to infantile experiences which were more than a mere need for emotional closeness. It indicates that the desired, rewarding love relationship must always have seemed in danger of disappearing. It must never

[29] This may be related to the claim that most professional clowns are sad people.

have been unconditional, but always dependent upon submission, upon childhood compliance with every parental demand.[30] The depressive adult is a person who has never succeeded in outgrowing his infantile need to get continual evidence that he will not be abandoned.

Reality adaptation. In their patterns of reality adaptation depressive personalities give many signs of the infantile needs and anxieties from which they have suffered and which they have tried to master. The stern lesson that they overlearned in early childhood was that any failure to comply with parental wishes meant an immediate loss of love and care, the desolate experience of loneliness and emptiness. No small child who is consistently given the alternative between love and desertion will choose desertion. He may rebel a thousand times against compliance; but if the punishment is always desertion and the reward is always love and care, the child will always surrender. He will learn to smother his rage and give up his bid for independence, if by such self-restriction he can get back a parent's love.

Such childhood training establishes a fixed pattern of pathological adaptation to external reality. The very needs and anxieties which the small child never really masters will remain always within him as his dominant needs and anxieties. As an adult, the depressive personality must adapt to external reality in such a way as to ensure the narcissistic supplies he cannot live without, to ensure a continual supply of love and care, or at least of envy and admiration. For a *cautious* adult this means making certain all the time that he does not forfeit the approval and support of others. For a more *enterprising* adult it means always striving for achievement and attractiveness, so as to stimulate expressions of love, admiration or envy, the outward signs that one is worthy and esteemed. Many retirement depressions of elderly achievers arise because of the loss of the source of such continual expressions.

Both standards of reality adaptation leave a person at the mercy of the indifference, criticism or rejection of other people. The life of the cautious depressive personality suffers because it must be limited to activities and opinions which will not turn others away from him. The life of the enterprising depressive is burdened with a continual need to achieve or to seem attractive, not so much as a source of pleasure as a safeguard against catastrophic loss. He is like a man who dances because someone is shooting at his feet.

A realistic conception of the external world is beyond the reach of such persons. In their childhood they construct a world dominated by infantile attempts at mastering threats of desertion. Their reality testing is continually distorted by an anxious emphasis upon securing narcissistic supplies. In

---

[30] Fromm-Reichmann, F., "Intensive psychotherapy of manic-depressives," in Bullard, D. M. (Ed.), *Psychoanalysis and Psychotherapy.* Chicago: Univ. of Chicago Press, 1959, pp. 221–226.

adulthood the basic unconscious orientation is still that of an insecure, help-less child in a world of powerful adults, who give love and care only when they are pleased, and without whose love and care even survival becomes impossible. The depressive acts as if the significant persons in his life were parents, not contemporaries, and as if he were called upon continually to demonstrate that he is innocent, compliant and worthy.[31]

Social interaction. The depressive person shows his personality defects clearly in his social relationships. His childhood experiences have left him unable to defend himself against his own self-destructive hostility unless he can get external reinforcements to bolster up his feeble self-esteem. His personality organization, we have said, is such that he must have an un-failing stream of love or esteem; but as a rule his childhood experiences have trained him neither to take the love and esteem of others for granted nor to live without them. He may be lucky enough to find external sources of continual approval and care. Otherwise he lives apprehensively, fearful that he will offend significant people, or that in some way he will fail, and so lose the reinforcements he must have. When this happens, as our clinical cases showed us, the nature of what depressive personalities have feared all their lives is revealed in their symptoms. It is an attack from their own internalized hostility, an attack from an archaic sadistic superego organiza-tion.

It is clear enough that, like paranoid personalities, the depressive lacks *realistic role representations.*[32] His pattern of distortion, however, is quite different. Paranoid persons expect others to attack them. They themselves feel innocent, and they stand on the offensive, ready to retaliate for the expected attack. The depressive expects others to desert him, to rebuff or belittle him. He stands ready to do whatever he can to appease others and win their approval. He feels guilty and expects punishment as expiation. He has one great advantage over paranoid persons: as long as he remains clinically well, he is able to accept closeness and to respond with pleasure to signs of affection and approval. His difficulty is that he can never get enough or be sure of a future supply.

Although the depressive personality has a far better understanding of other people than has the paranoid, his role attitudes still prevent him from having a realistic grasp of interactive situations in which he is per-sonally involved. He is overanxious to be loved, approved of, praised or admired. When he misinterprets it is always in the direction of being found unlovable or unacceptable. Indifference or neutrality in others seems to him a sign of depreciation, and he responds to this distortion by feeling worthless. Because he has such an exaggerated need for acceptance he

[31] Cohen, M. B., *et al.*, "An intensive study of twelve cases of manic-depressive psy-chosis," *Psychiatry*, 1954, *17*, 103–137.

[32] Cameron, N., and Margaret, A., "Social role-taking," in *Behavior Pathology.* Boston: Houghton Mifflin, 1951, pp. 114–122; Cameron, N., "Role-taking and behavior disorders," in *The Psychology of Behavior Disorders.* Boston: Houghton Mifflin, 1947, pp. 89–102.

leaves himself wide open to disappointment and disillusionment, like many a normal adolescent.

In spite of all this, depressive personalities usually get along better in social interrelationships than do paranoids. One reason is that they are basically compliant persons who need closeness and affection. They have experienced complete acceptance and approval throughout early childhood, even though this entailed loss of freedom. They have also learned to expect rejection and desertion the moment they refuse to comply. As an adult the depressive continues to act as though this were still true. He feels that he must gain constant approval just to be safe. He must have tangible evidence that he will not be left to his own devices without external support. This comes not from basic trust, but from contingent trust, that is, from a certainty of love in exchange for compliance.

A depressive personality can manage to live in reasonable comfort and security if he can find a situation that repeats in some form the one in which he grew up. Some adults actually go on living with their parents indefinitely and perpetuate a childlike emotional relationship. A depressive man may marry a woman who treats him much as his mother did; a depressive woman may find a husband who is willing to be a second father to her. Even in business and professional careers such a person may find it possible to play a childlike role successfully. He may subordinate himself to the dictates of parental figures or arouse continual expressions of admiration such as a dependent small child seeks from his mother.

Not every depressive personality is as fortunate as this; and even those who are may discover that human interrelationships are subject to change without notice. Husbands grow less attentive and indulgent; wives get tired of always giving protection and getting none in return; the patterns of employers and of fellow workers are seldom stable; or one's competence and attractiveness may begin to wane. One day a depressive personailty may do something which others cannot forgive; or he may grow tiresome with his constant self-blame and self-disparagement. If this sensitiveness to hurt and rebuff forces everyone to be overcareful, it can lead eventually to resentment, to the very rejection which the depressive personality cannot tolerate.

Hostility. Depressive personalities, like the paranoid, face the same basic problem of excessive internalized hostility.[33] But whereas in frank paranoid personalities the hostility is obvious, even when they are not psychotic, in depressives it usually is not. The difference is to some extent a difference in target, to some extent a difference in technique. Paranoid personalities, with their denial and projection, turn their hostility upon the environment and suffer from exaggerated innocence. Depressive personalities rely instead upon introjection. They turn their hostility upon themselves and suffer from exaggerated guilt.

[33] Fromm-Reichmann, F., "Psychoanalytic remarks on the clinical significance of hostility," in Bullard, D. M. (Ed.), *Psychoanalysis and Psychotherapy.* Chicago: Univ. of Chicago Press, 1959, pp. 277–282.

Clinical experience leads us to believe that there are large numbers of well-compensated depressive personalities who have mastered the techniques of ensuring the stream of narcissistic supplies which they must have. These people show no unusual signs of hostility unless the equilibrium they have established is seriously disturbed. The same is true of many inhibited characters, like Constance Q., who build a drab and rigid world which embraces both self-punishment and protection from emotional frustration. The relative ease with which many severe depressive psychoses develop, however, indicates that for both compensated and inhibited depressives the internalized excessive hostility remains always a dangerous threat.[34]

In less well-compensated depressive personalities there is an unmistakable undercurrent of hate. Many are emotionally ambivalent toward everyone whom they love. Such ambivalence has its roots in early childhood when love and care were made contingent upon compliance and expressions of hate were suppressed. Like a small child, the depressive resents his emotional dependence and hates the people whom he must always please; but unlike the small child, the depressive adult has long since denied and repressed his hate. Each time that he re-experiences some of the frustration and coercion that belongs to his early childhood, he revives basic infantile conflicts over hating loved persons, and this stimulates his morbid guilt. The repeated reactivation of infantile conflicts and frustrations helps to account for the depressive personality's overuse of introjection.

This is the general background against which the depressive may develop a vicious circle. His need for love and esteem is so great and so continuous that he can never feel satisfied or secure. He must therefore live perpetually frustrated by those from whom he needs love or esteem, because from his standpoint what he gets is too little and too uncertain. His frustration makes him angry, but to be angry with a loved one is doubly dangerous. For one thing it attacks his source of narcissistic supplies, and for another it increases his sense of guilt by increasing his own superego aggression. His increased guilt now calls for more love and reassurance to counteract the superego aggression; this increased demand, which no one can meet, invites still more anger, more guilt, and again more need. It is easy to see why an external loss of love or security, which a normal adult might handle well, can be disastrous to someone who lives in such unstable equilibrium.[35]

Distorted defensive structure. When a depressive person develops a frank psychotic depression, it is obvious that repression has failed and that introjection has become a dominant defense. What is not so obvious is that depressive personalities suffer from defective repression all their adult lives, and that a lifelong overuse of introjection is responsible for their characteristically *oral orientation.* As long as no psychosis develops, repression remains

---

[34] Rado, S., "The problem of melancholia," in *Psychoanalysis of Behavior.* New York: Grune & Stratton, 1956, pp. 47–63.

[35] For a cross-cultural study, see Iga, M., "Cultural factors in suicide of Japanese youth with focus on personality," *Sociol. Soc. Res.,* 1961, *46,* 75–92.

the key defense just as it does in normal and neurotic adults; but it is relatively weak, while introjection is relatively strong. In short, the balance of forces within the defensive structure of depressive personalities is always different from that in nondepressive personalities.

We see the influence of this defensive distortion in some of the behavioral characteristics and attitudes of depressive personalities. We already know that, because of weak repression and the constant threat of superego aggression, the depressive is driven always to enlist and retain the emotional support of outsiders. But what is equally striking is the infantile technique by which he seeks to achieve his end. It is a clinging technique, a parasitic technique, often an obviously aggressive oral technique. The depressive, for example, may cling to a marital partner, expecting and demanding emotional nourishment and protection like a big baby. The partner sometimes complains of the relationship as a draining, emotionally exhausting one.[36]

Metaphorically speaking, the adult depressive behaves toward loved ones as though he were a suckling. He seems to "swallow up" a marital partner, an employer or an associate, to make the other seem as much a part of him as his own mother once was. There is also the matriarchal mother with an infantile depressive personality who, in effect, swallows up the children she produces so that their lives become only an expression of her own. Even the husband may become incorporated into such a structure.

For the depressive personality to fail in such maneuvers is to be left exposed to superego attack, and therefore to experience feelings of desertion, insignificance and helplessness. To succeed means to acquire external objects which keep him safe as long as he can manipulate them. An external object, which supplies a depressive personality with the emotional support that he needs, may be potentially as dangerous as the original introjected objects, the ones that formed the nuclei of his archaic superego.

In both success and failure the depressive personality cannot free himself from an infantile dependence upon others. He cannot escape the constant danger of rejection. All his dependent relationships arouse frustration and hostility in him, usually unconscious but always intense. If he is meek, his meekness is a beggar's meekness, forced upon him by his own lack of resources. Like a beggar, he may secretly or unconsciously hate the people for whose bounty he is obliged always to appear grateful.

Oral traits. Oral traits are present in every human being, some symbolic and some direct; but in depressive personalities these are exaggerated in degree and primitive in function. We have just given general examples of symbolic sucking and engulfing in interpersonal relationships. There are also innumerable examples in individual needs and preferences. Such are, for example, an unusual devotion to eating and drinking for their own sake, addiction to smoking and chewing, exceptional pleasure in mouthing, suck-

---

[36] Cohen, M. B., *et al.*, "An intensive study of twelve cases of manic-depressive psychosis," *Psychiatry*, 17, 103–137.

ing, biting and the process of talking. Even the practice of making one's listeners into a captive audience is an oral clutching of other people.

Oral incorporation normally generalizes to other receptive channels, for example, devouring with one's eyes, eating another's words, breathing in an essence, the sense of possession that comes with an embrace, and the mutual engulfment of the sex act. None of these is pathological unless the degree of need and what it represents fall well outside the normal range. Only then can we speak of a depressive oral trait.

Precocious depressive ego development. The mother of a depressive does function as a substitute ego for her infant — that is, she does protect him from overwhelming primal anxiety and she helps him to overcome his primal phobias. She does these things, however, only as long as he meets her expectations. The moment he fails to comply with her wishes she withdraws her protection and help, in effect deserting her child and leaving him helpless. This a small child cannot tolerate. The major task of such a child is to avoid the sudden desertions to which his mother or mother substitute exposes him. This he can do only by learning to anticipate his tyrant's wishes. And we must remember that he is faced with the task of anticipation long before he has developed even the rudiments of secondary process thinking, long before he is capable of logic and abstraction.

This premature need for compliance, to avoid primal anxiety, leads the child to develop a precocious ego organization. In so doing he will make use of a readily available technique of defense and adaptation which we call *introjection.* This technique is modeled after the physical act of oral incorporation, the means through which the small child has already learned to overcome the loneliness and emptiness of hunger. Now he symbolically incorporates a tyrannical mother image into his developing personality. This he establishes as a permanent internal object. It demands and threatens implacably as the mother seemed to demand and threaten. The precocious ego system of the potential depressive now contains this foreign body inclusion.[37] In relation to it, as a forerunner of the superego, the infant and child will organize his dominant attitudes and actions, his primitive defensive and adaptive maneuvers, and eventually his role-expectations and his concepts of a self.

The internal object, thus acquired, operates as a primitive control. It is the mother's representative. If the child subordinates his action always to such an internal object, he need never fear desertion by his actual mother, since the demands of one correspond to the demands of the other. Thus he masters his chief fears and gains security at the price of subjecting himself to an internal tyrant whom he openly fears and secretly hates. The infantile anxieties that will persist into depressive adulthood are anxieties over meeting the expectations of this internal object. They persist unconsciously as a permanent sense of guilt, and consciously as a feeling of inferiority and a

[37] Klein, M., *Contributions to Psychoanalysis.* London: Hogarth, 1950.

hunger for love. Along with the infantile anxieties there will also persist a submerged and poorly repressed emotional ambivalence, in which one finds the sadistic fantasies of a badly frustrated child with impulses to hate the ones he loves.

The formation of a precocious ego, with its excessive use of introjective methods, means that all later maturation sequences will be distorted. Repression will never reach the degree of effectiveness, as the key defense, that it reaches in normals and neurotics. The overdeveloped introjection, even though it eventually becomes an auxiliary of repression, remains always an abnormally prominent auxiliary. Its expressions will always remain close to primitive incorporation. It is this that accounts for the orality of depressive personalities, for their tendencies to be parasitic, dependent, angry and engulfing.

Because repression never becomes normally effective in depressive personalities, they also suffer from poorly repressed sadistic fantasies and conflicts in their emotional relationships. Whenever they are exposed to deprivation or frustration, these fixated infantile trends are reactivated. They threaten to erupt into preconscious life. If they do erupt, of course, we have the conditions for the ego disintegration and regression characteristic of depressive psychosis.

The depressive superego. The introjected internal object, which we have described, forms a nucleus within the ego around which an archaic and later a mature superego will crystallize. This internal object, a nucleus of future superego organization, begins as an archaic representation of maternal demands and threats, as we have seen. We must bear in mind, however, that it was originally formed in response to an intense, intolerable anxiety, that it is a product of absolute deprivation and frustration.

Even the most well-integrated adult, in a moment of panic, is apt to perceive an ordinary danger as a frightful catastrophe. He may distort what he perceives almost beyond recognition. Something like this appears to happen to the frightened, deserted infant. What he internalizes, and what may form the nucleus of his future superego, may seem a cruel, murderous monster or a heartless, implacable judge. In other words, what the child internalizes is an expression of what he experiences at the time, not what the mother seems to herself to have been. It is this infantile monster that we see emerging in a depressive psychosis. It is expressed in adult terms, but its primitive and even savage character is quite unmistakable.

Such an infant retains his hostile internal object primarily because it works. It is the product of external deprivation, and it operates in such a way as to anticipate further external deprivation and to avoid it. Compliant behavior, organized in relation to the internal object's stern demands and threats, will please the actual demanding mother. It will ensure that she will provide love and support. The child, in short, becomes a slave to his internal object in order that he may be free of primal anxiety which threatens to destroy him. This procedure unfortunately condemns him to a life of servitude, to the perpetual feeling that he is inferior. It permanently distorts his social personality and restricts his freedom of action.

In the first place, the depressive must always appease the unconscious superego that organizes around his hostile introject. In the second place he must also appease anyone who tends to stir up his unconscious infantile conflicts and thus increases his superego aggression. To oppose such people makes him feel guilty, although he does not know why. And, finally, he must build his life around ensuring external love and support to offset the chronic aggression of his demanding unconscious superego.

The depressive superego has peculiarities quite different from those of the paranoid.[38] The depressive superego is certainly infantile; but it is a unified system of moral self-control which seems much better integrated than the paranoid superego. Perhaps because denial and projection are minimal, while introjection is prominent, the depressive feels his chief danger as coming from within himself. He only appeases others because they threaten to stir up self-hatred, either by denying him support or by stimulating his superego aggression. Because he tends to blame himself easily, and to belittle himself, he is less of a threat to others than the paranoid personality. Therefore he stands a better chance of being acceptable to others, of having close friends and confidants.

Childhood background of psychotic depressive reactions

We shall begin with a condensation of what has already been said on this subject, and then discuss it further. The adult who is especially vulnerable to psychotic depression is one who has experienced far more acceptance in childhood than the adult who is vulnerable to paranoid reactions. As a rule he gives the impression of greater stability when he is well. He usually succeeds in forming close personal interrelationships. Nevertheless, as a result of his traumatic early childhood, the depressive personality suffers from the following lifelong defects:

1. *An unstable ego organization,* which disintegrates if narcissistic supplies are cut off, either through actual loss or through the patient's own withdrawal.

2. *A powerful archaic superego system,* which is basically sadistic, gives rise to feelings of inferiority and worthlessness, and drives a person constantly to seek relationships which yield love or support, to offset his own superego aggression.

3. *A distorted defensive structure,* in which *repression* is chronically inadequate while *introjection* is overdeveloped and overused.

[38] Rosenfeld, H., "An investigation into the psychoanalytic theory of depression," *Internat. J. Psychoanal.*, 1959, *40*, 105–129.

4. *Vulnerability to traumatic anxiety* whenever dependent needs are frustrated and narcissistic supplies endangered, with a resultant intolerance for rejection because of the threat of his own superego attack.

5. *Powerful fixations in infantile conflicts* which center about love and hate, right and wrong, sin and forgiveness. Because *repression* is ineffectual, these conflicts penetrate into preconscious thinking and distort interpersonal relationships.

6. *Distorted reality-testing* which, while more competent in health than preparanoid reality-testing, is deflected by an excessive need to be reassured and dependent, by a hypersensitivity to signs of rejection or rebuff, and by an overuse of introjection.

Infantile experiences. The infant who will develop a depressive personality is one who gets full protection from excessive primal anxiety as long as he complies with his mother's wishes.[39] The important thing is not only that she be *present* but that she be *pleased.* If he fails to meet her expectations, he loses the support and love without which he cannot long survive. The demand made upon such a child is that he submit to severe restrictions of his freedom, including the freedom to express rage, in return for security and love. His pathology comes from a parental demand that is too severe and comes too early.

The thing to remember is that, no matter how obvious and natural a mother's demands may seem to her, they cannot seem obvious and natural to an infant. The mother, as an adult, acts in accordance with a set of principles. She has highly organized expectations, her own preconscious and unconscious standards as to what a mother is, and what a baby should be. The infant has no standards or principles. These are abstractions which for a long time a child cannot possibly develop.

Meanwhile he has nothing to go on but his own imperious needs. He learns slowly what is rewarded with approval and acceptance, and what is punished with rejection and desertion. For a long time he experiences the repeated shocks of sudden abandonment.[40] Even when the mother or mother substitute is physically present, a child may be left helpless, a prey to anxiety and loneliness, because she disapproves and withholds her love.

Throughout this long period of learning, the infant has no way of reliably anticipating his mother's sudden withdrawals of support and love. To him, her behavior must seem as startling and capricious as the behavior of some strange and powerful society seems to a man who is in its power, but who understands neither its intentions nor its language. The only way an infant can meet the situation is to choose behavior which ensures love and support. This means, in effect, to adopt a *dependent submissive role*, and at the same time to *introject the mother* as a frame of reference for playing such a role.

---

[39] In all statements of this kind it is to be understood that any person who gives mothering may be the mother substitute, even though the substitute be a sibling or the father.

[40] Cf. Bowlby, J., "Separation anxiety: a critical review of the literature," *J. Child Psychol. Psychiat.*, 1961, *1*, 251–269.

Even normal demands for compliance require a selective process on the child's part. This is a part of the process by which every infant and child constructs a realistic world in which he lives more or less realistically. Normal adaptation and mastery depend upon a certain amount of compliance. Of course, during infancy and early childhood the adaptive and defensive methods available are primitive. These work well enough under ordinary circumstances at first. They are normally superseded by more effective means of adaptation and defense as infant and child mature.

If, however, parental demands for compliance are *too sweeping and inflexible* during early infancy, the child is forced to make excessive use of his primitive adaptive and defensive methods. This excessive use does three things: (*a*) it gives the primitive methods a fixed and elaborate form in the developing organism; (*b*) it distorts the later developmental sequences; and (*c*) it induces structural changes in the personality system, such as we see in the distorted ego-superego interaction of depressives.

The depressive adult, we have said, is a person who has had to meet implacable demands for compliance during infancy by the *overuse of introjection. Introjection is a symbolic engulfing*, a perceptual taking in, the primitive forerunner of social role organization.[41] It is modelled upon the physical act of taking in food. The infant incorporates his mother symbolically, as he has previously incorporated his food, and sets her up inside as a regulating image. Instead of internalizing merely the role, as older children and adults do, *he internalizes the whole frightening image*, which then controls what he does.[42]

This introjective maneuver not only enables the infant to survive; it also enables him to evolve an adult personality which is more effective and socially acceptable than that of most paranoid and schizophrenic persons. This is mainly because the depressive personality is more compliant and conforming than the paranoid or schizophrenic. It is nevertheless true that the presence of a threatening internal object also hastens a precocious ego development in depressive personalities. A depressive ego organization is early committed to a lifelong overuse of introjective defenses and introjective adaptation. Repression is always relatively poor; and there is an eternal need for outside help against internal hostility. The ego is guilt-ridden, ruled by superego threat, and facing the world with feelings of inadequacy and weakness.

Advantages of depressive personalities. How is it that depressive personalities, with such a handicapped start, operate reasonably well unless they suffer an actual psychotic break? Why does the depressive in health give a much

[41] Cameron, N., *The Psychology of Behavior Disorders*. Boston: Houghton Mifflin, 1947, pp. 97–102; Mead, G. H., *Mind, Self, and Society*. Chicago: Univ. of Chicago Press, 1934.

[42] Adults do something approaching this after going through a traumatic experience. After a person has been in a horrible accident, for example, he may thereafter re-experience it in his fantasy whenever he is in danger, and use this as a controlling factor in what he does. The behavior resulting from such internalization can be ineffectual and even dangerous.

better impression as a social person than either the paranoid or the schizoid personality? Why is it that the person who develops a depressive psychosis usually makes an excellent recovery? We shall single out two reasons here for these superiorities.

1. *Consistent treatment during infancy.* Hard as it must be to learn strict compliance and submission, it is at least *possible* to learn if the mother provides consistent treatment. Consistency is a necessary condition for developing anticipation. The *internal object* which a consistently treated infant introjects is a *predictable one*, a *well-integrated one*. It permits *well-integrated reciprocal behavior* to develop in relation to it; and this lays the foundation for fairly *realistic role organization*. The infant who can count upon consistent severity, even though he suffers from much suppressed rage, is better off than one who never knows what to expect. The latter seems to be the plight of preschizophrenic infants, for example, who are offered no stable, consistent object to introject. They cannot, therefore, organize well-integrated role behavior early in life; and they cannot construct for themselves a realistic world. The depressive, on the other hand, has managed to develop reasonably good object relations and reasonably good integration.

2. *Emotional acceptance and closeness.* In return for his strict compliance and submission, the depressive is rewarded in infancy with *emotional acceptance* and *closeness*. The preparanoid infant, by contrast, is sadistically frustrated and rejected. Even though he is allowed to react with infant rage, the major lesson he learns is that he will be sadistically treated and rebuffed. The mothering of the preschizophrenic is even worse. It is not only inconsistent and unpredictable; it is also lacking in emotional acceptance and closeness. From this the characteristic feelings of futility develop. The child finds that no matter what he does it seems never to be right.

An infant who is consistently rewarded with closeness and affection can go ahead and construct a fairly realistic object world.[43] Since object-organization and ego-integration are interdependent, this means that he will develop a fairly well-integrated ego, one that includes close dependent emotional relationships.

This is the depressive personality's situation. His life will always be overshadowed by the effect of having introjected *sadistic internal objects;* but these objects, and the superego which evolves from them, are at least *predictable*. They are at least experienced as *a part of one's own personality;* they are neither denied nor projected. The depressive thus develops more effective *self-boundaries* than do paranoid and schizoid personalities. It is only when he suffers a sweeping regression that his self-boundaries become seriously defective; and even then he stands a good chance of re-establishing them as he recovers.

[43] Fairbairn, W. R. D., *An Object-Relations Theory of Personality.* New York: Basic Books, 1954.

Identification. In spite of their bad start, and in spite of a strong residual oral dependence, depressives seem to have developed in childhood a reasonably good capacity for identification. They give the impression of having made a good initial recovery from their early traumatic experiences of frustration and desertion, of having mastered the art of suppressing forbidden reactions. They seem to have enjoyed a considerable period of freedom from excessive anxiety during early childhood, a period during which they were able to participate in the power and qualities of their parents. The chief source of a child's self-esteem lies in identification with the strength and virtues of his parent-figures (*participative identification*).

Such identification has some of the characteristics of *primary identification*, the identification which antedates object relations. To a certain extent, the child participates in the power of his parents as though there were no difference between him and his parents, as though all their properties, deeds and knowledge were his also. He is fused with them into a single entity.[44]

Participative identification also has some of the characteristics of *secondary identification*, that is, identification in which the child distinguishes himself from objects and distinguishes one object from another. His two powerful and clever parents are separate from him. They come and go while he stays. They are often in recognizable opposition to him. They sometimes force him to do things, or to forego things, against his will. Even under these circumstances, however, the child's chief strength and self-esteem still come from the fact that he is a *participating member* of a powerful, influential, close-knit social unit. Its strength is his, just as a country's strength is felt by the citizen to be his own, and as also are its deeds, its prestige and its possessions. Only a feeling of complete rejection and exclusion from such a participating membership can remove these strong sources of a small child's sense of strength and self-esteem.

There is clinical evidence from the pattern of psychotic depressions that the person vulnerable to them has in fact suffered from severe trauma in early life. When, as an adult, he goes into a psychotic depression, he reactivates a regressive organization which is quite different from the kinds that appear in paranoid and schizophrenic regressions. He becomes deeply preoccupied with the derivatives of an ego-superego struggle which, while it is certainly infantile, seems more mature than the paranoid pseudocommunity, and much better integrated than schizophrenic diffusion.

Nevertheless, the pattern of the psychotic depression is a strange one. The depressed patient may or may not speak freely with those around him; but whether he does or not, he seems to have become oblivious to the social facts of external reality, and to have retreated like a dog with a bone, to gnaw on his sorrows alone, to dwell endlessly and delusionally upon his sense of

---

44 This was discussed in Chapter 2 as part of the normal symbiotic mother-child relationship. See also Jacobson, E., "Contribution to the metapsychology of cyclothymic depressions," in Greenacre, P. (Ed.), *Affective Disorders.* New York: Internat. Univ. Press, 1953, pp. 49–83; Jacobson, E., "Contribution to the metapsychology of psychotic identifications," *J. Amer. Psychoanal. Ass.*, 1954, 2, 239–262.

worthlessness, hopelessness and guilt. To help in trying to understand this strange adult clinical picture, there has been developed an hypothesis known as *the primal depression*.

The primal depression hypothesis

The primal depression hypothesis states that *every adult who becomes psychotically depressed has suffered a primal depression*, somewhere toward the end of his edipal phase, in his fourth or fifth year.[45] The assumption is analogous to the one made about adult phobias, that they are based upon transient childhood phobias which are almost universal in normal childhood during the same period.

The primal depression hypothesis goes on to say that when an adult who has suffered a childhood depression meets a situation of loss, desertion or deep humiliation, he undergoes an ego-superego regresssion to something like the pattern of the childhood or "primal" depression. In other words, his childhood experience has fixated a primitive ego-superego struggle at unconscious levels, and the adult experience of loss, desertion or humiliation lights up this primitive, childlike struggle. In adulthood, the struggle is expressed in adult terms; but its structure is the structure of the late edipal fixation.

The primal depression hypothesis has often been criticized as one that begs the question. It says, in effect, that we can explain the adult depression by assuming a childhood pattern which is like it. But what about the assumed childhood pattern?

It is an established fact that some children do develop a recognizable depression toward the end of their edipal phase of development, that is, around the fourth or fifth year. They give an exaggerated reaction to their experiences of disillusionment and humiliation, which we described in Chapter 2 as inevitable, even in the normal resolution of the edipal complex. These children withdraw emotionally from their frustrating parents. They seem sad and preoccupied, as well as resentful. In time, they work through their primal depression and resume their advance toward maturity.

The primal depression hypothesis assumes that a great many children go through such an experience without its being recognized as a childhood depression. The hypothesis assumes that the depressive withdrawal and regression of the primal depression leaves indelible traces in the child's personality, even after he has recovered and gone on with his maturing. These indelible traces constitute the pattern of fixation to which the psychotic depressive regresses in adulthood.

As more and more clinical studies of childhood depressions[46] accumulate,

[45] Jacobson, E., "The edipus complex in the development of depressive mechanisms," *Psychoanal. Quart.*, 1943, *12*, 541–560.

[46] Freud, A., and Burlingham, D., *War and Children*. New York: Internat. Univ. Press, 1943; Spitz, R., "Anaclitic depression," in *The Psychoanalytic Study of the Child*. New York: Internat. Univ. Press, 1946, vol. 2, pp. 313–342; Bierman, J. S., Silverstein, A. B., and Finesinger, J. E., "A depression in a six-year-old boy with acute poliomyelitis," in *The Psychoanalytic Study of the Child*. New York: Internat. Univ. Press, 1958, vol. 13, pp. 430–450.

it may be possible to confirm or refute the hypothesis that a primal depression in childhood sets the pattern for adult regression in psychotic depressions. At present it remains as a useful assumption for clinicians who work with psychotically depressed adults.

We turn now to *manic psychoses,* which seem to be the opposites of depressions, but are dynamically related to them. Adult superego controls seem to be eliminated in the manic attack. In place of the depressive ego-superego struggle there is a flight into unrestrained elation or aggression, with delusions of grandeur and childlike optimism taking the place of delusions of self-depreciation and despair. We know that these opposites are paradoxically related because of two reasons, which we shall repeat in the next chapter. One is that manic patients often have sudden, momentary bursts of sadness, even to the point of crying, expressing a feeling of hopelessness and making a suicidal attempt. The other is that a few depressed persons *alternate* between manic excitement and psychotic depression. This relationship has been openly recognized in the literature for hundreds of years.

16

Mania and Manic-Depressive Cycles

⳹

MANIC REACTIONS ARE MOOD DISORDERS, WITH DELUSIONS, WHICH ARE USUALLY exaggerations and distortions of normal elation or self-assertion. They are often mistaken at first for happiness. They resemble the changes that come over many people after they have had an alcoholic drink or two, but the manic reaction lasts for weeks or months, not hours, and no sign of intoxication is present.

Manic patients seem at first glance to be in good contact with their human environment, and their talk, though rambling, seems to spread freely over a wide range of topics. A closer examination, however, always reveals that both impressions are mistaken. The manic patient's contact with others is shallow and fleeting. His talk is actually limited in scope as compared with that of a normal happy person.[1] Mania is deeply regressive. Manic patients use their environment in the service of fantasies and conflicts which are still more primitive than those of paranoid persons. Their defenses, as we shall see, relate them to psychotic depressions, in spite of the prevailing opposite mood. We shall find no general disintegration, such as one finds in a high proportion of schizophrenics, and there are no hallucinations in typical cases.

Definition. Manic reactions are psychotic excitements characterized by overactivity and by delusional elation or self-assertion, but without disorgan-

---

[1] Lorenz, M., and Cobb, L., "Language behavior in manic patients," *Arch. Neurol. Psychol.*, 1952, 67, 763–770; Lorenz, M., "Language behavior in manic patients: an equalitative study," *Arch. Neurol. Psychol.*, 1953, 69, 14–26.

ization. The behavior of the manic patient is a caricature of joy, optimism or self-assurance, often a childish caricature. The patient makes no secret of the power he feels. He tells everything about himself that comes to his mind, and about other people as well, without even the ordinary reservations which he observes when he is well.

Relatives and other associates easily recognize well-developed cases of mania as abnormal. They usually call for outside help more quickly than in the case of comparably ill depressives because they feel more threatened themselves. They can no more control the manic patient's excesses than he himself can. There are real dangers in mania, the danger of self-injury, the danger of starvation and physical exhaustion, of financial and erotic adventures and, strange to say, even of suicide. The pervasive sense of aggressive self-assertion or seeming joy is dampened little or not at all by what other people say and do.[2] If there is any change because of attempts at outside control it is most likely to be a change to irritability and increased self-assertion. Genuine communication is next to impossible.[3] The manic patient's overactivity is self-propelled. His thoughts and acts run away with him. His talk flits quickly and irrationally from one thing to another. It is full of puns, sound associations and wit, the sure signs of primary process thinking, but there is no general disorganization, such as we often find in schizophrenics.

Adaptation. There is little of adaptive value in mania. Regression is too deep, reality-testing too severely impaired. The manic patient is like an over-excited child who is unable to quiet down and unable to make use of his environment in adult ways. He behaves as though there were every reason for his being madly playful and aggressively, insistently self-assertive. His expansive and often silly talk, his often dangerous lack of consideration for others, his inability to run his own life and cope with his own daily needs — all these seem to the patient right and normal.

The only sense in which mania can be considered adaptive is that it does *deny a reality* which is too painful to be faced, a reality which would justify a psychotic depression in anyone with such a personality organization. In this sense the manic reaction can be considered as a defense against psychotic depression, as a refusal or inability to accept the intolerably painful truths of a reality situation. There are many cases on record, for instance, in which a personal loss such as the death of someone has precipitated mania where one would ordinarily expect profound grief or a depression. There is also the fact, recognized for centuries, that mania and psychotic depression sometimes follow one another in the same person. We shall take up the latter relationship later in the chapter, and illustrate it clinically, after dis-

---

2 Lichtenberg, J. D., "Theoretical and practical considerations of the management of the manic phase of the manic-depressive psychosis," *J. nerv. ment. Dis.*, 1959, *129*, 243–281.

3 Cohen, M., *et al.*, "An intensive study of twelve cases of manic-depressive psychosis," *Psychiatry*, 1954, *17*, 103–137.

cussing the clinical manifestations and dynamic background of manic reactions.

Clinical Manifestations of Manic Reactions

It is symptomatic of the confusion in our current classification system that, in the official *Diagnostic Manual,* there is only one hesitant, parenthetic phrase suggesting the possibility of a neurotic manic reaction.[4] No real place is made for it among the neuroses enumerated there. It will be remembered that mild depressions, in which patients can still make use of their environment to hold themselves together, are given a major place among the neuroses as *neurotic depressions.* It would be logical to make a place, not only for neurotic manic reactions, but also for neurotic paranoid reactions and neurotic schizophrenic reactions. In out-patient clinics and in office practice one certainly sees patients who merit such designations, that is, *manic, paranoid* and *schizophrenic* patients, whose hold on reality enables them to work reasonably well and to make use of their environment in ways that are quite out of the reach of fully psychotic persons. We have already stressed a neurotic component in paranoid reactions.[5] In the chapters on neurotic depressions and psychotic depressions we have emphasized their close relationship, not only in the symptomatology, but also in the precipitating factors and in the personality background.

Here we shall follow custom, for the sake of clarity and convenience, and distinguish between mild and severe manic reactions without calling one neurotic and the other psychotic. As usual, it is the severe reaction which demonstrates both the symptomatology and dynamics best. Minor, slight manic reactions, usually called *hypomania,* are too much like the mild elations and episodes of self-assertion which a majority of adults at some time experience to make them convincing illustrations of psychopathology. Indeed, some persons appear to remain in a more or less constant mild manic state, and to perform a prodigious amount of work or play because of this. We shall return to a discussion of them in the chapter on personality disorders. Here we shall begin with a discussion of the delusions of grandeur which, although not confined to manic reactions, are most typical of them.

Manic delusions of grandeur

The grandiose delusions of mania stand in contrast to the delusions of psychotic depression. They are often little more than mere exaggerations of ordinary self-assertive pride, boastfulness, optimism and self-aggrandizement. When this is the case, what makes them pathological is that the circumstances under which the delusions arise seem to the observer to call rather for sadness, discouragement, disappointment, or even self-depreciation.

[4] *Mental Disorders.* Diagnostic and Statistical Manual. Washington, D.C.: Amer. Psychiatric Ass., 1952.

[5] See Chapter 14, "Paranoid reactions."

Manic delusions often go much farther than this. As in the cases we shall describe, the patient makes extravagant and impossible claims. He says he is enormously wealthy, immensely powerful or clever, has unlimited talent, is irresistably attractive and has the right to do or say anything he feels like. He may boast of his great achievements, great conquests, the importance of his social and personal connections, of his potency and fruitfulness. The very exaggeration and the self-assertive, expansive manner of the patient give valuable hints that all of this is a rather childlike defense against admitting failure or inadequacy.[6] In keeping with their delusions manic patients often behave like vulgar clowns or become pompous, arrogant and provocative. They make it necessary for those who are caring for them to remind themselves that such behavior and such attitudes are the products of a regressive illness, that they arise from an *absolute necessity to deny things* of which the patient has already had some awareness, at least at preconscious levels. In short, manic delusions should be looked upon as "holding actions," as defensive denials which give the patient time and opportunity to work through something which he is at the same time denying. They may also be, and in our two cases actually were, acts of vengeance. These two patients were offended and indignant, and they acted out a regressive kind of identification with the person who had hurt their pride.

Precipitating factors

The precipitating factors seem in most cases to be no different from those which are effective in precipitating psychotic depressions, especially a *loss of love*, of *personal security* and *self-esteem*. These we have described in detail near the beginning of Chapter 15. In some cases there is a brief depressive reaction just before the manic attack.[7] In others, there seems to be no depressive reaction to usher in the manic attack. Nevertheless, the ease with which sadness or self-depreciation can be demonstrated in most manic reactions suggests that they are usually attempts, and often successful attempts, at staving off a psychotic depression.

The person who develops a manic reaction seems to differ from the one who develops a psychotic depression chiefly in his sweeping use of *denial*, and in his *reconstructing reality* by means of *grandiose delusions*. The manic patient seems hopelessly irresponsible, which he often actually is, and he seems uncontrollably expansive. He behaves as though he thought no one but himself mattered in the world, as though he were capable of doing anything he wanted, and as though any attempts to control him, or to deprive him of any immediate pleasure that he wanted, were intolerable injustices. These attitudes, of course, are childlike and unrealistic. They represent a serious loss of social perspective.

[6] Schwartz, D., "A unitary formulation of the manic-depressive reactions," *Psychiatry*, 1961, *24*, 238–245.

[7] Cohen, M. B., *et al.*, "An intensive study of twelve cases of manic-depressive psychosis," *Psychiatry*, 1954, *17*, 103–137.

What the manic patient does is to develop for himself a pseudocommunity which is quite different from the actual interpersonal relationships existing around him. With the development of his delusions of grandeur, his experience and behavior are organized in terms of a pseudocommunity in which he is a great and leading figure. When he achieves this, he gives the impression of being very far indeed from sadness, dejection and self-depreciation. In other words, since he cannot face his intolerable anxiety, he denies external reality.[8] He also denies the attacks of his own superego, both at primitive and at more mature levels.

Onset of manic reactions

It is important to recognize the fact that manic reactions always begin after a phase of increased tension and anxiety, even though they sometimes have an abrupt onset and seem to be precipitated by a single incident. The patient, who has usually been suffering from an unhappy ambivalent conflict, finds himself in an acutely anxiety-provoking situation. The setting is thus one of unrelieved stress and strain. Usually the patient goes through a phase in which he attempts to meet the challenge, which the situation presents, in terms primarily of the social community. That is, he is at first oriented in relation to the functionally integrated group of which he is a member. It is only after he has failed in this attempt that he develops his grandiose delusional pseudocommunity.

One of our patients, Amy H., developed a full-fledged manic attack within a few hours of the death of her husband, to whom she had been unhappily married for twenty years. Lest this be mistaken for excessive joy, let it be said that this patient became psychotically depressed after she had recovered from her manic attack.

Another patient, an unmarried farmer aged twenty-five, who had been greatly overworked by his father, burst into tears when his father harshly criticized him. He tried to get a gun and kill himself. Later the same day he was found excited, sobbing, and distressed over his failure to complete his work. The very next day he developed a full-fledged manic attack, in which he was tremendously overactive and elated, with plans that were delusional and grandiose.

In both of these cases there was reason to assume a basically ambivalent, and somewhat infantile attitude toward a loved person, and in both we see a sweeping regression which seems to make both external reality and the

---

[8] Intolerable anxiety arises often in somatic disease, and especially when there is a reduction in competency of the brain as an organ. Carmichael reports a patient with typhoid fever who wrote him a check for a million dollars during the illness. The writer has witnessed numerous attacks of pathological elation in patients suffering from high fevers, infections and intoxications which reduced the effectiveness of cerebral function and allowed *denial* to appear in primitive, childlike forms.

critical functions of the superego ineffectual. Both patients seemed to escape a depression by the use of denial once they had regressed.[9]

In cases of gradual onset, the patient goes through a more obvious preliminary phase of tension and anxiety. He becomes overactive, restless, irritable, excited and self-assertive. He is characteristically intolerant of criticism or restraint; but he himself is usually critical of others, domineering, impatient and outspoken. He easily becomes angry and combative when interfered with, or even when remonstrated with. He is in open rebellion; but at the same time he has regressed to a point where he can no longer take into account the consequences of what he does and says, nor can he exert normal self-scrutiny and self-control. He may show a striking increase in initiative with, at the same time, an elementary want of adult judgment. One patient, near the beginning of an acute attack that led to hospitalization, tried to hire a fleet of trucks for a grandiose business enterprise, and actually did engage a nationally famous dance orchestra and a dance hall to entertain his friends, even though he did not have the money to pay for them.

The manic reaction deepens

As the manic reaction deepens the patient becomes more and more excited, elated and aggressive. At the same time, unlike either the paranoid psychotic or the psychotic depressive, he becomes exceedingly distractible. He cannot remain at any one thing for long. He shifts quickly from one thing to another, without having become really engaged in doing anything; or, if he does stick at anything for awhile, he works feverishly and with little regard for consequences. Nowhere is the superficiality and distractability more obvious than in the continuous flow of manic talk which, without becoming incoherent or bizarre, shifts without pause from one topic to another (*flight of ideas or flight of topics*). If elation dominates the clinical picture, the talk is interspersed with quips, puns, rhyming, witticisms and personal references, some of which may be vulgar or obscene.[10] If aggressive self-assertion is dominant the talk has less wit and more anger, boasting and threat.

In extreme instances the patient sings and shouts himself hoarse, adorns himself or strips himself naked, goes through calisthenic exercises, walks in circles, teases others, plays pranks and acts the fool. He may have neither time nor attention for the ordinary routines of eating, eliminating and resting. Sleep is sometimes as little as half an hour in twenty-four. A prevalent belief that manic patients are generally hungry and will gobble food is not supported by clinical experience. Unless the patient is carefully looked after,

[9] Recamier, P. C., "From anxiety to mania in its relationship to depression," *L'Evolution psychiatrique*, 1957, *III*, 554–594; abstract by Almansi, R. J., *Psychoanal. Quart.*, 1961, *30*, 156; Deutsch, H., "Absence of grief," *Psychoanal. Quart.*, 1937, *6*, 12–22.

[10] Katan, M., "Mania and the pleasure principle," in Greenacre, P., (Ed.), *Affective Disorders*. New York: Internat. Univ. Press, 1953, pp. 140–207.

he is likely to become starved and dehydrated because, like an overexcited child, he cannot take time to eat and drink. Gastrointestinal motility seems actually to be slowed during manic attacks. In spite of all the overactivity and excitement, the acutely manic patient does not show the kind of ego disintegration that an excited schizophrenic patient does.

A case of aggressive, self-assertive manic reaction

Arnold B., a married man of fifty-eight, worked at a racetrack. His income depended upon the racetrack's prosperity. Both had been steadily declining. It hurt his pride when he had to move his family to a poor neighborhood; but even this move did not save him from finally coming to the end of his resources. He was the only child of an aged father, whom he still called "my daddy," and of whom he was still afraid. The father had inherited a large income late in life on which he was living in comfortable idleness. He was said to be squandering large amounts of money on horses and horse-racing, on friends and women, apparently on everything but the patient and his family.

When Arnold had nowhere else to turn for money he appealed to his father. The father, however, refused over and over to help him. Instead he criticized Arnold harshly, calling him stupid, no good, and a poor thing. Arnold felt humiliated, angry and at his wit's end. For a month he seemed to his wife tense and discouraged. He appeared to be brooding constantly and he could not sleep.

One day he showed up at a racing event a changed man. He was garrulous, excited, argumentative and belligerent. This surprised his friends, for he had always been known as an even-tempered man, somewhat overconscientious but generally cheerful. At home he now became extremely critical and hard to please. Things went on like this for another month. Arnold's financial situation grew worse and worse. His father showed no signs of relenting.

Then an important racing event came up and Arnold entered two horses in it. This act seemed to provide the spark that touched off the conflagration. Arnold became suddenly excited, jovial and expansive. He could scarcely sleep at all. He wrote letters incessantly; he telephoned friends all over the country about horses and racing, even in the middle of the night; he even began sending radiograms offering to buy expensive horses. Finally he bought several hundred dollars worth of gear for his horses which was unnecessary and entirely beyond his means. At this point he was hospitalized.

In the hospital Arnold indulged in childlike boasting, in loud self-assertion and unrealistic optimism. He talked excitedly, telling everyone that he was going to make a fortune on his horses. Every patient was to get a radio, the nurses were to have mink coats, and he would give the hospital $100,000. He promised his own nurse $50,000 and wanted to marry her, ignoring the fact that he himself was already married. He said he never felt better in his life. He liked the hospital, he said, even if it was like a jail — "No, worse than a jail because you sometimes get out of a jail."

Not far beneath the surface there was sadistic aggression, as irresponsible as his boasts and promises. Arnold made cruel antisemitic tirades in front of a confused and frightened schizophrenic Jewish youth. These could be ended only by taking Arnold to his room and keeping him there until he had quieted down. He told an agitated, depressed clergyman that he had heard the doctors making plans to castrate him. For a few weeks Arnold continued aggressive, loud, self-assertive, erotic and grandiose. Then the attack subsided, he made his peace with his father — who had been footing the bills — and he went home almost well.

Discussion. As in the case of the agitated depressed woman, Constance Q., we see here someone faced with disillusionment in relation to an ambivalently loved person and subjected to harsh criticism. Yet the result is not a clearcut depression but a clearcut manic excitement. Arnold could certainly have felt himself to be a hopeless failure, unsuccessful, unlucky and unloved. He even went through an initial period of preoccupation, as Constance did. Then for some reason there came a sweeping denial of his intolerable frustration, a period of hopelessly unrealistic self-assertion, boasting and aggression.

By means of his expansive, grandiose delusions, Arnold reconstructed his world,[11] building a pseudocommunity which made him appear to himself as a wealthy spendthrift. He played the irresponsible child in his boasts, his promises and his love. At the same time he identified, also in a childlike way, with his spendthrift father. He had boundless wealth. He squandered money on horses and horse-racing; and he would squander more on his friends, the patients, the nurses and the hospital. He seldom so much as mentioned his wife and children. It was as though he were young again and could marry his nurse.

There were also hostility and vengeance in the picture. Arnold's noisy pushing behavior on the ward was as aggressive as the insistent demands of the depressed woman, Constance Q. He spoke cruelly to frightened patients. He made his father pay handsomely for his manic illness and said so. In the end, his illness brought him the help from his father that he needed.

A case of elated manic reaction

Stella S., a childless married woman aged thirty-four, had been living for the ten years of her married life with her husband's parents, in spite of her repeated insistence upon having a home of her own. For three months she had been working at a summer resort in upper Michigan, after telling her husband before she left that she would leave him if he did not provide her a separate home. Two weeks before she left Michigan for home a visiting relative found her downcast, irritable and in tears about her husband's having done nothing about moving.

[11] Katan, M., "Mania and the pleasure principle," in Greenacre, P. (Ed.), *Affective Disorders.* New York: Internat. Univ. Press, 1953, pp. 140–207.

The day before she left she was hurt and humiliated because her husband did not drive up to get her as he had promised. She arrived home the next day alone and went to her husband's place of business, kissed him and gave him a dressing-down for neglecting her. This was a week before her admission to the clinic.

During the next five days Stella was uncommunicative and unfriendly to her husband and his family. She herself was away from home most of the time because she was helping her lodge to prepare for a forthcoming town celebration. Even when she was at home she seemed to be engrossed in memorizing the part she was supposed to play in the festivities. Two days before her admission to the clinic Stella suddenly appeared at her husband's lodge to see if he was really there; and when she found that he was, she merely left with a smile. This visit seems to have been the beginning of her excitement.

When Stella left her husband's lodge she did not go home but went instead to the local hotel where she made the proprietor play cards with her until midnight. Then she insisted that he and a guest drive her around town looking for her husband. She laughed and sang as they went through the streets in the middle of the night.

Around one o'clock Stella arrived home to find her husband already in bed. She undressed but could not settle down. She was overactive and overtalkative, jumping from one topic to another, reciting the piece she had been memorizing, singing, laughing and making up rhymes. At two-fifteen the fire whistle blew and the patient dashed out of the house in pajamas, bedroom slippers and a coat. Her husband found her in another building, hiding behind a door. It took him an hour to get her home, and then in a few minutes she was out again. She walked up and down the streets, laughing and singing, stole a banana from a truck, and sat on the hotel steps with her husband for two hours. She finally got home and went to bed at six in the morning, but half an hour later she was up again.

All the next day the patient talked, laughed and sang. She swore at her father-in-law, made scenes, and once struck her husband in the face. To everyone around her she kept saying, "I told you this would happen!" On the day following she was taken to the city where she and her husband stayed at a friend's home. When they were out driving she threatened playfully to jump out of the car. All the next night she stayed up, working around the house with a dust mop, talking, singing and praying. She entered the hospital the next morning.

In the hospital Stella continued much as she had been before entering it. She was not disoriented, intoxicated or disorganized. There was no evidence of physical illness. When her husband left her the next day to return home she became agitated and wept for a short period; then she brightened up and resumed her previous overactive and overtalkative behavior. The following sample of talk shows flight of ideas, rhyming, punning and distractibility:

"You go out and stand pat — pat, you hear? Who was Pat? What does he wear when he's in Ireland? . . . See this pillow (raising it behind her head)? Now is it even or odd? Even or odd, by God.

I take it even, by God. By God we live; by God we die. And that's my allegiance to these United States. See my little eagle (bedsheet wrapped around her feet and stretched taut)? These are my wings. No, I have wings of a girl." Patient sings *Prisoner's Song*, making flying movements with her arms to accompany the lines, "Over these prison walls I would fly." Then she sings "One little Indian, two little Indians," and shouts "Heap big Indian chief! I'm not afraid. I got a heart right here. I've got a key to my heart. . . ."

In her outpouring of talk, during the first week following her admission to the hospital, Stella revealed her chief concerns, her ambivalent attitudes toward her husband and herself, and her underlying anxiety and unhappiness. She said she was going to have a baby, would conduct an orchestra, boasted about her bridge playing and her evening dresses. In the tubs she pretended to be swimming, laughed and sang, skipping from one song to another without finishing any. Within a week after admission she had quieted down to an almost normal level of general activity and talk. She was irritable and had occasional temper outbursts.

Five weeks after admission Stella went with her husband to spend the night at her mother's house. There she quarreled with him because he had stopped her charge account. She returned to the clinic the next day tense, overactive and overtalkative. At first she was fearful, irritable and sleepless. She spoke of fears that she would die and her husband also. Within four more days she was again elated. She laughed and sang, rhymed, punned, swore, and said she would divorce her husband. She told everyone of her desire for children. Her recovery after this was slow. There were episodes of irritability, resentment and angry crying, but no sadness. Four months after admission she was discharged as recovered.

Discussion. As in the preceding case, there is a background that might have been expected to precipitate a depression — a married woman's desperation over not having a home or a child after ten years of marriage. Stella's three-month separation from her husband and her ultimatum to him had produced no results whatever. She felt deserted and unloved. Yet the clinical picture that we see is full of singing, laughter, rhyming, punning and swearing. All of this seems to be a denial of her underlying hopelessness and despair. The anxiety, fear and anger managed to penetrate the defense and appear in Stella's general behavior and her talk. Nevertheless, she did not actually become depressed, unless we choose to call her brief episodes of crying depressions, and she recovered from her whole illness without special treatment within four months.

Dynamic and Developmental Background

Early in the chapter we remarked that mania can be considered adaptive in the sense that it denies painful realities which might justify a psychotic depression. In both our major cases there was an obvious threat of depression in the background, in the one before the manic excitement took over, in the other both before and during the manic reaction (Stella S.). It is not enough, however, to depict mania simply as a defense against psychotic depression. It probably always is this, even when no depressive signs are present, but it is also dynamically more than simple denial.

The history of mania and the depressions is one that repeatedly, almost continuously, has emphasized that however opposite their mood and activity may seem they are closely interrelated. This relationship was specifically stated in the first century A.D., given the name of *manic-depressive insanity* in the seventeenth century, and called *circular insanity* by Falret in 1851.[12] Kraepelin incorporated it in his classification late in the nineteenth century. Nevertheless, as Bertram Lewin has pointed out in his brilliant essay on elation,[13] one cannot dismiss mania as merely an alternating phase, of which the other phase is depression, nor regard it as simply a defense against depression,[14] even though it often seems to operate in this way. The dynamics of mania are much more complex than defensive denial alone.

We shall present mania here as a substitute method of working through problems which threaten to precipitate a depression. The reasons for doing this are both clinical and theoretical. Clinically, it has long been recognized that mania may follow or precede depression. Both of our major cases had been brooding over trouble for some time before their manic attacks supervened. Both had been more or less realistically struggling with genuine external situations which they could not resolve, the man with the reality of poverty and an unjust refusal of help, the woman with an unjust refusal to provide her with a home of her own. Their final manic attacks came, not as an access of joy or as a triumph, but as an overwhelming aggression which plunged them both into deep regressions.

We propose that the *latent content* in both these cases, and in other manias, is profoundly *depressive* and *pathologically dependent;* while it is the *manifest content* that appears superficially to be the *opposite* of this. Arnold B. was almost successful in defending against his underlying depression, but he bristled with hostility, which happy people do not, and occasionally made dejected references to the bad treatment he had received from his "daddy." Stella, in spite of showing more elation than Arnold, was much less successful in keeping her latent depression under cover. She gave abundant evidence of fear, anxiety and suicidal wishes, sometimes

---

[12] Cameron, N., "Functional psychoses," in Hunt, J. McV. (Ed.), *Personality and the Behavior Disorders.* New York: Ronald, 1944, pp. 861–921.

[13] Lewin, B. D., *The Psychoanalysis of Elation.* New York: Norton, 1950.

[14] Lewin, B. D., "Some psychoanalytic ideas applied to elation and depression," *Amer. J. Psychiat.,* 1959, *116,* 38–43; Schwartz, D. A., "Some suggestions for a unitary formulation of the manic-depressive reactions," *Psychiatry,* 1961, *24,* 238–245; Gibson, R. W., Cohen, M. B., and Cohen, R. A., "On the dynamics of the manic-depressive personality," *Amer. J. Psychiat.,* 1959, *115,* 1101–1107.

disguised as "playful," sometimes openly expressed along with agony, dread and depletion. Both patients were furiously angry.

The ancient linking of mania with depressions seems to be justified, not only by their clinical descriptive aspects and their close association often in the same patient, but also by their dynamic characteristics. Both occur in fundamentally oral dependent persons; both represent a deep oral regression,[15] and both are unable to make use of external reality relationships because of superego and ego defects. Let us turn to the dynamic aspects of mania.

Fixation and regression in manic reactions

In manic reactions the regression seems to be at least as deep as it is in psychotic depressions. In some respects it seems to be even deeper. The principal fixation levels represent oral dependent relationships. The orientation which manic regression reactivates depends upon very early severe oral frustration. This frustration is responsible for the aggression which appears in some form as an outstanding characteristic of manic patients. Rage is held in check by most manic patients with difficulty. Slight frustrations during the illness itself provoke violent outbursts which, however, are likely to vanish quickly if the provocation can be eliminated or the patient distracted. In this respect, the manic patient resembles the small child and is very different from an angry paranoid or schizophrenic person.

The situation with regard to object relations seems to be quite different from that in psychotic depressives and different from that in paranoid reactions also. In perhaps a majority of manic attacks, possibly in all of them, there is an initial withdrawal into brooding and silent preoccupation. This phase may be depressive in character; it is certainly not the vigilant, suspicious aloofness of the paranoid reaction. In the manic attack proper, however, the patient gives the impression of being outgoing and in contact with his surroundings in an overactive greedy way. This impression is belied by the fleeting, kaleidoscopic, rapidly shifting of the focus of the manic patient's attention. It is soon apparent that he is incapable of maintaining genuine adult object relations, that he is not really in effective contact with things or people, that he is as distractible and impulsive as a small child.[16]

The manic patient is often described as greedy, as hungry for new objects and new topics. This is true, but he is also literally insatiable. His attempts to satisfy his originally oral, dependent needs are not characteristically made through actual eating — the typical manic is too busy to concentrate on eating — but through all kinds of other "taking in" — visual, auditory

[15] B. D. Lewin, *op. cit.*, has made a detailed analysis of the deep regression and the oral character of *mania*, linking both to what he calls the *oral triad*, i.e., the wish *to devour, to be devoured* and *to sleep*.

[16] Rochlin, G., "The disorder of depression and elation," *Psychoanal. Quart.*, 1953, 22, 438–457.

and manual, as well as through the busy handling and destroying of whatever comes to hand. The reason he cannot satisfy his oral need is that he has regressed too deeply to be able to use the new objects or people in a meaningful adult way.

Defenses in manic reactions

The *regression* that occurs in manic reactions cannot be considered a defensive maneuver. It is the irresistible outcome of a massive breakthrough of unconscious material, in which aggression and derivatives of the primary process are dominant.[17] The manic attack is a sign that subtotal, psychotic regression has already occurred, a regression so sweeping and so deep that the patient can no longer deal with his environment effectually. It is also a sign that certain defenses have failed and that certain others have taken their place.

Defective repression. It is obvious from the manifest symptomatology that repression has grossly failed in manic reactions. Conscious and preconscious secondary process thinking is everywhere contaminated by primary process derivatives. Unbridled aggression wells up upon the least provocation. The derivatives appear in the unabashed clowning, the cruel teasing, the silly rhyming, punning, singing and laughing, even in the otherwise unaccountable overactivity. Manic patients are often compared to persons intoxicated by alcohol, and the comparison in many ways is apt. One of the major differences is that whereas the manic patients tend to be well coordinated, even when outrageously overactive, intoxicated persons tend to become poorly coordinated and disoriented. Later on, we shall attempt to relate the defective repression in mania to the development of a precocious ego with primitive defenses. First we shall discuss the role of denial and of reaction formation in manic reactions.

Denial. It is denial that seems to transform what might have been a psychotic depression into a manic reaction.[18] Denial in mania works in more than one direction. In the first place the circumstances which would justify at least some depression are denied. This was most obvious in the case of Arnold B. who, in spite of being hopelessly poor and without prospects, declared himself on the verge of becoming enormously wealthy. Certainly his lifetime experiences working at a racetrack would ordinarily have made him realize the tremendous odds against his becoming wealthy through his already manic investment in two horses. In the case of Stella S., denial of the sources of her unhappiness was less blatant. Nevertheless she did proclaim to everyone that she was going to have a baby, something she had always longed for, and that she was going to conduct an orchestra.

[17] Katan, M., "Mania and the Pleasure Principle," in Greenacre, P. (Ed.), *Affective Disorders.* New York: Internat. Univ. Press, 1953, pp. 140–207.

[18] Lewin, B. D., "Sleep, narcissistic neurosis and the analytic situation," *Psychoanal. Quart.*, 1954, 23, 487–510.

Denial also extends to the patient's present predicament. Here, again, Arnold was more successful in making merry, even though he was confined to a hospital, where liberty is inevitably limited, and one is separated from one's relatives and friends. It is true that he called the place worse than a jail; but, unlike a depressive, he did not behave in accordance with this complaint. Stella S. also denied her predicament, as well as her poor outlook, when she sang and laughed, punned, rhymed and shouted. Every now and then, however, the denial failed her; and she more realistically reacted with anxiety and fear, and even for short periods with weeping.

Reaction formation. We propose that the overactive, garrulous, superficially outgoing, laughing, teasing, singing, manic patient is reinforcing his strong denial and his weak repression by reaction formation. That is to say, he not only denies his depression and its causes, but also brings to bear in exaggerated form the apparent opposite of depression. In effect he shouts, boasts against, and laughs down the depression that is threatening him from within. This is what some cultures try to achieve by having professional clowns perform at all public funerals. The grim reality of a present death is denied and subjected to reaction formation by culturally demanded laughter and celebration. This is what among our own subcultures is achieved by the "wake," when it leads to heavy drinking, brawling and laughter among the mourners.

Identification. Identification may be prominent among manic defenses; but when it is, it does not lead to such primitive introjection as appears in psychotic depression, or at least not openly. In the case of Arnold B., the identification was extensive, clear and obviously delusional. It was his spendthrift father with whom Arnold was identifying — wealthy, irresponsible and erotic. He was no longer the even-tempered, somewhat overconscientious man whom his associates had known. Identification entered into the clinical picture of Stella's manic attack also. She suspected her husband of infidelity and, since she was declared to be fertile by her physicians, she blamed his failure to give her a child upon his supposed infidelity. Her manic attack began with definite erotic moves and with attempts to expose herself half-dressed around the town. This behavior was completely foreign to her normal conduct, but it probably represented an acting out of what she believed her husband to be doing. One gets the impression in all manic reactions that the patient is playing a role that is not his own. The manic role seems to be a variety of reaction formation, which buttresses the patient's denial of an underlying depression.

Ego-superego relationships in manic reactions

The ego-superego relationship in the regressed manic patient is very different from that in the psychotic depressed patient. In Chapter 15 we described the sadistic, primitive superego (or superego-precursor), which lashes out at the apparently cringing, but also angry, ego. Neither of these appears in manic reactions. The ordinary critical, restraining functions of the superego have virtually disappeared. There is a childlike abandonment to fleeting, shifting sources of momentary pleasure, as though no superego existed any more. The manic patient seems to be attempting to regain the lost "purified pleasure ego" of early childhood. The "purified pleasure ego,"[19] it will be remembered, is the ego presumed to be characteristic of a phase of infancy during which all that gave pleasure was embraced as *ego-syntonic*, as belonging to the ego, whereas all that was unpleasurable or painful was ejected as foreign to the ego, as *ego-alien*.

The resemblance just described is not a thoroughgoing one, and the defensive organization of the regressed manic is not the same as that of the infant.[20] The appearance that manics give of being carefree, happy-go-lucky children, or irresponsible, boastful, quarrelsome children, is nothing more than appearance. The manic patient is an adult, and he knows that he is an adult. Indeed, considering the degree of his excitement, it is remarkable to what an extent a trained therapist can get cooperation from a manic patient, at least for a while, by appealing to whatever is left of his impaired judgment.

We assume that the manic ego has suffered subtotal regression. In these circumstances, the greatest danger seems to be that of being overwhelmed by aggression and suffering a depression. It is therefore essential, from a defensive standpoint, to discharge aggression freely in all directions, either as anger and verbal attack, or as a tremendously busy, excited general over-activity. The apparent gaiety and exaggerated self-assertion, which we have said are only a mask, are best understood as *reaction formation supports* for the difficult task of *denial*. It is, of course, the defective repression that makes denial of primary importance.

Just how the critical functions of the superego have been disposed of in manic attacks is difficult to understand. They certainly do seem to disappear, and to leave a regressed, childish ego free to act out all kinds of outrageous impulses in a way that is quite foreign to the patient when he is well.

It may be the denial which is responsible for all this. But, even so, we are still left without an explanation of the selective character of the denial. For, although the critical functions of the superego seem to have been put out of commission, the loving, supporting functions of the superego, functions which are usually ascribed to the *ego-ideal*, seem to have been regressively strengthened. The manic patient acts as though he had a completely, absurdly permissive, fond mother-figure as his guide, and as though everything that he wants to do is right just because he wants to do it.

Many workers in this field believe that, in manic reactions, the ego has fused with the ego-ideal, and that this accounts for the wildly boastful,

[19] Klein, M., *Contributions to Psychoanalysis*. London: Hogarth, 1948.
[20] Rochlin, G., "The disorder of depression and elation," *Psychoanal. Quart.*, 1953, 22, 438–457.

childishly happy façade, with its almost total lack of self-criticism and self-restraint. If this is the case, then manic reactions must represent an even deeper regression than do psychotic depressive reactions. The ego-ideal, at least in this brash form, is considered to be of earlier origin than the critical superego. This suggests that the critical superego has been lost by way of a very deep regression.

It has also been suggested that regression in mania may reach a level at which *separate internal objects* operate in place of an integrated superego system.[21] This is a level of operation assumed to have been characteristic very early in everyone's life. The suggestion is that the regressed manic patient identifies with the *good internal objects*, and thus feels approved of, loved and always right. Such an interpretation does not take into account the signs of depression that lurk behind all, or nearly all, manic façades. Neither does it take into account the superficially good external object relations which characterize most manic attacks, and which suggest an ego-superego regression not nearly as deep as one to the original internal objects. We have a great deal yet to learn about the dynamics of mania.

Summary of psychodynamics in manic reactions

The manic attack appears to be a substitute method of working through problems which threaten to precipitate a psychotic depression. The *latent content* in mania is deeply depressive; but the *manifest content* is superficially playful, boastful, aggressive, overactive. The general personality of the manic, like that of the depressive, is pathologically oral dependent; and manic regression, like that of the psychotically depressive, leaves the patient unfit to handle external reality in effectual adult ways. Adult frustration seems likewise to arouse regressively deep oral frustrations, belonging to infancy.

Mania often, perhaps always, begins with preoccupation; but it soon becomes an apparently outgoing overactivity. Object relations, although numerous, are fleeting, superficial, ineffectual and unsatisfying. For this reason the manic's hunger for objects cannot be gratified in his adult surroundings; it is a hunger for early oral satisfaction.

Because repression is grossly defective in manic personalities, unconscious material threatens to break through and contaminate the conscious and preconscious organizations. In a *manic attack*, this threat is realized. Primitive fantasies and primary process material appear in the symptoms of the manifest mania. Denial, reinforced by reaction formation, transforms what might have been a depression into an elation which, although superficially the opposite of depression, is actually "forced," and has many signs of depression near the surface. Identifications may be prominent, especially if these support the defense or provide outlets for the excessive aggression.

[21] Klein, M., "Mourning and its relation to manic-depressive states," in Klein, M., *Contributions to Psychoanalysis*. London: Hogarth, 1948.

The regressive organization of ego and superego is still an unsolved problem. The ego is often compared with the *purified pleasure ego*, theoretically supposed to exist very early in ego development. It includes all that is pleasurable and ejects the rest. In some unknown way, the critical functions of the superego are suppressed in mania, perhaps by an extension of denial to include the denial of these functions. The pathological degree of self-approval, boastfulness, claims of omnipotent power, etc., indicate that other aspects of the superego, those of a regressed *ego-ideal*, are in the saddle. This would suggest a very deep regression as far as the superego is concerned, since this kind of ego-ideal belongs to a very early phase of indulgent development. Even though the ego's object relations are fleeting, facile and ineffectual, they are sufficiently developed and maintained to suggest that the *ego-superego as a whole* does not regress nearly as deeply as the ego-ideal might indicate.

Manic-Depressive Cycles

It is relatively rare for a manic reaction to be immediately followed by a clinically recognizable depressive reaction; and it is still rarer for a psychotic depression to pass over into a full-fledged manic reaction. Custom, however, is a strong force here as elsewhere. In spite of the clinical occurrence and recurrence of manic attacks, without more than the hint of a depressive episode, the official classification still classifies mania as merely a part of manic-depressive reactions, even though it gives to psychotic depression a separate status. In a leading review of the literature up to 1952[22] there is still no chapter on manic reactions; and in a much older one,[23] the 24 per cent of cases listed as "cyclothymics" consist mainly of those whose manic and depressive attacks were separated by years of good health, or separated by several recurrent attacks of the first one. Such situations hardly constitute "cycles."

Undoubtedly the recognition for more than 1600 years that mania and depression are intimately related has a great deal to do with this custom, especially after Bonet reported a case in which one state immediately followed the other and which he named *folie maniaco-mélancolique*.[24] Moreover, it is true that following a psychotic depression there may be a trace of euphoria for a few days or weeks, and after a manic attack or before it there may be some sadness or preoccupation. We have seen, particularly in the case of Stella S., sudden changes from boisterous elation to brief episodes of anxiety, fear and outspoken bitter unhappiness, and back again to

[22] Bellak, L., *Manic-Depressive Psychosis and Allied Conditions.* New York: Grune & Stratton, 1952.

[23] Rennie, T., "Prognosis in manic-depressive psychoses," *Amer. J. Psychiat.,* 1942, 98, 801–814.

[24] Cameron, N., "The functional psychoses," in J. McV. Hunt (Ed.), *Personality and the Behavior Disorders.* New York: Ronald, 1944, pp. 861–921; Schwartz, D. A., "Some suggestions for a unitary formulation of the manic-depressive reactions," *Psychiatry,* 1961, 24, 238–245; Gibson, R. W., Cohen, M. B., and Cohen, R. A., "On the dynamics of the manic-depressive personality," *Amer. J. Psychiat.,* 1959, 115, 1101–1107.

boisterous elation. The sameness of precipitating factors — death may bring a manic attack instead of the expected depression — the ambivalence seen in both, and the common prodromal period of tension and anxiety, all emphasize the close relationship between manic excitements and psychotic depressions.

Perhaps on the basis of Kraepelin's hypothesis, that both mania and depression were endogenous diseases, more or less unaffected by life situations and external factors, it has been widely assumed for a long time that mania represented merely an automatic swing, from one pole of metabolic activity, a depressive one, to the opposite metabolic pole. The biological evidence for this assumption is absent. Biologically considered, there is more correlation between agitated depression and mania than between agitated depression and retarded depression.[25] The determining factor appears to be rather *the level of general activity* than the prevailing mood.

We come back again to the conception of the manic reaction as a coordinate substitute for depression, which not only defends the patient from having a psychotic depression, but seems able in some way to work through the same general unconscious problems. It is in this sense that we must understand the relatively rare *manic-depressive cycle* which does occur. Here a full-fledged manic attack leads right over into a full-fledged depression; or a full-fledged psychotic depression leads right over into a full-fledged manic attack.[26]

What seems to happen in the first case is that the manic defenses of denial and reaction formation for some reason fail. The underlying depression then appears in the manifest clinical picture. In the second case, after a period of manifest psychotic depression, the defenses of denial and reaction formation dominate the manifest scene, and boisterous gaiety or aggression take the place of despair. We assume that, when this happens, the underlying depression becomes latent, in the same sense that desperate dream thoughts often remain latent behind a façade of manifest dream gaiety and even laughter.

The following case, already mentioned in discussing sudden onset in manic reactions, will illustrate such a succession.

Amy H., a middle-aged widow, developed a manic attack immediately after her husband's death. She had not fully recovered from this manic attack, which had all the classical symptoms of self-assertion, forced gaiety, boastfulness, overactivity and insomnia, when she went into a deep depression, which lasted more than a year. After this she had two more manic attacks, separated by periods of apparently good health.

In all of these illnesses, manic as well as depressive, Amy complained of loneliness and of her need for close affection. She was obviously an

---

[25] Cameron, N., "The place of mania among the depressions from a biological standpoint," *J. Psychol.*, 1942, *14*, 181–195.

[26] Arieti, S., "Manic-depressive psychosis," in Arieti, S. (Ed.), *American Handbook of Psychiatry*. New York: Basic Books, 1959, pp. 419–454.

orally dependent person who had never achieved emotional maturity. Even as an adolescent, Amy had been known as a person who concealed her shyness, timidity and dependence behind a mask of witty, happy-go-lucky sociability.

When she married, Amy exchanged a stern, domineering father for a similar husband. In this way, she continued well into middle life as an habitually dependent, dominated, dissatisfied woman. She had no children, who might have given her the chance to mature emotionally as they matured, that is, by identifying with a growing child and adolescent.

Her husband's sudden death seemed to promise Amy the freedom that she had always claimed she wanted. But her own emotional immaturity made his death a disaster, since she no longer had a dominant person upon whom to depend. She denied this need, and she denied the critical attacks of her superego, in her manic attacks. When the first of these subsided, however, the basic depression appeared, and plunged her into pathological mourning. This was in turn succeeded by another manic attack, which was more successful than the first, since it was not followed by a depression. It should be noted in passing that the psychiatrist, in whose care Amy was during her first two manic attacks, witnessed clear episodes of crying and despair, sometimes lasting only a few minutes, but impressive for their marked contrast to the then prevailing boisterous gaiety and self-assertion.

We have already said that, while psychotic regression revives childhood orientations, fantasies and conflicts, it does not make the patient into anything resembling a child. The palpable absurdities in manic attacks make this pathetically clear. At most, the manic patient succeeds in achieving a caricature of childlike irresponsibility. His boisterous joy covers up an overwhelming sadness; what looks like a wealth of object relations turns out to be a shallow pretense and a real poverty; what seems to be a regression into infantile omnipotence only emphasizes the patient's helplessness.

In the light of what is to follow, it should be pointed out here that, for all their defects, both the manic and the depressive reactions are relatively well organized. Contact with reality, even though fleeting and shallow in the manic patient, is maintained at an apparently playful level, at least without the patient's losing completely his hold upon external reality. His delusional reconstructions, even though they baldly deny important aspects of reality, do not become strange, mystical or dreamlike. They are easily intelligible and tend rather to arouse empathy in a normal observer than to arouse anxiety. The manic ego-superego organization may be deeply regressed; but it is not fragmented and dispersed among many fixation points.

As we turn now to the *schizophrenias*, we shall see that deep regressions which do lead to ego fragmentation and dispersal can produce clinical pictures which confuse the normal observer and make him anxious. We shall also see a much greater use of primitive *internal good objects* and *bad objects* than we have so far seen.

17

Schizophrenic Reactions

✣

SCHIZOPHRENIC REACTIONS ARE THE MOST FASCINATING IN ALL BEHAVIOR pathology. Fifteen thousand professional articles and books have been written about them. More clinicians and research workers are interested in them today than ever before, and schizophrenia is the subject of lively controversies from every angle. In this chapter we shall limit ourselves to the most prominent characteristics of schizophrenic reactions, leaving it to the reader to pursue its many details in the easily available literature on the subject.[1]

To begin with, schizophrenic reactions show a bewildering wealth of symptoms. Some of these seem on the surface to be quite contradictory although, as we shall see, they really are not. The official classification still lists the *types* which Kraepelin set up more than half a century ago, as if these were separate forms of the illness. Experience meanwhile has clearly demonstrated that a great many patients, perhaps a majority, belong to more than one of these *types*, and many patients slip from one *type* into another. We can no longer regard them as anything more than changeable groups

[1] See the comprehensive review in book form covering the literature of 1946–56. In this work the references are discussed according to subject matter, so that a reader can follow whatever line he wishes. Bellak, L. (Ed.), *Schizophrenia: A Review of the Syndrome.* New York: Logos Press, 1958. The more recent literature, which is growing more and more abundant, can be found in the *Psychological Abstracts,* published bi-monthly by the American Psychological Association, C. T. Morgan (Ed.). There is also Grinstein, A., *The Index of Psychoanalytic Writings.* New York: Internat. Univ. Press, vol. 6, *Subject Index,* 1960.

SCHIZOPHRENIC REACTIONS

of symptoms, as conveniences which are not mutually exclusive. They certainly are not separate diseases, not even separate subtypes of a disease.

The best way to approach schizophrenic reactions is to recognize that all the symptoms are signs of a breakthrough from primary processes in the unconscious. There is nothing in schizophrenia that cannot be traced to the intrusion of primary process material which should have been kept out of secondary process conscious and preconscious organizations. The intrusion occurs along a wide front, and it comes from several different levels simultaneously or in quick succession. This multiplicity of origins contributes to the appearance of disorganization which characterizes schizophrenia.

During recent years schizophrenia has taken its place beside the dream as a royal road to the unconscious. This is not to say that schizophrenic reactions and dreams are the same, although such a claim has been made more than once in the past. Unlike the dreamer, the schizophrenic patient is awake and usually responsive to his immediate surroundings, however strange his responses may seem. If one lives among schizophrenic persons, after dark as well as during the day, during quiet periods as well as during excitements, one gets an impression very different from the impressions derived from indirect reports and from occasional, formal contacts. Many of the classical descriptions of schizophrenia have come from persons who derived their information largely from formal clinical sessions and tests. These are misleading.

Schizophrenia seems destined to become not only a royal road to the unconscious, to the nature of primary processes, but also a royal road to basic information about normal infancy and early childhood. Many of the most fruitful hypotheses concerning early infantile object relations and early ego differentiation were originally derived from the study of deeply regressed schizophrenic adults. Nowadays the recognition of early autism in children has led to the direct study of childhood schizophrenia, and such study is throwing a new and unexpected light upon normal infancy as well as upon adult schizophrenia. The rapid growth of direct studies of normal infants and little children has at the same time supplemented, checked and enriched our total understanding of the beginnings of mental organization.

There is one other point to be made before going on to the clinical study of schizophrenia. If it has not gone too far, or lasted too long, the schizophrenic reaction can usually be much ameliorated through expert psychotherapy. Sometimes it can be recognized early and headed off. It can often be cured.[2] We stress these facts at the beginning because there is a wide-

Cf. Bychowski, G., *Psychotherapy of Psychosis.* New York: Grune & Stratton, 1952; Brody, E. B., and Redlich, F. C. (Eds.), *Psychotherapy with Schizophrenics.* New York: Internat. Univ. Press, 1952; Hill, L., *Psychotherapeutic Intervention in Schizophrenia.* Chicago: Univ. of Chicago, Press, 1955; Bellak, L. (Ed.), *Schizophrenia: A Review of the Syndrome.* New York: Logos Press, 1958; Fromm-Reichmann, F., *Psychoanalysis and Psychotherapy.* Chicago: Univ. of Chicago Press, 1959. For a detailed account of a borderline adolescent, see Parker, B., *My Language is Me: Psychotherapy with a Disturbed Adolescent.* New York: Basic Books, 1962.

spread belief that schizophrenia is hopeless, that it almost always leads to deterioration, and that it can only be treated by drugs or electric shock. None of these beliefs is justified. Nevertheless it is worth repeating that schizophrenia is one of the most serious and disabling disorders in behavior pathology and that, especially if it has developed insidiously or has remained untreated for long, the outlook for substantial improvement is poor.[3]

Instead of starting in the conventional way, with an account of each official *type*, or symptom group, and a recital of how such *types* originated historically, we shall begin with the account of an actual clinical case. This case has the merit of being a response to a situation which everyone can understand. It is, therefore, much more intelligible than schizophrenic reactions which develop because of weird ways of thinking, some of them lifelong, or because of situations which are unknown.

The schizophrenic reaction we are about to describe begins and ends rapidly. The sudden onset we can safely ascribe to the personally catastrophic nature of the situation. The quick recovery has at least two explanations. One is that the patient unquestionably had a basically strong, though defective, defensive and adaptive system. If it had not been basically *strong* she could never have reorganized her personality system so well after her widespread regression. If her defensive and adaptive system had not been basically *defective* the experience of uncomplicated surgery would never have made her regress as she did. There was another important factor in her quick recovery. This was the calm but expert understanding of her therapists. This patient, as we shall see, was originally a surgical patient; and it was from the surgical staff, particularly from the nurses, that we obtained the early information which enabled us to proceed intelligently. Because of the patient's fear of hospital personnel she received little psychotherapy. She also received no medication. Yet she was able not only to recover promptly but to return to a home environment which was essentially unchanged.

A case with sudden onset and quick recovery

Mabel T., a single woman aged thirty, owned and operated a small dress shop. As long as she could remember she had been terribly afraid of hospitals. She would even cross the street to avoid passing near one. Whenever a relative or a friend was hospitalized she could not make herself go to the hospital. She always sent flowers and an apology.

Two weeks before her own sudden hospitalization Mabel developed recurrent abdominal pains and vomiting. Her family physician diagnosed appendicitis and advised surgery. For these two weeks Mabel rejected the advice. One night, however, she became so frightened by an attack that she allowed herself to be taken to the hospital where she was almost immediately operated upon. The appendix, when removed, showed only chronic inflammation, and recovery from surgery was uneventful.

The surgeons requested psychiatric consultation soon after the operation because Mabel was behaving strangely. She seemed in a daze. She spoke vaguely about having cancer, about dying, about giving birth to a baby, and about seeing angels and flowers. When the psychiatric consultant saw her, Mabel was lying almost motionless in bed. Her eyes most of the time were closed and her eyeballs rolled upwards. Her limbs were limp, her lips moved occasionally, and every now and then a faint but serene smile lit up her face.

It was difficult to communicate with Mabel in her semistuporous state. Most of the time she was unresponsive. When she did speak, her talk was fragmentary and often appeared irrelevant. She spoke slowly and disconnectedly of angels and music, of "the garden," of cancer and of dying. Several times she said, "All the beautiful flowers." Once she remarked that she might have been baptized a Baptist or have gone to a Methodist kindergarten. (Actually she had had a Catholic upbringing in a Catholic family).

After she had finished speaking she would stare at the ceiling with a tranquil look and a faint smile. Then she would close her eyes again. Mabel was well oriented, as she might not have been had she been suffering from a severe systemic intoxication. She missed the date by only two days; she got the month and the year right; she named the hospital she was in and the city; she knew that the persons around her were nurses, doctors and patients.

With the surgeons' blessing Mabel was transferred to the psychiatric service, kept out of bed and given a full regime of planned activity under the close supervision of a resident and the head nurse. She required constant pressure during the day to prevent her from lapsing into deep preoccupation and immobility. When left alone for a few minutes she would slump in her chair and sometimes slip down on to the floor. It is worth pointing out that at this point Mabel was obviously trying to escape her frightening reality by taking refuge in complete inaction and unresponsiveness. If she had been neglected she would almost certainly have slipped into a stupor. She would then have been diagnosed as a case of *catatonic schizophrenia,* and it is quite possible that her unresponsiveness might have become chronic. We shall need to recall this when we come to identify the classical schizophrenic *types.* As it was, she was kept active enough to prevent a flight into stupor.

Mabel refused to eat or drink spontaneously. Because of her terrible fear of hospitals and of medical procedures, she was not given intravenous feeding. With great patience and kind persistence, the nurses spoon-fed and cup-fed her like a baby. Enemas were discontinued entirely when they were found to be making her acutely anxious. She complained that snakes were being put into her body, and that they would gnaw her insides.

Within a week after her transfer to the psychiatric service, Mabel was able to give a retrospective account of the development of her psychiatric illness on the surgical ward. The objective facts in it were checked against observations made by the surgeons, the surgical nurses and the family. This retrospective account revealed more than one source of intense anxiety, some of them unknown to the staff and the family.

When Mabel went under the general anesthetic she was dominated by two fears: one that she would die, and the other that she would reveal to everyone a misdeed belonging to her adolescence which was on her conscience. When she came out of the anesthetic she was frightened at being on a surgical service. She thought she was dying; and she kept saying, "Take care of father and mother." The day after her operation a doctor brought some nurses to her bedside and discussed her case. She could not understand all that he said, but in her frightened state she gathered that something terrible was the matter with her. She asked about her appendix and was told that it had not been found acutely inflamed.

This last information might have reassured Mabel if it had not been for an unnoticed visit from another patient who was resentful over what had been done to her surgically. This patient heightened Mabel's already intense anxiety about herself by advising her never to trust the doctors and nurses. She also had been told, she said to Mabel, that she had had appendicitis; but what she really had was cancer and they had been lying to fool her. "Now look what they've done to me," she said, and she showed Mabel her colostomy wound under the surgical dressings. Although this ghoulish visitor did not actually say so, the implication was clear to Mabel that she, too, had been fooled by this talk about appendicitis.

In her helpless anxiety Mabel came to the following frightening conclusions: there was a conspiracy to keep the truth from her; things more terrible would happen to her in the hospital; she was dying; the nurses and doctors were against her; she must have made her secret public under the anesthetic and everyone would now disown her; she had cancer or "a disease"; she had given birth to a baby; something crooked was going on around her; she was being killed by a "dry gas"; her blood was gone or it was bad.

If these convictions had been communicated to anyone at the time, Mabel would undoubtedly been diagnosed as a case of *paranoid schizophrenia*. This changeability emphasizes the important fact that the so-called *types* are only groups of symptoms. They reveal the psychotic regression and some of the defenses at the time. As this case demonstrates, neither the regression nor the psychotic defenses need become fixed, especially if the patient is protected by an understanding environment and given adequate normal stimulation.

The day after Mabel had been visited by the colostomy patient, with her resentment and her strange wound, Mabel's family was upset to hear her say that they must get her out of the place, that the nurses would give her no attention and were trying to get rid of her. She asked her sister to pray for her soul and said that she had cancer or "a disease." These complaints were all the more surprising because Mabel had never before confided in anyone and had rarely criticized anyone.

During the night that followed Mabel heard her mother's voice saying,

"Do the best you can for her. No use taking her home now." Another voice spoke of killing her sister and of throwing a rock through the window. These voices might have been parts of dreams; but Mabel accepted them as real happenings outside her. The next day she was openly suspicious of everyone and refused all food and fluids.

Then Mabel began seeing and hearing angels in the daytime. They were in the air above her; and they kept saying, "Come up into the garden," which meant to die. There were beautiful flowers and there was music. Mabel said to the nurses, "I feel like I'm going up and away." This all sounds like experiences of death, resurrection and ascension, during which the patient was apparently in a partial trance. The belief that she was dying or was already dead, about which more will be said later, represented products of her unmanageable fears. The angels and the "garden" sound like delusional and hallucinatory reconstructions which served a defensive or reassuring function. The flowers and the music could certainly have belonged to a funeral; but Mabel's almost ecstatic reaction to them made them also a refuge from the external reality that was frightening her.

Later on, Mabel described her experiences further. "I would just start to wander up in the air, rise and leap, then find I was in bed. . . . I was dreamy all the time, from morning to night, just dreamy. I couldn't wake myself up. I've been dreaming for two days. (*Are you coming out of it?*) I hope so. (*Did you enjoy it?*) Oh, no! I had everybody in my dreams — angels, flowers all around. They thought I ought to come up there. I thought I was. I thought I had cancer. (*Before the operation?*) No, after that."

The instability of Mabel's organization at this time comes out clearly. She was asked when she had had her operation; and she replied correctly, "Monday." But, probably because this brought her fears to the fore again, she immediately closed her eyes and went limp, in what might have become a catatonic episode. When aroused she at once asked, "Why did my blood go out? I'm waiting for the gas to go through and touch my heart. When it fills up it'll put me to sleep. They'll put me in the morgue. I'm not afraid to die now." The content is quite different now from the angels and the beautiful flowers, and the level of communication was definitely lower than in the preceding talk.

On the psychiatric service, two days after Mabel had become practically symptom-free, she suffered another sudden regression and both delusions and hallucinations reappeared. Fortunately they did not last long. They began when a fellow patient, who assumed that Mabel was married, asked her how many children she had at home. She became greatly disturbed. Soon after she told the resident that she now believed that all her fears about revealing her secret under the anesthetic had been well founded. That evening she heard the radio broadcasting the news about her, and she insisted that an "extra" had been gotten out by the newspaper to tell her life story. She interpreted crying on the ward as a sign that others knew she was doomed. She seemed fearful, suspicious and bewildered. She said, "I'm drawing my last breath. I beg you to send me home so they can put me in the graveyard. . . . It's too late now to think anything." Later she said, "I guess I'm only a spirit now and these are angels around me, the nurses. It's all too good to be true. I know they are real. I'll be dead and you can throw me in a furnace." It is not difficult to see that these experiences, while certainly delusional, expressed much more uncertainty about death and the angels than the earlier ones.

The next day Mabel seemed much improved. She said, "I don't know if it was all a nightmare or what," which clearly expressed an ability now to tolerate doubt. There were no further episodes of fear and confusion. She was finally discharged, clinically well, three weeks after her operation. Because of her fear of hospitals Mabel did not return for a follow-up. A relative, who saw her often, reported during the ensuing two years that she seemed to have recovered completely. After this, the hospital lost track of her.

Discussion of the case. Even though we know little about Mabel's childhood, we have chosen her case as a beginning because it seemed to have understandable precipitating factors, clear-cut schizophrenic symptomatology, and an uncomplicated recovery. A fear of hospitals is still widespread today in spite of their being far more often the road to recovery than ever before. The fear that one will disclose secrets under a general anesthetic is not only widespread but quite justified. Anxiety before and after surgery may also be counted as a normal reaction, though not in the extreme form that Mabel showed it. Indeed, careful psychological studies of surgical patients indicate that moderate pre-operative anxiety helps prepare a person for the inevitable physiological shock of the operation and its immediate consequences.[4] The complaint that one is not getting enough attention after surgery is often only an expression of dependency needs which the emergency and the helplessness have brought to the surface.

Nonetheless Mabel reacted to stress with frankly psychotic symptoms. Her delusions and her hallucinations do not fall within normal limits as postoperative reactions. Neither does her tendency to fall into a stupor which could not be justified on physiological grounds. Taken together these symptoms constitute a schizophrenic reaction. Mabel denied the simple realities of her situation, because of her fright and her regression, and she replaced them with experiences that lie outside those of a normal or neurotic person who is awake. Mabel projected her fears of death in the form of delusions that she was already dead or was being deliberately killed. She projected her fear of betraying a secret in the form of delusions and hallucinations that everyone knew about her and that her secret was being made public through the radio and press. She also projected her wishes and fears regarding death and resurrection in her experiences of having angels hovering over her and of rising toward heaven or "the garden"; but she also projected them in her belief that she was dying, that all the blood had run out of her, and that she would be sent to a morgue or thrown into a furnace.

The attacks of extreme lassitude, in which Mabel slumped in her chair

[4] Janis, I., *Psychological Stress.* New York: Wiley, 1958.

and slipped on to the floor, may have represented her own death to herself. They might, like the earlier trance states, represent only a flight from the frightening situation into immobility and unresponsiveness. We have no way of knowing which of these possibilities her catatonic symptoms of immobility and unresponsiveness expressed; but we have an enormous amount of information from other patients that either of these meanings may have dominated.

It is obvious from a clinical account which includes frank delusions and hallucinations that Mabel was psychotic. It is also obvious that we cannot call her psychosis either mania or a psychotic depression. What little ecstasy she experienced was strictly in the service of a defense against the delusion that she was dying or dead. She had childlike visions of angels and flowers without genuine elation or aggression. What depressive experiences she had were of a macabre character, mingled with fears that she had cancer, that she had given birth to a baby, and that she was being gassed. These assorted delusions have in them the themes of birth and death, but strangely unorganized, as though each delusion appeared without relation to the others. There was no sign of a persecuting superego such as we saw in psychotic depressions.

We cannot call Mabel's psychosis a paranoid reaction because the delusions were poorly organized, vague, unfocused, shifting, dreamlike. Moreover Mabel had outspoken hallucinations, which do not appear in paranoid reactions, and she intermittently lost effective contact with extreme reality. Indeed, she would have abandoned external reality, and sought to flee into a catatonic stupor, if she had been left alone. It is of passing interest that when the residents met to decide upon a final diagnosis after Mabel had been discharged they were divided as to whether she ought to be called a paranoid schizophrenic with catatonic episodes or a catatonic schizophrenic with paranoid delusions. This illustrates the defects and the difficulties in our current conceptualization of schizophrenia.

Definition. Schizophrenic reactions are regressive attempts to escape tension and anxiety by abandoning realistic interpersonal object relations and constructing delusions and hallucinations. As we said at the beginning of the chapter, schizophrenic reactions show a bewildering wealth of symptoms. Some of them seem to be the opposite of others, but all of them result from the breaking through of primary process material along a wide front. The manifest symptoms of schizophrenia are thus as varied and complex as are manifest dreams. Some of these reach a depth of regression unequaled in the rest of psychopathology.[5] When profound regression completely overwhelms a patient, as it almost overwhelmed Mabel, we may witness the relatively simple external picture of a psychogenic stupor. But this outcome

___

[5] Pious calls the deepest point of schizophrenic regression the *nadir*. See Pious, W. L., "A hypothesis about the nature of schizophrenic behavior," in Burton, A. (Ed.), *Psychotherapy of the Psychoses*. New York: Basic Books, 1961, pp. 43–68.

is relatively rare. As a rule the schizophrenic person regresses gradually; and as he regresses he keeps trying to regain his lost contact with objective reality, at various levels of organization, and for varying periods.[6]

The clinical results of such oscillations are bewildering both to the patient and to those who try to understand him. The manifest behavior in schizophrenia is often a conglomeration of regressive products, of reconstructive attempts to recover reality contacts, and of whatever residuals of normal behavior and experience the patient is still capable. Even such frankly pathological symptoms as delusions and hallucinations may express not only regression but also a renewed attempt to deal constructively with the shared social environment. In this sense they can be signs of improvement as well as signs of illness. We shall leave a description of schizophrenic symptomatology for a later section.

Adaptation. Schizophrenic reactions can be considered adaptive in the limited sense that regression and withdrawal may protect a person from a frightening social reality. Withdrawal has the virtue of reducing the complexity and the pressure of external reality; but it leaves the patient helpless. Delusions and hallucinations are adaptive if they provide satisfactory substitutes for whatever the patient has lost in his object relations. The advantages of such adaptive attempts are lost if the schizophrenic patient, when he regresses and withdraws into fantasy, finds himself either in an objectless world, which is in itself frightening, or encounters the kinds of primitive experiences that normal adults meet in dreams. Since the schizophrenic person is not asleep he cannot escape from desolate or frightening fantasies by waking up. Moreover, as we shall see later, the instability of ego-superego organization in the potentially schizophrenic person makes regression and withdrawal two perilous procedures. Such maneuvers may lead to disaster instead of adaptation.

Varieties of Schizophrenic Reactions

The current official classification appears to differentiate eight varieties of adult schizophrenia. Three of these, however, we can eliminate at once. The *acute undifferentiated type* and the *chronic undifferentiated type* are merely convenient labels for the cases that are difficult to classify. The same is true of the *residual type*. This leaves us with the four classical varieties, *simple, hebephrenic, catatonic* and *paranoid schizophrenia*, plus a fifth, the *schizo-affective type*, which makes room for the inevitable compromise between schizophrenic and manic or depressive reactions actually encountered in practice.

The bringing together of the four classical types, as varieties of a single

[6] The consistency of the symptomatology over a period of a century is indicated by Klaf, F. S., and Hamilton, J. G., "Schizophrenia: a hundred years ago and today," *J. ment. Sci.*, 1961, *107*, 819–827.

illness, we owe to the classificatory genius of Kraepelin. Before his conceptualization, each of these four varieties was regarded as a more or less independent disease. One of them, *catatonia*, was even considered to be a neurological syndrome, comparable in specificity with general paresis. On the basis of his extensive clinical experience, and his gift for organization, Kraepelin was able to recognize that these apparently diverse symptom pictures belong together. In line with existing prejudices about the alleged incurability of these psychoses, he conceptualized them as variations of early deterioration. He therefore applied to them all a term which was already current, *dementia praecox*, setting them in opposition to *dementia senilis*. *Dementia praecox* was thus first looked upon as a dementia that occurs precociously, in young people. Actually there need be no *dementia* at all.

The Kraepelinian *types* have been under fire ever since they were first formulated; but so far no one has come up with a better scheme.[7] In a voluminous and classical monograph, Bleuler helped to get rid of the misleading term *dementia praecox*, which was an advance since the illness which Kraepelin had described is neither necessarily a dementia nor precocious. Bleuler coined the term *schizophrenia* to emphasize the fragmentation which is evident even on a descriptive level. He also made extensive reinterpretations of the symptomatology along psychodynamic lines, for at the time he was under the influence of Freud and of Freud's disciples, as he clearly indicates in his preface.[8] In the end, however, even though he openly expressed his reluctance, Bleuler retained the Kraepelinian types because he did not know how to improve upon them.

We are in the same boat today. Nobody is satisfied with the Kraepelinian *types*, in part because they are purely descriptive, in part because actual living schizophrenic persons too often exhibit symptoms which belong to more than one type, as the case of Mabel T. has shown, and as other cases which we shall describe later also show. Nevertheless, schizophrenic symptoms are so numerous and complex that we need some kind of subdivision if we are merely to be able to hold on to them and talk about them.[9] The current situation is that we still have the Kraepelinian types with us; and they do have the advantage of being old established forms upon which we can all more or less agree. Let us see what they are.

Simple type

What we call the *simple type* conforms closely to the old concept of dementia praecox. This form was recognized and described almost 300 years

---

[7] Cameron, N., "The functional psychoses," in Hunt, J. (Ed.), *Personality and the Behavior Disorders*. New York: Ronald, 1944, pp. 861–921.

[8] Bleuler, E., *Dementia Praecox of the Group of Schizophrenias* (trans. J. Zinkin). New York: Internat. Univ. Press, 1950.

[9] The writer has attempted to subdivide schizophrenic reactions into *aggressive, submissive* and *detached* types. See Cameron, N., *The Psychology of Behavior Disorders*. Boston: Houghton Mifflin, 1947, pp. 468–484.

ago by Willis, the man who is noted for his description of the basic arterial arrangement in the brain (*Circle of Willis*). In 1674 he wrote of "young persons, lively and spirited, and at times even brilliant in their childhood, who passed into obtuseness and hebetude during adolescence." In the simple type we emphasize today a slow, insidious onset and an undramatic downhill course. The whole process looks like a slow fading of the promise of child-hood, a gradual arrest of personality growth, followed by a monotonous, inexorable decline. It should be noted, however, that in many of these cases the patient has never been particularly lively, spirited or brilliant. It is interesting, and it may be of some dynamic significance, that in the *simple type* neither delusions nor hallucinations seem to play a part. Delusions and hallucinations are often active attempts to regain lost object relations and hold on to them.

After a steady downward course, the decline may come to a halt at some relatively low level of adaptation. Here the patient often lives an idle, in-effectual and apparently meaningless life. If his level of adaptation is very low, or his behavior too unpredictable, he may require permanent institutional care. If not, he may lounge about the house or the neighborhood as an irresponsible idler, or wander aimlessly from place to place as a vagrant. Some patients in this group are able and willing to hold temporary jobs which are, however, far below the level of their original promise. They can easily be distinguished from mentally retarded persons, if they will cooperate, by their often surprisingly good score on intelligence tests. In short, what looks like simple deterioration is actually something much more complex. A general reduction in adaptive level is not always inconsistent with a high level of creativity in some special field, that is, sometimes a person who is unable or unwilling to maintain ordinary social relationships may show ex-ceptional talent in some creative work of his own.

Hebephrenic type

Hebephrenic schizophrenia is a caricature of early normal adolescence which it often replaces. The term *hebephrenia* really means literally *mind of youth*. The onset may be slow and insidious; but it may also be sudden, following quickly upon a personal loss or failure. Silly, disorganized be-havior is common. Giggling, smiling and laughter occur which seem empty and irrelevant to the observer. If, on the other hand, there is sadness it seems shallow, and if there is weeping it may appear inexplicable. There may be outbursts of anger.

A young woman, for example, newly admitted to a hospital, spent several days sobbing, crying real tears and seeming to be in terrible distress. Yet she could not account for her weeping, even to herself. All she could say was that she had lost something. As it turned out, she had lost the world of object relations, and she never succeeded in reorganizing so as to get it back. With these emotional expressions go also gestures, postures and mannerisms, which appear to be symbolic, but are usually strange, more or less fragmentary, and often bizarre. Speech becomes manneristic also, even to the point of being incoherent and including made-up words (*neologisms*). The delusions which develop are also likely to be bizarre and incoherent, including often weird notions of body change. Hallucinations are usually prominent, although if the patient is uncommunicative they may have to be inferred from the behavior.

With time, the hebephrenic often withdraws more and more into preoccupation with private fantasy until he becomes almost completely desocialized and inaccessible. He may even wet and soil like a baby. He may have to be helped to eat, or he eats greedily like a starved person. Occasionally a hebephrenic patient who has regressed almost to a vegetative level manages to reorganize and regain his lost object relations, with the help of an undaunted and gifted psychotherapist. As a rule, however, there is no complete return.

Catatonic type

The stress in this subtype of schizophrenia is laid upon motor disturbances. At one extreme a patient may be in a disorganized excitement; at the other extreme he may be mute and motionless, as though in a stupor. All kinds of combinations of such symptoms may appear in the same person. In catatonic excitement there may be the same degree of incessant activity that one sees in mania, the same inability to sleep, the same unwillingness to eat or drink. It differs from mania, however, in seeming weird, unrealistic, incoherent. In catatonic stupor the behavior seems constricted, sometimes negativistic and sometimes overcompliant. The patient may lie rigidly, eyes closed and with a masklike face, as though he were dramatizing his own death. Or he may sit or stand staring blankly ahead or at the floor, for hours at a time.

In both the excited and the immobile catatonic patient there are delusions, persecutory in character or mystical and miraculous. There are nearly always hallucinations also. These consist predominantly of terrifying visions, unintelligible apparitions, religious visitations, or voices and other sounds having fearsome or mysterious meanings. One can often learn something about the character of these delusions and hallucinations during relatively clear phases in the illness; but the chief source of information is the retrospective account which many patients are willing and able to give after partial recovery. Catatonic schizophrenia is more likely than the other types to come on suddenly and to clear up suddenly. This statement must, however, be tempered by the realization that pure types seldom appear.

Paranoid type

Delusions hold the spotlight in this group. The paranoid schizophrenic patient has usually been having serious interpersonal difficulties for many years before he becomes ill. He is characteristically tense, uneasy and distrustful, with a tendency to read hostile and belittling meanings into other people's comments and to apply these to himself. He may have tried to compensate for his mistrust by keeping a watchful, suspicious eye on whatever goes on around him, so as to be ready for anything that happens. He may, instead, have remained for many years defensively aloof, asocial and withdrawn, so that nothing can touch him. His lifelong custom is to mull things over alone, looking for explanations which seem plausible to him. Naturally, his personal fears, needs, wishes and uncertainties will play a large part in such lonely brooding.

The onset of paranoid schizophrenia comes when a person begins to lose his grip on reality, substitutes his misinterpretations and fantasies for the realities of shared social operations, and acts upon these as though they were publicly accepted fact. When this happens, the paranoid schizophrenic person regresses more quickly and further than the person with a paranoid reaction. His delusions are likely to be vague, bizarre and unconvincing, as we shall see when we come to our two detailed clinical cases. Their structure varies all the way from a mere succession of disjoined fragments to the most florid, imaginative jungles. Some are full of contradictions, of condensations and displacements, and of archaic symbolism such as we find in ordinary dreaming. Persecutory delusions are common, as are also delusions of influence and of grandeur, with ideas of reference. There are admixtures of the magical, mystical, religious and sexual, often in weird combination. Somatic delusions are characteristically bizarre. One finds sometimes vivid delusions of catastrophe, world destruction, salvation and world reconstruction.[10] We shall leave the details and illustrations for the next section where case material is presented.

Hallucinations are nearly always present, and in greater profusion than in any other major syndrome, with the exception of toxic and infectious states. The hallucinations usually support and enrich delusional beliefs. Auditory hallucinations are the most common; visual the next most common. Hallucinations of smell, taste, body equilibrium and skin sensation may also appear as important expressions of the patient's dynamics.

Emotional involvement is usual in paranoid schizophrenia, at least while the illness is active. The persecuted patient is terrified, indignant, belligerent. He may go into a whirlwind of furious retaliation, or plan revenge relentlessly for an imagined wrong. Even when the patient's response is submissive and compliant, he usually shows emotional feeling appropriately. Likewise, grandiose schizophrenic patients look grandiose; delusions of royalty make a person look proud and lofty; the transfigured patient usually looks as he

---

[10] Detailed accounts of schizophrenic delusions can be found in Cameron, N., *The Psychology of Behavior Disorders.* Boston: Houghton Mifflin, 1947, Chapters 13 and 15; and in Cameron, N., and Magaret, A., *Behavior Pathology.* Boston: Houghton Mifflin, 1951, Chapters 13, 14 and 16. For an autobiographical account, see Schreber, P., *Memoirs of My Nervous Illness* (1903) (trans. I. Macalpine and R. A. Hunter). London: Dawson, 1955.

feels. It is still true, however, that more schizophrenic patients exhibit emotional incongruities than other patients do, and we are still not certain why.

Recovery from paranoid schizophrenia is most likely to occur during the first year or two of frank psychosis. Such recovery does not mean that the patient will necessarily create a new personality. The goal of helping a decompensated patient back to as good an equilibrium as he had before his psychotic break is a realistic one. It is sometimes possible to guard against a second break by helping the patient to understand his areas of vulnerability, so that he can try to avoid the kind of situation which helped precipitate the first. The experience of having been able to confide in a therapist can be a new and strengthening one, to which the patient may return in times of later stress.

If the paranoid schizophrenic patient does not get well he is likely to undergo some further disorganization. Delusions grow more and more vague and unintelligible, or they become fixed and stereotyped. The patient gives up trying to account for them. Speech may also grow less organized and become limited in scope, stereotyped and jumbled. Mannerisms become established. Emotional responses lose their flexibility and may become unpredictable. In the end, patients who remain ill tend, as in the other subtypes, to live a greatly impoverished, desocialized life. If not made angry, they may lead an aimless, detached life of surly, silent defiance. It is not unusual for catatonic or hebephrenic characteristics to appear, or for the person to suffer a general decline like that of the simple type.

Schizo-affective type

The schizo-affective type is exactly what the name implies, a mixture of schizophrenic symptoms with manic or depressive ones. It is nothing more than a necessary convenience in classification, although it may also have dynamic implications. Essentially the clinical picture is one of an elation or a depression, in which delusions are more weird, vaguer and less well organized than usual. Hallucinations are common, as they are not in mania and depression. Estrangement, depersonalization and bizarre somatic delusions are common. On the other hand, the elated or depressive component is more stable, better organized and deeper than in most other schizophrenic illnesses. The mode of onset, course and outcome are as variable as in other types, but the chances for recovery are perhaps better. If there are recurrences, after recovery, the schizophrenic features grow more prominent and the chances for recovery grow poorer.

Clinical Illustrations of Schizophrenic Reaction

Having now described the classical subtypes of the schizophrenic reaction we shall give in some detail an account of two cases which will illustrate many of the typical symptoms. It will be seen that characteristics of more than one so-called type enter into each case, as is true of most schizophrenic patients in real life. For example, the high school girl exhibits almost typical paranoid delusions, goes through weird, semimagical rituals, and at times suddenly becomes catatonic. The man suffers from weird somatic delusions and later on seems to deteriorate and become hebephrenic as well as mute. Both patients heard voices. Neither of them recovered. Both of them lost an important person through death, a person who had probably been helping to hold together a basically defective maladaptive personality in the patient. The girl was mixed up in a confusing edipal conflict for three years before hospitalization. The man was so strongly attached to his mother that he could not marry. He also showed signs of serious confusions regarding his sexual identity.

A schizophrenic reaction in an adolescent girl

Joan R., a Kansas City high school girl, was admitted to a psychiatric clinic after she had attempted suicide by drinking iodine. We shall begin with her childhood. She had suffered the loss through death of two important mother figures, one when she was two years old, the other when she was fourteen. These are critical ages in personality development, ages when a mother figure plays her most significant roles. Joan's mother had been ill for some time before her death, so that the little girl lacked the ego support which should have been available to her for the structuring of her early personality. At fourteen, when an adolescent normally lives through in altered form the edipal conflicts of early childhood, Joan's foster mother died, and Joan was again left with no one to help her build her adolescent personality. To further complicate matters for Joan, her foster mother was her father's sister, a domineering widow with a daughter of her own. It will be simplest if we present briefly the patient's life history.

As we have said, Joan was two years old when her mother died. Her father's sister moved at once into the home, taking Joan's mother's place, and bringing with her Peggy, an eight-year-old daughter. We shall see how Joan tried to repeat what her foster mother had done as soon as death left her place vacant. Peggy's mother was an anxious, probably superstitious woman who encouraged Joan to be over-dependent. The two girls apparently hated each other. When Peggy's mother died, Joan was fourteen and Peggy was a grown woman of twenty. The household now consisted of Joan, Peggy and Joan's father, a scholar with little psychological understanding.

To her father's surprise Joan showed no sorrow over the death of her foster mother. Instead, she tried at once to take her place in the home, just as her foster mother had immediately taken her own mother's place. She became self-assertive, arrogant and demanding. The home, she said, was now hers, and Peggy could henceforth obey her orders. Joan's father spent the next two years trying unsuccessfully to keep the peace between these two girls, rivals for control of the home.

Without a mother figure and without a stable personality of her own, Joan soon got out of control. She continued for the time being to be affectionate to her father, but she also behaved toward him as a nagging wife rather than as a young adolescent daughter. She openly criticized his appearance and his ways, even in front of guests. She demanded that he give her more attention and more money. She reminded her father that her foster mother, her father's sister, had been afraid of the house, often saying that there was a curse upon it. She protested violently against his going out in the evening and leaving the latchkey under the mat, where strangers might find it. As we shall see Joan was already beginning to develop delusional fears in relation to this evening situation. Toward Peggy, her grownup cousin, she remained relentlessly hostile. Once during a quarrel over the radio she bit Peggy severely, giving her a wound that took two weeks to heal. From other evidence it is clear that Joan's emotional problems, with which no one helped her, were precipitating a general personality disorganization.

When Joan was sixteen her cousin married. This removed her rival from the home; but it also left Joan, in a state of emotional turmoil, alone in the house with her father. Her attitude toward him abruptly changed. She no longer gave or accepted tokens of affection. The hate that she had visited upon her cousin she now directed toward her father. She behaved insolently toward him, accusing him even before visitors of mistreating her. These accusations, which completely mystified her father, were actually the product of delusional experiences that she was having, experiences in which weird primary process fears and wishes had escaped repression and were mingling with preconscious and conscious organization. What these were we shall soon see. Whenever Joan had frightening dreams she would make her father join her in bed, as her aunt had always done, but later she would rail against him for having done this and accuse him of mistreatment. He was greatly disconcerted by all this contradiction and confusion; but he did not know what to do about it. He thought she would outgrow it. One night he came home late to find his daughter thrashing about the room with a cane — killing snakes, she said. She used to keep her light on all night long because she was having "frightening dreams," which were probably delusional and hallucinatory experiences rather than dreams.

As might be expected, after the aunt's death, when Joan was fourteen, her school work grew poorer and poorer. She seemed bored, inattentive and irritable. By the time she was fifteen and a half she needed a tutor to keep her from being dropped from school. Eventually even this help was not enough. When she was sixteen, Joan was dropped from school, and her father was told to consult a psychiatrist. The psychiatrist recommended immediate treatment, but his recommendation was not followed. Joan simply stayed at home.[11]

Joan showed a corresponding decline in her social relationships. Un-

[11] Bower, E. M., Shellhamer, T. A., and Daily, J. M., "School characteristics of male adolescents who later became schizophrenic," *Amer. J. Orthopsychiat.*, 1961, *30*, 712–739.

doubtedly because of her personality defects, and because she was overdependent upon her foster mother, Joan had never reached an adequate level of social skill. She frightened and repelled the neighborhood children with her temper tantrums and uncompromising demands. As an adolescent she was far too much involved in the rivalry with her cousin for domination of the home, in her own revived edipal conflicts and her preoccupations with frightening experiences to be able to interact normally with her peers, the boys and girls around her.

The climax came when Joan was sixteen, a year before she came to the hospital. She bought a new dress for a high school dance, but when her escort arrived she refused at first to see him. After considerable persuasion she finally consented to go with him; half an hour later she returned home without her escort. Perhaps she knew that her father had arranged to have her escorted when he found that nobody had invited her to the dance. At any rate this was her last social engagement. Following Joan's withdrawal from school, her father arranged little parties for her, "to help her get well," but she would shut herself in her room until the guests left the house. The best he could do about the situation was to engage a housekeeper.

During the months between leaving school and entering the hospital Joan was living in a nightmare. She was afraid to sleep at night because of all that seemed to be going on. During the day she lay around the house, preoccupied, worn out and doing next to nothing. Her behavior became obviously strange, reflecting the hopeless confusion of her thinking. For example, her father gave her forty dollars to buy some clothes, and she spent it all on history books which she never read. On another occasion she went out and spent twelve dollars on cosmetics, but a few days later she destroyed the lot. She got up early one morning, collected all the playing cards in the house and burned them, saying that they were sinful. She began talking about religion, the church, sin, charity and the hereafter. She gave the housekeeper five dollars because she had to be charitable "to get to heaven."

Joan said that all her troubles came from masturbation. At fifteen she concluded without telling anyone that this was driving her crazy. Her conclusion increased her already intolerable guilt, anxiety and confusion, and contributed to her belief that she would burn in hell for her sins, and that her hands were diseased. "I have leprosy!" she said at the hospital, "look at my hands. But that's not punishment enough for all my evil. Faust, yes, he gave himself to the devil. That's what I've done. Don't touch me! You'll be sorry, you'll get leprosy too!"[12]

The girl's unconscious material, which ultimately emerged and overwhelmed her, seems to have appeared first as anxiety dreams and frightening nighttime fantasies — of snakes, assault, strangers in the house and murder. "I used to read stories and things," she said, "and then I'd go to bed and lie awake and think about them. I'd be scared silly to be in the room by myself. That house is so spooky." The last statement repeats what her foster mother had always said. When Joan

---

[12] Compare this with the neurotic compulsive reaction to soiled hands, as in the case of Sally J., who washed and scrubbed her hands when she had evil thoughts.

closed her eyes and tried to sleep, she would have horrible visions, and see faces that seemed to grow enormous.[13] She thought men were walking on the roofs, which were flat and connected with one another, and that they were climbing in the window. Eventually a man across the street seemed to control the house; and she began hearing voices. Finally a man's voice dominated, telling her to do whatever she was told.

Joan now used weird delusions to reconstruct the reality that she had lost in her steady regression and disorganization, delusions which would help explain her previously unconscious fantasies, now fully conscious. Her home, she told herself, was now the headquarters of a dope ring. Her father had been murdered and an imposter put in his place. "My father wouldn't treat me the way this man has treated me," she said. "My father and I were friends. This man will get into bed with me. I've been love-starved and forsaken; and I thought someone was bringing in opium." The similarity of this tale to the common dope ring mystery story is obvious, and its appeal is probably to the same unconscious needs.

In her fantasies, which Joan considered real, people seemed to beat her and tie her up. They seemed able to read her mind, to control her by reading her thoughts. She tried to keep back her thoughts; but the effort hurt the back of her head.[14]

Joan began having horrible dreams and fantasies of killing her father and other people, of cutting them up and chewing their flesh, of being God, and of being murdered as a sacrifice.[15] She felt at times that she was someone else, that her body was changing, that she might be going to have a baby, that she had a brain tumor and was going crazy.

In the hospital, where people listened to her when she spoke, some of her sadomasochistic fantasies became obvious. Joan said that her suicidal attempt was an act of self-punishment. She was going to hell for her sins, she thought, and the quicker she got there the better. "I thought it would make me suffer. If I hadn't become so hardened it would have hurt terribly." At times she was sure she would be executed for her crimes, which seemed real to her, or that she would get life imprisonment. She wished that she would "get black smallpox or something." She said, "I got hipped on the subject of Christianity. I thought I should torture myself. . . . I try to figure out ways of torturing people. It seems I have been in so much pain; and I want other people to have the same thing."

Joan had many outbursts of rage. One night a nurse found her trem-

---

[13] Such changes in size have been reported by normal adults who have studied their visions when falling asleep. Cf. Silberer, H., "Report on a method of eliciting and observing certain symbolic hallucination-phenomena," in Rapaport, D. (Ed.), *Organization and Pathology of Thought.* New York: Columbia Univ. Press, 1951; Isakower, O., "A contribution to the pathopsychology of phenomena associated with falling asleep," *Internat. J. Psychoanal.*, 1938, *19*, 331–345.

[14] When adults anticipate a small child's actions, it must seem to the child that they know his thoughts. Such childhood experiences are probably the origins of this common form of schizophrenic delusion.

[15] Cannibalistic dreams are not rare among neurotic persons. Such dreams and the fantasies of this patient probably revive early childhood feeding fantasies which, in the adult, take on a more definite form.

bling and wringing her hands. "I think I'm pushing people's eyes in. I'm dreadfully wicked. . . . It's those awful thoughts that go through my head." Once in the daytime she cried to a group of patients, "If I had the strength of Christ I would kill every one of you! Yes, I would kill you all because a more horrid doom awaits you than death." There is a sign of confusion between herself and the others in this histrionic statement. Another day Joan became angry and struck an inoffensive depressed patient. "That's nothing in comparison with what I'm going to do," she cried, "I'm going to chop off your heads, every one of you. You'd better go home and chop off your families' heads. . . . You're not going to keep me here and make me bear children!" In the more permissive atmosphere of the hospital, Joan was giving vent to the violent aggression that she had felt for years at home.[16] After expressing it, she excused herself on the grounds that she would be saving the patients from something worse by killing them.

There were grandiose delusions also. Joan said that she felt she had a powerful influence over people and was responsible for everything that happened. She thought that she might get superhuman ideas, "such as how Christ turned water into wine — I had to find out how it was done." As God, she thought, she must suffer to help others; and because of her sins she ought to kill herself. But the attempt failed. "So," she said, "I came to the conclusion that I would have to forget. As time goes on, I'll forget all my troubles, my experiences and so forth." This was just what Joan seemed to be achieving. She expressed, in well-organized secondary process speech, the disintegration which she was experiencing, and to which she was resigned.

Years before, when her foster mother died, Joan had begun a struggle at home with a tangled personal situation involving real persons, her father, her cousin and herself. For such a struggle, with no one around to understand her, Joan's personality organization was unprepared. As time went on, this shared social community was gradually replaced by the even greater complexities of Joan's delusional pseudocommunity, with its mixture of real and imagined persons, of fact and reconstructed delusion. Now she seemed to be making a final retreat. She was withdrawing into an autistic community which consisted mainly of fantasied persons and action with the background of her own private fantasies.[17]

There were two definite catatonic episodes. One day, while telling her therapist that she liked dreamy states, Joan slipped into a stupor. Her eyes closed, her eyeballs rolled upward, and her limbs went limp. Her eyelids resisted opening, however, and her jaws and limbs grew stiffer as they were manipulated. When she was left alone she soon recovered. Another day Joan was lying on her side on her bed, just before lunch, when there was a sudden loud clap of thunder close by.

---

[16] There is a recent discussion of sadomasochism in relation to aggression in Gero, G., "Sadism, masochism and aggression," *Psychoanal. Quart.*, 1962, *31*, 31–42.

[17] For a comparison of *pseudocommunity* and *autistic community*, see Cameron, N., and Magaret, A., *Behavior Pathology*. Boston: Houghton Mifflin, 1951, Chapters 13 and 14.

Joan instantly became so rigid that the nurses could pick her up and place her in a sitting position with no more change in her posture than if she had been a statue. Then the lunch trays arrived, and an experienced nurse began coaxing her gently and spoon-feeding her. After about ten minutes of this, the girl suddenly got up, rubbed her eyes as though she had just awakened, and ate her lunch with the others as if nothing had happened.

Therapy was unsuccessful with Joan. She slept well at night without medication, in spite of occasional disturbing dreams. In the daytime she spent most of her time daydreaming. She became less and less communicative, her talk developed more and more disorganization. She was frequently observed talking excitedly to herself. Sometimes she smiled and laughed as though she were hallucinating. Often she stood straight against the wall with her hands high above her head; but she would give no explanation of this posturing. Her father decided to place Joan in a state hospital near her home. Her prognosis for social recovery was poor.

Discussion. In this case we see the progressive disorganization of an adolescent girl during a period of over three years. Joan suffered two severely traumatic losses. Her mother fell ill and died when Joan was only two, before she had had time to establish her own childhood personality. Her foster mother confused the child by immediately taking the dead mother's place, and by introducing a rival girl into the home. The fact that the woman who took the place of Joan's mother in the house was the sister of Joan's father must have added to the confusion, although we have no information about this. What we do know, however, is that neither girl seems to have been adequately protected from the hostility of the other, at least, after the foster mother died. The death of her domineering foster mother when Joan was only fourteen was the second severe trauma. It was compounded by the father's ineptness in handling emotional situations.

The affectional situation was suddenly complicated when the foster mother died. If Joan had been four years older or younger, she might have weathered it, in spite of having always been overdependent and overprotected. We have seen how unskilfully Joan tried to identify with her dead foster mother and take over the household immediately, as her foster mother had done. Her growing confusion can in part be attributed to the conflicts and contradictions, the tumult of early adolescent love and hate, which Joan's ineffectual attempts must have stimulated. A fourteen-year-old girl with such a background could hardly take the role of a domineering mother toward her twenty-year-old cousin; neither could she transform her dependent daughter role into that of the woman of the house in relation to her father. She had been reared an anxious, socially immature child without adequate opportunity to develop a mature ego-superego organization. As such, she was left alone to work out her multiple conflicts, including her clearly expressed guilt over sex and hostility, in a household with a man who did not understand her and a woman whom she hated.

Another important factor in promoting Joan's disorganization was the progressive intrusion of primary process fantasy into her nighttime and daytime thinking, once she had been abandoned to the complex home situation by the death of her aunt. Long before her aunt's death, probably throughout her life, Joan had found difficulty in distinguishing between dream and daydream. She had utilized fantasy freely in satisfying need, and she had also experienced terrifying dreams and hypnagogic visions which drove her to seek the protection of her aunt's bed. We have seen how she carried her conflicts, her wishes, fears and furies, over into her waking and sleeping fantasy life after her aunt was dead.

This procedure settled nothing. On the contrary, the confusion of fantasy and fact only increased Joan's anxiety and complicated her problems. There was now no adult to whom she could flee for comforting in the night, no adult who could act as substitute ego in support of her own inadequate one. The childhood fantasies came tumbling out of repression, through the defective defensive boundaries, and into Joan's daytime thinking. She was able to halt her regression by constructing fantastic delusions, which sounded like murder mystery stories, but this halt did not last. Even before she was admitted to the hospital Joan had already regressed into the jungles of primary process thinking. Therapy did not succeed in rescuing her. She continued regressing into an autistic world of fantasy where she ignored all of her surroundings that she could.

A schizophrenic reaction in an unmarried man of thirty

Donald J. had been trained as an electrical engineer. In part because of adverse business conditions, in part because of his own awkwardness and immaturity, he had never succeeded in establishing himself in his profession. Instead, he had been in succession a draftsman, an amateur inventor, and a mechanic's assistant. His early life throws light upon his failure in ego development.

Donald's mother died a few days after he was born. He had always felt in some way responsible for this. He was almost immediately adopted by a childless couple and separated from his siblings. His foster parents were unusually indulgent, his foster mother was domineering and possessive, and Donald had no children to play with at all until he began school at the late age of eight years. He said that he had always been happy playing imaginative, solitary games. He regarded his foster mother as perfect, an opinion that was not shared by his relatives, who described her as demanding, nagging and short-tempered.

When Donald was fourteen he began to masturbate, and he developed great concern and guilt about it. By the time he was fifteen he had developed what may have been an adolescent schizophrenic flurry. He was extremely anxious. He imagined terrible things happening to him because of his sin, among them the feeling that his blood had been turned into a snake which whirled about in his body. This illness lasted about six months, but it never kept him from school for more

than a few days at a time. He had two similar episodes in engineering
college, of short duration, each developing in a setting of stress, fatigue
and failure in examinations. At the age of twenty-two Donald was
graduated from engineering college, obtained employment as a draftsman whose task it was to devise and test electrical circuits, and returned
to live with his foster mother, who had meantime been widowed.

Although the patient speaks of this phase of his life as "the happy
days," it must also have been difficult for him. His foster mother was
soon paralyzed by a stroke and became, according to relatives, a terrible old lady, cantankerous, an "impossible" invalid. Donald had to
run the house and the finances, and look after his foster mother, at the
same time that he was holding down an exacting job. In spite of all
this he managed to devise and patent a new kind of wheel chair in
his spare time.

During this period Donald fell in love with a girl and asked her to
marry him. She accepted his proposal on condition that he give up
his mother. He decided to stay with his mother and give up the girl.
When he was twenty-eight Donald lost his job and, failing to get another, he began making and selling his patented wheel chairs. This only
brought him about two hundred dollars a year. Then he came down
with influenza and gave it to his foster mother, so he said, and she
suddenly died. He had to get out of a sickbed to make the funeral
arrangements and attend her burial. It reminded him of his feeling that
he was responsible for his mother's death.

When it was all over, and he had sold the home and gone to live
with acquaintances, he still felt ill and sad. He had made few close
friends while his foster mother lived, and now he felt life to be lonely
and empty. He tried hard to establish himself in the affections of his
siblings, behaving as though he had been brought up with them. They
were cool to him, and their failure to accept him hurt his feelings and
bewildered him. His only consolation was the friendship of a girl
whose acquaintance he had made at this time. He did not propose to
her until later, but he took it for granted that when he did so the girl
would accept him.

A year after his foster mother's death, and eight months prior to his
admission to the clinic, Donald succeeded in getting a job as mechanic's
assistant in another city. Here he worked with a gang of good-natured
but earthy men. As an awkward, socially inexperienced person he
quickly became the butt of his fellow workers' witticisms. He admitted
one day that he had never had sexual intercourse, and from then on
he was called a virgin. His virginity, with its possible implications,
was repeatedly discussed and commented upon in his presence. Since
teasing of this kind usually includes ambiguous references to the sex
of the person being teased, it is highly probable that this banter contributed to Donald's confusion about his sex identity, which came out
clearly as soon as he fell ill.

For recreation Donald spent weekends in his home city where he
visited acquaintances and his girl friend. During the week he went
occasionally to public dance halls where dancing partners were fur-

nished by the management. One night he found an abrasion on his genitals after he had indulged in sex play with a girl at the dance hall. A few days later a rash appeared on his body, and he leaped to the conclusion that he had developed syphilis. This he regarded as punishment for his sex play, but he did nothing about it except to worry.

Two months before admission to the clinic Donald developed back pains after changing to harder work. At about the same time his girl friend told him that she was in love with someone else and not interested in him. The pains then became worse and spread to his abdomen and his groin. His fears about syphilis finally drove Donald to seek medical help. In the course of diagnostic investigation he was cystoscoped. This was not only painful, it also resulted in genital paresthesias and heightened his already intense anxiety about himself.

According to Donald, he was told that he had a kidney infection, given a bottle of medicine, and told not to worry because the kidneys had been washed out. Unfortunately he believed in the popular superstition that tampering with the kidneys may change a man's sexual powers. He said later, "It all started after I had my kidneys cleaned out. . . . The medicines cleaned me out front and back; and I was practically hollow there." He returned to work but "everything seemed like a dream," his eyesight was dim and he saw spots before his eyes. He returned to his physican twice, "to see what it was all about," but the medicines prescribed made him feel more upset than ever. With this focus Donald quickly developed bizarre somatic delusions, some of which he experienced as dreams, some as waking experiences.

It seemed to Donald that his two sides were no longer working together. The right seemed to be stronger than the left. One night he awakened to find that he seemed to have grown a female breast on the left, and to have acquired boy's genitals which were not a part of himself. He believed that he could choose which of these three persons he might become — the man, the woman or the child. But the medicines, he said, made the boy win out. His voice seemed to grow boyish, his hands became soft, his heart felt weak, only one side of his intestines was working, and a hernia which had been corrected in boyhood seemed to come back. At one time Donald was sure that he had three hearts, one on the right, one on the left, and one in his genitals. He thought that his father's blood was in the right side and his mother's in the left.[18] The blood rushed back and forth between these two sides.

Donald heard a voice telling him to drink much more milk and this would make him well. He was not sure whether it was God's voice or the devil's. At night he had horrifying dreams. In the daytime he began walking the streets alone, feeling that terrible things were happening to him. He dreamed, for example, that he was giving birth to a litter of kittens, all chewing and scratching. Another time, after an anxiety dream, he turned the light on to find that his body had turned white. One night he dreamed that his body had shriveled up, and he

[18] Identification of the right side with masculinity and the left side with femininity is common in schizophrenic thinking. It is probably a product of primary process identification of *strength* with *the right* and *weakness* with *the left*.

awoke expecting death. In his fright he made a will and sat down in a chair to die. His body seemed to go stiff and then he knew he was dead, but after a while he felt better and went out for food. The next morning he was so weak that he could scarcely walk. His food fell through him like a stone, and then he realized that there was a snake in him.

Of this last episode he said, "I've been bothered by seeing myself all kinds of shapes after I'd taken that medicine. . . . My body was shrinking up, and I felt death creeping up on me, and I ate sour fruit. Next morning the snake was in my belly and then in my back; and it's been traveling around in me ever since. . . . When I walk, I walk like a snake." Donald said that his blood rushed around his body "like a wriggling snake." This is the same complaint that he made in adolescence when he was worried about masturbating.

Donald went in desperation to his home city for help. His old family physician advised him to go to a psychiatric clinic. His friends told him that he was getting on their nerves. He telephoned his former girl friend, but she only said, "You must paddle your own canoe." To himself he said, "There's no one in the world to help me now." Back in the city where he worked he at first wandered about indecisively; but he eventually appeared at the out-patient psychiatric clinic. Here he complained that a snake was in his belly, and that he was three persons in one — a man, a woman and a child. He was admitted to the in-patient service at once.

After a few days of confusion Donald appeared to improve rapidly. He dismissed his former complaints as "crazy stuff," saying that he "must have been nuts." At the end of four weeks, since he was in the hospital on a voluntary basis, he was discharged at his own request to return to work. Arrangements were made for him to report to the out-patient clinic for further psychotherapy.

Donald disappeared for eleven days. He was readmitted on the in-patient service, dirty and disheveled, agitated, suspicious and con-fused. He could not say where he had been. His complaint now was that he was "falling to pieces," a complaint which seemed justified by his behavior. In the ensuing five months he improved only super-ficially. Then he was taken by relatives to a hospital near his home. According to a report received a year later from that hospital efforts at therapy had been fruitless. Donald had become mute and with-drawn. He spent his time sitting alone, smirking and giggling, and apparently hallucinating. He was evidently living in an autistic com-munity, that is, in a private world of fantasied things, people and sit-uations, at a greatly regressed level.[19]

Discussion. We have presented this case because of the fantastic somatic delusions it illustrates, and because of the frantic but inept attempts the patient made to establish object relations with other people after his foster mother died. The symptoms are exceedingly bizarre, showing an invasion

[19] For a fuller discussion of the *autistic community*, see Cameron, N., and Magaret, A., *Behavior Pathology.* Boston: Houghton Mifflin, 1951, Chapters 13 and 14.

of thinking by concrete primary process interpretations. As in the case of Joan R., the patient was unable to distinguish clearly between dream, fantasy and fact, once he became seriously upset. This kind of confusion, appearing in a person who is not toxic, indicates serious defects in ego organization, ego defense and ego adaptation. It indicates that normal boundaries between ego, id, superego, somatic reality and external reality, had never been firmly established.

If we look at his early childhood, we find that Donald was denied the ordinary opportunities for interacting with other children, or for that matter with anyone but his tyrannical foster mother and perhaps his foster father, until he was eight years old. He seems to have lived almost all of his life in bondage to a person who demanded obedience and affection, but gave nothing in return. His play was confined to solitary imagining. There is no hint in his life story of anything approaching normal independence of action or thinking.

Donald weathered three illnesses during his adolescence in which somatic symptoms of a bizarre character appeared. It is probable that he weathered them because he could rely upon the strength of his tyrannical foster mother. During his adolescence, he had a strong mother figure in the background who could provide ego support at times when he was on the point of "falling to pieces." When he finally did fall ill, it was only after his foster mother had died, when he tried turning in all directions to find someone to save him from disintegrating.

We do not know the childhood origin of Donald's confusion of sex identity, a symptom common among schizophrenic patients. We do know that the teasing by his fellow workers, with all the implied ambiguity, seemed to bring it out clearly in his bizarre somatic complaints.[20] Added to all the other anxiety-provoking confusions was also Donald's feeling that he had killed his own mother and his foster mother.

Having now presented three clinical cases, let us summarize the principal schizophrenic symptoms, before going on to the dynamics.[21]

A Summary of Schizophrenic Symptoms

In presenting the three cases and in discussing the five subtypes of schizophrenia we have described a great many symptoms, without finding a place for their organized discussion. In our discussion of the five subtypes we could do little more than give a listing of symptoms and point out that

[20] For a discussion of the dynamics of teasing and being teased, see Brenman, M., "On teasing and being teased," *The Psychoanalytic Study of the Child.* New York: Internat. Univ. Press, 1952, vol. 7, pp. 264–285.

[21] For other case descriptions of schizophrenic reactions, emphasizing other aspects of the illness, see Cameron, N., *The Psychology of Behavior Disorders.* Boston: Houghton Mifflin, 1947, Chapter 15; Cameron, N., and Magaret, A., *Behavior Pathology.* Boston: Houghton Mifflin, 1951, Chapter 16; and Arieti, S., *Interpretation of Schizophrenia.* New York: Brunner, 1955.

they overlap from one type to another. In our case presentations we were able to describe how even the strangest symptoms seem to emerge out of an intelligible life history, or at least out of an intelligible situation. Nevertheless, the symptomatology of schizophrenic reactions is much richer than these accounts reveal; and it needs to be broken down into some of the traditional groupings of human function, such as thinking, feeling and action. What we shall do now is to present the symptoms of schizophrenia briefly in such a way that the reader can retain an organized picture as he turns later to the dynamic and developmental background of schizophrenic reactions.[22]

Precipitating factors

Although precipitating factors are not symptoms, they are often necessary to recognize if one is to understand the onset and character of symptoms. This was true in each of our case presentations. It has often been said that anything which will precipitate a neurotic reaction may precipitate a schizophrenic reaction in someone whose infancy and childhood have predisposed him to general ego disintegration under stress. This is probably true. Nonetheless the preschizophrenic, like all other prepsychotic personalities with basic ego defects, seems especially vulnerable to five general situations: (1) *the loss or threatened loss of a major source of gratification*; (2) *the loss or threatened loss of basic security*; (3) *an upsurge of erotic or hostile impulses*; (4) *a sudden increase in guilt* — conscious, preconscious or unconscious; and (5) *reduced general effectiveness of ego adaptation or defense*.[23]

Mabel T., our first case, suffered a sweeping schizophrenic regression when she was exposed to a situation which terrified her. She lost her basic security; and perhaps the physiological shock of surgery, for which Mabel was unprepared, reduced the general effectiveness of her ego adaptation and defense. We know that when the level of brain function is lowered by intoxication, infection, fever or cerebral damage, a schizophrenic picture may appear.

Joan R., the Kansas City high school girl, illustrates the disintegrative effects of loss of security and love, of her upsurges of erotic and hostile

---

[22] In a review of the literature, Dastur finds no evidence for a specific change in body tissues or systems to account for schizophrenic reactions. Dastur, D. K., "The pathology of schizophrenia: a historical review," *Arch. Neurol. Psychiat.*, 1959, *81*, 601–614. Likewise Herron finds no significant evidence to support the old distinction between a "process-organic" and a "reactive-psychogenic" formulation of schizophrenic etiology. Herron, W. G., "The process-reactive classification of schizophrenia," *Psychol. Bull.*, 1962, *59*, 329–343. Goldman follows Werner in presenting an ontogenetic etiology. See Goldman, A. E., "A comparative developmental approach to schizophrenia," *Psychol. Bull.*, 1962, *59*, 57–69.

[23] These five situations are discussed in Chapter 13, "Symptom Formation," near the end, under the heading of *Precipitating factors*. See also Abrahams, J., and Varon, M., *Maternal Dependency and Schizophrenia*. New York: Internat. Univ. Press, 1953.

impulses and of suddenly increased guilt. It is possible that, if she had re-ceived active psychotherapy three years earlier, the outcome of her illness might have been quite different.

Donald J., our third case, seems never to have reached an effectual level of personality development. We saw that he was severely deprived of essential human contacts during his first eight years. It is doubtful if he ever succeeded in developing a viable ego-superego organization, one that would survive even ordinary stress without the continued support of the foster mother who ran his life. In such a case we must not be surprised to see the personality system "fall to pieces," as Donald described his predicament, under conditions which in someone else might have led only to a period of mourning.

Onset

The mode of onset of an illness is part of its symptomatology. Sudden onset and quick recovery, such as Mabel T. showed, point to a personality which in spite of its fragility includes basically sound object relations. The delusions and hallucinations that Mabel developed cannot be explained solely by her exposure to surgery. Millions of patients go through an uncompli-cated appendectomy, such as hers, without developing such symptoms. We must assume that Mabel's personality structure made regression to deep, dispersed infantile fixation points easy and inevitable under conditions of extreme fear.

A slow, indefinite, insidious onset is common in schizophrenia. There are some patients who seem never to have been able to meet the ordinary demands of everyday routine, who never develop reasonably good object re-lations or a sense of reality, and who either remain all through childhood and into adolescence socially incompetent, or else progress somewhat in personality development until puberty and then succumb in the face of adolescent problems. There are others who, in spite of a basically defective ego organization, manage to escape signs of psychotic regression until a personally severe crisis faces them, or until they suffer loss, somatic injury or serious illness.

Sudden onset is often more apparent than real in schizophrenia. Joan R.'s suicidal attempt, which led to her emergency admission, is an example of this. She had been sending up psychotic distress signals throughout a period of at least three years. Even her dramatic decline in school work, and her daydreaming in class, might have alerted others to what was hap-pening to her, as it eventually did the school authorities. Such failure to recognize a psychotic development often comes from the fear of what schizo-phrenia may mean. Like the fear of cancer, this fear may actually prevent a patient from getting early help. It is essential that therapists, as well as relatives, think in terms of possible improvement rather than only in terms of cure, if they are to have the optimism necessary for early therapeutic attempts. This goal of improvement, rather than that of cure, has prevailed for centuries in the treatment of many human illnesses. In schizophrenic reactions it has only recently been recognized as a thoroughly valid one.

1. Disturbances in relation to reality[24]

There is often a gross *disturbance in adaptive capacity* among schizophrenic patients, resulting in behavior that is maladaptive or even inappropriate to the socially shared situation. It may lead to an inability to adapt to normal routines or to ordinary changes in them, both with respect to social relations and to impersonal ones. We have seen such disturbances in adaptive capacity in all three of our cases at the height of their illnesses, and particularly in the terminal withdrawal of Joan R. and Donald J. Normal role-taking becomes obviously impossible when social maladaptation reaches such heights.

Delusions and hallucinations. Disturbances in *reality-testing* lead to distortions of experienced reality, and to attempts to reconstruct reality with the help of *delusions* and *hallucinations.* When these occur in schizophrenic patients, we find products of primary process thinking, previously unconscious, which have escaped repression massively along a wide front, and have invaded their preconscious and conscious organizations. One method by which the schizophrenic patient attempts to deal with these confusing, strange and often frightening invasions is to deny and project them, to make them outside himself as things going on in the external world or in his body. Because their ego or self boundaries are always inadequate, many schizophrenic persons remain perpetually in doubt as to whether what they deny and project is inside them or outside them. They may also be in grave doubt and confusion as to whether outside things, events and even people are really separate from them or a part of them. This is very different from the situation in paranoid reactions and in mania and depression. One result of the defective boundaries and the fluctuating regression in schizophrenia is that delusions and hallucinations are usually confusing and poorly organized. Sometimes they shift and fuse and separate in the same way that manifest dreams do. An understanding of such changes helps to make the strange behavior of schizophrenics more intelligible.

Delusions of persecution in schizophrenia are basically like those in paranoid reactions, so that a separate discussion of them is unnecessary. They tend to be vague and uncertain because of the general disintegration of thinking. The patient may not get beyond the conviction that something is

[24] The organization of this and the following four subsections follows the outline on pp. 7-8 of Bellak, L. (Ed.), *Schizophrenia: A Review of the Syndrome.* It is based upon the article by Beres, D., "Ego deviation and the concept of schizophrenia," *The Psychoanalytic Study of the Child.* New York: Internat. Univ. Press, 1956, vol. 11, pp. 164-235

wrong, that something mystifying and uncanny is going on. There may be nothing approaching a coherent plot. Often the vague delusions sound like the more or less chaotic fears and suspicions of manifest dreams.

Delusions of grandeur are likewise dreamlike, fantastic, romantic or submissive, unlike those in mania. Some patients describe themselves as president or dictator, or as God or an historical personage, and seek recognition from others around them. Others assert that there is something important which they have been entrusted to perform, hear voices and have visions, but are unable to formulate clearly what their mission is or to put their convictions into organized action. Sometimes the delusions of grandeur follow an actual humiliating failure.

Among schizophrenic patients, delusions of persecution and of grandeur often go hand in hand. Imaginary persecutions are explained away by delusions of greatness, by a conviction that greatness naturally arouses envy, and envy leads to hostile attempts. As in the case of Joan R., delusions of grandeur often arouse guilt and the fear of punishment; and these in turn lead to construction of a persecuting pseudocommunity or to self-punitive reactions, and even to suicidal attempts. Delusions of world destruction, of salvation and of world reconstruction usually are grandiose. They represent as a rule the projection on to the outside world of what the patient feels is happening to himself. Sometimes they represent reactions to catastrophic guilt.

Somatic delusions are often attempts by schizophrenic persons to account for experiences which they cannot understand and which they manage to project imperfectly. That is to say, the experiences coming from unconscious fantasies and conflicts which have escaped repression are projected as body changes, and not as completely external events. The weird delusions of Donald J. gave us examples of this process. They were obviously tied up with his confusion over sex identity and his sense of being immature. Donald expressed both these confusions in the concrete terminology that is characteristic of schizophrenia. He did not say that he was womanish or like a boy. He said that part of his body was female and that his hands were becoming the hands of a boy. Still more bizarre somatic delusions than those of Donald J. are encountered in schizophrenia.[25]

Hallucinations are more common among schizophrenic reactions than anywhere else in behavior pathology with the exception of the toxic psychoses. Their distinctive trait is that they occur when the patient is free from the disorientation and the memory disturbances characteristic of toxic

[25] For a detailed discussion of the varieties of delusions and hallucinations, see Cameron, N., *The Psychology of Behavior Disorders*. Boston: Houghton Mifflin, 1947, Chapter 13. See also Cleveland, S. E., "Judgments of body size in a schizophrenic and a control group," *Psychol. Rep.*, 1960, *1*, 304.

and organic psychoses. They are usually auditory, less often visual, and occasionally involve taste, smell and skin sensitivities.[26] The organization of schizophrenic hallucinations varies all the way from a continuous stream of visions, or a voice with which the patient holds long conversations, to the most fragmentary sound — a word or phrase out of context, a scream, laughter, a rumble or a whisper. Patients are sometimes frightened and startled by their hallucinations. Sometimes they welcome them and use them as a means of "communicating" with relatives or friends, or with persons in another world.

Like delusions, hallucinations are the result of denial and projection. Something occurring within the schizophrenic person himself, after penetrating to preconscious or conscious levels, is experienced as coming from the outside. The something may represent an unsatisfied need, a fear or a wish. To a certain extent the occurrence of hallucination is a product of the person's perceptual isolation, as it also is in the normal adult subjected to sensory deprivation. The great difference is that in schizophrenia the isolation or deprivation is not imposed arbitrarily from the outside, but is a product of the patient's own withdrawal and of the ego disintegration that he develops in spite of external conditions adequate for a normal perceptual input. It is to be hoped that studies both of sensory deprivation (perceptual isolation)[27] and of experimentally induced toxic psychoses[28] will throw more light upon the production and functions of hallucinations.

Estrangement and depersonalization. These experiences, which we discussed in Chapter 10, on the dissociative reactions, are nowhere more common than in schizophrenia. Often they are the first complaints to appear. They are statements that something strange has happened to the patient or to his interaction with his surroundings. Often these changes are expressed as perceptual changes or emotional changes — things somehow look or feel different from the way they used to look or feel. In thus describing the change in his own reactions, which he usually denies and projects as inexplicable changes in the environment, the patient is unwittingly describing his own ego disintegration, his own inability to perceive or feel what he used to be able to perceive or feel. This change we can also ascribe to the breakdown of defensive processes, as the result usually of personal stress, and the altered sense of reality which invasions of primary process material are bound to produce.

Difficulties in distinguishing the ego, the self or the body from other objects and other people are also prominent symptoms in schizophrenic reactions. Some patients feel that everything happening around them happens inside them, or that everything done by others is being done by them. They

---

[26] The last are difficult to distinguish from perceptual distortions.
[27] Solomon, P. (Ed.), *Sensory Deprivation.* Cambridge, Mass.: Harvard Univ. Press, 1961.
[28] Uhr, L., and Miller, J. G. (Eds.), *Drugs and Behavior.* New York: Wiley, 1960.

obviously cannot distinguish any more between themselves and others — a distinction which is among the earliest and most significant signs of personality development. Other schizophrenic persons feel that nothing they do is real, that nothing happening around them really happens. All these disturbances have their roots in defective ego-boundaries or self-boundaries.[29]

It is worth special note that many persons with relatively severe disturbances in their relation to reality can nevertheless carry on normal activities in a competitive society. This is in part a result of something characteristic of schizophrenic regression, namely, that it fluctuates from shallow to extremely deep, even within the period of a few minutes. We shall return to a discussion of this phenomenon when we take up the dynamic background of schizophrenia.

Fixations, it will be remembered, are more widely dispersed in schizophrenia than in any other syndrome. Patients in treatment often confuse their therapists, as well as themselves, by ranging from deeply regressive, primitive material to something quite mature, and then back again to the archaic, within a single therapeutic session.[30] The so-called "lucid interval" seen in deeply regressed patients, and many of the sudden inexplicable "spontaneous recoveries," are manifestations of this wide regressive fluctuation. If a patient *loses* his ability to fluctuate from one level to another, and becomes fixed at a very primitive level, we have a picture of what looks like chronic deterioration. But even when this fixity appears, it is still not impossible that the patient may recover, even after years of hospitalization.

2. Disturbances in emotional or drive control

Outbursts of rage, such as Joan R. exhibited, are not uncommon in schizophrenic reactions. Less common are phases of frankly erotic behavior, in which the patient, usually a woman, behaves as though she were greatly beloved even by strangers.[31]

To this group of disturbances belong the catatonic excitements and the catatonic muteness and inaction. All of these are evidence of ego disintegration. Many of them have symbolic as well as disintegrative significance. Thus, a patient may express the salient features of a delusional belief in some disturbance of motility, just as we saw happen in conversion reactions without delusions. As a result of their ego disintegration, some patients become impulsive and unpredictable, and some lose sphincter control as part of their regression.

In the past a great deal was made of the so-called *emotional incongruity* and *affective flattening* in schizophrenia. Some writers even maintained that

---

29 Davie, J., and Freeman, T., "Disturbances of perception and consciousness in schizophrenic states," *Brit. J. Med. Psychol.*, 1961, *34*, 33–41.

30 Pious, W. L., "A hypothesis about the nature of schizophrenic behavior," in Burton, Arthur (Ed.), *Psychotherapy of the Psychoses*. New York: Basic Books, 1961.

31 Arey, L. B., The indirect representation of sexual stimuli by schizophrenic and normal subjects," *J. abnorm. soc. Psychol.*, 1960, *61*, 424–431.

a schism between supposed faculties of intellect and emotion was basic to the disorder. Actually there is seldom a lack of emotional response early in the illness. This usually takes the form of anxiety[32] which, considering the basic breakthrough of primary process material, can hardly be regarded as unwarranted. It is true that schizophrenic patients often tell of something terrible that is happening to them, or of something frightful that they have fantasied, planned or done, without anything approaching the emotional participation that a normal person expects. We do not have a complete explanation for this strange emotional vacuum, but we do know that in a large number of cases it appears late in the illness, and that it usually follows a phase of appropriate emotional expression.

It was true of all three cases presented in this chapter that the emotional component was originally appropriate and adequate. Mabel T. was terribly frightened by something that had always terrified her, and her delusional and hallucinatory experiences kept pace with identifiable anxieties from which she suffered. Joan R. was frightened and angry for years before she finally broke down and attempted suicide. Donald J., for all his strangeness, was obviously frightened by or frightened into his hypochondriacal somatic delusions. The emotional apathy in the two patients who did not recover came late in their illness; and even then it seemed more apathy toward outside happenings than apathy toward their own private world.

Many patients, like concentration camp victims, develop emotional apathy as a *secondary defense* against anguish. Others, like Donald J., seem not to mean what they say, in the same sense that the hearer would mean it, if he were to say it (e.g., that a snake is inside the abdomen devouring the intestines).

3. Disturbances in object-relations

Some of these have already been mentioned in this chapter, especially confusions of the ego, or the self, with other persons, and the production of delusions and hallucinations through denial and projection. Others will be discussed later on, in the section on the childhood background of schizophrenic adults. These disturbances remind one of the autistic and symbiotic phases of infancy, described in Chapter 2.

In one of our cases, Donald J., there was a pathologically close relationship between the patient and his foster mother. When Donald was faced with the choice between staying with his foster mother and marrying a wife, he gave up the wife. When, later on, his foster mother suddenly died, Donald tried desperately to form some new relationship to replace the one he had lost. He fell to pieces when this maneuver failed.

Among adult schizophrenic patients there can often be found a fear of closeness to anyone. So permeable are the ego or self boundaries of such

---

[32] See Bellak, L., "The schizophrenic syndrome," in Bellak, L. (Ed.), *Schizophrenia, A Review of the Syndrome.* New York: Logos Press, 1958, pp. 3–63.

individuals that closeness threatens them with being engulfed. Therefore, they must maintain a degree of physical and emotional aloofness that will ensure their being able to keep from being swallowed up. The trouble with this arrangement is that it also prevents the patient from having any close emotional ties, often from having any emotionally meaningful experiences in adult life.

Along with the fear of closeness, or as an alternative to it, is the sense of being always left out, of being on the outside while the rest of the world seems to be having meaningful experiences. To some extent this rests upon a failure to develop meaningful role-taking functions. The patient is then not properly integrated with his social community. He remains always on its fringe like a stranger who watches others having a party to which he is not invited.

4. Disturbances in defensive function

Although discussion of this topic belongs with the dynamic background of schizophrenia, and will be taken up specifically there, it is pertinent at this point to repeat what has been said earlier, that practically all of the symptoms of schizophrenia are results of the emergence of primary process material into secondary process thinking. There is a breakthrough along a wide front, and at many different levels, of drives, conflicts and fantasies which have previously been unconscious, or at least partially unconscious. Now they enter preconscious and conscious organizations on a massive scale and disrupt them.

In the case of Joan R.[33] we saw that the patient had always experienced difficulty in separating her fantasies from socially objective fact, her dreams from her daytime reality and fantasies. When she found herself deserted emotionally by her foster mother's death and her father's inability to understand her predicament, when she was left alone to battle first with her grownup cousin, and later with her multiplicity of fears and wishes, Joan began to disintegrate. First she had horrible experiences when falling asleep, then she developed delusions of being in the power of a dope ring, and finally she believed that her thoughts were being read and that she was controlled by someone outside the home who had murdered her father. We saw how Donald J. lost the last vestiges of defensive function when he was allowed to leave the hospital and return to work with no one to give him the emotional support that he needed. Even the relatively mature, successful Mabel T., when she found herself on the terrifying surgical ward, suffered a dramatic breakthrough which revealed the instability of her defensive organization.

5. Disturbances in language and thought

Because man is above all a thinking being it has been impossible to avoid discussing his schizophrenic reactions without including discussions of his

---

[33] The cases are listed alphabetically in the index under the general heading of *Cases*.

disturbances of thought. When we were considering man's *adaptive capacity*, his *reality-testing* and his *sense of reality* we were considering processes which, in both normal and schizophrenic persons, involve a great deal of thinking. The same is true, of course, in discussing delusions and hallucinations. Even when it came to emotional disturbances we had to assume an arbitrary distinction in order to make the emotional aspects of human activity seem separate from its thinking aspects. In real life, as we all know, the two are part of a unitary activity.

In the present section we shall deal specifically with thinking as it is related to language, a relationship which includes such basic functions as social expression, social communication and socially organized private fantasy. During the past fifty years the peculiarities of language and thought in schizophrenia have attracted a great deal of attention.[34] Their direct study has been supplemented by investigations into the normal patterns of childhood thought, particularly by the work of Piaget.[35] From such investigations it has become clear that human beings do not achieve *logical justification* until somewhere around their tenth year. What this means is that the child must organize his world of reality long before he can reason as adults reason. Today we take it for granted that infants and young children begin by conceiving of their world in ways that resemble what we have been calling the primary process. In childhood schizophrenia this seems to remain the dominant form of thinking.

In adult schizophrenic reactions the situation is different. The adult patient has achieved proficiency in secondary process thinking, that is, he has learned to think logically whenever necessary. It is only when he regresses that he loses this ability; and even then there will be some residual logic which, while it may only confuse him, will nevertheless complicate the symptom picture. The attempts at logical thought which adult schizophrenic patients make are not the same as a child's logic.[36]

[34] See, for example, Bleuler, E., *Dementia Praecox or the Group of Schizophrenias* (1911) (trans. J. Zinkin). New York: Internat. Univ. Press, 1950; Cameron, N., *Reasoning, Regression and Communication in Schizophrenics. Psychol. Monogr.*, 1938, No. 221; Cameron, N., "Schizophrenic thinking in a problem-solving situation," *J. ment. Sci.*, 1939, 85, 1012–1035; Cameron, N., "Experimental analysis of schizophrenic thinking," in Kasanin, J. (Ed.), *Language and Thought in Schizophrenia.* Berkeley, Calif.: Univ. of Calif. Press, 1944, pp. 50–64; Hanfmann, E., and Kasanin, J., *Conceptual Thinking in Schizophrenia. Nerv. ment. dis. Monogr.*, 1942, No. 68; Cameron, N., and Magaret, A., "Experimental studies in thinking," *J. exper. Psychol.*, 1949, 39, 617–627; Arieti, S., *Interpretation of Schizophrenia.* New York: Brunner, 1955; Arieti, S. (Ed.), *American Handbook of Psychiatry.* New York: Basic Books, 1959.

[35] J. Piaget has published more than a score of books containing his studies of childhood thinking, most of them available in English translation. See esp., *Origins of Intelligence in Children* (trans. M. Cook). New York: Internat. Univ. Press, 1952; *Construction of Reality in the Child* (trans. M. Cook). New York: Basic Books, 1954; *Play, Dreams and Imitation in Childhood* (trans. C. Gattegno and F. M. Hodgson). New York: Norton, 1951.

[36] A comparison between the logic of normal children and of schizophrenic adults is included in the paper, with its misleading title, by Cameron, N., "A study in thinking in senile deterioration and schizophrenic disorganization," *Amer. J. Psychol.*, 1938, 51, 650–665.

A schizophrenic patient's talking and thinking may show no greater change than an indefinable vagueness, with perhaps complaints of being unable to think clearly. A school teacher, for example, said, "I just exactly can't talk as clearly. I'd give a pretty dime to talk like I like or place my words in talking with people noticing." Of her thinking this schizophrenic young woman said, "It slips because you go on and talk and have imaginations and try for others and seems just to come back to you." A high school boy of sixteen, in an experimental test situation, completed the phrase, *My hair is fair because*, with the statement, "Because of something else, it's on my head, it comes from my mother." After partial recovery he completed the same phrase with, "Because I inherited it from my parents." To the test phrase, *The wind blows because*, he replied while he was ill, "Just cosmic dust," but after partial recovery his answer became, "Because of atmospheric air currents changing." It is hardly necessary to repeat that such language distortions involve the patient's thinking along with his talking.[37]

In severe language disorganization the schizophrenic patient may reach a level of verbal discontinuity at which his talk becomes useless as an instrument of communication. Conventional sequences of words and the use of appropriate connectives disappear, and the flow of talk becomes disjointed. The result is not the same as aphasic speech, but it can be just as disabling socially to the patient. Early in a schizophrenic illness this verbal discontinuity, usually called *scatter*, may be evident only in relation to personal conflicts, much as one finds it in an embarrassed adolescent. If the illness goes on, however, it may include everything but a few stereotyped replies to stereotyped questions. New words (*neologisms*) appear in the talk of some patients. Sometimes these are *condensations* typical of the primary process; sometimes they represent the development of a highly individualized *expressive language* which communicates little to others.[38]

Related to the latter is the development in schizophrenia of a mode of language which uses words and phrases with approximately their common meaning, but with enough imprecision to confuse the average listener in the same way that an imperfectly known foreign language confuses him. The

[37] For other examples, see Cameron, N., *Reasoning, Regression and Communication in Schizophrenics, Psychol. Monogr.*, 1938; No. 221; also Cameron, N., "Experimental analysis of schizophrenia," in Kasanin, J. (Ed.), *Language and Thought in Schizophrenia.* Berkeley, Calif.: Univ. of Calif. Press, 1944, pp. 50–64.

[38] See, for example, Searles, H. F., "Schizophrenic communication," *Psychoanalysis & Psychoanal. Rev.*, 1961, *48*, 3–50; Lorenz, M., "Problems posed by schizophrenic language," *Arch. gen. Psychiat.*, 1961, *4*, 603–610; Gottschalk, L. A., Gleser, G. C., Magliocci, E. B., and D'Zmura, T. L., "Further studies on the speech patterns of schizophrenic patients," *J. nerv. ment. Dis.*, 1961, *132*, 101–113; Bruch, H., and Palombo, S., "Conceptual problems in schizophrenia," *J. nerv. ment. Dis.*, 1961, *132*, 114–117; Lothrop, W. W., "A critical review of research on the conceptual thinking of schizophrenics," *J. nerv. ment. Dis.*, 1961, *132*, 118–126; Burstein, A. G., "Some verbal aspects of verbal primary process thought in schizophrenia," *J. abnorm. soc. Psychol.*, 1961, *62*, 155–157; Hall, G. C., "Conceptual attainment in schizophrenics and non-psychotics as a function of task structure," *J. Psychol.*, 1962, *53*, 3–13; Chapman, L. J., "A reinterpretation of some pathological disturbances in conceptual breadth," *J. abnorm. soc. Psychol.*, 1961, *62*, 514–519.

private idiom which some patients develop and use as speech may be unintelligible until it has been translated. To be able to make the translation one must usually study the patient's speech in relation to his personal difficulties, his verbal habits, his delusions and even his history. An example of this follows.

A patient states that he is alive, "Because you really live physically because you have menu three times a day. That's the physical." (*What else is there besides the physical?*) "Then you're alive mostly to serve a work from the standpoint of methodical business." A knowledge of the patient's habitual idiom and his preoccupation with serving the world makes this translation possible: "You live physically because you have three meals a day and you live to perform a service in your daily routines." The use of such personal idiom, even without other disorganization, is in effect to cut the patient off from the interpersonal relations that he needs. Neither his family nor the other patients were willing to make the constant effort which was necessary to communicate with this man. He himself gave the impression of not caring whether he communicated with anyone or not. He had been hospitalized for several years.

Mutism is not uncommon in schizophrenic reactions. Its most distinctive characteristics are the abruptness with which it may begin and end, and its often obvious relationship to the rest of the patient's behavior. The abruptness of onset and ending may be related to the fluctuation in fixation level which defines schizophrenia. It may also be a direct product of the situation. Here are some examples.

One schizophrenic patient was put under too much pressure by her therapist to tell her troubles. After having done so she said, "I've talked too much," and she remained mute for almost a year. Another patient, mute for several months, awakened one night and asked to see her therapist. When he came she conversed with him for over an hour. Her manner was somewhat dreamy and her sentences sometimes trailed off without a finish, but the general form of her talk was otherwise normally relevant and coherent. She spoke as one who had been in another world and had just returned — which was one of her beliefs — asking questions about the hospital, the nurses and attendants, the other patients and her family. Finally she said she wanted to go back to bed. The next morning she was mute as ever. A month later she began to speak in the daytime, and eventually she made a social recovery. A third patient, mute even before admission, received an unexpected visit from her relatives. She jumped up from her chair at once to greet them and conversed freely and naturally. When her therapist appeared she became mute, but resumed speaking as soon as he left. As soon as her visitors left she stopped talking. Some months later she also recovered. None of these mute patients explained their long silences when they recovered. In each the reason may have been a different one.

6. Overinclusion in schizophrenia

It is obvious that ego organization in perceptual and cognitive operations, as well as in autonomous functions, depends as much upon what is kept out as upon what is included. There are advantages, of course, in allowing a certain amount of instability and inclusiveness in unstructured, developing situations. For then ego organization is flexible enough to be able to adapt to unforeseen changes in the field. When it comes to structured situations, where one needs precision in close-knit sequential operations, there must be a stable ego organization which excludes competing and contradictory impulses. It is the failure to exclude competing, contradictory and even irrelevant impulses that characterizes overinclusion. This failure is obviously related to defects in defensive as well as in adaptive functions. It appears most clearly in schizophrenic reactions where defective ego boundaries permit both perceptual confusion and the invasion of cognitive organizations by primary process material.

We may define *overinclusion* as *the result of unstable ego organization which fails to limit the number and kind of simultaneously effective excitants to a relatively few coherent ones.* The concept of overinclusion was first developed operationally in studies of sorting according to classes by schizophrenic patients.[39] Since then its use has been expanded to include a wide range of behavior disorganization,[40] but it is in schizophrenic reactions that one sees it most clearly. This may be related to the fact that schizophrenic patients attempt to interact with their environment in terms of their private fantasies.

The following verbatim statements illustrate the confusion that a regressive disorganization can bring. They were made by a patient while he was engaged in the task of sorting colored blocks of several shapes into a specified number of groups. Throughout the task this schizophrenic young man was earnest and cooperative. He showed, as will be seen, an irresistible tendency to include in the task all kind of actually irrelevant objects — the desk blotter, parts of the room, things he pulled from his pockets, racial problems, a man outside and even the experimenter himself. Here are some of this patient's comments which illustrate the disorganizing effects of overinclusion.

"I've got to pick it out of the whole room. I can't confine myself to the game. . . . Three blues — now, how about that green blotter? Put it in there too. (Green) peas you eat, you can't eat them unless you write on it (the green blotter).[41] Like that wrist watch (experimenter's). I

[39] Cameron, N., "Schizophrenic thinking in a problem-solving situation," *J. ment. Sci.,* 1939, *85,* 1012–1035.

[40] See the review of this literature in Payne, R. W., "Cognitive abnormalities," in Eysenck, H. J. (Ed.), *Handbook of Abnormal Psychology.* New York: Basic Books, 1961, pp. 193–261; Payne, R. W., Mattussek, P., and George, E. I., "An experimental study of schizophrenic thought disorder," *J. ment. Sci.,* 1959, *105,* 627–652.

[41] The patient had just come from a meal at which he had eaten green peas.

don't see any three meals coming off that watch. . . . White and blue (blocks) is Duke's Mixture. This (pulling out cigarette paper) is white. All this wood and Japan (pulling out match box). There's a man out there with a white tie; that's got something to do with white suits. . . . To do this trick *you'd* have to be made of wood. You've got a white shirt on, and the white blocks, you have to have them cut out of *you!* You've got a white shirt on. This (white block) will hold you and never let you go. I've got a blue shirt on; but it can't be a blue shirt and still go together. And the room's got to be the same." Contemplating a grouping of similar white and yellow blocks, he asked, "Are there any Chinese working here? (*No*). Only white ones, then you can't put *them* together."

Dynamic and Developmental Background

We said at the beginning of this chapter that schizophrenic reactions show a bewildering wealth of symptoms and that all of them can be traced to the massive intrusion of primary process material. This intrusion, we said, comes from different levels of early fixation, the various levels finding expression either simultaneously or in quick succession. The distinctive appearance of disorganization in schizophrenia is in part a product of this multiplicity of origins. In part it also reflects the presence of primary process function along with residuals of normal secondary process function. In some patients the primary processes are considerably modified by ego defenses which are still operating, although usually at primitive levels. In other patients there is little defensive modification. In still others, the degree and even the kind of ego defensive action fluctuate through wide ranges.

The clinical picture which a given schizophrenic patient presents at any time will depend, of course, upon what defenses are being used and how effective they are in protecting preconscious and conscious organizations from primary process invasion. In office practice one meets many basically schizophrenic persons who are able to function reasonably well in a normal, competitive human environment — some of them exceptionally well even in comparison to their normal associates — in spite of persistent regressive tendencies which occasionally may lead to delusions and hallucinations. Only a few persons, sometimes only the therapist and the patient, know about the psychotic trends. To the rest of the world the person appears normal or at most neurotic. For these persons the designation *neurotic schizophrenic* has often been suggested; but whatever they are ultimately called, the personality structure is basically prepsychotic, that is, basically dependent upon primitive ego defenses, grossly defective in ego- or self-boundaries, and vulnerable to deep and varied ego-superego regression.

At least since Bleuler's monograph on *the group of schizophrenias*, published more than fifty years ago, it has been generally recognized that what we today call *schizophrenic reactions* consist of many manifest illnesses, not just one or even four or five. As we have seen in our clinical cases, schizophrenic persons seldom correspond to a single Kraepelinian type and frequently shift from one type to another. Joan R., for example, began as a paranoid schizophrenic but soon after hospitalization she developed clear-cut catatonic episodes. It was difficult at first to assign Donald J. to any of the Kraepelinian subtypes, but in time he presented a clinical picture which could be definitely called *hebephrenic*. A great many schizophrenic patients go in and out of the different types or never fall within any one of them.[42] Hence the presence in the official classification of three different subclasses for the otherwise unclassifiable patient.

The great variability of the manifest clinical form of schizophrenic reactions makes the task of describing their dynamic and developmental background all but impossible. To take into account all of the common variations would be to present an almost unintelligible complexity of exposition. What we shall do instead is to focus upon certain core characteristics of the schizophrenic and preschizophrenic personality, characteristics which describe the defects of those who are or have been seriously ill with deep regression and with delusional and hallucinatory episodes. Such a core group can be easily distinguished from neurotic persons and from those with organized paranoid psychotic reactions, or with psychotic depression, mania or toxic psychosis. It will include patients who never get well and patients who, in spite of deep regression, eventually recover and return to their previous level.

1. Fixation and regression in schizophrenic reactions

In schizophrenic reactions the adult regresses to fixation points which are deeper and more widely dispersed than in any other form of behavior pathology. As he regresses, the schizophrenic patient revives fears, wishes, conflicts and fantasies belonging to the earliest phases of personality development, phases in which no genuine object relationships exist. He may then live in a sort of dream world where he himself and the actual objects around him, including both people and things, seem to lose their identity and appear to merge. He himself and these others may undergo shifts from object to subject. What is happening outside the patient seems to happen inside, and what is going on only within a person's thinking seems to be happening outside it. Most of us have experienced this kind of perplexing, kaleidoscope change in our manifest dreams. One moment we are watching something going on; the next moment we are doing it or it is being done to us. At one moment you are the subject and at the next the object. Regression for many schizophrenic patients reaches levels such as these, comparable in depth and confusion to the regression of dreams and of *sensory deprivation* (*perceptual isolation*).[43]

We have said that fixation points to which regression carries a person in

[42] A lucid psychodynamic account of sudden shifts in schizophrenic symptoms can be found in Jacobson, E., "Contribution to the metapsychology of psychotic identification," *J. Amer. Psychoanal. Ass.*, 1954, *2*, 239–262.

[43] Sedman, G., "'Brain-washing' and 'sensory deprivation' as factors in the production of psychiatric states: the relation between such states and schizophrenia," *Conf. Psychiat.*, 1961, *4*, 28–44.

schizophrenic reactions are widely dispersed as well as deep. This dispersion adds to the patient's confusion. The effect of this situation is that he fluctuates from one level to another, even within a single hour. One moment regression carries a patient to a level where he is out of realistic contact with persons and things; the next moment he may emerge from this objectless world and either resume realistic contacts or operate at some intermediate level between that of a world without objects and a world of fully separable people, self and things.

Normally the process which we call *reality-testing* helps us to establish and to maintain a differentiation between *fantasy-oriented* and *reality-oriented* experience and behavior. It helps us distinguish between what is contributed to perception and cognition from the outside, and what is contributed to perception and cognition from internal need, wish, fantasy or emotional drive. We all know that these distinctions are rarely absolute, even in the most normal person. There is always some contribution of internal wish or fear, of fantasy or emotional drive, to modify realistic perception and cognition; and external reality is always modifying our private fantasies, even in our dreaming at night.

Nevertheless, the distinctions that we ordinarily make are complete enough for the practical business of coping realistically with our external, socially organized environment, and for the pleasurable or anxiety-provoking business of make-believe, story or daydream. We may enter into the make-believe fantasy of a play wholeheartedly, even to the point where we feel ourselves to be a part of it; but this does not prevent our switching to reality during the intermission, and again after the last curtain falls. A great deal of the emotional enjoyment — the warmth, depth and devotion of life — is made possible by our ability to fuse fantasy with reality when we want to, and to use primary processes in the service of the grownup self.

Failure of reality-testing mixes fantasy with fact. Most of us are able to return to a clear distinction between fantasy and fact when circumstances call for it. A minority of persons cannot achieve this distinction. Included in this minority are those persons who, like Joan R., have always relied upon fantasy to a much greater degree than do normal persons. Under conditions of stress, such persons are likely to develop a schizophrenic illness.

A basic source of confusion between reality and fantasy, in schizophrenic regression, is a defect in the development of a clear *self-image*, that is, an image of the *self*, which is distinct from the *surroundings*. We have reason to believe that this defect in reality-testing has its deepest roots in failures to resolve the early symbiotic relationship between mother and infant. Because of such a failure, the child never succeeds in establishing himself as a separate person, and never succeeds in seeing himself as a really separate person. He remains more or less fixated at an undifferentiated level. As soon as he regresses, he begins to lose his unstable differentiations of *self* from *not-self*, of *self* from *others*.

At these deep levels of regression, as we shall see in a moment, *repression* grows incompetent. The dominant defenses and methods of coping are once more the infantile ones: *primary identification, introjection* and *projection.* There is no longer a clear separation between what has been preconscious and what has been unconscious. What has been unconscious now becomes easily accessible. Primitive modes of thinking again dominate preconscious and conscious thinking. Representations of the self commingle with representations of other people. They now pass easily across the boundaries that should separate them because the boundaries have become vague and pathologically permeable. They fuse and they interchange positions, just as they do in everyone's nightly dreaming. In deep schizophrenic regression, the contributions of primitive, archaic fantasy and of primary processes to perception and cognition become great, while the contributions of external reality become correspondingly small.

Attempts to re-establish reality contacts. When a regressed schizophrenic patient attempts to re-establish his relations with external reality, under these conditions, it is understandable that he may experience intense estrangement and depersonalization.[44] Such experiences often generate enough anxiety to drive a person back into deep regression and isolation once more. The appearance of primitive and previously unconscious material, in the patient's preconscious and conscious thinking further increases his anxiety. He is now pushed once more into the attempt to escape, by regaining effective contact wtih external reality. This is his one hope of escaping from the fantasies that have emerged from his internal, previously unconscious reality. It is the kind of thing that persons do when they become intolerably anxious in sensory deprivation experiments, and ask to be released. It is the kind of thing we all do when we wake up from a nightmare. The regressed schizophrenic patient cannot be asked to be released, because his experiences are not experimentally produced. He cannot escape by waking up, because he is already awake.

The successions of deep regression and attempts at regaining effective relations with external reality give us clues as to what is going on during the fluctuations in level of regression, which we observe in clinically active schizophrenic patients. When a patient gives up trying to regain effective contact with external reality, he can only escape the anxiety which his primitive experiences tend to arouse by becoming apathetic, or by allowing himself to live his life of primitive fantasy, without letting external reality penetrate into his thinking.

This last is what we see clinically in the so-called *deteriorated* or *vegetative* schizophrenic patient. Donald J. presented such a clinical picture after he had given up; and so did Joan R. The "deterioration" that then develops is a defensive maneuver, a way of keeping out whatever the patient cannot

---

[44] For a discussion of *estrangement* and *depersonalization*, see Chapter 10 on dissociative reactions.

handle. However hopeless it may appear, we have the fact that many "deteriorated" schizophrenic patients can be rehabilitated after years of withdrawal, so that they are willing and able to lead a fairly normal life.

Constructive functions of delusions and hallucinations. We have indicated earlier in this chapter,[45] as well as in Chapter 14 on paranoid reactions, that delusions and hallucinations are not only signs of illness; they are also often signs that a patient is actively trying to cope with his regressed situation, that he is actively trying to get well. The patient's greatest problem is posed by his need to include the eruptions from his previously unconscious material in his present conscious and preconscious perception and cognition.

In the first place, the psychotic patient cannot exclude this material because repression has failed him on a massive scale. He cannot ignore these intrusions any more than a dreaming man can ignore his dreams while he is dreaming. They are often vivid experiences which press forward vigorously into consciousness and seem to the patient fully as real as external reality. This is because, by regressing, he has lost the reality-testing functions necessary for making distinctions between external reality and fantasy. The delusion and the hallucination often represent attempts to synthesize these products of previously unconscious need, wish, fear, conflict and fantasy, with the external reality which the patient is trying to handle.

The delusion, as we have already pointed out, is an attempt to include internally generated fantasy material with the representations of external reality. The denied and projected material that has escaped repression is mingled with the products of external reality on an equal footing. Internally generated wishes, fears, needs, conflicts and fantasies are attributed in part to real persons and in part to imaginary persons.[46] Joan R., for example, attributed her fears and fantasies to the activities of real persons, like her own father, as well as to "master minds." The apparent community of plotters that arises from such denial and projection — in the presence of a still effective external reality — is a form of pseudocommunity.

Because of the greater regression in schizophrenia, and because schizophrenic patients tend to fluctuate from one level of fixation to another, their delusions are usually less well organized and less realistic than the delusions of paranoid patients. The relatively greater penetration by primary process products gives schizophrenic delusional reconstructions a vagueness, contributes bizarre and often contradictory components, and makes them usually incommunicable.

Sometimes florid schizophrenic delusions and hallucinations suddenly disappear for no apparent reason. The patient has somehow managed suddenly to re-establish effective repression, to shut down the hatch, and once more

[45] In the section *Disturbances in relation to reality* of the present chapter.
[46] Cameron, N., "The paranoid pseudocommunity," *Amer. J. Sociol.*, 1943, *49*, 32–38; Cameron, N., "The paranoid pseudocommunity revisited," *Amer. J. Sociol.*, 1959, *65*, 52–59; Cameron, N., "Paranoia and paranoid states," in Arieti, S. (Ed.), *American Handbook of Psychiatry.* New York: Basic Books, 1959, pp. 508–539.

to "contain" his archaic unconscious activities. Even those of us who have witnessed such an extraordinary change have not been able to understand how it was achieved. Apparently, even the patient does not understand it, or at any rate he declines to discuss it. We have to remind ourselves that repression is itself an unconscious defense which operates without a person's being aware of it.

Hallucinations are more of a mystery than delusions, perhaps because they occur during states of deep regression. Patients who are able and willing to communicate while they are hallucinating assert that their hallucinatory experiences are as vivid and as real as their perceptions of socially shared reality. Often they say frankly that the only way they have of distinguishing between the two is to rely upon their therapist to tell them the truth about what he perceives and what he does not. We know today — from experiments with sensory deprivation, with hallucinogenic drugs, and with metabolic disturbances — that hallucination, even though difficult to explain, is within the reach of almost everyone.[47]

2. Defenses in schizophrenic reactions

The wide dispersal of fixation points in schizophrenic disorders, and the often rapid fluctuation from one level to another in the regressions of active cases, make it difficult to say anything definite about schizophrenic defensive maneuvers which will hold for all cases, or even for a single case over a long period of time. When regression is relatively slight, and does not lead to isolation of the patient from his surroundings, it may serve defensive functions in simplifying a schizophrenic patient's world by reducing the number and complexity of effective stimulations. The patient becomes less effectual but does not disintegrate. At the other extreme, when a patient withdraws and becomes stuporous, he may also preserve some ego-superego integration by shutting out the confusion of external stimulation almost completely. He then becomes ineffectual and helpless; but as long as he does not also disintegrate he may be protecting himself against the destruction of his personality structure by shutting out both the internal and the external realities which threaten him.[48]

These two conditions, the slight regression and the stuporous withdrawal without disintegration, are not the commonest results of schizophrenic regression. No matter how important they may be for successful therapy, they are best eliminated from our discussion of schizophrenic defenses, so

[47] Children can experience hallucinations without becoming psychotic. See Weiner, M. F., "Hallucinations in children," *Arch. gen. Psychiat.*, 1961, 5, 544–553. For a comparison of hallucinations with eidetic imagery, see Barber, T. X., "The 'eidetic image' and 'hallucinatory' behavior: a suggestion for further research," *Psychol. Bull.*, 1959, 56, 236–239.

[48] M. Katan regards hallucinations as defenses against delusions. See "The non-psychotic part of the personality in schizophrenia," *Internat. J. Psychoanal.*, 1954, 35, 119–128.

that we may consider the core of schizophrenic cases which make up the great majority, the middle ground.

Within the middle ground, we find the majority of psychotic schizophrenic reactions, those in whom regression varies from slight to subtotal, and in whom regression often reaches depths not reached in mania, depression or paranoid reactions. Such regression, with its unpredictable fluctuations and its abysmal depths, can only be called defensive in a very limited sense, in the sense that it may protect the patient from "falling to pieces," as schizophrenic patients themselves spontaneously describe their experience. What happens in deep schizophrenic regression is the greatest loss of differentiation of personality or psychic structure so far seen, a loss of differentiation which allows self-images and object images to merge and separate again, and then merge once more, which replaces even the archaic superego by early infantile introjected objects — usually "bad objects." The struggles of an infantile regressive ego against such introjected objects is often aided by projection, as we shall see, which at least allows the patient to battle against them as outside persecutors. When schizophrenic regression occurs in a person who has managed to get along reasonably well up to the time of onset of his illness, it occurs because of the failure of repression.

Defective repression. In persons who react to stress with a schizophrenic regression there has apparently always been an inadequacy of repression. This is probably related to the multiple fixation points in preschizophrenic personalities. Their multiplicity indicates that almost from the beginning of life the patient has been exposed repeatedly to excessive tension and anxiety, that he has never received adequate protection from unavoidable internal and external stress. The evidence available points to sadomasochistic experiences in relation to the patient's mother or mother substitute. In short, persons who are especially vulnerable to schizophrenic reactions are persons who have never had the opportunity to establish *basic trust*.[49] It is immaterial whether this is the "fault" of the mother or of the infant himself. For our present purposes it is enough to recognize that the adult who develops schizophrenia has such experiences as his background.

We take it for granted, as we also did in relation to paranoid reactions, that the person vulnerable to schizophrenic regression is one who was exposed to excessive tension and anxiety before repression had matured as an ego defense. The mother or mother figure of such a person was unsuccessful in providing him with a substitute ego at a time when his own ego was still poorly differentiated. This accounts for the overdevelopment of denial and projection regularly seen in schizophrenic reactions; and, as we have seen, such an overdevelopment early in life interferes with the normal develop-

49 We say *especially vulnerable* because recent experimental evidence from work with sensory deprivation, and with hallucinogenic drugs, indicates that schizophrenic-like disintegration is within the realm of *possibility* for almost everyone. See, for example, Solomon, P., *et al.* (Eds.), *Sensory Deprivation.* Cambridge, Mass.: Harvard Univ. Press, 1961.

ment of a defensive organization in which a strong repressive barrier is the keystone.

In schizophrenic reactions, however, we find also some of the most primitive forms of identification, introjection and incorporation. This is not merely theory. Patients themselves, without foreknowledge, complain of their archaic incorporation fantasies. Joan R. is by no means unique in her experiences of chewing people up and eating them. Such fantasies, undoubtedly derived from early nursing experiences and from such common adult remarks as, "You look good enough to eat!" appear in a large percentage of schizophrenic experiences. We may take them as evidence of fixation at early phases when identification was still equated with taking a person in through the mouth. Here, as in psychotic depression, there is evidence that introjection had to be used too much and too early, before repression had matured, and while introjection still was conceived or experienced as incorporation. Such early uses and overdevelopment of introjection (and archaic identification) would interfere with the growth of a normal defensive system in which there was mature repression as the keystone.

We have already pointed out, in discussing paranoid reactions, that mature repressive defenses are directly responsible for maintaining a functional barrier that separates unconscious processes from preconscious and conscious organizations. The failure of schizophrenic adults to develop adequate repressive defenses in early childhood leaves them always susceptible to invasions by primary process material, unconscious fantasies and the like. They are therefore defective in their subordination of primitive drives and needs to the demands of social reality. They are subject to interferences with attempts at realistic logical thinking. They are less tolerant of ambiguity than normal persons because of their inability to control and channel their emotional drives. They have serious difficulties in evolving reciprocal role behavior and in structuring a coherent self that will resist intrusions from external reality.

These difficulties are compounded in schizophrenic reactions by the regression to phases when there was no stable ego or superego, but only *internal objects* which were in the process of crystallizing out an ego differentiated from the id, and a superego — however archaic — differentiated from the ego. These internal objects are originally the result of introjection, at first with an incorporative meaning, and of identification, at first apparently total. However incomprehensible the introjection of whole persons may seem to us, even at a symbolic level, this seems to occur during early infancy. The least we can say is that it seems to have occurred in persons who become schizophrenic. These persons, if they are able and willing to communicate, tell us about their internal objects if we let them. Moreover some of them proceed to reproject what they originally introjected; and when they do this, the reprojected object seems to have retained all the characteristics of a childhood mother figure. It is hallucinated and it speaks as it did when the patient was a child, with the same intonations and the same admonitions. The schizophrenic patient, when he regresses deeply, tries to defend himself against the accusing, admonishing *internal objects*, denying that what they seem to be saying is true or just.

Denial and projection. Schizophrenic patients depend heavily upon primitive forms of denial and projection. Although denial is used first of all against parts of external reality, which have managed to break through into preconscious and conscious infantile perception, it is eventually used also against primary process intrusions from unconscious internal reality.[50] When schizophrenic patients suffer severe regression, and when their always inadequate repression fails them almost completely, they utilize denial and projection to get rid of the primary process material and the unconscious fantasies which threaten to overwhelm them. Since they are threatened mainly by upsurges of primitive aggressive drives, what they deny and project is chiefly aggressive and hostile in character, although not exclusively so.

Denial and projection in schizophrenia, as we have said earlier, lead to delusions and hallucinations, in which the patient's own irrepressible and uncontrollable emotional drives and fantasy productions seem to him to be embodied in outside existences. The degree of ego-superego regression that has occurred will usually determine the degree of communicability and intelligibility of the delusions and hallucinations, as well as their primitive character. Occasionally we find a patient with deeply regressive, archaic experiences who is willing and able to communicate them. From such persons we get insights which enable us to understand and interpret the much more common weird and fragmentary communication of archaic material.

It is worth repeating at this point, because it is so often overlooked, that delusions and hallucinations may not only be symptoms of a deep pathological regression, and therefore signs of illness, but also attempts by the patient to understand what is going on, and therefore signs of recovery. The recovery may fail because a patient cannot get his primary process material and his unconscious fantasies under repression again. But the delusion and the hallucination are attempts to reconstruct external reality in such a way as to include the parts of internal reality which have to be dealt with somehow because they have escaped repression.

In some schizophrenic patients, regression revives situations in which there are virtually no ego or self boundaries. When this is so, projection is a very primitive process, and the delusions and hallucinations which develop only succeed in confusing external and internal reality, in much the same way that manifest dreams do. Things and events which should be experi-

---

[50] See the discussion of denial in Lewin, B., *The Psychoanalysis of Elation.* New York: Norton, 1950; Jacobson, E., "Denial and repression," *J. Amer. Psychoanal. Ass.,* 1957, 5, 61–92. Normal infants and young children openly deny the existence of external realities that frighten them. An infant brought into a room full of strangers may, for example, simply stare straight ahead as though no one were there. An older child shuts his eyes or says outright that a frightening something does not exist.

enced as internal seem to be external, or fluctuate between seeming internal and external. At the same time, because of fluctuating and permeable boundaries, parts of the external world seem to be internal, and parts of the self seem to be outside the self. It is probable that in patients who regress deeply, and do not improve, representatives of the self and of the external world, including somatic parts, swim in an almost undifferentiated objectless dream world.

Introjection and identification. We have already discussed these under repression because they antedate the maturation of repression, and are overused in primitive forms by persons who have been exposed in infancy to excessive tension and anxiety. Here it is only necessary to add a few words. Introjection is a symbolic incorporation, that is to say, it is a symbolic act which is modelled upon the act of swallowing. Drinking in through the eyes and ears, tasting goodness and evil, chewing one's cud in relation to some decision, swallowing bait, propaganda and one's words, engulfing with ones' arms — these are only a few samples of thousands of introjective expressions, with incorporative implication, which are current in everyday speech. In schizophrenic regression, fantasies of introjection appear with openly archaic incorporation expressed.

A schizophrenic girl, who expressed many other incorporative fantasies, became frightened when her violin case was mislaid. She was immediately sure that she had swallowed it and persisted in this belief until the violin case was found, in spite of the nurses' attempts to tell her that swallowing it was impossible. To her this probably sounded as irrelevant as telling someone who was drinking in scenery that scenery cannot be swallowed.

Identification may also be derived from introjection as well as from imitation. This is especially obvious in processes of normal mourning and in psychotic depression. In schizophrenic regression identification may become imitative and introjective, but in childlike archaic forms. A patient may imitate the behavior of someone else, not playfully or ambitiously, but merely to increase self-control or to have within him the powers that he supposes the other person to have. This is a form of sympathetic magic. A patient may also identify with another person by feeling that he is fusing with the other person.[51] This is probably a return to *primary identification,* that is, to phases of childhood development in which self-images and object-images lacked clear boundaries and could be experienced as merging, separating and merging again. This, again, is something which all of us experience in dreams. To experience it while awake must be as confusing as a delirium.

Other defenses. During fluctuations of regression, while a person is beginning to disintegrate, and when he is returning again toward health, most of the other ego defenses commonly used appear in schizophrenic reactions.

[51] See the case reported in Jacobson, E., "Contribution to the metapsychology of psychotic identification," *J. Amer. Psychoanal. Ass.,* 1954, 2, 239–262.

Thus, for example, the defenses most characteristic of obsessive compulsive reactions — reaction formation, undoing, displacement, isolation — are common precursors of a schizophrenic breakthrough. Without question many persons escape a schizophrenic illness by rigidly adhering to obsessive compulsive defenses. We pointed out the similarity of obsessive doubting to schizophrenic reactions; and indeed one may lead over into the other. A relationship between hysterical reactions — that is, conversion and dissociative reactions — has long been recognized. The somatic disturbances in both may look alike. The isolation or split in the ego which characterizes dissociation also appears in schizophrenic reactions. Finally, we know that schizophrenia usually involves severe anxiety at some phase and that phobic defenses may be a vulnerable person's chief defenses against a schizophrenic psychosis.

It is an old story among therapists that one should always look behind a *neurotic façade* to see, if possible, whether or not it hides *psychotic trends.* Likewise, though this is not as often commented upon, in treating a schizophrenic person one looks for signs that neurotic defenses are being constructed. It is a triumph to be able to help a psychotic schizophrenic person to become neurotic instead, even though he cannot progress beyond becoming neurotic. A neurotic personality is less in danger of disintegration than a psychotic one. A regressing schizophrenic person is in danger of the deepest of all disintegrations short of intoxication and brain damage.

3. Ego-superego regression in active schizophrenic reactions[52]

As in the other psychoses, ego-superego regression in schizophrenia is *subtotal.* It is not merely partial, as in the neuroses. Much of the time, the greater part of ego-superego function operates at infantile levels, sometimes at regressive levels so deep that distinctions between the self and others are lost.

We have emphasized throughout this chapter the instability of the active schizophrenic regression, how it may fluctuate from fairly good object relations to their utter loss, sometimes over a period of weeks, sometimes within a single therapeutic hour. This extraordinary fluctuation in *level of regression,* we have said, reveals multiple fixation points, many of which appear to be more primitive than even the deepest psychotic depressive fixations. We have stated, moreover, that the *proportion of the ego-superego organization* involved in schizophrenic regression also fluctuates widely, varying from total psychotic withdrawal, such as one sees in catatonic stupors, to minimal loss of contact, that is, to minimal disturbance of ego-superego organization.[53]

[52] By *active schizophrenia* we mean simply reactions in which the patient is actively trying to find a solution, and has neither given up nor retreated into a persistent withdrawn state.

[53] Moriarty, D. M., "Observations of the superego in a schizophrenic patient," *Psychoanalysis & Psychoanal. Rev.,* 1961, 48, 3–18.

These wide fluctuations have double significance. They help us to understand the sudden changes in adaptive capacity and in the ability to communicate and interact effectually with other people. A suddenly increased involvement of the ego-superego organization would account for the sudden massive withdrawals that we witness clinically. A suddenly decreased involvement would account for the sudden good contact which we also witness. A knowledge of these wide fluctuations help the psychotherapist to be prepared for sudden increased cooperativeness, on the part of the patient, and to be ready to take advantage of it. The therapist can likewise be reconciled to sudden unexpected regressions and can console himself with the expectation that they may suddenly end.

Interest in schizophrenic ego-superego regression has never been higher or more productive of clinical and theoretical contributions than today. The complexity of the clinical picture and the spirited controversies over theoretical interpretations combine to give us a stimulating and challenging literature, nearly all of it based upon active participation in the theoretical investigation of active schizophrenic patients. The literature is also confusing. This is both because of the confused clinical picture that schizophrenic patients present, with all the archaic material in it expressed in unfamiliar symbolic form, and because of the basic controversies in fundamental psychodynamic theory which prevail in this field. We refer not only to the controversial British group centering about the work of Melanie Klein, whose views apparently can neither be wholly accepted nor wholly rejected by opponents, but also to the Sullivanian group, and even to the opposition of the more conservative writers who stress *aggressive drives* instead of libidinal drives. There are, naturally, also those who stress both. And finally there is the pioneer work of Federn which emphasizes the prime importance of *ego boundaries* and *ego feeling* in schizophrenics.[54]

No attempt will be made here to cover the literature on schizophrenia. A review of publications appearing between 1946 and 1956 alone amounts to more than a thousand pages and includes about 4000 references.[55] There is no indication that the rate of publication on this topic has decreased.

Childhood background of schizophrenic reactions

In a group of such variegated clinical pictures as we find among the schizophrenias it is too much to expect a simple statement about the probable childhood background of adult schizophrenic patients. Since the pioneer

---

[54] Federn, P., *Ego Psychology and the Psychoses.* New York: Basic Books, 1952. J. Piaget, gives abundant protocols indicating such fluidity in the perception and cognition of young infants, and evidence of their seeming to accept the disappearance and reappearance of objects as if these were unconnected phenomena or miracles. See *Origins of Intelligence.* New York: Internat. Univ. Press, 1952; *Construction of Reality in the Child* (trans. M. Cook). New York: Basic Books, 1954.

[55] Bellak, L. (Ed.), *Schizophrenia: A Review of the Syndrome.* New York: Logos Press, 1958.

work of Lidz and Lidz,[56] a great deal of attention has been devoted to the question of whether or not schizophrenics have an identifiable family background that is different from the family background of nonschizophrenic persons. One of the most ambitious and thoroughgoing study is being carried out at the present time at Yale by Lidz, Fleck and associates.[57]

There seems to be a good deal of evidence that many schizophrenic persons have lived as children in a pathological family organization. In some of these families every child has developed into a schizophrenic or a schizoid adult. In some families, one child appears to have been unconsciously "selected" by the others to carry the burden of a schizophrenic development, like a scapegoat, so that the other children and the parents might be protected from becoming themselves overtly psychotic. It is today a not uncommon finding that a potentially psychotic parent manages to keep clinically well by unconsciously encouraging a child or an adolescent to be psychotic. Whenever the families of such schizophrenic persons are studied intensively, they reveal abnormalities which a brief contact or a traditional history taking fails to bring out.

We are faced once more with the question of moral responsibility. Who is to blame for the development of schizophrenic persons in a pathological family, with perhaps a potentially psychotic parent? The question can be answered in those cases where the parent has been obviously sadistic, neglectful or indifferent, so that the child has had no chance to develop normal interpersonal relationships and no chance to internalize a stable parent image.

The question is much more difficult to answer when a potentially psychotic parent, who does not even realize that he is potentially psychotic, defends himself unconsciously by encouraging psychotic developments in a child, without in the least realizing what he is doing or why he is doing it. It is just as difficult to answer in those families which seem to have unconsciously "selected" one child to be the psychotic scapegoat, to carry the burden of psychosis, and free the rest of the family from the threat. Such maneuvers, like individual unconscious defense mechanisms, go unrecognized simply because they *are* unconscious. If they became conscious, they would inflict the defended persons with the very psychosis against which they are defending themselves. We are dealing here with sick people, sick parents and often sick family organizations, rather than with consciously evil people, evil parents or evil families. The promise for the future is that the ongoing

[56] Lidz, R. W., and Lidz, T., "The family environment of schizophrenic patients," *Amer. J. Psychiat.*, 1949, *106*, 332–345.

[57] Lidz, T., Cornelison, A., Fleck, S., and Terry, D., "The interfamilial environment of the schizophrenic patient: the father," *Psychiatry*, 1957, *20*, 329–342; Fleck, S., Cornelison, A., Norton, N., and Lidz, T., "Interaction between hospital staff and families," *Psychiatry*, 1957, *20*, 343–350; Lidz, T., and Fleck, S., "Schizophrenia, human integration and the role of the family," in Jackson, D. D. (Ed.), *The Etiology of Schizophrenia*. New York: Basic Books, 1960, pp. 323–345. See also Bowen, M., "A family concept of schizophrenia," in Jackson, D. D. (Ed.), *The Etiology of Schizophrenia*. New York: Basic Books, 1960, pp. 346–372.

studies of the families of schizophrenic patients will lead in the direction of eliminating the kind of situation which breeds children vulnerable to adult schizophrenia.[58]

We shall now turn to a brief consideration of the so-called "involutional psychotic reactions," before going on to the group of *personality disorders*, many of which resemble schizophrenic reactions, and some of which have identifiable origins in family pathology.

[58] Further discussions of the families of schizophrenics can be found in Bellak, L. (Ed.), *Schizophrenia: A Review of the Syndrome.* New York: Logos Press, 1958. See also Rosenthal, D., "Familial concordance by sex with respect to schizophrenia," *Psychol. Bull.*, 1962, *59*, 401–421; Sanua, V. D., "Sociocultural factors in families of schizophrenics," *Psychiatry*, 1961, *24*, 246–265; Garmezy, N., Clarke, A. R., and Stockner, C., "Child-rearing attitudes of mothers and fathers as reported by schizophrenic and normal patients," *J. abnorm. soc. Psychol.*, 1961, *63*, 176–182; Horowitz, F. D., and Lovell, L. L., "Attitudes of mothers of female schizophrenics," *Child Develpm.*, 1960, *31*, 299–305; Wolman, B. B., "The fathers of schizophrenic patients," *Acta Psychother. Psychosom.*, 1961, *9*, 193–210; Foudraine, J., "Schizophrenia and the family: a survey of the literature 1956–1960 on the etiology of schizophrenia," *Acta Psychother. Psychosom.*, 1961, *9*, 82–110; Rosenbaum, C. P., "Patient-family similarities in schizophrenia," *Arch. gen. Psychiat.*, 1961, *5*, 120–126.

18

Involutional Psychotic Reactions

⊹

WHAT IS MEANT BY AN *involutional psychotic reaction?* ALL THAT THIS designation means is that, if one of the psychotic reactions which we have already described in preceding chapters appears for the first time in middle or late middle life, it may be called involutional. At this period of life a psychosis is most likely to be depressive or paranoid. Only occasionally is it manic and only rarely schizophrenic.

This grouping called *involutional psychotic reactions* has little value in practice, since middle and late middle life are among the commonest periods in which depressive and paranoid reactions occur, and it has no value in psychodynamics. It seems unlikely to survive the next revision of the current classification, but since it is still with us we might as well make use of it. For one thing we can give a brief history of the concept which will make its present survival intelligible; for another, we can take this opportunity to point out some of the difficulties which beset men and women when they reach middle or late middle life.

The concept of involutional psychotic reaction goes back to the old concept of *involutional melancholia.* What used to be called involutional melancholia turned out to be an agitated depression occurring in women. It was supposed to be a direct, metabolic product of glandular changes in the menopause.[1] This kind of classification, centering around female reproductive functions, was taken for granted until recent decades before psycho-

[1] Other terms for the menopause are the *climacterium* and the *change of life.*

logical factors had been recognized as effective precipitating factors. Thus, as recently as 1928 we find a section in an authoritative handbook of psychiatry devoted to such supposed entities as *postpartum* and *puerperal psychoses,* and even to *gestation* and *lactation psychoses.*[2] These have disappeared from the literature meanwhile, because of the recognition that being pregnant, giving birth to a child and nursing it, may for one reason or another give rise to conflicts, frustration and fantasies which are deeply regressive in character, regressive enough to precipitate psychoses in vulnerable personalities.[3] When, in the relatively recent past, there was talk of a *male climacterium,* thought to be the equivalent of the female menopause, the concept of involutional melancholia gained a new lease on life. If men also experienced a *climacterium,* or change of life, then perhaps this was the explanation of middle life and late middle life depressions in the male.

In 1952 our present official classification was adopted by the American Psychiatric Association, and in it we find that the time-honored *involutional melancholia* has vanished. In its place is the so-called *involutional psychotic reaction,*[4] which is obviously a compromise between the old thinking and the new. Although one is warned in the 1952 diagnostic manual not to include psychotic reactions in this category "merely because of their occurrence within this age group," the symptoms listed under this heading are those commonly found in the psychoses we have already described. There is no cluster of symptoms that can conceivably be regarded as distinctive. Age remains the only criterion in spite of the manual's warning.

In actual practice even the age range is not a useful criterion. Diagnosticians and statisticians have shown, in the past, a confusing tendency to stretch the age range in both directions. If a woman grows depressed at the age of forty, sometimes even as early as thirty-five, and her depression includes bitterness, inflexibility and a tendency to remain chronic, she is often said to be "approaching the menopause." Her depression is then considered to be the direct result of the hormonal imbalance of an early involution, in other words, *involutional melancholia.* If another woman has her first depression at sixty, she may be said to be suffering from "a delayed effect of the menopause," actually long past, and therefore she too is called *involutional.* This elastic age range actually covers the period of most depressions occurring before senility. When it comes to the male, no one seems to be quite sure that he really goes through anything that can be called a climacterium or change of life. Those clinicians who think he does, vary in their opinion as to when this change occurs, placing it anywhere between forty and sixty-five.

[2] There was still a section on the reproductive psychoses of women in Bumke, O., *Handbuch der Geisteskrankheiten.* Berlin: Springer, 1928, vol. 7, pp. 118–150.

[3] Markheim, S., "A comparative evaluation of psychotic and nonpsychotic reactions to childbirth," *Amer. J. Orthopsychiat.,* 1961, *31,* 565–578.

[4] See also Davidoff, E., "The involutional psychoses," in Kaplan, O. (Ed.), *Mental Disorders in Later Life.* (2nd ed.), Stanford, Calif.: Stanford Univ. Press, 1956, pp. 244–261.

All in all, the concept of *involutional melancholia* proved not to be justified, and the substitution of an *involutional psychotic reaction* seems no more than a nod to the history we have just sketched. It should be given up because it is confusing and unreliable as well as useless. Ageing raises difficulties for most people. It must be considered as one factor leading to dissatisfaction in some persons, neuroses in others, psychoses in still others, and psychosomatic disorders or character disorders in persons vulnerable for some reason to these.

Factors Leading to Psychopathology in Middle Life

This leaves us only with a discussion of the difficulties in middle and late middle life which often lead to a neurotic or a psychotic reaction, a psychosomatic or a character (personality) disorder, and which often act to prolong such pathology.

One thing that no one can escape is a gradual *decline in biological effectiveness.* Most people adapt to this gradually; some regard it as a growing defeat; some try to deny it and resist it strenuously.

Another factor is the *socio-economic* one. During the forties, fifties and sixties, a person's sources of social prestige and economic security may be threatened or may actually disappear. Middle-aged women find themselves with little to occupy them beyond cooking and housecleaning. Middle-aged men are more and more in danger of losing their jobs and not finding new ones, or at least of being passed over when there are promotions to be made.[5]

A third factor is the *personal* one. Granted the same general biological decline and the same socio-economic threat, some persons show themselves less flexible, less able to adapt to the inevitable than others. Whereas one person shifts easily his interests, his habitual rhythms, and his demands on life, another person stubbornly tries to keep everything the same, even though everything is changing. We shall take up each of these factors now in more detail, keeping in mind always that they are not really separable, even though they merit separate discussion.

Biological factors

As everyone knows, the human organism begins to slow down long before it begins to wear out. This was dramatized in World War II, when air force pilots over forty were regarded as nearing the end of their flying careers. It has recently been dramatized afresh by public discussions of the age qualifications for astronauts. But decreasing biological effectiveness with the loss of youth has been recognized for centuries, probably for aeons. In our own time, it has been taken for granted for decades that baseball

---

[5] Botwinick, J., "Drives, expectancies and emotions," pp. 739–768, and Busse, E. W., "Psychopathology," pp. 364–399, in Birren, J. E. (Ed.), *Handbook of Aging and the Individual.* Chicago: Univ. of Chicago Press, 1959.

players would have to retire in their thirties, because they had become too old for their jobs, not quick enough or not well enough coordinated, or with too little endurance.

In almost everyone, the autonomous ego functions of motor coordination, perceptual grasp and new learning show impairment as one moves into the forties and fifties. In most persons, sensory acuity and sensory adaptation also diminish. The need for reading glasses seems to some middle-aged persons a personal affront or a narcissistic wound. Some take years and years to adapt to the use of bifocal glasses which to others seem merely a temporary nuisance. Impairment of hearing, which many escape, can lead in those who experience it to all kinds of adaptive difficulty. It is said that the incidence of paranoid reactions among the hard-of-hearing is roughly eight times the incidence in the total population. All these and many other changes involve cerebral function. There is no reason to suppose that the brain escapes the general slowing down of middle life. On the outside of the head, the hair grows sparse with age, even in women. In men it may virtually disappear. The body skin gradually loses its elasticity, becomes wrinkled, dry and discolored. Such changes in skin are especially important to women, as the billions of dollars spent in this country on cosmetics each year testify. For any woman who cannot accept her inescapable loss of youth they may be critical.

People in their forties and fifties find that they fatigue more easily than they used to, and that they recover from exertion slowly. There are also involutional changes in the viscera which, although invisible in themselves, may appear as physiological disturbances in visceral function. Gastrointestinal, urinary and genital disturbances are among the most common. The blood vessels, like the skin, lose their elasticity with age. They cannot respond as well as they could in youth to sudden or prolonged strain. Hormonal changes, which are most dramatic in the menopause, occur also at other times and in other systems, both in men and in women. To all these we must finally add the residuals of accidents and illnesses, which leave behind them their scars and their reduced effectiveness.

If any person's physical attractiveness or strength determines his general status, it is not difficult to understand the powerful impact of its loss. The result may be an intensification of neurotic reaction, a psychotic regression, a psychosomatic or a character (personality) disorder, depending upon the modes of expression that a person habitually uses, his defenses, and his vulnerability to partial or subtotal regression. Several factors which may increase or decrease the impact remain to be discussed.

There is first of all the factor of *individual difference* in the *age* at which significant involutional changes appear and the *degree* to which they interfere with normal living. We all know that signs of ageing are much less marked in some individuals than in others of the same chronological age. There are also individual differences in the *kind of function most affected* by ageing. Early cardiac ageing, for example, is more threatening and disabling for most persons than gastrointestinal ageing. The loss of sensory acuity, or early ageing of the skin, may require greater adaptive effort in persons whose security and prestige depend upon sensory acuity or youthful appearance than even cardiac impairment. The socio-economic and the personal factors, to which we have already alluded, will be taken up in more detail in the sections that follow.

Socio-economic factors

It is inevitable that one generation shall one day supersede the previous generation in the active control and direction of affairs. It is not until middle and late middle life that this socio-economic threat begins to materialize for most persons. What will happen? Must the middle-aged person give up his old established patterns of living, his style of life, and adapt himself unwillingly to patterns that are strange and uncongenial? Will he become a person of no significance and even a burden to others?

It is so difficult today for a man over forty to find employment once he loses his job (whether through company mergers, through cost cutting, through the relocation of plants or through automation) that special associations are being formed to provide mutual aid in locating new openings. This is true at the executive level as well as at the level of skilled and unskilled worker, and at clerical levels.

How and where can a person live without a job? Must he lose his home and his hard-won independence? Will he suffer the nightmare of having to live in the household of an offspring who does not want him? Even though in more patriarchal times this was an established custom, there is much evidence that the parent often had to put up with indignities and deprivations in the home of his married offspring.[6] The son or son-in-law, the daughter or daughter-in-law, is now in the position of command once held by the now dispossessed parent. Motives of revenge, often unconscious, may determine how the dependent parent is treated. At the least, he represents an expense and a curtailment of freedom for the younger persons with whom he may have to live.

The threat of becoming a helpless dependent may arouse anxiety, tension, fatigue, dejection and resentment in middle life, long before there is any immediate prospect of being helpless and dependent. The hypersensitivity that middle-aged people develop, in relation to their dwindling independence and significance, leaves them wide open to the development of psychopathol-

---

[6] In our folklore there is the classical story of *The Divided Horsecloth*. A man tells his son to turn the grandfather out of doors with nothing but a horsecloth. The son cuts the cloth in two, gives his grandfather only half, and returns to his father's house with the other half. When his father asks why he has done this, he replies that he is saving one-half for the time when he turns his father out of doors himself. There is also a similar story about the son who angrily drags his father to the edge of a field, beating him as he evicts him. His father finally cries out, "No more! No more! This is as far as I dragged my father when I beat him!"

ogy, including depressive delusions that they are unloved and about to be abandoned, and paranoid delusions that everyone is against them or is plotting against them.

The specter of lost significance and lost prestige is difficult to put down. Men retain their sense of significance in part through their earnings and through whatever prestige and power they have experienced on the job. Women usually retain theirs through their control of domestic arrangements and their children. Both men and women need also to hold their places in the affairs of the home, of the neighborhood, and of their circle of relatives and friends. It is self-evident that a sudden change from high prestige to little or none is much more difficult to weather than a gradual change from moderate prestige to relatively little. One of the chief obstacles in the way of adaptation to reduced power and prestige is that the same qualities of domination and possessiveness which helped a person to achieve and hold his position in life may now prevent his accepting any compromise in which domination and possession are minimal. It is never easy to be moved from the center of the stage to the sidelines. For a person who has always identified his integrity and worth with his continuing to hold the center of the stage, to be moved from it when he may still feel strong and able may be to invite regression and psychopathology.

It should be mentioned in passing that many socio-economic factors are not inevitable in the same sense that biological decline is inevitable. Some of them are being mitigated and even eliminated in this country today. As a result large numbers of persons in middle and late middle life are already escaping some of the worst threats that plagued ageing persons a decade or two ago. Our society is beginning to realize that socio-economic security is not just a luxury, but a potent factor in preserving the health of men and women who can find no work or are unable to work. This is only a beginning. It is limited to a very few nations. It is subject to abuse by persons who could manage without pensions and unemployment pay. It is subject to denunciation by persons who do not understand the dangers to national morale and social stability of deeply dissatisfied people who have lost hope. The trend toward providing economic security has already become so well established that nothing short of a general catastrophe can halt it. Nevertheless, enough uncertainty still prevails to make socio-economic insecurity a dominant concern for persons in middle and late middle life.

Personal factors

There are finally the personal factors to be considered, the individual ways of reacting to biological decline and to a reduction in socio-economic level. We have said that differences in flexibility mean differences in adaptability, that persons who can shift their interests, habitual rhythms and demands are more likely to come to terms with the changes which appear in middle and late middle life. One person, for example, with relatively little biological decline may react to that little with serious personality disturbances; while another person, who recognizes his biological waning, is able to accept it with equanimity. Likewise, one person can accept a reduction in socio-economic level which to another seems intolerable. The latter is much more likely than the former to react in middle life with neurotic, psychosomatic, psychotic or character disorder.

Many persons treat a reduction in physical strength or attractiveness as nothing short of a disaster. This is especially likely when the change comes suddenly, following an illness or an accident, or in the wake of the loss of a loved one through death, separation or desertion. To a minority, as we have already seen in the preceding chapters, such losses may lead to a collapse of defensive and adaptive systems. The regression that ensues will then light up long buried anxieties, conflicts, fantasies and guilt. Depressive or paranoid psychoses may then develop; but when they do they are not different from other depressions and paranoid reactions in persons who feel hopeless, anxious, guilty and unloved. The delusions by means of which such regressed persons may attempt to reconstruct their external reality are the delusions with which we are already familiar.

Some persons in their forties and fifties, finding that increased effort and overcompensation are not enough to maintain them, or to reinstate them, in a position of prestige, give up and become depressed at once. Those who have good object relations will be neurotically depressed; those with poor object relations will regress subtotally and become psychotically depressed. Other persons in the same situation wear themselves down by continued effort, grow anxious, sleepless and irritable, and eventually arrive by a different route at an agitated depression. Once more, the depressions are not essentially different from depressions at other times, or from depressions developing in patients who have been depressed before in life.[7]

Paranoid personalities may develop paranoid reactions under the same circumstances. In middle life they will feel unappreciated, discriminated against and unwanted. It is only a step from this feeling to the development of regressive delusional reconstructions, such as we have described, for example, in the formation of a pseudocommunity.[8] Paranoid delusional reactions, like psychotic depressions, develop more often in middle life than in adolescence and in early adulthood. It is for this reason that it has always been easy to attach the label *involutional* to these psychoses.

The bizarre somatic delusions, mentioned specifically in the official classification, are usually attempts to justify and account for changes in the body image in schizoid personalities. Body changes which a person cannot escape, and can neither adapt to nor accept, are denied and projected as strange happenings in the body. If our case of Donald J., the electrical engineer,

---

[7] One of the stipulations for an involutional psychotic reaction is that it must not be a *second* depressive or paranoid reaction. This stipulation has been carried over directly from the older concept of involutional melancholia. It is equally irrational in both.

[8] See the chapter on paranoid reactions.

had been that of a man fifteen years older, he could certainly have qualified as one of involutional psychotic reaction with bizarre somatic delusions. Yet he could still have been included, more intelligibly, among the schizophrenic reactions.

In conclusion, we may accept the fact that middle and late middle life pose special problems, just as adolescence and senility do. The psychotic reactions that emerge during middle and late middle life, however, are in no way distinctive in the sense of being of direct metabolic origin. They are products of subtotal regression in the face of frustration, conflict, guilt and fantasy. They belong with the other psychoses which have already been described and discussed. Let us turn now to a consideration of the miscellaneous but highly interesting group of *personality disorders*.

19

Personality Disorders

$$\maltese$$

UNDER THIS GENERAL HEADING THE OFFICIAL CLASSIFICATION HAS MADE A heroic attempt to gather together under one large tent a number of miscellaneous disturbances. Many of them are highly important in behavior pathology. Unfortunately the result has been rather to confuse than to clarify.

The confusion becomes obvious the moment we look at the official descriptions of what are usually called *character disorders,* there divided between "personality trait disturbances," some of which are neurotic, others nonspecific, and "personality pattern disturbances," most of which are prepsychotic personalities. The overall definition of personality disorders states without qualification that patients experience "minimal subjective anxiety"; but descriptions of subgroups go on to ignore this important stipulation. Thus, patients with personality trait and pattern disturbances (character disorders) are called fearful, sensitive, elated, sad, suspicious, envious and extremely jealous. Surely no one supposes that such characteristics reach pathological levels without strong anxiety, even strong subjective anxiety. One subgroup is said openly to suffer from "strong and poorly controlled hostility, guilt and anxiety." Another subgroup, with three subtypes, is described as frequently having anxiety reactions superimposed upon it.

When we turn to the *sociopathic personality disturbances* (the ones that used to be called psychopathic states and impulse disorders), we find no mention of anxiety or anxiety equivalents. Yet we know that careful clinical studies of *antisocial* and *dissocial* persons — who fight against or seem to disregard social sanctions — have revealed over the past fifty years that anxiety is a leading factor, even subjective anxiety, appearing in the midst of reactively hostile or defensively callous behavior. In *deviant sexuality, drug addiction* and *alcoholism,* also classified under personality disorders, it is well known to contemporary authors and playwrights, to say nothing of contemporary therapists, that intense objective and subjective anxiety appear as part of the behavior pathology. Yet minimal subjective anxiety still stands as the official description of the whole group of personality disorders, which includes these.

Finally, we come to a heterogeneous class called *transient situational personality disorders.* These are described as acute symptomatic reactions to overwhelming stress occurring temporarily in persons who seem not to have an underlying personality disturbance. They include responses to civilian catastrophe and military combat, certainly a timely topic today, and adaptive failures at various age levels from infancy to normal senility.

This last grouping is not without practical usefulness. In the case of military personnel, for example, experience has taught that, when diagnoses are made in terms of neurotic, psychotic or psychosomatic reactions, such diagnoses may be interpreted outside of the medical corps in ways unnecessarily detrimental to the military patient. Transient situational personality disorder is a euphemism that avoids stigmatizing a patient in his own eyes and in the eyes of others. The grouping is also useful in emphasizing the vulnerability of everyone to personality disturbances when stress is great enough, something which we have been emphasizing all through this book. The crises in adaptation at different age levels are also universally recognized and are an integral part of our understanding of behavior pathology. Aside from these emphases and practical uses, there is no good reason for looking upon transient disturbances as fundamentally different from neurotic, psychotic and psychosomatic disorders. We have already described cases which last only a few days and seem to clear up without leaving permanent new defects. Even in a catastrophe or in combat the personality disturbances which appear always involve internal forces that are highly personal and by no means simply situational. Again, we point out that everyone is vulnerable to personality disorganization, given enough stress, and that his response to the threat or the actual beginnings of disorganization will depend upon what his defenses and coping mechanisms are and how well they function under the stress circumstances.

We shall try to clarify the confusion existing today in relation to this heterogeneous group of personality disorders by first of all omitting entirely the transient situational disturbances, since they have nothing special about them excepting their temporary duration. Their dynamics and their therapy can best be understood in terms of the extreme stresses and the different demands and opportunities made at different ages, and under various situations, both of which have been already discussed.

As for the rest of the personality disturbances assigned officially to this general section, we shall regroup them in a way that is not only more consistent but is the way most active therapists and diagnosticians group them. If it is understood that our conceptualization of these disorders is still vague, in spite of a growing dynamic and legal interest in them, the somewhat vague nature of the grouping will be better tolerated. There is neither practical advantage nor scientific integrity in pretending that we are sure when we are not.

The regrouping of personality disorders, as we shall describe them, gives us the following clinical disorders:

1. *Character disorders.* These include all of the personality trait and pattern disturbances in the official classification that correspond to neurotic and prepsychotic personality structures, and one, the *hysterical*, which the official classification has overlooked.

2. *Inadequate and unstable personalities.* This group includes the *inadequate*, the *emotionally unstable*, and the *passive-aggressive personalities*, as these are described in the official classification.

3. *Sociopathic personality disturbances.* We include three subgroups under this heading: (i) *irresponsible and emotionally shallow persons,* who seem to commit repeated offenses without anxiety and with little material gain; (ii) *antisocial persons* in open aggressive rebellion against society who may or may not express anxiety; (iii) *dissocial persons* who are easily corrupted, but seem neither antisocial nor emotionally shallow. Clinicians who specialize in work with patients in these three groups feel that there is no justification for grouping cases of sexual deviation, of alcohol addiction or of drug addiction with them. We are accordingly giving these a separate place.[1]

4. *Sexual deviation.* This group is substantially the same as that in the official classification, which does little more than name a few deviations. We shall discuss six of the most common: (i) *overt homosexuality;* (ii) *exhibitionism;* (iii) *voyeurism;* (iv) *fetishism;* (v) *transvestism;* and (vi) *sadomasochism.*

5. *Addiction.* As in the official classification, we include here separately addiction to alcohol and addiction to drugs, since both research workers and clinicians find basic differences between the character of the two addictions.

Character Disorders

In the *character disorders* — called "personality trait and pattern disturbances" in the official classification — some distortion of the personality develops early in life and persists as a person's style, as the characteristic

[1] Cf. the detailed criticism made by Cleckley, H., "Psychopathic states," in Arieti, S. (Ed.), *American Handbook of Psychiatry.* New York: Basic Books, 1959, pp. 567–589.

way in which he copes with his environment and defends himself. A character disorder may never be experienced as something abnormal or intrusive, and may therefore never give rise to anxiety once it becomes established. It is the bent twig of childhood which distorts the form of the personality and gives rise to compensatory changes to offset the distortion. The end-result may be an adult who seems always inhibited in certain areas of function, or who shows exaggerations of certain personality characteristics, or who stands chronically apart from the affairs of the marketplace, or rushes impetuously into every quickening stream that passes near him. If such an adult and those who are close to him accept his peculiarities as simply his nature he is not likely to find them disturbing or seek to change them. He may be proud of them and consider them, not incorrectly, as signs of his individuality.[2]

It is only when a person with a character distortion realizes that something is wrong with him, with his attempts at adaptation, defense, mastery and satisfaction, that he experiences his difficulties as ego-alien, usually without knowing precisely what they are or why he feels as he does. The realization often comes with repeated failures and dissatisfactions which a person cannot explain away. It may come because new circumstances force a person to compare himself with others, and the comparison raises self-doubt, dissatisfaction and perhaps anxiety. He may even recognize that some of what he has regarded as his special virtue or his mark of individuality may be in fact a pathological need, fear or incapacity. He may find, for example, that his vaunted firmness rests upon a rigidity which keeps him from changing even when a change is necessary, or that his widely known affability is actually a fear of displeasing anyone, or that his willingness to compromise stems from an inability to take a firm stand.

One of the simplest ways of illustrating how a character disorder may be mistaken for a virtue is to look into the motives and the methods of conforming. Every child learns to conform to what is expected of him. This is an integral part of growing up from babyhood through childhood and adolescence to adulthood. It is also the basis of cross-cultural differences in adult personality. The child in each different society is provided with unique models for identification and with adult guidance in learning to conform to these models.

A child in any culture may learn to conform gladly and willingly, but still without achieving normal, effective adulthood. If, for example, a parent demands unquestioning conformity of a child, regardless of the circumstances and of the child's changing needs, the child is most likely to be what he is compelled to be, even if this means serious distortion in his personality or character organization. If a child receives love in return for self-effacement,

[2] See the panel discussion in Valenstein, A. F. (reporter), "Psychoanalytic concept of character," *J. Amer. Psychoanal. Ass.*, 1958, 6, 567–575. See also Peck, R. F., Havighurst, R. J., Cooper, R., Lilienthal, J., and More, D., *The Psychology of Character Development.* New York: Wiley, 1960.

and if no other significant adult counteracts this trend, he will grow to adulthood as a chronically self-effacing person who even seeks out a marital partner who will also reward his self-effacement. This may be an acceptable situation, satisfying to all concerned, but it is not a normal personality organization.

Neither is the personality organization normal that is built around the *masochistic acceptance of punishment or restraint as an inevitable part of parental love*, nor one built around *infantile dependence*. Nevertheless if a parent treats a child consistently with *sadistic affection*, the child is likely to develop a reciprocal *masochistic acceptance of sadistic affection* which may last into adult life, as we have seen in some of our neurotic and psychotic patients. If a parent keeps a child consistently in a state of *infantile dependence*, no matter how this is rationalized, the child may always seek out situations and persons that encourage his lifelong pattern.[3]

The important point here is that unquestioning conformity, self-effacement, masochistic suffering and infantile dependence are often acceptable and even sometimes highly valued by society. That is, persons who are themselves relatively free of character distortions often admire them in others, without stopping to consider why these others have them while they themselves do not. It is self-evident that persons who cannot be comfortable unless they are conforming, who enjoy self-effacement and masochistic suffering, or who live contentedly in infantile dependence, are not likely to get into trouble unless they carry their characterological needs to extremes. To avoid common misunderstandings, it is essential to state here that courage, integrity, dependability, normal self-sacrifice and the ability to accept dependence upon others are not signs of character disorder. It is only when these seeming *qualities* turn out to be *demands*, upon a human environment which does not want them, and does not gain in warmth or understanding from them, that we call them disorders rather than virtues.

If a person with a character disorder seeks therapeutic help it is because he has for some reason become dissatisfied with the way he is organized, or with the way he operates, and because he hopes through therapy to acquire a different, happier and more effective way of living. Nowadays it is this hope that motivates a large percentage of patients who turn spontaneously to psychotherapy and psychoanalysis. The hope is an ambitious one. It implies the possibility of making fundamental changes in a personality organization that has determined the patient's very style of life, perhaps from early childhood. Sometimes such a hope can be fulfilled; more often it cannot. If a patient's hope can be so modified that he expects improvement rather than a radical change, his chances of reaching his goal will be greatly increased, and the chances of therapeutic disillusionment will be correspondingly lessened.

[3] Under exceptional circumstances, an adult who has shown no significant character distortion may acquire one permanently, because of exceedingly traumatic conditions. This has been true of concentration camp victims, and of persons who have suffered a crushing personal blow in adulthood.

Classification. The problem of classifying character disorder has not yet been solved. We have today two competing systems of classification. Neither of them is satisfactory and the two overlap. One of them takes off from the principle of erogenous zonal development. A recent presentation equates genital or phallic traits with hysterical character, anal-sadistic traits with compulsive character, and oral narcissistic traits at least in part with depressive character.[4] The other system is the one adopted by the official classification. It recognizes *compulsive, paranoid, cyclothymic* (*manic-depressive*) and *schizoid personalities,* to which we shall add *hysterical personality.* Because of the overlapping of these two systems, and because of the still unsettled state of the grouping, we shall follow the official classification to the extent that it parallels neurotic and psychotic reactions.

Before going on to discuss the major varieties of character disorder it might be well to state in what way these differ from neurotic and psychotic reactions. They differ in representing a variety of personality structures which are in some way distorted but manage to achieve a stability that includes the distortion. For example, a compulsive personality or character is so organized that the person having it can operate — as an overconscientious, inhibited, rigid individual — without developing symptoms of an acute conflict, such as we saw in the cases described under obsessive compulsive reactions. Similarly, a manic-depressive (cyclothymic) personality may exhibit unmistakable mood swings that carry the person to euphoric heights and depressive depths, without his becoming psychotically or even neurotically manic or depressed. In short, there is a distortion of character which more or less permanently alleviates anxiety, but leaves a person with less flexibility, less maneuverability than normal.

Under stress, such a distorted personality organization may develop its own characteristic peculiarities to the point where a neurotic or psychotic or psychosomatic illness appears, with symptoms which are only exaggerations of the distortion. For example, an overconscientious, inhibited, rigid person may develop typical obsessive compulsive symptoms, thereby becoming frankly neurotic. There is also the possibility, repeatedly seen in practice, that such a person may regress under stress and develop a psychotic reaction.

This possibility is of more than theoretical interest. In entering upon the treatment of personality or character disorders one must bear in mind the risk of a psychotic regression resulting from therapeutic disturbance of the pathological equilibrium. Effective psychotherapy and psychoanalysis often involves risk, just as surgical interference does. The therapist who takes such inevitable risks into account is not to be blamed if, in spite of all reasonable precaution, they materialize in the course of therapy. He must be ready, of course, to change his methods and even to taper off therapy, if the dissolution of a character disorder seems to be leading toward psychotic

---

[4] For an elaboration of this system, see Michaels, J. J., "Character structure and character disorders," in Arieti, S. (Ed.), *American Handbook of Psychiatry.* New York: Basic Books, 1959, pp. 353–377.

regression or has actually precipitated one. No surgeon makes an incision without thereby endangering his patient's health and life; but without this danger there can be no surgery. No psychotherapist or psychoanalyst opens up the old conflicts crystallized in personality distortion without endangering his patient's equilibrium; but without this danger there can be no effective psychotherapy or psychoanalysis.

Varieties of character disorder or personality distortion

1. *Compulsive personality or character.* There are some compulsive trends in every normal person. They appear as automatic orderliness, neatness, frugality and obstinacy, and as automatic conformity, inhibition and conscientiousness. Without these relative inflexibilities a stable society would be impossible. Even taking pleasure in being neat, orderly and frugal, in standing one's ground, in conforming, in practicing inhibition and being conscientious is in itself far from abnormal. Such pleasure is one of the major sources of satisfaction in being an acceptable member of society. Its roots are in the child's early need to be a member of his family, of his later need to belong to neighborhood and school groups, and of his pressing adolescent need to be one of the crowd.

We speak of a *compulsive personality* or *character* only when these trends are so pronounced and insistent that severe anxiety appears when people or circumstances interfere with their exercise. It is this threat of severe anxiety that forces some people to practice extreme conformity, to be excessively conscientious, and to exhibit crippling inhibitions in areas where initiative or active participation is essential for normal function, especially in sex and aggression. People with compulsive personality or character distortions suffer from life-long unwarranted concern over conforming, over conflicts as to what is good and bad, right and wrong, clean and dirty. They may overcompensate for their compulsive trends by immersing themselves in work to the virtual exclusion of relaxation and recreation. These are the "driven" persons. One sees examples of such overcompensation in business and professional men, in housewives and mothers, who neglect all the other phases that would make their lives well balanced by filling up their time completely with overwork. One sees other examples in persons whose rigid conformity to some set of standards, sometimes the standards of a rebellious group, makes them incapable of an intelligent flexibility in meeting new situations which society actively fosters.

There are advantages in recognizing extreme rigidity in dealing with everyday life, or with a personal or social crisis, as part of a character distortion built into the compulsive personality. It makes the inflexibility and insistence of compulsive relatives, friends, and public officials easier to understand and accept. It also prepares us for the possibility that a person with a life-long compulsive distortion, if he is exposed to more stress than he can tolerate, may develop a fullblown obsessive compulsive reaction easily. He may, instead, develop an anxiety reaction, or a serious phobia to protect himself from anxiety. The anxiety reaction and the phobia will be contaminated by obsessive compulsive symptoms like those in the case of Ramona M. The possibility of regression into psychosis has already been discussed.

Traditionally, the compulsive personality or character has been linked to anal-sadistic trends. Its origins have been located in the childhood struggle with parents over bowel control, and in a childhood regression after failure to solve edipal conflicts at a genital level.[5] This is not difficult to accept if we recall how some of our clinical cases of obsessive compulsive reactions were outspokenly and intolerably anxious over contamination, feces and soiling.[6] We had no reason for hesitating there in relating such compulsive concern with a partial regression to childhood levels of conflict over bowel control and the struggle for independence from parental figures. In some of the cases no inferences were necessary. The patients spontaneously recalled the unreasonable demands made upon them in these universal childhood adaptations.

In *obsessive compulsive neuroses* we see the failure of repression and the emergence in acute form of anal-sadistic impulses and of ego defenses against them — reaction formation, displacement, isolation, undoing, countermeasures, doubt and rumination. In *compulsive personality* or *character distortions* we see the same kind of symptomatic structure; but the symptoms are neither extreme nor acute, and they are built into the adult personality. In the case of Sally J. we saw a person with an obvious *personality* or *character distortion*, evident even in early childhood, who suffered an *acute obsessive compulsive reaction* when sexually aroused.

The great majority of compulsive personality or character disorders never break down in an acute neurosis or psychosis. They remain inhibited, rigid, obstinate, excessively neat and orderly, overconscientious; or they mix some of these compulsive characteristics with their opposites to form a contradictory picture. Thus, compulsive disorderliness and dirtiness may coexist with inhibitions, rigidity and obstinacy. The same man may be compulsively stingy and a compulsive spendthrift.

2. *Hysterical personality or character.* This common clinical variety was unaccountably omitted from the official classification. It is characterized by a lifelong tendency to be histrionic, exhibitionistic, narcissistic and emotionally shallow. We are retaining the old term *hysterical* both because the clinical picture is close to the commonsense meaning of the word, and because neither conversion nor dissociative reactions — the successors to hysterical

---

[5] Michaels, J. J., "Character structure and character disorders," in Arieti, S. (Ed.), *American Handbook of Psychiatry.* New York: Basic Books, 1959, pp. 353–377; Fenichel, O., *The Psychoanalytic Theory of the Neuroses.* New York: Norton, 1945, pp. 278–284.

[6] See especially the cases of Ramona M. and Sally J. in Chapter 11.

reactions — can be equated with this histrionic, narcissistic personality or character distortion which we are about to describe.

There are some hysterical trends in most normal persons just as there are compulsive trends. Without some tendency to be dramatic, boastful or frivolous on occasion a normal personality would seem dull, solemn and emotionally uninvolved. The person who can be "the life of the party" is often a person with normal dramatic or frivolous trends. A narcissistic, boastful enthusiasm over what one is doing can be entertaining to others and lift their morale. The origins of such behavior are in the normal "showing off" and silliness of little children, who have been allowed a limited, healthy expression by parents who understand a child's need to be childishly gay. Its normal adult product is sometimes the artist of screen, stage or television, the scientist, the politician and the writer, those who remain stable and develop their talents as their profession.

We speak of hysterical personality or character only when histrionic, narcissistic, exhibitionistic display continues into adulthood almost as it appeared in childhood, and when criticism of display or interference with it provokes unreasonable anger, sullenness or self-depreciation. In mild instances, "the life of the party" soon becomes a public nuisance. In more pronounced cases, the person with hysterical personality or character seems never to have grown up. He seems always to be an actor who insists upon being the center of attention. He does things to shock, amuse or impress people, not so much because he needs self-expression — everybody needs self-expression — but because of a pathological narcissism, a consuming need to be noticed, to be admired or feared, but always to be conspicuous. His fleeting and shallow emotional attachments are to some extent the consequence of such a general orientation, and to some extent its cause. The impression of instability, insincerity and superficiality is also a consequence of an orientation which places attention-getting at the top of the motivational hierarchies.

Traditionally, the hysterical personality or character has been linked with failure to resolve edipal conflicts and with fixation in a phallic phase of sexual development. The contrast is striking between compulsive hostility, with its concern over contamination, and the erotic display of a great many hysterical characters. Hysterical personalities or characters conform more closely to normal feminine patterns of needing to be attractive, to be noticed and to be loved, than to the masculine patterns of aggression, initiative and relative independence. It is for this reason that we find hysterical distortions of personality or character much more frequently among women than among men.

The decompensation of a hysterical personality may lead to one of several regressions. Among these is, of course, the development of an outspoken conversion reaction. Here display takes the form of a disabling symptom which, even though unconsciously produced, serves the purpose of forcing people to pay continual attention to the patient. Another possibility is that needs for narcissistic supplies may become powerful enough to lead to a depressive illness, neurotic or psychotic, when they are frustrated. A third possibility is that deeper and more diffuse fixations may result in the transformation of hysterical distortion into a schizophrenic reaction. This last possibility, more prominently discussed a few decades ago than now, is still something to remember in dealing therapeutically with hysterical personality or character distortion.

3. *Paranoid personality.* The paranoid personality is one that has its origin in a lack of basic trust.[7] There is evidence that in many cases the paranoid person has received sadistic treatment during early infancy and that he has, in consequence, internalized sadistic attitudes toward himself and others. Because of his basic lack of trust in others the paranoid personality must be vigilant in order to safeguard himself against sudden deception and attack. He is exquisitely sensitive to traces of hostility, contempt, criticism or accusation in the attitudes of other people. These traces, often slight and usually unconscious, the paranoid personality treats as though they were fully conscious and of prime importance. His lack of basic trust hampers the paranoid personality in carrying out reality testing operations. He magnifies unconscious hostility or unconscious homosexual trends in other persons; and he always assumes that what is clear to him must also be clear to other people. At the same time, the paranoid person is characteristically unaware of his own hostile, contemptuous, critical and accusing attitudes. Consequently, he is unable to understand why anyone else should behave toward him with resentment or hostility.

The exquisite sensitiveness of the paranoid personality toward relatively slight and often wholly unconscious trends in others comes from his readiness to detect aggression, seductiveness and deceit in his surroundings. This in turn originates in early childhood experiences of being treated sadistically, or at least in experiencing whatever treatment he received as being sadistic, belittling, critical and accusing.

We can assume that the lack of basic trust in infancy interfered with the development of a normal symbiotic relationship with the available mother figure. This, in turn, means that ego and later superego identifications would not lead to the formation of effective ego boundaries, or to the normal maturation of the superego and the ego ideal. Defective ego boundaries and an immature superego, with its ego-ideal component, interfere grossly with reality-testing so that the paranoid personality cannot distinguish effectively between what is external shared social fact and what is internal imagined private fantasy. On the other hand, the essentially neurotic fixations present in paranoid persons keep them in better overall contact with external reality than is the case with depressive and schizoid personalities.

A significant result of the defective ego boundaries is that the paranoid

---

[7] A more detailed account of the origins of paranoid trends and the organization of the paranoid pseudocommunity appears in Chapter 14; see also Cameron, N., "The paranoid pseudocommunity revisited," *Amer. J. Sociol.*, 1959, *65*, 52–58.

personality must depend heavily upon denial and projection. Denial, as an ego defense, is called into action when something has managed to penetrate into preconscious or conscious organization. Denial, in other words, repudiates something which is already present, and projection changes it into something that appears to come from the outside. This maneuver is certainly primitive and childlike; but it is the maneuver of preference for a great many otherwise mature persons. These persons exhibit a paranoid distortion, a personality or character structure which leaves them unusually prone to suspicion, envy, jealousy and obstinacy.

The degree and the manner in which homosexuality enters into the organization of the paranoid personality is still the subject of controversy. We have elsewhere reviewed some of the significant literature, beginning with Freud's dynamic interpretations, and proceeding with the part played by excessive love to counteract excessive hate, by delusional masochism, by sadism and a very early superego, by superego nuclei, by denial, projection and the pseudocommunity.[8]

Objections to assuming a central role for homosexuality in the paranoid personality have been spelled out by MacAlpine and Hunter in their introduction to the translation of Schreber's *Memoirs of My Nervous Illness* and in their discussion of Freud's views which appears at the end of their translation.[9] These objections have been reinforced by the observation that whereas paranoid men complain of homosexual advances and homosexual persecution, paranoid women complain principally of accusations that they are prostitutes.[10] Further objections have been raised in relation to paranoid psychoses and narcissism, with considerable emphasis upon the work of Federn, which would seem to carry paranoid experiences back to phases of development earlier than edipal conflicts.[11] The genuineness of homosexuality in paranoid mechanisms has also been called into question.

The question of the role of homosexuality in paranoid personalities must still be considered a moot one. It is even possible that male and female homosexuality have different bases, since the evolution of sexuality in the two sexes follows different lines. In any case, a differentiation between latent and manifest homosexuality still needs to be emphasized. Delusions and hallucinations, like manifest dreams, are conscious and preconscious experiences which may require interpretation before their evidence can be accepted. This caution applies both to the pro's and con's of the basic question.

[8] Cameron, N., "Paranoid conditions and paranoia," in Arieti, S. (Ed.), *American Handbook of Psychiatry.* New York: Basic Books, 1959, pp. 508–539.

[9] MacAlpine, I., and Hunter, R. A., "Introduction," and "Discussion," in Schreber, D. P., *Memoirs of My Nervous Illness* (1903) (trans. MacAlpine and Hunter). London: Dawson, 1955, pp. 1–28 and pp. 369–411.

[10] Klein, H. R., and Horwitz, W. A., "Psychosexual factors in the paranoid phenomena," *Amer. J. Psychiat.*, 1949, *104*, 697–704.

[11] Grauer, D., "Homosexuality and the paranoid psychoses as related to the concept of narcissism," *Psychoanal. Quart.*, 1955, *24*, 516–526.

4. *Cyclothymic (manic-depressive) personality.* The existence of a cyclo-thymic or manic-depressive personality is based upon the presence in some persons of a mood fluctuation which is apparently not paralleled by external events that justify the fluctuations. It is also based upon the persistence in some persons of a euphoric or a depressed mood without fluctuations. The official classification implies that the warmth, friendliness and generosity of cyclothymic persons is only apparent or superficial.[12] It seems to accept the time-worn view that depressive and manic moods are endogenous, that is, generated from within, presumably independent of or almost independent of external factors and internal conflicts or fantasies.

This is no place to join the battle over endogenous and exogenous per-sonality disturbances. The view that manic and depressive moods are of metabolic or other biochemical origin is both ancient and honorable. It has been reviewed a number of times within recent years.[13] One critical review emphasizes the statistical decline of manic and depressive illnesses in the United States and other countries, and weighs carefully ecological, cultural and social factors which may play a part in the apparently rapid decline in the United States.[14] These figures apply strictly to psychotic developments; but they are not without relevance to problems of origin and incidence of fluctuating moods as character disorders, or of persistent hypomanic and depressive moods without psychosis. The depressive personality has already been discussed in Chapter 15, on psychotic depression. Manic reactions have been discussed, both in relation to historical perspectives and to mania as a defense against threatening depression, in Chapter 16, on manic reactions and manic-depressive cycles. The interrelation of the latter has been considered in the same chapter.

5. *Schizoid personality.* The schizoid personality, like the paranoid, is presumed to originate in a lack of basic trust, which dates back to the symbi-otic mother-child relationship of early infancy, and in anxieties, fears and sadism aroused during and after this early phase. The character of the childhood and adolescence of schizoid personalities, suggests strongly that they have never felt fully accepted, even in the direct form of close body contact during infancy, and that, unlike paranoids, they have not been allowed to express the rage they must have felt, in many instances not even ordinary normal aggression. They are often described as having been quiet, shy, obedient children, oversensitive to the criticisms and rejections of others, shrinking from interpersonal relationships while at the same time feeling lonely and out of things.

Many such children avoid competitive games and the close relationship

[12] *Mental Disorders.* Diagnostic and Statistical Manual. Washington, D.C.: Amer. Psychiatric Ass., 1952.

[13] Cameron, N., "The functional psychoses," in Hunt, J. McV. (Ed.), *Personality and the Behavior Disorders.* New York: Ronald, 1944, pp. 861–921.

[14] Arieti, S., "Manic-depressive psychosis," in Arieti, S. (Ed.), *American Handbook of Psychiatry.* New York: Basic Books, 1959, pp. 419–454.

of their peers. They may be looked upon by their peers as odd, queer or snobbish. Consequently they are often the targets for teasing which wounds them more than it should. They may take refuge in omnipotent and often vengeful fantasies. Many of them are avid readers, lone students of nature, or poets or artists. Most schizoid personalities have a defective defensive system; and this keeps them in closer contact with primary process material than average. Some are able to make use of their "intuitive" feelings in their fantasy, their poetic or artistic endeavors, and their unity with nature. Nevertheless, all schizoid personalities pay for whatever intuition they may have by remaining detached, uncomfortable with others, lonely and aloof. This is not the picture of primitive joy but of a pervasive loneliness for which the schizoid child, adolescent and adult try to compensate as best they can.

The adulthood of the schizoid personality seems to be simply a continuation of early childhood trends in more mature forms. In adolescence there may be a period of active, hostile rebellion, of angry distrust and obstinacy; or there may be a period of heightened asceticism with moralizing and intolerance for the behavior of others. This is only an exaggeration of what adolescence brings out in a large proportion of normal persons. The adult schizoid personality is typically aloof, unsociable, secretive and uncomfortable in the close proximity of others, especially of members of the opposite sex. He sometimes gives an impression of being self-sufficient, but this impression arises from a defensive refusal to trust anyone, to confide in anyone.

Unlike the paranoid personality, the schizoid cannot as a rule express hostility or even ordinary aggression. For this reason, and because of his distrust, he usually avoids open competition. He is the prototype of the ivory tower detached and abstract thinker. His relative lack of interaction with others may make him seem a colorless person, which he may actually be, but it is also possible that he has a rich and vivid fantasy life behind the drawbridge and the moat of his solitary castle. Occasionally a schizoid person is able to pour out feelings in writing or drama which astonish those who know him personally. Usually, however, the isolation of a lifetime leaves the interior of the castle bleak. If a schizoid person meets losses, frustrations or intrusion which he cannot handle, there is always the possibility that he will regress into a schizophrenic reaction as we have already described it in an earlier chapter.

Inadequate and Unstable Personalities

Under this general heading we shall discuss a miscellaneous group of personality disorders that do not belong with the character disorders which we have just described. Chronically inadequate and unstable personalities seem to have their origins early in life, and they persist throughout adulthood. Some investigators take this to mean that the defects are congenital, perhaps hereditary. Others take it to mean that the defects come from very early infantile experience, including early disturbances of physiology. The work of Spitz and others, who have demonstrated the baneful influences of early infantile deprivation upon personality integration, makes it all the more difficult to differentiate the hereditary or congenital from the experiential.[15]

For our purposes this differentiation is not crucial. It would be unreasonable to assume that everyone starts out in life with the same degree of biological fitness, or with the same potentialities for emotional response.[16] It would be equally unreasonable to assume that infantile experiences do not sometimes determine the course of further development, including further physiological development. Either factor or both may be involved in the development of inadequacy or instability. We shall leave the task of making such distinctions to the investigations now in progress and to those which are currently proposed. In the virtual absence of conclusive findings we shall confine ourselves in this section to a brief description of inadequacy and instability.

1. *Inadequate personality.* In this group the official classification places persons whose response to the ordinary demands of life — intellectual, emotional, social and physical — are generally ineffectual. These persons seem not to be grossly deficient according to mental tests and physical examinations. Nevertheless, they are inept in life, show poor judgment continually, are usually improvident and lacking in a normal sense of responsibility. They are often good-natured, easy-going and no trouble to others, except for their inability to persevere in anything, even when they are in sight of reward. In spite of normal or above-normal intelligence, the inadequate personality pursues immediate pleasure like a child, unable to postpone it in the interest of the reality principle. He is usually described as lacking in physical as well as in emotional stamina, a description that suggests the old conception of the "constitutionally inferior psychopath."

There can be no question that the inadequate personality is for some reason unable to carry through a normal maturing process that would lead to a responsible adulthood. There is room for doubt, however, that physical inadequacy explains the syndrome, if indeed the inadequate personality really constitutes a syndrome. As matters stand today, the inadequate personality whose physical and intellectual defects do not show up in tests and examinations remains one of our many unsolved psychopathological and psychody-

[15] Spitz, R., "Anxiety in infancy: a study of its manifestations in the first year of life," *Internat. J. Psychoanal.*, 1950, *31*, 138–143; Spitz, R., "Hospitalism: an inquiry into the genesis of psychiatric conditions in early childhood," *The Psychoanalytic Study of the Child.* New York: Internat. Univ. Press, 1951, vol. 6, pp. 255–278.

[16] Bergman, P., and Escalona, S. K., "Unusual sensitivities in very young children," *Psychoanalytic Study of the Child.* New York: Internat. Univ. Press, 1949, vol. 3, pp. 333–352; Leitch, M., and Escalona, S. K., "The reaction of infants to stress," *The Psychoanalytic Study of the Child.* New York: Internat. Univ. Press, 1949, vol. 3, pp. 121–140; Escalona, S. K., "Emotional development in the first year of life," in Senn, M. (Ed.), *Problems of Infancy and Childhood.* New York: Josiah Macy, Jr. Foundation, 1953.

namic problems. The study of actual cases reveals a pervasive immaturity which seems to be a result of abnormalities in the family structure.[17] The inadequate personality reflects ineffectualities in personal interaction within the family that reared him. It seems more than ever doubtful today that he can be dismissed as "poor stuff," as he used to be before the age of psychodynamics.

2. *Emotionally unstable personality.* Like the inadequate personality just discussed, the emotionally unstable personality is described in the official classification as a failure to achieve mature self-control, without considering possible psychodynamic origins. Emphasis is upon the presence of strong and poorly controlled hostility, guilt and anxiety, which together with impulsiveness make it impossible for the emotionally immature person to establish and maintain meaningful, stable interpersonal relationships.[18] The emotionally unstable person is said to react at times with explosive intensity to relatively slight external stress. In the course of such an emotional reaction he may shout, threaten, assault others or destroy things. He is described as being jealous and quarrelsome in relation to persons of the opposite sex. He may even attempt suicide to relieve himself of an intolerable situation. When he is not emotionally disturbed he may be outgoing and friendly.

The impression one gets from clinical descriptions suggests an adult who is impulsive, unpredictable, hostile and sometimes dangerous to himself and others. These descriptions also suggest that perhaps the emotional instability of the patient is contagious. Much that is described fits into the frame of paranoid reactions and paranoid personality. It seems to be the immaturity of emotional control that leads to this diagnosis of emotionally unstable personality. The patient appears to suffer from a child's impulsiveness and lack of emotional control; and he expresses himself episodically with all the physical power, but not the emotional integration, of an adult. There have been attempts to give these emotionally unstable persons the benefit of a psychodynamic approach.[19] Perhaps such studies will enable us to understand them and classify them more intelligently.

3. *Passive-aggressive personalities.* In this subgroup the official classification includes a continuum of immature dependent personalities which are divided into three types. The *passive dependent type* is openly passive and childishly dependent. The *passive aggressive type* shows aggression in passive ways, comparable to civil disobedience and the sit-down strike. The *aggressive type,* although deeply dependent beneath the surface, is reactively hostile and provocative. A few words will be sufficient to describe each of these three types.

[17] For two detailed case studies, see Cameron, N., and Magaret, A., *Behavior Pathology.* Boston: Houghton Mifflin, 1951, pp. 199–206.

[18] Cf. Frosch, J., and Wortis, S. B., "A contribution to the nosology of the impulse disorders," *Amer. J. Psychiat.,* 1954, *111,* 132–138.

[19] Michaels, J. J., "Character structure and character disorders," in Arieti, S. (Ed.), *American Handbook of Psychiatry.* New York: Basic Books, 1959, pp. 353–377.

(i) *Passive dependent type.* These persons seem to be helpless, indecisive and clinging, as though they were still small children. In spite of an underlying hostile attitude toward others, they avoid the show of aggression, appear fearful and timid, and shrink from situations expressing hostility. They appear to be frightened, angry grown-up babies.[20]

(ii) *Passive aggressive type.* These persons act out in their personal lives the principles of civil disobedience. Their passive aggression can be as infuriating to their associates as the sit-down strike is to employers. Civil disobedience and the sit-down strike were utilized by persons who felt badly used by authority figures against whom they could not employ violence without provoking the authority figures to violent countermeasures. Adults who are not actually in the same danger, but who are emotionally immature, may behave as though they actually were. They become sullen and stubborn, use inefficiency and procrastination to defeat their superiors, complain of bad treatment and tend to demoralize others. Underneath it all, these are fearful, anxious persons who treat authority, and even their equals, as though they were domineering tyrants.

(iii) *Aggressive type.* The aggressive persons in this group are fundamentally no less fearful and dependent than the others. Their aggression is purely reactive and defensive. It is more like that of a rebellious child or adolescent than of an adult. The aggression takes the forms familiar to anyone who has worked with rebellious children and adolescents. Sarcasm, provocative acts and talk, argumentativeness, competitiveness and demands for special attention are common components of the picture. Some of the members of this group seem constantly irritable, develop temper tantrums and become destructive with relatively little provocation. Often they seem to encourage others to retaliate. Some individuals are ambitious and some indulge in grandiose daydreams.

The fact that these persons are not actually adolescent, and that they seem to persist in their reactive aggressive behavior no matter what others do, makes them difficult problems for their adult associates and for authority figures.[21] It is probable that a great many of these and some of the previously discussed types are paranoid or schizoid personalities. It would be instructive to have follow-up studies made of these groups to see what happens to them as time goes on and their dependency needs and frustrations continue to grow.

Sociopathic Personality Disturbances

This group corresponds to what used to be called *psychopathic personality* and is now called *sociopathic personality disturbance* in the official classifica-

[20] For an interesting account of unmet dependent needs, see Josselyn, I., *The Happy Child.* New York: Random House, 1955.

[21] The overlapping of this group with the *antisocial personality* will be obvious in the next section. In our present state of ignorance, a clearer distinction does not seem warranted.

tion. We have, however, excluded sexual deviations and the addictions because, as Cleckley has pointed out,[22] these disorders are not necessarily related in actual clinical cases. The *sociopathic personality* seems unable to learn, that is, to profit by his experiences, in certain areas of interpersonal relationship. He may be of average or superior intelligence. Yet he repeatedly acts out in such a way as to invite social ostracism and often legal prosecution, without being able to change his impulsive behavior. As a rule the sociopathic person cannot fully realize that what he does is socially wrong or dangerous, or that he has any responsibility to society to control his behavior.

It is common experience among therapists who work in this field to find the sociopathic person expressing apparently deep remorse and sincere good intentions, only to repeat what he has just been reprimanded or punished for, as though his remorse and sincerity were pure sham. Sometimes his expressions are sham, often they are not. When they are not, the sociopath seems to have conscious, but shallow and fleeting, feelings of remorse and good intentions. He cannot, however, control unconscious impulses to repeat what he has been repeating, regardless of his words and the punishment inflicted upon him. The exasperation that others feel over this apparent deception is easy to understand. Even experts in this field often express exasperation in their clinical reports. Sometimes this is what the patient wants the therapist and others to feel. Their defeat and despair are his strange triumph and revenge.[23]

During the nineteenth century there was a great deal of interest in the persons we now call sociopathic. They were stigmatized a century ago as moral imbeciles or as being morally insane. These names were intended to distinguish between intellectual deficit and moral deficit. In harmony with prevailing conceptions at that time, the sociopath was considered to be suffering from an inborn, incurable character defect which nothing could modify. The original change of terminology to *psychopathic personality* was intended to escape the implication of moral condemnation, which is foreign to modern psychiatry. Unfortunately the old conviction that the disorder was innate and unmodifiable clung to the new name and has persisted down to the present time. In once again changing the name, to *sociopathic,* we have reasons for hoping that the old pessimism may lift since, as we shall see in a moment, a beginning has been made toward understanding the dynamics underlying adult sociopathic distortions.[24]

It should be said at the outset that current psychotherapy and psycho-

---

[22] Cleckley, H., "Psychopathic states," in Arieti, S. (Ed.), *American Handbook of Psychiatry.* New York: Basic Books, 1959, pp. 567–588.

[23] Cf. Karpman, B., *The Sexual Offender and His Offense.* New York: Julian Press, 1954.

[24] Cf. Albert, R. S., Brigante, T. R., and Chase, M., "The psychopathic personality: a content analysis of the concept," *J. gen. Psychol.,* 1959, *60,* 17–28; Painting, D. H., "The performance of psychopathic individuals under conditions of positive and negative partial reinforcement," *J. abnorm. soc. Psychol.,* 1961, *62,* 353–355.

analysis have little success in dealing with adults in this group. Nevertheless, it is worth reflecting that seventy years ago the neuroses were generally regarded as untreatable. Moreover, as the records show all too clearly, neurotic patients used to exasperate clinicians then in much the same way that sociopathic personalities do today. It is difficult for a therapist to tolerate situations in which therapeutic failure is so consistent and the disorder seems so completely irrational. It is also worth remembering that thirty years ago there were few who regarded psychotic patients as amenable to psychotherapy or psychoanalysis, and that today a great many psychiatrists are seeking occult physiological disturbances for the psychoses, just as a great many psychiatrists blamed physiological disturbances for the neuroses before psychodynamic therapy demonstrated the genetic and unconscious origins of neurotic symptoms which we all accept today.

When a gross distortion of organization turns out not to be explicable in terms of inheritance or the accidents of intrauterine life and birth traumata, the clinician and the research worker turn to the conditions of childhood which may have produced the adult distortion. We see this as established practice in research and clinical therapy when one deals with adult deformities of body structure. The aim of such work, of course, is to prevent the occurrence of the adult distortion.

This is the situation today with regard to sociopathic disturbances. Since the adult sociopath seems to be little benefitted by psychotherapeutic and psychoanalytic procedures, with few exceptions, we look to childhood conditions in the hope that these may be changed in such a way as to prevent the development of sociopathic distortions. Perhaps while progress is being made in this direction there may also be progress made in relation to helping the adult.

A major obstacle to therapeutic success is the patient's own attitude, especially when he insists that there is nothing wrong with him, that he does not need help and will not accept it. It has been said in this connection that you cannot sentence a person to psychotherapy. This obstacle is not limited, however, to the treatment of sociopathic persons. Every clinician sees patients who seem to do everything they can to make themselves worse. You cannot, for example, sentence a cardiac patient to keep his weight down or to rest and exercise as he should. Such problems are also psychological ones, and as every practitioner knows they can defeat both therapist and patient.

Within these limitations, optimism has been aroused in the last two decades by the new light shed upon conditions in childhood which seem responsible for adult sociopathic distortions. This new light has come from the simultaneous psychotherapeutic — in some patients psychoanalytic — treatment of parent and child. The therapeutic advances have been definite but modest; the therapeutic understanding which the clinicians have gained has been great. As one worker in this field has put it, "The genesis of some of the human characteristics included in the definition of psychopathic personality (sociopathic personality) is no greater mystery than other syndromes in psychopathology."[25] He goes on to say that when both parent and offending child are studied therapeutically at the same time it is almost always possible to reconstruct the chief dynamics involved. In actual cases studied, the more significant parent — usually but not always the mother — has been observed encouraging amoral or antisocial behavior in the child without consciously realizing it. Evidently the neurotic needs of the parent — domineering, dependent, hostile or erotic — were finding vicarious gratification in the child's behavior.

In some cases reported, a parent showed unmistakable relish while the child was telling the therapist about his misdeeds, as though the recital were pleasurably wicked, but once the tale was told the parent turned immediately moralistic and condemned it and the child. In some instances the parent egged the child on with his story, supplying hints and missing bits of information which he or she had been treasuring up. In still others, the parent said angrily or shouted what the child was not to do, often thereby suggesting something which the child had not thought of doing. In one case, the child reporting alone to the therapist said, "That's what she *wants* me to do!" In another, both parents openly enjoyed and laughed about the petty thefts and lawbreaking of their children, but could not understand how these children, grown to adolescence, could possibly commit delinquent crimes showing disregard for other people's safety and property.[26]

The questions posed by these and many other studies and observations seem directly concerned with adult sociopathic personality disturbances in which some distortion interferes with the integration of ego-superego standards. How is a child who has openly ambivalent and often unconsciously corrupting parents to develop consistent ego and superego attitudes himself? Early in life the significant parent or both parents must be the main sources of identification, and therefore the chief determinants of his personality structure. Faced with such inconsistent, ambiguous or even corrupting attitudes, how is the child to know which he shall internalize, or whether to internalize them all? Every child, early in life, has only parental approval and disapproval, parental love and parental rejection, to guide him in what he selects. If a significant parent, while perhaps voicing strong disapproval, at the same time shows so much relish that even strangers pick it up, what can he or she expect of the child who inevitably senses both? When, for example, a parent insists upon hearing every detail of a misdeed, listens with rapt attention, and then angrily condemns the child, what sort of confusion does this introduce into the child's perception of reality. Early in life children are especially sensitive to unconscious attitudes, which often strike them with a clarity denied to adults. If these are furtively corrupting, the child

[25] Szurek, S., "Notes on the genesis of psychopathic trends," *Psychiatry*, 1942, 5, 1–6.

[26] Johnson, A. M., "Sanctions for superego lacunae of adolescents," in Eissler, K. R. (Ed.), *Searchlights on Delinquency*. New York: Internat. Univ. Press, 1949, pp. 225–245; Redl, F., and Wineman, D., *The Aggressive Child*. Glencoe, Ill.: Free Press, 1957; Cloward, R. A., and Ohlin, L. E., *Delinquency and Opportunity: A Theory of Delinquent Gangs*. Glencoe, Ill.: Free Press, 1960.

will probably be corrupted. Like his parent, he may himself come to condemn verbally what he secretly and perhaps unconsciously enjoys. Another possibility, which we see actualized in some sociopathic personality disturbances, is that as a child grows up in such an atmosphere, he becomes unable to take any social injunction seriously and even fails to establish any stable emotional relationship.[27]

At first glance it may seem that the two opposed forces present in the ambiguous behavior of a parent are about equal. This may be true objectively. But we must remember that when a small child is forming his basic identifications he is at the same time struggling with forbidden impulses and fantasies from within. Shall he go along with these asocial or antisocial impulses and fantasies or shall he resist them? What is reality saying to him from the outside, an "outside" which he scarcely recognizes as separate from himself? When there is no unified superego, and while the superego is still rudimentary or immature, the child needs a lot of outside help in handling the powerful impulses of the moment. He needs help that is unambiguous, clearcut and without anxiety or ulterior motive. At such a time the child is testing reality, constructing his world and constructing a social self within himself. If he is confronted by grossly inconsistent, ambiguous or corrupting identification models, he can hardly escape constructing his world and himself in distorted ways. All this we have known for a long time. It remained for the simultaneous study of the child offender and the parent to reveal actual observation confirming such interrelationships.

Theoretically, the child whose identification figures — the significant parents — are capricious, inconsistent or emotionally neglectful should grow into adulthood with irresponsible or emotionally shallow and meaningless attitudes toward others. This picture we actually see in many sociopathic personalities. If a child receives verbal rebukes and nonverbal encouragement for acting out his nonsocial and antisocial impulses or fantasies — and every little child experiences such impulses and fantasies — we should expect theoretically that he would grow to be an adult who says all the right things and does all the wrong ones. This, also, we know to be a leading characteristic of many sociopathic personalities.

If, after a child's nonsocial and antisocial acting out is covertly encouraged and vicariously enjoyed by a parent, the child is suddenly punished when the parent realizes what is happening, he is likely to grow up not only inconsistent or antisocial but also with a deep resentment toward authority figures in general.

If, as happens perhaps more often in sexual deviation than in sociopathic personality disturbance, a parent unconsciously or consciously seduces a child in the direction of acting out forbidden impulses and fantasies, and repeatedly frustrates the child, the child may be expected to develop serious superego defects as well as deep resentment. There are cases among socio-

[27] Cf. Knight, J. A., "Acting out through the child," *Amer. J. Orthopsychiat.*, 1960, **30**, 422–423.

pathic personality disturbances in which the patient approves of everything he does, no matter what it is, and uses secondary processes mainly in providing rationalizations for whatever behavior is socially inacceptable. This is not delusional behavior, but it seems to be close to it.

The question is often raised as to why only one child in a family of several should grow up with a sociopathic personality disturbance. We could say, as we do also in relation to neuroses and psychoses, that in all genetic and dynamic development there is involved a multiplicity of factors. This is true; but some of the case studies of sociopathic disturbances in children have also shown that, for some as yet unknown reason, a whole family seems to select one child as the scapegoat. The child is chosen as the one to act out the forbidden impulses and fantasies of parents and siblings, while they may be able to enjoy vicariously what the scapegoat does without themselves experiencing responsibility or guilt for it.

This observation confirms others made especially in the family relationships of schizophrenic patients. Here, also, one child may seem to have been predestined from an early age to act out the delusional fantasies of a potentially psychotic parent, sometimes with the abetment of other siblings who call attention to anything strange about the selected child. Attempts at treating such a patient, grown to psychotic adulthood, are often met clinically by anxious resistance on the part of the parent. Sometimes the threat of recovery in the patient precipitates a parental crisis, in some cases amounting to an outspoken psychosis. Once more, we find that there are comparisons possible at genetic and dynamic levels between sociopathic personality disturbances and the neuroses and psychoses. Such a relationship is likely in the future to stimulate further efforts at finding suitable therapy for sociopathic personality disturbances.

We shall turn now to a descriptive account of sociopathic personality disturbances. Classification within the group is highly unsatisfactory, in part because we do not understand these disturbances well, in part because in the past they have been comparatively neglected by dynamically oriented therapists, just as used to be the case with the psychoses. The three types we shall distinguish are not dynamically established. They are merely descriptive subgroups whose characteristics to a large degree overlap.

Irresponsible and emotionally shallow sociopathic personalities

In this subgroup we include persons who seem incapable of assuming adult responsibilities, who pursue goals of immediate gratification, without regard for social demands or the rights and feelings of other persons. They typically find the self-discipline necessary for the attainment of a stable social status distasteful, and whatever they find distasteful they experience as intolerable. They strike others as lacking in conscience, or at least in a dependable conscience, and for this reason acquaintances become wary of them in self-defense. In a society that depends heavily upon the personal integrity of individuals these persons pose a grave threat because they feel free to enter into agreements, or to benefit from situations of mutual trust, with no compunctions whatever about violating agreements and trust.

Some of these persons seem emotionally warm and attractive. They may be good talkers who inform themselves superficially on a number of topics, so that they are entertaining to others and come to be respected for what appears to be a cultured background. This kind of thing is all the easier for them to attain since they actually do approve of what they say and do. They accept themselves at face value. Because of the defects in identification, about which we have spoken earlier, these irresponsible and emotionally shallow persons lack adequate ego-superego structure for a stable, dependable personality, and for meaningful emotional relationships with others. Their sense of reality remains arrested at an infantile level where impulse and fantasy are as important as social demands, or even more important.

Some irresponsible sociopathic personalities seem emotionally shallow. Nothing appears to involve them excepting their immediate desire for gratification, and even this desire often seems childish. Their emotional instability is usually much more obvious than in adults who appear emotionally warm but actually are not. The emotionally shallow person quickly abandons one interpersonal relationship for another without giving evidence that the sudden shift in apparent loyalty means anything to him. Like the emotionally warm, but superficial, irresponsible person, he is always able to rationalize what he does and to make it seem reasonable and just.

Irresponsible psychopathic personalities, whether superficially warm or not, make excessive demands upon other persons or upon society at large, without having the least empathy for others and without being able to understand why their demands are excessive and their performance defective. In some cases the irresponsibility, restlessness and shallow affect seem to come and go with unpredictable changes in general mood. Sometimes they are apparent only in certain special situations, for example, in relations to authority but not otherwise, or in relation to sexual partners but not to others. The general picture in irresponsible and emotionally shallow sociopathic personality disturbances is one of severe ego-superego distortion or of seriously arrested development in ego-superego relations. We have already indicated the probable dynamics of such defects in the preceding paragraphs.

Antisocial sociopathic personality reactions

Juvenile delinquents[28] and adult criminals, even habitual adult criminals, are by no means necessarily sociopathic personalities. The juvenile delinquent is often the understandable product of his social environment. He may have passionate stable loyalties toward other members of his group or

---

[28] Glueck, S., and Glueck, E., "Reflections on basic research in juvenile delinquency," *World ment. Hlth.*, 1960, *12*, 6–17.

gang, which itself may be the source of the delinquent's antisocial behavior. There are often high standards of morality or ethics within a gang which, even though they do not correspond to prevailing codes outside the gang and in adult life, nevertheless demonstrate a capacity for self-control and even self-sacrifice which seems remarkable in a social offender. Much the same can be said for the majority of criminals. They have embarked upon a way of life, often through accident, which brings them profit as an illegal industry. But if they recognize what they are doing, and the risks they run, they cannot be classified as sociopathic personalities. After all, the successful political rebellions which we see almost everywhere today are carried on by persons who knowingly break the law and challenge established authority, just as did our own patriots two centuries ago. These are not the persons whom we identify as sociopathic personalities.

Antisocial reactions occur in sociopathic personalities for different reasons. The reasons are much the same as those which we have already discussed for irresponsible and emotionally shallow sociopaths; but the typical antisocial reaction is neither feckless nor unemotional. On the contrary, it is often a deeply emotional rebellion against authority which owes its intensity and persistence to its origins in the childhood family life.[29] Its defects, the failures to profit by experience or to circumvent the law, and the overall appearance of defiant hatred, even to those who offer help, are marks left by the betrayals suffered in childhood within the family, by the lack of stable, dependable, protecting identification models in the parents.[30]

The antisocial sociopathic adults who present an especially difficult challenge are those who, in spite of an apparently favorable environment, show a progressive inability to control and channel their aggressive impulses. They seem incapable of utilizing their aggression in the service of socially acceptable initiative and competitive achievement. As with the irresponsible persons discussed above, they are unable to take the role of other persons, to see themselves even approximately as others see them, or to understand why others treat them as they do. Some continue as offenders against the law, without profiting as much from their activities as they would by legal means, because they are unable to empathize with other persons and understand society and its laws as attempts to organize against the laws of the jungle. They also rationalize their behavior by the use of secondary process reasoning. It must be confessed that the daily newspaper recounts not only crimes, but also antisocial statements from persons who consider themselves leaders of society. What the effect of such reporting may have upon the potential antisocial sociopathic personality it is impossible to judge.

The crimes committed by antisocial sociopathic personalities are the same

[29] Witmer, H. L., and Kotinsky, R. (Eds.), *New Perspectives for Research on Juvenile Delinquency."* Washington, D.C.: U.S. Child. Bur. Pub., 1956, No. 356.

[30] Cf. Bennett, I., *Delinquent and Neurotic Children: A Comparative Study with One Hundred Case Histories.* New York: Basic Books, 1960; Glaser, D., Grant, J. D., and Wilkins, L., *Research and Potential Application of Research in Probation, Parole and Delinquency Prediction.* New York: New York School Soc. Work, 1961.

as those commmitted by others. They include all manner of crimes of violence, embezzlement, forging and swindling. What distinguishes them is the lack of feeling which the criminal shows toward his victim and toward himself as having committed a crime. He justifies and rationalizes what he has done, not as a chance he has taken, but as something laudable for which he is being mistreated. Just as it is difficult to draw a clear-cut line between the normal and the neurotic or psychotic, and between the neurotic or psychotic and the irresponsible psychopathic personality, so also it is hard to distinguish sometimes between the sociopathic antisocial personality and the criminal and, for that matter, between the criminal and the law-abiding citizen who cheats on income taxes and smuggles luxuries into his country. The extremes are easy enough to recognize apart, and for these we have abundant case material in the studies of juvenile delinquency.

Dissocial sociopathic personality reactions

This group provides a place for individuals who are in a sense the victims of an abnormal human environment, and who are capable of strong loyalties and deep emotional attachments within such an environment. They typically come into conflict with prevailing social and moral codes because these codes differ from the ones according to which they have learned to live. Thus a child brought up in one subculture, who has identified in its terms, might become sociopathic in relation to another subculture because its demands are ones with which he is unfamiliar or to which he is actively opposed. This is in part the dilemma presented in our country by recent mass migrations. The migratory adults rear their children according to standards of conduct which were acceptable in the cultures from which they have migrated, but are not acceptable in the new one. Even more common than this, however, is the migratory parent who cannot understand the ways of the new environment and offers nothing in the way of a useful identification model to the child. Both the parent and the child may react to their disappointments in the hardships and the discriminations they experience in their new haven as if the new environment were a sadistic, corrupting parent. The major difference to be expected in the dissocial reaction, as compared with the antisocial and the irresponsible or emotionally shallow personality, is that the dissocial reaction will usually respond favorably to environmental changes, whereas the others usually require a more thoroughgoing personality change before they can learn to adapt to the realities of social living.

Sexual Deviations

Sexual deviations are tied up in the public mind with degeneracy, violence and antisocial reactions. This linkage does occur, as the lurid accounts in newspapers and weekly magazines testify, but at least in Western culture it is a rare exception. By far the majority of sex deviants are neither degenerate nor antisocial. Most of them tend to be basically timid rather than violent. Cross-cultural studies report that many forms of deviant sexuality appear in religious observances and pubertal initiation among preliterate societies today, and that in ancient times they were sometimes encouraged socially among the precursors of Western culture.[31]

The typical sex deviant in our culture today is an emotionally immature person whose sexual development has been arrested or distorted early in life. Often he has been exposed as a young child to conscious or unconscious seduction by an older child or an adult long before his own sexual development had reached a mature genital level. Often he seems not to have been exposed to seduction but to have suffered an arrested or distorted sexual development because of intense childhood anxiety. In both arrested and distorted developments there has been a childhood fixation which has interfered with later maturational sequences and left the child to grow into an adult sex deviant. During early adolescence, when an upsurge of sex drive normally occurs, distortions originating in early childhood may be reactivated and grow into a fixed pattern that persists into adulthood as a perversion. Thus the adolescent or adult sex deviant, like the neurotic and the psychotic person, is a product of childhood maldevelopment.

Sexual deviations or perversions are patterns of sex behavior which do not culminate in heterosexual intercourse when this outcome is permissible and objectively possible. Some deviants prefer sex relations with persons of their own sex when members of the opposite sex are available. Others find their major sources of sexual gratification in activities that are only a part of the foreplay in normal intercourse, for example, exhibiting and sexual looking. Still others become sexually excited by contact with an inanimate thing, such as a shoe, instead of a live person. Some seek to identify with the opposite sex by dressing like them without being homosexual. Others derive sexual pleasure from sadism or masochistic suffering, or from both, apparently because of fixation in infantile misinterpretations of masculine aggression and feminine submission in adult sex relationships. In all of these deviations the elimination of a reciprocal partner of the opposite sex robs the deviant of many of the most significant emotional experiences of normal adult life, to say nothing of the dangers to which they expose him if he comes into conflict with the law. Something will be said about probable genetic and dynamic origins when we describe each deviation by itself.

Although much has been made in the literature of departures from normal sex intercourse, both cross-culturally and in relation to ancient precursors of Western civilization, the trend has always been overwhelmingly in the

---

[31] Friedman, P., "Sexual deviations," in Arieti, S. (Ed.), *American Handbook of Psychiatry.* New York: Basic Books, 1959, pp. 589–613; Lorand, S., and Balint, M. (Eds.), *Perversions: Psychodynamics and Therapy.* New York: Random House, 1956.

direction of condemning sex deviation as immoral and unnatural. Judaic, Christian and Moslem scriptures have for centuries proscribed homosexuality and intercourse with animals. During medieval times these were punishable by death. The Napoleonic code abolished punishment for sexual deviation, provided that minors were not seduced and public decency was not offended. This general attitude apparently prevails legally in most European countries. In the United States homosexual relations constitute a serious crime, regardless of the circumstances, although female homosexuality is looked upon with much greater leniency than male. Almost all sex deviations are condemned by United States law if they are practiced in public. In some states the elements of normal heterosexual foreplay are considered to be crimes, even when practiced in private by a married couple. Since legal proscription is an expression and a determinant of public cultural attitudes in a country, it must be taken into account as a part of social reality which demands personal adaptation.

Freud long ago formulated sexual deviation, or perversion, as the opposite of neurosis because he believed at the time that sex offenders acted out their conflicts and fantasies without suffering anxiety, just as many sociopathic personalities seem to do. Further clinical experience, however, convinced him that his earlier formulation applied only to a narrow range of conscious attitudes, and that sex deviants always suffer unconscious anxiety and often conscious or preconscious anxiety. He thus came to relate sex deviation to the castration complex, as a defense against forbidden sexual and aggressive impulses toward parents or siblings. He and subsequent writers have put sex deviations beside the common neuroses and psychoses, of which they are frequently a part.

Freud had always recognized the importance of seduction by older persons — real or fantasied, conscious or unconscious — in producing the fixations underlying sex deviations. In an important series of papers he added the possibility of a defensive origin, the defense operating in the absence of actual seduction.[32] An arrested or distorted sexual pattern may result, for example, from early childhood anxiety which forces the child to abandon an opposite-sexed parent or sibling as his sex object, and leads him to select a person of the same sex who seems less dangerous. Such anxiety may instead make a child regress to sadistic and masochistic fantasies, fixate him in some sexual interest normal to early childhood (such as looking, peeping or exhibiting), lead him to substitute an inanimate object as his sexual fetish, or make him identify with members of the opposite sex and try to be as much like them as possible.

In turning now to a description of sexual deviations, whose name is legion, we shall confine ourselves to the most common ones, and to those which show a minimum of other neurotic and psychotic manifestations. These common deviations are: (1) *overt homosexuality;* (2) *genital ex-*

[32] See the panel discussion, Arlow, J. A., "Perversions: theoretical and therapeutic aspects," *J. Amer. Psychoanal. Ass.,* 1954, 2, 336–345.

hibitionism; (3) *voyeurism* or *sexual looking;* (4) *fetishism;* (5) *transvestism;* and (6) *sadomasochism.* Often a combination of two or more deviations appears in one person; but often only one seems to be present. Since, as we have already implied, sexual deviation always involves some reality distortion, at conscious, preconscious or unconscious levels, neurotic symptoms often complicate the clinical picture, and occasionally psychotic phenomena appear. In our descriptions we shall largely ignore these combinations and complications so as to present relatively clear pictures.

1. Overt homosexuality

Among contemporary civilizations the most common sex deviation seems to be that of overt homosexuality. Historians report that it has been a serious problem for thousands of years, in Western, oriental and African societies. Students of preliterate societies find it among many contemporary primitive cultures. In some of these it plays a part in religious ceremonies or in the privileges accorded a chief. Sometimes it is accepted as an inevitable phase of maturing; sometimes it is severely condemned.[33] It has been observed as a frequent aberration among subhuman mammals.[34]

In spite of all these sources of information, overt homosexuality is still little understood by contemporary psychopathologists, and still less by laymen. Homosexuality in women is regarded by the average layman as a harmless joke. In men it is treated as a serious crime. The law in general accepts the layman's view, perhaps because it is less ambiguous than the opinions of experts.

Neither the attitudes of laymen nor those of the law are justified by available facts. Even though there is disagreement about other points among experts, they all agree that homosexuality is a form of psychopathology which is not "degenerate" and probably not congenital. Whether or not homosexual persons themselves regard their sex orientation as normal is beside the point. Most sex deviants look upon their anomalies as "natural," simply because they have always had them as long as they can remember. Homosexuality becomes a crime, socially considered, when it is practiced in public and offends others for this reason, and when it is used to seduce children or young adolescents. When it merely arouses anxiety or anger in unconsciously ambivalent adults, the question again becomes one of psychopathology, not only in the homosexual person, but also in the emotionally ambivalent one.

One reason for the relative paucity of accurate information about this common deviation is that homosexual persons who are satisfied with their

---

[33] Bieber, I., *et al. Homosexuality: A Psychoanalytic Study of Male Homosexuals.* New York: Basic Books, 1962; Wiedemann, G. H., "A survey of psychoanalytic literature on overt male homosexuality," *J. Amer. Psychoanal. Ass.,* 1962, *10,* 386–410.

[34] Ford, C. S., and Beach, F. A., *Patterns of Sexual Behavior.* New York: Harper, 1951.

way of life do not seek therapy. Consequently, we are less likely to have them as patients than in the case of neuroses and psychoses. Another is the not unjustified fear of exposure and legal reprisal, which does not hang over neurotic and psychotic persons. That we lack both accurate knowledge and personal objectivity in relation to overt homosexuality, especially in males, becomes obvious in such contemporary documents as the *Wolfenden Report,* made public in Great Britain in 1957.[35] This semiofficial document has been characterized as being marred by confused, contradictory, naive and vengeful statements. These in themselves may reflect unclear and conflict-ridden thinking. It is remarkable that none of the members chosen for this committee seems to have been an expert in the special field being investigated, and that apparently no effort was made by the committee to obtain expert testimony.

A source of added confusion in this area is that the proposition is widely accepted in the current literature to the effect that everyone has *latent* homosexual trends. In the vast majority of adults, however, there is no threat of overt homosexual action. The trend seems not to appear even in the great majority of manifest dreams, fantasies and daydreams. It may be that our difficulty in understanding overt homosexuality is in part a product of our successful ego defenses against latent unconscious trends. Ego defenses which are only partially successful may account for the exaggerated anxiety and anger which some adults show with regard to homosexuality, and for the openly seductive behavior of a small minority of law enforcement officers.

Technically, we speak of overt homosexuality when an adult prefers sex relations with his or her own sex, in spite of the availability of potential partners of the opposite sex. By common consent, we except adults who are barred for long periods from association with the opposite sex. We also except young adolescents who experiment homosexually but do not develop overt homosexual trends in adulthood. We except young children whose sex play among their peers is sometimes more or less indiscriminate.

A note on the therapy of overt homosexual persons is in place at this point. The prevailing attitude today is that unless a homosexual adult is unhappy over his plight, or is also suffering from neurotic anxiety which makes him want to change, there is little use in undertaking therapy aimed at helping him to become heterosexual. Therapy in this, as in other sex deviations, has had only moderate success, probably because the patient has accepted his deviation nearly all his life as an essential part of him. It is experienced, in other words, as *ego-syntonic* and not as *ego-alien.* A change in so fundamental an orientation is likely to be time-consuming and effortful even for those who voluntarily seek it. Bieber *et al.* report, for example, that only two of twenty-eight such patients, psychoanalytically

35 Wolfenden Report on Homosexuality, Report of the Committee on Homosexual Offences and Prostitution, in Allen, C., and Berg, C., *The Problem of Homosexuality.* New York: Citadel, 1958.

treated, became heterosexual in fewer than 150 hours of analysis, and only nine of forty who had between 150 and 349 hours of psychoanalysis became heterosexual.[36]

Although theories about the origins of adult overt homosexuality have been developed from limited biased samples, they are all that we have to go on at the present time. Our discussion of them will be brief.

Anatomical and physiological hypotheses. True hermaphroditism, that is, the presence in the same individual of the genitalia of both sexes, is such a rarity that it contributes nothing to an understanding of homosexuality. In past decades it used to be popular to emphasize anomalies in secondary sex characteristics — in body form, muscularity, hair distribution, voice pitch, etc. — but these also have no significant bearing on the problem. The same anomalies are just as common, if not commoner, among normally heterosexual adults. Moreover, the majority of overt homosexual adults appear to be anatomically normal males or females, both as to genital development and as to secondary sex characteristics.

When it comes to sex hormones the situation is more complex. Normal males secrete estrogen, a female sex hormone, as well as testosterone, and normal females secrete testosterone, a male sex hormone, as well as estrogen. No correlation has been found between the amount of opposite-sex hormone secreted by an individual and his choice of sex object. Moreover, in spite of sporadic claims to the contrary, attempts to treat overt homosexuality by means of hormone administration have been uniformly unsuccessful. A great deal of experimental study is going on at the present time with regard to sex determination in the genes of sperm and ovum; but nothing has yet appeared to throw light upon homosexuality in the human being.

Psychodynamic hypotheses. Overt homosexuality has been receiving increased attention within recent years among therapists with psychodynamic training. Although progress has been slow and controversy great, a few solid gains have been made, which we shall sketch here.

Until Freud's early papers[37] appeared it was generally assumed that heredity was the decisive factor, that an inborn disposition was paramount in the etiology of homosexuality. Freud himself never gave up the possibility that a constitutional predisposition might be an etiological factor in the development of homosexuality; but in the decades that followed he placed more and more emphasis upon psychodynamic factors. He eventually abandoned his original formulation of perversions or sex deviations as the negatives of neuroses, but retained his observation that homosexual

[36] Bieber, I., *et al.*, *Homosexuality: A Psychoanalytic Study of Male Homosexuals.* New York: Basic Books, 1962.

[37] Freud, S., "Three essays on the theory of sexuality," (1905), Standard Edition, 1953, vol. 7.

adults show a predominance of archaic mechanisms.[38] These have been more recently re-emphasized and made specific.[39]

Contemporary trends have laid particular stress upon pre-edipal phases of development without losing sight of the important role of edipal conflicts or of the later reactivation of infantile impulses during pubertal and early adolescent identity crises. The role of narcissistic choice of love object, which Freud was the first to recognize, has also received general acceptance among the chief etiological factors. The homosexual adult thus may love himself as he sees himself in others of his own sex, trying to repeat the situation in which he was loved by his mother, from whom he cannot detach himself. The sex deviation may be a remnant of a person's infantile sexuality, which he experiences as ego-syntonic and uses defensively against separation fears, castration fears, and fears of merging again symbiotically with the mother. The last-named fear is one that we have met in schizophrenic reactions, the fear of disappearing or ceasing to exist as a person.

As might be expected in dealing with anything as nonspecific as homosexuality, a number of different situations have been found to be effective in the background of different patients. Failures to resolve the early symbiotic relationship with the mother not only lead to primitive defensive and adaptive maneuvers but also interfere with optimal resolution of edipal conflicts later on. There are such obvious forms of deprivation and seduction as rearing a boy among females, dressing him as a girl and treating him as one. Less obvious are instances of powerful identification with the mother, which Freud also emphasized, in which the boy feels himself to be a part of his mother, or internalizes her image as a dominant part of himself.

The complexity of the childhood interrelationships can be illustrated by the way in which opposite conditions seem to produce similar deviations. Thus, *if a boy fears his father* so much that he cannot identify with him, he may also not dare to love *his mother or any other woman.* On the other hand, *if it is his mother who seems dangerous and frightening* to a boy, he may renounce *all women* as too frightening. In both instances the outcome may be homosexuality.

A child of either sex is likely to develop distortions in basic object relationships, including homosexuality, when the mother is strong and dominant in the home while the father is weak, ineffectual, or habitually neglectful of his children. A boy may be unable to identify with such a father and develop instead a feminine identification by default. A girl may be unable to take such a man as her love object. She may not only identify with her powerful mother but also take over her mother's attitudes of mascu-

[38] For a brief review of this development, see Socarides, C. W. (reporter), "Theoretical and clinical aspects of overt male homosexuality," *J. Amer. Psychoanal. Ass.,* 1960, 552–566. Also Socarides, C. W. (reporter), "Theoretical and clinical aspects of overt female homosexuality," *J. Amer. Psychoanal. Ass.,* 1962, 10, 579–592.

[39] Bychowski, G., "Homosexuality and psychosis," in Lorand, S., and Balint, M. (Eds.), *Perversions: Psychodynamics and Therapy.* New York: Random House, 1956, pp. 97–130.

line domination, thus making her unfit to play a normal feminine role. It must be emphasized, however, that such family constellations occur often in the background of neurotic and psychotic patients. We have as yet insufficient data to indicate why one of these three solutions — neurosis, psychosis or sex deviation — is "chosen" unconsciously in some cases and another solution is "chosen" in other cases.[40]

2. Exhibitionism

Genital exhibitionism is almost exclusively confined to men. It is a post-pubertal and usually a post-marital phenomenon. Typically an exhibitionist compulsively shows his genitals to young women or mature women in a public place, such as a street, a park or a doorway, sometimes in a bus, a train, a plane or a shop. This may be repeated several times in a single day, each time with great anxiety on the part of the exhibitionist.[41] It is often said that he does this to stimulate women to do the same, either to see if they have male genitals or to reassure himself of his own intactness. This may be the basic unconscious motivation. The exhibitionist himself usually maintains that he is not interested in looking, but only in being seen. Such a claim suggests a basic narcissism.

Most exhibitionists seem to be sexually inhibited and timid. Some have an unexplained tendency to spy upon and betray other exhibitionists, a tendency which may have its origin in narcissistic rivalry and enmity or indicate unconscious homosexual trends. Some appear to have a need to be caught, but when this happens the person seems bewildered and is unable to explain his behavior. Legal punishment is reported to have no effect.

The psychodynamic origins of genital exhibitionism are not clear. Castration anxiety and narcissism are the factors most often cited; and they appear obvious in the light of the patient's behavior. Also cited are free and easy genital exhibition in the home and an early intimate relationship with a girl. We are still in the dark as to this "choice" of deviation.[42] The normal sex curiosity in early childhood leads to mutual exhibitionism, as in the "doctor game," but this does not account for either the intense anxiety or the lack of interest in the woman as a sex object to whom the genitals are exhibited. Deep-seated personality disorders are indicated by the com-

[40] Fleischmann, O., "Comments on the 'choice of homosexuality' in males," *J. Amer. Psychoanal. Ass.*, 1960, *8*, 562–563. Similar seductions are reported by Johnson, A. M., "Etiology and therapy of overt homosexuality," *Psychoanal. Quart.*, 1955, *24*, 506–515; Bacon, C., "A developmental theory of female homosexuality," in Lorand, S., and Balint, M. (Eds.), *Perversions: Psychodynamic and Therapy.* New York: Random House, 1956, pp. 131–159.

[41] Christoffel, H., "Male genital exhibitionism," in Lorand, S., and Balint, M. (Eds.), *Perversions: Psychodynamics and Therapy.* New York: Random House, 1956, pp. 243–264.

[42] A case of seduction in the direction of *exhibitionism* is described in Litin, E. M., Giffin, M. E., and Johnson, A. M., "Parental influences in unusual sexual behavior in children," *Psychoanal. Quart.*, 1956, *25*, 37–55.

bination of an unusual form of aggression with timidity, of a general sexual inhibition with anxious public acting out, and of the betrayal of others to the police with impulses to be caught. Some clinicians regard the exhibitionst as fixated in the phallic phase of development. It is certainly true that small boys sometimes unexpectedly show their penis to visitors; but when they do, it is with a naive pride, not with anxiety. The rarity of exhibitionism in women may be related to genital differences, as well as to the fact that it is considered normal in our culture for women to call attention to their secondary sex characteristics through their way of dressing — e.g., the breasts, hips, figure and smooth skin. Even in the strip tease the performer is less likely to be considered pathological than the watchers.

3. Voyeurism

We speak of voyeurism when a person obtains his major sexual gratification, sometimes his sole sexual gratification, through looking at the sexual organs, the naked body conformation or the sexual activities of others. Male voyeurs are usually inhibited sexually, and often impotent, but nearly always heterosexual as regards their object. One of the commonest forms is that of a man peeping at women who are undressed or undressing as, for example, in women's dormitories. As an unwarranted invasion of personal privacy it leads typically to police action. The Lady Godiva legend, with its naked woman riding through the streets and its furtive "peeping Tom" who spies on her, is a folklore assertion of the right of a woman to exhibit, if her cause is a good one, and the universal condemnation of the voyeur.

The psychodynamics of voyeurism are probably similar to those of exhibitionism. The voyeur, like the exhibitionist, remains fixated at an infantile level. Sexual looking is certainly related to the normal sex curiosity of small children, both as regards one another and as regards the primal scene, that is, the observation of parental intercourse. Freud pointed this out more than half a century ago;[43] and even the biblical equation of sexual looking with adultery made two thousand years ago was not new then. Sexual looking and sexual display are normal precursors of adult sex intercourse, not only in mature human beings but in other mammals.[44] It is only when they become major or sole sources of sexual satisfaction, which do not lead to heterosexual intercourse, that we call them sex deviations. Within recent years there has been an increased interest in the aggressive, sadistic components of sex deviations. Thus, for example, the intrusive attacking characteristics of both exhibitionism and voyeurism are worth considering in any attempt to evaluate exhibitionists and voyeurs.

[43] Freud, S., "Three Essays on the theory of sexuality," Standard Edition, 1953, vol. 7, pp. 125–244.
[44] Ford, C. S., and Beach, F. A., *Patterns of Sexual Behavior*. New York: Harper, 1951.

4. Fetishism

Fetishism gets its name from the use of some special and usually in-animate object in the religious practices of preliterate (primitive) societies which ascribe power, comfort or welfare to the magical object or fetish. Sex deviants in our culture similarly use something, usually inanimate, as their sexual object instead of using a sex partner; or they require that such an object be present for sexual intercourse to proceed. Fetishists are nearly always men; and their commonest fetish is a woman's shoe. This choice has been variously explained in the past (*a*) as the object last seen in the frustrated sex curiosity of small children, an interpretation that certainly does not apply to modern women as it might have in the nineteenth century; (*b*) as a mere exaggeration of the lover's attachment to something worn by his beloved; (*c*) as the expression of a masochistic wish to be trod upon; and (*d*) as a female symbol that also enclosed the foot as a masculine symbol. Fetishists may be predominantly asexual, interested only in their chosen inanimate object, or heterosexual but with the pathological demand that the fetish be present as a condition for successful intercourse.

As in other sex deviations, the origins of fetishism are still obscure. Fetishism does have normal counterparts which, while they do not account for the deviation, make it more understandable. There is, for example, the almost universal attachment of small children to teddy bears, dolls, blankets and the like — even to fragments of a blanket as it falls apart. Such normal fetishes seem to operate as sources of security, especially at bedtime when the child is left alone in the dark. The almost universal reliance of adults in all cultures upon charms, amulets and tokens has already been described in the chapter on obsessive compulsive reactions. But none of these uses appears to be primarily sexual. One of the most widely accepted hypotheses is that the fetish is a substitute for a sex partner, a substitute that makes no demands and is not in itself dangerous. Another is that some forgotten or repressed compulsive demand, originating in early childhood, asserts itself in the adult fetishist.

Current emphasis upon aggression in sex deviations calls to mind the braid cutters. Hair fetishism was long ago attributed by Freud[45] to an interest in the hair of the *mons veneris,* part of the external female genital, an interest in denying the absence of male genitalia in women.[46] The aggression is exhibited by those who lop off the braids of girls and women, especially in public conveyances where the fetishist aggressor can escape detection. Such aggression not only deprives the female of something that she prizes, something that is characteristically feminine in our culture; but it can also represent a symbolic castration, and thus a double vengeance, even though it is doubly irrational.[47]

[45] Freud, S., "Three Essays on the theory of sexuality," Standard Edition, 1953, vol. 7, pp. 125–244.

[46] Freud, S., "Fetishism," (1927), Standard Edition, 1961, vol. 21, pp. 149–166.

[47] Fenichel, O., *The Psychoanalytic Theory of Neurosis.* New York: Norton, 1945, p. 349.

5. Transvestism

The term *transvestism* means literally *cross-dressing*. In this deviation, gratification is obtained, or identification with the opposite sex is symbolized, by *wearing the clothes* of the opposite sex. Like fetishism, it is largely confined to males. Two exceptions need to be mentioned. We do not speak of transvestism when homosexual men wear women's clothes to attract ambivalent male sex partners, since cross-dressing is used in these circumstances, not for itself, but as a means toward homosexual ends. Neither do we speak of transvestism when normal women wear clothes which used to be considered masculine, such as slacks, blue jeans and shorts, as a matter of convenience. Within the past two decades, women have adapted these previously masculine garments in such a way that they do not detract from their femininity, but rather emphasize it.

There is general agreement that women who dress completely as men are usually homosexually inclined. There is a great deal of disagreement as to the status of men who dress in women's clothes. This may represent an actual heterogeneity among male transvestists or a lack of clear evidence. In a recent publication on sex behavior, for example, exactly opposite views are expressed about this question by different contributors, and with equal conviction. Some insist that all male transvestites must be homosexual; others are equally insistent that a majority of them are not. Allen, citing Stekel in support of his views, feels that transvestism is always a manifestation of homosexuality, but he modifies this statement with the observation that often this seems to shade off into narcissism.[48] Brown is equally positive that transvestists are almost always heterosexual, although also narcissistic, that they are not fetishists, and that most of them marry and have a family.[49]

A minority of male transvestists are also fetishists who can achieve full potency only while wearing some item of women's clothing. Some transvestists have brief compulsive episodes, during which they have an irresistible urge to wear clothing of the opposite sex, but appear the rest of the time to be normal. A few are so narcissistic that they have little or no interest in finding a sex partner. In this they resemble narcissistic, frigid, asexual women; and in fact some of them seem to have identified with such women.

The origins of transvestism are sometimes obvious, sometimes obscure. Since they usually go back as far as the preverbal phase of development, it may be necessary to rely upon the mother's memory, and not the patient's; and if the mother is responsible for the deviation she is likely to be a reluctant and an unreliable witness. Psychoanalytic interpretations stress

[48] Allen, C., "Sexual perversions," in Ellis, A., and Abarbanel, A. (Eds.), *The Encyclopedia of Sexual Behavior.* New York: Hawthorn Books, 1961, pp. 802–811.

[49] Brown, D. G., "Transvestism and sex-role inversion," in Ellis, A., and Abarbanel, A. (Eds.), *The Encyclopedia of Sexual Behavior.* New York: Hawthorn Books, 1961, pp. 1012–1022.

the importance of castration anxiety. Thus, for example, a male transvestist can identify with the childhood image of a phallic mother; but he need not imitate her object-choice, that is, he may still be attracted to women as love objects.

In the past it has often been asserted that transvestists have not been subjected to early seduction, that they represent in fact an *intersex*. Recent studies, however, in which parents and their children have been treated simultaneously, describe clear-cut cases of parental seduction, and regard parental pathology as the source of transvestism. Some mothers, for example, gave extra love to a son when he dressed as a girl. In some instances the boy was dressed as a girl and treated as one for several years, even to the point of complimenting him on looking "so pretty" in dresses. One transvestist in these studies stated that he had always regarded himself as a girl, even though at conscious levels he knew that he was not. Another tried to be as much as possible like his younger sister, because his mother expressed open preference for her daughter and disdain for her son. In some cases of transvestism, one or both parents had wanted a child of the opposite sex, and seemed to have encouraged the development of cross-dressing unconsciously as a fulfillment of their consciously remembered wish. Mothers of some transvestite boys in therapy express frank hatred of men.

Female transvestism, that is, the wearing of boys' and men's clothing that is not adapted to feminine appearance, is not only comparatively rare, but usually more obscure as to its origins than is the male form. Envy of boys may play a leading role; but envy of boys is extremely common among girls, whereas transvestism is rare. Parental sanctions must play an important part. This sometimes appears as a *mother's* pathological, vicarious pleasure in seeing her daughter look and behave in accordance with her own preconscious or unconscious wishes. Sometimes it stems from a *father's* disdain of women, and from his disappointment at not having a son with whom he can identify. Friedman has pointed out that female transvestism has more of a make-believe character than male, since wearing men's clothing cannot give a woman the illusion that she has male genitals. Latent homosexual trends have been invoked as an explanation for both male and female transvestism; but since it is also invoked to account for both neuroses and psychoses, it cannot explain the "choice" of this sex deviation.[50]

6. Sadomasochism

Sadism means sexual pleasure in inflicting pain, restriction or humiliation. *Masochism* means sexual pleasure in suffering it. *Sadism* is looked upon as fixation in an infantile misinterpretation and distortion of the *male role*

[50] Lukianowicz makes a distinction between transvestists and persons who desire and sometimes seek a change in sex organs. The latter he calls transsexualists. Lukianowicz, N., "Survey of various aspects of transvestism in the light of our present knowledge," *J. nerv. ment. Dis.*, 1959, *128*, 36–64.

in sex intercourse, which the adult as a child misinterpreted as a brutal attack. *Masochism* is looked upon as fixation in an infantile misinterpretation and distortion of the *female role*, which the adult as a child misinterpreted as pleasure in being cruelly attacked and physically injured. These attitudes take it for granted that the child has witnessed sexual intercourse in the parental bedroom (*primal scene*). Even today a large proportion of infants and small children sleep in the parental bedroom, where it is almost inevitable that they should witness parental intercourse.

Because sadistic and reciprocal masochistic attitudes, of abnormal intensity, are usually present in the same person — that is, if a person fantasies sadistic acts he also fantasies the masochistic experiences which they would arouse, and vice versa — the term *sadomasochism* is commonly used to designate this sex deviation. Even when sadism appears alone, the sadistic person seems to identify strongly with his victim; and where it is masochism that prevails, the masochist seems to experience pleasure in fantasying about what sadists do.[51]

We do not usually speak of *sadism* in connection with normal male aggression in sex relations, or of *masochism* in normal female submission and receptiveness. In theoretical discussions, however, these designations are frequently employed.[52]

Both sadism and masochism are traditionally interpreted as defenses against castration anxiety. The frequent presence of remnants of cross-identification, however, suggests the possibility of a still earlier origin. Simultaneous therapeutic study of parents and children have revealed some of the sources of sadomasochistic deviation;[53] and we have also discussed this briefly at the beginning of the section on *character disorders*. A recent paper interprets sadomasochism as basically *erotic*, rather than *aggressive*.[54] This eliminates the need for invoking the concept of instinctual or emotional drive defusion as an explanation.

Addiction

The term *addiction* is used nowadays to describe so many things that its meaning has been blunted. Thus, for example, we speak of addiction, not only to drugs, but indiscriminately to such things as golf, television and the movies, to food fads, gambling and racing, without being much concerned

[51] Patients whose prevailing conscious *fantasies* are *masochistic* sometimes report *sadistic dreams*; and some *sadistic* patients have *masochistic dreams*. Cf. Ruffler, G., "The analysis of a sadomasochist," in Lorand, S., and Balint, M. (Eds.), *Perversions: Psychodynamics and Therapy.* New York: Random House, 1956, pp. 209–230.

[52] Cf. Loewenstein, R. M., "Psychoanalytic theory of masochism," *J. Amer. Psychoanal. Ass.*, 1957, 5, 197–234. See also articles by Brenner, C., Bromberg, N., Bychowski, G., Eidelberg, L., and Blumstein on masochism in *J. Amer. Psychoanal. Ass.*, 1959, 7, 197–298.

[53] Johnson, A. M. and Szurek, S., "The genesis of antisocial acting out in children and adults," *Psychoanal. Quart.*, 1952, 21, 323–343.

[54] Gero, G., "Sadism, masochism and aggression: their role in symptom formation," *Psychoanal. Quart.*, 1962, 31, 31–42.

about our careless use of the word. This generalization has the advantage of calling attention to the close relationship between a pathological dependence upon specific chemical substances and an apparently incurable dependence upon certain activities, situations and people. It brings together the physiological, the cultural and the psychological. The generalization suffers from disadvantages also. It tends to equate many things which are fundamentally dissimilar, most of which yield easily to treatment. It distracts attention from certain forms of specific, self-perpetuating, asocial dependence, such as occur in alcoholism and in narcotic addiction.

With modern advances in chemistry the number of potential sources of chemical addiction has greatly increased. Nevertheless, two familiar forms still dominate contemporary thinking. One of these, by far the commonest of all, is not subject to effective legal restraint. The other is strictly controlled. Both involve physiological, cultural and psychological problems which remain unsolved. In what follows, we shall restrict discussion to these two, *chronic alcoholism* and *opiate addiction*, which present both society and the patient with quite different problems. Our discussion must of necessity be brief; but whole volumes have been devoted to them by experts,[55] and an internationally famous journal on alcoholism is on the shelves of most university libraries.[56]

Alcoholic addiction (chronic alcoholism)

Addiction to alcohol is an illness. It has been estimated that about four and a half million persons in the United States are alcohol addicts. The rate per 100,000 persons is half again as great as that reported for France, our nearest rival in this respect, two-and-a-half times as great as that given for our near northern neighbor, Canada, and almost four times as great as that for England, where the same language and many similar conventions prevail. Why? There is always, of course, the problem of accuracy in reporting, but probably no one in the United States conversant with alcoholism would question its importance. It was not until 1956 that the American Medical Association officially recognized it as an illness. The great majority of laymen, not only in this country but in many others, still vacillate between regarding alcoholism as a sin and regarding it as a joke. Why? Few who imbibe consider alcohol as an unmitigated evil; few who abstain do not.

[55] Cf. Jellinek, E. M., *Effects of Alcoholism on the Individual*. New Haven, Conn.: Yale Univ. Press, 1947; Jellinek, E. M., *Recent Trends in Alcoholism and Alcohol Consumption*. New Haven, Conn.: Hillhouse Press, 1947; Lindesmith, A. R., *Opiate Addiction*. Bloomington, Ind.: Principia Press, 1947; Wikler, A., *Opiate Addition*. Springfield, Ill.: Thomas, 1952; Gibbins, R. J., *Chronic Alcoholism and Alcoholic Addition*. Toronto, Can.: Toronto Univ. Press, 1953; Kruse, H. D. (Ed.), *Alcoholism as a Medical Problem*. New York: Hoeber, 1956; Thompson, G. N. (Ed.), *Alcoholism*. Springfield, Ill.: Thomas, 1956; Nyswander, M., *The Drug Addict as a Patient*. New York: Grune & Stratton, 1956; Himwich, H. E., *Alcoholism: Basic Aspects and Therapy*. Washington, D.C.: Amer. Ass. Adv. Sci., 1957.

[56] *Quarterly Journal of Studies on Alcohol*, 1939–date.

Nearly fifty years ago the people of the United States attempted to outlaw the use of alcohol by enacting a constitutional amendment. This attempt was direct and courageous; but because it was not accompanied by public re-education, nor by a full-scale study of an almost universal need for tranquilizers, in the face of universal human anxiety, the attempt was both unintelligent and irresponsible. After less than fifteen years another constitutional amendment was adopted to make alcohol available without restriction to everyone. Once more, no attempt was made at federal levels to study the problem of alcohol addiction, considered by many to be the greatest of all mental problems today. The futility of legislative prohibition in the face of a general opposition was fully demonstrated. It is generally conceded by students of crime today that the prohibition of alcohol in this country, which was almost universally flouted, gave immense financial resources to organized crime in the United States for the first time. Many of our major current problems stem from the immense fortunes amassed during this era and from the perfection of techniques of evasion and revenge. This is perhaps the greatest legacy of legislative prohibition and certainly its most evil and regrettable one. Let other nations who have not tried this courageous but unintelligent expedient point the finger. They may have shown more intelligence but less courage.

The problem of alcoholic addiction was largely ignored here during legal prohibition. It had been legislated out of existence. Nevertheless it remained with us as a fact of life and it is still with us. Although there have been and still are a great many able and devoted scientists working in this field the problem of chronic alcoholism remains virtually unsolved. It has been well said that the study of alcoholism requires research in physiological, cultural or socio-economic, and psychological fields.[57]

It will not help the average inexpert person to be given the details of physiological research related to alcoholic addiction. The variables involved, however important they may eventually turn out to be, are for the most part unfamiliar and unintelligible to any but specialists in the physiology of metabolism. Suffice it to say here that alcohol is almost unique in having instant metabolic effects of potentially far-reaching significance. One of the immediate effects of alcohol in most persons is to reduce anxiety — hence its almost universal use — to relieve hunger, and to alter the functioning of the brain, especially of the cerebral cortex.

To the changes in cortical function are ascribed such well-known immediate effects, if the dosage is small, as increased sociability and self-confidence, talkativeness, and a general sense of relaxation and well being. The effects of large dosages, at the time and on the next day, are also well known. One sees heavy drinking during the watching of television programs (which perhaps the emptiness of some programs promotes), at social

[57] See the concise review by Zwerling, I., and Rosenbaum, M., "Alcoholic addiction and personality (non-psychotic conditions)," in Arieti, S. (Ed.), *American Handbook of Psychiatry*. New York: Basic Books, 1959, pp. 623–644. This review also includes data from new and original studies.

gatherings such as the cocktail hour, in taverns, and sometimes on the street. The hangover experienced by heavy drinkers the next day is a common source of malaise, ill temper and inefficiency. It is significant that many surgeons, psychotherapists and psychoanalysts refuse alcohol during an evening that precedes a working day, because their profession demands a high degree of efficiency and concentration, a steady hand and an unclouded mind. All this, of course, is not a matter of addiction but of simple alcohol ingestion.

It is in the details of physiological change, especially when it comes to chronic alcoholism, that physiological complexities arise and controversy grows rife. There is no doubt that eventually brain changes develop in alcohol addiction; but it is not known if these changes come directly from the alcohol, from intermediate products of alcohol, or from damage to other organs, particularly to the liver. Serious and often fatal changes in the liver itself have been demonstrated in relation to alcoholism for many decades; but just how these come about, and what relation they have to general malnutrition, avitaminosis, disturbances in hormone production, and other metabolic deficiencies has not yet been worked out. Zwerling and Rosenbaum point out that disputes among physiologically-oriented research workers are as acrimonious as the disputes between them and the more psychodynamically-oriented research workers. Such bitter disagreement is hard for the layman to understand because he has an image of the cool, judicious scientist as his ideal model. Actually, the amount of personal involvement that scientific research demands, if one is to be a devoted, unselfish worker, makes a certain degree of personal bias inevitable. The cool, judicious unbiased scientist may be an ideal, but he is an impractical ideal.

The fact remains, whatever its ultimate interpretation, that alcohol can act as a magical tranquilizer in a world full of unconquerable anxieties. Its action is quick and sure, while adaptation by other means may be slow and uncertain. Alcoholic addiction seems to arise from the effects of alcohol upon the organism as a whole. It helps create internal conditions, including its local effects upon the gastrointestinal system, which can be most easily alleviated by drinking more alcohol. Thus, even within a physiological account, there are conditions sufficient for addiction.

The moment we stop to reflect, however, we find cultural or socio-economic influences at work. Among persons born in the United States, and living here all their lives, we find alcoholic addiction rare or absent among Moslems, Jews, Mormons and Chinese, but disproportionately frequent among persons of Irish descent. Since alcohol is equally available to all of these groups, and since there is a religious but not genuine ethnic difference between some of them, neither a strict physiological nor a strict psychological approach seems indicated. In all of them there seems to be an early influence, transmitted culturally, which contributes to attitudes as fundamental in human life as any metabolic factors. Thus, even among human beings with a built-in physiological potentiality for alcoholic addiction, we must take into account the effects of differences in subcultures within the United States. We have to find room for the fact that five times as many men as women become alcoholic addicts in our country.[58]

This brings us to psychological factors, that is, to questions of basic personality structure or character. As might be expected there is no general agreement as to what personality organization makes a person who belongs to a subculture that permits drinking more vulnerable to addiction than those around him. If there are four and a half million alcoholics in the United States, there are about seventy million adults who do not become addicted, even though alcohol is readily available. The alcoholic addict is most often characterized as an oral dependent person. The evidence for orality is obvious, since the alcoholic drinks his agent. But it is also true that the chronic alcoholic may be using alcohol to combat anxieties, conflicts and frustrations at any or all levels,[59] many of them similar to those facing the opium addict who does not take in his agent through the mouth. It has been suggested that persons who become addicted to alcohol may be incapable of developing neurotic, psychotic or psychosomatic structures. This is contradicted, however, by the clinical fact that alcoholism can be found among persons with any of the common neurotic, psychotic and psychosomatic disorders, or, for that matter, among most of the personality disorders described earlier in the present chapter.

A recent study suggests instead that a basic character disorder underlies alcoholic addiction, or chronic alcoholism, even though its symptomatological picture may vary considerably. This study finds that most of the alcoholics studied were *dependent, depressed, schizoid, hostile* and *sexually immature*.[60] These findings were the result of clinical studies. Psychological tests tended to support them. Separate perceptual tests, using Witkin's procedures, disclosed a unique pattern which was interpreted as a pervasive dependent attitude, but with a primitive insulating narcissism. The alcoholics studied were *field-dependent* when they had to manipulate an object in relation to a frame forming the *field;* but they were *field-independent* when it came to aligning their bodies with the pull of gravity, in the presence of indicators forming the field which contradicted gravity.[61]

These patients showed *passive-dependent* attitudes in relying irrationally upon external agents for care and security, and upon other people to satisfy

---

58 The factor of greater conformity among women is suggested by the fact that before narcotic addiction was made illegal, there were three female addicts for every male, whereas now their are four male addicts for every female addict. Cf. Nyswander, M., "Drug addiction," in Arieti, S. (Ed.), *American Handbook of Psychiatry.* New York: Basic Books, 1959, pp. 614–622.

59 Cf. Higgins, J. W., "Psychodynamics in the excessive drinking of alcohol," *Arch. Neurol. Psychiat.,* 1953, 69, 713–717.

60 Zwerling, I., and Rosenbaum, M., "Alcoholic addiction and personality," in Arieti, S. (Ed.), *American Handbook of Psychiatry.* New York: Basic Books, 1959, pp. 623–644.

61 Witkin, H. A., *et al., Personality through Perception.* New York: Harper, 1954. The concepts of *field-dependence* and *field-independence* are operationally defined in this reference.

their insatiable demands for food, love, comfort and acceptance. They looked upon the world passively, as determining their fate quite without regard for anything they themselves might do. Often there was a façade of aggressive vigilant activity in relation to the impulsive gratification of a wish or to protection against loss.

They were *depressed*, with basic attitudes of sadness and futility, self-depreciation and sometimes there were suicidal attempts. Many had a front of gaiety or joviality which seemed not directly related to the underlying depression.

These patients were also called *schizoid* because they seemed emotionally detached from others, with a sense of being aloof, separate, odd-man-out. At the same time a feeling of omnipotence might be expressed, such as that of being invulnerable. A *paranoid* concern with the motives of people close to them was also characteristic.

Pathological *hostility* appeared openly in some as an overwhelming rage during intoxication, in a few even when sober. Some who concealed and channeled their rage, even when drunk, had murderous dreams or hallucinations. Some felt sure, after a binge, that they had killed someone; one would give himself up to the homicide squad after a binge. The investigators thought that probably all the patients had self-destructive or self-loathing attitudes.

Sexual immaturity seemed to arise from a basic failure in masculine identification. Attitudes ranged from *reaction formation* which implied a feminine identification to open envy of women's lot. Sex behavior ranged from markedly reduced heterosexual activity to homosexual relationships. In view of the prevalent view that alcoholism is related to homosexual strivings, it is interesting that none of the forty-six patients studied was completely homosexual, and only one engaged in more homosexual than heterosexual activity.

This study has been cited in some detail because it is recent, because it has a psychodynamic approach, because it uses clinical interviews, psychological and perceptual tests, and physiological studies. The last-named suggested liver damage and the creation of physiological states which demanded more alcohol as relief. These are not new findings. The study is cited also because it does not indulge in name-calling and because its multi-discipline method seems to hold special promise.

No one doubts the damaging effect of excessive alcoholic intake upon the body, especially upon the brain, if it is long continued. The details of *delirium tremens* and of *alcoholic deterioration* are familiar to almost everyone in our urban communities. In turning now to opiate addiction we turn to a form of addiction which, according to one of the country's leading experts, does not lead to brain damage but does lead to extreme social deterioration and to crime, when crime is necessary to obtain the addictive drug.[62]

[62] Nyswander, M., "Drug addiction," in Arieti, S. (Ed.), *American Handbook of Psychiatry*. New York: Basic Books, 1959, pp. 614–622.

Opiate addiction

Among the opiates are included opium itself, morphine, heroin, codein and a number of minor opium derivatives which are addictive. Within recent years new synthetic drugs with most of the properties of morphine have been developed. They are addictive in much the same way. Government regulation of the use of opiates was begun in 1914. It has been stringent and its application has been extended to the newer synthetic morphine equivalents. The incidence of addiction to opiates and their synthetic equivalents is not known. It has been estimated that there are between 60,000 and 180,-000 addicts in the United States. The reversal of the sex ratio after passage of the Harrison Narcotic Act has already been mentioned, from 75 per cent female before 1914 to 20 per cent female today. Ready availability, as a contributing factor, is obvious from its occurrence among physicians and nurses, the highest incidence among professional groups. Otherwise, opiate addiction is characteristic of unskilled workers, perhaps because early contact and use interrupts all schooling. The family background, while definitely pathological in 50 per cent of the cases, does not seem to be specific. There is the familiar dominant mother and the hostile, indifferent or absent father. In about half the families overpermissiveness toward the future addict extended to his not being encouraged to continue school or learn a vocation, even though he might be of superior intelligence.[63]

The British define an addict as a person who feels normal on drugs. This definition is inadequate since it would include such persons as diabetics who feel comfortable on insulin. Wikler's definition, which restricts the term addiction to the compulsive use of drugs harmful to the individual or society, is closer to the mark.[64] Tolerance for opiates develops quickly. A dose effective at first may be ineffective within a matter of weeks. The basis of *tolerance* is unknown, but it appears to be pharmacological. *Dependence* upon opiates likewise appears to be on a pharmacological basis. Both can be developed easily in experimental animals by simply giving them injections. Withdrawal symptoms in human beings are specific and may become alarming. They can be avoided by gradual reduction in dosage with substitutes of a less addictive drug and eventual complete withdrawal of all drugs.

Successful treatment depends, not only upon special experience, but upon the willingness of the patient to give up the drug and his ability to cooperate faithfully. Institutionalization is stipulated by the law, but morphine addicts have been successfully treated in office practice by physicians with special expertness in this field.[65] It is noteworthy that even those who consider psychotherapy or psychonanlysis essential for a genuine recovery believe

63 Nyswander, M., "Drug addiction," in Arieti, S. (Ed.), *American Handbook of Psychiatry.* New York: Basic Books, 1959, pp. 614–622.

64 Wikler, A., *Opiate Addiction.* Springfield, Ill.: Thomas, 1953.

65 Savitt, R. A., "Extramural psychoanalytic treatment of a case of narcotic addiction," *J. Amer. Psychoanal. Ass.,* 1954, 2, 494–502; Nyswander, M., *et al.,* "The treatment of drug addicts as voluntary out-patients," *Amer. J. Ortho.,* 1958, 28, 714–718.

that opiate addiction is primarily a pharmacological problem, that is, they feel that the need has been created physiologically, regardless of the personality of the patient.

Opiate addiction is said to differ fundamentally from alcoholic addiction in that it does not itself harm the brain, even after as much as fifty years of addiction. Neither does it release criminal aggression, or antisocial acting out, in the way that alcoholism often does.[66] The social deterioration that is so common appears to come largely from self-neglect, increasing preoccupation with getting hold of the drug, and the experience of being a social outcast who must often associate with habitual criminals. In Great Britain, where physicians are now allowed to give small doses to patients who are registered with the government as addicts, there seems to be nothing in the way of crime in relation to addiction.

There is general uncertainty today as to whether or not a specific premorbid personality pattern underlies opiate addiction.[67] It is interesting to note that over a hundred years ago it was asserted that addiction was impossible if a hypodermic needle was used because, as long as the narcotic did not reach the stomach, a person could not develop hunger for it. This is a peculiar restriction of the meaning of hunger when one considers that for thousands of years hunger and need have been equated in both sacred and secular writings. The question raised here is that of whether the opium addict is to be regarded as fundamentally an oral-dependent, passive person. He is frequently inadequate, often suffers from a character disorder, and is often neurotic. These can hardly be looked upon as specific, however, and no one thinks that they are. Neither can their major sources of anxiety — given by one of the leading experts in this field as pain, sexuality and the expression of aggression.

What does seem characteristic is the feeling, during addiction, of being sexually satisfied, full of food, free from anxiety and pain, and free of aggressive strivings. This suggests the picture of an artificial attempt to reinstate the all around satisfaction that infants probably experience when they are pacified, wellfed and contented. Such a speculation may err in making opium addiction appear too primitive and regressive. It may in fact be less primitive than the direct autonomic discharge characteristic of psychosomatic disorders to which we shall now turn.

[66] Nyswander, M., "Drug addiction," in Arieti, S. (Ed.), *American Handbook of Psychiatry*. New York: Basic Books, 1959, pp. 614–622.

[67] Chein, I., and Rosenfeld, E., "Juvenile narcotic use," *Law & Contemporary Problems*, 1957, *22*, 52–68; Felsinger, J. M., *et al.*, "Personality and reaction to drugs," *J. Amer. Med. Ass.*, 1955, *157*, 1113–1115; Gerard, D., and Kornetsky, C., "Adolescent opiate addiction," *Psychiat. Quart.*, 1955, *29*, 457–486; Gold, L., "Toward an understanding of adolescent drug addiction," *Fed. Probation*, 1957, *22*, 42–48.

20

Psychosomatic Disorders

⚕

IN THESE DISORDERS THE PATIENT REACTS TO STRESS, TENSION AND ANXIETY
WITH DIRECT PHYSIOLOGICAL MALFUNCTION, WHICH MAY LEAD TO IRREVERS-
IBLE ORGAN OR TISSUE DAMAGE. Unlike the neuroses, they do not involve
symbolic expressions of conflict or, if they do, the expression is incidental.
There is no significant distortion of reality such as we see in the psychoses.
The official classification advises that we utilize the term *psychophysiological
autonomic and visceral disorders*. But the moment one tries to make an
adjective out of this polyglot phrase, or even attempts to use it frequently
in discussions, the survival of the original term *psychosomatic* is easy to
understand. A brief comparison with some of the neuroses and the psychoses
will help to clarify the position of the psychosomatic disorders.

Neurotic *anxiety reactions,* for example, are dominated by an apprehension
which stems from the threatened emergence of unconscious conflicts and
fantasies. The patient attempts to discharge his tension and reduce his
anxiety by increasing his bodily activity, especially the activity of his general
(skeletal) musculature. The *psychosomatic patient* need not be apprehensive
at all, and his discharge takes the form of autonomic and vegetative malfunction. In *conversion reactions*, which were most often confused with psychosomatic disorders in the past, unconscious conflicts are expressed symbolically by some change in a body part — usually in a sense organ or in the
skeletal musculature — and this symbolic change can be translated into language without doing violence to the symptom. If there is any damage to

679

organs or tissues it is only secondarily, through disuse. The general impression which a conversion symptom gives, while it is also primitive and regressive, is that of a more sophisticated use of the body part involved. While, as in any other field, one often sees intermediate clinical syndromes, a well-defined *neurosis* can easily be differentiated from a well-defined *psychosomatic disorder*.

A striking feature of the *psychoses* is the distortion of reality through delusions, and sometimes hallucinations, both of which may be spontaneous attempts at self-cure but tend to incapacitate the patient in his interpersonal relations. Without going into further detail, it is only necessary to say that delusions and hallucinations are not essential characteristics of *psychosomatic disorders*. In fact, there is occasionally a tendency for a psychosomatic patient to develop a frank psychosis when he loses his physiological disorder. This helps to point up the differentiation. Here are two brief case excerpts to illustrate psychosomatic illnesses.

A businessman, aged thirty-five, had been working hard under great pressure to build up his advertising agency. He was a typical "achiever" or "go-getter," full of energy, initiative and push, never able to relax, and driving himself to the limit. When one of his close associates left the firm to establish a rival agency, the patient developed a peptic ulcer. To a psychiatric consultant he at first presented a bland picture of indifference; but after reaching the point where he was able to express angry resentment over what he considered a betrayal by his former associate, his medical course showed marked improvement.

A man, aged thirty-two, who was rising steadily in a highly competitive academic situation, seemed on the surface to be stable and matter-of-fact. Nevertheless, whenever he felt that his wife was not paying enough attention to his needs — which he couched mainly in terms of food and sex — he developed attacks of bronchial asthma and episodes of dermatitis. At other times he was symptom-free. We shall present another asthmatic case later on in more detail, which had both allergic and emotional components.

Origins of the concept of psychosomatic disorders

A realization that emotional disturbances are tied up with physiological overactivity, which can lead to illness and even to death, is not new. It is confined neither to our times nor to our culture. The ancients wrote about it, and what they wrote has been confirmed and expanded through the ages. During the nineteenth and twentieth centuries, the rapid advances in knowledge about infectious diseases, metabolic disorders and surgical intervention, however, focussed attention upon laboratory and surgical techniques, with a corresponding decrease of interest in the patient as a person.[1]

[1] Lidz, T., "General concepts of psychosomatic medicine," in Arieti, S. (Ed.), *American Handbook of Psychiatry*. New York: Basic Books, 1959, pp. 647–658.

During the past few decades an interest in the *patient as a person* has been revived. Physicians recognized that certain illnesses were often influenced significantly by emotional disturbances, physiologists contributed information about this relationship, more and more psychiatrists turned their attention to various aspects of the problem, and both experimental and clinical psychologists entered the field. Psychosomatic medicine and the study of emotional problems in relation to illness express the convergence of this interest from all directions.

The establishment of *psychosomatic disorders* as a separate group within the framework of psychopathology — by whatever name we choose to call it — is relatively recent. The publication of Dunbar's annotated survey of the literature in 1935 gave great impetus to an already lively interest in working out the relations between emotion and bodily illness. So did later editions of the same work, even though they gave up the attempt to cover the later literature.[2] A journal with monographic supplements was soon established which devoted itself entirely to psychosomatic medicine; more recently another journal has been established which is devoted to psychsomatic research. Even these innovations cover only a fraction of the publications on psychosomatic disorders. Reviews have been appearing annually in other journals, attempting to keep up with the growth of knowledge, which has been great, and with the growth of controversy, which has also been great.[3] When Dunbar frankly declined to give more than a sampling of the subsequent literature, beyond the more than 2000 articles and books reviewed in the first edition of her major work, she was assessing realistically the inhuman burden which any conscientious reviewer of the whole field of psychosomatic disorders would have to assume.

Today there is no longer any danger that this field will be neglected, either in its therapeutic or in its investigative aspects. The danger now is that the term will lose its meaning, that the field will lose its boundaries. It has long been accepted that disturbance in the homeostatic balance of the body is a determinant of physical illness. More recently, personality disturbances have also been recognized as determinants of physical illness. Now it has become clear that susceptibility to any illness may be influenced by emotional disturbances, either directly or through unconscious neglect and exposure.[4] The same is true of the onset, course and outcome of any illness,

2 Dunbar, F., *Emotions and Bodily Change.* (3rd ed.), New York: Columbia Univ. Press, 1946; Dunbar, F., *Psychosomatic Diagnosis.* New York: Hoeber, 1943.

3 Cf. the journal, *Psychosomatic Medicine,* and its monograph series, and the various psychiatric, psychoanalytic and psychological journals. Also Alexander, F., and French, T. M. (Eds.), *An Approach to the Cause and Treatment of Vegetative Disturbances.* New York: Ronald, 1948; Alexander, F., *Psychosomatic Medicine.* New York: Norton, 1950; Grinker, R. R., *Psychosomatic Research.* New York: Norton, 1953; Grinker, R. R., and Robbins, F. P., *Psychosomatic Case Book.* New York: Blakiston, 1954; Wittkower, E. D., and Cleghorn, R. A. (Eds.), *Recent Developments in Psychosomatic Medicine.* Philadelphia: Lippincott, 1954; Jores, A., and Freyberger, H., *Advances in Psychosomatic Medicine.* New York: Brunner, 1961.

4 Lidz, T., "General concepts of psychosomatic medicine," in Arieti, S. (Ed.), *American Handbook of Psychiatry.* New York: Basic Books, 1959, pp. 647–658.

and of the success or failure of surgical procedures.[5] The need today is for a redefinition of *psychosomatic disorders* as illnesses in which *emotional maladaptation is dominant and may lead to irreversible organ or tissue damage.*

Emotional stress and bodily illness

In all normal activity there is involvement of the internal organs and tissues, even though most of the time we are not aware of it. The heart varies in beat and in blood volume, the lungs expand and contract, the genitourinary systems change in pace and pattern, and the gastrointestinal system undergoes muscular and glandular changes — all as parts of ordinary everyday living. Even the skin, which both separates a person from his environment and makes important contacts with it, shows vascular and glandular changes which are not under voluntary control. It flushes and blanches in much the same way that mucous membranes flush and blanch.

With increased general activity, all of these systems may change their functioning to meet the extra demand. In emotional experience and behavior, even when these fall within normal limits, the visceral (or internal organ) involvement becomes marked. The heart beats faster and harder, a person may gasp or pant, the genitourinary systems may change their pattern, and the gastrointestinal system increases or decreases its activity. The skin of an emotionally aroused person may turn pale or blush deeply; we know that his gastric mucosa also turns pale or becomes engorged.

When a person is exposed to unusual stress, whether the stress is internally or externally generated, he is likely to become physiologically alerted, to show a readiness for fight or flight. As originally interpreted by Cannon, such preparation is mediated through the adrenal glands and the autonomic or vegetative nervous system.[6] Since the autonomic nervous system also functions in such a way as to regulate the equilibrium of the internal organs throughout the body, and the skin as well, these become inevitably involved in the preparation for emergencies. The autonomic or vegetative nervous system has widespread, diffuse effects because of its anatomical distribution and its physiological mode of operation.[7]

If overt action is possible, if anger can be aggressively expressed or fear leads to immediate flight, the energy mobilized in the visceral reactions is dissipated and used up. If, however, there is no possible outlet, if no overt expression or action can occur, the visceral changes are likely to persist. Visceral tension, unrelieved by action, may include a wide range of physiological alteration. It is when this kind of thing becomes chronic, or recurs repeatedly, that visceral changes apparently go beyond normal limits, become pathological, and lead to a *psychosomatic disorder*. Such an origin is cur-

[5] Janis, I., *Psychological Stress.* New York: Wiley, 1958.

[6] Cannon, W. B., *The Wisdom of the Body.* New York: Norton, 1932.

[7] For a more detailed discussion of this see the chapter on "Symbolization, role-taking and emotional reactions," in Cameron, N., and Magaret, A., *Behavior Pathology.* Boston: Houghton Mifflin, 1951, pp. 88–129.

rently ascribed to many cases of peptic ulcer, bronchial asthma, ulcerative colitis, hypertension, migraine and arthritis.[8]

Although Cannon's experiments, and Dunbar's attempts to establish personality profiles, succeeded in breaking new ground and calling general attention to psychosomatic disorders, their interpretations have turned out to be oversimplifications. According to Grinker, the same is true of the so-called "specificity" studies, that is, the investigations which have aimed at finding specific life situations and specific psychodynamic origins for the variety of visceral disorders now ascribed to emotional disturbance. He has found several different visceral disorders at different times in the same patient, and he maintains that the same kind of visceral disorder may result from widely different life situations and psychodynamic patterns.[9] With the recent differentiation of *noradrenalin*, thought to be involved in anger, from *epinephrin*, thought to be involved in fear, even the physiological mechanisms and concomitants of emotional disturbances have become matters of controversy. There is still a great deal to be learned in this area; but it has become firmly established as a legitimate field of inquiry which promises innumerable practical applications.

The fact that the mucous membrane of the stomach undergoes visible changes during emotional experiences was first reported by the American physician, Beaumont, early in the nineteenth century.[10] He was stationed at an isolated frontier post when he was called upon to treat a guide and hunter who had suffered a gunshot wound. The patient recovered from his injury, but there remained a permanent opening in his stomach wall. Beaumont seized the opportunity to make a series of direct observations of gastric activity over a period of years. Although he had only the most primitive means at hand, and even though his patient periodically disappeared from the post, Beaumont's carefulness, accuracy and intelligent persistence were rewarded by discoveries about digestion, and about gastric participation in emotional disturbances, which were nothing short of epoch-making.

Two decades ago, in a more sophisticated series of brilliant observations, which had the advantage of a modern hospital setting, Wolf and Wolff have added greatly to our knowledge of the effects of fear and anger in gastric functioning.[11] These have been further extended by Mirsky, Margolin and others.[12] Many other studies have added to a growing understanding of

[8] Cf. the reviews of these syndromes in "Psychosomatic medicine," (various) in Arieti, S. (Ed.), *American Handbook of Psychiatry*. New York: Basic Books, 1959, pp. 647–794. Each review includes a bibliography. Other reviews can be found in current issues of *Psychosomatic Medicine, The American Journal of Psychiatry*, as well as in the sources indicated in footnote 3 of this chapter.

[9] Cf. Grinker, R. R., *Psychosomatic Research*. New York: Norton, 1953; Grinker, R. R., and Robbins, F. P., *Psychosomatic Case Book*. New York: Blakiston, 1954.

[10] Beaumont, W., *Experiments and Observations on the Gastric Juice and the Physiology of Digestion*. Pittsburgh: F. P. Allen, 1833.

[11] Wolf, S., and Wolff, H. G., *Human Gastric Function*. New York: Oxford, 1943.

[12] See the review by Lidz, T., and Rubenstein, R., "Psychology of gastrointestinal disorders," in Arieti, S. (Ed.), *American Handbook of Psychiatry*. New York: Basic Books, 1959, pp. 678–689. Reviews of psychosomatic disorders in other systems appear in the same work as *Part 5, Psychosomatic Medicine*.

physiological and psychodynamic interrelations with respect to the *central nervous system*, the *autonomic nervous system*, the *hypothalamus*, the *reticular and limbic systems*, and the various *metabolic* and *hormonal changes* — all with their after-effects and feedbacks. Attempts have been made to establish a *general adaptation syndrome* for physiological stress.[13]

Beginning with the brilliant pioneering work of the Russian physiologist, Pavlov, near the turn of the century, there has grown up another great literature demonstrating the ways in which internal organs and the skin come to respond to stimulation which had not previously provoked a reaction.[14] Pavlov's first experiments were on the manner in which gastric secretion could be altered by previously ineffective stimulus sources. From this beginning has arisen a vast number of experimental demonstrations of conditioning and learning, including whole philosophies of learning based upon the proposition that all learning can ultimately be reduced to conditioning.[15] Pavlov's work and that of his followers throughout the world have provided the basis for understanding some of the ways in which the functions and malfunctioning of the viscera become tied up with life experiences, including social situations, and particularly the social relationships *early in life*.

A great deal of what has already been said about feeding, maternal care, love and protection, applies to psychosomatic disorders. If we recall that a young infant can do little more than breathe, move and eliminate without human help, it is obvious that most of what we call the *oral phase of development* centers around feeding, comforting, holding and other primitive need-satisfaction situations. Out of his experiences in such situations, the infant will develop many of his most fundamental orientations and responses, including his emotional growth, his predominant emotional patterns, his prevailing modes of seeking and getting satisfaction, and his major avenues of expressing frustration, deprivation, longing, dependency, love and hatred. The psychosomatic disorders are widely interpreted as examples of *deep regression*, or *dedifferentiation*, to a *primitive visceral level*, where emotional disturbances directly alter visceral functioning; if this alteration becomes chronic or recurrent, the result may be tissue or organ damage.

Psychosomatic disorders as adaptations

Psychosomatic disorders can threaten the life of a patient. They always mean some distortion or loss of function, or at the very least discomfort or disfigurement. How then can we call them adaptive? They can be adaptive in the same sense that disabling neuroses and psychoses can. If they begin

---

[13] Cf. Selye, H., *The Stress of Life*. New York: McGraw-Hill, 1956.

[14] Pavlov, I. P., *The Work of the Digestive Glands* (trans. W. H. Thompson). London: Griffin; Pavlov, I. P., *Conditioned Reflexes* (trans. G. V. Anrep). London: Oxford Univ. Press, 1927; Pavlov, I. P., *Conditioned Reflexes and Psychiatry* (trans. H. Gantt). New York: International Publishers, 1941. See also the review by Liddell, H. S., "Conditioned reflex method and experimental neurosis," in Hunt, J. McV. (Ed.), *Personality and the Behavior Disorders*. New York: Ronald, 1944, pp. 389–412.

[15] Cf. Hilgard, E. R., *Theories of Learning*. (2nd ed.) New York: Appleton-Century-Crofts, 1956.

by protecting the patient from something worse, then they begin as adaptations, no matter what their later course may be. In other words, psychosomatic disorders are maladaptive, but they at least begin by achieving something which the patient cannot achieve in other ways. We must always remember that the psychosomatic disorder, like the neurosis and the psychosis, is not something that a person thinks out consciously. It is something that happens to him when he is under stress. The process of developing the disorder is an unconscious one; the patient does not know what he is doing. With this general orientation, we can approach psychosomatic disorders which, even though they are maladaptations, do perform certain functions. Some of these adaptive functions follow.

1. *A psychosomatic disorder puts an apparent or an actual physical illness in place of an intolerable current situation.* It makes a person physically sick instead of neurotic or psychotic. In most cultures today, a *physical illness* is honorable no matter how deplorable it may be, whereas a *neurotic illness* is looked upon as a weakness which is not honorable, and a *psychosis* is called crazy. It is more dignified to suffer from a psychosomatic disorder, as long as the patient believes in the physical origin of his illness.

2. Although psychosomatic disorders often involve *primary anxiety* — the diffuse, regressive anxiety of a small child — this may be *easier to bear* than a secondary anxiety based upon conscious conflicts over childhood impulses, which a person cannot otherwise control and does not recognize. The end-result may be a serious illness and even death; but the patient does not foresee this danger. The whole process is unconscious; and its symptoms are those of a physical illness which seems as unavoidable as any other physical illness. A great many psychosomatic disorders are of mild or moderate degree, and do not lead to death.

3. *A psychosomatic disorder may protect a patient from developing a frank psychosis,* which is in itself frightening, and may lead to a prison-like confinement with loss of civil rights. This danger is known to every citizen, even to children, and although the processes leading to psychosis or psychosomatic disorder are unconscious, this does not mean that they lack some unconscious "choice." Although there is a difference in opinion among experts as to the frequency with which the loss of psychosomatic symptoms is followed by psychosis, no one working in the field denies that there sometimes seems to be a close relationship between the two. For example, some patients with ulcerative colitis develop a paranoid psychosis when they improve, and others become psychotically depressed, as though the psychosomatic disorders and the psychoses were interchangeable.[16] This suggests

[16] Cf. West, R., "The place and recognition of emotional factors in the etiology and treatment of chronic non-specific colitis," in Jores, A., and Freyberger, H., *Advances in Psychosomatic Medicine.* New York: Brunner, 1961, pp. 270–279; Grace, W. J., Wolf, S., and Wolff, H. G., *The Human Colon.* New York: Hoeber, 1951.

caution in treating chronic psychosomatic disorders which do not threaten life, and prepares the therapist for the possibility that he may be called upon to treat psychotic trends as his patient recovers.

4. *Psychosomatic disorders give the patient the privileges of a sick person,* without interfering with his freedom or lowering his self-esteem. The *secondary gain,* as this is called, and the relationship of an unconsciously needed dependency upon a parent-figure, the clinician, can bring valuable gratifications to a basically immature person. These gratifications should not be scorned. They sometimes protect a person from disabling neurotic or psychotic developments; and they often give meaningful interpersonal relationships to an otherwise empty life. It should be added that many emotionally immature, dependent men and women hide their needs, from themselves as well as from others, behind an energetic, independent façade. The needs are still there, however, and they are still unsatisfied.

5. Finally, there remains to be considered the intensification of a physical illness by a psychosomatic disorder. The patient may *use his physical illness as a means of eliciting concern, care and affection,* which he has needed all along, but has been unable to get as long as he remained well. This also should not be scorned. Life is objectively more difficult and less rewarding for some persons than for others; and subjectively it may seem bleak, even though objectively it is considered fortunate. The psychotherapeutic aim in treating psychosomatic disorders, is to bring the need to verbal expression, if this can be done skilfully and safely, so that, as a patient improves physically, he also matures psychodynamically. To give support and to permit dependence during the *early stages* of therapy is usually the most important part of the treatment of psychosomatic disorders.

Varieties of Psychosomatic Disorder

Psychosomatic disorder may involve the skin and any of the viscera, in any one of a number of different ways. It may complicate the course and affect the outcome of any physical illness. For this reason the psychiatrist, no matter how well versed he may be in medical and surgical problems, cannot expect to take over the work of the specialist, who is an expert in treating the particular physical illness from which the patient is suffering. Neither can the specialist in other fields expect to be able to carry out psychotherapy, except in relatively simple situations. Successful treatment of psychosomatic disorders depends upon the intelligent and willing cooperation of two therapists, each skilled in his own specialty.

In what follows, we shall discuss briefly eight of the systems most commonly involved. In part because of the unusually complex relationship between physical disease and psychosomatic disorder, but chiefly because the concentrated study of them has been so recent, the discussion will be more tentative than in the case of neuroses, psychoses and personality disorders, which have a wealth of investigation behind them. Our aim here will be that of sketching some of the prevalent hypotheses without attempting much in the way of evaluation. The articles, journals and books cited will open the door to anyone who wishes to pursue the subject further.

Psychosomatic disorders and the gastrointestinal tract

It is hardly surprising that psychosomatic disorders commonly involve the gastrointestinal tract. During the first year of postnatal life, as we pointed out in Chapter 2, most of a child's significant sources of pleasure, relief and comfort, most of his sources of frustration and apparent anxiety, center around the mouth and feeding. In the beginning, most babies find delay in the feeding process intolerable. Their behavior, while they wait, looks like a desperate anxiety, which quickly vanishes when their mouth holds the nipple and they can suck. This frantic behavior gradually disappears as the infant learns, through repeated experiences, that he can depend upon someone's bringing him food when he needs it, that in this area of his restricted life he can begin building a *basic trust.* We know also that *pleasure-sucking,* unrelated to food intake, is a source of infantile gratification, which sometimes begins even before birth and often lasts for years after it.

Still more important than oral pleasure and oral frustration is the growth of oral dependence. At first, the infant seems not to differentiate between being hungry and needing love, between being fed lovingly and being loved. Nevertheless, it is through the feeding situation, with its sucking and swallowing and gastric comforting, that every infant makes his most important close relationship with another person. It is through his mouth that he first incorporates part of his external world and learns the art of symbolic introjection. Before long, this differentiates into reactions to *the one who feeds and loves the infant,* as well as reactions to the *feeding itself.* It is also through the inevitable delays and frustrations during oral dependence that the early steps are taken in organizing an ego system. The child learns to look beyond his own body for sources of relief, pleasure and comfort.

What is particularly relevant here is that early in life the infant does not differentiate between his physiological functions and his earliest experiences of love and care. To some extent these remain undifferentiated, although distinguishable, in all adults. We all tend to equate *being asked to dinner* with *being loved,* or if love seems too strong a word, at least with *being accepted.* We never lose some pleasures of the mouth, of eating and drinking, or the healthy comfort of a satisfied stomach. We never wholly lose symbolic expressions of rejection and disgust that must also involve gastric action. The adult who develops gastric function as a psychosomatic disorder seems to be one whose regression under stress carries some of these reactions back to their infantile intensity and who uses them habitually in expressing his extremes of tension and anxiety.

Peptic ulcer. This term refers to ulcers occurring most frequently in the stomach and duodenum. They are usually single and sharply demarcated from the normal or near-normal tissue that surrounds them. They may occur at any age, even in the newborn. Their direct cause is related to digestion of gastric or duodenal tissue by acid digestive juices. It cannot be taken for granted that every case of peptic ulcer is precipitated by emotional problems, but the ones that *are emotional in origin* present a formidable proportion. Anything that increases gastric acidity or gastric motility may indirectly precipitate and perpetuate a peptic ulcer. We have already cited the classical studies of Beaumont, early in the nineteenth century, and those of Wolf and Wolff, of Mirsky and of Margolin within recent years. Peptic ulcer may even be present without specific symptoms. In a recent study, for example, it was found that in a group of eight-five adults, either healthy at the time or else hospitalized for non-gastrointestinal disorders, "silent" duodenal ulcer appeared in the X-ray examination of 20 per cent of young soldiers, 4 per cent of older civilian men, and 4 per cent of young women.[17] In general, fewer women than men suffer from peptic ulcer; but when they do, they are usually sicker than are the men.

As a group, adults who develop peptic ulcer seem to be relatively stable. According to some studies, many of them are obviously dependent persons; but the majority are apparently self-sufficient, with much energy, drive and initiative.[18] The popular image of the man with peptic ulcer is that of a successful business executive, who works hard, drives himself, eats and drinks a great deal, and keeps a pill of some sort handy in case of trouble. Such a man would never be suspected of having imperious dependency needs — of wanting or needing to be taken care of. What is more important, such a man cannot allow himself even to become aware of his own dependency needs, let alone express them to others. To the world he presents the façade of the strong, successful achiever. To himself he appears as the image of the independent, powerful man who need depend upon no one else.

When it is studied psychodynamically, this façade often turns out to be overcompensatory, a strong expression of self-sufficiency which is basically a *reaction formation* against powerful dependency needs. The man has built up a style of life which hides his strong dependency needs defensively, and denies them even to himself. By means of this defense he remains unconscious of these needs. The mere suggestion of them would seem to him an insult. Whenever there is a threat to this life pattern, the man increases his strivings and feels more than ever the demand to be independent of everyone.

[17] Smith, V. M., Feldman, M., and Mead, J. A., "Frequency of silent peptic ulcer," *Amer. J. Gastroenterology*, 1962, 37, 55–63.

[18] Alexander, F., *Psychosomatic Medicine.* New York: Norton, 1950.

Such persons, whether actually executives or merely laborers, seem to develop peptic ulcer when an increase in dependency needs threatens to destroy their self-image. This may come from the loss, or even the threatened loss, of *someone* upon whom the patient is actually dependent, or of *the success* upon which he has counted. The precipitating factor may be the loss of mother, wife or child; it may be marital discord or business failure, or even the stress of keeping a business or a marriage successful. It is believed that, under such circumstances, there is a regression to primary anxiety, and that the anxiety over dependency is expressed by hypersecretion and overactivity in the stomach. The unmet need for dependency and love activates mechanisms which are normal for an infant who cannot distinguish between hunger and love. These mechanisms require that someone provide food, or infantile love, which differentiates out of this need and its satisfaction during infancy. Exactly what the physiological process is, that produces the peptic ulcer, nobody seems to be sure. But in many cases it is clear that the origins lie in tension, anxiety and chronic conflict, with the stomach bearing the brunt of the stress, perhaps in line with primary process thinking.

Obesity. Like peptic ulcer, obesity may be the result of many things, and among these many things must be counted strong irrational dependency needs. Obesity is frequently a psychosomatic disorder, and it can be a grave one. Chronic overweight is nearly always a result of overeating. Endocrine and metabolic disorders are seldom involved. Theoretically, the control of obesity should be an easy matter, a matter of controlling a person's food intake. In practice the control of obesity is exceedingly difficult in those persons for whom food and eating have imperious unconscious meanings.

Such persons behave as if they were food addicts; they seem unable to control their excessive need for food. They go on a diet over and over again; but as soon as they have lost weight they begin to overeat again, until they have gained back all that they had lost. A new kind of dieting may start the cycle all over again. For a time, weight is lost and the patient expresses enthusiasm and determination; but in the end obesity appears again, even though the patient knows that his life depends upon avoiding it.

In the study of obese children, Bruch has found that often their mothers could not give them true and mothering love, because of their own unmet needs to be dependent and be loved. They could, however, give their children food and conscientious care. The *giving of food* became a substitute for the *giving of love*, in the manner of primary processes, both in the mother and in the child. The child was left with an irrational craving for food because its cravings for love had never been met excepting at a primitive feeding level.[19] We see the same kind of thing in the lonely housewife who overeats, nibbling in moments of emptiness and boredom, and gorging herself when she feels especially neglected or rejected. The obese cardiac patient, whose life depends upon his losing weight, nevertheless treats himself to a huge,

[19] Bruch, H., *The Importance of Overeating.* New York: Norton, 1957.

delicious meal whenever he feels lonely, just as he may have done all his life. Whatever the situation, unless an obese patient with strong dependency needs — which are infantile and oral in their expression — is helped to work them through, the feeling of primary process hunger will defeat every attempt at cure.

Ulcerative colitis. This is another serious gastrointestinal disorder in which, as in peptic ulcer, emotional experiences, tensions and anxieties are generally accepted as playing important roles. Direct observation of the mucous membrane of the colon, while patients were experiencing conflicts over resentment and the desire to please, revealed that it became congested and hyperactive. In such a state, the colon becomes fragile, so that minor traumata can produce hemorrhage and ulceration.[20]

The patients reported in this study seemed at first sight passive, acquiescent, bland and sweet; but behind this façade there was anger and hostility. They were not frankly aggressive; but they were often querulous, demanding and sensitive, brooding over supposed personal slights. Their strong dependency needs (to be loved and accepted) were rivaled by angry feelings which stirred up guilt and the fear that a loved person would reject them in retaliation for their anger. The mothers of these patients were described as fostering an inordinate degree of dependency by their domination, but as being fundamentally hostile toward their offspring. Often the mothers seem borderline or frankly psychotic.

Clinicians working in this field are divided as to whether ulcerative colitis on a psychosomatic basis is more closely related to a paranoid psychosis or a psychotic depression.[21] Attacks are often precipitated by the loss, through death or separation, of an ambivalently loved person, when unconscious rage and guilt disturb colonic function. There is some evidence that psychosomatic ulcerative colitis may involve a psychotic depressive mechanism. On the other hand, it is reported that attacks come when a person is obliged to take steps toward greater maturity,[22] or to fulfill an obligation in an overall ambivalent situation.[23] This suggests to many a regression to the level of self-assertion and bowel control characteristic of small children.

During personality development, as we have seen, this is a period in which children seek at the same time to *assert themselves* and to *control themselves*. Since bowel control is of central importance in this phase, the bowel can express giving and withholding in relation to parental figures. There is pleasure in being dirty, and pleasure in getting approval for being clean. The control can become stubborn and frustrating to others; the lack of

[20] Grace, W. J., Wolf, S., and Wolff, H. G., *The Human Colon.* New York: Hoeber, 1951.

[21] For a discussion of this and the possible relation to oral and anal conflict, see Lidz, T., and Rubenstein, R., "Psychology of gastrointestinal disorders," in Arieti, S. (Ed.), *American Handbook of Psychiatry.* New York: Basic Books, 1959, pp. 678–689.

[22] Sperling, M., "Psychoanalytic study of ulcerative colitis in children," *Psychoanal. Quart.*, 1946, *15*, 302–312.

[23] Daniels, G., "Non-specific ulcerative colitis as a psychosomatic disease," *Med. Clinics of North America*, 1944, *28*, 593.

control can take the form of an angry attack. This is a period full of ambivalence about a great many things, not the least of which is the struggle over *being good and yielding* or *being bad and withholding*, or of *being bad and soiling*. The small child wants to please his mother and receive her love, but he also wants to be independent, and her attempts to control him make him angry. He grows guilty over his angry feelings, his dirty badness and his destructive fantasies. He may fear retaliation from his mother for all this, but even more, he is afraid that he will lose her love. These are some of the reasons given in the literature for linking ulcerative colitis to a deeply regressive process.

The case of a five-year-old boy with ulcerative colitis, as reported in the literature, presents some such picture. He had his first attack when he was three-and-a-half years old, on the day when summer school ended, and a maid left to whom he was devoted. He was tense and furious, but he dared not express his fury. He had both oral and anal aggressive impulses, and destructive fantasies in which people were represented as food and feces. The boy's mother, and most of the relatives in his environment, restrained their feeling and impulses in order to keep up a smooth social front. In them also there were primitive oral and anal destructive impulses, but they handled their own hostility by excessive self-control, and encouraged harsh superego development. Because of such an ego-superego structure, it is reported, eight of the twelve members of this family developed psychosomatic, rather than psychotic disorders. This interpretation is in line with a widely held view, already stated, that psychosomatic disorder may be an alternate to psychotic disorder.[24]

Another study of ulcerative colitis in children comes to somewhat different conclusions. These are that gratifications during the neonatal period had been both qualitatively and quantitatively inadequate in these patients. Josselyn, in reporting her work, stated that the patients showed fixations at many levels, and that the nature of the conflict precipitating an attack was not specific. When regression began in her patients, no gratification could be found at any of the levels. Accordingly, regression revived the "primary function level," that of a newborn baby, who reacts in a total or massive way. The disorder then becomes one of excitation and discharge, with a concomitant disintegration of ego structure, and a gross total "somatopsychic disturbance," which Josselyn calls a "physiological psychosis."[25]

The respiratory system

The respiratory system is involved in everyday emotional experience. There is the sigh of sadness, longing and regret, the gasp of surprise, the cry of fear and the wailing of grief. Crowds watching a tight-rope walker

[24] Blom, G. E., "Ulcerative colitis in a five-year-old boy," in Caplan, G. (Ed.), *Emotional Problems in Early Childhood*. New York: Basic Books, 1955, pp. 169–198.

[25] Josselyn, I., "Report of cases of ulcerative colitis," in Goliner, B. J. (reporter), "Psychosomatic diseases in children and adolescents," *J. Amer. Psychoanal. Ass.*, 1960, 8, 152–158.

hold their breath, and let it out audibly in relief when the act is finished. Mothers do the same when they watch a child pass through some danger of which he may not even be aware. One can often tell from a person's speech, from its pitch, rate and rhythm, that he is emotionally disturbed.

The most primitive form in which emotionality is expressed by the respiratory system is the commonplace breathholding spells of angry infants and small children. They express rage and frustration by crying and crying until they are literally blue in the face. Some infants even stop breathing completely and have convulsive movements because of the disturbed oxygen-carbon dioxide balance in the blood.

Tense adults who are anxious or angry, may breathe so that the *tidal air* does not reach the *alveolar air* of the lungs in such a way as to permit normal interchange of oxygen and carbon dioxide. Although they do not turn blue, as infants do, they experience dizziness, faintness and sometimes "blacking out." Patients are as a rule not aware that emotional disturbance is involved. They go for help because of the physical symptoms.[26]

Bronchial asthma. The most important of the psychosomatic disorders of respiration appears in the form of bronchial asthma. This involves constriction of the bronchioles which results in wheezing, choking sensations and gasping for breath. Some asthmatic patients are critically ill, and some are chronically disabled. Most of them experience remissions, in which they seem quite well, and periods of attacks, which can be severe.

It must not be supposed that all bronchial asthma is psychosomatic. Some asthmatic patients follow a distinctly seasonal cycle which parallels such seasonal cycles in allergens as we find in ragweed and cottonwood. Even those who are more or less constantly asthmatic may be physiologically hypersensitive to pollens and molds that are always present in the air. Many of these can be desensitized by physiological means alone.

There has been a great number of studies of bronchial asthma, both from an allergic and a psychosomatic point of view. In a controlled series of studies, Dekker *et al.* found that in their patients they could not differentiate between an *allergic* and a *psychogenic* group. They emphasize the role of conditioning in producing bronchial asthma in patients who are also sensitive to allergens.[27] It seems obvious that several contributing factors may be involved, e.g., specific allergic sensitivity, autonomic nervous system susceptibility, an unusually responsive respiratory system, and life experiences which include conflicts that are no longer conscious. The concurrence of different constellations in producing a psychosomatic disorder is exceptionally well illustrated in asthma. The following case shows this clearly, and

[26] Wittkower, E. D., and White, K. L., "Psychophysiological aspects of respiratory disorder," in Arieti, S. (Ed.), *American Handbook of Psychiatry*, New York: Basic Books, 1959, pp. 690–707.

[27] Dekker, E., Barendregt, J. T., and DeVries, K., "Allergy and neurosis in asthma," in Jores, A., and Freyberger, H. (Eds.), *Advances in Psychosomatic Medicine*. New York: Basic Books, 1961, pp. 235–240.

may be taken as representative of psychosomatic disorders in other systems as well.

Patricia M., a Baraboo school girl, fourteen years of age, was admitted to a general hospital because of severe attacks of bronchial asthma. The nurses reported that she entered the ward flanked by her frightened parents, the mother supporting her on one side and the father walking on the other side, carrying a syringe with adrenalin ready for instant use. This entrance was a dramatic representation of the attitudes which all three had developed during the four months of her asthmatic attacks. At home the father, after work, had been devoting himself entirely to the task of diverting Patricia, so as to minimize her attacks. Actually, the attacks had increased in frequency and severity following his arrival at home, but neither the parents nor the child seemed to suspect that there might be some connection involved. By the time she was brought to the hospital, her activities had been restricted to those of a person in imminent danger of collapse and sudden death.

Although a respiratory hypersensitivity to bacterial proteins was clearly demonstrated, it was obvious to everyone that the extreme anxiety of the child and her parents presented a major problem. At first, parental visits to the child, but not to the hospital, were limited. Both parents and the child received psychotherapy during the period of of her being desensitized to her specific allergens. When Patricia had asthmatic attacks they were treated competently and without anxiety on the part of the staff. When it was observed that she had an increase of attacks on "Protein Clinic" days, the allergist made arrangements to have her treated on the psychiatric ward, and the increase disappeared. Because of her long period of inactivity, it was necessary to schedule increasing activity until Patricia had regained the confidence that she had lost because of everyone's extreme anxiety. After four months, she was well enough to go home and resume a normal life. When asthmatic attacks then occurred, which they did at infrequent intervals, both the parents and the girl were able to handle the situation without alarm. Patricia was seen in office treatment for some time after discharge so that some of her personal problems could be worked through.

It is generally agreed that asthmatic attacks with psychosomatic components are found in persons with strong but repressed dependency needs, especially needs for protection. There is the familiar emotional ambivalence, with destructive wishes toward a loved person.[28] Different persons build up different patterns of defense against their conflicts. Asthmatic patients range all the way from passive, submissive persons to markedly impulsive, impatient, egocentric, domineering and even tyrannical ones.

The asthmatic attack has been interpreted as *a suppressed cry for help* from a mother figure, when the patient faces loss or separation. The patient can express his dependency only in an infantile way. Asthmatic persons

[28] Alexander, F., *Psychosomatic Medicine*. New York: Norton, 1950, pp. 132–141.

often report difficulty in crying, and relief from the asthma when they have *learned to cry.* Attacks in psychosomatic patients are also relieved sometimes by *confession,* if they have had conscious or unconscious feelings of guilt over their hostility, and fears of losing the love they need. Patients who discover that they are accepted, in spite of real or fantasied "badness," often experience relief.[29]

Some clinicians maintain that the dependency needs of asthmatic patients are inordinate because these were not met in childhood. Some feel that allergic children have been unusually sensitive, from birth on, so that they raise difficulties in early mother-child relationships and precipitate mutual frustration. Some of the mothers studied had obviously not solved their own dependency conflicts. They often showed their ambivalence by first holding their child so close as almost to choke it, and then pushing it away in a gesture of rejection. In these cases, the asthmatic attacks disappeared after the child was separated from his mother, so that his needs for love and protection were not in constant conflict with maternal demands for surrender and maternal rejection. This type of conflict, of course, is almost universal in small children; but in the asthmatic child it seems to be especially intense. *Early infection* may make the respiratory system chronically hypersensitive, so that conflict, frustration and anxiety lead to profound regression without symbolic expression.[30]

Cardiovascular disorders on a psychosomatic basis

Like other psychosomatic disorders, these are related to the normal occurrences of everyday life. It is the intensity, the exaggeration or the sustained character of the reaction that make them pathological. The cardiovascular system is normally in constant flux, even while the body is at rest. It responds with changes in blood flow and blood pressure under conditions of physical exertion, tension, vigilance and relaxation. Its shifts participate in all emotional experience and behavior. A man's heart beats faster, and his blood pressure may rise, when he feels joyous, angry or afraid, and even when he feels hurried or pushes himself. He may flush because of the heat or because he is embarrassed or angry. He may pale because he is tired or because he is anxious or frightened. Palpitation and skipped beats are by no means unusual in healthy men and women.

As we have already seen, in the *anxiety reactions,* even the most ordinary cardiovascular changes — in heart action, blood pressure or distribution of the flow — may themselves arouse anxiety and become the focus of new fears. Thus we find persons frightened at the prospect of a heart attack, and of impending death, when they are in no such danger. Behind the

---

[29] Jessner, L. *et al.,* "The asthmatic child and his mother," *The Psychoanalytic Study of the Child.* New York: Internat. Univ. Press, 1955, vol. 10, pp. 353–375.

[30] For a further discussion with bibliography, see Wittkower, E. D., and White, K. L., in Arieti, S. (Ed.), *American Handbook of Psychiatry.* New York: Basic Books, 1959, pp. 690–707.

symptoms there may be unexpressed anxiety, guilt or rage. When a person becomes enraged and *expresses* it, he gains some discharge through violent action or a verbal assault. The difficulty in social group living is that violence in action or speech may be met with violence, or at least by anger and disapproval. We must include in such reactions to one's anger or hate the forces of repression within the person himself, and the threat his fury may pose to his own self-image as a civilized and even perhaps a benevolent person. It seems to be when a chronically hostile person suppresses his anger that certain of the vascular concomitants of rage lead to psychosomatic disorders. We shall discuss two of the most common of these, *essential hypertension* and *migraine*.[31]

Essential hypertension. In about 75 or 80 per cent of persons suffering from chronic high blood pressure no consistent organic etiology can be found. Their hypertension is called *essential*, which really means that it is of unknown etiology. The active participation of cardiovascular mechanisms in all emotional changes and in all situations of stress has focused attention upon this group as one involving psychosomatic factors. It has been pointed out that *stress-discharge* implicates the same endocrine and autonomic mechanisms that mediate *diffuse arteriolar* and *peripheral blood vessel constriction*. The not unreasonable conclusion is then drawn that continued emotional stress stimulates pathophysiological activity which underlies the development of essential hypertension.[32]

While it is generally believed that constitutional, genetic and early traumatic experiences are responsible for the development of essential hypertension, there is no agreement as to the type of personality involved. Some hypertensive patients are affable and friendly; some are even passive and intimidated; all of them seem to have conflict in handling their aggressive impulses. The solution of their impasse is to develop great self-control or self-restriction, so that they dare not allow themselves to express *moderate* anger. In this group we again find persons with excessive dependency needs which have not been adequately met.

Some patients with essential hypertension report that they used to have temper outbursts, but changed suddenly to strict self-control.[33] This appears to mean that they reacted to frustration with anger, which is a normal reaction, but *suppressed the expression* of it and probably repressed the feel-

[31] For a more extended discussion and bibliography, see Reiser, M. F., and Bakst, H., "Psychology of cardiovascular disorders," in Arieti, S. (Ed.), *American Handbook of Psychiatry.* New York: Basic Books, 1959, pp. 659–677.

[32] Van der Valk, J. M., "Blood pressure changes under emotional influences with hypertension and control subjects," *J. psychosom. Res.*, 1957, 2, 134–145; Engel, B. T., and Bickford, A. F., "Response specificity: stimulus-response and individual response specificity in essential hypertensives," *Arch. gen. Psychiat.*, 1961, 5, 478–489; Kalis, B. L., Harris, R. E., Bennett, L. F., and Sokolow, M., "Personality and life history factors in persons who are potentially hypertensive," *J. nerv. ment. Dis.*, 1961, 132, 457–468.

[33] Alexander, F., *Psychosomatic Medicine.* New York: Norton, 1950.

ing as well. This does not mean, however, that they erased all physiological traces of the unexpressed anger. If the demands and the critical attitudes of a man's superior infuriate him and make him feel inferior, they may make him drive himself on to *prove* that he is competent. If he submits to ill-treatment during the process, feeling more hostile all the time, he may stir up deep-seated conflicts involving childhood dependency and hostility. This may begin the controlled hostile aggression and the blood pressure changes.

Neurotic patients often face the same general problem, of course, but they handle it through their characteristic defenses in different ways. We do not know why the psychosomatic patient develops essential hypertension. It may be that he inherits an unstable vasomotor system, since even normal individual differences in vasomotor reactivity are very great. It is most probable that some constellation of factors, as yet undetermined, accounts for this syndrome.

Migraine. This also is an illness of unknown etiology which many ascribe to psychosomatic sources. In its most characteristic form it consists of a unilateral periodic headache, often with nausea and vomiting, and some-times with diarrhea or constipation. An attack may be preceded, for hours or even days, by attacks of facial flushing or facial pallor; there are often signs of constriction in the arteries of the head, face, and eye-grounds, just before an attack begins. Paresthesias, vertigo and scintillating visual phe-nomena may provide a warning. Migraine is considered by many clinicians to be an epileptic equivalent; by others it is placed among the headaches, without definite commitment.[34]

Persons who suffer from migraine attacks seem to be hard-driving, per-fectionistic and ambitious, as well as irritable and resentful.[35] They become frustrated because they cannot keep up with their own demand upon them-selves. Alexander postulates that, in these patients, destructive impulses are inhibited in the fantasy stage of development, when planning and visual imagery are active. To this he ascribes the development of *migraine*, rather than of *essential hypertension* — in which he assumes that destructive im-pulses are inhibited during the stage of vegetative preparation — or of *rheumatoid arthritis,* where the inhibition of hostile impulses seems to occur in the *muscular phase.*

Rheumatoid arthritis

This is another common disorder of unknown etiology in which emotional stress is believed to play a part. Persons who develop rheumatoid arthritis are described as active, energetic achievers, who do not express their feel-ings freely. According to Alexander, the inhibition of rage occurs at the point of consummation of the hostile aggressive act itself. The simultaneous

---

[34] Cf. Wolff, H. G., *Headache and Other Head Pain.* New York: Oxford, 1948.
[35] Alexander, F., *Psychosomatic Medicine.* New York: Norton, 1950.

action of powerfully contracted muscles, some directed toward carrying out the aggressive act and the others directed toward restraining the act, may lead to injury of the joint itself. This is presented as a speculation, but an interesting one.

There are serious doubts as to what factors are involved in precipitating rheumatoid arthritis. Both an *increase in responsibility* and a *decrease in responsibility* have been reported. Such global phrases tell us little about the patient's experiences in either situation. The parents of patients who develop rheumatoid arthritis are said to have been restrictive and sometimes overprotective, while not allowing their child to express his anger through the usual motor channels when he was frustrated. The mother is usually described as a "cold" person who allows herself little emotional expression.

The last-mentioned characteristic, reported by adult patients giving their own histories, has been confirmed by a study of mothers whose children were suffering from rheumatoid arthritis.[36] The mother was often rigid, demanding and domineering; the father was passive and gentle. The child who feels rebellious because of his mother's strict control is so dependent upon her love that he does not dare to express his angry feelings. The guilt created by his own hostility adds an internal restricting pressure to the external restraint imposed by the mother.

Women arthritics are described as having been tomboys who were greatly interested in sports and often engaged in active competition. Many of them resented their feminine role, experienced marked rivalry with a brother or father, and chose as marital partners men who were passive, inadequate or suffering from a physical disability. These women *took control* of their families, but served husband and children *resentfully,* as martyrs. Sometimes the first arthritic attack comes when they lose the martyr role, and their guilt over their own hostility can no longer be controlled. The ambivalent conflict over dependency needs and resentment can no longer be worked out through service and self-sacrifice, but neither can the anger be openly expressed. These, too, are hypotheses which remain to be tested by further investigation.

The skin

The skin is a paradox and almost a miracle. It *separates* the organism from the surroundings; but it has unnumbered sensitive little sense organs which, together with the eyes, ears, nose and mouth, *connect* the organism with its surroundings. Taken as a unit, it is the most external of external organs; yet it originates from the same embryological layer as does the brain, the *ectoderm,* and it functions in many ways like an internal organ. A massive network of small blood vessels grows into it which include

[36] Blom, G. E., and Whipple, B., "A method of studying emotional factors in children with rheumatoid arthritis," in Jessner, L., and Pavenstedt, E., *Dynamic Psychopathology in Childhood.* New York: Grune & Stratton, 1959, pp. 124–165.

mesodermal derivatives; and the skin has innumerable glands and smooth muscle elements which relate it directly to the viscera. The skin also grows hair which on the face is the mark of the male, and on the head is called woman's crowning glory.

The skin is a major organ of body temperature control, of evaporation, excretion and secretion. Its blood vessels, glands and smooth muscles undergo all kinds of important changes which are not under conscious or preconscious control. They participate actively in the emotional components of experience and behavior. Early in life the skin is involved in need-satisfaction sequences which bring mother and child into a reciprocal relationship and help to establish the normal symbiotic mother-child relationship. Throughout life the skin has erotic functions as well as aggressive and hostile ones. It can as easily become the locus of injury as the source of comfort.

The skin shows some remarkable changes in less normal situations. When a person is greatly excited, ecstatic or under hypnosis, his skin may be insensitive to pain; it also may retain for a long time the mark of even a light scratch. It is not difficult to understand that the skin can react in all kinds of ways to all kinds of emotional disturbances. Eczema, urticaria and the dermatoses have all been found to be related to emotional factors. The skin is the site of so many malfunctions and diseases that specialists devote their whole professional lives to its study and therapy. Considering its complex structure, its diverse and often conflicting functions, its immediate visibility to others and its narcissistic value, there can be no doubt that the skin plays an important part in psychosomatic disorders. One of the foremost students of psychosomatics has derived significant theoretical contributions to the general field from his work in dermatology.[37]

In 75 per cent of the patients treated in certain dermatology clinics, psychological problems have been found that were related to the skin lesions for which treatment was sought. Some allergic patients, who develop contact dermatitis whenever they are exposed to their specific allergen, also develop the same kind of lesion in a stress situation when the allergen is absent. The stress or tension appears to act as though it were the allergic substance itself. This is similar to the situation which we described in the chapter on obsessive compulsive reactions, where once a compulsive ritual had been established in relation to some specific conflict, it was used also in unrelated states of tension and anxiety.

Some scratching seems to be compulsive, and the itching that provokes it resembles an equivalent of libidinal drives. The scratching then gives the impression of a regressive masturbatory action which reaches a crescendo

[37] Cf. Schur, M., "Comments on the metapsychology of somatization," *The Psychoanalytic Study of the Child.* Internat. Univ. Press, 1955, vol. 10, pp. 119–164; Schur, M., "The ego in anxiety," in Loewenstein, R. (Ed.), *Drives, Affects, Behavior.* New York: Internat. Univ. Press, 1953; Schur, M., "Basic problems of psychosomatic medicine," in Herma, H., and Kurth, G. M. (Eds.), *Elements of Psychoanalysis.* New York: World Publishing Co., 1950.

and is followed by relief. Sometimes the scratching is so extreme that it produces tissue injury, chronic irritation and pain. It then seems to serve self-punitive functions as well. Scratching is often associated with destructive impulses and fantasies in relation to other persons. It has been observed that the clawlike position of many patients' hands suggests that they are inhibiting the desire to scratch someone else. It may be the guilt over having such hostile impulses that leads to destructive self-scratching.

Many cases of skin lesions reveal exhibitionistic impulses and defenses against them. Schur maintains that conflicts over exhibitionism are present even before the initial lesion.[38] He found defective libido development in his patients, impairment in many ego functions, extreme emotional ambivalence, and tenuous object relationships built around narcissistic and pregenital needs. These patients seemed to have suffered severe early traumatization which left them with serious ego defects. In their psychological examinations they gave responses similar to those of borderline psychotic patients with primary process thinking.

According to Schur, treatment should be directed toward counteracting the regression by encouraging verbalization. Through this procedure the primary process use of the skin, to express feelings, impulses and thoughts cutaneously, is gradually replaced by expression through normal secondary process channels. In successful cases the skin disorder disappears.

Hyperthyroidism

It has long been recognized that psychological stress can precipitate hyperthyroidism, and that anxiety, irritability, restless overactivity and mood swings are among the most prominent symptoms. In this disorder the interaction between visceral functioning and psychological activity is especially clear. Excessive thyroid secretion increases anxiety, and the increased anxiety increases thyroid secretion, thus completing the vicious cycle.

People who suffer from hyperthyroidism usually appear to be responsible, active, sensitive and self-sufficient, but this appearance is evidently a defensive *reaction formation*. The patient has adopted a style of life which denies his dependency longings and the threats to his security early in life. A fear of loss through death seems to underlie many cases. This has sometimes been justified by the death of the mother when the patient was still a child. As part of an attempt to master the anxiety which comes from frustrated dependency longings, the patient may identify with the lost person by assuming an *attitude* of self-reliance which has no other basis. Even in childhood, he may assume responsibilities that are beyond his actual powers and keep him under constant pressure.

Alexander has speculated that the promotion and acceleration of growth in childhood is a thyroid function. According to him, the thyroid may

[38] Schur, M., "Comments on the metapsychology of somatization," *Psychoanalytic Study of the Child*. New York: Internat. Univ. Press, 1955, vol. 10, pp. 119–164.

again become preponderant under adult stress, and resume its childhood functions as part of a regression. The increased thyroid activity in adulthood then represents something which was appropriate in childhood, but is now pathological in its effects. This is somewhat analagous to the undifferentiated, infantile mode of functioning which is ascribed to the stomach of those who develop peptic ulcers. The hyperthyroid adult overdoes the process of trying to be self-sufficient and mature. He fails in this attempt and actually regresses to a level where thyroid hyperactivity was a normal part of growth acceleration.[39] Whether or not this is actually the mechanism underlying hyperthyroidism, and whether or not hereditary factors need also to be considered, are still matters of controversy.[40]

Diabetes mellitus

This is another endocrine disorder with important emotional components; but the emotional etiology of the disturbance in glucose metabolism is questionable. In *normal persons,* fear or anxiety does result in changes in the blood sugar level, but the changes are transient. Long lasting or widely fluctuating changes in blood sugar are characteristic of *diabetic persons* who are exposed to emotional stress. The common stresses seem to be frustration of dependency needs and the reactivation of dependency needs through loss. It is reported that when a patient feels cared for, when he receives the attention he requires, his blood sugar levels return to normal limits, and they can again be controlled by the dietary regimen to which he is accustomed, or by the insulin therapy which he had previously used. The dietary control of diabetes always involves food deprivation, and this may aggravate any conflict the patient has over dependency needs. A mother whose only expression of love is through feeding may find great difficulty in restricting her diabetic child's diet. The patient, whether child or adult, may feel deprived and unloved to such an extent that he eats what he should not, both to provide himself with the symbol of love and to punish an authority figure secretly. Whatever the etiological relationships, these factors must be kept in mind by those responsible for the care and treatment of diabetics.

Sexual dysfunction as a psychosomatic disorder

Because sexual dysfunction is almost universal in neurotic, psychotic and personality disorders, its place among the psychosomatic disorders is limited to those cases in which it plays a conspicuous specific role; even then it is usually symptomatic of some more widespread personality involvement. This is because normal heterosexual intercourse always involves the reciprocal participation of two differently organized persons, a male and a

---

[39] Alexander, F., *Psychosomatic Medicine.* New York: Norton, 1950.

[40] Alexander, F., Flagg, G. W., Foster, S., Clemens, T., and Blahd, W., "Experimental studies of emotional stress: I. Hyperthyroidism," *Psychosom. Med.,* 1961, *23,* 104–114.

female, whose anatomy, physiology, biochemistry, activity, experiences and expectations are radically different.

In the lower mammals it is the periodic physiological phase of "heat" in the female that determines copulation with an available male. There is no close-knit, lifelong family formation, in the human sense, no comparable assumption of male responsibility, and presumably no conflict on the part of either male or female. Speculations about human sexual function have often been based upon the animal model, but this procedure has proved to be erroneous. Even the higher subhuman species, such as the chimpanzees, do not conform to the sexual pattern of lower mammals. Among human beings, the promiscuous, ever-ready Don Juan seems to approach the male pattern of lower mammals; but he is atypical among the human species and he is almost always sexually abnormal.

There are many reasons for the differences between the sex life of man and that of lower mammals. Some of them are strictly biological. For example, women do not have a regularly recurrent period of "heat," with long periods during which sexual intercourse is consistently rejected. Other reasons seem to arise out of the edipal experiences of human children, which themselves depend upon man's unique pattern of close family living, his capacity for symbolization, and the long period during which a child cannot even survive without adult help. The powerful systematized ideals and taboos that all normal human beings internalize are also unique for the human species.

Man has no equal in his ability to learn, in the plasticity of his experience and behavior; this also makes close living in family groups a strong influence. Man incorporates symbolically, he introjects and identifies, in ways that set him apart from all other living beings. These activities make his sex life psychologically and culturally determined, as well as biologically determined. In fact, as we have seen in cross-identification and sex deviation, the influences of individual experience may overwhelm the biological factors. Even in sexually normal persons, individual likes and dislikes, individual expectations and ideals, are powerful determinants in courtship, mating and marital sex relationships. The *general course* of normal sexual maturing, however, is determined by anatomical and physiological factors which operate within the prevailing cultural framework.

We have already included an account of normal sexual development as a part of general personality development; and we have discussed sex deviations in the preceding chapter on personality disorders. In the present chapter we shall confine ourselves to certain specific complaints which patients commonly make about their sex life, even though these are usually part of a neurosis, a psychosis or a personality disorder. They provide good illustrations of the interdependence of physiological and psychodynamic factors.

Sexual dysfunction in the male. Impotence, premature and retarded ejaculation are among the commonest forms of sexual dysfunction in the male. These malfunctions are only rarely signs of physiological pathology; they are almost always the result of psychodynamic factors. It is true that potency and male sex performance depend upon complex physiological coordinations and sequences; but these proceed more or less automatically when conditions are favorable and the man is normal. Difficulties arise because anything that stimulates anxiety, guilt or fear may interfere with masculine sex functions; and so also may conflicts about sexuality, emotional ambivalence toward the woman, or a feminine identification. Such interfering factors may be not only irrational but also unconscious. The symptoms then appear not to involve the personality at all, and this in itself may increase a man's anxiety and his fear of a hidden illness. The conspicuous failure of hormone therapy in remedying psychosomatic sexual dysfunction over a period of more than half a century, to say nothing of its tendency to promote the development of cancer, has all but eliminated it from the field.

Psychotherapy and psychoanalysis have been more effective. According to Gutheil, male dysfunction can often be remedied at a superficial level, without going into the psychodynamic factors of childhood. Excessive pregenital stimulation, in adolescent masturbation or in foreplay, for example, may be an important factor. Folklore about the effects of masturbation often helps to implant unsound fears.[41] Be that as it may, most of the origins of male sexual dysfunction go back to the complex developments which we have discussed in Chapters 2 and 3 on personality development and in Chapter 19 on personality disorders.

There are the factors of distorted parental personality which lead to defective ego introjects and superego identifications. Both maternal overindulgence and maternal domination can leave a male at pregenital levels, either because he has remained sexually infantile or because the female seems dangerous to him when he experiences mature sex impulses. Perhaps a fear of engulfment and the loss of identity still lingers from failure to resolve the symbiotic phase. For example, a man may be timid and inhibited when he faces the genital engulfment which is normal to adult male sex experience. Perhaps edipal fears are still dominant in the system unconscious.

Sometimes a strict superego makes sexual activity seem sinful, dangerous, and even unthinkable with a respected woman. In this group belong males who are pathologically guilty over masturbation, and a special group that has learned to idealize "good" women as being superior to sexuality, while they can find sex satisfaction only with "bad" women, or prostitutes. This last is a pathological exaggeration of the edipal resolution which represses a child's sexual impulses toward his mother, but leaves his tender, almost asexual love for her intact in his preconscious and conscious life.

---

[41] Gutheil, E. A., "Sexual dysfunction in man," in Arieti, S. (Ed.), *American Handbook of Psychiatry*. New York: Basic Books, 1959, pp. 708–726. A review of the literature appears in Senoussi, A. E., Coleman, D. R., and Tauber, A. S., "Factors in male impotence," *J. Psychol.*, 1959, *48*, 3–46.

Still other unconscious determinants of male sexual dysfunction are the pre-edipal childhood fears of untamed rage and hostility in relation to a mother's suppression or coercion. In adulthood these reactions may be re-aroused by sexual intimacies with an eligible woman. It should be noted, however, that the aggression aroused by anger sometimes leads to effective male functioning. Thus, for example, sex relations immediately following an angry quarrel are successful in some males who find a willing, passive or receptive sex partner unattractive.

Unconscious resentment toward women, or even an infantile envy of their narcissism and reproductive role may interfere with male sexual function. Unresolved edipal fears of a father figure, who seemed dangerous in early childhood, sometimes result in an irrational inability to fulfill the male role adequately in adulthood. Whether or not such interferences with male performance should be treated as psychosomatic regressions, or as components of a neurosis, is still the subject of controversy.

Sexual dysfunction in the female. The more passive, receptive female sex functions pose different but no less difficult problems. Among the commonest are frigidity, menstrual difficulties, and pathological reactions to pregnancy, childbirth, and the care of babies and small children. There is a much greater incidence of physiological pathology in menstrual difficulties, pregnancy and childbirth than in male sexual dysfunction. This difference should not be overlooked. We shall confine our discussion to pathology which seems to be psychosomatic, that is, pathology in which emotional factors play a leading part.

Almost everyone knows that the menstrual cycle is sensitive to emotional disturbances, especially to anxiety and mood disorders, and that emotional factors may also play an important role in ovulation, conception, pregnancy and childbirth. When we come to the nursing and general care of babies and children we find ourselves once more in the realm of interpersonal behavior. The most far-reaching investigation of female dysfunction, in all of its aspects, is that of Benedek and Robbins, to which the reader is referred with the caution that much of it still needs confirmation.[42] The earlier pioneer work on the psychology of women by Helene Deutsch, in two volumes, also deserves careful attention.[43] No attempt will be made here to summarize these works, since they are easily available and much too extensive for a brief review.

There is widespread recognition today that gynecological disorders often involve important emotional factors. This is obvious in the practice of gynecologists and obstetricians who refer their patients with emotional problems to a psychiatrist who has also had some training in their field.

There seems to be a close relationship in women between gonadal function

[42] Benedek, T., and Rubenstein, B. B., *The Sexual Cycle in Women: The Relation Between Ovarian Function and Psychodynamic Process*. Washington, D.C.: National Res. Council, 1942.

[43] Deutsch, H., *The Psychology of Women* (1925). New York: Grune & Stratton, 1944-1945.

and emotional reactions. Gonodal hormones stimulate emotional manifesta-tions of sex drive; conversely, emotion influences the menstrual flow, as well as the time and the number of ovulations. A lack or a poverty of menstrual flow appears to be often a defense against sexuality. Painful menses may accompany incomplete sexual maturity or they may represent a regression. Latent sexual conflicts produce anxiety; and this in turn seems to predispose a woman to an increased reaction to the hormonal changes of the premenstrual period. Although menstruation is a normal physiological process, women describe it by such terms as "the curse" or "sickness," in part because of the negative attitudes attached to it by tradition and folklore.

Frigidity, or lack of a satisfying sexual responsiveness, is a common disturbance among women which, like impotence in men, is usually part of a neurosis, a psychosis, or a personality disorder. In the past, there has been a misleading tendency to regard the vagina as the female counterpart of the penis, and to depreciate the role of erectile tissue in the female as "pregenital fixations" which should be outgrown. This interpretation is contrary to the anatomical and physiological facts. Excepting at its orifice, the vagina contributes little in the way of erotic stimulation during normal intercourse, while the clitoris and other erectile structures contribute a great deal.[44] Frigidity involves failure on the part of the woman to respond with orgasm when these structures are stimulated in normal intercourse. This failure may result from a wide variety of sources, including current attitudes toward the man, anxieties over being physically damaged or be-coming pregnant, when pregnancy is not desired, and a matrix of negative feminine attitudes arising during childhood, latency and adolescence. The nature of the relationships between a woman's own parents often plays a significant part in determining these attitudes. So also do parental warnings and current folklore.[45]

Pregnancy itself results in a wide variety of personal reactions. Some women experience a pleasurable, narcissistic gratification. They say that they have never felt better in their lives. It is still unclear whether this feeling is the direct result of hormonal changes, or whether it comes more indirectly from the satisfaction of their increased dependency needs, or from a sense of increased significance as an expectant mother.

[44] Benedek, T., "Sexual functions in women and their disturbance," in Arieti, S. (Ed.), *American Handbook of Psychiatry.* New York: Basic Books, 1959, pp. 727–748; Marmor, J., "Some considerations concerning orgasm in the female," *Psychosom. Med.* 1954, *16,* 240–245.

[45] See the panel discussion in Moore, B. E. (reporter), "Frigidity in women," *J. Amer. Psychoanal. Ass.,* 1961, *9,* 571–584. See also Davids, A., de Vault, S., and Talmadge, M., "Psychological study of emotional factors in pregnancy: a preliminary report," *Psychosom. Med.,* 1961, *23,* 93–103; Wenar, C., Handlon, M. W., and Garner, A. M., "Pat-terns of mothering in psychosomatic disorders and severe emotional disturbances," *Merrill-Palmer Quart.,* 1960, *6,* 165–170; Ryle, A., "The psychological disturbances asso-ciated with 345 pregnancies in 137 women," *J. ment. Sci.,* 1961, *107,* 279–286.

Differences in the ways different women experience *childbirth* are clearly related to their fears and anxieties, or to their sense of triumph and creation, as well as to objective realities of the childbirth situation.[46] The so-called "natural childbirth" movement is based upon these relations. It attempts to train the pregnant woman in the cooperative use of her body during the birth process and to reduce her anticipatory anxiety. Many women who remain conscious throughout the process remember it as an ecstatic experience of fulfillment during which their creativity was fully expressed.

Breast-feeding represents another function in which emotional factors play a significant part. Some mothers enjoy the experience in their own way as much as the infant does. Others avoid it altogether. Still others attempt to breast-feed but are foiled by their own anxiety, which either interferes with milk-production, or else leaves the mother unable to relax and enter into breast-feeding pleasurably in spite of a plentiful milk supply. Self-criticism and self-doubts concerning maternal adequacy are common in this situation when an infant is restless, cries or refuses to nurse. In addition to all kinds of possible conflicts from the past, there is usually a sense of competing with other mothers in this respect, or of measuring up to the new mother's own standards, and those of her own mother.

Dynamic and Developmental Background of Psychosomatic Disorders

There are two questions which are basic to the psychopathology of psychosomatic disorders, neither of which has been as yet answered to everyone's satisfaction. The first asks why the patient reacts to stress with *primitive autonomic* and *vegetative changes* at a *physiological level*. The second question asks why *some particular tissue, organ* or *system* should be utilized by one patient and *some other one* by another patient.

Why does anyone get a psychosomatic disorder?

This question asks, in effect, why the patient does not react to stress with a neurosis or a psychosis.

The *neurotic patient,* as we have seen, manages his otherwise intolerable tension and anxiety by means of a compromise, the product of which we call the *neurotic symptom*. This compromise includes the regressive reactivation of infantile material, some of which escapes repression. But the neurotic patient's defensive organization is relatively intact, so that his symptom is usually limited in scope.

[46] Cf. Rosengren, W. R., "Some social psychological aspects of delivery room difficulties," *J. nerv. ment. Dis.*, 1961, *132*, 515–521.

In *psychotic patients*, the regression is deeper than in neurosis, and it is usually subtotal in extent. What we call the *psychotic symptom* is likewise an attempt at a compromise — e.g., the delusion or the hallucination — but unlike the neurotic compromise it involves serious distortions of reality. This is because of the massive breakthrough of primary process material which the symptom attempts to include by reconstructing external reality.

The person with a *psychosomatic disorder* neither forms a neurotic compromise nor seriously distorts external reality. Instead, he tries to discharge his tensions and relieve his anxiety through direct autonomous and visceral processes. How is this to be explained? A great many ingenious explanations have been offered by experts in this field. To do justice to them and their authors would require volumes. We shall have to be satisfied here with a small sampling of certain representative views.[47]

One point on which there is general agreement is that psychosomatic disorders are deep regressions to an almost undifferentiated phase of ego development. This agreement rests upon the primitive physiological character of the psychosomatic reaction. With few exceptions, a working distinction can be made even between the *psychosomatic disorders* and such neuroses as *anxiety reactions* and *conversions*. The neuroses employ obvious fantasy and symbol in creating the neurotic symptom, whereas there is an apparent lack of such fantasy and symbolization in the psychosomatic disorders.

A differentiation is sometimes difficult to make with respect to *anxiety reactions* because of their diffuse character. A careful study of the patients themselves, however, brings out a great deal of unconscious symbolism in anxiety reactions, as we saw in the case of Walter A. This is quite different from the lack or the paucity of symbolism in psychosomatic disorders.

As for *conversion symptoms*, they almost always use unconscious symbolization which involves sense organs or the skeletal musculature (paralyses, anesthesias, blindness, deafness, etc.). Their symbolization can usually be translated into relatively sophisticated verbal statements, which is not the case in psychosomatic disorders. We cannot expect a patient to exclude mixtures of the two methods of dealing with stress, of course, and this seems to happen when the symptoms overlap, such as in cases of anorexia, recurrent vomiting and pseudo-pregnancy.

The *deep physiological regression* characteristic of *psychosomatic dis-*

---

[47] For a recent overview, see the section on psychosomatic disorders in Arieti, S. (Ed.), *American Handbook of Psychiatry*. New York: Basic Books, 1959. pp. 647–696. See also Grinker, R. R., and Robbins, F. P., *Psychosomatic Case Book*. New York: Blakiston, 1954; Schur, M., "The ego in anxiety," in Loewenstein, R. M. (Ed.), *Drives, Affects, Behavior*. New York: Internat. Univ. Press, 1953, pp. 67–103; Jacobson, E., "The effects and their pleasure-unpleasure qualities in relation to the psychic discharge process," in Loewenstein, R. M., (Ed.), *Drives, Affects, Behavior*. New York: Internat. Univ. Press, 1953, pp. 38–66; Schur, M., "Comments on the metapsychology of somatization," *The Psychoanalytic Study of the Child*. Internat. Univ. Press, 1955, vol. 10, pp. 119–164 (includes 93 references); Delafresnaye, J. F. (Ed.), *Brain Mechanisms and Consciousness*. Oxford, England: Blackwell, 1954.

orders has received many interpretations. Purely physiological hypotheses are widely used. Since the autonomic nervous system, the internal organs and the skin are involved in a variety of different ways, we have many interpretations which are confined to interrelationships between the central nervous system and the autonomic nervous system, including the latter's central nervous system centers.

Within recent years, there have been rapid advances in knowledge of the physiology of these systems, a greater emphasis than ever upon feedback systems, new discoveries concerning the hypothalamus, the limbic system and the reticular systems, and a differentiation between the secretion of noradrenalin and epinephrin by the adrenal glands. All this has carried knowledge and speculation far beyond the phase in which Cannon formulated his relationship between the adrenal glands, the autonomic nervous system and emotional expression. To cite one example from among a multitude, peptic ulcers have been experimentally produced through direct stimulation of the hypothalamus, which itself acts upon the anterior pituitary gland, the reticular system, the vagus nerve and the adrenals.[48]

Attempts have been renewed to picture the sympathetic division of the autonomic nervous system as acting in opposition to the parasympathetic division, to explain certain emotional effects. In some functions these two divisions seem actually to be in opposition; but they also cooperate, a quick sympathetic discharge being followed by a slower parasympathetic discharge. A *general adaptation syndrome,* as well as *local adaptation syndromes,* have been invoked to account for general health and disease, in addition to psychosomatic disorders.[49] The weakness of all purely physiological approaches to the problems of psychosomatic disorders is that they all but ignore interpersonal relationships within the social structure of human beings, and the internal psychological interrelationships such as we have sketched in the chapter on the psychodynamic system.

The overwhelming importance of the internal psychic life of the human being, so different from anything found among other living organisms, and the intricately structured emotional interactions among human beings in a socially integrated society, cannot be slighted in dealing with the psychosomatic disorders, any more than can the physiological factors. We must always bear in mind the fact that, no matter how regressive a psychosomatic disorder may be, it occurs in an adult who has a lifetime of acquired experience and behavior built into his responsive equipment. As was the case also in the neuroses and the psychoses, regression in psychosomatic disorders is never the same thing as a return to infancy. Infants do not have the background of a long life of secondary process experience; and very early in their life they show little differentiation in their emotional responses to frustration.

[48] French, J. D., *et al.,* "Experimental observations on psychosomatic mechanisms. I. Gastrointestinal disturbances," *Am. Med. Ass. Arch. Neurol. Psychiat.,* 1954, *72,* 267.

[49] Selye, H., *The Stress of Life.* New York: McGraw-Hill, 1956.

The psychosomatic patient, in spite of his physiological regression, still has a highly organized ego system, a superego with its ego-ideal, immensely complex defensive systems, and a wealth of secondary process thinking. In short, the man who suffers from peptic ulcer or essential hypertension because of inappropriate, regressive emotional discharge, may at the same time be earning a good living in a difficult job, taking care of his family at an adult level, and contributing to his community in mature ways. As in the rest of psychopathology, we are dealing here not only with a regression to primitive levels, but also with the reactions of the adult personality to the regression, in so far as the adult personality remains maturely integrated. With this in mind, we can turn to the contributions toward understanding psychosomatic regression which Grinker and his associates have made, and those of Schur, as examples of modern thinking in this area.

Grinker points up the similarities between psychosomatic disorders and infantile emotional discharge. When a very young infant reacts to stress, he does so in a total way, using everything he has available in discharging tension. Even after he has progressed in differentiating his experience and behavior at preverbal levels, he still remains subject to emotional storms, occurring at a physiological level.[50] As time goes on, the infant differentiates the psychological or psychic from the physiological, and within the psychic systems he makes those differentiations which we have discussed as the *psychodynamic system* in Chapter 5. Grinker and others, including the independent work of Schur, maintain that when the psychosomatic patient regresses he loses his acquired reactions to the particular stress involved. In this sense, he suffers a *dedifferentiation*. He deals with *excessive tension* and *anxiety* in *primitive ways* which disturb and may damage visceral structures. The exact form of these primitive ways, which differ among different adults, are believed to have been determined by experiences during the first two years of life. They may then be used in meeting almost any form of adult stress, even though the psychosomatic response is wholly inappropriate in adulthood. This is the same phenomenon which we pointed out in the obsessive compulsive neuroses, where we saw a patient soiling herself slightly, and indulging in an orgy of handwashing, in response to almost *any increase in tension* — a generalization which developed, however, during the course of an adult neurosis.

Grinker brings to his interpretations a vast clinical experience, with combat personnel in the infantry and the air force, and with civilians in a metropolitan hospital which includes an institute devoted to psychosomatic research.[51] He describes a "field concept" in relation to psychosomatic disorders. He emphasizes the fact that every internal organ and system is

---

[50] Grinker, R. R., *Psychosomatic Research*. New York: Norton, 1953.
[51] Grinker, R. R., and Spiegel, J. P., *War Neuroses*. Philadelphia: Blakiston, 1945; Grinker, R. R., and Spiegel, J. P., *Men Under Stress*. Philadelphia: Blakiston, 1945; Grinker, R. R., and Robbins, F. P., *Psychosomatic Case Book*. New York: Blakiston, 1954.

intimately integrated with every other organ and system in the body, that each organ or system has all the other organs and systems as its environment, and in turn helps to make up the environment of each of the other internal organs and systems. The organism as a whole shares a total environment with other human beings, and interacts with them under conditions of stress.

Under conditions of extreme, traumatic stress, such as one meets in military combat situations, some adults lose their emotional differentiations. They react much as an infant reacts under emotional stress, with crying, vomiting, diarrhea, random movements and infantile postures. We can take this as the extreme example which illustrates *dedifferentiation* in physiological regression. It is not found in peacetime situations, even among paratroopers exposed to stress.[52] In lesser and more chronic stresses, or in repeatedly recurrent stress, changes may develop in an organ (e.g., smooth muscle alterations); and if the stress persists there may be damage to the tissues. In human beings, psychosomatic disorders are not expressions of symbolism, but rather expressions of excessive energy in the vegetative system which cannot find an outlet.

Schur links the *inability of the psychosomatic patient to find adequate outlets for his tensions* with his *regression to primary processes*, which the patient cannot recognize, and which he could not express adequately even if he did recognize them. Schur uses the concepts of *somatization, desomatization* and *resomatization* in describing what takes place in psychosomatic regression.[53] As the normal infant grows into normal childhood, says Schur, much of his experience and behavior becomes *desomatized*. It differentiates from the earlier global emotional experiences and expressions toward more mature patterns which include secondary process symbolization, motor coordination, thinking and communication. Libidinal and aggressive energies are progressively neutralized and brought under ego control for secondary process use. The primitive fantasying and daydreaming of early childhood is gradually replaced in the preconscious and conscious organizations by increasingly logical thinking, verbalization, communication, and controlled, differentiated emotional expression. This whole process may be called a *progressive desomatization*.

The psychosomatic patient, when he regresses, in part reverses this process. The work of desomatization — which leads normally from the phase of emotional storms to the establishment of secondary process thinking and emotional differentiation — is in part undone. The patient once more expresses his stresses, frustrations, sexuality, dependency needs or rage, directly in autonomic and visceral hyperactivity. This is a *resomatization* of

52 Basowitz, H., Persky, H., Korchin, S. J., and Grinker, R. R., *Anxiety and Stress.* New York: McGraw-Hill, 1955.

53 Schur, M., "The ego in anxiety," in Lowenstein, R. M. (Ed.), *Drives, Affects, Behavior.* New York: Internat. Univ. Press, 1933, pp. 67–103; Schur, M., "Comments on the metapsychology of somatization," *The Psychoanalytic Study of the Child.* New York: Internat. Univ. Press, 1955, vol. 10, pp. 119–164.

the emotional expression which, if it persists, may lead to increasing and irreversible tissue damage.

It is worth noting that, although most of Schur's clinical examples are taken from skin disturbances and allergies, his principles apply to psychosomatic disorders in general, and they do not contradict the major conclusions reached by Grinker from different material. We have already mentioned that the skin, even though it is the most external part of the body, behaves in many ways like an internal organ. Its extensive vascular and secretory activities are for the most part not under voluntary control, and neither are the changes that take place in its structure. Schur believes that skin lesions may function like conversion symptoms when they *first erupt*, but *not afterwards*. He makes interesting comparisons between psychosomatic skin disorders, conversion reactions and schizophrenia, which are beyond the scope of our discussion.[54] We turn now to our second question which is concerned with the choice of psychosomatic symptom.

"Choice" of organ or system

Why does one psychosomatic patient develop disturbances in one organ, system or tissue, while another psychosomatic patient develops disturbances in another? Why, for example, does one emotionally disturbed person develop peptic ulcer, another essential hypertension, and a third a skin disorder? This is basically the same question as that of the "choice" of neurosis; and our answers are similar. We have some interesting leads but no definitive conclusions.

Some of the leads have already been mentioned in the preceding discussions of the various systems involved in psychosomatic disorder. There seems to be a preponderance of passive dependent persons, who strive reactively to be self-sufficient, among patients with peptic ulcers; but some peptic ulcer patients feel angry and hostile inside. Bronchial asthma in some patients seems related to a cry for help or a need to confess to a mother figure, but it appears only in persons who are physiologically allergic. There is no reason to assume that every asthmatic patient belongs to this psychological group.[55]

In other words, we seem to be dealing with multiple factors in the "choice" of psychosomatic symptom, and not with a simple cause-and-effect relationship. Even among the most skeptical of experts there is a feeling that some as yet undiscovered complex relationship exists between consti-

[54] See Schur, M., "Comments on the metapsychology of somatization," *The Psychoanalytic Study of the Child.* New York: Internat. Univ. Press, 1955, vol. 10, pp. 119–164; Ittelson, W. H., Seidenberg, B., and Kutash, S. B., "Some perceptual differences in somatizing and nonsomatizing neuropsychiatric patients," *Psychosom. Med.*, 1961, 23, 219–223.

[55] French, T. M., Alexander, F., *et al.*, *Psychogenic Factors in Bronchial Asthma.* Parts I and II, *Psychosom. Med. Monogr.*, *IV* and *II*, Nos. I and II. Washington, D.C.: National Res. Council, 1941.

tution, personality type, infantile experiences and some special organic involvement, on the one hand, and the site of the psychosomatic disorder, on the other hand. No one has so far come up with a wholly satisfactory solution of the problem. Let us review briefly some of the attempts which have been made.

At one extreme are the hereditary, constitutional and congenital sensitivity theories. No one doubts that newborns differ in their autonomic nervous system patterns and in their potentialities for vegetative response to stress. We pointed out in Chapter 2 that no two newborns are anatomically and physiologically identical, even identical twins. Such individual differences must include the internal organs, the skin, the autonomic nervous system and its central nervous system representation. Even though newborns respond to stress with everything they have, as Grinker and Wolff have emphasized, there must be differences in their total patterns, both qualitatively and quantitatively.

The trouble with this kind of explanation is that it is too general, and so far it has been neither confirmed nor refuted. There seem to be familial tendencies to develop diabetes and essential hypertension, for example, quite apart from questions of psychosomatic disorder. As for peptic ulcer, it has been demonstrated among newborns, by Mirsky and others, when longings for dependence and striving for self-sufficiency do not exist.[56] Congenital differences in activity levels, sensitivity and responsiveness have been found, but even these are not simple factors because they involve interaction with the mother. A mother begins to respond with her own characteristic behavior to her newborn infant from the very start. Her responses must be increasingly important factors in the situation as the infant begins to develop his first primitive discriminations. The hereditary, constitutional and congenital sensitivity theories are really ways of saying, "He was born that way."

Closely related to hereditary, constitutional and congenital theories are those which try to explain the "choice" of psychosomatic disorder on the grounds of the *special weakness* or the *overuse* of a particular organ, tissue or system. Some writers maintain that emotional disturbances injure an already inadequate, abnormal body part, one that has developed abnormally during intrauterine life or early infancy, or one that has been damaged by childhood infection, metabolic deficiency or injury. Others point out that an originally normal body part might become the site of psychosomatic disorder because it has been a source of strength in early childhood, and has therefore borne the brunt of emotional stress. Such hypotheses also can be neither confirmed nor refuted at present.

At the other extreme are the "specificity" theories which seek to account for the site of psychosomatic disorders in terms of the constellation of problems facing the adult patient, and the specific pattern of his emotional

---

[56] Mirsky, I. H., "Psychoanalysis and the biological sciences," in Alexander, F., and Ross, H. (Eds.), *Twenty Years of Psychoanalysis.* New York: Norton, 1953, pp. 155–176.

response to the stress which these problems represent. No matter how diffuse the autonomic nervous system and the visceral responses may be, there are certainly marked differences in adult *experience* and *behavior* during fear, rage and love. Moreover, there are marked individual differences in the *specific patterns* of fear, rage and love among different adults. And among adults there are many who suppress their responses with the help of reaction formation, so that while they experience at some level one kind of emotional expression, they also experience its opposite at another level.

"Specificity" theories seemed at first to be borne out by the detailed, prolonged study of individual patients. As more reports appeared, and different investigators became interested in more and more kinds of psychosomatic disorder, the "specificity" theories as complete explanations came more and more into question, even among those who first proposed them. Some found their peptic ulcer patients to be passively dependent, for example, while others found them filled with rage, whether they longed for dependence or not. The complexity of emotional response in adults, the quick shifts from fear or passivity to fury and hostility, and the simultaneous presence of both dependent longings and hostile resentment over their frustrations, or even over having to be in a dependent position — all these contribute to the inadequacy of the "specificity" theories to account for the facts now at our disposal.[57]

A *compromise* between the extremes of *congenital weakness* and *adult conflict,* contained in Grinker's reports, has much to be said for it. This compromise begins with the observation that a young infant's emotional storms are not specific, but seem to involve the whole organism at once, just as the emotional storms of some severely traumatized combat personnel do. During the first two years of life, however, each child develops differentiations, in his emotional experiences and expressions, just as in the rest of his behavior and experience. This is normally one of an intimate mother-child relationship. The mother's reactions have to be considered as part of every interaction, and as important determinants of the child's emotional expression.

Even a child with normal emotional organization may suppress or distort his emotional discharge because of maternal anxiety, overconcern, indifference or hostility. A child burdened from the moment of birth with general hyperactivity in his emotional responses, with an unusual degree of anxiety or fury, or with a specific tendency for one organ, one system or one kind of tissue to take the burden of emotional expression, would be even more vulnerable to specific maternal reactions. During these first two years, as we saw in Chapter 2, oral dependent needs and later needs for self-assertion, which inevitably involve bowel training crises, are of great intensity. The

[57] Buck, C., and Hobbs, G. E., "The problem of specificity in psychosomatic illness," *Psychosom. Res.,* 1959, 3, 227–233.

infant and very young child has little chance of finding relief in substitute expressions or activities which play so important a role in adult emotional control and channelling.

Dependency needs persist in everyone throughout life, as normal components of human love and human interdependence. So also do needs for self-assertion and independence, and the ability to be angry on occasion and express it. The ability to be anxious, fearful, aggressive, trustful and loving, under appropriate conditions, are likewise normal aspects of human experience and behavior. The difficulty lies in achieving a good balance among these capacities, and in releasing emotional expressions appropriately, within reasonable bounds.

The preferred pattern of expressing emotional stress in adulthood may be a repetition of a pattern learned in early childhood, just as is often the case in neurotic symptoms. It is perhaps unreasonable to look for *specific adult patterns of stress* and *specific adult constellations of emotional expression* to account for the *form* of a psychosomatic disorder. The adult emotional expression, with its "choice" of symptomatology, may only represent something learned early in life which is irrationally repeated whenever the patient feels under stress. This would make it an exaggerated *visceral mannerism.*

We have several times called attention to the enormous enrichment of human life which comes from the ability to imagine, to plan and to remember. We have said also that these abilities expose human beings to hazards which seem not to be the lot of other living organisms. A person can worry about dangers weeks or years before they come, and about dangers that never come. He can become angry and remain angry for weeks or months over something which he cannot express, or which he expresses but keeps on generating a smouldering anger. He may not even realize at preconscious and conscious levels that he is angry, but his viscera go right on expressing the anger at unconscious levels. A person can remember and fantasy about past fears, past hates, past frustrations and past guilt, reviving as he does so all the visceral intensities which were part of the original experience.

All such reactions are inappropriate biologically, however justified or understandable they may be in a social sense. They are, in effect, misuses and abuses of biological mechanisms designed to alert the organism, to put it on an emergency basis, or to prepare it to endure an unusual hardship by mobilizing its biological resources. The visceral systems that are involved in *long-lasting emotional expression* cannot be expected to function normally in performing their *nonemotional tasks.* The continually hyperactive, hypersecretory stomach, for example, is not nearly as good a digestive organ as the stomach that increases its motility and secretion only during periods of hunger and the approach of food.

In the face of so much conflicting evidence and so much controversy, it seems wise to follow Lidz's suggestion that the search for some kind of specificity be continued critically, even though it has so far not met complete success.[58] With more sophisticated theoretical constructions, and with further clinical studies carried out under controlled conditions, it may some day be possible to be more specific about psychosomatic disorders, and to bring them under better therapeutic control. Whether or not they can, as a group, be prevented depends as much upon social and cultural factors as upon physiological ones, since individual modes of emotional experience and expression develop and differentiate within specific interpersonal relationships. A repressive society, or a repressive family structure, should result in more psychosomatic disorder than a freely expressive one.

We turn now to a consideration of *acute and chronic brain disorders* which result in, or are accompanied by, psychopathology related to the disturbance of brain function.

[58] Lidz, T., "General concepts of psychosomatic medicine," in Arieti, S. (Ed.), *American Handbook of Psychiatry*. New York: Basic Books, 1959, pp. 647–658.

21

Acute and Chronic Brain Disorders

THE BRAIN, EVEN TO A GREATER DEGREE THAN MOST OTHER ORGANS, depends upon the maintenance of physiological equilibrium within a relatively narrow range if it is to operate effectively. Anything that seriously interferes with this equilibrium will reduce cerebral competence, and may result in pathological behavior and experience. Among the common sources of disturbed equilibrium are marked changes in temperature, in water balance and in the concentration of electrolytes in the brain, interference with the supply of oxygen and food materials, and interference with the removal of waste products from the brain. The recent demonstration by our astronauts that human control of space flight may be more effective than automatic machine control has given new emphasis to the importance of maintaining an optimal equilibrium in brain physiology during space exploration. In the life of the ordinary earthbound human being such changes as the above are involved in the many forms of intoxication, in disorders of the cardiovascular system, in head injury, brain disease and brain deterioration.

If a disturbance in the physiological equilibrium of the brain is sudden and severe it may help precipitate one of the major clinical syndromes of acute brain disorder — *delirium, stupor* or *coma.* If, however, such a disturbance develops slowly, it may be paralleled by some degree of compensatory adaptation, psychological as well as physiological. In this case there may be little impairment of cerebral function for a long time, even in some cases for a lifetime. Nevertheless, in many instances there comes a sudden halt to the compensatory adaptation, the brain decompensates and precipitates an acute brain disorder.

The effectiveness of compensatory adaptation varies considerably from individual to individual, under comparable circumstances, and even in the same person under different physiological and psychological stresses.[1] In alcoholic intoxication, for example, if the dosage of alcohol is held constant, the same person will react differently when such conditions as food and water intake, work, rest, incentive and social stimulation are varied. When all these conditions are controlled and the dosage held constant, it is still possible to demonstrate marked individual differences in susceptibility to alcoholic intoxication. As we shall see later, there is also wide diversity among different individuals, and in the same person under different conditions, when it comes to other forms of intoxication, to cardiovascular disturbances, head injury, brain disease and brain deterioration.

Cerebral incompetence often develops gradually and progressively without an acute episode. Senile persons who develop progressive cerebral incompetence usually show a gradual, undramatic decline in their adaptive capacity.[2] Some of these decline even to the level of an almost vegetative existence without developing an acute behavioral disturbance of any consequence. Ultimately they may require institutionalization, but only because their home environment cannot provide the degree of protection and care which their incompetence demands.

Finally, there are many cases of head injury, brain infection, cerebral arteriosclerosis and even senile deterioration in which the progress of cerebral incompetence may be halted or even reversed. Persons with brain damage are often able to adapt satisfactorily to life at home, or outside the home as a boarder, or even in an institution, provided that enough is expected of them to make full use of their potential, but they are not exposed to more demand than they can meet. Institutional life usually offers the poorest prognosis. The lack of freedom and privacy, the monotony and boredom, the loss of friends and the sense of having been deserted are enough in themselves to lead to an irreversible deterioration. We shall return to a discussion of this toward the end of the chapter.

Today it is generally recognized that cerebral incompetence, unless it is sudden and severe or profound and inclusive, need not necessarily lead to outspoken psychopathology. When it does, there are usually other factors to be considered. For, on the one hand, we know that brain injury, infection or intoxication may help precipitate psychopathology which then becomes chronic, or grows progressively worse, even though meanwhile there has been complete recovery from the cellular effects of the cerebral damage.

---

[1] Cf. Phillips, L., and Zigler, E., "Social competence: the action-thought parameter and vicariousness in normal and pathological behavior," *J. abnorm. soc. Psychol.*, 1961, 63, 137–146.

[2] Cumming, E., and Henry, W. E., *Growing Old*. New York: Basic Books, 1961.

On the other hand, we know that severe neurotic or psychotic reactions may develop during senile deterioration, for example, and then clear up without a corresponding improvement in the senile picture.[3]

It is also recognized today that many neurotic and psychotic reactions appearing in the wake of cerebral incompetence are not actually *brain disorders*, but are the reactions of sick or injured persons to the fact or the consequences of being sick or injured. In this sense they are not fundamentally different from neurotic and psychotic reactions to illness or injury involving other parts of the body. Thus, for example, a person may develop an *anxiety reaction* to having broken his head as well as to having broken his leg. Another may react with an *agitated depression* or with *mania* to attacks of dizziness and fainting, whether these attacks result from cardiac disease or from cerebral arteriosclerosis. A third may develop a *conversion reaction* following head injury for the same reasons that he might have developed it following a back injury.

With these considerations as our general background we may pass on to a discussion of the syndromes of acute and chronic cerebral incompetence, their relation to personal and situational stress, and their misidentification by some patients who are reacting with psychopathology to being ill or to having had an accident.

Syndromes of Acute and Chronic Cerebral Incompetence

Acute and chronic brain disorders, when they involve cerebral incompetence, yield an almost infinite diversity of signs and symptoms, whose relative importance varies according to the special interests of the person studying them. For the sake of brevity and clarity, we shall restrict our discussion to those signs and symptoms which are of common occurrence and of special interest to the student of psychopathology. These we shall group into the syndromes of *acute cerebral incompetence*, usually of relatively short duration, and of *chronic cerebral incompetence*, which last long and often have a progressive downhill course.

Acute cerebral incompetence

The major syndromes of acute cerebral incompetence are *acute delirium*, *stupor* and *coma*. Of these, by far the most interesting from the standpoint of behavior pathology is the acute delirium. *Coma* is a state of maximal unreactivity short of death; it is what is popularly known as unconsciousness. In *stupor* a person is difficult to arouse and to keep aroused. In what follows we shall only mention coma and stupor incidentally. Our discussion of acute cerebral incompetence will deal mainly with delirium.

[3] Stein, M. R., Vidich, A. J., and White, D. M. (Eds.), *Identity and Anxiety*. Glencoe, Ill.: Free Press, 1960.

Acute delirium. Acute delirium is a syndrome of acute cerebral incompetence which is characterized by gross disorientation, defective memory, hallucinations and delusions. To an observer the delirious patient appears at first restless, irritable and confused. His attention is difficult to get and to hold; he seems uncertain as to his whereabouts and the identity of persons and objects around him; his talk becomes rambling or groping, and he misspeaks, slurs and mispronounces words. At night he sleeps fitfully and awakens often with a start. He complains of weird and terrifying dreams, and of dreamlike hypnagogic hallucinations when he shuts his eyes. He begins to show obvious defects in recent memory and immediate recall; but his remote memory may at first be relatively little affected.

As the delirium progresses the patient appears increasingly confused and disoriented. He now misidentifies persons and objects and grossly misinterprets what is going on in his environment. He may develop tremors which are particularly noticeable in the fingers, tongue and facial muscles. He may become ataxic, show marked reflex changes and sweat profusely. He grows more and more restless and sleepless, hallucinating now with his eyes wide open, in the daytime as well as at night.

Sometimes the delirious person speaks to those around him as though they were other people with different functions. Sometimes he seems to be listening to and talking to hallucinated persons in hallucinated settings. Every now and then he may attempt to get up and go out in response to imagined demands made upon him, or to imagined threats made against him, his relatives or friends. Often he engages in confused, fragmentary activities which resemble his usual occupation or some habitual mode of entertainment. When interfered with or restrained, he may quiet down for a time, or he may respond with angry or frightened combative behavior, which is sometimes dangerous to himself or to others.

The acute delirious syndrome may last a few hours, or persist for days or weeks, and in exceptional cases for many months. It is not rare for a person in the midst of a delirium to clear up suddenly for a brief period and then lapse into as great confusion as ever. This transient clearing-up is the so-called *lucid interval*.

An acutely delirious elderly man suddenly improved one afternoon and began asking for information as to where he was and what had happened to him. He conversed connectedly with the nurse and the physician, discussed persons and places of mutual interest, described accurately a previous visit to another division of the hospital, and appeared to understand his present situation. His speech was a little slow, there was some groping for words, and there were occasional long silences; but otherwise there was nothing unusual in his behavior. By evening, however, this man's talk was becoming less adequate, and by night he was again acutely delirious. His delirium had followed an arteriosclerotic cerebral accident or "stroke." He made a partial recovery after four months of delirium, but less than a year later death came as the result of a second cerebral accident.

Recovery from acute delirium may be a gradual affair, with progressive improvement in cerebral competence; or it may occur rapidly, following a deep sleep, as in many cases of febrile disease. If, on the other hand, the acutely incompetent brain becomes still more incompetent physiologically, the patient typically becomes less and less reactive. His noisy restlessness and insomnia give place to drowsiness and torpor, with occasional tossing about. His movements are slower, more aimless and disjunctive. His speech becomes fragmentary, incoherent and muttering. He may then become at first difficult to arouse and to keep aroused (*stupor*), and later on impossible to arouse (*coma*). In the moribund patient deepening stupor and coma are the usual preludes to death. The patient who recovers from a comatose state returns to normal as a rule by way of stupor. The stuporous patient, as he improves, sometimes passes through a delirious phase on the road to recovery.

When cerebral incompetence occurs suddenly, as in cases of head injury, cerebral hemorrhage, blood loss, massive infection or overwhelming intoxication, the comatose state may be almost instantaneously induced. Persons recovering from abruptly induced coma sometimes also pass through a delirious syndrome, after first passing through a stuporous phase.

A young adult who had sustained a severe head injury in an explosion spent several days in profound coma. Then, as he improved, he became active enough intermittently to be called stuporous. Finally he developed a typical acute delirium which lasted several weeks. Marked defects in orientation and recall persisted throughout most of the delirious period, but the ultimate recovery was complete, with no defects that could be detected on clinical examination.

Dynamic background of acute delirium. In acute delirium we see what happens to human behavior and experience when the body's chief organ of integration, the brain, suffers from an acute physiological disruption of function. We shall discuss first the changes that appear on the surface as behavioral disorganization. The normal continuity and relatedness of behavior disappears; and in its place we see behavior that is fragmentary, haphazard and chaotic.

The overt manifestations of behavioral disorganization may be considered under four major categories: (1) *incoordination;* (2) *interpenetration;* (3) *fragmentation;* and (4) *overinclusion.* These do not represent mutually exclusive categories, but merely four convenient groupings. None of them is confined to delirium.[4] It is only their combination with gross disorientation, memory defect, delusions and hallucinations which is specific to delirium.

---

[4] For a discussion of *behavioral disorganization,* which includes *delirium,* see Cameron, N., and Magaret, A., *Behavior Pathology.* Boston: Houghton Mifflin, 1951, Chapter 15.

1. *Incoordination.* Incoordination of behavior results from the inter-ference of disruptive tensions and movements which break up normal timing and harmony (*synergy*) of behavior. Unsteadiness and tremor destroy a person's precision. The uncoordinated person overreaches, underreaches, and misdirects his movements.[5] If disorganization of behavior becomes severe, a person can no longer stand, walk or manipulate objects adequately. He may sway, stagger, misstep, fumble and even lurch or fall to the ground. In speech and thinking the disorganized person manifests similar defects. His speech becomes slurred, disjointed and unsteady. He mispronounces and misspeaks. He may be unable to recall familiar words and names. He gives signs that his thinking changes its normal pace, loses direction and becomes both undependable and unpredictable. Often it is the loss of coordinated speech and thinking that appears earliest, and most disturbs the disorganizing person.[6]

2. *Interpenetration.* Here an intrusive movement, word or thought appears inappropriately in some ongoing activity which actually belongs to some other activity. In normal life many of the absurd actions performed by preoccupied persons are examples of interpenetration. A preoccupied man may go to a closet to get a jacket, only to find that he has put on his hat as though he were going out. The concept of interpenetration was originally formulated in relation to speech and thinking;[7] and it is in talking and thinking that we encounter the most significant examples from everyday life. Freud's early and systematic account of slips of the tongue and pen includes the interpenetration of preconscious and conscious thought and action by products of unconscious themes.[8] In delirium, as we shall see in a moment, the behavioral disorganization is compounded because of the invasion of pre-conscious and conscious processes by derivatives of unconscious primary processes.

3. *Fragmentation.* This refers to the appearance of discontinuous and abortive behavior, to the interruption of a theme begun, by its sudden termi-nation, often followed by a silence or by something quite unrelated. Surprise, shock and the demands of competing stimulation under stress may fragment behavior in normal persons. In delirium and in severe schizophrenic regres-sion we find the most dramatic examples of fragmentation, in which some-times no two successive actions or thoughts seem related to one another.

---

[5] Cf. Ferraro, A., "Presenile psychoses, senile psychoses and psychoses with cerebral arteriosclerosis," in Arieti, S. (Ed.), *American Handbook of Psychiatry*. New York: Basic Books, 1959, pp. 1021–1108.

[6] See the account of experimentally induced incoordination in Luria, A., *The Nature of Human Conflicts* (trans. H. Gantt). New York: Liveright, 1932.

[7] Cameron, N., "The geography of disordered reasoning," in Beck, S. J., and Molish, H. B., *Reflexes to Intelligence*. Glencoe, Ill.: Free Press, 1959, pp. 299–308.

[8] Freud, S., "The psychopathology of everyday life," (1901), Standard Edition, 1960, vol. 6, pp. 1–279.

Fragmentation also appears in delirious states when activity and thinking become stereotyped, repetitive and perseverative. This phenomenon seems often to represent an unsuccessful attempt to control behavior by limiting it and by fixating on some one aspect of it. In somewhat the same way frightened normal people sometimes stare at something, hang on to something, or repeat a meaningless action, which may not be relevant to their anxiety, but nevertheless serves as an anchor in their sea of emotional turmoil. The delirious patient, who is usually frightened by his nightmarish experience with a world that seems to have lost its stability, may utilize repetition, perseveration and stereotypy as his form of anchorage.

4. *Overinclusion.* This represents a failure to limit the number and kind of simultaneous excitants to a relatively few coherent ones. The concept of *overinclusion* was originally developed in relation to schizophrenic thinking, and we have already defined it and given a generous sample of it in the chapter on schizophrenic reactions. It has since then been extended to include perceptual and cognitive failure in other disorders.[9] In delirium, overinclusion results not only from the invasion of preconscious and conscious organizations by primary processes and previously unconscious fantasy, but also from the loss of perceptual and cognitive structure, which the delirious brain cannot sustain. The latter defect gives rise to the gross disorientation which is specific for delirium but not for schizophrenia. The schizophrenic confuses fantasy and fact, mixes primary process material together, hallucinates and has delusions; but in spite of all this he usually knows where he is and who the people are around him. He often misidentifies strangers as people whom he knows; but he does not typically suffer the utter confusion in relation to external reality that characterizes acute delirium.[10]

If we now supplement the overt manifestations of delirium, as just described, by a consideration of the delirious person's subjective experience, we can see at once that we are dealing with disturbances of cerebral competence. To the delirious patient, his surroundings seem to lose their stability unaccountably. Objects come and go unexpectedly. People seem to be doing things that are strange, inexplicable, inappropriate and disconnected. People and things often appear distorted in weird ways which lie entirely outside the delirious person's previous experience with waking adult life. The gross disturbances in perception may destroy normal perspectives, proportions and reality relationships in space and time. Little things may appear enormous and large things very small. Shapes and spatial organizations undergo all kinds of distortion. Sounds are misidentified, misunderstood and located incorrectly. Skin sensations give rise to all kinds of delusions and hallucina-

[9] For a review of the literature on *overinclusion*, see Payne, R. W., "Cognitive abnormalities," in Eysenck, H. J. (Ed.), *Handbook of Abnormal Psychology*. New York: Basic Books, 1961, pp. 193–261.

[10] This distinction is necessary to maintain in experimental work with hallucinogenic drugs, which produce a delirious rather than a schizophrenic state.

tions. Taste and smell may also be involved in strange ways. The gross disturbances in cognition, if these can be separated from perception, lead to all kinds of misinterpretation and misidentification. They render it impossible for the delirious patient to construct an intelligible whole out of his fragmented experience.

Acute delirium is sometimes compared to ordinary dreaming, in which the normal person is grosssly disoriented, witnesses kaleidoscopic and often wholly unintelligible changes, experiences perceptual and cognitive distortions, and suffers from an invasion of his preconscious thinking by unconscious and primary process products. The comparison in some respects is apt. The sleeping person who is dreaming has regressed to a level of activity at which repression is weak. Denial, projection and introjection may perform primitive defensive functions, primary process thinking rules, and ego or self boundaries dissolve. There is one great difference between delirium and the dream. This is that the normal person manages to dream by excluding most of his external stimulation, by entering into a state of perceptual isolation. The absence of nearly all external stimulation during sleep greatly simplifies the situation for the dreamer. Even a sleepwalker is much better organized with regard to this environment than an acutely delirious person.

Hallucinations and delusions may develop at first in acute delirium under conditions similar to those of ordinary dreaming. In fact, a delirium may be preceded by terrifying dreams. As cerebral incompetence increases, however, hallucinatory and delusional experiences begin to trouble the patient when he is between waking and sleeping, so that he may be afraid to close his eyes. Eventually, with growing instability of perceptual and cognitive structures, the boundaries between external and internal reality melt, daydreams and previously unconscious fantasies mingle with the shifting, unstable perceptual and cognitive processes, to form a confused and confusing mass of unintelligible experience.

Delirious experience is nearly always frightening. The delirious person is typically apprehensive, insecure and fearful. This is in part because of the loss of perceptual and cognitive stability, the loss of one's familiar world, with its familiar organization and its predictable happenings. We all depend upon the stability of our surroundings for our feelings of security. If we move to unfamiliar surroundings, where we do not know what to expect and cannot understand what is going on, we need all the cerebral competence we can muster to cope with our strange situation. The delirious person is like a normal person who has been dropped into a weird environment without warning, but he has nothing in the way of cerebral competence to cope with it.

In addition to perceptual and cognitive instability, the delirious person must also cope with a wholesale eruption of previously unconscious fantasies, with an invasion by primary process thinking, and with the reconstructions of external reality which he attempts by means of his delusions and hallucinations. Because of his acute cerebral incompetence, however, the delirious person cannot succeed in structuring his new world even in as organized fashion as many schizophrenic and most paranoid persons do. His one advantage is that he is almost sure to recover quickly from his delirium; and, when he does, he is nearly always able to reconstruct his external world of reality in accordance with a previously adequate construction.

The specific fears, suspicions, fantasies, needs and defenses appearing in a delirious picture belong, of course, to the specific personality organization of the individual patient. It has long been known that certain intoxicating drugs are more hallucinogenic than others; but even these produce hallucinatory experiences which reflect the individual characteristics of the person taking them. Sometimes a person in acute delirium is preoccupied chiefly with his habitual business or domestic routines which he acts out inappropriately wherever he is (*occupational delirium*). Usually his fears, fantasies, conflicts, wishes and perplexities appear in more or less disconnected, dreamlike episodes. Occasionally, as we shall see, these episodes lead to psychopathology which may outlast by weeks, months or even years the signs of actual cerebral incompetence. The fact that a person's habitual occupation or his personal fears and fantasies appear prominently in his delirious symptoms is no more surprising, of course, than the fact that, while delirious, he speaks his own familiar tongue.

The memory deficits characteristic of acute delirium are of complex origin. Poor recall of recent events may be due to their having occurred during early phases of the delirium, when cerebral incompetence was already present. Memory deficits may also be a consequence of the fragmentation, discontinuity and overinclusion in delirious perception and cognition. In addition, the delirious person experiences direct products of primary processes, which in themselves are extremely difficult for even the best organized and most effective person to remember. After he has recovered he may be unable to fit many events, which he partially recalls, into his now normal organization; they seem weird and unnatural to him, like the manifest dreams of normal persons. There are often islands of relatively good recall which probably correspond to periods of relatively high cerebral competence during the fluctuations of the delirium.

Having now described the syndrome of acute delirium we shall defer discussion of acute cases until we come to the psychopathology encountered in intoxication, head injury, general paresis and cerebral degeneration in senile and arteriosclerotic psychoses. Meanwhile we shall turn to a description of chronic and progressive cerebral incompetence.

Chronic and progressive cerebral incompetence

Chronic brain disorders are the result of relatively permanent, irreversible, diffuse brain damage. If the pathological process which underlies the brain damage is arrested, there will still remain a certain amount of brain defect. The rest of the brain will then have to function as best it can in relation to this residual damage. The residual defect may be so slight as to have little practical importance for the recovered patient. On the other hand, it may be so great as to interfere more or less permanently with normal orientation, memory, perception, cognition and action.

Many chronic brain disorders are progressive rather than stationary; and some of these carry patients all the way down to an almost vegetative existence. In the course of such progression there may develop a great deal of psychopathology, that is, pathology of activity and of experience, or there may develop very little until the brain has undergone a great deal of destruction. In what follows we shall confine ourselves to those chronic brain disorders which grow progressively worse, ignoring those which are arrested at one level or another.[11] In this way, by following the decline in cerebral competence, we shall get some conception of the various levels at which an arrested brain disorder may leave a patient stranded.

Progressive cerebral incompetence. Syndromes of progressive cerebral incompetence are characterized by decreasing adaptiveness, increasing loss of memory and cognitive grasp, and increasing signs of cerebral pathology. These defects may develop slowly and insidiously, running a course of gradual decline over a period of years and sometimes of decades. Many cases that begin with a slow and insidious development are suddenly interrupted by a convulsion, after which the symptoms of cerebral incompetence are generally more pronounced and the decline more rapid. Still other cases have an abrupt onset with transient confusion, acute delirium or a convulsion, followed by chronic progressive cerebral incompetence, and usually punctuated by convulsive episodes. Temporary remissions are not unusual. These occasionally last a few months, and rarely a few years. Regardless of the type of onset or the occurrence of remissions, the course of progressive cerebral incompetence is downhill. Some patients reach an almost vegetative level of existence before they die, their behavior reduced to little more than a few stereotyped acts, with perhaps a phrase or two uttered entirely out of context.

> An aged patient did nothing but sit and rock all day, wetting and soiling herself, and having to be fed, washed, dressed and undressed as though she were a baby. No matter what was said to her, whether this was a kind greeting or a threat, she always replied, "Yes, darling," "Why, of course, darling," or "Certainly, darling."

In progressive cerebral incompetence there is considerable variability in the order of appearance and the prominence of different symptoms, as well as in what changes are first noticed. The first observed change is usually a

---

[11] For an account of chronic, stationary brain disorder, see Kaplan, O. (Ed.), *Mental Disorders in Later Life.* (2nd ed.) Stanford, Calif.: Stanford Univ. Press, 1956; also, Arieti, S. (Ed.), "Organic conditions," *American Handbook of Psychiatry.* New York: Basic Books, 1959, pp. 1003–1316.

memory defect or some confusion with regard to orientation. The patient becomes increasingly forgetful. He cannot remember where he has left or hidden personal belongings; he does not recall having met recent acquaintances before; he forgets engagements, whether these are recreational or in the line of duty. He tends to repeat himself, telling the same thing over and over to the same person and with the same detail. He cannot learn new procedures and he becomes easily confused in a new environment.

A business executive in late middle life was first recognized as incompetent by his family when he could not find his way back to the hotel at an unfamiliar summer resort. Each day he would drive back from the beach and pass the hotel without recognizing it, in spite of the family's protests. He was a pleasant man and took the whole situation good-naturedly as a joke. The family, however, discussed his situation with his business associates and discovered that he had been showing poor judgment and defective memory for at least a year before this vacation. Following his retirement he had a brief delirious episode in which he suffered from delusions and hallucinations of a frightening character. For this he was hospitalized. He was able to leave the hospital for home after a few weeks of care and protection, but although he was still good-natured and cheerful, he had severe defects in memory and orientation. His prognosis was regarded as poor.

The loss in recent memory is often paralleled by a progressive change in character. Thus, a person with a senile or arteriosclerotic brain may seem a changed man, at first to his close friends and relatives, but eventually to everyone. He may become careless of his dress, appearance and deportment, react with indifference, anger, joviality or tears, to situations that would not have evoked these reactions before. He may show a degree of instability and unpredictability quite foreign to his habitual behavior. A previously adequate person may exhibit striking ineptitude in business, social or domestic matters. He squanders or gives away his own property and that of others, or dissipates his earnings by glaringly injudicious spending.

An unusually able, shrewd manufacturer suffered a stroke in late middle life which left him with muscular weakness on one side of his body. His previously well-controlled aggression now appeared in an attempt to force his industrial competitor to sell out to him at a price far above the market value of the rival concern. Only the ethical restraint of the competitior, who realized what the situation was, saved the patient and his family from financial ruin.

Some persons lose the respect and affection of their friends and relatives by becoming entangled in a sexual liaison of an inexplicable character, or through committing a sex offense in relation to minors, before their cerebral incompetence is realized. An inability to include the probable consequences and implications of an act, as controlling factors, is often one of the most striking defects in progressive cerebral incompetence, whether the incompetence is of toxic, traumatic, infective, arteriosclerotic or senile origin. A person may thus appear to be in good contact with his immediate environment while he is, at the same time, grossly defective with respect to past training and future probabilities. This involves, of course, the whole question of responsibility, legal and moral, in the person suffering from cerebral decline.

Dynamic background of progressive cerebral incompetence. The syndromes of slowly or relatively slowly developing progressive cerebral incompetence give us examples of the gradual deterioration of the brain as an organ. The slowness of the pathological process, where there is no stormy incident, allows for some compensatory adaptation, physiological as well as psychological, which varies from person to person. Our business executive who could not find his way back to a summer resort hotel is an example of fairly good adaptive compensation, since he had been carrying on well at home for at least a year after his defects were noticed in the more exacting situation in his business.

Because of the compensatory adaptation we do not see for a long time the overt manifestations of behavioral disorganization which characterize cerebral incompetence with an acute onset or with an acute episode. Thus *incoordination, interpenetration, fragmentation* and *overinclusion,* so obvious in acute delirium, may not appear in chronically progressive cases until a low level of decline has been reached, unless of course the slow decline is interrupted by an acute attack. The most successful adaptations usually occur in persons who voluntarily limit the scope of their activities as they deteriorate, and in those who remain good-natured and complacent. The aggressive, irritable person, like our case of the manufacturer who suffered a stroke, is not likely to hide his defects for long.

Compensatory adaptation probably depends upon the physiological flexibility of cerebral function, upon the physiological youth of undamaged parts, and perhaps upon vicarious activities of undamaged areas which are little used in ordinary life. Since outspoken delusions and hallucinations do not occur for a long time, or do not occur at all, in slowly progressive cerebral incompetence, the major requirements for successful adaptation are *compensations* for the inevitable memory losses, for the inability to carry out new and complex tasks, and for the disturbances of orientation — all of which are interrelated. Memory losses may be concealed by circumlocution; something forgotten is referred to in a roundabout way. They are also overcome by getting other people to supply the forgotten link. Some persons use confabulation, that is, they substitute imaginary happenings for the forgotten ones, a process closely related to delusion, and to what younger people do when they find that they cannot explain their behavior or their attitudes. The dislike many ageing persons show for new ways and new adventures is often sparked by their difficulties in orientation and in handling new and complex situations. *Conservatism* is one expression of this; *seclusion* is another. Both are defensive in function, and both may to a certain extent be necessary for the preservation of ego integration.

Ultimately progressive cerebral incompetence leads, with few exceptions, to deterioration which cannot be compensated. Progressively impaired retentivity and recall make a person less and less able to participate in the life around him. His interest flags with his decreasing span of attention and his increasing fatigue. He may fall back upon repetitive reminiscences because he can no longer keep up with current events. Remote memory at first suffers much less than recent memory; but eventually it also becomes hopelessly inadequate.

His decreasing effectiveness of retentivity and recall isolates a person from what is going on in his immediate environment. It may also promote disorientation. Present happenings are located in the daily routines of the early years which he remembers. If he realizes that he is not at home, or in a familiar place, he is less likely to say that he does not know where he is than to confabulate, that is, to make up a story that accounts for his predicament.

An institutionalized woman of eighty-three always gave her age as eighteen or nineteen. If questioned as to her whereabouts she would just say that she was resting awhile before going on home. Almost every evening on rounds she would ask if she could "stay in this hotel tonight," often adding that she had started out too late to get home before dark. She usually lamented, in a dignified way, her inability to help her father with the milking that evening. When asked her father's age, however, she often said, "Oh, he's been dead many years," apparently forgetting what she had said about helping him.

When a patient's recall of remote as well as of recent events grows fragmentary, when circumlocution fails and verbal confabulations no longer fill in the gaps, the continuity of his behavior virtually disappears. Certain relatively simple automatized sequences remain, such as walking, getting up and sitting or lying down, chewing and sucking. Often regression revives some more or less infantile patterns. Increased emotional lability (*emotional incontinence*) is common. It varies from mere exaggeration and perseveration of normal emotional expression to inappropriate as well as uncontrollable laughing, crying or shouting, which to the patient himself may seem unaccountable, if he still maintains some of his perspective.

Disturbances of language and thinking are particularly detrimental. Normally we all depend upon these functions, not only for communication with others, but also as points of reference in our own ongoing behavior. Their disturbance interferes with communication, thus further isolating and desocializing the patient, and deprives him of his habitual ways of representing external, somatic and internal reality to himself in terms of secondary processes.

As the brain deteriorates as an organ, ego disintegration becomes inevitable. In the end, even though a patient may avoid an acute delirium, his defensive functions deteriorate along with his adaptive ones, and he undergoes an irreversible regression. Previously unconscious fantasies, conflicts, wishes and impulses may come to the fore in undisguised forms, making the patient unpredictable and primitive. Why this kind of thing should happen early in some cases of progressive cerebral incompetence and not in others we do not know.

There are many indications of progressive cerebral incompetence other than those we have discussed. Some of them are important chiefly as clinical signs of brain damage and do not in themselves contribute significantly to psychopathology. Others do complicate the psychopathology. Among the latter may be mentioned the tremors which interfere with manipulation and speech, numerous forms of incoordination, muscular weakeness and paralyses, and sense-organ disturbances. Their maladaptive influences are obvious.[12] Let us turn now to the clinical description of four common forms of cerebral incompetence, acute as well as chronic and progressive.

Psychopathology in Brain Disorders

No one needs to be reminded that psychopathology sometimes develops in persons who at the time show signs of cerebral incompetence, as well as in persons whose brains appear to be functioning normally. What does deserve to be emphasized is that the mere presence of relative cerebral incompetence need not account for the presence of psychopathology. The clinician often finds that cerebral incompetence, although present, plays an insignificant part in the psychopathology. The patient in these cases does not differ significantly, either in the pattern of his reaction or in the ease with which he so reacts, from other patients exposed to similar stresses and strains, who give no evidence of cerebral incompetence. When the consequences of brain disorder contribute significantly to psychopathology — that is, to neurotic and psychotic reactions, to psychosomatic disorders and character changes — they may do so in one of several ways.

In the first place, a person may develop pathological self-reactions to behavior resulting from his own cerebral incompetence. Thus, during an acute delirium a patient's delusional and hallucinatory experiences may arouse such intense anxiety, and lead to so much ego disintegration, that a schizophrenic disorganization occurs, or a manic or depressive illness results, as we shall see in the section on acute intoxication.

Ego disintegration also contributes to the precipitation of psychopathology in acute and chronic progressive cerebral incompetence. Suppose, for example, that an individual develops cerebral incompetence who for decades has been successfully dealing with serious conflicts and inacceptable impulses by means of repression and other defensive measures. A significant reduction in cerebral competence is likely to result in failure of ego defenses and

[12] For a discussion of these complications, see Grinker, R. R., and Bucy, P. C., *Neurology*. (4th ed.) Springfield, Ill.: Thomas, 1951.

in the invasion of preconscious and conscious organizations by previously unconscious primary process material. The heightened tension and anxiety that follow such an invasion lead to psychopathology. The exact character of the psychopathology will correspond to the individual's dominant personality trends.

Psychopathology arises in some persons because they cannot recognize and accept their diminished competence. It is this inability which leads patients to attempt things of which they are no longer capable, as in the case of the competitive manufacturer who had suffered a stroke, and to resist aggressively the limitations which others attempt to impose upon them. One sees obvious examples in the irritable, self-assertive excitements of patients with cerebral intoxication or cerebral infection. The problem, however, is socially far more important and therapeutically more challenging in the maladaptations that develop among the millions of people whose cerebral incompetence progresses slowly. In ageing persons, for example, an inability to recognize and accept their own decline in competence, when the decline is inexorable but slow, often culminates in psychopathology which is at least potentially preventable.

An important challenging problem is also presented by those persons who cannot accept their changed social status. Some of them recognize and accept their diminished adequacy, but they cannot adapt to their reduced security and prestige. They cannot adapt to the neglect and prejudices which other people express, or to the restrictions placed upon their range of opportunity and their interests. Persons whose abilities have declined because of cerebral intoxication, injury, infection or deterioration, need emotional acceptance and emotional support. They need the prestige and the social status to which they have been accustomed. But because they are inefficient and a social burden, we tend to neglect and depreciate persons with cerebral incompetence. By so doing we give them a standing invitation to develop psychopathology which then further incapacitates them and makes them a still greater social burden.

In order to illustrate more specifically the precipitation of psychopathology in persons with cerebral incompetence we have selected four common and important clinical groups. (1) *Acute intoxication* will introduce us once more to the psychopathology of the delirious patient. (2) *Head injury* represents the physically traumatic basis of psychopathology. (3) *General paresis,* although less common and more treatable than it used to be, is a typical cerebral infection. (4) *Senile* and *arteriosclerotic brain disorders* are not only common examples of slowly and usually undramatic progressive cerebral incompetence, but also illnesses that are certain to be of increasing importance as our ageing population grows.

Psychopathology in acute intoxication

The most interesting direct consequence of acute intoxication is the acute delirium which we have already described. There is general agreement today that in delirium the exact character of the disorientation, the delusions and the hallucinations cannot be predicted solely on the basis of the kind of toxic substance involved. The personality organization of the intoxicated person, his past and present experiences must always be considered.[13]

One study, for example, included more than a hundred delirious persons. There was no specific relationship between a particular toxin and the character of the psychopathology appearing in the delirium. The behavior and experience of patients having more than one delirious episode was characteristic for the individual and not for the intoxicating agent. Every patient in this series, regardless of intoxicating agent, believed at some time during his illness that he was the victim of deliberate annoyance or persecution. Fear was expressed in the great majority of cases, but neither the presence nor the degree of fear bore any relationship to the nature of the intoxicating agent. Cultural attitudes were reflected in the greater proportion of women than of men who believed themselves to be accused of sexual promiscuity.[14]

The relative unimportance of the specific character of the toxin becomes still clearer when we examine the detailed symptoms of acute deliria. It is obvious, for example, that when bromides or alcohol intoxications produce a so-called *occupational delirium,* the occupation which the patient attempts to carry on belongs to his own life pattern. Neither bromides nor alcohol will make every delirious man a carpenter or every delirious woman a milliner.

The *disorientation* in deliria is likewise on a personal basis, just as it is in ordinary dreaming. The delirious seaman in a shore hospital believes himself to be on shipboard or at the waterfront. The delirious farmer behaves as though he were in the farmhouse, in the stables or the fields, or at a county fair. Even the most confused, weird disorientative behavior and experience are still the products of a patient's individual past and of his immediately present surroundings. The invasion by unconscious fantasies and primary process material is still an invasion from the patient's own unconscious.

The *delusional reconstructions* in acute delirium are also specific for the individual patient and not for the toxic agent. Except for the gross disorientation and impaired retentivity, there is nothing about delirious delusions that is essentially different from any other delusions. The particular components of a patient's external environment and his internal reality, to which he responds with delusions, he selects on the basis of his own ac-

---

[13] Certain drugs produce perceptual and cognitive distortions which may be indistinguishable from those reported by schizophrenic patients. The important difference is that schizophrenic patients give no evidence of being intoxicated. Further light has been focused upon this difference by the results of sensory deprivation, which also may produce a schizophrenic-like picture, without any question of intoxication being involved. Cf. Solomon, P., *et al.* (Eds.), Sensory Deprivation. Cambridge, Mass.: Harvard Univ. Press, 1961.

[14] Levin, M., "Toxic psychoses," in Arieti, S. (Ed.), *American Handbook of Psychiatry.* New York: Basic Books, 1959, pp. 1222–1230; Robinson, G. W., "The toxic delirious reactions of old age," in Kaplan, O. (Ed.), *Mental Disorders in Later Life.* (2nd ed.) Stanford, Calif.: Stanford Univ. Press, 1956, pp. 332–351.

quired reaction-sensitivities, whether at the moment he is confused or not. These will determine what interpretations he makes of what he thinks he sees, hears, does or imagines. We shall cite cases later on in which psychopathology in a delirium was strikingly similar to psychopathology in the same person at another time when there was no delirium.

Hallucinatory reconstructions, like delusions, are not specifically determined by the properties of the toxic agent. Intoxication may induce hallucinatory experiences, but *what* the individual hallucinates will depend upon his own unconscious, preconscious and conscious processes, and upon the whole previous learning of the individual and his general personality make-up, as well as upon the immediate environment in which he lives. In *delirium tremens,* for example, there are usually hallucinated voices which threaten, revile or accuse the alcoholic patient. But threatening, reviling and accusing voices are common in all deliria and common also in the auditory hallucinations of nondelirious patients.

There is a great deal of folklore about hallucinations in *delirium tremens* to the effect that pink elephants, rodents, green monkeys and spotted giraffes are commonly experienced by the delirious alcoholic. A study of 113 patients with delirium tremens, however, showed that dogs, insects and snakes are the commonest animal hallucinations, three groups which are regarded by nonalcoholic persons as dangerous also. Only one case reported seeing a pink elephant and one reported seeing rodents.[15] The influence of the immediate environment is clear in the prevalence of hallucinated fish and lobsters in *delirium tremens* patients being treated by continuous baths.

It is well known that schizophrenic reactions may be precipitated in acute deliria resulting from intoxication, infection, high fever and debilitating disease. Of thirteen cases reported in one study of bromide delirium none had previously shown schizophrenic symptoms. Of these patients two were severely disoriented on admission, seven were seriously disoriented for time but only occasionally for place or person, while four showed only fleeting disorientation. In ten cases the duration varied from four days to seven and one-half weeks; and in the remaining three cases the duration was five, ten and twelve months respectively.[16]

The most impressive evidence we have of the nonspecific effect of toxic agents comes from those cases in which the same behavior pathology occurs in both delirious and nondelirious settings. In one of the studies already cited, two patients had developed and recovered from psychopathology prior to their acute intoxication. In each, the psychopathology that appeared in the delirium showed the same characteristics as did the earlier illnesses which were not precipitated by a delirium. In other words, the psychopathology was specific for *the person* and not for *the toxin.*

[15] Dynes, J., "Survey of alcoholic patients admitted to the Boston Psychopathic Hospital in 1937," *New England Med. J.,* 1939, *220,* 195–203.

[16] Levin, M., "Toxic psychoses," in Arieti, S. (Ed.), *American Handbook of Psychiatry.* New York: Basic Books, 1959, pp. 1222–1230.

We shall present two of our own cases which illustrate the same point. One developed a manic attack in a bromide delirium and later developed another manic attack in a setting of marital discord uncomplicated by intoxication. The other suffered a manic attack during litigation that threatened to destroy her economic security, and thirty years later developed another when she became disoriented following an operation for a cataract.

Beatrice D., a married woman of thirty, was admitted to a psychiatric service in an acute delirium two weeks after she had undergone minor surgery. She had been apprehensive before the operation. On the first postoperative day she seemed so anxious that she was given small doses of morphine. This only alarmed her further. She thought she heard the attending surgeon saying that she had taken a turn for the worse. She spoke to her relatives of dying. On the fourth postoperative day bromide sedation was substituted for the morphine. As Beatrice continued apprehensive and irritable, she was given bromide sedation for the next ten days. When she became combative she was tied down on the bed. She was soon acutely delirious.

When transferred to the psychiatric service Beatrice was grossly disoriented and had obvious memory defects. She told of having had delusional fears of being poisoned and dreamlike visual and auditory hallucinations. She was dehydrated on admission and had a bright red body rash. As soon as Beatrice had received fluids and chlorides, restraint became unnecessary. She was free to move about the room and the adjacent ward. She remained fearful, confused and easily stirred to resentment, for another ten days. While she was still showing considerable fear, her talk became coherent, and then she began rhyming, punning, swearing and showing flight of ideas. She was distractible, aggressively overactive, overtalkative and erotic. This manic behavior persisted for three weeks after the delirious symptoms had disappeared. After another month the patient was discharged.

Three years later Beatrice was readmitted in a typical manic attack. Her behavior pathology in this attack closely resembled that in the first one, not only in her general behavior, but also in most of the specific details. This time, however, there was no delirium in the picture. The precipitating situation was one of severe marital discord. Recovery was complete after five months.

Irene T. was a widow aged sixty-five. She developed an acute delirium following an operation for cataract. The delirium began with disorientation, most obvious at night, and was soon accompanied by visual and auditory hallucinations and poor recall. As time went on, Irene became noisy, talked loudly, sang and occasionally shouted. Her speech became vulgar and profane. She rhymed, punned and showed some flight of ideas.

On the psychiatric service, Irene was typically manic, except for her behavior at night — when she was disoriented and hallucinating — and whenever she was restrained or interfered with, when she developed fearful delusions and misidentifications. The manic excitement subsided as the delirium disappeared, but at a slower rate. There was no clinical evidence to justify a diagnosis of cerebral arteriosclerosis or senile deterioration.

Thirty years earlier, when Irene was thirty-five years old, she developed a manic attack with closely similar behavior. The precipitating situation at that time was a lawsuit which threatened to destroy her security. Irene's husband had died when she was thirty-three. The aim of the lawsuit was to prove that she was not really the wife of the dead man, and to deprive her of a large inheritance, as well as to ruin her socially. She recovered from this illness just as she recovered from the one thirty years later. In one there was a delirious episode preceding the manic attack; in the other there was no delirium at all.

Psychopathology in head injury

Head injury does not necessarily mean brain injury. But when it does, and the resulting cerebral incompetence is extreme, the patient may go quickly into coma or stupor. If the brain damage is serious, and the injured man survives, he may pass from coma or stupor into a typical delirium. He may develop the disoriented *Korsakoff syndrome*, with memory defects and confabulation, before his behavior becomes more nearly adequate.[17] None of these syndromes, of course, is peculiar to head injury. The same phenomena are common in any severe cerebral incompetence, whether it occurs in intoxication, infection or brain degeneration. Even the apparent sequence of phases, when it occurs, is no more than a succession of recognizable clinical syndromes which represent different degrees of adequacy in a recovering organism.

In most cases of head injury that result in immediate severe cerebral incompetence, that is, in which the patient becomes "unconscious," the initial improvement is rapid. Neither acute delirium nor the Korsakoff syndrome appears. Instead, there may be only transient periods of confusion, mild ataxia, dulling and amnesia, events being forgotten which occurred before the brain injury, as well as after it. The course of convalescence after brain injury is highly variable. It can seldom be predicted from a consideration of the apparent brain damage alone. There is even doubt that progressive deterioration can result from moderate trauma alone in an otherwise healthy brain.

Nothing has brought out more clearly the intricate interweaving of biological and social factors in psychopathology than the study of reactions to head injury. For a long time professional interest was directed mainly toward the problem of recognizing and treating the consequences of brain damage — convulsive attacks, deformities, emotional storms and impaired performance. Whenever brain injury leaves such permanent residuals, a very considerable degree of adaptiveness may be demanded of the patient having them. But whether or not these sequelae are present in a given case,

---

[17] Brosin, H. W., "Psychiatric conditions following head injury," in Arieti, S. (Ed.), *American Handbook of Psychiatry.* New York: Basic Books, 1959, pp. 1175–1202.

there are still other aspects of head injury of equal importance, sometimes of greater importance, that deserve special consideration.

There are, for example, the reactions of the injured person to his accident, to the experience of having been hurt, helpless, frightened, in pain, comatose, forgetful or confused. Injury to the head in our society is apt to be an object of greater concern than injury to an arm or leg. There is also the necessity for adapting oneself to minor residuals, in themselves perhaps unimportant, which often become the focus of anxiety, worry and complaints of fatigue, and can lead to *conversion reactions* and *chronic invalidism.* Finally there are the *primary* and *secondary gains,* which we have already discussed in relation to conversion reactions.

Head injury is exceedingly common.[18] Almost every fair-sized community or neighborhood has persons in it who have suffered a permanent reduction in adequacy as a direct or indirect result of head trauma. In spite of this, according to Brosin, there were only about 400 papers on head injury in the literature up to 1957. Many of the earlier papers were chiefly concerned with an enumeration of symptoms, and with attempts to relate the most typical symptoms to known or inferred brain damage. A trend is growing, however, in the direction of relating chronic residual symptoms, not alone to neuro-physiology and neuropathology, but also to personality organization — to the patient's habitual attitudes, his premorbid needs and satisfactions, his preferred defenses and coping mechanisms, and the degree of social maturity he had achieved before his accident.[19]

One of the most carefully designed clinical studies of head injury has shown that in acute head injury the complaints made by the patients were related to the clinical signs. Accordingly, as one might expect, patients with evidence of brain damage had more complaints than those without. When, however, patients were studied later on, those who had suffered severe head injuries had few residual complaints, while those who had suffered minor head injury had many complaints. Moreover, the number of complaints tended to increase and to grow more diffuse in character the longer a post-traumatic syndrome lasted.[20]

Even headache is apparently not specific for head injury. It is much more common in persons without neurological signs of brain damage than in persons with residual signs. Only a small number of patients without neurological signs show personality changes that can be ascribed to the head injury. The majority had had difficulties in interpersonal relationships before their accident. Many seemed to have been chronically dissatisfied and

---

[18] Brosin estimates the morbidity from head injuries in automobile accidents alone as about one and a half million annually (*op. cit.*).

[19] Cf. Barker, R., Wright, B., Meyerson, L., and Gonick, M., *Adjustment to Physical Handicap and Illness.* (2d ed.) New York: Soc. Sci. Res. Council, 1953.

[20] Ruesch, J., Harris, R., and Bowman, K., "Pre- and post-traumatic personalities in head injuries," in *Trauma of the Central Nervous System.* Baltimore: Williams and Wilkins, 1945, pp. 507–544.

unhappy. Others gained through their symptoms what they had not been able to gain before. Persistence of complaints in these patients seems best understood as adaptive measures, comparable to neurotic reactions, through which tension and anxiety are reduced. It is the *pre-traumatic personality organization* of the patient with head injury that seems to determine what the *post-traumatic adaptation shall be.*

Psychopathology in general paresis

General paresis is an encephalitis, an inflammation of the brain which develops because of the presence in it of the spirochaete of syphilis. Although the spirochaete may be active throughout the cerebral cortex, it affects most intensely the frontal regions where, in cases that end fatally, the invading organism is most concentrated. The neurological signs of general paresis are less specific than this. All of them appear in other central nervous system disease in one combination or another. Among the most common paretic signs are the so-called *Argyll-Robinson pupil* (one that does not respond to light but does to accommodation of the eye for distance) and tremors of the fingers, tongue, eyelids and facial muscles. Speech is slow and slurred. Writing is tremulous, often illegible, with letters omitted or transposed. There is muscular weakness (*paresis*), and there are often convulsive attacks and attacks of transient paralysis. In untreated cases the course is a downhill one, death coming within two or three years. The course is usually uneventful, but if the inflammatory process should flare up there may be an episode of nonspecific excitement in which the patient is sometimes violent.

Apart from the occasional episodic excitement, cases of general paresis show a clinical picture of relatively rapid progressive cerebral incompetence, after an insidious onset and a gradual development of symptoms. The psychopathology that appears seems to be nonspecific. If there is an acute inflammatory episode it may lead to an excitement with expansive, aggressive, elated features. Otherwise the general principle set forth about thirty years ago still holds. "The type of psychosis or psychoneurosis exhibited [by the paretic patient] is that which the individual would have developed at that time, provided syphilis was absent, and any other adequate precipitating factor was present."[21] In other words, the brain made incompetent by this specific inflammatory and degenerative injury lowers the efficiency of adaptive and defensive systems. The paretic patient then reacts in accordance with his preparetic *personality organization,* but without the checks and balances provided by whatever adaptive-defensive structure he has developed through his preparetic years. Two case illustrations will illustrate this.

[21] Schube, P., "Emotional states of general paresis," *Amer. J. Psychiat.,* 1934, *94,* 625–638.

Louis Z. was a married job-carpenter aged forty-one. He was hospitalized because he had threatened to kill his competitors. His wife said that he had always been a jealous, insecure, suspicious man. Eight weeks before admission he seemed irritable, moody and fatigued. Three weeks before admission he told his wife that competitors were stealing his tools and putting inferior ones in their place. When he found his tools, he insisted that these alleged thieves had secretly returned them to make a fool of him. This kind of behavior, his wife said, was not at all out of character for him. When, however, Louis threatened to kill his supposed persecutors he was brought to the hospital. In addition to his delusions, he had tremors, a mild memory defect and sluggish pupils. His cerebrospinal fluid was typical for general paresis. Under malarial therapy his cerebrospinal fluid became normal. He was able then to return to work without, however, losing his suspicions.

Pierce B. had been a frugal, honest, hard-working man. He was generally considered in his home town to be a model citizen. Two years before he had to be hospitalized, he changed into an irritable, intolerant person with frequent angry outbursts. A month before his admission he became extremely irritable, forgetful and undependable in his work, surly and resentful when rebuked, and at home violently angry over trivial things. He was restless, talkative and excitable until finally he could not work, eat, or sleep as he had. He was full of grandiose schemes, like a manic patient, and he boasted about his abilities, his achievements and possessions. When humored he could be led; but when contradicted or frustrated he became explosively angry, threatening members of his family.

On admission to a hospital he was found to have slurred speech, tremors, pupils which reacted slightly to accommodation of the eyes for distance but not at all in response to light (*Argyll-Robertson pupils*), and paretic cerebrospinal fluid. His general excitement and his delusions were manic in character. His course was downgrade, with typical symptoms of progressive cerebral incompetence until he died.

With the advent of malarial therapy and, more recently, penicillin therapy on a wide scale, the hospital admissions for general paresis have dropped dramatically, from around 20 to 25 per cent to less than 2 per cent. Malarial therapy has resulted in complete recovery in 35 per cent of unselected cases of general paresis. Large doses of penicillin have raised it to 50 per cent.[22] The brilliant work of Latin-American scientists, who use a combination of different strains of penicillin, has brought the recovery rate up to 83 per cent.[23] When one stops to consider that general paresis used to be regarded as an incurable disease, this achievement of our Latin-American neighbors ranks very high among modern therapeutic advances.

[22] Bruetsch, W. L., "Neurosyphilitic conditions," in Arieti, S. (Ed.), *American Handbook of Psychiatry*. New York: Basic Books, 1959, pp. 1003–1020.

[23] Borges Fortes, A., "Tratamiento da paralasia general pela penicilina," *Arq. brasil. neurist. y psiquit.*, 1956, 5, 23–30 (cited by Bruetsch, *op. cit.*).

Psychopathology in senile and arteriosclerotic brain degeneration

In contrast to the rapid disappearance of general paresis as a major source of psychopathology, the incidence of cerebral degeneration, because of senile and arteriosclerotic brain changes, is rapidly increasing. This is to a large extent the direct result of the rapidly growing number of elderly persons in our population. It is inevitable that the ageing brain, as an organ, should undergo degenerative changes. If these changes affect the cerebrum gradually and diffusely we see the picture called *senile degeneration.* If the changes come suddenly, and are focal rather than diffuse, we speak of *arteriosclerotic cerebral degeneration.*[24] In the latter we find that certain areas of the cerebrum, the ones supplied by diseased blood vessels, will be more or less completely destroyed, while intervening cerebral areas, where the blood vessels are functioning adequately, will be fairly well preserved. As might be expected, many cases of cerebral degeneration show both kinds of anatomical change. Nevertheless, more or less pure cases of one or the other do occur, and even when the two are mixed there is usually a predominance of one process over the other.

The *onset* in *senile cerebral degeneration* is often so gradual and insidious that the progressive cerebral incompetence is not recognized until some particularly ineffectual performance calls attention to the change. If acute confusional or convulsive attacks occur at all, in senile degeneration, they come late in the degenerative process, or in response to a sudden emotional crisis. The business executive already described, who could not find his way back to the unfamiliar hotel, illustrates this kind of onset. The acute delirious episode from which he suffered after retirement was precipitated by a sudden fright; and he recovered from it without recovering full competence.

The *onset* in *arteriosclerotic cerebral degeneration* is usually sudden. It may be marked by an acute confusional episode or a convulsive attack. Neurological signs of focal damage are common. It occurs much more often in the fifties than the senile diffuse type, which appears usually in the sixties, seventies or eighties. Sudden remissions followed by sudden declines are also more common. The industrialist who almost ruined himself financially, described earlier in the chapter, illustrates this kind of onset.

The course is inevitably downhill in both types. Because senile degeneration is slow and gradual, it allows a person to adapt to the decline as it develops; this is particularly true if his surroundings support him. The sudden, stormy beginning in arteriosclerotic cerebral degeneration, with its confusional or convulsive attacks and the paralyses which so often accom-

[24] By custom, this term includes what is more accurately called *atherosclerosis.* The differentiation between *senile* and *arteriosclerotic cerebral degeneration,* as here presented, follows that of Rothschild, D., "Senile psychoses and psychoses with cerebral arteriosclerosis," in Kaplan, O. (Ed.), *Mental Disorders in Later Life.* (2nd ed.) Stanford, Calif.: Stanford Univ. Press, 1956, pp. 289–331.

pany it, presents much more difficult adaptive problems. Both the patient and his relatives, or other close associates, are called upon to make sudden adaptations to the sudden fluctuations. Otherwise the situations confronting patients in the two groups are more alike than dissimilar. Therefore, in the interest of simplicity and clarity of exposition, we shall confine further discussion mainly to the psychopathology that arises during senile cerebral degeneration, and treat arteriosclerotic cases as variants with their own special problems.

It has often been said that the ultimate prognosis in senile cerebral degeneration is hopeless. In the long run this is true. Nerve cells in the cerebrum disappear gradually with age. They cannot be replaced, and their progressive loss will finally incapacitate the ageing person. The work of brain pathologists demonstrates, however, that factors other than cell destruction must be taken into account.[25] Thus one finds relatively little cell loss in the cerebrum of many persons who have suffered a severe senile decline before dying; while many whose cerebrum shows extensive cell destruction have suffered little or no senile decline.

What is true of general senile decline is also true of specific psychopathology arising in old age. If the environment is exceptionally favorable, and the ageing person is stable and adaptable, his general behavior organization may be expected to remain adequate until his brain can no longer serve him adequately. The brain, as an organ, undoubtedly has a great deal of reserve potentiality with which to compensate for nerve cell losses. A favorable environment allows the ageing person to make full use of these potentialities. When, at last, he does suffer a decline, he may reach an almost vegetative level before any serious personal maladaptation appears. Such a course places the least burden upon society as well as upon the patient. It is the one least likely to call out resentment in others during the final decline, or remorse after it is over.

The average senile or late senescent person, as his biosocial adequacy declines, does not find that the general conditions of his life improve or that they provide new rewards to replace the old rewards which he no longer gets. On the contrary, for the great majority of ageing men and women the increase in years bring only an increase in handicaps — biological, personal, social and economic.

Psychosomatic disorders are common. The elderly have neither the strength nor the endurance of the young. Their visceral performance is often less effective and more easily disturbed than it was earlier in life. In the gastrointestinal system, and to a lesser degree in the cardiovascular and genitourinary systems, disturbances frequently appear which, although not in themselves a threat to continued health and life, are reacted to as if they were. Symptoms of gastrointestinal malfunction are common results of

    [25] Rothschild, D., "Senile psychoses and psychoses with cerebral arteriosclerosis," in Kaplan, O. (Ed.), *Mental Disorders in Later Life.* (2nd ed.) Stanford, Calif.: Stanford Univ. Press, 1956, pp. 289–331.

deficiencies and diseases in others systems, of general malnutrition, or of overexertion and lack of adequate sleep. All of these conditions appear more frequently in old age than in youth.

Once middle age has been reached, the older a person grows the more familiar he becomes with the incursions of illness and death among his associates, and the more likely he is to have been ill himself and to have undergone surgery. The accumulation of such incidents may make a person reaction-sensitive to signs that he may himself be in poor health or that he is beginning to decline, when actually neither is the case. Most ageing men and women in our culture have reason to feel neglected and in need of more attention, comfort and affection than they receive. The frustrations and the unhappiness that are imposed upon the elderly by restrictive social conventions, economic dependence, and reduced biosocial adequacy, do much to reinforce and to perpetuate such developments. What we have already said about the personal effects of ageing, in the preceding chapter, applies with particular force here.[26] Indeed, we might paraphrase in relation to senile cerebral incompetence what Schube has said about general paresis, and say that, if behavior pathology appears in a setting of senile decline, it is likely to be the same as what would have developed if cerebral incompetence had been absent and any other adequate precipitating factor present.

In other words, we are dealing with something more complicated, as a rule, than the direct effects of senile decay. We have to include also the patient's own reactions to his decreasing adequacy, security and prestige. And we must take into account the potentially deeply disturbing effects of socio-economic and rapid cultural change.[27] In the process of rapid urbanization, for example, ageing persons are increasingly exposed to the demands of relocation and of the increasing pace of daily life. As a person ages he finds it more and more difficult to adapt to any quick change, especially when this involves a change in living conditions, the loss of old friends and of long familiar surroundings. In the United States, where tradition does not provide increased age with increased respect, such changes bring nothing but loss without compensation.

Anxiety reactions in senile persons do not differ fundamentally from anxiety reactions at any other period of life. The same general factors precipitate them and perpetuate them. Only the details are peculiar to old age. The aged have many reasons for feeling insecure. Most of them become economically dependent upon the good will of others, sometimes upon the caprice of others. Unemployment compensation, the growth of local social welfare responsibility and the establishment of federal social

[26] Birren, J. E. (Ed.), *Handbook of Aging and the Individual.* Chicago: Univ. of Chicago Press, 1959; Cumming, E., and Henry, W. E., *Growing Old.* New York: Basic Books, 1961; Stein, M. R., Vidich, A. J., and White, D. M. (Eds.), *Identity and Anxiety.* Glencoe, Ill.: Free Press, 1960.

[27] Cameron, N., "Neuroses of later maturity," in Kaplan, O. (Ed.), *Mental Disorders of Later Life.* (2nd ed.) Stanford, Calif.: Stanford Univ. Press, 1956, pp. 201–243.

security benefits, have done a great deal to ameliorate the anxious dependence of the ageing person upon others; but they have not yet eliminated socio-economic sources of anxiety. A great many persons, who never actually become dependent, live in constant dread that some day they will. The high probability of ultimate infirmity and the certainty of death are also important sources of persistent anxiety in aged persons. Helplessness and dependence are much more dreaded than death.[28]

Guilt is also a common source of anxiety in ageing persons. A decline in the adequacy of adaptive and defensive maneuvers often allows primary process material to emerge, hostile and erotic impulses to gain expression, and fantasies which have previously been kept unconscious to become preconscious and conscious. The consequence may be a return of the repressed, the revival of conflicts and ambitendencies previously controlled, and sometimes the appearance of unwise and impulsive behavior. The ageing person may become involved in misconduct because his reactions to an immediate situation no longer include self-control in terms of future consequences. He may, on the other hand, develop guilt because of vengeful fantasies in relation to close relatives who appear to domineer, belittle or obstruct him. Sex conflicts and sex fantasies often play a part in the precipitation and perpetuation of guilt. Sometimes the lonely, unhappy senile person, like the adolescent, finds in sex need and sexual gratification what he cannot otherwise achieve.

Obsessive compulsive reactions appearing in senility often represent the regressive revival of a technique used earlier in life to cope with conflicts which have also been regressively revived. On the other hand, obsessive compulsive reactions may develop for the first time in old age, as a response to newly increased insecurity, conflict and anxiety. If an ageing person finds the complexities of his situation more than his adaptive capacity can manage, he may fall back upon stereotyped, perseverative or ritualistic reactions. This is also what children and adolescents do, and for that matter what the cerebrally competent adult may also do, when his adaptive efforts fail, and he falls back upon ritual and repetition.

Psychotic reactions occurring in senility do not lend themselves readily to a meaningful grouping if the standard classification is followed. Rothschild[29] recommends the following substitute classification into three groups:

1. *The psychotic reaction is an understandable outgrowth of long-standing personality difficulties.* Processes of ageing reduce the person's resources until they are not sufficient to maintain an adequate equilibrium. Situational stresses are often an added factor.

---

[28] Sands, S. L., and Rothschild, D., "Socio-psychiatric foundations for a theory of the reactions to ageing," *J. nerv. ment. Dis.*, 1952, *116*, 233–239.

[29] Rothschild, D., "Senile psychoses and psychoses with cerebral arteriosclerosis," in Kaplan, O. (Ed.), *Mental Disorders in Later Life*. (2nd ed.) Stanford, Calif.: Stanford Univ. Press, 1956, pp. 289–331; Gibson, A. C., "Psychosis occurring in the senium: a review of an industrial population," *J. ment. Sci.*, 1961, *107*, 921–925.

2. *Special stresses of a somatic or situational character precipitate a psychosis in persons with apparently well-integrated personalities.* Psychological stresses include those common to the aged, such as separation from or death of a spouse, breakup of the home, lack of employment, and others which we have earlier described. Sometimes it is the suddenness of the event or its combination with other unfavorable factors that makes it traumatic.

3. *A group in which neither personality defects nor dramatic events seem responsible.* This is the largest of the three groups. The picture is usually one of simple deterioration. It is possible that this represents complete surrender to the appalling isolation and the meaninglessness of the aged person's existence. Rothschild suggests that perhaps personal factors were present earlier in the senile deterioration, but that many do not arrive at psychiatric hospitals until deterioration is advanced.

A relatively high incidence of paranoid reactions in hospitalized senile patients may reflect in part the greater difficulty that relatives find in tolerating an aggressive, accusing, delusional senile person than a sad self-reproachful one, or a neurotic or psychosomatic person. It may also reflect a corresponding difference in the senile population as a whole. We know, for example, that serious impairment of hearing and sight at any age often gives rise to anxiety and suspiciousness. Senility is the period of life in which such losses are most frequent. We also know that, in our society, it is customary to belittle and restrict the aged, to deny them freedom of action and of opportunity, and to meet their protests and their resentment with evasiveness or counteraggression. These are optimal conditions for the development of paranoid reactions in susceptible persons at any age.

The rapid increase in numbers of aged persons surviving nowadays is fortunately being accompanied by a rapidly growing concern with their welfare. This concern includes attempts at preventing senile and arteriosclerotic reactions at physical, psychological and socio-economic levels, since critical situations at any or all three of these levels may precipitate such a reaction. It has also been recommended that people approaching middle life and old age be prepared for the inevitable changes which they will meet.[30] Therapeutic measures of all kinds are being utilized — psychotherapeutic and psychoanalytic, group and family therapy, pharmacological, surgical and shock therapy, and rehabilitation.

Individual and group therapy do not differ essentially in treating the aged, as compared with younger persons, excepting that less flexibility and more limited goals must be expected. Strikingly good results in cases of cerebral accidents ("strokes") have been obtained when a bloodclot in an accessible vessel can be removed promptly by surgery. Equally remarkable

[30] Lewis, N. D. C., "Mental hygiene in later maturity," in Kaplan, O. (Ed.), *Mental Disorders in Later Life.* (2nd ed.) Stanford, Calif.: Stanford Univ. Press, 1956, pp. 460–475.

have been the achievements in rehabilitating and retraining victims of cerebral accident who have not been helped by surgery.

In all aged persons the most important single consideration is to keep the individual in active contact with others, and to keep him working at his optimal capacity, which is usually considerably higher than his lowered initiative and self-esteem indicate. The universally recognized bad effects of retirement upon persons who are not thoroughly prepared for it make it mandatory that a retiring person maintain an active life at whatever level his strength permits. The alternative may be a general physical and psychological decline.

22

Therapy

✛

General Introduction

A BOOK ABOUT PSYCHOPATHOLOGY WITHOUT A CHAPTER ON THERAPY would be incomplete. This is particularly the case when it comes to psychotherapy. Nearly all of our modern conceptions about psychopathology have come directly from the work of psychotherapists and psychoanalysts actively engaged in treating sick people. As everyone nowadays knows, the breakthrough in psychological therapy was the result of one man's courageous, determined, laborious and inspired devotion to the problems presented by neurotic and psychotic patients during the last decades of the nineteenth century. We shall see that this man, Sigmund Freud, used psychological methods reluctantly, after years of therapeutic experience with hypnosis and electrical stimulation. He never quite gave up the hope that some day biochemical treatment would supersede the methods of personal interaction which he had inaugurated and developed into a system.

Freud is often pictured as a man obsessed with the importance of psychology, especially the psychology of sex. Nothing could be farther from the truth. If anything, Freud was convinced of the prime importance of physiology and biochemistry, a man forced by the inadequacy of physical and physiological methods to turn to the intricacies of personal interaction. Here he made discoveries so revolutionary that he could hardly believe them himself. A great many people still do not believe them; a great many more

743

accept them, and incorporate them into their own practice and theory without fully recognizing their source.

The search for some kind of biochemical therapy for psychopathology, some procedure that will replace psychotherapy, has continued to this day. With the marvels of new synthetic drugs before us, the development of insulin coma and the availability of electric shock therapy, this search has recently grown more widespread and intense than ever. Many persons, unfamiliar with the relatively recent past, hail the upsurge of interest in nonpsychological methods as the great new hope in the treatment of psychological ills. Actually this upsurge is the revival of an old hope, which antedated systematic studies of human interaction, and therefore did not understand the potentialities of human interaction for good and harm, or the intimate manner in which every human being internalizes the products of human interaction as integral parts of his own personality.

In this chapter our main emphasis will be upon expressive psychotherapies, since these are by far the most advanced and successful techniques we have for the understanding and treatment of persons suffering from psychopathology. They also fit into our modern conceptions of the psychogenic origin of most psychopathology, that is, the conceptions of psychopathology as the product of personal interaction, rather than of disturbed chemistry. We shall place less emphasis upon somatic methods — such as the use of drugs, insulin coma, and electric shock — even though, as we shall see, these can be valuable auxiliaries to psychotherapy. They may even be substituted for or precede psychotherapy in those patients whose illness makes them inaccessible to genuine communication.

It should not be surprising to the intelligent layman, or to the perceptive scientist or general physician, that the systematic, expert use of personal interaction can be made into a highly effective therapeutic tool. In ordinary everyday life, it is through the commonsense structuring of personal interrelationships that we all influence the attitudes and behavior of other persons. It is upon personal interaction, not upon changing body chemistry, that we depend in forming and maintaining our friendships and our business and professional relationships. Personal interaction determines the success or the failure of marital relations; and it is the core of a parent's chosen child-rearing practices, through which the parent hopes to see his children transformed into adequate adults. Finally, it is through his own imagining, thinking, talking and planning — not through taking medicines or receiving electric shock — that a man regulates his own behavior, determines his own experience, and forms a picture of himself as a member of his family and his community.

It is this same kind of personal interaction, imagining, thinking, talking, planning and self-regulation — refined, sophisticated and systematized — that makes up psychotherapy. This is the most appropriate and effective means of dealing with persons who are continually frustrated by their personal conflicts, threatened by overwhelming anxieties, badgered by their unacceptable impulses, oppressed by an irrational harsh conscience, or left without a rudder because their superego is defective. It is the most appropriate and effective means of helping those who have suffered an arrest of emotional development in some area of their personality, or an emotional distortion earlier in their life. This, then, is the kind of personal interaction, structured especially with such problems and deficiencies in view, that we call psychotherapy. It has many varieties and a fascinating history.

Definition. The term "psychotherapy" covers a wide range of treatment procedures whose common characteristic is that they deal with psychogenic illnesses by psychological methods, rather than by the use of medicines and other somatic procedures. Psychotherapy is also utilized in treating the psychopathology in psychosomatic disorders, in brain disorders, and in patients with general medical and surgical illnesses, with the cooperation of the physician or surgeon.

The relationship between psychological methods and somatic methods need not be mutually exclusive. Medicines are often used to lessen a patient's anxiety, when this is so great as to interfere with psychotherapy, and when it threatens a patient's security, his life or the life of others. Medication is widely employed today to decrease suffering and disturbance in psychotic patients, which in some cases makes possible a return to the home environment, and in others makes the patient accessible to psychotherapy. Both medication and shock treatment are used to break into the vicious cycle which seems to perpetuate many psychotic depressions and many chronic schizophrenias. Finally, medicines are sometimes used to enable a patient to relive a recent severe traumatic experience under controlled conditions, in the company of his therapist. While this last method seems to be successful only in cases of severe traumatic neuroses, such as one finds among combat personnel, its demonstrated usefulness in such cases merits its being given special mention.

What we have referred to as the *expressive psychotherapies* are the ones which permit and encourage the patient to talk freely or otherwise communicate whatever seems to be troubling him. This includes a wide variety of different methods. Sometimes it appears as if the promotion of free expression were the only thing that binds these methods together as a group; but such an appearance contradicts the history of their development.

The origins of expressive psychotherapy

However diverse may be the different varieties of expressive psychotherapy, they all go back to the revolutionary work of Freud. This is just as true of the varieties which openly reject Freud as it is of those which evade the issue, and of those which openly acknowledge Freud as their source. To illustrate this point, we shall present briefly here two outstanding examples of expressive psychotherapy, neither of which considers itself psychoanalytic, and neither of which is so considered by psychoanalysts. One of them has had an enormous influence upon the development of psychiatry in the United States and in Great Britain. The other has had an enormous influence upon the development of clinical psychology in the United States.[1]

Psychobiology. This is an approach to psychological medicine based upon a wholesome respect for the human being, sick or well, and a conviction that if a neurotic or psychotic person is given the opportunity to work through his problems with a trained therapist he will improve or recover. Psychobiology emphasizes the total personality, its integrity, and the use of what is still healthy to help restore mental health in a person who has lost it. It works predominantly at conscious and preconscious levels, although unconscious factors are recognized implicitly without giving them explicit expression. The emphasis is upon current problems, conflicts, frustrations, anxieties and pathological guilt. The influence of a patient's childhood is recognized as significant for his current problems, but this component does not receive the kind of attention that psychoanalysts give it.

Psychobiology was the creation of Adolf Meyer, a man who, like Freud, began his work with studies in neuroanatomy, and became interested in the clinical patient because the force of circumstances made the clinical patient the center of his attention. Circumstances also gave Meyer the extraordinarily fortunate opportunity to establish a psychiatric clinic in the heart of one of the great hospitals of the world, the Johns Hopkins Hospital, and to organize there a program of training in psychological medicine which remained for a long time unrivaled. Psychobiology cannot be understood excepting as an attempt to establish and maintain psychiatry as a co-equal with other branches of medicine, in a setting which from the very start was highly competitive and demanding.

Meyer liked to emphasize the role of symbolization in normal and pathological experience. He called the human being "an experiment of nature," and considered him the resultant of all his past experiences, his heredity, and his current situation.[2] Therapy in Meyer's day began with meticulous history-taking, and with a formal question-and-answer mental-status examination. After this formal beginning, psychotherapy proceeded with greater freedom, its course depending more upon the patient-therapist relationship than upon any set rules. It was quite permissible, as the writer has reason to know from his service on Meyer's staff, to give over whole hours merely to listening to the patient. Nevertheless, psychotherapy as

[1] For somatic methods sometimes used as therapy, see Arieti, S. (Ed.), *American Handbook of Psychiatry.* New York: Basic Books, 1959, pp. 1521–1582 (various authors).

[2] Meyer, A., *The Commonsense Psychiatry of Doctor Adolf Meyer.* (ed. A. Lief). New York: McGraw-Hill, 1948; Muncie, W., *Psychobiology and Psychiatry.* (2nd ed.) St. Louis: Mosby, 1948; Muncie, W., "Psychobiology," in Arieti, S. (Ed.), *American Handbook of Psychiatry.* New York: Basic Books, 1959, pp. 1317–1332.

practiced in psychobiology remained a face-to-face interview type of situation which tended to slight free association and unconscious influences.

Perhaps the most constructive contribution of psychobiology, under Meyer's aegis, was its insistence upon exact and minute clinical observation, and upon the formulation of what had been observed in ordinary, common-sense terms. It was first-class medicine applied to psychiatric practice, without apologies for psychogenic origins or for psychotherapeutic successes and failures. For many years, Meyer's service was the only place in the United States, and perhaps in the world, where a psychiatric resident in training was given full, mature responsibility for a small number of selected patients in the setting of a first-class teaching university hospital. It was a place where every patient on the in-patient service, no matter what he said or did, and no matter who he was, could be certain that he would be treated with complete respect as a human being. The setting was therapeutically permissive and, outside of the formal mental-status examination, a perceptive therapist could follow whatever procedures seemed promising, including those which the patient's preferences indicated.

Meyer himself called psychobiology *genetic-dynamic*. It drew its fundamental tenets from Freudian psychology without clearly recognizing this. Many of the men and women trained by Meyer later acquired training in classical psychoanalysis. A few of them became leaders in that field. Maurice Levine was one of the writer's first teachers on Meyer's staff. Adelaide Johnson shared the responsibilities of the assistant residency with him. The names of Kubie and Bertram Lewin kept showing up on Meyer's case histories.

Nevertheless, psychobiology failed to capture and hold the imagination of dynamic American psychiatry because it all but ignored Freud, it failed to give serious consideration to the unconscious, it soft-pedaled sexual and aggressive drives, and it made next to no use of free association and the significance of dreams. There were always individual exceptions to these restrictions, toward whom Meyer showed remarkable tolerance; but the restrictions were the rule, and they prevailed.

Nondirective or client-centered therapy. This movement, which Carl Rogers founded and developed with his students, has had as profound an effect upon clinical psychology during the past two decades as psychobiology had upon American psychiatry thirty or forty years ago. Like Meyer, Rogers was largely self-trained in clinical work with patients, whom he prefers to call *clients*. Unlike Meyer, he is gifted in self-expression as well as in leadership; and he has the advantage of not having to establish himself in psychological medicine as a pioneer, since he is not a medical man, and the field of psychological medicine has long been an accepted one.

There are many similarities between *nondirective* or *client-centered therapy* and *psychobiology*. Rogers and his followers also emphasize the importance and the integrity of the individual, the general tendency of sick or disturbed persons to improve or become well if circumstances permit.[3] Like Meyer's school, they utilize a face-to-face technique, and accept whatever the patient presents, with full respect for the patient (or client) as a person. They do not pass judgment upon clients, advise them, or challenge them. They always look past what the client is saying to hear what emotions he may be unwittingly expressing. Their general procedure is to formulate what the client seems to be expressing, including his emotional expression, and allow the client to lead the way. There is certainly less formality in nondirective therapy than in psychobiology, but there is the same emphasis upon current problems and upon conscious and preconscious processes, and the same avoidance of what might be going on at unconscious and infantile levels.

The nondirective or client-centered school of thought is quite explicit about its Freudian origins. The shyness which Meyer showed in this respect is notably absent. Nonetheless, the relationship between nondirective psychotherapy and psychoanalysis, like that between psychobiology and psychoanalysis, is not a simple one. In the late 1920's Otto Rank, one of the brilliant nonmedical followers of Freud, began drifting away from the master. He not only put intellectual distance between himself and Freud; he also began paying long visits to the United States. Here he lectured widely. His most important influence was upon social workers in New York and Philadelphia.[4] Jessie Taft was his sponsor; it was she who wrote two readable digests of Rankian psychology.[5] Frederick Allen, the distinguished Philadelphia child psychiatrist, also came under his influence.[6] It is from these roots, according to Hobbs, that client-centered or nondirective psychotherapy sprang.[7] Rogers has not only carried this development far into the traditional research interests of American clinical psychology; he has also organized a succession of outpatient clinics, connected with universities, where he continues his research and clinical practice.

Some origins of Freud's psychoanalysis. Since these two forms of psychotherapy, and practically all other expressive psychotherapies, can be

[3] The publications of this school number in many hundreds. One might begin with Rogers, C. R., *Client-Centered Therapy*. Boston: Houghton Mifflin, 1951. Earlier books by the same author are Rogers, C. R., *Clinical Treatment of the Problem Child*. Boston, Houghton Mifflin, 1939; and Rogers, C. R., *Counseling and Psychotherapy*. Boston: Houghton Mifflin, 1942.

[4] Munroe, R., *Schools of Psychoanalytic Thought*. New York: Dryden Press, 1955, pp. 575–598.

[5] Taft, J., *The Dynamics of Therapy in a Controlled Relationship*. New York: Macmillan, 1933; Taft, J., *Family Casework and Counseling: A Functional Approach*. Philadelphia: Univ. of Penna. Press, 1948.

[6] Allen, F., "Therapeutic principles applicable to work with children," *Amer. J. Psychiat.*, 1937, *94*, 673–677; Allen, F. H., *Psychotherapy with Children*. New York: Norton, 1942.

[7] Hobbs, N., "Client-centered therapy," in McCary, J. L. (Ed.), *Six Approaches to Psychotherapy*. New York: Dryden Press, 1955, pp. 11–60.

traced back to Freud's discoveries, their common origins may all become more intelligible if we begin with a brief account of how Freud made his discoveries and why. As almost everyone knows today, Freud began his career as a clinical neurologist who worked also in comparative neuro-anatomy. That he was not a limited man in those demanding fields is clear from his early publications which, in addition to some research papers, included a monograph on *aphasia* and a *classification of the cerebral palsies of children* which remained the standard in clinical neurology throughout the Western world for fifty years.

The necessity for earning a living outside of strictly academic circles drove Freud into private practice, where he soon found himself in contact with neurotic patients, and not a few whom we would probably call border-line psychotic today. Freud showed himself to be a man of extraordinary honesty, courage, obstinacy and inventiveness, with a capacity for creative understanding which can only be described as genius. Out of the complex matrix of his personal and professional background, we shall mention four among the most important influences.[8]

The first was the influence of his medical school teachers, Brücke and Meynert. Brücke was a distinguished physiologist at the University of Vienna, a sworn enemy of vitalism, who insisted upon naturalistic interpre-tations of all living human functions. Meynert was a famous neuroanatomist who also doubled as a psychiatrist. Freud worked in Meynert's laboratory and was once given the key to the psychiatric service. These men helped to set the seal of natural science upon Freud's outlook.

The second influence came from a senior colleague, Breuer, with whom Freud discussed their cases, and with whom he published the papers brought together in *Studies on Hysteria.*[9] It was one of Breuer's cases, a young woman, who was able to get rid of all her symptoms under hypnosis by just talking freely. She had to do this every few days in order not to have a galaxy of severe symptoms. It was she who called the treatment a "talk-ing cure," when she was serious, and "chimney-sweeping" when she joked. Freud and Breuer were good friends for about a dozen years, but eventually they had a permanent falling out, presumably over Freud's insistence upon the sexual character of the psychoneuroses (neuroses). The extent of their interchange can be gauged from the *Studies on Hysteria,* and from Volume One of *The Life and Work of Sigmund Freud.* For many years after their break, Freud continued to attribute what seems to have been an exaggerated proportion of their joint contribution to Breuer. The influence of Fliess, who followed Breuer as Freud's friend, but during most of the time at a distance, is not included here because Fliess appears to have been more a splendid listener and encourager than a coworker.

[8] Jones, E., *The Life and Work of Sigmund Freud.* New York: Basic Books, 1953–1957 (3 vols.).

[9] Breuer, J., and Freud, S., *Studies on Hysteria.* (1895), Standard Edition, 1955, vol. 2.

The third influence came from the year Freud spent at Charcot's clinic in Paris, in 1885, on a scholarship, and the short stay in 1889 with Bernheim, the professor of medicine at Nancy, who was also a distinguished hypnotist and psychotherapist. Charcot insisted that only hysterical patients could be deeply hypnotized, while Bernheim said that everyone could be. Charcot also emphasized the universal importance of sex in hysteria, and Freud wondered often why the great neurologist never came out with this in public. He was soon to find out. Back in Vienna, after the Paris year, Freud found that there were patients whom he could not hypnotize. In 1889, he took one of his unhypnotizable patients to Bernheim, only to be told that Bernheim really could not hypnotize everyone. It throws some light on the industriousness of Freud that he translated Charcot's lectures and two books by Bernheim into German during these early years.

A fourth influence was Freud's long period of dream analysis. He had apparently always been interested in dreams, even as a boy, and had always dreamed a good deal. He seems to have finished the work on *The Interpretation of Dreams* in 1895; but he did not publish it for another five years. At the same time, he was interested in his patients' dreams as well, as one can see in *Studies on Hysteria*. But the analysis of his own dreams stands out as one of the boldest and most self-revealing documents in history. As an achievement in systematic self-analysis, carried out alone without the support of another analyst — for there were no other analysts then — it is without a peer.

Freud sometimes challenged his critics to try the same thing with themselves; but there was no one stout-hearted enough to pick up the gauntlet. Even his followers did not emulate his example systematically in this direction. Anyone who has gone through his own dream analyses knows how painful and how revealing the process can be, even with the unspoken support of a training analyst. There is abundant evidence that Freud, for all his stoicism, was a sensitive man who was a stranger neither to mental nor to physical anguish. He writes quite bluntly that he went much farther with his self-analysis than the material he reported in *The Interpretation of Dreams*. We can be certain that he spared himself nothing in the process, and that it cost him years of pain. But if Freud had not subjected himself to these years of self-searching, to the solitary process of exploring his own dynamic unconscious, he would never have arrived at an understanding of the depths of human thinking, of the weird nature of the primary process, and of the structure of psychoneuroses and psychoses.

Academic questions are raised from time to time concerning the origins of Freud's dynamic hypotheses.[10] Just who were his intellectual progenitors and whose writings might have suggested this or that component of his

---

[10] For an account of the contributions of Jung, Adler, Rank and others, see Munroe, R. L., *Schools of Psychoanalytic Thought: An Exposition, Critique and Attempt at Integration.* New York: Dryden Press, 1955; and Jones, E., *The Life and Work of Sigmund Freud.* New York: Basic Books, 1953–1957 (3 vols).

theories? No one can answer these questions. Freud was an omnivorous reader, an enthusiastic listener, and a man with extraordinary retentive powers. He was surrounded in his formative years by a galaxy of stars in many fields. As with other geniuses — as with Van Gogh, for example, whose angry asocial character contrasts so vividly with the socially responsive, patient originator of psychoanalysis — Freud borrowed from whatever area he could, and proceeded to construct something unlike anything that preceded him. One has only to read his masterly review of the literature in *The Interpretation of Dreams* to see this.

Bernfeld has called attention to the fact that Freud attended Brentano's readings and seminars in 1874–76, the only nonmedical courses that he seems to have included during his medical studies.[11] Brentano was a leader of the *act psychology school* which stressed the constant push of ideas from within. In 1874, Brentano published one of his major works, in which he devoted an entire chapter to a detailed discussion of the concept of unconscious ideas, which he traced back to Thomas Aquinas.[12] It is unlikely that so alert and flexible a mind as Freud's was not influenced by his prolonged contact with Brentano, even though it may have been only a small cork floating on a vast sea of physiological and anatomical interests. In his biography, Jones dismisses Brentano as of no importance in Freud's development, and we shall never know whether Jones or Bernfeld was right.[13] In any case, it would have taken a genius to distill psychodynamics from the writings of Brentano, or from those whom Brentano discusses in his book.[14] Freud was a genius who took whatever material he needed from whatever source it came; and he built his own unique systems of theory and practice.

The beginnings of psychoanalytic therapy. Turning from these speculations to what we know was going on, we get the picture of an energetic, enquiring, adventurous young scientist, who questioned every opinion offered and every procedure employed, whether it was his own or that of someone else. He stuck with hypnosis and suggestion for years, and he gave his patients low-voltage electric shocks, after the custom of his day, even though his successes were as meager and transient as those of his contemporaries. He wore himself out insisting to his patients, also in the manner of practitioners of that time, that they would experience lasting improvement and the loss of their symptoms. Hypnosis and suggestion were the chief methods employed then, just as they are still the chief methods

[11] Bernfeld, S., "Freud's earliest theories and the school of Helmholtz," *Psychoanal. Quart.*, 1944, *13*, 341–362; see also Boring, E. G., *A History of Experimental Psychology.* (2nd ed.), New York: Appleton-Century-Crofts, 1950, 356–361.

[12] Brentano, F., *Psychologie vom empirischen Standpunkt.* (1874) Leipzig: Meiner, 1924, pp. 78–91 and pp. 141–194.

[13] Jones, E., *The Life and Work of Sigmund Freud.* New York: Basic Books, 1953–1957 (3 vols.).

[14] Cameron, N., "Dynamics in psychiatry," *Conn. State Med. J.*, 1954, *18*, 340–346. See also Whyte, L. L., *The Unconscious Before Freud.* New York: Basic Books, 1960.

today of suppressive symptomatic psychotherapy. We see the young Freud systematically hypnotizing his patients and trying out the various methods of suggestion employed then. He added some special refinements of his own, such as placing his hand on the patient's forhead, and authoritatively stating that, when he pressed hard, the forgotten idea would appear. He found that sometimes it did, and sometimes it did not.

Soon Freud, with his characteristic honesty, realized that he got as good or better results without hypnosis and without suggestion as with them. What to do with this enlightenment? He profited by Breuer's experience with the "talking cure" and "chimney-sweeping" in giving his patients free rein, first with hypnosis and then without it. In the end, all that remained of the methods of hypnosis was the couch, which even today is still the symbol of psychoanalysis, and is used in more superficial psychotherapy where relaxation seems desirable. Freud soon began sitting behind his reclining patients, where he could see them, but they could not see him. An early patient told him sharply that his interruptions interfered with her free associations. Freud tried limiting his comments, confrontations, and interpretations to a minimum, and found that this method worked well. Thus evolved the essential elements of early psychoanalysis — the couch, the invisible therapist, and the noninterference with free association unless it was clearly to the advantage of therapy to say something.

It was not long before Freud recognized the importance of resistance in his patients, the importance of their shying away from some painful topic as they approached it, of changing the topic abruptly, of making irrelevant remarks or becoming silent.[15] The patient who had come for help seemed now to be doing everything he could to avoid being helped. Freud quickly recognized that this "resistance" was closely related to repression, and that more often than not the patient was unaware of his evasion and the reasons for it. This led to the practice of calling the patient's attention to such incidents, and of urging him to follow the "basic rule," which is simply to say whatever comes to mind, regardless of how trivial, meaningless or embarrassing it may be. Freud found that his own relative silence and his invisibility allowed his patients to express themselves almost as though they were alone and as though they were fantasying aloud.

Transference and countertransference

The climax came when Freud discovered *transference*, the re-enacting or re-experiencing by adult patients of their childhood experiences in relation to parents and other authority figures, and even to the siblings of their childhood. Freud found that during the therapeutic hours patients often attributed all kinds of things to him which had no foundation in objective fact. They expressed admiration, love or gratitude which were strangely out

---

[15] See the symposium on *The Silent Patient*. (R. M. Loewenstein, chairman.) *J. Amer. Psychoanal. Ass.*, 1961, 9, 2–90.

of place. They expressed resentment, ridicule and open hostility that were not justified by the therapeutic situation.

A full realization of the power of transference came to Freud when a woman patient, as she was leaving the treatment hour, threw her arms around his neck. Something similar had happened to Breuer. The reaction of Breuer was one of embarrassment and shame. He made sure that this kind of thing would not be repeated. Freud also avoided a repetition of such acting out, but he seized upon this incident as something to study especially for its possible relation to the therapeutic situation.

This is the kind of thing that singles out the man of genius. Pavlov did something analogous. He found that his dogs secreted gastric juice when they were not supposed to secrete it. Instead of throwing out the disturbing data, Pavlov recognized that here was something worth studying in its own right. He and his followers proceeded to study this irregularity systematically, and vast forests of experimental psychology have grown up from this inspired recognition. Freud had found something in the emotional reactions of his patients that disturbed the therapist-patient relationship, and he likewise recognized that here he had something worth his special attention.

With this start, Freud went still further, and began studying *his own reactions* to patients, to see how much of the irrational and infantile entered into his therapeutic procedures. From such studies came the concept of *countertransference*. Not only may a patient contaminate therapy with his irrational and infantile emotional attitudes, but so may also a therapist with his own, unless he is alerted to the problem and able to face his own previously unconscious trends. It is one of the most serious defects of many forms of psychotherapy and counseling today that they minimize the importance of unconscious transference and countertransference factors in the treatment situation, or even ignore them entirely. Both transference and countertransference can give invaluable clues to a patient's basic fantasies, to his major unconscious defenses, his wishes and fears, his loves and his hates, the ways in which he experiences reality, and the pressures exerted by his superego.

In psychotherapy, it is by no means always essential to point out or to interpret a patient's transference reactions to him; it is often essential to avoid pointing them out or interpreting them.[16] On the other hand, the therapist who is not himself alert to these factors, and is not aware of his own countertransference tendencies, may still be able to give good counsel, but he cannot be a completely competent therapist.

Transference and countertransference, the revivals of emotional residues from childhood, are likely to be present in any therapeutic situation, simply

---

[16] There is a large literature on *transference* and *countertransference*, especially in the *Journal of the American Psychoanalytic Association*, the *International Journal of Psychoanalysis*, and the *Psychoanalytic Quarterly*. Some discussion of manipulation of *transference* can be found in Alexander, F., and French, T. M. (Eds.), *Psychoanalytic Therapy*. New York: Ronald, 1946. This book aroused a great deal of opposition and controversy when it first appeared.

because of the unique relationship between the patient and his therapist. This relationship is bound to include some of the components of parent-child interactions from the past of one or both participants, even in general medical and surgical situations. In all forms of psychotherapy there is no longer any doubt that transference and countertransference tendencies are present. It is only a question nowadays of their being recognized by the therapist, and of their being included in his evaluation and management of treatment.

With this account of the evolution of psychotherapy as our background, we shall be ready to take up the major varieties used today in treating persons who suffer from psychopathology. We shall begin with the protective, sheltering arrangements that are available to those persons who need protection and shelter from the ordinary human environment. These constitute a relatively small *minority* of patients, but their *number* is great. Then we shall go on to the ameliorative measures used to reduce acute anxiety and mental suffering, and to the empirical measures employed to break into certain psychotic processes which seem to have become vicious cycles. We call these last *auxiliary therapies* because they treat the *symptoms* and do not reach the distortions in human interaction which precipitate the psychosis. Finally we shall come to the varieties of psychotherapy, the most successful of all forms of treatment of psychopathology when they promote a therapist-patient relationship which is accepting, warm and expressive. But first let us look at the protective, ameliorative and auxiliary therapies.

Protective, Ameliorative and Auxiliary Therapies

The vast majority of persons who seek treatment for their psychopathology do not need protection, amelioration or auxiliary therapy. They are just as capable of facing psychotherapy as patients with strictly somatic disorders are capable of facing somatic therapy.[17] But there are perhaps a million patients in the United States who do need protection, amelioration or auxiliary therapy. To them we now turn.

1. Protective care

Patients with psychopathology need protective care when they themselves and their human environment cannot cope with the conditions of everyday living. These include hospitalized patients and a great many who would benefit from an adequate hospital environment if this were available. Some communities provide such care and some do not. In some the hospital care provided by the state is such that hospitalization for psychopathology is avoided by everyone whenever possible; when it can be no longer avoided, it provides the patient with only drab confinement and little personal treatment.

[17] Leighton, A. H., *My Name is Legion*. New York: Basic Books, 1959.

Hospitalization in a competent, well-run, community-supported situation has many advantages. It is a haven for adults who cannot keep up with the routine demands of everyday life, or who have been continually harassed by family, neighborhood or business situations. It is a haven for persons who feel themselves a terrible burden for their families, and who in many instances are. A well-run hospital, which gives individuals appropriate individual care, can help a patient to re-establish routines of living which a psychotic or near-psychotic episode has destroyed. It can give many persons a routine of living which is better than anything that they have been able to establish by themselves.

At the level of simply maintaining life, a competently run mental hospital makes sure that a patient too sick to look after himself — for example, in a psychotic depression, a manic excitement, schizophrenia or a brain disorder — is looked after in such basic things as eating, drinking, evacuating, sleeping and exercising. If a patient is capable of interacting with others, but has developed an aversion to human contact or a neglect of it by reason of his illness, the good hospital helps him use his residual capacities to re-establish human contact, but avoids forcing it upon him. The hospital environment allows a sick and incompetent adult to regain and maintain his self-respect by shielding him from relatives and friends, who normally make emotional demands upon him which, for the time being, he is unable to meet.

If a person is psychotically depressed, the good hospital does not surround him with anxiety, which would only make him more desperate. It does not exhort him to "snap out of it," because experience has taught its personnel that it is impossible to "snap out of it," and that such exhortation only makes a depressed person more depressed than ever. If the patient is in a manic excitement, he is helped to control his excitement, he is not exposed to dangerous stimulation, his physiological needs for food, rest and general body care are met as much as possible, and he is protected from doing damage to his human and inanimate environment. If he is schizophrenic, the hospital provides the patient with a simplified environment and with personnel that is not frightened or aggressive when he responds to delusional and hallucinatory experiences. If the patient is in a temporary panic, he finds whatever seclusion he needs from the ordinary, everyday environment which may have precipitated his panic.

Besides receiving these protective and custodial services, the hospitalized patient finds some satisfaction for his regressive, dependent needs in being taken care of, and treated as a sick person, which he is. The good hospital provides a framework of restrictions which prevents acting out, which gives many patients a needed sense of security in relation to impulses that they cannot control alone. It assuages the guilt of some, and reduces in still others their delusional fear of imprisonment, attack or execution. The medical setting of the good mental hospital ensures attention to possible medical and surgical complications through the services of consultants in or near the hospital itself. Among these must be included the treatment of deliria and deficiencies induced by metabolic disorders, alcohol or drugs, severe postoperative anxieties and brain damage. A hospital is also the safest place to carry out such auxiliary procedures as insulin coma and electric shock when a psychotic cycle has been set up by a patient's reactions to intolerable anxiety. Finally, a hospital should give patients who are ready for it the chance to begin psychotherapeutic work while they are too sick to go home.[18]

Hospital care also has potentially serious disadvantages for the mental patient. If it is incompetent, patients suffer damage from neglect or isolation, from not being treated with the respect accorded other sick persons, and from their own tendencies toward infantile regression. The combination of drab surroundings and impoverished inner resources can be particularly demoralizing. One sometimes sees mental hospitals where the lawns and flowerbeds outside get better care than the patients inside. It should be mentioned, however, that for the profoundly guilty depressed person, a drab hospital and the menial labor usually demanded of patients, seem to gratify a need for punishment. We saw this happen in the case of Agnes W., who did badly in a good mental hosiptal, where she constantly insisted that she be punished, and recovered in a drab, prison-like hospital where she was forced to do menial labor because all the other patients were. This does not justify poor hospital care, any more than it would justify execution, which Agnes W. also continually demanded.

Perhaps the greatest danger of prolonged hospitalization is that relatives and friends tend to desert the patient. This seems especially to be the case among poorly educated people from a low socio-economic level.[19] They look upon mental illness as incurable and as a family disgrace. The tendency then is to give up visiting the patient, to omit all mention of him to friends, and to obstruct efforts at obtaining his return to the community. There is also the important factor of tolerance by the human environment. If a family is in poor economic circumstances, and has many young children around the house, it becomes exceedingly difficult to make room for a recovering psychotic person, and often impossible to make room for a chronically psychotic one. It follows that the rate of discharge for persons who have suffered a psychotic break is far lower among these groups than it is among well-educated people who are also able financially to provide a place for the recovering and the chronically ill psychotic patient. It must be kept in mind that love and hope can be even more important in recovering from mental illness than from physical illness.

Within recent years a rapidly increasing use has been made of hospital night care and hospital day care. When a patient seems ready to return to

[18] Stanton, A. S., and Schwartz, M. S., *The Mental Hospital*. New York: Basic Books, 1954.
[19] Hollingshead, A. B., and Redlich, F. C., *Social Class and Mental Illness*. New York: Wiley, 1958.

his family, but is not yet ready to follow a home routine, hospital day care provides one. For some weeks or months, the patient spends the day or a good part of the day in the hospital, doing what the other patients do, but returning home for the evening and the night. In the opposite situation, when it is deemed unwise or impractical for a recovering patient to return home, he may go to work, or to a technical school or college, during the daytime, and return to the hospital for his evening meal and the night. In both varieties there is provision made for psychotherapy at the hospital. Out-patient clinics and rehabilitation centers, if they have the trained personnel, the space and the equipment, can perform the same functions as the hospital day care. In all of these, the advantages in preparing the patient for his re-entry into the community are obvious.

2. Ameliorative therapy

This has limited application. It has been found that a mild or moderate degree of anxiety, for example, may be a person's most important incentive in seeking therapy, and in keeping on with it until he can acquire more constructive incentives. The situation is then analogous to that of abdominal pain in surgery. The good surgeon does not eliminate the pain entirely until he has made his diagnosis and obtained the patient's cooperation. Such use of anxiety or pain often seems heartless to the layman. Actually, it is the product of self-discipline on the part of the good surgeon and the good psychotherapist, whose basic urge is to relieve suffering and who has the means at his disposal for doing so. For the patient, his therapist's self-discipline may make the difference between recovery and nonrecovery, and sometimes between life and death.

Acute or moderately severe anxiety and mental suffering interfere with therapy, by distracting or disorganizing the patient, and by leaving him with an intolerable burden. Sedatives, "tranquilizers," and antispasmodic drugs are used to control the physiological concomitants of emotion and to provide rest and sleep. Stimulants often enable depressed patients to go on with their work or, if they are in a hospital or at home, to participate actively in helpful routines. Such medicinal help does not reach the roots of a person's problems; it does nothing about the sources of anxiety. Psychotherapy is still needed; and patients should be clear about this. When a patient cannot accept his need for psychotherapy, or is too sick to profit from it, the temporary use of medicines to tide him over his crisis may be all that can be done.

Therapists working in large public mental hospitals report that the use of tranquilizers has made it possible to discharge many patients who would otherwise have had to be permanently hospitalized. Where chronically disturbed patients are present on public ward services in large numbers, the reduction in general tension and in impulsive, noisy behavior has made it possible for all of the patients to live more comfortably than before. The use of tranquilizers in one large public mental hospital has reduced the use of insulin coma and electric convulsive therapy, and increased more than ever the need for qualified psychotherapists in the hospital.[20]

3. Auxiliary therapies

It would be perhaps more accurate to call these *makeshift therapies,* but the term *auxiliary therapies* is already in the literature. Two such methods deserve special mention here. One of them consists of inducing coma in a patient, accompanied by a considerable degree of individual attention and general medical care. The other consists of inducing generalized convulsions by passing a high voltage electric current through the patient's head. There are serious dangers in both procedures, and although they rarely lead to death, this must be considered as a possible risk. They should be carried out only by thoroughly trained personnel in a hospital.

There is no known rationale for the use of insulin coma or electric convulsive therapy. Both are purely empirical. Insulin coma nowadays is usually limited to the treatment of young, acutely ill schizophrenic adults, in other words, to schizophrenic patients who have always had the best prognosis, regardless of what kind of therapy was employed. Electric convulsive treatment appears to be most useful in cutting psychotic depressions short. Neither procedure has any bearing upon possible sources of the illness, and there is some controversy as to whether either lessens the likelihood of a recurrence.

Insulin coma. Insulin coma was introduced by Sakel in 1928 for the treatment of excited states in morphine addicts during withdrawal of the narcotic. Sakel later extended this treatment to excited schizophrenic patients. In 1936 he brought his method to the United States, where it was widely hailed as the new cure for schizophrenia. This expectation has not been fulfilled. A great many schizophrenic patients respond well to psychotherapeutic methods, and many recover their previous equilibrium, or even improve upon it, through the process of psychotherapy. Many schizophrenic patients improve or recover through the use of electric convulsive therapy; and it has been known for ages that many improve and even recover without special treatment. It is therefore difficult to evaluate insulin coma as therapy, and impossible to regard it as a specific. A clinical anecdote will illustrate the complexity of the problem.

When the writer was serving as psychiatrist in a state hospital, where each psychiatrist's case load was numbered in the hundreds, he became acquainted with an adult male patient who had become a chronic

---

[20] Noyes, A. P., and Kolb, L. C., *Modern Clinical Psychiatry.* (5th ed.) Philadelphia: Saunders, 1958; Detre, T., and Jarecki, H., "A practical guide to the use of pharmacological agents in general practice," *Conn. State Med. J.,* 1961, *25,* 553–565.

schizophrenic several years before. He interested the writer especially because of certain peculiar gestures and mannerisms, which need not detain us here. He also interested the writer because he seemed to want to communicate something incommunicable, or, at least, something which no one around him was able to grasp. It was probably primary process material, although this is a mere guess.

Three years later, when the writer was chief resident psychiatrist at the Johns Hopkins Hospital, this same schizophrenic patient was admitted to the neurosurgical service because he had sustained a skull fracture at the state hospital when he fell down a flight of stairs. The neurosurgeons were not eager to keep him on their service once he regained consciousness. Accordingly he was transferred to the psychiatric service.

To the writer's great surprise, this man who had not been able to communicate for many years spoke clearly now. He seemed eager to tell all that he remembered about the state hospital, and it was obvious that he remembered a great deal. Notwithstanding the fact that he was treated in what was at one time called the "total push method," that is, he was kept active and in as normal contact as possible by an experienced personnel, he soon began to fade. Within three weeks he was again unable to communicate, he had reverted once more to his strange gestures and mannerisms, and it was soon obvious that we had "lost" him. He again sat on one heel, like a cowboy, though he had never seen a cowboy, and stared at the entrance door as though he expected something to come in which he could not name. Back at the state hospital, he was given insulin coma and metrazol shock therapy, which were then in high favor as a cure for schizophrenia, but he did not change at all, either for the better or for the worse. What should have been done? Should the patient have had less attention, no attention or more attention? We do not know. We know only that we had the man back in this world after his accident, and that we could not keep him there.

Treatment with insulin coma usually consists of daily intramuscular injections of insulin, which are increased until the patient becomes comatose, that is, unresponsive to a point short of death. Five or six treatments are given until the patient has had a total of fifty hours in coma.[21] Insulin coma treatment today is limited almost entirely to schizophrenic patients. The best results are for patients who are in their twenties, have had a stormy, sudden onset, and appeared previous to their illness to have been reasonably well integrated. This is the same group, as we mentioned earlier, that has always had the best prognosis, regardless of specific therapeutic procedure.

[21] For a brief discussion of methods, benefits and complications, see Noyes. A. P., and Kolb, L. C., *Modern Clinical Psychiatry*. (5th ed.) Philadelphia: Saunders, 1958; Horwitz, W. A., "Insulin shock therapy," in Arieti, S. (Ed.), *American Handbook of Psychiatry*. New York: Basic Books, 1959, pp. 1485–1498. It should be said here that both insulin coma and electrically induced convulsions are not without serious dangers; and sometimes they prove fatal to the patient.

It is the group which also responds best to psychotherapy. Insulin coma therapy seems to be gradually losing ground in public institutions, where electric convulsive therapy is replacing it.

Electric convulsive therapy. Many prefer this term to the older term, *electric shock therapy,* because convulsive seizures seem to be necessary if the treatment is to have any effect.[22] The objective of the treatment is to produce tonic and then clonic convulsions which resemble those in epilepsy. These are produced by passing a high voltage electric current through the patient's head. The method was introduced by two Italians, Cerletti and Bini, in 1938. The most dramatic effects occur among psychotic depressions, including the so-called "involutional melancholias," which are psychotic depressions appearing in middle life.

The vast majority of psychotically depressed persons recover without electric convulsive treatment; but there seems to be no doubt that electric convulsive therapy cuts down drastically the duration of the illness. Instead of being psychotically depressed for months or years, the patient given electrically induced convulsions may recover in a matter of weeks or months. Nobody knows why, just as nobody can explain our chronic schizophrenic patient's temporary remission after his skull fracture. For the time being, until we understand depressions better, electric convulsive therapy seems destined to widespread use. In addition to its effect in shortening the period of depressive suffering, which is often agonizing, convulsive therapy also shortens the period during which the depressed patient is a suicidal risk. There is no other psychopathology that can compare with psychotic depression when it comes to suicidal risk.

How are we to evaluate electric convulsive therapy? What happens to make the inaccessible patient accessible? We do not know. Why does electric convulsive therapy work better with patients who are inaccessible by reason of a psychotic depression than with those made equally inaccessible by reason of a schizophrenic illness? We do not know. Why in the first place do either of these psychotic people become inaccessible when everything depends upon their remaining in effective interaction with their human environment? We do not know. Within recent years a new synthetic drug has been introduced, called *Indoklon,* which produces convulsions when it is inhaled. It has been called the new cure for depressions and perhaps the new cure for other psychoses as well. Who knows?

Shall we give up psychotherapy and psychoanalysis because a small minority of patients are unable to profit from either? Shall we forsake psychotherapy and psychoanalysis because this minority benefits from crude empirical methods which have no beneficial effect whatever upon the vast number of persons with neurotic depressions and other neuroses, upon those with personality disorders, and even upon a large percentage of psychotic

---

[22] Kalinowsky, L. B., "Convulsive shock treatment," in Arieti, S. (Ed.), *American Handbook of Psychiatry.* New York: Basic Books, 1959, pp. 1499–1520.

patients? The answer seems to lie in obtaining a better understanding of what produces psychopathology, and in arriving sooner or later at methods which strike at its roots rather than those which drive a patient into a coma or into electrically induced convulsions. For the millions of persons who develop neuroses, personality disorders and psychosomatic disorders, and for most of those who become psychotic, the brightest hope is still where it was when Freud developed his methods of free association, when he learned to accept the neurotic and borderline psychotic patient as an equal among all the other patients whom mankind has learned to respect. This brings us to a consideration of some representative methods of psychotherapy.

Some Varieties of Psychotherapy

We have already indicated that the term *psychotherapy* extends over a wide range of treatment procedures which rely upon psychological methods in dealing with psychological illnesses, in dealing with the psychopathology in psychosomatic disorders and brain disorders, and with whatever psychopathology may arise during general medical and surgical illnesses, in convalescence and rehabilitation. We have said that psychological and somatic methods are not mutually exclusive; and we have discussed some aspects of their interrelationship, including the use of somatic therapies as auxiliary, preparatory or substitute forms of treatment. We have sketched briefly some of the origins, beginnings and applications of psychotherapy, and pointed out the inevitable presence of transference and countertransference factors with which the therapist must be prepared to deal. This last is just as true in therapeutic situations where the therapist restricts recognition of these factors to himself, as where the therapist exercises caution and wisdom in helping his patient to recognize the transference factors that are interfering with treatment. It remains now to discuss in a few words the major varieties of psychotherapy.

Before doing this, it might be well to mention certain procedures commonly employed in an effort to provide patients or clients with a more favorable environment than they have. In the old days, it was customary to advise a neurotic, mildly psychotic or ageing patient to take a vacation. When this advice was given conscientiously, and not just to be rid of a complaining person, it was given on the general principle that the environment as it was structured was too much for him to handle, that it included too many responsibilities or too great a conflict for a person not in the best of mental health and strength. Going on a vacation has often worked well. Indeed, taking a vacation is still one of the most widely used methods of temporarily ridding oneself of routines and responsibilities which have grown tiresome and burdensome, of benefiting by the refreshing experiences of a new environment and of days filled with recreation. For everyone, it means eventually coming back to the old situation. If a patient who goes off on a vacation does little or nothing about his essential problems, he will face them as soon as he comes back again, and he will more than likely find them wherever he goes to escape from them. Such environmental manipulation has limited and superficial uses.

It is in dealing with children that environmental manipulation has been most systematically developed, and most beneficially employed. Its simplest forms are those which include summer camps or boarding schools for children, where the company of other like-aged and like-sexed children, under the direction of intelligent and emotionally mature adults, may provide a child with many opportunities which he does not have at home. Something similar is offered the preschool child by those so-called "nursery schools" which provide something beyond the mere relief of care for the child's mother. Other common examples of environmental manipulation are the attempts to improve slum neighborhoods and provide community organizations which lessen the trends toward juvenile delinquency. These attempts take it for granted that whatever pathological behavior is encountered is the product rather of a pathological or pathogenic environment than of established psychopathology in the individual.

A similar assumption is present when action is taken to place a disturbed child in a foster home. The assumption is so often justified that such placement has become a major task of many social work agencies.[23] The procedure is neither simple nor easy. There is first of all the problem of getting parents or parent substitutes to give up the child. Then there is the problem of finding a foster home where the child will be well treated, as a member of the family, and not as a burden, a boarder, or a source of income. Finally, there is the problem of gaining the child's consent and cooperation. In some instances, the last-mentioned is the most difficult of all. Many children, reared in a home that is pathogenic for them, nonetheless resist every attempt to remove them to a home of strangers, no matter how wholesome and affectionate these strangers may be.

Nowadays attempts are increasing continually to get both a disturbed child and his parent into psychotherapy simultaneously, usually with a different therapist for each.[24] Even when this attempt succeeds it presents many special difficulties. The child continues to live with the parent, so that some communication about treatment is inevitable, and the parent controls the home situation completely. It is, for example, essential that a parent not be treated with hostility by a therapist lest this hostility be unwittingly passed on by the parent to the child, and even to the whole therapeutic situation. Parents are likely to feel "accused" by the mere fact that their child needs treatment. They may spend much of their time and effort in defensive maneuvers designed to show that the child's behavior is not their fault. Therapists in parent-child situations need to be as objective and empathic in relations to one patient as to the other.

[23] Lippman, H. S., *Treatment of the Child in Emotional Conflict.* New York: McGraw-Hill, 1956.

[24] Fanshel, D., "Studying the role performance of foster parents," *Soc. Work.,* 1961, 6, 74–81; Naughton, F. X., "Foster home placement as an adjunct to residential treatment," *Soc. Casework,* 1957, 38, 288–295.

Sometimes the mother of a disturbed child is unwilling to have the child in psychotherapy, but is willing to come for help herself. Sometimes it is the child who refuses to come. Under either condition a great deal of progress can be made through psychotherapy of the parent. It goes without saying that everything depends upon the parent's integrity. Any changes for the better which competent psychotherapy may bring about, will appear in the home as a changed environment in which the child has been living and in which he continues to live. Parents are, after all, the chief components of a child's human environment.

What we have just been discussing are methods of environmental manipulation, of changing the neighborhood or the home of a child, of jointly treating child and parent, and of treating children indirectly through giving psychotherapy to the parent. It should be added that sometimes one must also treat a marital partner indirectly through treating the spouse, when the marital partner refuses treatment. We turn now to the major forms of individual psychotherapy with adults. It is customary to divide these for convenience into four groups: (1) *suppressive;* (2) *supporting;* (3) *relationship;* and (4) *expressive psychotherapies.* We shall follow this custom in what follows.[25]

1. Suppressive psychotherapy

This form, if it can really be called psychotherapy, is used in the United States only where nothing is known about modern psychotherapy, or where it is known and despised. Fifty years ago, and for centuries before that, suppressive procedures were almost the rule. Their effect is to reinforce repression. The suppressive therapist behaves in an authoritative, dogmatic manner. He seeks to suppress all the manifestations of symptoms that he can, and to replace them with attitudes dominated by *reaction formation,* which is repression's handmaiden. In short, he treats the *symptoms* but leaves their *sources* untouched. Under these circumstances, a regressed patient may be enabled to pull himself together again; but he remains vulnerable to the same kind of stress that forced him into symptom formation, or other pathological behavior and experience, in the first place.

It cannot be denied that suppressive psychotherapy often works well, even though it does nothing about the patient's preconscious and unconscious conflicts, or about his frustrations, anxieties or guilt, excepting to forbid their expression. This can be much better than nothing. It provides the patient with a strong, inhibiting parent figure who treats him as a weakling or as a naughty child. Sometimes when a patient is frightened by the imminent eruption of unconscious material, which he is in no position to handle by himself, he may reap immediate benefits from the presence of a firm, authoritarian person who, in effect, exorcises the devils of the id and the superego, and drives them back where they belong. In practice, suppressive

[25] Levine, M., "Principles of psychiatric treatment," in Alexander, F., and Ross, H., *Dynamic Psychiatry.* Chicago: Univ. of Chicago Press, 1952, pp. 307–368.

psychotherapy is sometimes supplemented by hypnotic suggestion, a combination that was apparently much used in Freud's early years and, as a matter of fact, was used for a time by Freud himself.

The weaknesses of suppressive psychotherapy are the weaknesses that led Freud to give it up. It serves at best as a temporary expedient, a method which inflates the therapist's sense of power and plays upon the patient's need to be childishly dependent. It is sometimes important to give symptomatic treatment, to strengthen the repressive forces in dealing with a panic, or with a psychotic reaction which is on the verge of disorganizing a patient. The same end can be obtained, however, in supportive psychotherapy which provides firmness and a good parental figure, but is more lenient than forbidding, more like the good mother of childhood than the stern father. Suppressive psychotherapy belongs with exhortation and exorcism, as something which modern methods have made obsolete.

2. Supportive psychotherapy

Like suppressive psychotherapy, supportive psychotherapy does nothing about a patient's preconscious and unconscious conflicts. It relieves his anxiety by giving him acceptance and promoting his dependence during a period of physical illness or emotional turbulence, when his defensive organization is not adequate to meet his crises alone. If *suppressive psychotherapy* provides a *stern father figure*, who forbids symptomatic expression, *supportive psychotherapy* provides a *good mother figure* who protects, reassures and encourages the patient through therapeutic warmth, empathy and strength. The therapist functions for the time being as a mature ally of the patient's weakened ego.

Supportive psychotherapy is most successful in the treatment of traumatic neuroses, and of mild to moderate psychoses, in persons who have seemed to be reasonably adequate before they were exposed to unreasonable internal or external stress. It is also appropriate for persons who have been thrown into unexpected conflict, who cannot make necessary decisions alone, or who cannot escape without help from intolerable pressures, but whose only objective is to regain their former equilibrium, without any basic change in their personality. Once the crisis is over, the problem of the patient's dependence upon the therapist must be worked through. Psychotherapy restricted to supportive measures is often practiced where therapists are too few and patients too many, and where the available therapeutic personnel consists of persons untrained in or averse to relationship and expressive psychotherapy.

3. Relationship psychotherapy

As the name implies, this form of psychotherapy consists essentially in establishing an effective relationship between patient or client and psychotherapist. It may begin, as does supportive psychotherapy, merely with sincere accepting attitudes, with genuine respect for human beings, and with a mature understanding of the difficulties inherent in human life. Unlike supportive psychotherapy, however, the aims of relationship psychotherapy go on to include the production of fundamental changes in the personality organization of the patient or client, of helping his growth toward maturity, and of diminishing his vulnerability to emotional turmoil, frustration, conflict and pathogenic guilt.

The major emphases in relationship psychotherapy are upon the *life problems* and *life situations* which are at present disturbing the patient or client, and upon those of the remembered past. It consists of interviews extending over a period of weeks or months, in which the therapist is accepting but firm, nonjudgmental but more favorable toward signs of maturing independence than toward dependence and regression. The relationship psychotherapist provides a warm, friendly, wholesome adult in the therapeutic situation, who not only tolerates disagreement and opposition in his patient but expects tolerance from the patient when he expresses opposition or refuses to agree.

This is another therapy which deals primarily with conscious and readily available preconscious material. It does not concentrate upon unconscious material, and it does not bring the transference to the center of therapy. If the relationship therapist is able to recognize unconscious trends and transference maneuvers in his patient, and if he can also recognize his own countertransference tendencies, he will be in a better position to understand what is going on than if he is blind to them. If *suppressive psychotherapy* can be likened to the intervention of a stern, dictatorial father, and if *supportive psychotherapy* can be likened to the help of a good mother, *relationship psychotherapy* may be compared to the help which a friendly, warm, objective and more mature parent or older sibling might provide.

Relationship psychotherapy gives the patient the opportunity to make healthy identifications with the most mature aspects of his therapist's personality, and with the general attitudes and procedures of the good therapist. When we were discussing identification in relation to personality development, near the beginning of the book, we said that introjection and identification are not confined to the periods of infancy, childhood and adolescence, but may take place at any age. We all know that whenever a powerful political or religious leader appears on the adult scene, thousands and even millions of adults may identify with him. To the extent that they lead to more responsible attitudes and an increase in respect for human decency, such identifications have almost unlimited potentialities for good. To the extent that they lead to irresponsibility, impulsiveness and disrespect for human decency, such adult identifications have almost unlimited potentialities for evil. The good therapist in relationship psychotherapy offers himself as a good parent or a good older sibling, with whom the patient or client can identify. He does so with the implicit, usually unspoken expectation that the person whom he is treating will show himself capable of greater maturity, independence and responsibility. He expects to see not only some of these therapeutic attitudes and expectations incorporated, but also some tolerance for the failings and mistakes of others.

Relationship psychotherapy also provides the patient with what has been called "corrective emotional experience," that is, with experiences that are contradictory to those which he has always anticipated in others. He finds himself neither praised for dependence and submission nor condemned for self-assertion and independence. He is neither praised for defiance and opposition nor condemned for expressing his dependency needs. The therapist is consistently permissive but at the same time consistently firm. He never allows himself to be provoked into hostility or seduced into giving parental guidance. Such experiences lead the patient to recognize that his own hostility is not really dangerous, and that other adults are not as hostile as he had supposed them to be. It leads him to recognize that dependency needs are normal within normal limits, and that these limits are different from those which he had previously established. Relationship psychotherapy is often used for persons who cannot benefit from expressive therapies, either because they are too prejudiced or too sick. It is also used by therapists who themselves are not ready or not trained to carry on expressive psychotherapeutic procedures. As we turn now to a discussion of expressive psychotherapy, it will be obvious that relationship psychotherapy is also an integral part of most expressive psychotherapies.

4. Expressive psychotherapy

Early in this chapter we said that *expressive psychotherapies* include many procedures in which the only tie seems to be their promotion of free expression. There we discussed very briefly such divergent methods as the *psychobiological approach* in psychiatry,[26] and the neo-Rankian *client-centered psychotherapies* developed by Rogers and his followers, and extensively used by counselors and clinical psychologists.[27] We should also mention the *existential approach*,[28] *psychodrama*,[29] and the increasingly important *group therapies*.[30] Most of these make little or no use of the powerful unconscious and concealed preconscious forces which often play a determinative part in human behavior and experience. *Psychoanalytically oriented psychotherapy* is also a form of psychotherapy which is growing rapidly in favor, as more and more persons gain experience with its concepts through a personal psy-

[26] Muncie, W., "The psychobiological approach," in Arieti, S. (Ed.), *American Handbook of Psychiatry*. New York: Basic Books, 1959, pp. 1317–1332.

[27] Rogers, C. R., and Dymond, R. F. (Eds.), *Psychotherapy and Personality Change*. Chicago: Univ. of Chicago Press, 1954.

[28] May, R., "The existential approach," in Arieti, S. (Ed.), *American Handbook of Psychiatry*. New York: Basic Books, 1959, pp. 1348–1361.

[29] Moreno, J. L., "Psychodrama," in Arieti, S. (Ed.), *American Handbook of Psychiatry*. New York: Basic Books, 1959, pp. 1375–1396.

[30] Frank, J. D., and Powdermaker, F. B., "Group psychotherapy," in Arieti, S. (Ed.), *American Handbook of Psychiatry*. New York: Basic Books, 1959, pp. 1362–1374.

choanalysis or by other means.[31] Whether or not *psychoanalysis* itself should be considered a form of expressive psychotherapy is still a matter of considerable controversy. As we have indicated earlier, there can be no doubt that nearly all forms of contemporary expressive psychotherapy owe their existence to Freud and the development of psychoanalysis, however much they may wish to ignore or deny their spiritual parent.

Since this book is not devoted exclusively to psychobiology, to client-centered or nondirective therapy, to psychodrama, existentialism, group therapy or psychoanalysis, we shall direct our discussion of expressive psychotherapy to those forms which are in keeping with the general approach used throughout the rest of the book. Anyone interested in studying the other forms can easily find his way to them by consulting the references provided in the footnotes, and the references provided by these references. We must emphasize once again, however, that a mere intellectual acquaintance with the various expressive psychotherapies does not guarantee an adequate understanding of them. They are all methods of human interaction. Their mere description must necessarily remain pale, insubstantial and incomplete. To try to explain them to a person who has had little or no clinical experience is something like explaining baseball to an Englishman who has never seen it, or explaining cricket to an American. We shall therefore confine our discussion to a brief account of individual psychotherapy as it is carried on today.

Most competent expressive psychotherapy, that goes beyond counseling and the paraphrasing of feeling tones, is psychoanalytically oriented, even though its practitioners may not have been themselves psychoanalyzed.[32] There are two reasons for this situation. One is that people who come for psychotherapy manifest the phenomena which psychoanalysis describes, although they do not themselves know anything about psychoanalysis. We must remember that Freud got his ideas from his patients, not from theories or books. The other reason is that, once a therapist allows himself to become aware of unconscious and deep preconscious processes, he finds therapies which confine themselves to conscious material, and to material that is readily made conscious, to be shallow and timid. The unconscious and deeply stratified preconscious material is there, whether you ignore it or not; so also are the transference and the countertransference forces, the defenses and the resistances. These are all factors which actually operate in every psychotherapy. They are not just theories.

Ever since Freud, it has been established practice among competent psy-

[31] See (various) "Psychoanalytic therapies," in Arieti, S. (Ed.), *American Handbook of Psychiatry*. New York: Basic Books, 1959, pp. 1397–1465; Alexander, F., and French, T. M., (Eds.), *Psychoanalytic Therapy*. New York: Ronald, 1946.

[32] Colby, K., *A Primer for Psychotherapists*. New York: Ronald, 1951; Hill, L. B., *Psychotherapeutic Intervention in Schizophrenia*. Chicago: Univ. of Chicago Press, 1955; Bychowski, G., *Psychotherapy of Psychosis*. New York: Grune & Stratton 1952; Ekstein, R., and Wallerstein, R. S., *The Teaching and Learning of Psychotherapy*. New York: Basic Books, 1958.

chotherapists to treat patients and their complaints with respect, warmth and understanding, to meet the emotional aspects of their behavior with empathy, that is, with thorough emotional understanding. At the same time, however, the situation is always kept a therapeutic and not a social one. The patient must feel free to establish psychological closeness with his therapist, or to put psychological distance between himself and his therapist, without fear of arousing personal affection or personal offense. The therapist, for his part remains always friendly, warm, firm and accepting, but he avoids anything that approaches a personal entanglement with his patient.

The competent psychotherapist is not vulnerable to any attempts a patient may make — through flattery, automatic compliance, facetiousness or seduction — to change the therapeutic situation into a social one. He is not offended by a patient's coolness, criticism, hostility or provocation. If he has been trained by thorough supervision, over a long period, to recognize these often subtly expressed resistances, so much the better. If he has not received prolonged supervisory training, he must do his best alone to recognize a patient's positive and negative emotional reactions as possible resistances, and to treat them objectively, with proper timing, during therapeutic sessions. All this he must do without seeming to reject the patient unless, of course, a hypersensitivity to rejection is one of the patient's leading characteristics, which demand special attention.

The good psychotherapist must also be on the watch for subtle expressions of his own countertransference. In the beginning he learns to inhibit them during the therapeutic hour, but he reviews them objectively afterwards. He will find that, until he gains mastery over them, his own countertransference reactions have the same tendency to repeat themselves which the patient's neurotic transference reactions have. The two are often interrelated.

Above all, it is essential for the psychotherapist with a dynamic orientation not to slight the reality situations and current events in his patient's life. He must bear in mind the fact that his patient does not, and indeed must not talk, think and act in terms of the components of his psychodynamic system, that is, in terms of ego, id, superego and the rest. Therapy conducted in such terms is not therapy at all, but only a pseudointellectual game. True expressive psychotherapy is carried out by both patient and therapist alike in ordinary everyday terms.

The general objectives of expressive psychotherapy are the same as those of relationship therapy. Both aim at providing the patient with opportunities for having spontaneous corrective emotional experiences through interaction with a good therapist. The therapeutic experience, as well as the professional objectivity and warmth of the therapist himself, should give the patient new perspectives and new sources of identification. In successful expressive psychotherapy, these become the starting points for new attitudes on the patient's part toward himself and toward persons outside the therapeutic hour. This is not a matter of limitation, but of deep, gradual personal reorganization, which includes the maturing of infantile, childish and adolescent needs, conflicts, drives and perspectives.

The more specific goals of expressive psychotherapy depend upon the variety of therapy employed. In all of them, the therapist himself should be aware of unconscious as well as conscious and preconscious processes, so that he need not deny or omit their consideration for personal reasons. It is not essential, as we have already said, to communicate all these deeper and more infantile processes to the patient. Sometimes such communication does more harm than good; sometimes it can be of great benefit to a patient, especially if it is phrased in commonsense terms and utilized sparingly and cautiously. The good psychotherapist always adopts some of the patient's own terms in their communication, always being sure that he does this without artificiality, condenscion or facetiousness. When a patient says approvingly, "You speak my language," this may well be a sign that the therapist is reaching the patient at a commonsense, personal level.

Most patients who enter into psychotherapy today are aware that much is going on within them at unconscious levels, without knowing what it is or how to express their realization.[33] They may be afraid of their unconscious processes and harbor superstitious attitudes toward them; but they usually reveal their awareness in one way or another. They may say that they suppose they have this or that defense, this or that unacceptable impulse, this or that resistance, ambivalence or dependency need. There is no harm in tentatively agreeing with the patient's supposition, if the therapist feels reasonably sure that it lies near the surface, and that the patient is capable of dealing with it constructively. There is no harm in ignoring the patient's supposition, if that seems best, or in saying casually, "You may be right," or "I'm not sure about that," or "Let's wait and see." There is no harm in echoing or paraphrasing some part of what the patient says, but with a casual and enquiring air which may lead the patient to say more about it if he wants to.

It is the therapist's duty to move his patient gradually into problems that he has been avoiding because they make him anxious, or because he is afraid of losing his therapist's approval and respect.

The good therapist does not, of course, coerce his patient or move too rapidly into sensitive areas. He never allows his own personal or scientific curiosity to take precedence over his primary therapeutic goals. As French has often expressed it, the good therapist, like the good gardener, waits until he recognizes something which is struggling to emerge, and then makes it easier for it to emerge. The good gardener may loosen the soil which is preventing a maturing plant from reaching the surface. He never pulls the plant up into the air. The good psychotherapist helps the patient to loosen up his defenses, so that what is ready to emerge can do so. He never tries to drag anything up from the unconscious or deep preconscious into awareness. This would be sheer folly, and it might even lead to a psychotic break.

---

[33] See the account given in Gill, M., Newman, R., and Redlich, F. C., *The Initial Interview*. New York: Internat. Univ. Press, 1954.

What emerges when it is ready to emerge can then be dealt with on a communicative level.

Some relationship and expressive psychotherapists have made it appear as though their particular variety originated the method of letting the patient take the lead, express himself freely, and find out that his therapist fully accepts and understands his feelings. Actually it was Freud who developed and openly advocated these procedures. It was he who practiced them with his patients from the beginning of the century, and for more than thirty years thereafter. They have always been, and still are, essential components of all expressive psychotherapy.

At the same time, most expressive psychotherapists do not leave it entirely up to the patient to decide what he shall talk about and what he shall avoid. There are many ways of making it easier for a patient to bring sensitive personal problems into the therapeutic situation, and many ways of making pathogenic defenses unnecessary. When this is done frankly, but conservatively, the patient is in no danger of divulging too much or exploring too deeply. Unconscious material can become conscious, when necessary and appropriate, current problems and life situations, with all their emotions and feeling tones can be met and understood, interpersonal relationships can include much that is unsaid, much that a patient cannot formulate in words, but which he communicates at unverbalized, emotional levels.

From the time of Freud the goal of expressive psychotherapy, and particularly of psychoanalytically oriented psychotherapy, has been avowedly to promote maturation. The verbalization of previously unverbalized attitudes, fantasies and beliefs — some of them almost incredibly infantile — helps in the maturing process. To verbalize is often to conceptualize something in communicable terms, to hear oneself say something newly said, and to share it with an accepting, nonjudgmental therapist. The re-experiencing and recognition of feelings and emotions, which may be components of infantile, childhood, adolescent or adult relationships, also helps in the process of maturing. It is here that the importance of allowing the patient to enter areas previously defended against is most obvious. If the therapist conspires with the patient to keep him away from his own anxieties he will also prevent him from maturing wherever he is afraid to mature.

The expressive psychotherapist must always proceed cautiously and patiently when he deals with pathogenic defenses. He needs always to remember that even a pathogenic defense may serve essential functions, at least for the time being. Compulsive rituals sometimes protect a person from a schizophrenic regression or a psychotic depression. There may be rigid paranoid trends behind an anxiety neurosis or a phobia. A conversion symptom may guard a person from regressing into a paranoid psychosis or into schizophrenia. Even the well-known rigid character structure is not rigid for nothing. It usually constitutes an armoring which, like a well-defended fortress, contains within it much that is soft and vulnerable. A therapist has to be able to think of all these possibilities when he begins the treatment of a new patient.

The question of how transference shall be used, whether simply as a guide for the therapist, who says nothing about it, or as something which can be skilfully utilized by singling it out and calling it a name, is too involved to be dealt with here. Earlier in the chapter we discussed transference and countertransference, and said there that both are apt to be present in any psychotherapy that goes beyond a conversation. This is true whether their presence is recognized or not by the therapist, and whether he elects to consider them or to ignore them.

Psychoanalysis

There are many psychoanalytically oriented psychotherapies today that call themselves psychoanalysis; there are many psychotherapists who consider themselves to be psychoanalysts. Is there really any difference and, if there is, just what is it? There are several differences between expressive psychotherapies and psychoanalysis. A very few of the characteristics peculiar to psychoanalysis will be mentioned here. For full descriptions the reader will have to go to works on psychoanalysis written by psychoanalysts.[34] It is extremely difficult, if not impossible, to understand psychoanalysis fully without being psychoanalyzed oneself, and then psychoanalyzing patients under the supervision of training analysts. As this consumes a period of several years, and as it is restricted to the few who seem eligible to a qualified psychoanalytic training institute, the average person must be content with what he can read, just as he remains content with reading about heart surgery and about the experiences of an astronaut in flight.

Psychoanalysis has always used the couch, although even today some standard psychoanalyses are carried out from start to finish without it. Lying on a couch can be relaxing and comfortable. It promotes free association by providing the patient with minimal distraction. The psychoanalyst keeps himself out of sight, but keeps his patient where he can always see him. He says very little at all times, but especially during the early weeks, when the patient is groping for his own means of expression, and establishing his initial transference reactions. The myth of the analyst as a blank screen, however, belongs to the history of psychoanalysis, not to its current practice. When the psychoanalyst does speak, it is to encourage the free flow of verbalized thought and emotion, to comment upon something that needs comment, sometimes to repeat a fragment which seems promising, to confront the patient with what he is expressing, and once in a while to make an interpretation.

The competent psychoanalyst is exceedingly sparing with his interpretations. This is in part because of their power, and in part because too frequent

[34] For example, Kubie, L. S., *Practical and Theoretical Aspects of Psychoanalysis.* New York: Internat. Univ. Press, 1950; Hendrick, I., *Facts and Theories of Psychoanalysis.* (3rd ed.) New York: Knopf, 1958; Glover, E., *The Technique of Psychoanalysis.* New York: Internat. Univ. Press, 1955; Brenner, C., *An Elementary Textbook of Psychoanalysis.* New York: Internat. Univ. Press, 1955; Braatoy, T., *Fundamentals of Psychoanalytic Technique.* New York: Wiley, 1954.

interpretation turns the psychoanalytic situation into a didactic one. It should be mentioned here that the so-called "didactic analysis" is merely the personal psychoanalysis of someone who is a candidate at a training institute. It need not differ in any way from the psychoanalysis of any other person.

When the psychoanalyst makes an interpretation, it is usually to reformulate what the patient is expressing, and to relate it to unconscious material which has neared the surface. If the patient rejects or ignores the interpretation, the psychoanalyst may repeat it or he may wait weeks or months before he judges the time has come to repeat it. He repeats it then only because the patient is again expressing the same kind of thing as before. Every psychoanalyst knows that some of his interpretations will be incorrect, that some will be half correct, and that some will be correct but ill-timed. What seemed ready to emerge was not actually ready. It may have been near the surface, but too laden with anxiety to be released into conscious awareness. It should be abundantly clear that psychoanalysis today does not haul things from the unconscious into consciousness, as many of its critics seem to assume. Neither is it an intellectual exercise.

The psychoanalyst makes use of everything and anything that appears in his patient's behavior. He notices how the patient comes in and how he leaves, what he says, how he looks, his mannerisms, his movements and his postures. A sigh, a blush, a change in breathing or in the speed of talking, a stammer, a flooding of free associations, the patient's restlessness, or his very want of appropriate feelings, may any one of them be much more important than what the patient happens to be saying.

If the patient reports a manifest dream, the psychoanalyst listens to everything that the patient reports, but especially to the feeling tone of the dream and the report, and to what the patient seems to be omitting.[35] Manifest dreams are so complex, so loaded with primary process displacement, condensation and symbolization, so likely to express defensive maneuvers, resistances and superego reactions, that it is by no means always possible to understand them or to interpret them. Often one finds that only a fragment makes sense; and even this fragment, taken out of the context of this person, this life history, and this therapeutic process, may seem itself to be senseless. Some patients try to use their dreaming defensively, that is, they bring dreams into their psychoanalysis in such a way or in such quantities as to keep them from free associations in other areas which make them more anxious. This is but one example of the use of the so-called "basic rule," to say everything that comes to mind, in such a manner that it defeats the goals of therapy.

Two things more about psychoanalysis deserve special mention here. One of them is that psychoanalysis takes a long time; the other is that it requires almost daily therapeutic sessions. There is much public misunderstanding about both of these characteristics.

[35] French, T. M., *The Integration of Behavior: Volume Two: The Integrative Process in Dreams.* Chicago: Univ. of Chicago Press, 1954.

Psychoanalysis takes a long time because it is a process of working through a patient's difficulties, of allowing a transference neurosis to develop and be resolved, of reworking things left unsettled in a person's early childhood. It is not just a means of restoring the patient to his previous level of adjustment. In psychoanalysis, the same neurotic conflict or anxiety may appear over and over in different guises and behind different defenses. Each time it reappears it must be dealt with anew. The very goal of psychoanalysis, which is that of giving a patient the chance to reexperience his persistent infantile and childhood anxieties and conflicts, but this time with an adult ego, makes it impossible to shortcut the growth process.

The frequency of therapeutic sessions has been the subject of heated controversy, even among psychoanalysts themselves. Freud insisted, on the basis of his own clinical experience, that sessions almost every day were essential if a patient were not to evade anxiety-provoking problems and deep neurotic conflicts. The great majority of psychoanalysts have found this to be true. The actual quality of what a patient says appears to change when he is shifted from four or five sessions a week to one or two. The former promotes regressive experiences and brings the transference phenomena into bold relief. The latter helps the patient to cover up what he finds too painful or what he considers dangerous to expose. Many psychoanalysts make use of this difference in tapering off an analysis before they terminate it. The patient who has been coming four or five times a week for two or three years, begins to come twice a week and then once a week. During this reduction there may be a temporary increase in regressive behavior, but as a rule the material which the patient brings into analysis grows more and more like that in late sessions of good expressive psychotherapy.

The little that has just been said about psychoanalysis is not intended to be a full, exact description. Even those books by psychoanalysts which are wholly devoted to a description of the process of psychoanalysis cannot communicate it to a person who has not himself been analyzed. They succeed in describing some of the procedures, some of the basic goals and attitudes, and some of the special difficulties. They do not communicate, because they cannot, the emotional experiences of the person being analyzed or of the analyst while he is analyzing. They cannot capture the quality of the interaction, which often shifts rapidly during a single session. The analysand, the person who is being analyzed, may feel as lonely at times as an astronaut who has lost communicative contact with the earth, but in reality he is interacting with an accepting person throughout every analytic hour. Eventually he comes to recognize that this is so without ever being told.

Conclusion

This brings our long journey through the mental development of human beings, their peculiarly human problems, their mental illnesses and therapies to an end. To study psychopathology, one must study living human beings, the mentally healthy and the mentally sick, in treatment hours and out of them, in homes and hospitals, alone as well as in communities, wherever they are to be found. To understand the mature adult, one must know what infants and children seem to experience, and how they operate. For within every living adult there are the old, primitive primary processes of infancy and early childhood still at work. We know this because every night of our lives they take control of our thinking for awhile in dreams. There are also at work all the feelings, emotions, perceptions, imaginings and thought that belong to adult preconscious and conscious systems. An infinity of memories is always present which may lead to any level of operation.

All the things which we have been describing and discussing are in themselves only fragments, the products of observation, examination, analysis and theory. Taken together they go into what we conceive of as the make-up of a man, a woman and a child as we experience them. In the end we come face to face with the miracle of the human being — with the body of an animal, the mind of a dreamer, the ability to communicate beyond imagining, and a capacity for goodness, for evil, for greatness and for suffering, which no other being on earth can ever share. It is this human being, the creator and the destroyer, that we must be able to watch with great objectivity and understand with great compassion.

Name Index

Subject Index

Abstraction, scientific, 132–133

Acrophobia, 280–285

Acting out, anxiety reaction and, 264

Activity levels, newborn, 31–32

Adaptation: anxiety reaction and, 249; cerebral, 715–716; conversion symptom and, 308; ego (*see* Ego adaptation); neurosis and, 451–453; persistence of behavior and, 265–267; phobic, 278; psychosis and, 466, 474–475; psychosomatic disorder and, 684–686, 707–710

Adaptation syndrome, 707

Addiction, alcoholic, 672–676

Addiction, opiate, 677–678

Adolescence, 99–111; identification conflicts in, 103–105; peer culture in, 107–109; psychodynamic system and, 105–107; reality-testing in, 106–107; rebellion in, 103–105; reorganization in, 109–110; revival of edipal and pre-edipal problems in, 103–105; sex differences in, 101

Adoption, childhood, 267–268

Adulthood, 111–114

Affect, schizophrenic, 607–608

Aged, increased numbers of, 7, 741–742

Ageing, psychopathology of, 738–742

Aggression: enjoyment of, 130; frustration and, 174; neurotic depression and, 432–433; paranoid reaction and, 505–508

Aggressive personality, 650–651

Agoraphobia, 289–292

Alcoholism, 672–676

Alternating personality, 358–359

Ambivalence, emotional, 65; mourning and, 538–539

Amnesia, massive normal, 367–368; pathological, 355–360

Anal fixation, 65 (*see also* Sphincter)

Analysis, didactic, 772

Anesthesia, "glove," 315; "stocking," 315

Anorexia, conversion reaction and, 322–323

Anticipation, oral, 43–44

Anxiety: anticipation and, 223–224; anxiety reaction and, 246, 259–265; body-image and, 227–228; castration, 71–72, 95–97; changes in childhood patterns, 222–227; childhood adoption of prevailing patterns, 267–268; cultural inheritance of, 267–268; defective ego boundaries and, 230–231; defensive functions of, 220–221; diabetes and, 700; ego boundaries and, 227–231; hyperthyroidism and, 699–700; internalization of, 267–268; loss of love and, 225–227; neurotic, 248–250; normal, 219–220; object representation and, 227–228; overpermissive parents and, 269–270; overprotective parents and, 268–269; patho-logical, 221; primary, 222–225, 230–231, 260; psychosomatic, 685, 689; realistic activity and, 233–234; ritual and, 243–244; secondary, 231; self-image and, 227–228; separation, 224–225; sex deviation and, 661; superego and, 229–230; surgery and, 220–221; symptoms and, 453–454, 463–465; training in, 268–271; traumatic, 220–221

Anxiety attacks, 256–257

Anxiety neurosis, 250–256

Anxiety reaction: adaptation and, 249; brief cases of, 246–247; chronic, 250–266; conversion reactions and, 325; defenses in, 271–272; definition of, 249; developmental background, 259–273; dynamic background, 259–273; fixation and, 262; phobia and, 297; primary anxiety in, 260–261; projection and, 272–273; psychosomatic disorders and, 679; regression in, 272; repression in, 272–273; symptoms of, 250–253; tension discharge in, 271–272; therapy and, 274–275; varieties of, 250

Apathy, frustration and, 174

Appetite, loss of (*see* Anorexia)

Arthritis, rheumatoid, 696–697

Association, free (*see* Free association)

Asthma, dependency needs and, 693–694

Autism, infantile, 60–61, 214

Autonomic disorders (*see* Psychosomatic disorders)

Autonomy, infant, 60

Barrier, protective, 179

Basic trust, 26–27, 56–58, 117; paranoid reaction and, 480; paranoid personality and, 645–646; schizoid personality and, 647–648

Behavior, persistence of nonadaptive, 265–267

Biological factors, psychopathology and, 630–632

Bodily illness, emotional stress and, 682–684

Body-image, 195–196; anxiety and, 227–228, 345–346; denial in, 346; phantom limb and, 346; regression and, 346; somatic estrangement and, 345–346

Body language, conversion reaction and, 305, 308, 315, 320–321, 330–332; normal, 306

Borderline psychoses, 20

Boundaries, ego, 78–79, 227–231, 262–265; paranoid personality and, 645–646; repression and, 238–239, 299–302

Bowel: infantile control, 63–65; ulcerative colitis and, 690–691

Dream: anxiety and, 252; characteristics of, 210–212; conversion and, 329; day's residues in, 161–162; daytime preparation of, 15; defenses in, 211–212; fixation and, 213–214; Freud's analysis of, 750–751; functions of, 210–212; manifest symptoms and, 205–206, 457–458; nonsensical manifest, 158–161; nonverbal, 122–123; normal, 14–16; phobia and, 301–302; primary process and, 211–212; psychoanalysis and, 772; regression and, 210–214; schizophrenia and, 578; superego and, 190–191; unconscious roots of, 158–161
Dreamlike states, 349–355
Dreamwork, daytime and nighttime, 205
Drive: abstraction and, 125–126, 137–138; adolescent, 105–107; aggressive, 127–129, 133–135; as construct, 132–133; definition of, 130–133; ego control of, 135–138; Freud's changing formulation of, 138–140; fusion of, 129–130; id and ego in, 153–154, 206–208; instinct and, 130–132; pathologically aggressive, 119–121; pre-edipal, 65–67; regression of, 218–219; sexual, 126–127, 133–135; summary of, 136, 153–154; superego control of, 135–138

Eating: fantasies of, 323–324; sexuality and, 323–325; symbolic significance of, 321
Edipal boy, 70–72
Edipal complex, inverted, 94–95; negative, 94–95; resolution of, 187–188; revival in adolescence, 103–105
Edipal conflicts, mastery of, 74–76; neuroses and, 68
Edipal frustration, 74–76
Edipal girl, 72–74
Edipal legend, 68
Edipal phase, 67–76; failures to resolve, 86–98
Ego: aggression in neurotic depression, 433; autonomous, 59, 177–178, 233–234; boundaries, 227–231; central nervous system and, 186; conflict and, 176; conflict-free sphere, 177–178; conscious, 164; definition of, 164; drive control and, 135–138; early organization and, 205–206; ears and, 47–49; eyes and, 47–49; goals of, 166–167; growth through introjection and identification, 207–208; id and, 170–171, 206–208; as intervening variable, 137; language and, 62; maturation of preconscious, 171–173; mother as temporary, 56–58; mouth and, 41–47; precocious in depressive personalities, 549–550; preconscious, 164–165, 186–

188; repressed, 228–229; secondary process and, 164-168; separation of unconscious from preconscious and conscious, 187–188; summary of, 136, 186–187; synthetic function of, 206; three worlds of, 180–186; unconscious, 147–148, 165, 187–188
Ego adaptation, defenses and, 179–180; mastery and, 178; neurosis and, 451–453
Ego boundaries, 78–79; defenses and, 59, 148; dissolution of, 51–53; lack of, 51–53; normality and, 13 (see also Boundaries, ego)
Ego development: conflict and, 176–177; delay and, 173–174; frustration and, 174–175
Ego differentiation: defense mechanisms and, 171; maturation of preconscious ego and, 171–173; organization and, 170–172; reality-testing and, 171
Ego disintegration: neurotic symptom and, 454–455; psychotic symptom and, 465; unconscious intrusions and, 207–208
Ego-ideal, 190, 194–195, 208–210
Ego-identity, 196
Ego introjects, 59–60, 175
Ego-splitting: dissociative reactions and, 363–364; isolation and, 242 (see also Isolation)
Ego strength, adolescent, 105–107
Ego-superego split, psychotic depression and, 541–542
Ego-syntonic, definition of, 165
Elaboration, secondary (see Secondary elaboration)
Electric convulsive therapy, 760–761
Elevators, fear of, 286–287
Emotion: hypertension and, 695–696; infantile in psychosomatic disorders, 708–710; psychosomatic disorder and, 680–686; psychotherapy and, 766; schizophrenia and, 607–608
Emotional support, need for in latency, 84–86
Energy: deaggressivized, 179–180; desexualized, 179–180; neutralized, 179–180
Energy of organization: 166, 222–224; anxiety reactions and, 261; conversion reactions and, 328–329; paranoid reactions and, 487; phobia and, 297–298
Envy, penis, 95–97
Eros, Freud on, 138–140
Estrangement: body-image and, 345–346; normal, 339–340; object, 343–345; pathological, 343–348; psychotic depression and, 521–522; schizophrenic, 606–607; self and, 346–348; somatic, 345–346
Ethology, instinct and, 131–132
Exclusion, normal, 16–17, 326–327

Speech, loss in conversion reactions, 309–311; psychosomatic disorder and, 692 (*see also* Language)

Sphincter control, phase of, 61–67

Split-level functioning, anxiety reactions and, 263–265; neurotic symptom formation and, 450–451; phobias and, 302; regression and, 212–213, 229–230, 263

Starvation, as conversion symptom, 322–323

Stimulation, infant need for, 56–57

Stimulus-response, inadequacy of concept, 122–125

Stress: emotional and bodily illness, 682–684; infantile, 222; internal, 12–13; latency, 86–98; primary anxiety and, 222–224; psychosomatic disorder and, 707–710; regression and, 121–122

Stupor, psychogenic, 354–355

Sublimation, 201–202, 244–245

Sucking, pleasure (*see* Pleasure sucking)

Superego: adolescent, 105–107; advantages of, 193–195; aggression in neurotic depression, 432–433, 439–440; anxiety and, 229–231; archaic functions in obsessive compulsive reactions, 403–411; conflict and, 208–210; conscience and, 189–190; cultural inheritance in, 97–98; defective, 97–98, 403–411; definition of, 188; depressive, 550–551; development of, 187–188, 208–209; dreaming and, 190–191; drive control and, 135–138; identification and introjects, 191–192; immaturity in early childhood, 67; as intervening variable, 137; introjects and, 60; object representation and, 97; origins of, 191–192; postedipal, 78, 193–195; precursors of, 67, 191–194, 395, 403–410; reaction formation and, 192; regression of, 218–219, 403–411; self-representation and, 97; summary of, 136; unconscious, 147–148, 187–188, 279–280

Supplies, narcissistic, 432

Surgery, anxiety and, 220–221

Symbiosis, 53–61; dissolution of, 59–61; failure to resolve, 60–61; growth of, 55–58; fixation in, 215; identity and, 117; mother in, 54–55; newborn in, 55; psychopathology and, 54–58

Symbol: opposite meanings of, 293–294; primary process and, 157–158

Symbolization: conflict and, 202–203; conversion reactions and, 307–308, 327–328

Symptom: adaptive function of, 451–453; anxiety and, 453–454; "choice" of psychosomatic, 710–714; ego disintegration and, 453–454; manifest dream and, 205–206, 457–458; neurotic emergence of, 458–459; overdetermination in conversion, 307; reactivation of conflict in, 456–

457; regression and, 455–456; secondary gain in, 461–462; tension and, 453–454

Symptom formation: anxiety reaction and, 263–265, 446; fantasy and, 459–461; neurotic phases, 453–462; paranoid, 483–487, 506–508, 512–513; primary gain and, 461; psychotic, 462–468; psychosomatic, 705–714; review of neurotic cases, 446–450

System: psychodynamic (*see* Psychodynamic system); unconscious, 232–233

Talion principle, 72

Tension: anxiety reactions and, 259–265, 271–272; neurotic symptoms and, 453–454; nonverbal communication of, 267–268; pleasurable, 179; psychotic symptoms and, 463–465

Thanatos, 138–140

Therapy: anxiety reactions and, 274–275; beginnings of psychoanalytic, 751–752; chemical, 744–745; client-centered, 747–748; countertransference and, 752–754; environmental manipulation and, 761–763; expressive, 745–754; fear of, 286–287; Freud and, 743–745, 748–754; insulin coma and, 758–760; neurotic depression and, 423–425, 440–441; nondirective, 747–748; phobias and, 284–285; protective, 754–757; senility and, 741–742; transference and, 752–754

Thinking: childhood forms in normal adults, 203–204; confused in normal children, 203–204; need-satisfaction and, 122–123; nonverbal, 122–123; normal and delusional, 470–472; prelogical, 79; schizophrenic disturbances in, 609–614

Tic, as conversion reaction, 318–320

Tolerance, frustration (*see* Frustration tolerance)

Torticollis, spasmodic, 319–320

Trance state, 353–354

Transference, therapy and, 752–754

Transvestism, 669–670

Tremor, as conversion symptom, 317

Trust, basic (*see* Basic trust)

Turning-against-the-self, defensive, 241

Twilight state, 351–355

Ulcer, peptic, as psychosomatic disorder, 688–689

Ulcerative colitis, as psychosomatic disorder, 690–691

Unconscious: enlivening influence of, 329–330; incomplete separation from preconscious, 187–188; repression and, 238–239

Undoing: defensive, 243–244; normal, 387–388; obsessive compulsive, 386–395, 402–403